GREAT BOOKS OF THE WESTERN WORLD

GREAT BOOKS
OF THE WESTERN WORLD

ROBERT MAYNARD HUTCHINS, *EDITOR IN CHIEF*

11.

EUCLID

ARCHIMEDES

APOLLONIUS OF PERGA

NICOMACHUS

THE THIRTEEN BOOKS OF EUCLID'S ELEMENTS

THE WORKS OF ARCHIMEDES INCLUDING THE METHOD

ON CONIC SECTIONS
BY APOLLONIUS OF PERGA

INTRODUCTION TO ARITHMETIC
BY NICOMACHUS OF GERASA

WILLIAM BENTON, *Publisher*

ENCYCLOPÆDIA BRITANNICA, INC.

CHICAGO · LONDON · TORONTO · GENEVA · SYDNEY · TOKYO · MANILA

The Thirteen Books of Euclid's *Elements* and *The Works of Archimedes*,
including *The Method*, translated by Sir Thomas L. Heath,
are reprinted by arrangement with CAMBRIDGE UNIVERSITY PRESS

Conics is reprinted by arrangement with the translator, R. Catesby Taliaferro.
Copyright, 1939, by R. Catesby Taliaferro

Nicomachus of Gerasa: *Introduction to Arithmetic*, by Martin Luther D'Ooge,
Frank Egleston Robbins, and Louis Charles Karpinski, is reprinted by arrangement with
The Regents of the University of Michigan (THE UNIVERSITY OF MICHIGAN PRESS).
Copyright, 1926, by Francis W. Kelsey

THE UNIVERSITY OF CHICAGO

The Great Books
is published with the editorial advice of the faculties
of The University of Chicago

1952
BY ENCYCLOPÆDIA BRITANNICA, INC.
NINETEENTH PRINTING, 1971
COPYRIGHT UNDER INTERNATIONAL COPYRIGHT UNION

ALL RIGHTS RESERVED UNDER PAN AMERICAN AND UNIVERSAL COPYRIGHT
CONVENTIONS BY ENCYCLOPÆDIA BRITANNICA, INC.

Library of Congress Catalog Card Number: 55–10320
International Standard Book Number: 0–85229–163–9

GENERAL CONTENTS

EUCLID'S ELEMENTS

BIOGRAPHICAL NOTE

EUCLID, *fl. c.* 300 B.C.

EUCLID is said to have been younger than the first pupils of Plato but older than Archimedes, which would place the time of his flourishing about 300 B.C. He probably received his early mathematical education in Athens from the pupils of Plato, since most of the geometers and mathematicians on whom he depended were of that school. Proclus, the Neo-Platonist of the fifth century, asserts that Euclid was of the school of Plato and "intimate with that philosophy." His opinion, however, may have been based only on his view that the treatment of the five regular ("Platonic") solids in Book XIII is the "end of the whole *Elements*."

The only other fact concerning Euclid is that he taught and founded a school at Alexandria in the time of Ptolemy I, who reigned from 306 to 283 B.C. The evidence for the place comes from Pappus (fourth century A.D.), who notes that Apollonius "spent a very long time with the pupils of Euclid at Alexandria, and it was thus that he acquired such a scientific habit of thought." Proclus claims that it was Ptolemy I who asked Euclid if there was no shorter way to geometry than the *Elements* and received as answer: "There is no royal road to geometry." The other story about Euclid that has come down from antiquity concerns his answer to a pupil who at the end of his first lesson in geometry asked what he would get by learning such things, whereupon Euclid called his slave and said: "Give him a coin since he must needs make gain by what he learns."

Something of Euclid's character would seem to be disclosed in the remark of Pappus regarding Euclid's "scrupulous fairness and his exemplary kindness towards all who advance mathematical science to however small an extent." The context of the remark seems to indicate, however, that Pappus is not giving a traditional account of Euclid but offering an explanation of his own of Euclid's failure to go further than he did with his investigation of a certain problem in conics.

Euclid's great work, the thirteen books of the *Elements*, must have become a classic soon after publication. From the time of Archimedes they are constantly referred to and used as a basic text-book. It was recognized in antiquity that Euclid had drawn upon all his predecessors. According to Proclus, he "collected many of the theorems of Eudoxus, perfected many of those of Theatetus, and also brought to incontrovertible demonstration the things which were only loosely proved by his predecessors." The other extant works of Euclid include: the *Data*, for use in the solution of problems by geometrical analysis, *On Divisions* (of figures), the *Optics*, and the *Phenomena*, a treatise on the geometry of the sphere for use in astronomy. His lost *Elements of Music* may have provided the basis for the extant *Sectio Canonis* on the Pythagorean theory of music. Of lost geometrical works all except one belonged to higher geometry.

Since the later Greeks knew nothing about the life of Euclid, the mediaeval translators and editors were left to their own devices. He was usually called *Megarensis*, through confusion with the philosopher Eucleides of Megara, Plato's contemporary. The Arabs found that the name of Euclid, which they took to be compounded from *ucli* (key) and *dis* (measure) revealed the "key of geometry." They claimed that the Greek philosophers used to post upon the doors of their schools the well-known notice: "Let no one come to our school who has not learned the *Elements* of Euclid," thus transferring the inscription over Plato's Academy to all scholastic doors and substituting the *Elements* for geometry.

CONTENTS

BOOK ONE

DEFINITIONS

1. A *point* is that which has no part.
2. A *line* is breadthless length.
3. The extremities of a line are points.
4. A *straight line* is a line which lies evenly with the points on itself.
5. A *surface* is that which has length and breadth only.
6. The extremities of a surface are lines.
7. A *plane surface* is a surface which lies evenly with the straight lines on itself.
8. A *plane angle* is the inclination to one another of two lines in a plane which meet one another and do not lie in a straight line.
9. And when the lines containing the angle are straight, the angle is called *rectilineal*.
10. When a straight line set up on a straight line makes the adjacent angles equal to one another, each of the equal angles is *right* and the straight line standing on the other is called a *perpendicular* to that on which it stands.
11. An *obtuse angle* is an angle greater than a right angle.
12. An *acute angle* is an angle less than a right angle.
13. A *boundary* is that which is an extremity of anything.
14. A *figure* is that which is contained by any boundary or boundaries.
15. A *circle* is a plane figure contained by one line such that all the straight lines falling upon it from one point among those lying within the figure are equal to one another;
16. And the point is called the *centre* of the circle.
17. A *diameter* of the circle is any straight line drawn through the centre and terminated in both directions by the circumference of the circle, and such a straight line also bisects the circle.
18. A *semicircle* is the figure contained by the diameter and the circumference cut off by it. And the centre of the semicircle is the same as that of the circle.
19. *Rectilineal figures* are those which are contained by straight lines, *trilateral* figures being those contained by three, *quadrilateral* those contained by four, and *multilateral* those contained by more than four straight lines.
20. Of trilateral figures, an *equilateral triangle* is that which has its three sides equal, an *isosceles triangle* that which has two of its sides alone equal, and a *scalene triangle* that which has its three sides unequal.
21. Further, of trilateral figures, a *right-angled triangle* is that which has a right angle, an *obtuse-angled triangle* that which has an obtuse angle, and an *acute-angled triangle* that which has its three angles acute.

1

22. Of quadrilateral figures, a *square* is that which is both equilateral and right-angled; an *oblong* that which is right-angled but not equilateral; a *rhombus* that which is equilateral but not right-angled; and a *rhomboid* that which has its opposite sides and angles equal to one another but is neither equilateral nor right-angled. And let quadrilaterals other than these be called *trapezia*.

23. *Parallel* straight lines are straight lines which, being in the same plane and being produced indefinitely in both directions, do not meet one another in either direction.

POSTULATES

Let the following be postulated:

1. To draw a straight line from any point to any point.
2. To produce a finite straight line continuously in a straight line.
3. To describe a circle with any centre and distance.
4. That all right angles are equal to one another.
5. That, if a straight line falling on two straight lines make the interior angles on the same side less than two right angles, the two straight lines, if produced indefinitely, meet on that side on which are the angles less than the two right angles.

COMMON NOTIONS

1. Things which are equal to the same thing are also equal to one another.
2. If equals be added to equals, the wholes are equal.
3. If equals be subtracted from equals, the remainders are equal.
[7] 4. Things which coincide with one another are equal to one another.
[8] 5. The whole is greater than the part.

BOOK I. PROPOSITIONS

PROPOSITION 1

On a given finite straight line to construct an equilateral triangle.

Let *AB* be the given finite straight line.

Thus it is required to construct an equilateral triangle on the straight line *AB*.

With centre *A* and distance *AB* let the circle *BCD* be described;   [Post. 3]
again, with centre *B* and distance *BA* let the circle *ACE* be described;   [Post. 3]
and from the point *C*, in which the circles cut one another, to the points *A*, *B* let the straight lines *CA*, *CB* be joined.   [Post. 1]

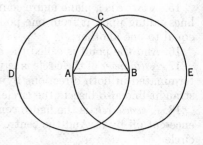

Now, since the point *A* is the centre of the circle *CDB*,
　　　　　　　AC is equal to *AB*.   [Def. 15]
Again, since the point *B* is the centre of the circle *CAE*,
　　　　　　　BC is equal to *BA*.   [Def. 15]
But *CA* was also proved equal to *AB*;
　　　therefore each of the straight lines *CA*, *CB* is equal to *AB*.
And things which are equal to the same thing are also equal to one another;
　　　　　　　therefore *CA* is also equal to *CB*.   [C. N. 1]
Therefore the three straight lines *CA*, *AB*, *BC* are equal to one another.

Therefore the triangle ABC is equilateral; and it has been constructed on the given finite straight line AB.

(Being) what it was required to do.

PROPOSITION 2

To place at a given point (as an extremity) a straight line equal to a given straight line.

Let A be the given point, and BC the given straight line.

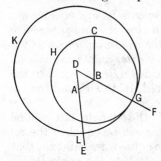

Thus it is required to place at the point A (as an extremity) a straight line equal to the given straight line BC.

From the point A to the point B let the straight line AB be joined; [Post. 1]
and on it let the equilateral triangle DAB be constructed. [I. 1]
Let the straight lines AE, BF be produced in a straight line with DA, DB; [Post. 2]
with centre B and distance BC let the circle CGH be described; [Post. 3]
and again, with centre D and distance DG let the circle GKL be described. [Post. 3]

Then, since the point B is the centre of the circle CGH,
BC is equal to BG.
Again, since the point D is the centre of the circle GKL,
DL is equal to DG.
And in these DA is equal to DB;
therefore the remainder AL is equal to the remainder BG. [C.N. 3]
But BC was also proved equal to BG;
therefore each of the straight lines AL, BC is equal to BG.
And things which are equal to the same thing are also equal to one another; [C.N. 1]
therefore AL is also equal to BC.

Therefore at the given point A the straight line AL is placed equal to the given straight line BC.

(Being) what it was required to do.

PROPOSITION 3

Given two unequal straight lines, to cut off from the greater a straight line equal to the less.

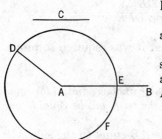

Let AB, C be the two given unequal straight lines, and let AB be the greater of them.

Thus it is required to cut off from AB the greater a straight line equal to C the less.

At the point A let AD be placed equal to the straight line C; [I. 2]
and with centre A and distance AD let the circle DEF be described. [Post. 3]

Now, since the point A is the centre of the circle DEF,

AE is equal to AD. [Def. 15]

But C is also equal to AD.

Therefore each of the straight lines AE, C is equal to AD;

so that AE is also equal to C.   [C.N. 1]

Therefore, given the two straight lines AB, C, from AB the greater AE has been cut off equal to C the less.

(Being) what it was required to do.

PROPOSITION 4

If two triangles have the two sides equal to two sides respectively, and have the angles contained by the equal straight lines equal, they will also have the base equal to the base, the triangle will be equal to the triangle, and the remaining angles will be equal to the remaining angles respectively, namely those which the equal sides subtend.

Let ABC, DEF be two triangles having the two sides AB, AC equal to the two sides DE, DF respectively, namely AB to DE and AC to DF, and the angle BAC equal to the angle EDF.

I say that the base BC is also equal to the base EF, the triangle ABC will be equal to the triangle DEF, and the remaining angles will be equal to the remaining angles respectively, namely those which the equal sides subtend, that is, the angle ABC to the angle DEF, and the angle ACB to the angle DFE.

For, if the triangle ABC be applied to the triangle DEF,

and if the point A be placed on the point D

and the straight line AB on DE,

then the point B will also coincide with E, because AB is equal to DE.

Again, AB coinciding with DE,

the straight line AC will also coincide with DF, because the angle BAC is equal to the angle EDF;

hence the point C will also coincide with the point F, because AC is again equal to DF.

But B also coincided with E;

hence the base BC will coincide with the base EF.

[For if, when B coincides with E and C with F, the base BC does not coincide with the base EF, two straight lines will enclose a space: which is impossible.

Therefore the base BC will coincide with EF] and will be equal to it. [C.N. 4]

Thus the whole triangle ABC will coincide with the whole triangle DEF, and will be equal to it.

And the remaining angles will also coincide with the remaining angles and will be equal to them,

the angle ABC to the angle DEF,

and the angle ACB to the angle DFE.

Therefore etc.

(Being) what it was required to prove.

PROPOSITION 5

In isosceles triangles the angles at the base are equal to one another, and, if the equal straight lines be produced further, the angles under the base will be equal to one another.

Let ABC be an isosceles triangle having the side AB equal to the side AC;

and let the straight lines *BD*, *CE* be produced further in a straight line with *AB*, *AC*.   [Post. 2]

I say that the angle *ABC* is equal to the angle *ACB*, and the angle *CBD* to the angle *BCE*.

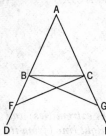

Let a point *F* be taken at random on *BD*;
from *AE* the greater let *AG* be cut off equal to *AF* the less;   [I. 3]
and let the straight lines *FC*, *GB* be joined.   [Post. 1]
Then, since *AF* is equal to *AG* and *AB* to *AC*,
the two sides *FA*, *AC* are equal to the two sides
GA, *AB*, respectively;
and they contain a common angle, the angle *FAG*.
Therefore the base *FC* is equal to the base *GB*,
and the triangle *AFC* is equal to the triangle *AGB*,
and the remaining angles will be equal to the remaining angles respectively,
namely those which the equal sides subtend,
that is, the angle *ACF* to the angle *ABG*,
and the angle *AFC* to the angle *AGB*.   [I. 4]
And, since the whole *AF* is equal to the whole *AG*,
and in these *AB* is equal to *AC*,
the remainder *BF* is equal to the remainder *CG*.
But *FC* was also proved equal to *GB*;
therefore the two sides *BF*, *FC* are equal to the two sides *CG*, *GB* respectively;
and the angle *BFC* is equal to the angle *CGB*,
while the base *BC* is common to them;
therefore the triangle *BFC* is also equal to the triangle *CGB*, and the remaining angles will be equal to the remaining angles respectively, namely those which the equal sides subtend;
therefore the angle *FBC* is equal to the angle *GCB*,
and the angle *BCF* to the angle *CBG*.
Accordingly, since the whole angle *ABG* was proved equal to the angle *ACF*,
and in these the angle *CBG* is equal to the angle *BCF*,
the remaining angle *ABC* is equal to the remaining angle *ACB*;
and they are at the base of the triangle *ABC*.
But the angle *FBC* was also proved equal to the angle *GCB*;
and they are under the base.

Therefore etc.   Q. E. D.

PROPOSITION 6

If in a triangle two angles be equal to one another, the sides which subtend the equal angles will also be equal to one another.

Let *ABC* be a triangle having the angle *ABC* equal to the angle *ACB*;
I say that the side *AB* is also equal to the side *AC*.
For, if *AB* is unequal to *AC*, one of them is greater.
Let *AB* be greater; and from *AB* the greater let *DB* be cut off equal to *AC* the less;
let *DC* be joined.
Then, since *DB* is equal to *AC*,
and *BC* is common,

the two sides *DB*, *BC* are equal to the two sides *AC*, *CB* respectively;
and the angle *DBC* is equal to the angle *ACB*;
therefore the base *DC* is equal to the base *AB*,
and the triangle *DBC* will be equal to the triangle *ACB*,
the less to the greater:
which is absurd.
Therefore *AB* is not unequal to *AC*;
it is therefore equal to it.
Therefore etc.   Q. E. D.

PROPOSITION 7

*Given two straight lines constructed on a straight line (from its extremities) and
meeting in a point, there cannot be constructed on the same straight line (from its
extremities), and on the same side of it, two other straight lines meeting in another
point and equal to the former two respectively, namely each to that which has the
same extremity with it.*

For, if possible, given two straight lines *AC*, *CB* constructed on the straight
line *AB* and meeting at the point *C*, let two other straight
lines *AD*, *DB* be constructed on the same straight line
AB, on the same side of it, meeting in another point *D*
and equal to the former two respectively, namely each to
that which has the same extremity with it, so that *CA* is
equal to *DA* which has the same extremity *A* with it, and
CB to *DB* which has the same extremity *B* with it; and let
CD be joined.

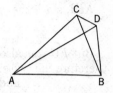

Then, since *AC* is equal to *AD*,
the angle *ACD* is also equal to the angle *ADC*;   [I. 5]
therefore the angle *ADC* is greater than the angle *DCB*;
therefore the angle *CDB* is much greater than the angle *DCB*.
Again, since *CB* is equal to *DB*,
the angle *CDB* is also equal to the angle *DCB*.
But it was also proved much greater than it:
which is impossible.
Therefore etc.   Q. E. D.

PROPOSITION 8

*If two triangles have the two sides equal to two sides respectively, and have also the
base equal to the base, they will also have the angles equal which are contained by
the equal straight lines.*

Let *ABC*, *DEF* be two triangles having
the two sides *AB*, *AC* equal to the two sides
DE, *DF* respectively, namely *AB* to *DE*, and
AC to *DF*; and let them have the base *BC*
equal to the base *EF*;
I say that the angle *BAC* is also equal to
the angle *EDF*.

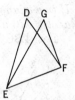

For, if the triangle *ABC* be applied to the triangle *DEF*, and if the point *B*
be placed on the point *E* and the straight line *BC* on *EF*,
the point *C* will also coincide with *F*,

because BC is equal to EF.

Then, BC coinciding with EF,

BA, AC will also coincide with ED, DF;

for, if the base BC coincides with the base EF, and the sides BA, AC do not coincide with ED, DF but fall beside them as EG, GF,

then, given two straight lines constructed on a straight line (from its extremities) and meeting in a point, there will have been constructed on the same straight line (from its extremities), and on the same side of it, two other straight lines meeting in another point and equal to the former two respectively, namely each to that which has the same extremity with it.

But they cannot be so constructed.   [I. 7]

Therefore it is not possible that, if the base BC be applied to the base EF, the sides BA, AC should not coincide with ED, DF;

they will therefore coincide,

so that the angle BAC will also coincide with the angle EDF, and will be equal to it.

If therefore etc.   Q. E. D.

PROPOSITION 9

To bisect a given rectilineal angle.

Let the angle BAC be the given rectilineal angle.

Thus it is required to bisect it.

Let a point D be taken at random on AB;

let AE be cut off from AC equal to AD;   [I. 3]

let DE be joined, and on DE let the equilateral triangle DEF be constructed;

let AF be joined.

I say that the angle BAC has been bisected by the straight line AF.

For, since AD is equal to AE,

and AF is common,

the two sides DA, AF are equal to the two sides EA, AF respectively.

And the base DF is equal to the base EF;

therefore the angle DAF is equal to the angle EAF.   [I. 8]

Therefore the given rectilineal angle BAC has been bisected by the straight line AF.   Q. E. F.

PROPOSITION 10

To bisect a given finite straight line.

Let AB be the given finite straight line.

Thus it is required to bisect the finite straight line AB.

Let the equilateral triangle ABC be constructed on it,   [I. 1]

and let the angle ACB be bisected by the straight line CD;   [I. 9]

I say that the straight line AB has been bisected at the point D.

For, since AC is equal to CB,

and CD is common,

the two sides AC, CD are equal to the two sides BC, CD respectively;

and the angle ACD is equal to the angle BCD;

EUCLID

therefore the base AD is equal to the base BD. [I. 4]

Therefore the given finite straight line AB has been bisected at D. Q. E. F.

PROPOSITION 11

To draw a straight line at right angles to a given straight line from a given point on it.

Let AB be the given straight line, and C the given point on it.

Thus it is required to draw from the point C a straight line at right angles to the straight line AB.

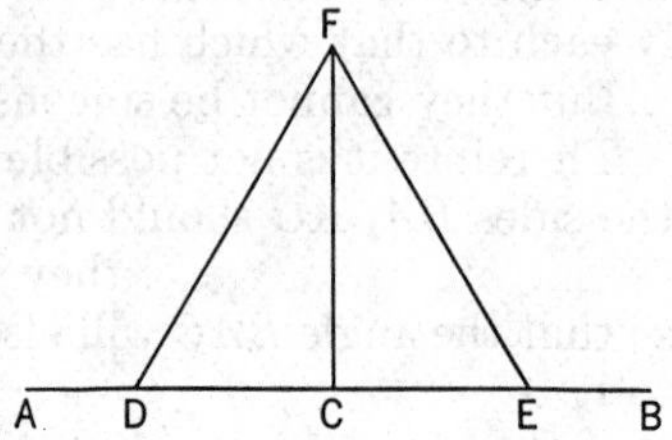

Let a point D be taken at random on AC;

let CE be made equal to CD; [I. 3]

on DE let the equilateral triangle FDE be constructed, [I. 1]

and let FC be joined;

I say that the straight line FC has been drawn at right angles to the given straight line AB from C the given point on it.

For, since DC is equal to CE,

and CF is common,

the two sides DC, CF are equal to the two sides EC, CF respectively;

and the base DF is equal to the base FE;

therefore the angle DCF is equal to the angle ECF; [I. 8]

and they are adjacent angles.

But, when a straight line set up on a straight line makes the adjacent angles equal to one another, each of the equal angles is right; [Def. 10]

therefore each of the angles DCF, FCE is right.

Therefore the straight line CF has been drawn at right angles to the given straight line AB from the given point C on it. Q. E. F.

PROPOSITION 12

To a given infinite straight line, from a given point which is not on it, to draw a perpendicular straight line.

Let AB be the given infinite straight line, and C the given point which is not on it;

thus it is required to draw to the given infinite straight line AB, from the given point C which is not on it, a perpendicular straight line.

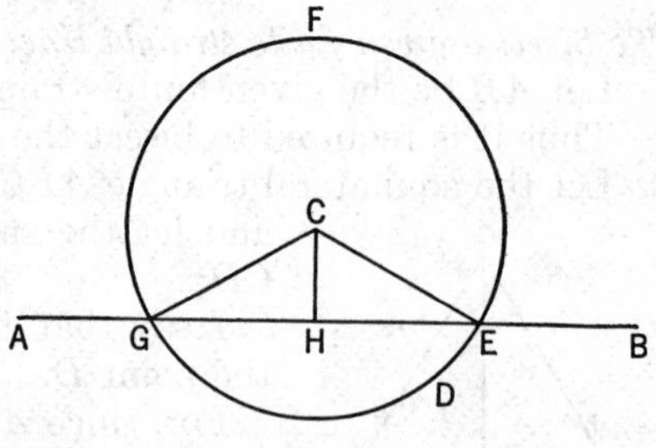

For let a point D be taken at random on the other side of the straight line AB, and with centre C and distance CD let the circle EFG be described; [Post. 3]

let the straight line EG be bisected at H, [I. 10]

and let the straight lines CG, CH, CE be joined. [Post. 1]

I say that CH has been drawn perpendicular to the given infinite straight line AB from the given point C which is not on it.

For, since GH is equal to HE,

and HC is common,

the two sides GH, HC are equal to the two sides EH, HC respectively;
and the base CG is equal to the base CE;
therefore the angle CHG is equal to the angle EHC.   [I. 8]
And they are adjacent angles.

But, when a straight line set up on a straight line makes the adjacent angles equal to one another, each of the equal angles is right, and the straight line standing on the other is called a perpendicular to that on which it stands.
[Def. 10]

Therefore CH has been drawn perpendicular to the given infinite straight line AB from the given point C which is not on it.   Q. E. F.

PROPOSITION 13

If a straight line set up on a straight line make angles, it will make either two right angles or angles equal to two right angles.

For let any straight line AB set up on the straight line CD make the angles CBA, ABD;
I say that the angles CBA, ABD are either two rights angles or equal to two right angles.

Now, if the angle CBA is equal to the angle ABD, they are two right angles.   [Def. 10]

But, if not, let BE be drawn from the point B at right angles to CD;   [I. 11]
therefore the angles CBE, EBD are two right angles.

Then, since the angle CBE is equal to the two angles CBA, ABE,
let the angle EBD be added to each;
therefore the angles CBE, EBD are equal to the three angles CBA, ABE, EBD.   [C.N. 2]

Again, since the angle DBA is equal to the two angles DBE, EBA,
let the angle ABC be added to each;
therefore the angles DBA, ABC are equal to the three angles DBE, EBA, ABC.   [C.N. 2]

But the angles CBE, EBD were also proved equal to the same three angles;
and things which are equal to the same thing are also equal to one another;
[C.N. 1]

therefore the angles CBE, EBD are also equal to the angles DBA, ABC.
But the angles CBE, EBD are two right angles;
therefore the angles DBA, ABC are also equal to two right angles.
Therefore etc.   Q. E. D.

PROPOSITION 14

If with any straight line, and at a point on it, two straight lines not lying on the same side make the adjacent angles equal to two right angles, the two straight lines will be in a straight line with one another.

For with any straight line AB, and at the point B on it, let the two straight lines BC, BD not lying on the same side make the adjacent angles ABC, ABD equal to two right angles;
I say that BD is in a straight line with CB.

For, if BD is not in a straight line with BC, let BE be in a straight line with CB.

Then, since the straight line AB stands on the straight line CBE,
the angles ABC, ABE are equal to two right angles.   [I. 13]
But the angles ABC, ABD are also equal to two
right angles;
therefore the angles CBA, ABE are equal to the
angles CBA, ABD.   [Post. 4 and *C.N.* 1]
Let the angle CBA be subtracted from each;
therefore the remaining angle ABE is equal to the remaining angle ABD,
                                                                      [*C.N.* 3]
              the less to the greater: which is impossible.
Therefore BE is not in a straight line with CB.
Similarly we can prove that neither is any other straight line except BD.
Therefore CB is in a straight line with BD.
Therefore etc.   Q. E. D.

PROPOSITION 15

If two straight lines cut one another, they make the vertical angles equal to one another.

For let the straight lines AB, CD cut one another at
the point E;
I say that the angle AEC is equal to the angle DEB,
     and the angle CEB to the angle AED.
For, since the straight line AE stands on the straight
line CD, making the angles CEA, AED,
              the angles CEA, AED are equal to two right angles.   [I. 13]
Again, since the straight line DE stands on the straight line AB, making the
angles AED, DEB,
              the angles AED, DEB are equal to two right angles.   [I. 13]
But the angles CEA, AED were also proved equal to two right angles;
   therefore the angles CEA, AED are equal to the angles AED, DEB.
                                                            [Post. 4 and *C.N.* 1]

Let the angle AED be subtracted from each;
therefore the remaining angle CEA is equal to the remaining angle BED.
                                                                      [*C.N.* 3]
Similarly it can be proved that the angles CEB, DEA are also equal.
Therefore etc.   Q. E. D.
[PORISM. From this it is manifest that, if two straight lines cut one another,
they will make the angles at the point of section equal to four right angles.]

PROPOSITION 16

*In any triangle, if one of the sides be produced, the exterior angle is greater than
either of the interior and opposite angles.*

Let ABC be a triangle, and let one side of it BC be produced to D;
I say that the exterior angle ACD is greater than either of the interior and
opposite angles CBA, BAC.
Let AC be bisected at E [I. 10], and let BE be joined and produced in a
straight line to F;
                   let EF be made equal to BE,   [I. 3]
let FC be joined [Post. 1], and let AC be drawn through to G.   [Post. 2]

Then, since AE is equal to EC, and BE to EF,
the two sides AE, EB are equal to the two sides CE, EF respectively;

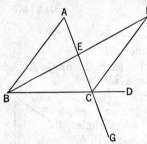

and the angle AEB is equal to the angle FEC,
for they are vertical angles.   [i. 15]
Therefore the base AB is equal to the base FC,
and the triangle ABE is equal to the triangle CFE,
and the remaining angles are equal to the remaining angles respectively, namely, those which the equal sides subtend;   [i. 4]
therefore the angle BAE is equal to the angle ECF.

But the angle ECD is greater than the angle ECF;   [C.N. 5]

therefore the angle ACD is greater than the angle BAE.

Similarly also, if BC be bisected, the angle BCG, that is, the angle ACD [i. 15], can be proved greater than the angle ABC as well.

Therefore etc.   Q. E. D.

PROPOSITION 17

In any triangle two angles taken together in any manner are less than two right angles.

Let ABC be a triangle;
I say that two angles of the triangle ABC taken together in any manner are less than two right angles.

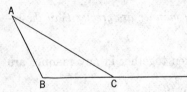

For let BC be produced to D. [Post. 2]
Then, since the angle ACD is an exterior angle of the triangle ABC,
it is greater than the interior and opposite angle ABC.   [i. 16]
Let the angle ACB be added to each;

therefore the angles ACD, ACB are greater than the angles ABC, BCA.
But the angles ACD, ACB are equal to two right angles.   [i. 13]
Therefore the angles ABC, BCA are less than two right angles.

Similarly we can prove that the angles BAC, ACB are also less than two right angles, and so are the angles CAB, ABC as well.

Therefore etc.   Q. E. D.

PROPOSITION 18

In any triangle the greater side subtends the greater angle.

For let ABC be a triangle having the side AC greater than AB;
I say that the angle ABC is also greater than the angle BCA.

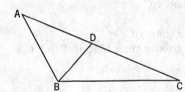

For, since AC is greater than AB, let AD be made equal to AB [i. 3], and let BD be joined.

Then, since the angle ADB is an exterior angle of the triangle BCD,
it is greater than the interior and opposite angle DCB.   [i. 16]

But the angle ADB is equal to the angle ABD,
since the side AB is equal to AD;

therefore the angle ABD is also greater than the angle ACB;
therefore the angle ABC is much greater than the angle ACB.
Therefore etc.

Q. E. D.

PROPOSITION 19

In any triangle the greater angle is subtended by the greater side.

Let ABC be a triangle having the angle ABC greater than the angle BCA;
I say that the side AC is also greater than the side AB.

For, if not, AC is either equal to AB or less.

Now AC is not equal to AB;
for then the angle ABC would also have been equal to the angle
ACB;　　　　　　　　　　　　　　　　　　　　　　　　[I. 5]

but it is not;
therefore AC is not equal to AB.

Neither is AC less than AB,
for then the angle ABC would also have been less than the angle ACB;　[I. 18]
but it is not;
therefore AC is not less than AB.

And it was proved that it is not equal either.
Therefore AC is greater than AB.
Therefore etc.

Q. E. D.

PROPOSITION 20

In any triangle two sides taken together in any manner are greater than the remaining one.

For let ABC be a triangle;
I say that in the triangle ABC two sides taken together in any manner are greater than the remaining one, namely

BA, AC greater than BC,

AB, BC greater than AC,

BC, CA greater than AB.

For let BA be drawn through to the point D, let DA be made equal to CA,
and let DC be joined.

Then, since DA is equal to AC,
the angle ADC is also equal to the angle ACD;　[I. 5]
therefore the angle BCD is greater than the angle ADC.

[C.N. 5]

And, since DCB is a triangle having the angle BCD greater
than the angle BDC,
and the greater angle is subtended by the greater side, [I. 19]
therefore DB is greater than BC.

But DA is equal to AC;
therefore BA, AC are greater than BC.

Similarly we can prove that AB, BC are also greater than CA, and BC, CA
than AB.

Therefore etc.

Q. E. D.

PROPOSITION 21

If on one of the sides of a triangle, from its extremities, there be constructed two

*straight lines meeting within the triangle, the straight lines so constructed will be
less than the remaining two sides of the triangle, but will contain a greater angle.*

On *BC*, one of the sides of the triangle *ABC*, from its extremities *B*, *C*, let
the two straight lines *BD*, *DC* be constructed meeting within the triangle;

I say that *BD*, *DC* are less than the remaining two sides of the triangle *BA*,
AC, but contain an angle *BDC* greater than the angle *BAC*.

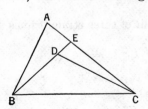

For let *BD* be drawn through to *E*.

Then, since in any triangle two sides are greater
than the remaining one,   [I. 20]
therefore, in the triangle *ABE*, the two sides *AB*,
AE are greater than *BE*.

Let *EC* be added to each;
therefore *BA*, *AC* are greater than *BE*, *EC*.

Again, since, in the triangle *CED*,
the two sides *CE*, *ED* are greater than *CD*,
let *DB* be added to each;
therefore *CE*, *EB* are greater than *CD*, *DB*.

But *BA*, *AC* were proved greater than *BE*, *EC*;
therefore *BA*, *AC* are much greater than *BD*, *DC*.

Again, since in any triangle the exterior angle is greater than the interior
and opposite angle,   [I. 16]
therefore, in the triangle *CDE*,
the exterior angle *BDC* is greater than the angle *CED*.

For the same reason, moreover, in the triangle *ABE* also,
the exterior angle *CEB* is greater than the angle *BAC*.

But the angle *BDC* was proved greater than the angle *CEB*;
therefore the angle *BDC* is much greater than the angle *BAC*.

Therefore etc.   Q. E. D.

PROPOSITION 22

*Out of three straight lines, which are equal to three given straight lines, to construct
a triangle: thus it is necessary that two of the straight lines taken together in any
manner should be greater than the remaining one.*   [I. 20]

Let the three given straight lines be *A*, *B*, *C*, and of these let two taken together in any manner be greater than the remaining one,

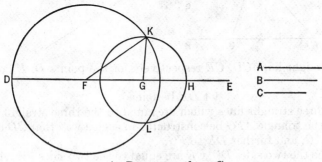

namely   *A*, *B* greater than *C*,
                         A, *C* greater than *B*,
and   *B*, *C* greater than *A*;

thus it is required to construct a triangle out of straight lines equal to A, B, C.

Let there be set out a straight line DE, terminated at D but of infinite length in the direction of E,

and let DF be made equal to A, FG equal to B, and GH equal to C.   [I. 3]

With centre F and distance FD let the circle DKL be described;

again, with centre G and distance GH let the circle KLH be described;

and let KF, KG be joined;

I say that the triangle KFG has been constructed out of three straight lines equal to A, B, C.

For, since the point F is the centre of the circle DKL,

FD is equal to FK.

But FD is equal to A;

therefore KF is also equal to A.

Again, since the point G is the centre of the circle LKH,

GH is equal to GK.

But GH is equal to C;

therefore KG is also equal to C.

And FG is also equal to B;

therefore the three straight lines KF, FG, GK are equal to the three straight lines A, B, C.

Therefore out of the three straight lines KF, FG, GK, which are equal to the three given straight lines A, B, C, the triangle KFG has been constructed.

Q. E. F.

PROPOSITION 23

On a given straight line and at a point on it to construct a rectilineal angle equal to a given rectilineal angle.

Let AB be the given straight line, A the point on it, and the angle DCE the given rectilineal angle;

thus it is required to construct on the given straight line AB, and at the point A on it, a rectilineal angle equal to the given rectilineal angle DCE.

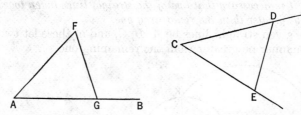

On the straight lines CD, CE respectively let the points D, E be taken at random;

let DE be joined,

and out of three straight lines which are equal to the three straight lines CD, DE, CE let the triangle AFG be constructed in such a way that CD is equal to AF, CE to AG, and further DE to FG.   [I. 22]

Then, since the two sides DC, CE are equal to the two sides FA, AG respectively,

and the base DE is equal to the base FG,

the angle DCE is equal to the angle FAG.   [I. 8]

Therefore on the given straight line AB, and at the point A on it, the rectilineal angle FAG has been constructed equal to the given rectilineal angle DCE.   Q. E. F.

PROPOSITION 24

If two triangles have the two sides equal to two sides respectively, but have the one of the angles contained by the equal straight lines greater than the other, they will also have the base greater than the base.

Let ABC, DEF be two triangles having the two sides AB, AC equal to the two sides DE, DF respectively, namely AB to DE, and AC to DF, and let the angle at A be greater than the angle at D;

I say that the base BC is also greater than the base EF.

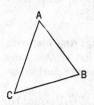 

For, since the angle BAC is greater than the angle EDF, let there be constructed, on the straight line DE, and at the point D on it, the angle EDG equal to the angle BAC;   [I. 23]
let DG be made equal to either of the two straight lines AC, DF, and let EG, FG be joined.

Then, since AB is equal to DE, and AC to DG,
the two sides BA, AC are equal to the two sides ED, DG, respectively;
and the angle BAC is equal to the angle EDG;
therefore the base BC is equal to the base EG.   [I. 4]

Again, since DF is equal to DG,
the angle DGF is also equal to the angle DFG;   [I. 5]
therefore the angle DFG is greater than the angle EGF.

Therefore the angle EFG is much greater than the angle EGF.

And, since EFG is a triangle having the angle EFG greater than the angle EGF,
and the greater angle is subtended by the greater side,   [I. 19]
the side EG is also greater than EF.

But EG is equal to BC.

Therefore BC is also greater than EF.

Therefore etc.   Q. E. D.

PROPOSITION 25

If two triangles have the two sides equal to two sides respectively, but have the base greater than the base, they will also have the one of the angles contained by the equal straight lines greater than the other.

Let ABC, DEF be two triangles having the two sides AB, AC equal to the two sides DE, DF respectively, namely AB to DE, and AC to DF; and let the base BC be greater than the base EF;

I say that the angle BAC is also greater than the angle EDF.

For, if not, it is either equal to it or less.

Now the angle BAC is not equal to the angle EDF; for then the base BC would also have been equal to the base EF,   [I. 4]
but it is not;

therefore the angle BAC is not equal to the angle EDF.

Neither again is the angle *BAC* less than the angle *EDF*; for then the base
BC would also have been less than the base *EF*,   [I. 24]

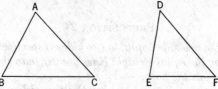

but it is not; therefore the angle *BAC* is not less than the angle *EDF*.
But it was proved that it is not equal either;
   therefore the angle *BAC* is greater than the angle *EDF*.
Therefore etc.   Q. E. D.

PROPOSITION 26

*If two triangles have the two angles equal to two angles respectively, and one side
equal to one side, namely, either the side adjoining the equal angles, or that subtending one of the equal angles, they will also have the remaining sides equal to the
remaining sides and the remaining angle to the remaining angle.*

Let *ABC*, *DEF* be two triangles having the two angles *ABC*, *BCA* equal to
the two angles *DEF*, *EFD* respectively, namely the angle *ABC* to the angle
DEF, and the angle *BCA* to the angle *EFD*; and let them also have one side
equal to one side, first that adjoining the equal angles, namely *BC* to *EF*;
 I say that they will also have the remaining sides equal to the remaining
sides respectively, namely *AB* to *DE* and *AC* to *DF*, and the remaining angle
to the remaining angle, namely the angle *BAC* to the angle *EDF*.

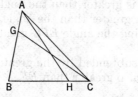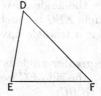

For, if *AB* is unequal to *DE*, one of them is greater.
Let *AB* be greater, and let *BG* be made equal to *DE*; and let *GC* be joined.
Then, since *BG* is equal to *DE*, and *BC* to *EF*,
 the two sides *GB*, *BC* are equal to the two sides *DE*, *EF* respectively;
   and the angle *GBC* is equal to the angle *DEF*;
   therefore the base *GC* is equal to the base *DF*,
  and the triangle *GBC* is equal to the triangle *DEF*,
and the remaining angles will be equal to the remaining angles, namely those
which the equal sides subtend;   [I. 4]
   therefore the angle *GCB* is equal to the angle *DFE*.
But the angle *DFE* is by hypothesis equal to the angle *BCA*;
   therefore the angle *BCG* is equal to the angle *BCA*,
    the less to the greater: which is impossible.
Therefore *AB* is not unequal to *DE*,
    and is therefore equal to it.
But *BC* is also equal to *EF*;

therefore the two sides AB, BC are equal to the two sides DE, EF respectively,

and the angle ABC is equal to the angle DEF;

therefore the base AC is equal to the base DF,

and the remaining angle BAC is equal to the remaining angle EDF. [I. 4]

Again, let sides subtending equal angles be equal, as AB to DE;

I say again that the remaining sides will be equal to the remaining sides, namely AC to DF and BC to EF, and further the remaining angle BAC is equal to the remaining angle EDF.

For, if BC is unequal to EF, one of them is greater.

Let BC be greater, if possible, and let BH be made equal to EF; let AH be joined.

Then, since BH is equal to EF, and AB to DE, the two sides AB, BH are equal to the two sides DE, EF respectively, and they contain equal angles;

therefore the base AH is equal to the base DF,

and the triangle ABH is equal to the triangle DEF,

and the remaining angles will be equal to the remaining angles, namely those which the equal sides subtend;   [I. 4]

therefore the angle BHA is equal to the angle EFD.

But the angle EFD is equal to the angle BCA;

therefore, in the triangle AHC, the exterior angle BHA is equal to the interior and opposite angle BCA:

which is impossible.   [I. 16]

Therefore BC is not unequal to EF,

and is therefore equal to it.

But AB is also equal to DE;

therefore the two sides AB, BC are equal to the two sides DE, EF respectively, and they contain equal angles;

therefore the base AC is equal to the base DF,

the triangle ABC equal to the triangle DEF,

and the remaining angle BAC equal to the remaining angle EDF. [I. 4]

Therefore etc.   Q. E. D.

PROPOSITION 27

If a straight line falling on two straight lines make the alternate angles equal to one another, the straight lines will be parallel to one another.

For let the straight line EF falling on the two straight lines AB, CD make the alternate angles AEF, EFD equal to one another;

I say that AB is parallel to CD.

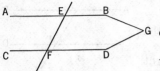

For, if not, AB, CD when produced will meet either in the direction of B, D or towards A, C.

Let them be produced and meet, in the direction of B, D, at G.

Then, in the triangle GEF,

the exterior angle AEF is equal to the interior and opposite angle EFG:

which is impossible.   [I. 16]

Therefore AB, CD when produced will not meet in the direction of B, D.

Similarly it can be proved that neither will they meet towards A, C.

But straight lines which do not meet in either direction are parallel;

[Def. 23]

therefore AB is parallel to CD.

Therefore etc.   Q. E. D.

PROPOSITION 28

If a straight line falling on two straight lines make the exterior angle equal to the interior and opposite angle on the same side, or the interior angles on the same side equal to two right angles, the straight lines will be parallel to one another.

For let the straight line EF falling on the two straight lines AB, CD make the exterior angle EGB equal to the interior and opposite angle GHD, or the interior angles on the same side, namely BGH, GHD, equal to two right angles;

I say that AB is parallel to CD.

For, since the angle EGB is equal to the angle GHD,

while the angle EGB is equal to the angle AGH,

[I. 15]

the angle AGH is also equal to the angle GHD;

and they are alternate;

therefore AB is parallel to CD.   [I. 27]

Again, since the angles BGH, GHD are equal to two right angles, and the angles AGH, BGH are also equal to two right angles,   [I. 13]

the angles AGH, BGH are equal to the angles BGH, GHD.

Let the angle BGH be subtracted from each;

therefore the remaining angle AGH is equal to the remaining angle GHD;

and they are alternate;

therefore AB is parallel to CD.   [I. 27]

Therefore etc.   Q. E. D.]

PROPOSITION 29

A straight line falling on parallel straight lines makes the alternate angles equal to one another, the exterior angle equal to the interior and opposite angle, and the interior angles on the same side equal to two right angles.

For let the straight line EF fall on the parallel straight lines AB, CD;

I say that it makes the alternate angles AGH, GHD equal, the exterior angle EGB equal to the interior and opposite angle GHD, and the interior angles on the same side, namely BGH, GHD, equal to two right angles.

For, if the angle AGH is unequal to the angle GHD, one of them is greater.

Let the angle AGH be greater.

Let the angle BGH be added to each;

therefore the angles AGH, BGH are greater than the angles BGH, GHD.

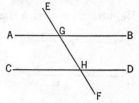

But the angles AGH, BGH are equal to two right angles;   [I. 13]

therefore the angles BGH, GHD are less than two right angles.

But straight lines produced indefinitely from angles less than two right angles meet;   [Post. 5]

therefore AB, CD, if produced indefinitely, will meet;

but they do not meet, because they are by hypothesis parallel.
Therefore the angle AGH is not unequal to the angle GHD,
and is therefore equal to it.
Again, the angle AGH is equal to the angle EGB;   [I. 15]
therefore the angle EGB is also equal to the angle GHD.   [C.N. 1]
Let the angle BGH be added to each;
therefore the angles EGB, BGH are equal to the angles BGH, GHD. [C.N. 2]
But the angles EGB, BGH are equal to two right angles;   [I. 13]
therefore the angles BGH, GHD are also equal to two right angles.
Therefore etc.   Q. E. D.

PROPOSITION 30

Straight lines parallel to the same straight line are also parallel to one another.
Let each of the straight lines AB, CD be parallel to EF; I say that AB is also
parallel to CD.

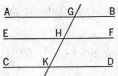

For let the straight line GK fall upon them.
Then, since the straight line GK has fallen on the parallel straight lines AB, EF,
the angle AGK is equal to the angle GHF. [I. 29]
Again, since the straight line GK has fallen on the parallel straight lines EF, CD,
the angle GHF is equal to the angle GKD.   [I. 29]
But the angle AGK was also proved equal to the angle GHF;
therefore the angle AGK is also equal to the angle GKD;   [C.N. 1]
and they are alternate.
Therefore AB is parallel to CD.   Q. E. D.

PROPOSITION 31

*Through a given point to draw a straight line parallel to a given straight
line.*
Let A be the given point, and BC the given straight line;
thus it is required to draw through the point A a straight line parallel to the
straight line BC.

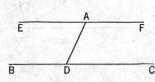

Let a point D be taken at random on BC,
and let AD be joined; on the straight line DA,
and at the point A on it, let the angle DAE be
constructed equal to the angle ADC [I. 23]; and
let the straight line AF be produced in a straight
line with EA.
Then, since the straight line AD falling on the two straight lines BC, EF has
made the alternate angles EAD, ADC equal to one another,
therefore EAF is parallel to BC.   [I. 27]
Therefore through the given point A the straight line EAF has been drawn
parallel to the given straight line BC.   Q. E. F.

PROPOSITION 32

*In any triangle, if one of the sides be produced, the exterior angle is equal to the two
interior and opposite angles, and the three interior angles of the triangle are equal
to two right angles.*

Let ABC be a triangle, and let one side of it BC be produced to D;

I say that the exterior angle ACD is equal to the two interior and opposite angles CAB, ABC, and the three interior angles of the triangle ABC, BCA, CAB are equal to two right angles.

For let CE be drawn through the point C parallel to the straight line AB.

[I. 31]

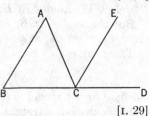

Then, since AB is parallel to CE,
    and AC has fallen upon them,
the alternate angles BAC, ACE are equal to one another.   [I. 29]

Again, since AB is parallel to CE,
  and the straight line BD has fallen upon them,
the exterior angle ECD is equal to the interior and opposite angle ABC.   [I. 29]

But the angle ACE was also proved equal to the angle BAC;
therefore the whole angle ACD is equal to the two interior and opposite angles BAC, ABC.

Let the angle ACB be added to each;
therefore the angles ACD, ACB are equal to the three angles ABC, BCA, CAB.

But the angles ACD, ACB are equal to two right angles;   [I. 13]
therefore the angles ABC, BCA, CAB are also equal to two right angles.

Therefore etc.   Q. E. D.

Proposition 33

The straight lines joining equal and parallel straight lines (at the extremities which are) in the same directions (respectively) are themselves also equal and parallel.

Let AB, CD be equal and parallel, and let the straight lines AC, BD join them (at the extremities which are) in the same directions (respectively);

I say that AC, BD are also equal and parallel.

Let BC be joined.

Then, since AB is parallel to CD, and BC has fallen upon them,
the alternate angles ABC, BCD are equal to one another.   [I. 29]

And, since AB is equal to CD,
            and BC is common,
the two sides AB, BC are equal to the two sides DC, CB;
and the angle ABC is equal to the angle BCD;
        therefore the base AC is equal to the base BD,
        and the triangle ABC is equal to the triangle DCB,
and the remaining angles will be equal to the remaining angles respectively, namely those which the equal sides subtend;   [I. 4]
        therefore the angle ACB is equal to the angle CBD.

And, since the straight line BC falling on the two straight lines AC, BD has made the alternate angles equal to one another,
                AC is parallel to BD.   [I. 27]

And it was also proved equal to it.

Therefore etc.
                                                                            Q. E. D.

PROPOSITION 34

In parallelogrammic areas the opposite sides and angles are equal to one another, and the diameter bisects the areas.

Let $ACDB$ be a parallelogrammic area, and BC its diameter;
I say that the opposite sides and angles of the parallelogram $ACDB$ are equal
to one another, and the diameter BC bisects it.

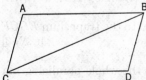

For, since AB is parallel to CD,
and the straight line BC has fallen upon them,
the alternate angles ABC, BCD are equal to one
another.   [I. 29]

Again, since AC is parallel to BD, and BC has
fallen upon them,
the alternate angles ACB, CBD are equal to one another.   [I. 29]
Therefore ABC, DCB are two triangles having the two angles ABC, BCA
equal to the two angles DCB, CBD respectively, and one side equal to one side,
namely that adjoining the equal angles and common to both of them, BC;
therefore they will also have the remaining sides equal to the remaining
sides respectively, and the remaining angle to the remaining angle;   [I. 26]
therefore the side AB is equal to CD,
and AC to BD,
and further the angle BAC is equal to the angle CDB.
And, since the angle ABC is equal to the angle BCD,
and the angle CBD to the angle ACB,
the whole angle ABD is equal to the whole angle ACD.   [C.N. 2]
And the angle BAC was also proved equal to the angle CDB.
Therefore in parallelogrammic areas the opposite sides and angles are equal
to one another.
I say, next, that the diameter also bisects the areas.
For, since AB is equal to CD,
and BC is common,
the two sides AB, BC are equal to the two sides DC, CB respectively;
and the angle ABC is equal to the angle BCD;
therefore the base AC is also equal to DB,
and the triangle ABC is equal to the triangle DCB.   [I. 4]
Therefore the diameter BC bisects the parallelogram $ACDB$.   Q. E. D.

PROPOSITION 35

Parallelograms which are on the same base and in the same parallels are equal to one another.

Let $ABCD$, $EBCF$ be parallelograms on the same base BC and in the same
parallels AF, BC;
I say that $ABCD$ is equal to the parallelogram $EBCF$.

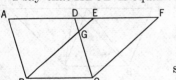

For, since $ABCD$ is a parallelogram,
AD is equal to BC.   [I. 34]
For the same reason also
EF is equal to BC,
so that AD is also equal to EF;   [C.N. 1]
and DE is common;

therefore the whole AE is equal to the whole DF.   [C.N. 2]
But AB is also equal to DC;   [I. 34]
therefore the two sides EA, AB are equal to the two sides FD, DC respectively,
and the angle FDC is equal to the angle EAB,
the exterior to the interior;   [I. 29]
therefore the base EB is equal to the base FC,
and the triangle EAB will be equal to the triangle FDC.   [I. 4]
Let DGE be subtracted from each;
therefore the trapezium $ABGD$ which remains is equal to the trapezium $EGCF$ which remains.   [C.N. 3]
Let the triangle GBC be added to each;
therefore the whole parallelogram $ABCD$ is equal to the whole parallelogram $EBCF$.   [C.N. 2]
Therefore etc.   Q. E. D.

PROPOSITION 36

Parallelograms which are on equal bases and in the same parallels are equal to one another.

Let $ABCD$, $EFGH$ be parallelograms which are on equal bases BC, FG and in the same parallels AH, BG;
I say that the parallelogram $ABCD$ is equal to $EFGH$.
For let BE, CH be joined.
Then, since BC is equal to FG, while

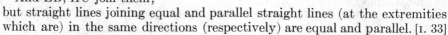

FG is equal to EH,
BC is also equal to EH.   [C.N. 1]
But they are also parallel.
And EB, HC join them;
but straight lines joining equal and parallel straight lines (at the extremities which are) in the same directions (respectively) are equal and parallel. [I. 33]
Therefore $EBCH$ is a parallelogram.   [I. 34]
And it is equal to $ABCD$;
for it has the same base BC with it, and is in the same parallels BC, AH with it.   [I. 35]
For the same reason also $EFGH$ is equal to the same $EBCH$;   [I. 35]
so that the parallelogram $ABCD$ is also equal to $EFGH$.   [C.N. 1]
Therefore etc.   Q. E. D.

PROPOSITION 37

Triangles which are on the same base and in the same parallels are equal to one another.

Let ABC, DBC be triangles on the same base BC and in the same parallels AD, BC;
I say that the triangle ABC is equal to the triangle DBC.
Let AD be produced in both directions to E, F;
through B let BE be drawn parallel to CA,   [I. 31]

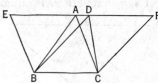

and through C let CF be drawn parallel to BD.   [I. 31]

Then each of the figures $EBCA$, $DBCF$ is a parallelogram; and they are equal,

for they are on the same base BC and in the same parallels BC, EF. [I. 35]

Moreover the triangle ABC is half of the parallelogram $EBCA$; for the diameter AB bisects it.   [I. 34]

And the triangle DBC is half of the parallelogram $DBCF$; for the diameter DC bisects it.   [I. 34]

[But the halves of equal things are equal to one another.]

Therefore the triangle ABC is equal to the triangle DBC.

Therefore etc.   Q. E. D.

PROPOSITION 38

Triangles which are on equal bases and in the same parallels are equal to one another.

Let ABC, DEF be triangles on equal bases BC, EF and in the same parallels BC, AD;

I say that the triangle ABC is equal to the triangle DEF.

For let AD be produced in both directions to G, H;

through B let BG be drawn parallel to CA,   [I. 31]

and through F let FH be drawn parallel to DE.

Then each of the figures $GBCA$, $DEFH$ is a parallelogram;

and $GBCA$ is equal to $DEFH$;

for they are on equal bases BC, EF and in the same parallels BF, GH.   [I. 36]

Moreover the triangle ABC is half of the parallelogram $GBCA$; for the diameter AB bisects it.   [I. 34]

And the triangle FED is half of the parallelogram $DEFH$; for the diameter DF bisects it.   [I. 34]

[But the halves of equal things are equal to one another.]

Therefore the triangle ABC is equal to the triangle DEF.

Therefore etc.   Q. E. D.

PROPOSITION 39

Equal triangles which are on the same base and on the same side are also in the same parallels.

Let ABC, DBC be equal triangles which are on the same base BC and on the same side of it;

[I say that they are also in the same parallels.]

And [For] let AD be joined; I say that AD is parallel to BC.

For, if not, let AE be drawn through the point A parallel to the straight line BC,   [I. 31]

and let EC be joined.

Therefore the triangle ABC is equal to the triangle EBC;

for it is on the same base BC with it and in the same parallels.   [I. 37]

But ABC is equal to DBC;

24 EUCLID

therefore *DBC* is also equal to *EBC*,   [*C.N.* 1]
the greater to the less: which is impossible.
Therefore *AE* is not parallel to *BC*.
Similarly we can prove that neither is any other straight line except *AD*;
therefore *AD* is parallel to *BC*.
Therefore etc.   Q. E. D.

PROPOSITION 40

Equal triangles which are on equal bases and on the same side are also in the same parallels.

Let *ABC*, *CDE* be equal triangles on equal bases *BC*, *CE* and on the same side.
I say that they are also in the same parallels.
For let *AD* be joined;
I say that *AD* is parallel to *BE*.
For, if not, let *AF* be drawn through *A* parallel to *BE*
[I. 31], and let *FE* be joined.
Therefore the triangle *ABC* is equal to the triangle
FCE;

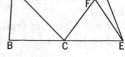

for they are on equal bases *BC*, *CE* and in the same parallels *BE*, *AF*.   [I. 38]
But the triangle *ABC* is equal to the triangle *DCE*;
therefore the triangle *DCE* is also equal to the triangle *FCE*,
                               [*C.N.* 1]
the greater to the less: which is impossible.
Therefore *AF* is not parallel to *BE*.
Similarly we can prove that neither is any other straight line except *AD*;
therefore *AD* is parallel to *BE*.
Therefore etc.   Q. E. D.

PROPOSITION 41

If a parallelogram have the same base with a triangle and be in the same parallels, the parallelogram is double of the triangle.

For let the parallelogram *ABCD* have the same base *BC* with the triangle *EBC*, and let it be in the same parallels *BC*, *AE*;
I say that the parallelogram *ABCD* is double of the triangle *BEC*.
For let *AC* be joined.
Then the triangle *ABC* is equal to the triangle *EBC*;
for it is on the same base *BC* with it and in the same parallels *BC*, *AE*.   [I. 37]
But the parallelogram *ABCD* is double of the triangle *ABC*;
for the diameter *AC* bisects it;   [I. 34]
so that the parallelogram *ABCD* is also double of the triangle *EBC*.
Therefore etc.   Q. E. D.

PROPOSITION 42

To construct, in a given rectilineal angle, a parallelogram equal to a given triangle.

Let *ABC* be the given triangle, and *D* the given rectilineal angle;
thus it is required to construct in the rectilineal angle *D* a parallelogram equal

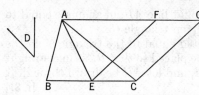

to the triangle ABC.

Let BC be bisected at E, and let AE be joined;
on the straight line EC, and at the point E on it, let the angle CEF be constructed equal to the angle D;   [I. 23]

through A let AG be drawn parallel to EC, and   [I. 31]
through C let CG be drawn parallel to EF.

Then $FECG$ is a parallelogram.

And, since BE is equal to EC,
        the triangle ABE is also equal to the triangle AEC,
for they are on equal bases BE, EC and in the same parallels BC, AG; [I. 38]
        therefore the triangle ABC is double of the triangle AEC.

But the parallelogram $FECG$ is also double of the triangle AEC, for it has the same base with it and is in the same parallels with it;   [I. 41]
        therefore the parallelogram $FECG$ is equal to the triangle ABC.

And it has the angle CEF equal to the given angle D.

Therefore the parallelogram $FECG$ has been constructed equal to the given triangle ABC, in the angle CEF which is equal to D.   Q. E. F.

Proposition 43

In any parallelogram the complements of the parallelograms about the diameter are equal to one another.

Let $ABCD$ be a parallelogram, and AC its diameter;
and about AC let EH, FG be parallelograms, and BK, KD the so-called complements;

I say that the complement BK is equal to the complement KD.

For, since $ABCD$ is a parallelogram, and AC its diameter,
        the triangle ABC is equal to the triangle ACD.   [I. 34]

Again, since EH is a parallelogram, and AK is its diameter,
        the triangle AEK is equal to the triangle AHK.

For the same reason
        the triangle KFC is also equal to KGC.

Now, since the triangle AEK is equal to the triangle AHK,
                and KFC to KGC,
the triangle AEK together with KGC is equal to the triangle AHK together with KFC.   [C.N. 2]

And the whole triangle ABC is also equal to the whole ADC;
therefore the complement BK which remains is equal to the complement KD which remains.   [C.N. 3]

Therefore etc.   Q. E. D.

Proposition 44

To a given straight line to apply, in a given rectilineal angle, a parallelogram equal to a given triangle.

Let AB be the given straight line, C the given triangle and D the given rectilineal angle;

thus it is required to apply to the given straight line AB, in an angle equal to the angle D, a parallelogram equal to the given triangle C.

Let the parallelogram $BEFG$ be constructed equal to the triangle C, in the angle EBG which is equal to D [I. 42]; let it be placed so that BE is in a straight line with AB; let FG be drawn through to H, and let AH be drawn through A parallel to either BG or EF.   [I. 31]

Let HB be joined.

Then, since the straight line HF falls upon the parallels AH, EF, the angles AHF, HFE are equal to two right angles.
                         [I. 29]

Therefore the angles BHG, GFE are less than two right angles;
and straight lines produced indefinitely from angles less than two right angles meet;   [Post. 5]
         therefore HB, FE, when produced, will meet.

Let them be produced and meet at K; through the point K let KL be drawn parallel to either EA or FH,   [I. 31]
         and let HA, GB be produced to the points L, M.

Then $HLKF$ is a parallelogram,
HK is its diameter, and AG, ME are parallelograms, and LB, BF the so-called complements, about HK;
                         therefore LB is equal to BF.   [I. 43]
But BF is equal to the triangle C;
                         therefore LB is also equal to C.   [C.N. 1]
And, since the angle GBE is equal to the angle ABM,   [I. 15]
              while the angle GBE is equal to D,
         the angle ABM is also equal to the angle D.

Therefore the parallelogram LB equal to the given triangle C has been applied to the given straight line AB, in the angle ABM which is equal to D.
                                        Q. E. F.

PROPOSITION 45

To construct, in a given rectilineal angle, a parallelogram equal to a given rectilineal figure.

Let $ABCD$ be the given rectilineal figure and E the given rectilineal angle; thus it is required to construct, in the given angle E, a parallelogram equal to the rectilineal figure $ABCD$.

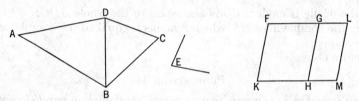

Let DB be joined, and let the parallelogram FH be constructed equal to the triangle ABD, in the angle HKF which is equal to E;   [I. 42]
let the parallelogram GM equal to the triangle DBC be applied to the straight

line GH, in the angle GHM which is equal to E.   [I. 44]

Then, since the angle E is equal to each of the angles HKF, GHM,

the angle HKF is also equal to the angle GHM.   [C.N. 1]

Let the angle KHG be added to each;

therefore the angles FKH, KHG are equal to the angles KHG, GHM.

But the angles FKH, KHG are equal to two right angles;   [I. 29]

therefore the angles KHG, GHM are also equal to two right angles.

Thus, with a straight line GH, and at the point H on it, two straight lines KH, HM not lying on the same side make the adjacent angles equal to two right angles;

therefore KH is in a straight line with HM.   [I. 14]

And, since the straight line HG falls upon the parallels KM, FG, the alternate angles MHG, HGF are equal to one another.   [I. 29]

Let the angle HGL be added to each;

therefore the angles MHG, HGL are equal to the angles HGF, HGL.   [C.N. 2]

But the angles MHG, HGL are equal to two right angles;   [I. 29]

therefore the angles HGF, HGL are also equal to two right angles.   [C.N. 1]

Therefore FG is in a straight line with GL.   [I. 14]

And, since FK is equal and parallel to HG,   [I. 34]

and HG to ML also,

KF is also equal and parallel to ML;   [C.N. 1; I. 30]

and the straight lines KM, FL join them (at their extremities); therefore KM, FL are also equal and parallel.   [I. 33]

Therefore $KFLM$ is a parallelogram.

And, since the triangle ABD is equal to the parallelogram FH,

and DBC to GM,

the whole rectilineal figure $ABCD$ is equal to the whole parallelogram $KFLM$.

Therefore the parallelogram $KFLM$ has been constructed equal to the given rectilineal figure $ABCD$, in the angle FKM which is equal to the given angle E.

Q. E. F.

PROPOSITION 46

On a given straight line to describe a square.

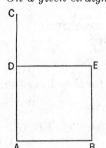

Let AB be the given straight line; thus it is required to describe a square on the straight line AB.

Let AC be drawn at right angles to the straight line AB from the point A on it [I. 11], and let AD be made equal to AB;

through the point D let DE be drawn parallel to AB, and through the point B let BE be drawn parallel to AD.   [I. 31]

Therefore $ADEB$ is a parallelogram;

therefore AB is equal to DE, and AD to BE. [I. 34]

But AB is equal to AD;

therefore the four straight lines BA, AD, DE, EB are equal to one another; therefore the parallelogram $ADEB$ is equilateral.

I say next that it is also right-angled.

For, since the straight line AD falls upon the parallels AB, DE,

the angles BAD, ADE are equal to two right angles.   [I. 29]

But the angle *BAD* is right;

therefore the angle *ADE* is also right.

And in parallelogrammic areas the opposite sides and angles are equal to one another; [I. 34]

therefore each of the opposite angles *ABE*, *BED* is also right.

Therefore *ADEB* is right-angled.

And it was also proved equilateral.

Therefore it is a square; and it is described on the straight line *AB*. Q. E. F.

PROPOSITION 47

In right-angled triangles the square on the side subtending the right angle is equal to the squares on the sides containing the right angle.

Let *ABC* be a right-angled triangle having the angle *BAC* right;

I say that the square on *BC* is equal to the squares on *BA*, *AC*.

For let there be described on *BC* the square *BDEC*, and on *BA*, *AC* the squares *GB*, *HC*; [I. 46]
through *A* let *AL* be drawn parallel to either *BD* or *CE*, and let *AD*, *FC* be joined.

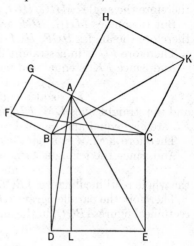

Then, since each of the angles *BAC*, *BAG* is right, it follows that with a straight line *BA*, and at the point *A* on it, the two straight lines *AC*, *AG* not lying on the same side make the adjacent angles equal to two right angles;

therefore *CA* is in a straight line with *AG*. [I. 14]

For the same reason
BA is also in a straight line with *AH*.

And, since the angle *DBC* is equal to the angle *FBA*: for each is right:

let the angle *ABC* be added to each;

therefore the whole angle *DBA* is equal to the whole angle *FBC*. [C.N. 2]
And, since *DB* is equal to *BC*, and *FB* to *BA*,

the two sides *AB*, *BD* are equal to the two sides *FB*, *BC* respectively;

and the angle *ABD* is equal to the angle *FBC*;

therefore the base *AD* is equal to the base *FC*,

and the triangle *ABD* is equal to the triangle *FBC*. [I. 4]

Now the parallelogram *BL* is double of the triangle *ABD*, for they have the same base *BD* and are in the same parallels *BD*, *AL*. [I. 41]

And the square *GB* is double of the triangle *FBC*,

for they again have the same base *FB* and are in the same parallels *FB*, *GC*. [I. 41]

[But the doubles of equals are equal to one another.]

Therefore the parallelogram *BL* is also equal to the square *GB*.

Similarly, if *AE*, *BK* be joined,

the parallelogram *CL* can also be proved equal to the square *HC*;

therefore the whole square *BDEC* is equal to the two squares *GB*, *HC*. [C.N. 2]

And the square *BDEC* is described on *BC*,

and the squares GB, HC on BA, AC.

Therefore the square on the side BC is equal to the squares on the sides BA, AC.

Therefore etc.   Q. E. D.

Proposition 48

If in a triangle the square on one of the sides be equal to the squares on the remaining two sides of the triangle, the angle contained by the remaining two sides of the triangle is right.

For in the triangle ABC let the square on one side BC be equal to the squares on the sides BA, AC;

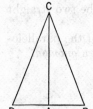

I say that the angle BAC is right.

For let AD be drawn from the point A at right angles to the straight line AC, let AD be made equal to BA, and let DC be joined.

Since DA is equal to AB,

the square on DA is also equal to the square on AB.

Let the square on AC be added to each;

therefore the squares on DA, AC are equal to the squares on BA, AC.

But the square on DC is equal to the squares on DA, AC, for the angle DAC is right;   [I. 47]

and the square on BC is equal to the squares on BA, AC, for this is the hypothesis;

therefore the square on DC is equal to the square on BC,

so that the side DC is also equal to BC.

And, since DA is equal to AB,

and AC is common,

the two sides DA, AC are equal to the two sides BA, AC;

and the base DC is equal to the base BC;

therefore the angle DAC is equal to the angle BAC.   [I. 8]

But the angle DAC is right;

therefore the angle BAC is also right.

Therefore etc.   Q. E. D.

BOOK TWO

DEFINITIONS

1. Any rectangular parallelogram is said to be *contained* by the two straight lines containing the right angle.

2. And in any parallelogrammic area let any one whatever of the parallelograms about its diameter with the two complements be called a *gnomon*.

BOOK II. PROPOSITIONS.

PROPOSITION 1

If there be two straight lines, and one of them be cut into any number of segments whatever, the rectangle contained by the two straight lines is equal to the rectangles contained by the uncut straight line and each of the segments.

Let A, BC be two straight lines, and let BC be cut at random at the points D, E;

I say that the rectangle contained by A, BC is equal to the rectangle contained by A, BD, that contained by A, DE and that contained by A, EC.

For let BF be drawn from B at right angles to BC;   [I. 11]
let BG be made equal to A,   [I. 3]
through G let GH be drawn parallel to BC,
[I. 31]
and through D, E, C let DK, EL, CH be drawn parallel to BG.

Then BH is equal to BK, DL, EH.

Now BH is the rectangle A, BC, for it is contained by GB, BC, and BG is equal to A;
BK is the rectangle A, BD, for it is contained by GB, BD, and BG is equal to A;
and DL is the rectangle A, DE, for DK, that is BG is equal to A. [I. 34]
Similarly also EH is the rectangle A, EC.

Therefore the rectangle A, BC is equal to the rectangle A, BD, the rectangle A, DE and the rectangle A, EC.

Therefore etc.   Q. E. D.

PROPOSITION 2

If a straight line be cut at random, the rectangle contained by the whole and both of the segments is equal to the square on the whole.

For let the straight line AB be cut at random at the point C;

I say that the rectangle contained by AB, BC together with the rectangle contained by BA, AC is equal to the square on AB.

For let the square *ADEB* be described on *AB* [I. 46], and let *CF* be drawn through *C* parallel to either *AD* or *BE*.   [I. 31]

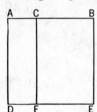

Then *AE* is equal to *AF*, *CE*.

Now *AE* is the square on *AB*;

AF is the rectangle contained by *BA*, *AC*, for it is contained by *DA*, *AC*, and *AD* is equal to *AB*;

and *CE* is the rectangle *AB*, *BC*, for *BE* is equal to *AB*.

Therefore the rectangle *BA*, *AC* together with the rectangle *AB*, *BC* is equal to the square on *AB*.

Therefore etc.   Q. E. D.

PROPOSITION 3

If a straight line be cut at random, the rectangle contained by the whole and one of the segments is equal to the rectangle contained by the segments and the square on the aforesaid segment.

For let the straight line *AB* be cut at random at *C*;

I say that the rectangle contained by *AB*, *BC* is equal to the rectangle contained by *AC*, *CB* together with the square on *BC*.

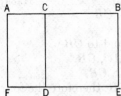

For let the square *CDEB* be described on *CB*; [I. 46]

let *ED* be drawn through to *F*,

and through *A* let *AF* be drawn parallel to either *CD* or *BE*.   [I. 31]

Then *AE* is equal to *AD*, *CE*.

Now *AE* is the rectangle contained by *AB*, *BC*, for it is contained by *AB*, *BE*, and *BE* is equal to *BC*;

AD is the rectangle *AC*, *CB*, for *DC* is equal to *CB*;

and *DB* is the square on *CB*.

Therefore the rectangle contained by *AB*, *BC* is equal to the rectangle contained by *AC*, *CB* together with the square on *BC*.

Therefore etc.   Q. E. D.

PROPOSITION 4

If a straight line be cut at random, the square on the whole is equal to the squares on the segments and twice the rectangle contained by the segments.

For let the straight line *AB* be cut at random at *C*;

I say that the square on *AB* is equal to the squares on *AC*, *CB* and twice the rectangle contained by *AC*, *CB*.

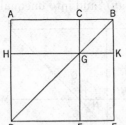

For let the square *ADEB* be described on *AB*,

[I. 46]

let *BD* be joined;

through *C* let *CF* be drawn parallel to either *AD* or *EB*,

and through *G* let *HK* be drawn parallel to either *AB* or *DE*.   [I. 31]

Then, since *CF* is parallel to *AD*, and *BD* has fallen on them,

the exterior angle *CGB* is equal to the interior and opposite angle *ADB*.   [I. 29]

But the angle *ADB* is equal to the angle *ABD*,

since the side *BA* is also equal to *AD*;   [I. 5]

therefore the angle CGB is also equal to the angle GBC,
so that the side BC is also equal to the side CG. [I. 6]
But CB is equal to GK, and CG to KB; [I. 34]
therefore GK is also equal to KB;
therefore $CGKB$ is equilateral.
I say next that it is also right-angled.
For, since CG is parallel to BK,
the angles KBC, GCB are equal to two right angles. [I. 29]
But the angle KBC is right;
therefore the angle BCG is also right,
so that the opposite angles CGK, GKB are also right. [I. 34]
Therefore $CGKB$ is right-angled;
and it was also proved equilateral;
therefore it is a square;
and it is described on CB.
For the same reason
HF is also a square;
and it is described on HG, that is AC. [I. 34]
Therefore the squares HF, KC are the squares on AC, CB.
Now, since AG is equal to GE,
and AG is the rectangle AC, CB, for GC is equal to CB,
therefore GE is also equal to the rectangle AC, CB.
Therefore AG, GE are equal to twice the rectangle AC, CB.
But the squares HF, CK are also the squares on AC, CB; therefore the four areas HF, CK, AG, GE are equal to the squares on AC, CB and twice the rectangle contained by AC, CB.
But HF, CK, AG, GE are the whole $ADEB$,
which is the square on AB.
Therefore the square on AB is equal to the squares on AC, CB and twice the rectangle contained by AC, CB.
Therefore etc. Q. E. D.

PROPOSITION 5

If a straight line be cut into equal and unequal segments, the rectangle contained by the unequal segments of the whole together with the square on the straight line between the points of section is equal to the square on the half.

For let a straight line AB be cut into equal segments at C and into unequal segments at D;
I say that the rectangle contained by AD, DB together with the square on CD is equal to the square on CB.
For let the square $CEFB$ be described on CB, [I. 46]
and let BE be joined;
through D let DG be drawn parallel to either CE or BF,
through H again let KM be drawn parallel to either AB or EF,
and again through A let AK be drawn parallel to either CL or BM. [I. 31]
Then, since the complement CH is equal to the complement HF, [I. 43]

let *DM* be added to each;
therefore the whole *CM* is equal to the whole *DF*.

But *CM* is equal to *AL*,
since *AC* is also equal to *CB*;   [I. 36]
therefore *AL* is also equal to *DF*.

Let *CH* be added to each;
therefore the whole *AH* is equal to the gnomon *NOP*.

But *AH* is the rectangle *AD*, *DB*, for *DH* is equal to *DB*,
therefore the gnomon *NOP* is also equal to the rectangle *AD*, *DB*.

Let *LG*, which is equal to the square on *CD*, be added to each;
therefore the gnomon *NOP* and *LG* are equal to the rectangle contained by *AD*, *DB* and the square on *CD*.

But the gnomon *NOP* and *LG* are the whole square *CEFB*, which is described on *CB*;
therefore the rectangle contained by *AD*, *DB* together with the square on *CD* is equal to the square on *CB*.

Therefore etc.   Q. E .D.

PROPOSITION 6

If a straight line be bisected and a straight line be added to it in a straight line, the rectangle contained by the whole with the added straight line and the added straight line together with the square on the half is equal to the square on the straight line made up of the half and the added straight line.

For let a straight line *AB* be bisected at the point *C*, and let a straight line *BD* be added to it in a straight line;

I say that the rectangle contained by *AD*, *DB* together with the square on *CB* is equal to the square on *CD*.

For let the square *CEFD* be described on *CD*,   [I. 46]
and let *DE* be joined;
through the point *B* let *BG* be drawn parallel to either *EC* or *DF*,
through the point *H* let *KM* be drawn parallel to either *AB* or *EF*,
and further through *A* let *AK* be drawn parallel to either *CL* or *DM*. [I. 31]

Then, since *AC* is equal to *CB*,
AL is also equal to *CH*.   [I. 36]
But *CH* is equal to *HF*.   [I. 43]
Therefore *AL* is also equal to *HF*.
Let *CM* be added to each;
therefore the whole *AM* is equal to the gnomon *NOP*.
But *AM* is the rectangle *AD*, *DB*,
for *DM* is equal to *DB*;

therefore the gnomon *NOP* is also equal to the rectangle *AD*, *DB*.

Let *LG*, which is equal to the square on *BC*, be added to each;
therefore the rectangle contained by *AD*, *DB* together with the square on *CB* is equal to the gnomon *NOP* and *LG*.

But the gnomon *NOP* and *LG* are the whole square *CEFD*, which is described on *CD*;
therefore the rectangle contained by *AD*, *DB* together with the square on *CB* is equal to the square on *CD*.

Therefore etc.   Q. E. D.

Proposition 7

If a straight line be cut at random, the square on the whole and that on one of the segments both together are equal to twice the rectangle contained by the whole and the said segment and the square on the remaining segment.

For let a straight line AB be cut at random at the point C;

I say that the squares on AB, BC are equal to twice the rectangle contained by AB, BC and the square on CA.

For let the square $ADEB$ be described on AB,   [I. 46]

and let the figure be drawn.

Then, since AG is equal to GE [I. 43], let CF be added to each;

therefore the whole AF is equal to the whole CE.

Therefore AF, CE are double of AF.

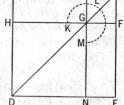

But AF, CE are the gnomon KLM and the square CF; therefore the gnomon KLM and the square CF are double of AF.

But twice the rectangle AB, BC is also double of AF; for BF is equal to BC;

therefore the gnomon KLM and the square CF are equal to twice the rectangle AB, BC.

Let DG, which is the square on AC, be added to each;

therefore the gnomon KLM and the squares BG, GD are equal to twice the rectangle contained by AB, BC and the square on AC.

But the gnomon KLM and the squares BG, GD are the whole $ADEB$ and CF,

which are squares described on AB, BC;

therefore the squares on AB, BC are equal to twice the rectangle contained by AB, BC together with the square on AC.

Therefore etc.   Q. E. D.

Proposition 8

If a straight line be cut at random, four times the rectangle contained by the whole and one of the segments together with the square on the remaining segment is equal to the square described on the whole and the aforesaid segment as on one straight line.

For let a straight line AB be cut at random at the point C;

I say that four times the rectangle contained by AB, BC together with the square on AC is equal to the square described on AB, BC as on one straight line.

For let [the straight line] BD be produced in a straight line [with AB], and let BD be made equal to CB;

let the square $AEFD$ be described on AD, and let the figure be drawn double.

Then, since CB is equal to BD, while CB is equal to GK, and BD to KN,

therefore GK is also equal to KN.

For the same reason

QR is also equal to RP.

And, since BC is equal to BD, and GK to KN,

therefore CK is also equal to KD, and GR to RN.   [I. 36]

But CK is equal to RN, for they are complements of the parallelogram CP;

[I. 43]

therefore *KD* is also equal to *GR*;
therefore the four areas *DK*, *CK*, *GR*, *RN* are equal to one another.
Therefore the four are quadruple of *CK*.

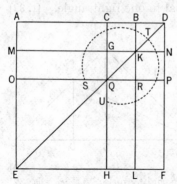

Again, since *CB* is equal to *BD*,
while *BD* is equal to *BK*, that is *CG*,
and *CB* is equal to *GK*, that is *GQ*,
therefore *CG* is also equal to *GQ*.

And, since *CG* is equal to *GQ*, and *QR* to *RP*,
AG is also equal to *MQ*, and *QL* to *RF*. [I. 36]

But *MQ* is equal to *QL*, for they are complements of the parallelogram *ML*;   [I. 43]
therefore *AG* is also equal to *RF*;
therefore the four areas *AG*, *MQ*, *QL*, *RF* are equal to one another.

Therefore the four are quadruple of *AG*.

But the four areas *CK*, *KD*, *GR*, *RN* were proved to be quadruple of *CK*;
therefore the eight areas, which contain the gnomon *STU*, are quadruple of *AK*.

Now, since *AK* is the rectangle *AB*, *BD*, for *BK* is equal to *BD*,
therefore four times the rectangle *AB*, *BD* is quadruple of *AK*.

But the gnomon *STU* was also proved to be quadruple of *AK*;
therefore four times the rectangle *AB*, *BD* is equal to the gnomon *STU*.

Let *OH*, which is equal to the square on *AC*, be added to each;
therefore four times the rectangle *AB*, *BD* together with the square on *AC* is equal to the gnomon *STU* and *OH*.

But the gnomon *STU* and *OH* are the whole square *AEFD*,
which is described on *AD*;
therefore four times the rectangle *AB*, *BD* together with the square on *AC* is equal to the square on *AD*.

But *BD* is equal to *BC*;
therefore four times the rectangle contained by *AB*, *BC* together with the square on *AC* is equal to the square on *AD*, that is to the square described on *AB* and *BC* as on one straight line.

Therefore etc.   Q. E. D.

PROPOSITION 9

If a straight line be cut into equal and unequal segments, the squares on the unequal segments of the whole are double of the square on the half and of the square on the straight line between the points of section.

For let a straight line *AB* be cut into equal segments at *C*, and into unequal segments at *D*;
I say that the squares on *AD*, *DB* are double of the squares on *AC*, *CD*.

For let *CE* be drawn from *C* at right angles to *AB*, and let it be made equal to either *AC* or *CB*;
let *EA*, *EB* be joined,
let *DF* be drawn through *D* parallel to *EC*,
and *FG* through *F* parallel to *AB*,
and let *AF* be joined.

Then, since AC is equal to CE,

the angle EAC is also equal to the angle AEC.

And, since the angle at C is right,

the remaining angles EAC, AEC are equal to one right angle.   [I. 32]

And they are equal;

therefore each of the angles CEA, CAE is half a right angle.

For the same reason each of the angles CEB, EBC is also half a right angle;

therefore the whole angle AEB is right.

And, since the angle GEF is half a right angle.

and the angle EGF is right, for it is equal to the interior and opposite angle ECB,   [I. 29]

the remaining angle EFG is half a right angle;   [I. 32]

therefore the angle GEF is equal to the angle EFG,

so that the side EG is also equal to GF.   [I. 6]

Again, since the angle at B is half a right angle,

and the angle FDB is right, for it is again equal to the interior and opposite angle ECB,   [I. 29]

the remaining angle BFD is half a right angle;   [I. 32]

therefore the angle at B is equal to the angle DFB,

so that the side FD is also equal to the side DB.   [I. 6]

Now, since AC is equal to CE,

the square on AC is also equal to the square on CE;

therefore the squares on AC, CE are double of the square on AC.

But the square on EA is equal to the squares on AC, CE, for the angle ACE is right;   [I. 47]

therefore the square on EA is double of the square on AC.

Again, since EG is equal to GF,

the square on EG is also equal to the square on GF;

therefore the squares on EG, GF are double of the square on GF.

But the square on EF is equal to the squares on EG, GF;

therefore the square on EF is double of the square on GF.

But GF is equal to CD;   [I. 34]

therefore the square on EF is double of the square on CD.

But the square on EA is also double of the square on AC;

therefore the squares on AE, EF are double of the squares on AC, CD.

And the square on AF is equal to the squares on AE, EF, for the angle AEF is right;   [I. 47]

therefore the square on AF is double of the squares on AC, CD.

But the squares on AD, DF are equal to the square on AF, for the angle at D is right;   [I. 47]

therefore the squares on AD, DF are double of the squares on AC, CD.

And DF is equal to DB;

therefore the squares on AD, DB are double of the squares on AC, CD.

Therefore etc.   Q. E. D.

Proposition 10

If a straight line be bisected, and a straight line be added to it in a straight line, the square on the whole with the added straight line and the square on the added straight line both together are double of the square on the half and of the square described on the straight line made up of the half and the added straight line as on one straight line.

For let a straight line *AB* be bisected at *C*, and let a straight line *BD* be added to it in a straight line;
I say that the squares on *AD*, *DB* are double of the squares on *AC*, *CD*.

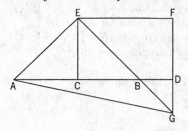

For let *CE* be drawn from the point *C* at right angles to *AB* [I. 11], and let it be made equal to either *AC* or *CB* [I. 3];
let *EA*, *EB* be joined;
through *E* let *EF* be drawn parallel to *AD*, and through *D* let *FD* be drawn parallel to *CE*.   [I. 31]
Then, since a straight line *EF* falls on the parallel straight lines *EC*, *FD*,
the angles *CEF*, *EFD* are equal to two right angles;   [I. 29]
therefore the angles *FEB*, *EFD* are less than two right angles.
But straight lines produced from angles less then two right angles meet;   [I. Post. 5]
therefore *EB*, *FD*, if produced in the direction *B*, *D*, will meet.
Let them be produced and meet at *G*,
and let *AG* be joined.
Then, since *AC* is equal to *CE*,
the angle *EAC* is also equal to the angle *AEC*;   [I. 5]
and the angle at *C* is right;
therefore each of the angles *EAC*, *AEC* is half a right angle.   [I. 32]
For the same reason
each of the angles *CEB*, *EBC* is also half a right angle;
therefore the angle *AEB* is right.
And, since the angle *EBC* is half a right angle,
the angle *DBG* is also half a right angle.   [I. 15]
But the angle *BDG* is also right,
for it is equal to the angle *DCE*, they being alternate;   [I. 29]
therefore the remaining angle *DGB* is half a right angle;   [I. 32]
therefore the angle *DGB* is equal to the angle *DBG*,
so that the side *BD* is also equal to the side *GD*.   [I. 6]
Again, since the angle *EGF* is half a right angle,
and the angle at *F* is right, for it is equal to the opposite angle, the angle at *C*,   [I. 34]
the remaining angle *FEG* is half a right angle;   [I. 32]
therefore the angle *EGF* is equal to the angle *FEG*,
so that the side *GF* is also equal to the side *EF*.   [I. 6]
Now, since the square on *EC* is equal to the square on *CA*,
the squares on *EC*, *CA* are double of the square on *CA*.
But the square on *EA* is equal to the squares on *EC*, *CA*;   [I. 47]

therefore the square on EA is double of the square on AC.   [$C.N.$ 1]
Again, since FG is equal to EF,
the square on FG is also equal to the square on FE;
therefore the squares on GF, FE are double of the square on EF.
But the square on EG is equal to the squares on GF, FE;   [I. 47]
therefore the square on EG is double of the square on EF.
And EF is equal to CD;   [I. 34]
therefore the square on EG is double of the square on CD.
But the square on EA was also proved double of the square on AC;
therefore the squares on AE, EG are double of the squares on AC, CD.
And the square on AG is equal to the squares on AE, EG;   [I. 47]
therefore the square on AG is double of the squares on AC, CD.
But the squares on AD, DG are equal to the square on AG;   [I. 47]
therefore the squares on AD, DG are double of the squares on AC, CD.
And DG is equal to DB;
therefore the squares on AD, DB are double of the squares on AC, CD.
Therefore etc.   Q. E. D.

PROPOSITION 11

To cut a given straight line so that the rectangle contained by the whole and one of the segments is equal to the square on the remaining segment.

Let AB be the given straight line;
thus it is required to cut AB so that the rectangle contained by the whole and one of the segments is equal to the square on the remaining segment.
For let the square $ABDC$ be described on AB;   [I. 46]
let AC be bisected at the point E, and let BE be joined;
let CA be drawn through to F, and let EF be made equal
to BE;
let the square FH be described on AF, and let GH be
drawn through to K.
I say that AB has been cut at H so as to make the rectangle contained by AB, BH equal to the square on AH.
For, since the straight line AC has been bisected at E, and
FA is added to it,
the rectangle contained by CF, FA together with the square
on AE is equal to the square on EF.   [II. 6]
But EF is equal to EB;
therefore the rectangle CF, FA together with the square on AE is equal to the square on EB.
But the squares on BA, AE are equal to the square on EB, for the angle at A is right: [I. 47]
therefore the rectangle CF, FA together with the square on AE is equal to the squares on BA, AE.
Let the square on AE be subtracted from each;
therefore the rectangle CF, FA which remains is equal to the square on AB.
Now the rectangle CF, FA is FK, for AF is equal to FG;
and the square on AB is AD;
therefore FK is equal to AD.
Let AK be subtracted from each;

therefore *FH* which remains is equal to *HD*.
And *HD* is the rectangle *AB*, *BH*, for *AB* is equal to *BD*;
and *FH* is the square on *AH*;
therefore the rectangle contained by *AB*, *BH* is equal to the square on *HA*.
therefore the given straight line *AB* has been cut at *H* so as to make the rectangle contained by *AB*, *BH* equal to the square on *HA*.   Q. E. F.

PROPOSITION 12

In obtuse-angled triangles the square on the side subtending the obtuse angle is greater than the squares on the sides containing the obtuse angle by twice the rectangle contained by one of the sides about the obtuse angle, namely that on which the perpendicular falls, and the straight line cut off outside by the perpendicular towards the obtuse angle.

Let *ABC* be an obtuse-angled triangle having the angle *BAC* obtuse, and let *BD* be drawn from the point *B* perpendicular to *CA* produced;
I say that the square on *BC* is greater than the squares on *BA*, *AC* by twice the rectangle contained by *CA*, *AD*.

For, since the straight line *CD* has been cut at random at the point *A*,
the square on *DC* is equal to the squares on *CA*, *AD* and twice the rectangle contained by *CA*, *AD*. [II. 4]
Let the square on *DB* be added to each;
therefore the squares on *CD*, *DB* are equal to the squares on *CA*, *AD*, *DB* and twice the rectangle *CA*, *AD*.

But the square on *CB* is equal to the squares on *CD*, *DB*, for the angle at *D* is right;   [I. 47]
and the square on *AB* is equal to the squares on *AD*, *DB*;   [I. 47]
therefore the square on *CB* is equal to the squares on *CA*, *AB* and twice the rectangle contained by *CA*, *AD*;
so that the square on *CB* is greater than the squares on *CA*, *AB* by twice the rectangle contained by *CA*, *AD*.
Therefore etc.   Q. E. D.

PROPOSITION 13

In acute-angled triangles the square on the side subtending the acute angle is less than the squares on the sides containing the acute angle by twice the rectangle contained by one of the sides about the acute angle, namely that on which the perpendicular falls, and the straight line cut off within by the perpendicular towards the acute angle.

Let *ABC* be an acute-angled triangle having the angle at *B* acute, and let *AD* be drawn from the point *A* perpendicular to *BC*;
I say that the square on *AC* is less than the squares on *CB*, *BA* by twice the rectangle contained by *CB*, *BD*.
For, since the straight line *CB* has been cut at random at *D*,
the squares on *CB*, *BD* are equal to twice the rectangle contained by *CB*, *BD* and the square on *DC*.
                                                            [II. 7]

Let the square on DA be added to each;
therefore the squares on CB, BD, DA are equal to twice the rectangle contained by CB, BD and the squares on AD, DC.

But the square on AB is equal to the squares on BD, DA, for the angle at D is right;　　　　　　　　　　　　　　　　　　　　　　　　[I. 47]
　　　　and the square on AC is equal to the squares on AD, DC;
therefore the squares on CB, BA are equal to the square on AC and twice the rectangle CB, BD,
so that the square on AC alone is less than the squares on CB, BA by twice the rectangle contained by CB, BD.

Therefore etc.　　　　　　　　　　　　　　　　　　　　　　　Q. E. D.

PROPOSITION 14

To construct a square equal to a given rectilineal figure.

Let A be the given rectilineal figure;
thus it is required to construct a square equal to the rectilineal figure A.

For let there be constructed
the rectangular parallelogram BD
equal to the rectilineal figure A.
　　　　　　　　　　　　　　　　[I. 45]

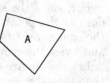 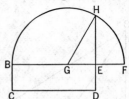

Then, if BE is equal to ED,
that which was enjoined will
have been done; for a square BD
has been constructed equal to the rectilineal figure A.

But, if not, one of the straight lines BE, ED is greater.

Let BE be greater, and let it be produced to F;
　　　　let EF be made equal to ED, and let BF be bisected at G.

With centre G and distance one of the straight lines GB, GF let the semicircle BHF be described; let DE be produced to H, and let GH be joined.

Then, since the straight line BF has been cut into equal segments at G, and into unequal segments at E,
the rectangle contained by BE, EF together with the square on EG is equal to the square on GF.　　　　　　　　　　　　　　　　　　　　　　　[II. 5]

But GF is equal to GH;
therefore the rectangle BE, EF together with the square on GE is equal to the square on GH.

But the squares on HE, EG are equal to the square on GH;　　　[I. 47]
therefore the rectangle BE, EF together with the square on GE is equal to the squares on HE, EG.

Let the square on GE be subtracted from each;
therefore the rectangle contained by BE, EF which remains is equal to the square on EH.

But the rectangle BE, EF is BD, for EF is equal to ED;
　　　　therefore the parallelogram BD is equal to the square on HE.

And BD is equal to the rectilineal figure A.

Therefore the rectilineal figure A is also equal to the square which can be described on EH.

Therefore a square, namely that which can be described on EH, has been constructed equal to the given rectilineal figure A.　　　　　Q. E. F.

BOOK THREE

DEFINITIONS

1. *Equal circles* are those the diameters of which are equal, or the radii of which are equal.

2. A straight line is said to *touch a circle* which, meeting the circle and being produced, does not cut the circle.

3. *Circles* are said to *touch one another* which, meeting one another, do not cut one another.

4. In a circle straight lines are said *to be equally distant from the centre* when the perpendiculars drawn to them from the centre are equal.

5. And that straight line is said to be *at a greater distance* on which the greater perpendicular falls.

6. A *segment of a circle* is the figure contained by a straight line and a circumference of a circle.

7. An *angle of a segment* is that contained by a straight line and a circumference of a circle.

8. An *angle in a segment* is the angle which, when a point is taken on the circumference of the segment and straight lines are joined from it to the extremities of the straight line which is the *base of the segment,* is contained by the straight lines so joined.

9. And, when the straight lines containing the angle cut off a circumference, the angle is said to *stand upon* that circumference.

10. A *sector of a circle* is the figure which, when an angle is constructed at the centre of the circle, is contained by the straight lines containing the angle and the circumference cut off by them.

11. *Similar segments of circles* are those which admit equal angles, or in which the angles are equal to one another.

BOOK III. PROPOSITIONS

PROPOSITION 1

To find the centre of a given circle.

Let *ABC* be the given circle;
     thus it is required to find the centre of the circle *ABC*.

Let a straight line *AB* be drawn through it at random, and let it be bisected at the point *D*;
from *D* let *DC* be drawn at right angles to *AB* and let it be drawn through to *E*; let *CE* be bisected at *F*;
     I say that *F* is the centre of the circle *ABC*.

For suppose it is not, but, if possible, let *G* be the centre,

41

and let *GA, GD, GB* be joined.

Then, since *AD* is equal to *DB*, and *DG* is common,
the two sides *AD, DG* are equal to the two sides *BD, DG* respectively;
and the base *GA* is equal to the base *GB*, for they are
radii;

therefore the angle *ADG* is equal to the angle *GDB*.
[I. 8]

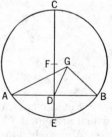

But, when a straight line set up on a straight line
makes the adjacent angles equal to one another, each of
the equal angles is right;   [I. Def. 10]
therefore the angle *GDB* is right.

But the angle *FDB* is also right;
therefore the angle *FDB* is equal to the angle *GDB*,
the greater to the less: which is impossible.

Therefore *G* is not the centre of the circle *ABC*.

Similarly we can prove that neither is any other point except *F*.

Therefore the point *F* is the centre of the circle *ABC*.

PORISM. From this it is manifest that, if in a circle a straight line cut a
straight line into two equal parts and at right angles, the centre of the circle is
on the cutting straight line.   Q. E. F.

PROPOSITION 2

*If on the circumference of a circle two points be taken at random, the straight line
joining the points will fall within the circle.*

Let *ABC* be a circle, and let two points *A, B* be taken at random on its circumference;

I say that the straight line joined from *A* to *B* will fall within the circle.

For suppose it does not, but, if possible, let it fall outside, as *AEB*;
let the centre of the circle *ABC* be taken [III. 1], and let it be *D*; let *DA, DB* be
joined, and let *DFE* be drawn through.

Then, since *DA* is equal to *DB*,
the angle *DAE* is also equal to the angle *DBE*.   [I. 5]
And, since one side *AEB* of the triangle *DAE* is produced,
the angle *DEB* is greater than the angle *DAE*. [I. 16]

But the angle *DAE* is equal to the angle *DBE*;
therefore the angle *DEB* is greater than the angle
DBE.

And the greater angle is subtended by the greater
side;   [I. 19]
therefore *DB* is greater than *DE*.

But *DB* is equal to *DF*;
therefore *DF* is greater than *DE*,
the less than the greater: which is impossible.

Therefore the straight line joined from *A* to *B* will not fall outside the circle.

Similarly we can prove that neither will it fall on the circumference itself;
therefore it will fall within.

Therefore etc.   Q. E. D.

PROPOSITION 3

If in a circle a straight line through the centre bisect a straight line not through the centre, it also cuts it at right angles; and if it cut it at right angles, it also bisects it.

Let ABC be a circle, and in it let a straight line CD through the centre bisect a straight line AB not through the centre at the point F;

I say that it also cuts it at right angles.

For let the centre of the circle ABC be taken, and let it be E; let EA, EB be joined.

Then, since AF is equal to FB, and FE is common,
two sides are equal to two sides;
and the base EA is equal to the base EB;
therefore the angle AFE
is equal to the angle BFE.   [I. 8]
But, when a straight line set up on a straight line makes the adjacent angles equal to one another, each of the equal angles is right;   [I. Def. 10]
therefore each of the angles AFE, BFE is right.

Therefore CD, which is through the centre, and bisects AB which is not through the centre, also cuts it at right angles.

Again, let CD cut AB at right angles;

I say that it also bisects it, that is, that AF is equal to FB.

For, with the same construction,
since EA is equal to EB,
the angle EAF is also equal to the angle EBF.   [I. 5]
But the right angle AFE is equal to the right angle BFE, therefore EAF, EBF are two triangles having two angles equal to two angles and one side equal to one side, namely EF, which is common to them, and subtends one of the equal angles;
therefore they will also have the remaining sides equal to the remaining sides;   [I. 26]
therefore AF is equal to FB.

Therefore etc.   Q. E. D.

PROPOSITION 4

If in a circle two straight lines cut one another which are not through the centre, they do not bisect one another.

Let $ABCD$ be a circle, and in it let the two straight lines AC, BD, which are not through the centre, cut one another at E;

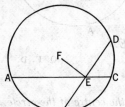

I say that they do not bisect one another.

For, if possible, let them bisect one another, so that AE is equal to EC, and BE to ED;
let the centre of the circle $ABCD$ be taken [III. 1], and let it be F; let FE be joined.

Then, since a straight line FE through the centre bisects a straight line AC not through the centre,
it also cuts it at right angles;   [III. 3]
therefore the angle FEA is right.

Again, since a straight line FE bisects a straight line BD,
it also cuts it at right angles;   [III. 3]
therefore the angle FEB is right.

But the angle FEA was also proved right;
therefore the angle FEA is equal to the angle FEB, the less to the greater:
which is impossible.

Therefore AC, BD do not bisect one another.

Therefore etc.   Q. E. D.

PROPOSITION 5

If two circles cut one another, they will not have the same centre.

For let the circles ABC, CDG cut one another at the points B, C;
I say that they will not have the same centre.

For, if possible, let it be E; let EC be joined, and let EFG be drawn through
at random.

Then, since the point E is the centre of the circle
ABC,

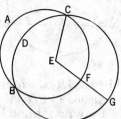

EC is equal to EF.   [I. Def. 15]

Again, since the point E is the centre of the circle
CDG,

EC is equal to EG.

But EC was proved equal to EF also;
therefore EF is also equal to EG, the less to the
greater: which is impossible.

Therefore the point E is not the centre of the circles ABC, CDG.

Therefore etc.   Q. E. D.

PROPOSITION 6

If two circles touch one another, they will not have the same centre.

For let the two circles ABC, CDE touch one another at the point C;
I say that they will not have the same centre.

For, if possible, let it be F; let FC be joined, and let FEB be drawn through
at random.

Then, since the point F is the centre of the circle
ABC,

FC is equal to FB.

Again, since the point F is the centre of the
circle CDE,

FC is equal to FE.

But FC was proved equal to FB;
therefore FE is also equal to FB, the less to the
greater: which is impossible.

Therefore F is not the centre of the circles ABC, CDE.

Therefore etc.   Q. E. D.

PROPOSITION 7

*If on the diameter of a circle a point be taken which is not the centre of the circle,
and from the point straight lines fall upon the circle, that will be greatest on which
the centre is, the remainder of the same diameter will be least, and of the rest the*

nearer to the straight line through the centre is always greater than the more remote, and only two equal straight lines will fall from the point on the circle, one on each side of the least straight line.

Let *ABCD* be a circle, and let *AD* be a diameter of it; on *AD* let a point *F* be taken which is not the centre of the circle, let *E* be the centre of the circle, and from *F* let straight lines *FB, FC, FG* fall upon the circle *ABCD*;

I say that *FA* is greatest, *FD* is least, and of the rest *FB* is greater than *FC*, and *FC* than *FG*.

For let *BE, CE, GE* be joined.

Then, since in any triangle two sides are greater than the remaining one,

[i. 20]

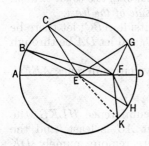

EB, EF are greater than *BF*.

But *AE* is equal to *BE*;

therefore *AF* is greater than *BF*.

Again, since *BE* is equal to *CE*, and *FE* is common,

the two sides *BE, EF* are equal to the two sides *CE, EF*.

But the angle *BEF* is also greater than the angle *CEF*;

therefore the base *BF* is greater than the base *CF*.

[i. 24]

For the same reason

CF is also greater than *FG*.

Again, since *GF, FE* are greater than *EG*,

and *EG* is equal to *ED*,

GF, FE are greater than *ED*.

Let *EF* be subtracted from each;

therefore the remainder *GF* is greater than the remainder *FD*.

Therefore *FA* is greatest, *FD* is least, and *FB* is greater than *FC*, and *FC* than *FG*.

I say also that from the point *F* only two equal straight lines will fall on the circle *ABCD*, one on each side of the least *FD*.

For on the straight line *EF*, and at the point *E* on it, let the angle *FEH* be constructed equal to the angle *GEF* [i. 23], and let *FH* be joined.

Then, since *GE* is equal to *EH*,

and *EF* is common,

the two sides *GE, EF* are equal to the two sides *HE, EF*;

and the angle *GEF* is equal to the angle *HEF*;

therefore the base *FG* is equal to the base *FH*.   [i. 4]

I say again that another straight line equal to *FG* will not fall on the circle from the point *F*.

For, if possible, let *FK* so fall.

Then, since *FK* is equal to *FG*, and *FH* to *FG*,

FK is also equal to *FH*,

the nearer to the straight line through the centre being thus equal to the more remote: which is impossible.

Therefore another straight line equal to *GF* will not fall from the point *F* upon the circle;

therefore only one straight line will so fall.

Therefore etc.   Q. E. D.

PROPOSITION 8

If a point be taken outside a circle and from the point straight lines be drawn through to the circle, one of which is through the centre and the others are drawn at random, then, of the straight lines which fall on the concave circumference, that through the centre is greatest, while of the rest the nearer to that through the centre is always greater than the more remote, but, of the straight lines falling on the convex circumference, that between the point and the diameter is least, while of the rest the nearer to the least is always less than the more remote, and only two equal straight lines will fall on the circle from the point, one on each side of the least.

Let ABC be a circle, and let a point D be taken outside ABC; let there be drawn through from it straight lines DA, DE, DF, DC, and let DA be through the centre;

I say that, of the straight lines falling on the concave circumference $AEFC$, the straight line DA through the centre is greatest,

while DE is greater than DF and DF than DC;

but, of the straight lines falling on the convex circumference $HLKG$, the straight line DG between the point and the diameter AG is least; and the nearer to the least DG is always less than the more remote, namely DK than DL, and DL than DH.

For let the centre of the circle ABC be taken [III. 1], and let it be M; let ME, MF, MC, MK, ML, MH be joined.

Then, since AM is equal to EM, let MD be added to each;

therefore AD is equal to EM, MD.

But EM, MD are greater than ED;

therefore AD is also greater than ED.

Again, since ME is equal to MF,

and MD is common,

therefore EM, MD are equal to FM, MD;

and the angle EMD is greater than the angle FMD;

therefore the base ED is greater than the base FD.   [I. 24]

Similarly we can prove that FD is greater than CD; therefore DA is greatest, while DE is greater than DF, and DF than DC.

Next, since MK, KD are greater than MD,   [I. 20]

and MG is equal to MK,

therefore the remainder KD is greater than the remainder GD,

so that GD is less than KD.

And, since on MD, one of the sides of the triangle MLD, two straight lines MK, KD were constructed meeting within the triangle,

therefore MK, KD are less than ML, LD;   [I. 21]

and MK is equal to ML;

therefore the remainder DK is less than the remainder DL.

Similarly we can prove that DL is also less than DH;

therefore DG is least, while DK is less than DL, and DL than DH.

I say also that only two equal straight lines will fall from the point D on the circle, one on each side of the least *DG*.

On the straight line *MD*, and at the point *M* on it,
let the angle *DMB* be constructed equal to the angle *KMD*, and let *DB* be
joined.

Then, since *MK* is equal to *MB*,
                    and *MD* is common,
    the two sides *KM*, *MD* are equal to the two sides *BM*, *MD* respectively;
                and the angle *KMD* is equal to the angle *BMD*;
            therefore the base *DK* is equal to the base *DB*.   [I. 4]

I say that no other straight line equal to the straight line *DK* will fall on
the circle from the point *D*.

For, if possible, let a straight line so fall, and let it be *DN*.

Then, since *DK* is equal to *DN*,
                while *DK* is equal to *DB*,
                DB is also equal to *DN*,

that is, the nearer to the least *DG* equal to the more remote: which was proved
impossible.

Therefore no more than two equal straight lines will fall on the circle *ABC*
from the point *D*, one on each side of *DG* the least.

Therefore etc.   Q. E. D.

PROPOSITION 9

If a point be taken within a circle, and more than two equal straight lines fall from
the point on the circle, the point taken is the centre of the circle.

Let *ABC* be a circle and *D* a point within it, and from *D* let more than two

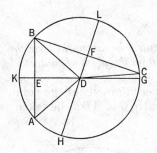

equal straight lines, namely *DA*, *DB*, *DC*, fall on
the circle *ABC*;

I say that the point *D* is the centre of the circle
ABC.

For let *AB*, *BC* be joined and bisected at the
points *E*, *F*, and let *ED*, *FD* be joined and drawn
through to the points *G*, *K*, *H*, *L*.

Then, since *AE* is equal to *EB*, and *ED* is common,

the two sides *AE*, *ED* are equal to the two sides
BE, *ED*;

and the base *DA* is equal to the base *DB*;
    therefore the angle *AED* is equal to the angle *BED*.   [I. 8]

Therefore each of the angles *AED*, *BED* is right;   [I. Def. 10]
    therefore *GK* cuts *AB* into two equal parts and at right angles.

And since, if in a circle a straight line cut a straight line into two equal parts
and at right angles, the centre of the circle is on the cutting straight line,

[III. 1, Por.]

        the centre of the circle is on *GK*.

For the same reason
        the centre of the circle *ABC* is also on *HL*.

And the straight lines *GK*, *HL* have no other point common but the point *D*;
    therefore the point *D* is the centre of the circle *ABC*.

Therefore etc.   Q. E. D.

PROPOSITION 10

A circle does not cut a circle at more points than two.

For, if possible, let the circle *ABC* cut the circle *DEF* at more points than two, namely *B, C, F, H*;

let *BH, BG* be joined and bisected at the points *K, L*,

and from *K, L* let *KC, LM* be drawn at right angles to *BH, BG* and carried through to the points *A, E*.

Then, since in the circle *ABC* a straight line *AC* cuts a straight line *BH* into two equal parts and at right angles,

the centre of the circle *ABC* is on *AC*.

[III. 1, Por.]

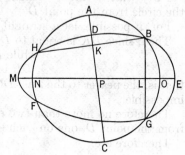

Again, since in the same circle *ABC* a straight line *NO* cuts a straight line *BG* into two equal parts and at right angles,

the centre of the circle *ABC* is on *NO*.

But it was also proved to be on *AC*, and the straight lines *AC, NO* meet at no point except at *P*;

therefore the point *P* is the centre of the circle *ABC*.

Similarly we can prove that *P* is also the centre of the circle *DEF*; therefore the two circles *ABC, DEF* which cut one another have the same centre *P*: which is impossible. [III. 5]

Therefore etc.

Q. E. D.

PROPOSITION 11

If two circles touch one another internally, and their centres be taken, the straight line joining their centres, if it be also produced, will fall on the point of contact of the circles.

For let the two circles *ABC, ADE* touch one another internally at the point *A*, and let the centre *F* of the circle *ABC*, and the centre *G* of *ADE*, be taken;

I say that the straight line joined from *G* to *F* and produced will fall on *A*.

For suppose it does not, but, if possible, let it fall as *FGH*, and let *AF, AG* be joined.

Then, since *AG, GF* are greater than *FA*, that is, than *FH*,

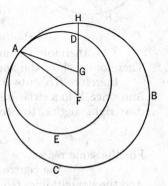

let *FG* be subtracted from each;

therefore the remainder *AG* is greater than the remainder *GH*.

But *AG* is equal to *GD*;

therefore *GD* is also greater than *GH*. the less than the greater: which is impossible.

Therefore the straight line joined from *F* to *G* will not fall outside;

therefore it will fall at *A* on the point of contact.

Therefore etc.

Q. E. D

PROPOSITION 12

If two circles touch one another externally, the straight line joining their centres will pass through the point of contact.

For let the two circles *ABC*, *ADE* touch one another externally at the point *A*, and let the centre *F* of *ABC*, and the centre *G* of *ADE*, be taken;

I say that the straight line joined from *F* to *G* will pass through the point of contact at *A*.

For suppose it does not, but, if possible, let it pass as *FCDG*, and let *AF*, *AG* be joined.

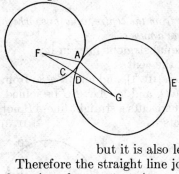

Then, since the point *F* is the centre of the circle *ABC*,

FA is equal to *FC*.

Again, since the point *G* is the centre of the circle *ADE*,

GA is equal to *GD*.

But *FA* was also proved equal to *FC*;

therefore *FA*, *AG* are equal to *FC*, *GD*,

so that the whole *FG* is greater than *FA*, *AG*;

but it is also less [I. 20]: which is impossible.

Therefore the straight line joined from *F* to *G* will not fail to pass through the point of contact at *A*;

therefore it will pass through it.

Therefore etc.   Q. E. D.

PROPOSITION 13

A circle does not touch a circle at more points than one, whether it touch it internally or externally.

For, if possible, let the circle *ABDC* touch the circle *EBFD*, first internally, at more points than one, namely *D*, *B*.

Let the centre *G* of the circle *ABDC*, and the centre *H* of *EBFD*, be taken.

Therefore the straight line joined from *G* to *H* will fall on *B*, *D*.   [III. 11]

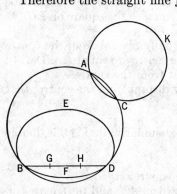

Let it so fall, as *BGHD*.

Then, since the point *G* is the centre of the circle *ABCD*,

BG is equal to *GD*;

therefore *BG* is greater than *HD*;

therefore *BH* is much greater than *HD*.

Again, since the point *H* is the centre of the circle *EBFD*,

BH is equal to *HD*;

but it was also proved much greater than it: which is impossible.

Therefore a circle does not touch a circle internally at more points than one.

I say further that neither does it so touch it externally.

For, if possible, let the circle *ACK* touch the circle *ABDC* at more points than one, namely *A*, *C*, and let AC be joined.

Then, since on the circumference of each of the circles $ABDC$, ACK two points A, C have been taken at random, the straight line joining the points will fall within each circle; [III. 2]

but it fell within the circle $ABDC$ and outside ACK [III. Def. 3]: which is absurd.

Therefore a circle does not touch a circle externally at more points than one. And it was proved that neither does it so touch it internally.

Therefore etc. Q. E. D.

PROPOSITION 14

In a circle equal straight lines are equally distant from the centre, and those which are equally distant from the centre are equal to one another.

Let $ABDC$ be a circle, and let AB, CD be equal straight lines in it;

I say that AB, CD are equally distant from the centre.

For let the centre of the circle $ABDC$ be taken [III. 1], and let it be E; from E let EF, EG be drawn perpendicular to AB, CD, and let AE, EC be joined.

Then, since a straight line EF through the centre cuts a straight line AB not through the centre at right angles, it also bisects it. [III. 3]

Therefore AF is equal to FB;

therefore AB is double of AF.

For the same reason

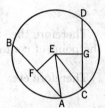

CD is also double of CG;

and AB is equal to CD;

therefore AF is also equal to CG.

And, since AE is equal to EC,

the square on AE is also equal to the square on EC.

But the squares on AF, EF are equal to the square on AE, for the angle at F is right;

and the squares on EG, GC are equal to the square on EC, for the angle at G is right; [I. 47]

therefore the squares on AF, FE are equal to the squares on CG, GE,

of which the square on AF is equal to the square on CG, for AF is equal to CG;

therefore the square on FE which remains is equal to the square on EG,

therefore EF is equal to EG.

But in a circle straight lines are said to be equally distant from the centre when the perpendiculars drawn to them from the centre are equal [III. Def. 4];

therefore AB, CD are equally distant from the centre.

Next, let the straight lines AB, CD be equally distant from the centre; that is, let EF be equal to EG.

I say that AB is also equal to CD.

For, with the same construction, we can prove, similarly, that AB is double of AF, and CD of CG.

And, since AE is equal to CE,

the square on AE is equal to the square on CE.

But the squares on EF, FA are equal to the square on AE, and the squares on EG, GC equal to the square on CE. [I. 47]

Therefore the squares on EF, FA are equal to the squares on EG, GC,

of which the square on EF is equal to the square on EG, for EF is equal to EG;

therefore the square on AF which remains is equal to the square on CG;
$$\text{therefore } AF \text{ is equal to } CG.$$
And AB is double of AF, and CD double of CG;
$$\text{therefore } AB \text{ is equal to } CD.$$
Therefore etc.   Q. E. D.

PROPOSITION 15

Of straight lines in a circle the diameter is greatest, and of the rest the nearer to the centre is always greater than the more remote.

Let $ABCD$ be a circle, let AD be its diameter and E the centre; and let BC be nearer to the diameter AD, and FG more remote;

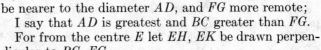

I say that AD is greatest and BC greater than FG.

For from the centre E let EH, EK be drawn perpendicular to BC, FG.

Then, since BC is nearer to the centre and FG more remote, EK is greater than EH.   [III. Def. 5]

Let EL be made equal to EH, through L let LM be drawn at right angles to EK and carried through to N, and let ME, EN, FE, EG be joined.

Then, since EH is equal to EL,
$$BC \text{ is also equal to } MN.$$ [III. 14]
Again, since AE is equal to EM, and ED to EN,
$$AD \text{ is equal to } ME, EN.$$
But ME, EN are greater than MN,   [I. 20]
$$\text{and } MN \text{ is equal to } BC;$$
$$\text{therefore } AD \text{ is greater than } BC.$$
And, since the two sides ME, EN are equal to the two sides FE, EG,
$$\text{and the angle } MEN \text{ greater than the angle } FEG,$$
therefore the base MN is greater than the base FG.   [I. 24]
But MN was proved equal to BC.

Therefore the diameter AD is greatest and BC greater than FG.

Therefore etc.   Q. E. D.

PROPOSITION 16

The straight line drawn at right angles to the diameter of a circle from its extremity will fall outside the circle, and into the space between the straight line and the circumference another straight line cannot be interposed; further the angle of the semicircle is greater, and the remaining angle less, than any acute rectilineal angle.

Let ABC be a circle about D as centre and AB as diameter;

I say that the straight line drawn from A at right angles to AB from its extremity will fall outside the circle.

For suppose it does not, but, if possible, let it fall within as CA, and let DC be joined.

Since DA is equal to DC,
$$\text{the angle } DAC \text{ is also equal to the angle } ACD.$$ [I. 5]
But the angle DAC is right;
$$\text{therefore the angle } ACD \text{ is also right:}$$
thus, in the triangle ACD, the two angles DAC, ACD are equal to two right angles: which is impossible.   [I. 17]

Therefore the straight line drawn from the point A at right angles to BA will not fall within the circle.

Similarly we can prove that neither will it fall on the circumference;

therefore it will fall outside.

Let it fall as AE;

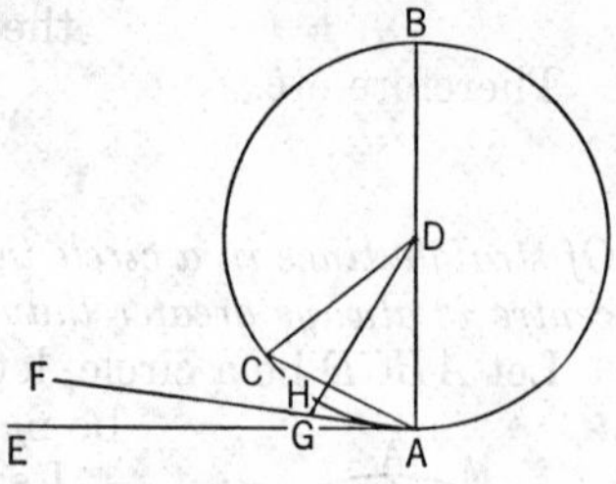

I say next that into the space between the straight line AE and the circumference CHA another straight line cannot be interposed.

For, if possible, let another straight line be so interposed, as FA, and let DG be drawn from the point D perpendicular to FA.

Then, since the angle AGD is right,

and the angle DAG is less than a right angle,

AD is greater than DG. [I. 19]

But DA is equal to DH;

therefore DH is greater than DG, the less than the greater: which is impossible.

Therefore another straight line cannot be interposed into the space between the straight line and the circumference.

I say further that the angle of the semicircle contained by the straight line BA and the circumference CHA is greater than any acute rectilineal angle,

and the remaining angle contained by the circumference CHA and the straight line AE is less than any acute rectilineal angle.

For, if there is any rectilineal angle greater than the angle contained by the straight line BA and the circumference CHA, and any rectilineal angle less than the angle contained by the circumference CHA and the straight line AE, then into the space between the circumference and the straight line AE a straight line will be interposed such as will make an angle contained by straight lines which is greater than the angle contained by the straight line BA and the circumference CHA, and another angle contained by straight lines which is less than the angle contained by the circumference CHA and the straight line AE.

But such a straight line cannot be interposed;

therefore there will not be any acute angle contained by straight lines which is greater than the angle contained by the straight line BA and the circumference CHA, nor yet any acute angle contained by straight lines which is less than the angle contained by the circumference CHA and the straight line AE.—

PORISM. From this it is manifest that the straight line drawn at right angles to the diameter of a circle from its extremity touches the circle. Q. E. D.

PROPOSITION 17

From a given point to draw a straight line touching a given circle.

Let A be the given point, and BCD the given circle;

thus it is required to draw from the point A a straight line touching the circle BCD.

For let the centre E of the circle be taken; [III. 1]

let AE be joined, and with centre E and distance EA let the circle AFG be described;

from D let DF be drawn at right angles to EA,

and let EF, AB be joined;

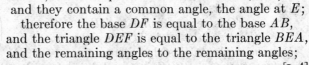

I say that *AB* has been drawn from the point *A* touching the circle *BCD*.

For, since *E* is the centre of the circles *BCD*, *AFG*,

EA is equal to *EF*, and *ED* to *EB*;

therefore the two sides *AE*, *EB* are equal to the two sides *FE*, *ED*;

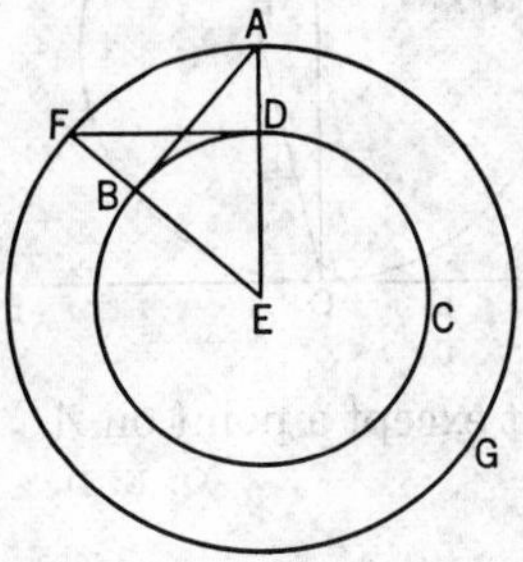

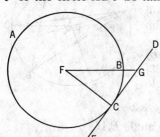

and they contain a common angle, the angle at *E*;

therefore the base *DF* is equal to the base *AB*,

and the triangle *DEF* is equal to the triangle *BEA*,

and the remaining angles to the remaining angles;

[I. 4]

therefore the angle *EDF* is equal to the angle *EBA*.

But the angle *EDF* is right;

therefore the angle *EBA* is also right.

Now *EB* is a radius;

and the straight line drawn at right angles to the diameter of a circle, from its extremity, touches the circle;   [III. 16, Por.]

therefore *AB* touches the circle *BCD*.

Therefore from the given point *A* the straight line *AB* has been drawn touching the circle *BCD*.   Q. E. F.

PROPOSITION 18

If a straight line touch a circle, and a straight line be joined from the centre to the point of contact, the straight line so joined will be perpendicular to the tangent.

For let a straight line *DE* touch the circle *ABC* at the point *C*, let the centre *F* of the circle *ABC* be taken, and let *FC* be joined from *F* to *C*;

I say that *FC* is perpendicular to *DE*.

For, if not, let *FG* be drawn from *F* perpendicular to *DE*.

Then, since the angle *FGC* is right,

the angle *FCG* is acute;   [I. 17]

and the greater angle is subtended by the greater side;   [I. 19]

therefore *FC* is greater than *FG*.

But *FC* is equal to *FB*;

therefore *FB* is also greater than *FG*,

the less than the greater: which is impossible.

Therefore *FG* is not perpendicular to *DE*.

Similarly we can prove that neither is any other straight line except *FC*;

therefore *FC* is perpendicular to *DE*.

Therefore etc.   Q. E. D.

PROPOSITION 19

If a straight line touch a circle, and from the point of contact a straight line be drawn at right angles to the tangent, the centre of the circle will be on the straight line so drawn.

For let a straight line *DE* touch the circle *ABC* at the point *C*, and from *C* let *CA* be drawn at right angles to *DE*;

I say that the centre of the circle is on *AC*.

For suppose it is not, but, if possible, let *F* be the centre, and let *CF* be joined.

Since a straight line *DE* touches the circle *ABC*,
and *FC* has been joined from the centre to the point of contact,

FC is perpendicular to *DE*;   [III. 18]
therefore the angle *FCE* is right.

But the angle *ACE* is also right;
therefore the angle *FCE* is equal to the angle *ACE*,

the less to the greater: which is impossible.
Therefore *F* is not the centre of the circle *ABC*.

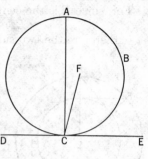

Similarly we can prove that neither is any other point except a point on *AC*.
Therefore etc.   Q. E. D.

PROPOSITION 20

In a circle the angle at the centre is double of the angle at the circumference, when the angles have the same circumference as base.

Let *ABC* be a circle, let the angle *BEC* be an angle at its centre, and the angle *BAC* an angle at the circumference, and let them have the same circumference *BC* as base;

I say that the angle *BEC* is double of the angle *BAC*.

For let *AE* be joined and drawn through to *F*.

Then, since *EA* is equal to *EB*,
the angle *EAB* is also equal to the angle *EBA*; [I. 5]
therefore the angles *EAB*, *EBA* are double of the angle *EAB*.

But the angle *BEF* is equal to the angles *EAB*, *EBA*;   [I. 32]
therefore the angle *BEF* is also double of the angle *EAB*.

For the same reason

the angle *FEC* is also double of the angle *EAC*.

Therefore the whole angle *BEC* is double of the whole angle *BAC*.

Again let another straight line be inflected, and let there be another angle *BDC*; let *DE* be joined and produced to *G*.

Similarly then we can prove that the angle *GEC* is double of the angle *EDC*,

of which the angle *GEB* is double of the angle *EDB*;

therefore the angle *BEC* which remains is double of the angle *BDC*.
Therefore etc.   Q. E. D.

PROPOSITION 21

In a circle the angles in the same segment are equal to one another.

Let *ABCD* be a circle, and let the angles *BAD*, *BED* be angles in the same segment *BAED*;

I say that the angles *BAD*, *BED* are equal to one another.

For let the centre of the circle *ABCD* be taken, and let it be *F*; let *BF*, *FD* be joined.

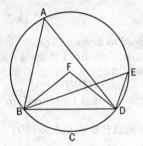

Now, since the angle *BFD* is at the centre,
and the angle *BAD* at the circumference,
and they have the same circumference *BCD* as base,
therefore the angle *BFD* is double of the angle *BAD*.   [III. 20]

For the same reason
the angle *BFD* is also double of the angle *BED*;
therefore the angle *BAD* is equal to the angle *BED*.

Therefore etc.   Q. E. D.

PROPOSITION 22

The opposite angles of quadrilaterals in circles are equal to two right angles.

Let *ABCD* be a circle, and let *ABCD* be a quadrilateral in it;
I say that the opposite angles are equal to two right angles.

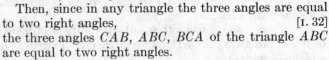

Let *AC*, *BD* be joined.

Then, since in any triangle the three angles are equal to two right angles,   [I. 32]
the three angles *CAB*, *ABC*, *BCA* of the triangle *ABC* are equal to two right angles.

But the angle *CAB* is equal to the angle *BDC*, for they are in the same segment *BADC*;   [III. 21]
and the angle *ACB* is equal to the angle *ADB*, for they are in the same segment *ADCB*;

therefore the whole angle *ADC* is equal to the angles *BAC*, *ACB*.

Let the angle *ABC* be added to each;
therefore the angles *ABC*, *BAC*, *ACB* are equal to the angles *ABC*, *ADC*.

But the angles *ABC*, *BAC*, *ACB* are equal to two right angles;
therefore the angles *ABC*, *ADC* are also equal to two right angles.

Similarly we can prove that the angles *BAD*, *DCB* are also equal to two right angles.

Therefore etc.   Q. E. D.

PROPOSITION 23

On the same straight line there cannot be constructed two similar and unequal segments of circles on the same side.

For, if possible, on the same straight line *AB* let two similar and unequal segments of circles *ACB*, *ADB* be constructed on the same side;
let *ACD* be drawn through, and let *CB*, *DB* be joined.

Then, since the segment *ACB* is similar to the segment *ADB*,
and similar segments of circles are those which admit equal angles [III. Def. 11],
the angle *ACB* is equal to the angle *ADB*, the exterior to the interior: which is impossible.   [I. 16]

Therefore etc.   Q. E. D.

PROPOSITION 24

Similar segments of circles on equal straight lines are equal to one another.

For let AEB, CFD be similar segments of circles on equal straight lines AB, CD;

I say that the segment AEB is equal to the segment CFD.

For, if the segment AEB be applied to CFD, and if the point A be placed on C and the straight line AB on CD,

the point B will also coincide with the point D, because AB is equal to CD;

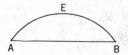 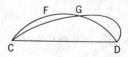

and, AB coinciding with CD,

the segment AEB will also coincide with CFD.

For, if the straight line AB coincide with CD but the segment AEB do not coincide with CFD,

it will either fall within it, or outside it;

or it will fall awry, as CGD, and a circle cuts a circle at more points than two: which is impossible.   [III. 10]

Therefore, if the straight line AB be applied to CD, the segment AEB will not fail to coincide with CFD also;

therefore it will coincide with it and will be equal to it.

Therefore etc.   Q. E. D.

PROPOSITION 25

Given a segment of a circle, to describe the complete circle of which it is a segment.

Let ABC be the given segment of a circle;

thus it is required to describe the complete circle belonging to the segment ABC, that is, of which it is a segment.

For let AC be bisected at D, let DB be drawn from the point D at right angles to AC, and let AB be joined;

the angle ABD is then greater than, equal to, or less than the angle BAD.

First let it be greater;

and on the straight line BA, and at the point A on it, let the angle BAE be constructed equal to the angle ABD; let DB be drawn through to E, and let EC be joined.

Then, since the angle ABE is equal to the angle BAE,

the straight line EB is also equal to EA.   [I. 6]

And, since AD is equal to DC, and DE is common,

the two sides AD, DE are equal to the two sides CD, DE respectively;

and the angle ADE is equal to the angle CDE, for each is right;

therefore the base AE is equal to the base CE.

But AE was proved equal to BE;

therefore BE is also equal to CE;

therefore the three straight lines AE, EB, EC are equal to one another.

Therefore the circle drawn with centre E and distance one of the straight lines AE, EB, EC will also pass through the remaining points and will have been completed.   [III. 9]

Therefore, given a segment of a circle, the complete circle has been described.

And it is manifest that the segment ABC is less than a semicircle, because the centre E happens to be outside it.

Similarly, even if the angle ABD be equal to the angle BAD,

AD being equal to each of the two BD, DC,

the three straight lines DA, DB, DC will be equal to one another,

D will be the centre of the completed circle,

and ABC will clearly be a semicircle.

But, if the angle ABD be less than the angle BAD, and if we construct, on the straight line BA and at the point A on it, an angle equal to the angle ABD, the centre will fall on DB within the segment ABC, and the segment ABC will clearly be greater than a semicircle.

Therefore, given a segment of a circle, the complete circle has been described.   Q. E. F.

PROPOSITION 26

In equal circles equal angles stand on equal circumferences, whether they stand at the centres or at the circumferences.

Let ABC, DEF be equal circles, and in them let there be equal angles, namely at the centres the angles BGC, EHF, and at the circumferences the angles BAC, EDF;

I say that the circumference BKC is equal to the circumference ELF.

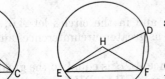

For let BC, EF be joined.

Now, since the circles ABC, DEF are equal,

the radii are equal.

Thus the two straight lines BG, GC are equal to the two straight lines EH, HF;

and the angle at G is equal to the angle at H;

therefore the base BC is equal to the base EF.   [I. 4]

And, since the angle at A is equal to the angle at D,

the segment BAC is similar to the segment EDF;   [III. Def. 11]

and they are upon equal straight lines.

But similar segments of circles on equal straight lines are equal to one another;   [III. 24]

therefore the segment BAC is equal to EDF.

But the whole circle ABC is also equal to the whole circle DEF;

therefore the circumference BKC which remains is equal to the circumference ELF.

Therefore etc.   Q. E. D.

PROPOSITION 27

In equal circles angles standing on equal circumferences are equal to one another, whether they stand at the centres or at the circumferences.

For in equal circles *ABC, DEF,* on equal circumferences *BC, EF,* let the angles *BGC, EHF* stand at the centres *G, H,* and the angles *BAC, EDF* at the circumferences;

I say that the angle *BGC* is equal to the angle *EHF,*

and the angle *BAC* is equal to angle *EDF.*

For, if the angle *BGC* is unequal to the angle *EHF,*
one of them is greater.

Let the angle *BGC* be greater: and on the straight line *BG,* and at the point *G* on it, let the angle *BGK* be constructed equal to the angle *EHF* [I. 23].

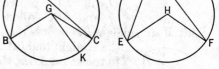

Now equal angles stand on equal circumferences, when they are at the centres;   [III. 26]

therefore the circumference *BK* is equal to the circumference *EF.*

But *EF* is equal to *BC;*

therefore *BK* is also equal to *BC,* the less to the greater: which is impossible.

Therefore the angle *BGC* is not unequal to the angle *EHF;*

therefore it is equal to it.

And the angle at *A* is half of the angle *BGC,*

and the angle at *D* half of the angle *EHF;*   [III. 20]

therefore the angle at *A* is also equal to the angle at *D.*

Therefore etc.   Q. E. D.

PROPOSITION 28

In equal circles equal straight lines cut off equal circumferences, the greater equal to the greater and the less to the less.

Let *ABC, DEF* be equal circles, and in the circles let *AB, DE* be equal straight lines cutting off *ACB, DFE* as greater circumferences and *AGB, DHE* as lesser;

I say that the greater circumference *ACB* is equal to the greater circumference *DFE,* and the less circumference *AGB* to *DHE.*

For let the centres *K, L* of the circles be taken, and let *AK, KB, DL, LE* be joined.

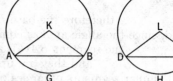

Now, since the circles are equal,
the radii are also equal;

therefore the two sides *AK, KB* are equal to the two sides *DL, LE;*

and the base *AB* is equal to the base *DE;*

therefore the angle *AKB* is equal to the angle *DLE.*   [I. 8]

But equal angles stand on equal circumferences, when they are at the centres;   [III. 26]

therefore the circumference *AGB* is equal to *DHE.*

And the whole circle *ABC* is also equal to the whole circle *DEF;*

therefore the circumference *ACB* which remains is also equal to the circumference *DFE* which remains.

Therefore etc.   Q. E. D.

PROPOSITION 29

In equal circles equal circumferences are subtended by equal straight lines.

Let *ABC*, *DEF* be equal circles, and in them let equal circumferences *BGC*, *EHF* be cut off; and let the straight lines *BC*, *EF* be joined;

I say that *BC* is equal to *EF*.

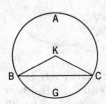 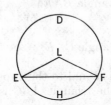

For let the centres of the circles be taken, and let them be *K*, *L*; let *BK*, *KC*, *EL*, *LF* be joined.

Now, since the circumference *BGC* is equal to the circumference *EHF*,

the angle *BKC* is also equal to the angle *ELF*.   [III. 27]

And, since the circles *ABC*, *DEF* are equal,

the radii are also equal;

therefore the two sides *BK*, *KC* are equal to the two sides *EL*, *LF*; and they contain equal angles;

therefore the base *BC* is equal to the base *EF*.   [I. 4]

Therefore etc.   Q. E. D.

PROPOSITION 30

To bisect a given circumference.

Let *ADB* be the given circumference;

thus it is required to bisect the circumference *ADB*.

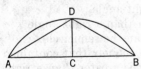

Let *AB* be joined and bisected at *C*; from the point *C* let *CD* be drawn at right angles to the straight line *AB*, and let *AD*, *DB* be joined.

Then, since *AC* is equal to *CB*, and *CD* is common.

the two sides *AC*, *CD* are equal to the two sides *BC*, *CD*;

and the angle *ACD* is equal to the angle *BCD*, for each is right;

therefore the base *AD* is equal to the base *DB*.   [I. 4]

But equal straight lines cut off equal circumferences, the greater equal to the greater, and the less to the less;   [III. 28]

and each of the circumferences *AD*, *DB* is less than a semicircle;

therefore the circumference *AD* is equal to the circumference *DB*.

Therefore the given circumference has been bisected at the point *D*.

                                                    Q. E. F.

PROPOSITION 31

In a circle the angle in the semicircle is right, that in a greater segment less than a right angle, and that in a less segment greater than a right angle; and further the angle of the greater segment is greater than a right angle, and the angle of the less segment less than a right angle.

Let *ABCD* be a circle, let *BC* be its diameter, and *E* its centre, and let *BA*, *AC*, *AD*, *DC* be joined;

I say that the angle BAC in the semicircle BAC is right,
the angle ABC in the segment ABC greater than the semicircle is less than a right angle,
and the angle ADC in the segment ADC less than the semicircle is greater than a right angle.

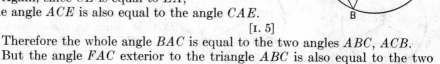

Let AE be joined, and let BA be carried through to F.

Then, since BE is equal to EA,
the angle ABE is also equal to the angle BAE.

                                                        [I. 5]

Again, since CE is equal to EA,
the angle ACE is also equal to the angle CAE.

                                                        [I. 5]

Therefore the whole angle BAC is equal to the two angles ABC, ACB.

But the angle FAC exterior to the triangle ABC is also equal to the two angles ABC, ACB;   [I. 32]
therefore the angle BAC is also equal to the angle FAC;
therefore each is right;   [I. Def. 10]
therefore the angle BAC in the semicircle BAC is right.

Next, since in the triangle ABC the two angles ABC, BAC are less than two right angles,   [I. 17]
and the angle BAC is a right angle,
the angle ABC is less than a right angle;
and it is the angle in the segment ABC greater than the semicircle.

Next, since $ABCD$ is a quadrilateral in a circle,
and the opposite angles of quadrilaterals in circles are equal to two right angles,   [III. 22]
while the angle ABC is less than a right angle,
therefore the angle ADC which remains is greater than a right angle;
and it is the angle in the segment ADC less than the semicircle.

I say further that the angle of the greater segment, namely that contained by the circumference ABC and the straight line AC, is greater than a right angle;
and the angle of the less segment, namely that contained by the circumference ADC and the straight line AC, is less than a right angle.

This is at once manifest.

For, since the angle contained by the straight lines BA, AC is right,
the angle contained by the circumference ABC and the straight line AC is greater than a right angle.

Again, since the angle contained by the straight lines AC, AF is right,
the angle contained by the straight line CA and the circumference ADC is less than a right angle.

Therefore etc.

                                                        Q. E. D.

PROPOSITION 32

If a straight line touch a circle, and from the point of contact there be drawn across, in the circle, a straight line cutting the circle, the angles which it makes with the tangent will be equal to the angles in the alternate segments of the circle.

For let a straight line EF touch the circle $ABCD$ at the point B, and from the point B let there be drawn across, in the circle $ABCD$, a straight line BD cutting it;

I say that the angles which BD makes with the tangent EF will be equal to the angles in the alternate segments of the circle, that is, that the angle FBD is equal to the angle constructed in the segment BAD, and the angle EBD is equal to the angle constructed in the segment DCB.

For let BA be drawn from B at right angles to EF,

let a point C be taken at random on the circumference BD,

and let AD, DC, CB be joined.

Then, since a straight line EF touches the circle $ABCD$ at B,

and BA has been drawn from the point of contact at right angles to the tangent, the centre of the circle $ABCD$ is on BA.   [III. 19]

Therefore BA is a diameter of the circle $ABCD$;

therefore the angle ADB, being an angle in a semicircle, is right. [III. 31]

Therefore the remaining angles BAD, ABD are equal to one right angle.
[I. 32]

But the angle ABF is also right;

therefore the angle ABF is equal to the angles BAD, ABD.

Let the angle ABD be subtracted from each;

therefore the angle DBF which remains is equal to the angle BAD in the alternate segment of the circle.

Next, since $ABCD$ is a quadrilateral in a circle,

its opposite angles are equal to two right angles.   [III. 22]

But the angles DBF, DBE are also equal to two right angles;

therefore the angles DBF, DBE are equal to the angles BAD, BCD,

of which the angle BAD was proved equal to the angle DBF;

therefore the angle DBE which remains is equal to the angle DCB in the alternate segment DCB of the circle.

Therefore etc.   Q. E. D.

PROPOSITION 33

On a given straight line to describe a segment of a circle admitting an angle equal to a given rectilineal angle.

Let AB be the given straight line, and the angle at C the given rectilineal angle;

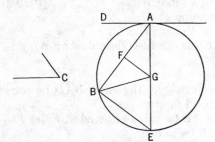

thus it is required to describe on the given straight line AB a segment of a circle admitting an angle equal to the angle at C.

The angle at C is then acute, or right, or obtuse.

First, let it be acute, and, as in the first figure, on the straight line AB, and at the point A, let the angle BAD be constructed equal to the angle at C;

therefore the angle BAD is also acute.

Let AE be drawn at right angles to DA, let AB be bisected at F, let FG be drawn from the point F at right angles to AB, and let GB be joined.

Then, since AF is equal to FB,

and FG is common,

the two sides AF, FG are equal to the two sides BF, FG;

and the angle AFG is equal to the angle BFG;

therefore the base AG is equal to the base BG.   [I. 4]

Therefore the circle described with centre G and distance GA will pass through B also.

Let it be drawn, and let it be ABE;

let EB be joined.

Now, since AD is drawn from A, the extremity of the diameter AE, at right angles to AE,

therefore AD touches the circle ABE.   [III. 16, Por.]

Since then a straight line AD touches the circle ABE,

and from the point of contact at A a straight line AB is drawn across in the circle ABE,

the angle DAB is equal to the angle AEB in the alternate segment of the circle.   [III. 32]

But the angle DAB is equal to the angle at C;

therefore the angle at C is also equal to the angle AEB.

Therefore on the given straight line AB the segment AEB of a circle has been described admitting the angle AEB equal to the given angle, the angle at C.

Next let the angle at C be right; and let it be again required to describe on AB a segment of a circle admitting an angle equal to the right angle at C.

Let the angle BAD be constructed equal to the right angle at C, as is the case in the second figure; let AB be bisected at F, and with centre F and distance either FA or FB let the circle AEB be described.

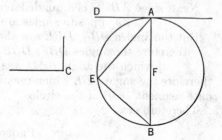

Therefore the straight line AD touches the circle ABE, because the angle at A is right.   [III. 16, Por.]

And the angle BAD is equal to the angle in the segment AEB, for the latter too is itself a right angle, being an angle in a semicircle.   [III. 31]

But the angle BAD is also equal to the angle at C.

Therefore the angle AEB is also equal to the angle at C.

Therefore again the segment AEB of a circle has been described on AB admitting an angle equal to the angle at C.

Next, let the angle at C be obtuse;

and on the straight line AB, and at the point A, let the angle BAD be constructed equal to it, as is the case in the third figure;

let AE be drawn at right angles to AD, let AB be again bisected at F, let FG be drawn at right angles to AB, and let GB be joined.

Then, since AF is again equal to FB,
and FG is common,

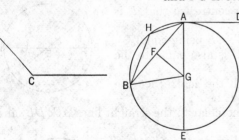

the two sides AF, FG are equal to the two sides BF, FG;
and the angle AFG is equal to the angle BFG;
therefore the base AG is equal to the base BG. [I. 4]

Therefore the circle described with centre G and distance GA will pass through B also; let it so pass, as AEB.

Now, since AD is drawn at right angles to the diameter AE from its extremity,

$\qquad\qquad$ AD touches the circle AEB. $\qquad$ [III. 16, Por.]

And AB has been drawn across from the point of contact at A;
therefore the angle BAD is equal to the angle constructed in the alternate segment AHB of the circle. $\qquad$ [III. 32]

But the angle BAD is equal to the angle at C.

Therefore the angle in the segment AHB is also equal to the angle at C.

Therefore on the given straight line AB the segment AHB of a circle has been described admitting an angle equal to the angle at C. $\qquad$ Q. E. F.

PROPOSITION 34

From a given circle to cut off a segment admitting an angle equal to a given rectilineal angle.

Let ABC be the given circle, and the angle at D the given rectilineal angle; thus it is required to cut off from the circle ABC a segment admitting an angle equal to the given rectilineal angle, the angle at D.

Let EF be drawn touching ABC at the point B, and on the straight line FB, and at the point B on it, let the angle FBC be constructed equal to the angle

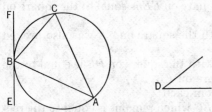

at D. $\qquad$ [I. 23]

Then, since a straight line EF touches the circle ABC,
and BC has been drawn across from the point of contact at B,
the angle FBC is equal to the angle constructed in the alternate segment BAC. $\qquad$ [III. 32]

But the angle FBC is equal to the angle at D;
therefore the angle in the segment BAC is equal to the angle at D.

Therefore from the given circle ABC the segment BAC has been cut off admitting an angle equal to the given rectilineal angle, the angle at D. $\qquad$ Q. E. F.

PROPOSITION 35

If in a circle two straight lines cut one another, the rectangle contained by the segments of the one is equal to the rectangle contained by the segments of the other.

For in the circle $ABCD$ let the two straight lines AC, BD cut one another at the point E;

I say that the rectangle contained by AE, EC is equal to the rectangle contained by DE, EB.

If now AC, BD are through the centre, so that E is the centre of the circle $ABCD$,
   it is manifest that, AE, EC, DE, EB being equal, the rectangle contained by AE, EC is also equal to the rectangle contained by DE, EB.

Next let AC, DB not be through the centre; let the centre of $ABCD$ be taken, and let it be F;
from F let FG, FH be drawn perpendicular to the straight lines AC, DB, and let FB, FC, FE be joined.

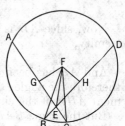

Then, since a straight line GF through the centre cuts a straight line AC not through the centre at right angles,
it also bisects it;   [III. 3]
therefore AG is equal to GC.

Since, then, the straight line AC has been cut into equal parts at G and into unequal parts at E,
the rectangle contained by AE, EC together with the square on EG is equal to the square on GC;   [II. 5]
Let the square on GF be added;
therefore the rectangle AE, EC together with the squares on GE, GF is equal to the squares on CG, GF.

But the square on FE is equal to the squares on EG, GF, and the square on FC is equal to the squares on CG, GF;   [I. 47]
therefore the rectangle AE, EC together with the square on FE is equal to the square on FC.

And FC is equal to FB;
therefore the rectangle AE, EC together with the square on EF is equal to the square on FB.

For the same reason, also,
the rectangle DE, EB together with the square on FE is equal to the square on FB.

But the rectangle AE, EC together with the square on FE was also proved equal to the square on FB;
therefore the rectangle AE, EC together with the square on FE is equal to the rectangle DE, EB together with the square on FE.

Let the square on FE be subtracted from each;
therefore the rectangle contained by AE, EC which remains is equal to the rectangle contained by DE, EB.

Therefore etc.   Q. E. D.

PROPOSITION 36

If a point be taken outside a circle and from it there fall on the circle two straight lines, and if one of them cut the circle and the other touch it, the rectangle contained by the whole of the straight line which cuts the circle and the straight line intercepted on it outside between the point and the convex circumference will be equal to the square on the tangent.

For let a point D be taken outside the circle ABC, and from D let the two straight lines DCA, DB fall on the circle ABC; let DCA cut the circle ABC and let BD touch it;

I say that the rectangle contained by AD, DC is equal to the square on DB.

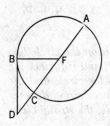

Then DCA is either through the centre or not through the centre.

First let it be through the centre, and let F be the centre of the circle ABC; let FB be joined;

       therefore the angle FBD is right.   [III. 18]

And, since AC has been bisected at F, and CD is added to it,

the rectangle AD, DC together with the square on FC is equal to the square on FD.   [II. 6]

But FC is equal to FB;

therefore the rectangle AD, DC together with the square on FB is equal to the square on FD.

And the squares on FB, BD are equal to the square on FD;   [I. 47]

therefore the rectangle AD, DC together with the square on FB is equal to the squares on FB, BD.

Let the square on FB be subtracted from each;

therefore the rectangle AD, DC which remains is equal to the square on the tangent DB.

Again, let DCA not be through the centre of the circle ABC;

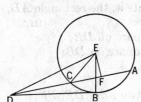

let the centre E be taken, and from E, let EF be drawn perpendicular to AC;

let EB, EC, ED be joined.

Then the angle EBD is right.   [III. 18]

And, since a straight line EF through the centre cuts a straight line AC not through the centre at right angles,

       it also bisects it;   [III. 3]

therefore AF is equal to FC.

Now, since the straight line AC has been bisected at the point F, and CD is added to it,

the rectangle contained by AD, DC together with the square on FC is equal to the square on FD.   [II. 6]

Let the square on FE be added to each;

therefore the rectangle AD, DC together with the squares on CF, FE is equal to the squares on FD, FE.

But the square on EC is equal to the squares on CF, FE, for the angle EFC is right;   [I. 47]

and the square on ED is equal to the squares on DF, FE;

therefore the rectangle AD, DC together with the square on EC is equal to the square on ED.

And EC is equal to EB;

therefore the rectangle AD, DC together with the square on EB is equal to the square on ED.

But the squares on EB, BD are equal to the square on ED, for the angle EBD is right;   [I. 47] therefore the rectangle AD, DC together with the square on EB is equal to the squares on EB, BD.

Let the square on EB be subtracted from each;

therefore the rectangle AD, DC which remains is equal to the square on DB.

Therefore etc.   Q. E. D.

Proposition 37

If a point be taken outside a circle and from the point there fall on the circle two straight lines, if one of them cut the circle, and the other fall on it, and if further the rectangle contained by the whole of the straight line which cuts the circle and the straight line intercepted on it outside between the point and the convex circumference be equal to the square on the straight line which falls on the circle, the straight line which falls on it will touch the circle.

For let a point D be taken outside the circle ABC; from D let the two straight lines DCA, DB fall on the circle ABC; let DCA cut the circle and DB fall on it; and let the rectangle AD, DC be equal to the square on DB.

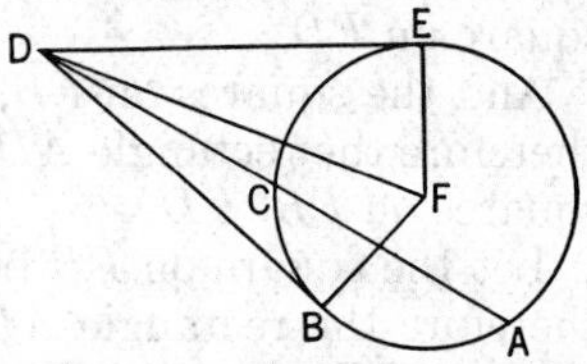

I say that DB touches the circle ABC.

For let DE be drawn touching ABC; let the centre of the circle ABC be taken, and let it be F; let FE, FB, FD be joined.

Thus the angle FED is right.   [III. 18]

Now, since DE touches the circle ABC, and DCA cuts it, the rectangle AD, DC is equal to the square on DE.   [III. 36]

But the rectangle AD, DC was also equal to the square on DB;

therefore the square on DE is equal to the square on DB;

therefore DE is equal to DB.

And FE is equal to FB;

therefore the two sides DE, EF are equal to the two sides DB, BF;

and FD is the common base of the triangles;

therefore the angle DEF is equal to the angle DBF.   [I. 8]

But the angle DEF is right;

therefore the angle DBF is also right.

And FB produced is a diameter;

and the straight line drawn at right angles to the diameter of a circle, from its extremity, touches the circle;   [III. 16, Por.]

therefore DB touches the circle.

Similarly this can be proved to be the case even if the centre be on AC.

Therefore etc.   Q. E. D.

BOOK FOUR

DEFINITIONS

1. A rectilineal figure is said to be *inscribed in a rectilineal figure* when the respective angles of the inscribed figure lie on the respective sides of that in which it is inscribed.

2. Similarly a figure is said to be *circumscribed about a figure* when the respective sides of the circumscribed figure pass through the respective angles of that about which it is circumscribed.

3. A rectilineal figure is said to be *inscribed in a circle* when each angle of the inscribed figure lies on the circumference of the circle.

4. A rectilineal figure is said to be *circumscribed about a circle*, when each side of the circumscribed figure touches the circumference of the circle.

5. Similarly a circle is said to be *inscribed in a figure* when the circumference of the circle touches each side of the figure in which it is inscribed.

6. A circle is said to be *circumscribed about a figure* when the circumference of the circle passes through each angle of the figure about which it is circumscribed.

7. A straight line is said to be *fitted into a circle* when its extremities are on the circumference of the circle.

BOOK IV. PROPOSITIONS

PROPOSITION 1

Into a given circle to fit a straight line equal to a given straight line which is not greater than the diameter of the circle.

Let *ABC* be the given circle, and *D* the given straight line not greater than the diameter of the circle;

thus it is required to fit into the circle *ABC* a straight line equal to the straight line *D*.

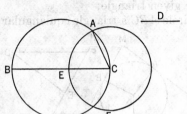

Let a diameter *BC* of the circle *ABC* be drawn.

Then, if *BC* is equal to *D*, that which was enjoined will have been done; for *BC* has been fitted into the circle *ABC* equal to the straight line *D*.

But, if *BC* is greater than *D*, let *CE* be made equal to *D*, and with centre *C* and distance *CE* let the circle *EAF* be described; let *CA* be joined.

Then, since the point *C* is the centre of the circle *EAF*,

67

$$CA \text{ is equal to } CE.$$

But CE is equal to D;

$$\text{therefore } D \text{ is also equal to } CA.$$

Therefore into the given circle ABC there has been fitted CA equal to the given straight line D.   Q. E. F.

PROPOSITION 2

In a given circle to inscribe a triangle equiangular with a given triangle.

Let ABC be the given circle, and DEF the given triangle;
thus it is required to inscribe in the circle ABC a triangle equiangular with the triangle DEF.

Let GH be drawn touching the circle ABC at A [III. 16, Por.]; on the straight line AH, and at the point A on it, let the angle HAC be constructed equal to the angle DEF,

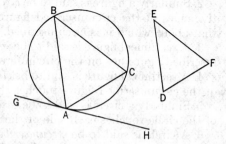

and on the straight line AG, and at the point A on it, let the angle GAB be constructed equal to the angle DFE;   [I. 23]

let BC be joined.

Then, since a straight line AH touches the circle ABC,
and from the point of contact at A the straight line AC is drawn across in the circle,
therefore the angle HAC is equal to the angle ABC in the alternate segment of the circle.   [III. 32]

But the angle HAC is equal to the angle DEF;

$$\text{therefore the angle } ABC \text{ is also equal to the angle } DEF.$$

For the same reason

$$\text{the angle } ACB \text{ is also equal to the angle } DFE;$$

therefore the remaining angle BAC is also equal to the remaining angle EDF.   [I. 32]

Therefore in the given circle there has been inscribed a triangle equiangular with the given triangle.   Q. E. F.

PROPOSITION 3

About a given circle to circumscribe a triangle equiangular with a given triangle.

Let ABC be the given circle, and DEF the given triangle;
thus it is required to circumscribe about the circle ABC a triangle equiangular with the triangle DEF.

Let EF be produced in both directions to the points G, H,
let the centre K of the circle ABC be taken [III. 1], and let the straight line KB be drawn across at random;
on the straight line KB, and at the point K on it, let the angle BKA be constructed equal to the angle DEG,

$$\text{and the angle } BKC \text{ equal to the angle } DFH;$$ [I. 23]

and through the points A, B, C let LAM, MBN, NCL be drawn touching the circle ABC.   [III. 16, Por.]

Now, since LM, MN, NL touch the circle ABC at the points A, B, C, and KA, KB, KC have been joined from the centre K to the points A, B, C, therefore the angles at the points A, B, C are right.   [III. 18]

And, since the four angles of the quadrilateral $AMBK$ are equal to four right angles, inasmuch as $AMBK$ is in fact divisible into two triangles, and the angles KAM, KBM are right, therefore the remaining angles AKB, AMB are equal to two right angles. But the angles DEG, DEF are also equal to two right angles;   [I. 13] therefore the angles AKB, AMB are equal to the angles DEG, DEF, of which the angle AKB is equal to the angle DEG; therefore the angle AMB which remains is equal to the angle DEF which remains.

Similarly it can be proved that the angle LNB is also equal to the angle DFE; therefore the remaining angle MLN is equal to the angle EDF. [I. 32]

Therefore the triangle LMN is equiangular with the triangle DEF; and it has been circumscribed about the circle ABC.

Therefore about a given circle there has been circumscribed a triangle equiangular with the given triangle.   Q. E. F.

PROPOSITION 4

In a given triangle to inscribe a circle.

Let ABC be the given triangle;
thus it is required to inscribe a circle in the triangle ABC.

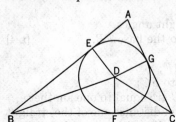

Let the angles ABC, ACB be bisected by the straight lines BD, CD [I. 9], and let these meet one another at the point D; from D let DE, DF, DG be drawn perpendicular to the straight lines AB, BC, CA.

Now, since the angle ABD is equal to the angle CBD, and the right angle BED is also equal to the right angle BFD, EBD, FBD are two triangles having two angles equal to two angles and one side equal to one side, namely that subtending one of the equal angles, which is BD common to the triangles; therefore they will also have the remaining sides equal to the remaining sides;   [I. 26]
therefore DE is equal to DF.

For the same reason
DG is also equal to DF.

Therefore the three straight lines DE, DF, DG are equal to one another; therefore the circle described with centre D and distance one of the straight lines DE, DF, DG will pass also through the remaining points, and will touch the straight lines AB, BC, CA, because the angles at the points E, F, G are right.

For, if it cuts them, the straight line drawn at right angles to the diameter of

the circle from its extremity will be found to fall within the circle: which was
proved absurd;   [III. 16]
therefore the circle described with centre D and distance one of the straight
lines DE, DF, DG will not cut the straight lines AB, BC, CA;
therefore it will touch them, and will be the circle inscribed in the triangle
ABC.   [IV. Def. 5]
    Let it be inscribed, as FGE.
    Therefore in the given triangle ABC the circle EFG has been inscribed.

                                                                             Q. E. F.

Proposition 5

About a given triangle to circumscribe a circle.
    Let ABC be the given triangle;
    thus it is required to circumscribe a circle about the given triangle ABC.

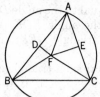 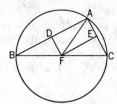 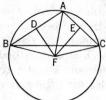

    Let the straight lines AB, AC be bisected at the points D, E [I. 10], and from
the points D, E let DF, EF be drawn at right angles to AB, AC;
they will then meet within the triangle ABC, or on the straight line BC, or
outside BC.
    First let them meet within at F, and let FB, FC, FA be joined.
    Then, since AD is equal to DB,
                        and DF is common and at right angles,
                therefore the base AF is equal to the base FB.   [I. 4]
Similarly we can prove that
                        CF is also equal to AF;
                    so that FB is also equal to FC;
    therefore the three straight lines FA, FB, FC are equal to one another.
    Therefore the circle described with centre F and distance one of the straight
lines FA, FB, FC will pass also through the remaining points, and the circle
will have been circumscribed about the triangle ABC.
    Let it be circumscribed, as ABC.
    Next, let DF, EF meet on the straight line BC at F, as is the case in the se-
cond figure; and let AF be joined.
    Then, similarly, we shall prove that the point F is the centre of the circle
circumscribed about the triangle ABC.
    Again, let DF, EF meet outside the triangle ABC at F, as is the case in the
third figure, and let AF, BF, CF be joined.
    Then again, since AD is equal to DB,
                        and DF is common and at right angles,
                therefore the base AF is equal to the base BF.   [I. 4]
Similarly we can prove that
                        CF is also equal to AF;
                    so that BF is also equal to FC;

therefore the circle described with centre F and distance one of the straight lines FA, FB, FC will pass also through the remaining points, and will have been circumscribed about the triangle ABC.

Therefore about the given triangle a circle has been circumscribed.

Q. E. F.

And it is manifest that, when the centre of the circle falls within the triangle, the angle BAC, being in a segment greater than the semicircle, is less than a right angle;

when the centre falls on the straight line BC, the angle BAC, being in a semicircle, is right;

and when the centre of the circle falls outside the triangle, the angle BAC, being in a segment less than the semicircle, is greater than a right angle.   [III. 31]

PROPOSITION 6

In a given circle to inscribe a square.

Let $ABCD$ be the given circle;

thus it is required to inscribe a square in the circle $ABCD$.

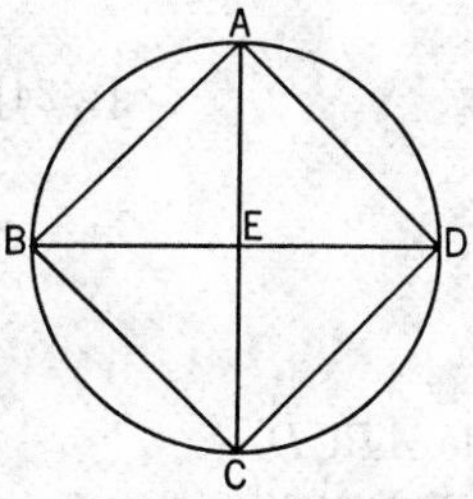

Let two diameters AC, BD of the circle $ABCD$ be drawn at right angles to one another, and let AB, BC, CD, DA be joined.

Then, since BE is equal to ED, for E is the centre, and EA is common and at right angles,

therefore the base AB is equal to the base AD. [I. 4]

For the same reason

each of the straight lines BC, CD is also equal to each of the straight lines AB, AD;

therefore the quadrilateral $ABCD$ is equilateral.

I say next that it is also right-angled.

For, since the straight line BD is a diameter of the circle $ABCD$,

therefore BAD is a semicircle;

therefore the angle BAD is right.   [III. 31]

For the same reason

each of the angles ABC, BCD, CDA is also right;

therefore the quadrilateral $ABCD$ is right-angled.

But it was also proved equilateral;

therefore it is a square;   [I. Def. 22]

and it has been inscribed in the circle $ABCD$.

Therefore in the given circle the square $ABCD$ has been inscribed. Q. E. F.

PROPOSITION 7

About a given circle to circumscribe a square.

Let $ABCD$ be the given circle;

thus it is required to circumscribe a square about the circle $ABCD$.

Let two diameters AC, BD of the circle $ABCD$ be drawn at right angles to one another, and through the points A, B, C, D let FG, GH, HK, KF be drawn touching the circle $ABCD$.   [III. 16, Por.]

Then, since FG touches the circle $ABCD$,

and EA has been joined from the centre E to the point of contact at A,

therefore the angles at A are right.   [III. 18]

For the same reason

the angles at the points B, C, D are also right.

Now, since the angle AEB is right,

and the angle EBG is also right,

therefore GH is parallel to AC.   [I. 28]

For the same reason

AC is also parallel to FK,

so that GH is also parallel to FK.   [I. 30]

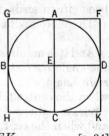

Similarly we can prove that

each of the straight lines GF, HK is parallel to BED.

Therefore GK, GC, AK, FB, BK are parallelograms;

therefore GF is equal to HK, and GH to FK.   [I. 34]

And, since AC is equal to BD,

and AC is also equal to each of the straight lines GH, FK,

while BD is equal to each of the straight lines GF, HK,   [I. 34]

therefore the quadrilateral $FGHK$ is equilateral.

I say next that it is also right-angled.

For, since $GBEA$ is a parallelogram,

and the angle AEB is right,

therefore the angle AGB is also right.   [I. 34]

Similarly we can prove that

the angles at H, K, F are also right.

Therefore $FGHK$ is right-angled.

But it was also proved equilateral;

therefore it is a square;

and it has been circumscribed about the circle $ABCD$.

Therefore about the given circle a square has been circumscribed.   Q. E. F.

PROPOSITION 8

In a given square to inscribe a circle.

Let $ABCD$ be the given square;

thus it is required to inscribe a circle in the given square $ABCD$.

Let the straight lines AD, AB be bisected at the
points E, F respectively,   [I. 10]
through E let EH be drawn parallel to either AB or
CD, and through F let FK be drawn parallel to either
AD or BC;   [I. 31]
therefore each of the figures AK, KB, AH, HD, AG,
GC, BG, GD is a parallelogram, and their opposite
sides are evidently equal.   [I. 34]

Now, since AD is equal to AB,

and AE is half of AD, and AF half of AB,

therefore AE is equal to AF,

so that the opposite sides are also equal;

therefore FG is equal to GE.

Similarly we can prove that each of the straight lines GH, GK is equal to
each of the straight lines FG, GE;

therefore the four straight lines GE, GF, GH, GK are equal to one another.

Therefore the circle described with centre G and distance one of the straight lines GE, GF, GH, GK will pass also through the remaining points.

And it will touch the straight lines AB, BC, CD, DA, because the angles at E, F, H, K are right.

For, if the circle cuts AB, BC, CD, DA, the straight line drawn at right angles to the diameter of the circle from its extremity will fall within the circle: which was proved absurd;   [III. 16]
therefore the circle described with centre G and distance one of the straight lines GE, GF, GH, GK will not cut the straight lines AB, BC, CD, DA.

Therefore it will touch them, and will have been inscribed in the square $ABCD$.

Therefore in the given square a circle has been inscribed.   Q. E. F.

PROPOSITION 9

About a given square to circumscribe a circle.

Let $ABCD$ be the given square;
    thus it is required to circumscribe a circle about the square $ABCD$.
For let AC, BD be joined, and let them cut one another at E.
Then, since DA is equal to AB, and AC is common,

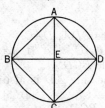

therefore the two sides DA, AC are equal to the two sides BA, AC;
    and the base DC is equal to the base BC;
therefore the angle DAC is equal to the angle BAC.
                                                        [I. 8]
Therefore the angle DAB is bisected by AC.
    Similarly we can prove that each of the angles ABC, BCD, CDA is bisected by the straight lines AC, DB.
Now, since the angle DAB is equal to the angle ABC,
    and the angle EAB is half the angle DAB,
    and the angle EBA half the angle ABC,
    therefore the angle EAB is also equal to the angle EBA;
        so that the side EA is also equal to EB.   [I. 6]
Similarly we can prove that each of the straight lines EA, EB is equal to each of the straight lines EC, ED.

Therefore the four straight lines EA, EB, EC, ED are equal to one another.

Therefore the circle described with centre E and distance one of the straight lines EA, EB, EC, ED will pass also through the remaining points;
    and it will have been circumscribed about the square $ABCD$.
Let it be circumscribed, as $ABCD$.

Therefore about the given square a circle has been circumscribed. Q. E. F.

PROPOSITION 10

To construct an isosceles triangle having each of the angles at the base double of the remaining one.

Let any straight line AB be set out, and let it be cut at the point C so that the rectangle contained by AB, BC is equal to the square on CA;   [II. 11]
    with centre A and distance AB let the circle BDE be described,
and let there be fitted in the circle BDE the straight line BD equal to the straight line AC which is not greater than the diameter of the circle BDE.   [IV. 1]

Let AD, DC be joined, and let the circle ACD be circumscribed about the triangle ACD.   [IV. 5]

Then, since the rectangle AB, BC is equal to the square on AC,

and AC is equal to BD,

therefore the rectangle AB, BC is equal to the square on BD.

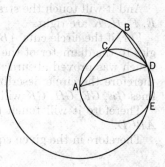

And, since a point B has been taken outside the circle ACD,

and from B the two straight lines BA, BD have fallen on the circle ACD, and one of them cuts it, while the other falls on it,

and the rectangle AB, BC is equal to the square on BD,

therefore BD touches the circle ACD.   [III. 37]

Since, then, BD touches it, and DC is drawn across from the point of contact at D,

therefore the angle BDC is equal to the angle DAC in the alternate segment of the circle.   [III. 32]

Since, then, the angle BDC is equal to the angle DAC,

let the angle CDA be added to each;

therefore the whole angle BDA is equal to the two angles CDA, DAC.

But the exterior angle BCD is equal to the angles CDA, DAC;   [I. 32]

therefore the angle BDA is also equal to the angle BCD.

But the angle BDA is equal to the angle CBD, since the side AD is also equal to AB;   [I. 5]

so that the angle DBA is also equal to the angle BCD.

Therefore the three angles BDA, DBA, BCD are equal to one another.

And, since the angle DBC is equal to the angle BCD,

the side BD is also equal to the side DC.   [I. 6]

But BD is by hypothesis equal to CA;

therefore CA is also equal to CD,

so that the angle CDA is also equal to the angle DAC;   [I. 5]

therefore the angles CDA, DAC are double of the angle DAC.

But the angle BCD is equal to the angles CDA, DAC;

therefore the angle BCD is also double of the angle CAD.

But the angle BCD is equal to each of the angles BDA, DBA;

therefore each of the angles BDA, DBA is also double of the angle DAB.

Therefore the isosceles triangle ABD has been constructed having each of the angles at the base DB double of the remaining one.   Q. E. F.

PROPOSITION 11

In a given circle to inscribe an equilateral and equiangular pentagon.

Let $ABCDE$ be the given circle;

thus it is required to inscribe in the circle $ABCDE$ an equilateral and equiangular pentagon.

Let the isosceles triangle FGH be set out having each of the angles at G, H double of the angle at F;   [IV. 10]

let there be inscribed in the circle $ABCDE$ the triangle ACD equiangular with the triangle *FGH*, so that the angle *CAD* is equal to the angle at *F* and the angles at *G*, *H* respectively equal to the angles *ACD*, *CDA*;   [IV. 2]

therefore each of the angles *ACD*, *CDA* is also double of the angle *CAD*.

Now let the angles *ACD*, *CDA* be bisected respectively by the straight lines *CE*, *DB* [I. 9], and let *AB*, *BC*, *DE*, *EA* be joined.

Then, since each of the angles *ACD*, *CDA* is double of the angle *CAD*,

and they have been bisected by the straight lines *CE*, *DB*,

therefore the five angles *DAC*, *ACE*, *ECD*, *CDB*, *BDA* are equal to one another.

But equal angles stand on equal circumferences;   [III. 26]
therefore the five circumferences *AB*, *BC*, *CD*, *DE*, *EA* are equal to one another.

But equal circumferences are subtended by equal straight lines;   [III. 29]
therefore the five straight lines *AB*, *BC*, *CD*, *DE*, *EA* are equal to one another;

therefore the pentagon *ABCDE* is equilateral.

I say next that it is also equiangular.

For, since the circumference *AB* is equal to the circumference *DE*, let *BCD* be added to each;

therefore the whole circumference *ABCD* is equal to the whole circumference *EDCB*.

And the angle *AED* stands on the circumference *ABCD*, and the angle *BAE* on the circumference *EDCB*;

therefore the angle *BAE* is also equal to the angle *AED*.   [III. 27]

For the same reason

each of the angles *ABC*, *BCD*, *CDE* is also equal to each of the angles *BAE*, *AED*;

therefore the pentagon *ABCDE* is equiangular.

But it was also proved equilateral;

therefore in the given circle an equilateral and equiangular pentagon has been inscribed.   Q. E. F.

PROPOSITION 12

About a given circle to circumscribe an equilateral and equiangular pentagon.

Let *ABCDE* be the given circle;

thus it is required to circumscribe an equilateral and equiangular pentagon about the circle *ABCDE*.

Let *A*, *B*, *C*, *D*, *E* be conceived to be the angular points of the inscribed pentagon, so that the circumferences *AB*, *BC*, *CD*, *DE*, *EA* are equal;   [IV. 11]

through *A*, *B*, *C*, *D*, *E* let *GH*, *HK*, *KL*, *LM*, *MG* be drawn touching the circle;
                                                        [III. 16, Por.]

let the centre *F* of the circle *ABCDE* be taken [III. 1], and let *FB*, *FK*, *FC*, *FL*, *FD* be joined.

Then, since the straight line *KL* touches the circle *ABCDE* at *C*,

and *FC* has been joined from the centre *F* to the point of contact at *C*,

therefore *FC* is perpendicular to *KL*;   [III. 18]

therefore each of the angles at C is right.
For the same reason
          the angles at the points B, D are also right.
And, since the angle FCK is right,
    therefore the square on FK is equal to the squares on FC, CK.
For the same reason   [I. 47]
the square on FK is also equal to the squares on
FB, BK;

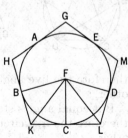

so that the squares on FC, CK are equal to the
squares on FB, BK,
of which the square on FC is equal to the square on
FB;

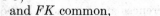

therefore the square on CK which remains is equal
to the square on BK.
Therefore BK is equal to CK.
And, since FB is equal to FC,
                    and FK common,
the two sides BF, FK are equal to the two sides CF, FK; and the base BK
equal to the base CK;
          therefore the angle BFK is equal to the angle KFC,   [I. 8]
              and the angle BKF to the angle FKC.
Therefore the angle BFC is double of the angle KFC,
              and the angle BKC of the angle FKC.
For the same reason
          the angle CFD is also double of the angle CFL,
              and the angle DLC of the angle FLC.
Now, since the circumference BC is equal to CD,
              the angle BFC is also equal to the angle CFD.   [III. 27]
And the angle BFC is double of the angle KFC, and the angle DFC of the
angle LFC;
          therefore the angle KFC is also equal to the angle LFC.
But the angle FCK is also equal to the angle FCL;
therefore FKC, FLC are two triangles having two angles equal to two angles
and one side equal to one side, namely FC which is common to them;
therefore they will also have the remaining sides equal to the remaining sides,
and the remaining angle to the remaining angle;   [I. 26]
          therefore the straight line KC is equal to CL,
              and the angle FKC to the angle FLC,
And, since KC is equal to CL,
              therefore KL is double of KC.
For the same reason it can be proved that
              HK is also double of BK.
And BK is equal to KC;
              therefore HK is also equal to KL.
Similarly each of the straight lines HG, GM, ML can also be proved equal to
each of the straight lines HK, KL;
              therefore the pentagon $GHKLM$ is equilateral.
I say next that it is also equiangular.
For, since the angle FKC is equal to the angle FLC,

and the angle *HKL* was proved double of the angle *FKC*,
and the angle *KLM* double of the angle *FLC*,
therefore the angle *HKL* is also equal to the angle *KLM*.

Similarly each of the angles *KHG*, *HGM*, *GML* can also be proved equal to each of the angles *HKL*, *KLM*;
therefore the five angles *GHK*, *HKL*, *KLM*, *LMG*, *MGH* are equal to one another.

Therefore the pentagon *GHKLM* is equiangular.

And it was also proved equilateral; and it has been circumscribed about the circle *ABCDE*.   Q. E. F.

PROPOSITION 13

In a given pentagon, which is equilateral and equiangular, to inscribe a circle.
Let *ABCDE* be the given equilateral and equiangular pentagon;
    thus it is required to inscribe a circle in the pentagon *ABCDE*.

For let the angles *BCD*, *CDE* be bisected by the straight lines *CF*, *DF* respectively; and from the point *F*, at which the straight lines *CF*, *DF* meet one another, let the straight lines *FB*, *FA*, *FE* be joined.

Then, since *BC* is equal to *CD*, and *CF* common,

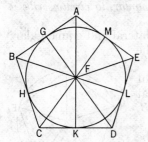

the two sides *BC*, *CF* are equal to the two sides *DC*, *CF*;
    and the angle *BCF* is equal to the angle *DCF*;
    therefore the base *BF* is equal to the base *DF*,
and the triangle *BCF* is equal to the triangle *DCF*, and the remaining angles will be equal to the remaining angles, namely those which the equal sides subtend.   [I. 4]
    Therefore the angle *CBF* is equal to the angle *CDF*.

And, since the angle *CDE* is double of the angle *CDF*,
    and the angle *CDE* is equal to the angle *ABC*,
    while the angle *CDF* is equal to the angle *CBF*;
    therefore the angle *CBA* is also double of the angle *CBF*;
    therefore the angle *ABF* is equal to the angle *FBC*;
    therefore the angle *ABC* has been bisected by the straight line *BF*.

Similarly it can be proved that
the angles *BAE*, *AED* have also been bisected by the straight lines *FA*, *FE* respectively.

Now let *FG*, *FH*, *FK*, *FL*, *FM* be drawn from the point *F* perpendicular to the straight lines *AB*, *BC*, *CD*, *DE*, *EA*.

Then, since the angle *HCF* is equal to the angle *KCF*,
    and the right angle *FHC* is also equal to the angle *FKC*,
FHC, *FKC* are two triangles having two angles equal to two angles and one side equal to one side, namely *FC* which is common to them and subtends one of the equal angles;
therefore they will also have the remaining sides equal to the remaining sides;
                                                                  [I. 26]
    therefore the perpendicular *FH* is equal to the perpendicular *FK*.
Similarly it can be proved that

each of the straight lines FL, FM, FG is also equal to each of the straight lines FH, FK;

therefore the five straight lines FG, FH, FK, FL, FM are equal to one another.

Therefore the circle described with centre F and distance one of the straight lines FG, FH, FK, FL, FM will pass also through the remaining points;

and it will touch the straight lines AB, BC, CD, DE, EA, because the angles at the points G, H, K, L, M are right.

For, if it does not touch them, but cuts them,

it will result that the straight line drawn at right angles to the diameter of the circle from its extremity falls within the circle: which was proved absurd.

[III. 16]

Therefore the circle described with centre F and distance one of the straight lines FG, FH, FK, FL, FM will not cut the straight lines AB, BC, CD, DE, EA;

therefore it will touch them.

Let it be described, as $GHKLM$.

Therefore in the given pentagon, which is equilateral and equiangular, a circle has been inscribed.   Q. E. F.

Proposition 14

About a given pentagon, which is equilateral and equiangular, to circumscribe a circle.

Let $ABCDE$ be the given pentagon, which is equilateral and equiangular; thus it is required to circumscribe a circle about the pentagon $ABCDE$.

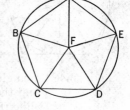

Let the angles BCD, CDE be bisected by the straight lines CF, DF respectively, and from the point F, at which the straight lines meet, let the straight lines FB, FA, FE be joined to the points B, A, E.

Then in manner similar to the preceding it can be proved that the angles CBA, BAE, AED have also been bisected by the straight lines FB, FA, FE respectively.

Now, since the angle BCD is equal to the angle CDE,
    and the angle FCD is half of the angle BCD,
        and the angle CDF half of the angle CDE,
    therefore the angle FCD is also equal to the angle CDF,
        so that the side FC is also equal to the side FD.   [I. 6]

Similarly it can be proved that

each of the straight lines FB, FA, FE is also equal to each of the straight lines FC, FD;

therefore the five straight lines FA, FB, FC, FD, FE are equal to one another.

Therefore the circle described with centre F and distance one of the straight lines FA, FB, FC, FD, FE will pass also through the remaining points, and will have been circumscribed.

Let it be circumscribed, and let it be $ABCDE$.

Therefore about the given pentagon, which is equilateral and equiangular, a circle has been circumscribed.   Q. E. F.

PROPOSITION 15

In a given circle to inscribe an equilateral and equiangular hexagon.

Let *ABCDEF* be the given circle;
thus it is required to inscribe an equilateral and equiangular hexagon in the
circle *ABCDEF*.

Let the diameter *AD* of the circle *ABCDEF* be drawn;

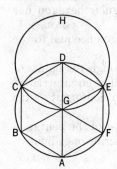

let the centre *G* of the circle be taken, and with centre *D*
and distance *DG* let the circle *EGCH* be described;
let *EG*, *CG* be joined and carried through to the points
B, *F*,

and let *AB*, *BC*, *CD*, *DE*, *EF*, *FA* be joined.

I say that the hexagon *ABCDEF* is equilateral and
equiangular.

For, since the point *G* is the centre of the circle
ABCDEF,

GE is equal to *GD*.

Again, since the point *D* is the centre of the circle
GCH,

DE is equal to *DG*.

But *GE* was proved equal to *GD*;

therefore *GE* is also equal to *ED*;

therefore the triangle *EGD* is equilateral;

and therefore its three angles *EGD*, *GDE*, *DEG* are equal to one another, inasmuch as, in isosceles triangles, the angles at the base are equal to one another.

[I. 5]

And the three angles of the triangle are equal to two right angles;   [I. 32]

therefore the angle *EGD* is one-third of two right angles.

Similarly, the angle *DGC* can also be proved to be one-third of two right
angles.

And, since the straight line *CG* standing on *EB* makes the adjacent angles
EGC, *CGB* equal to two right angles,

therefore the remaining angle *CGB* is also one-third of two right angles.

Therefore the angles *EGD*, *DGC*, *CGB* are equal to one another;

so that the angles vertical to them, the angles *BGA*, *AGF*, *FGE* are equal.

[I. 15]

Therefore the six angles *EGD*, *DGC*, *CGB*, *BGA*, *AGF*, *FGE* are equal to
one another.

But equal angles stand on equal circumferences;   [III. 26]

therefore the six circumferences *AB*, *BC*, *CD*, *DE*, *EF*, *FA* are equal to one
another.

And equal circumferences are subtended by equal straight lines;   [III. 29]

therefore the six straight lines are equal to one another;

therefore the hexagon *ABCDEF* is equilateral.

I say next that it is also equiangular.

For, since the circumference *FA* is equal to the circumference *ED*,

let the circumference *ABCD* be added to each;

therefore the whole *FABCD* is equal to the whole *EDCBA*;

and the angle *FED* stands on the circumference *FABCD*,

and the angle AFE on the circumference $EDCBA$;
therefore the angle AFE is equal to the angle DEF.   [III. 27]

Similarly it can be proved that the remaining angles of the hexagon $ABCDEF$ are also severally equal to each of the angles AFE, FED;
therefore the hexagon $ABCDEF$ is equiangular.

But it was also proved equilateral;
and it has been inscribed in the circle $ABCDEF$.

Therefore in the given circle an equilateral and equiangular hexagon has been inscribed.   Q. E. F.

PORISM. From this it is manifest that the side of the hexagon is equal to the radius of the circle.

And, in like manner as in the case of the pentagon, if through the points of division on the circle we draw tangents to the circle, there will be circumscribed about the circle an equilateral and equiangular hexagon in conformity with what was explained in the case of the pentagon.

And further by means similar to those explained in the case of the pentagon we can both inscribe a circle in a given hexagon and circumscribe one about it.

                                                              Q. E. F.

PROPOSITION 16

In a given circle to inscribe a fifteen-angled figure which shall be both equilateral and equiangular.

Let $ABCD$ be the given circle;
thus it is required to inscribe in the circle $ABCD$ a fifteen-angled figure which shall be both equilateral and equiangular.

In the circle $ABCD$ let there be inscribed a side AC of the equilateral triangle inscribed in it, and a side AB of an equilateral pentagon;

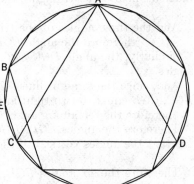

therefore, of the equal segments of which there are fifteen in the circle $ABCD$, there will be five in the circumference ABC which is one-third of the circle, and there will be three in the circumference AB which is one-fifth of the circle;
therefore in the remainder BC there will be two of the equal segments.

Let BC be bisected at E;   [III. 30]
therefore each of the circumferences BE, EC is a fifteenth of the circle $ABCD$.

If therefore we join BE, EC and fit into the circle $ABCD$ straight lines equal to them and in contiguity, a fifteen-angled figure which is both equilateral and equiangular will have been inscribed in it.   Q. E. F.

And, in like manner as in the case of the pentagon, if through the points of division on the circle we draw tangents to the circle, there will be circumscribed about the circle a fifteen-angled figure which is equilateral and equiangular.

And further, by proofs similar to those in the case of the pentagon, we can both inscribe a circle in the given fifteen-angled figure and circumscribe one about it.   Q. E. F.

BOOK FIVE

DEFINITIONS

1. A magnitude is a *part* of a magnitude, the less of the greater, when it measures the greater.

2. The greater is a *multiple* of the less when it is measured by the less.

3. A *ratio* is a sort of relation in respect of size between two magnitudes of the same kind.

4. Magnitudes are said to *have a ratio* to one another which are capable, when multiplied, of exceeding one another.

5. Magnitudes are said to *be in the same ratio*, the first to the second and the third to the fourth, when, if any equimultiples whatever be taken of the first and third, and any equimultiples whatever of the second and fourth, the former equimultiples alike exceed, are alike equal to, or alike fall short of, the latter equimultiples respectively taken in corresponding order.

6. Let magnitudes which have the same ratio be called *proportional*.

7. When, of the equimultiples, the multiple of the first magnitude exceeds the multiple of the second, but the multiple of the third does not exceed the multiple of the fourth, then the first is said to *have a greater ratio* to the second than the third has to the fourth.

8. A proportion in three terms is the least possible.

9. When three magnitudes are proportional, the first is said to have to the third the *duplicate ratio* of that which it has to the second.

10. When four magnitudes are <continuously> proportional, the first is said to have to the fourth the *triplicate ratio* of that which it has to the second, and so on continually, whatever be the proportion.

11. The term *corresponding magnitudes* is used of antecedents in relation to antecedents, and of consequents in relation to consequents.

12. *Alternate ratio* means taking the antecedent in relation to the antecedent and the consequent in relation to the consequent.

13. *Inverse ratio* means taking the consequent as antecedent in relation to the antecedent as consequent.

14. *Composition of a ratio* means taking the antecedent together with the consequent as one in relation to the consequent by itself.

15. *Separation of a ratio* means taking the excess by which the antecedent exceeds the consequent in relation to the consequent by itself.

16. *Conversion of a ratio* means taking the antecedent in relation to the excess by which the antecedent exceeds the consequent.

17. A ratio *ex aequali* arises when, there being several magnitudes and another set equal to them in multitude which taken two and two are in the same proportion, as the first is to the last among the first magnitudes, so is the first to the last among the second magnitudes;

Or, in other words, it means taking the extreme terms by virtue of the removal of the intermediate terms.

18. A *perturbed proportion* arises when, there being three magnitudes and another set equal to them in multitude, as antecedent is to consequent among the first magnitudes, so is antecedent to consequent among the second magnitudes, while, as the consequent is to a third among the first magnitudes, so is a third to the antecedent among the second magnitudes.

BOOK V. PROPOSITIONS

PROPOSITION 1

If there be any number of magnitudes whatever which are, respectively, equimultiples of any magnitudes equal in multitude, then, whatever multiple one of the magnitudes is of one, that multiple also will all be of all.

Let any number of magnitudes whatever AB, CD be respectively equimultiples of any magnitudes E, F equal in multitude;

I say that, whatever multiple AB is of E, that multiple will AB, CD also be of E, F.

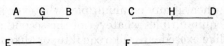

For, since AB is the same multiple of E that CD is of F, as many magnitudes as there are in AB equal to E, so many also are there in CD equal to F.

Let AB be divided into the magnitudes AG, GB equal to E,
          and CD into CH, HD equal to F;
then the multitude of the magnitudes AG, GB will be equal to the multitude of the magnitudes CH, HD.

Now, since AG is equal to E, and CH to F,
          therefore AG is equal to E, and AG, CH to E, F.

For the same reason
          GB is equal to E, and GB, HD to E, F;
therefore, as many magnitudes as there are in AB equal to E, so many also are there in AB, CD equal to E, F;
therefore, whatever multiple AB is of E, that multiple will AB, CD also be of E, F.

Therefore etc.   Q. E. D.

PROPOSITION 2

If a first magnitude be the same multiple of a second that a third is of a fourth, and a fifth also be the same multiple of the second that a sixth is of the fourth, the sum of the first and fifth will also be the same multiple of the second that the sum of the third and sixth is of the fourth.

Let a first magnitude, AB, be the same multiple of a second, C, that a third, DE, is of a fourth, F, and let a fifth, BG, also be the same multiple of the second, C, that a sixth, EH, is of the fourth F;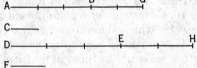

I say that the sum of the first and fifth, AG, will be the same multiple of the second, C, that the sum of the third and sixth, DH, is of the fourth, F.

For, since AB is the same multiple of C that DE is of F, therefore, as many magnitudes as there are in AB equal to C, so many also are there in DE equal to F.

For the same reason also,
as many as there are in BG equal to C, so many are there also in EH equal to F; therefore, as many as there are in the whole AG equal to C, so many also are there in the whole DH equal to F.

Therefore, whatever multiple AG is of C, that multiple also is DH of F.

Therefore the sum of the first and fifth, AG, is the same multiple of the second, C, that the sum of the third and sixth, DH, is of the fourth, F.

Therefore etc. Q. E. D.

PROPOSITION 3

If a first magnitude be the same multiple of a second that a third is of a fourth, and if equimultiples be taken of the first and third, then also ex aequali the magnitudes taken will be equimultiples respectively, the one of the second, and the other of the fourth.

Let a first magnitude A be the same multiple of a second B that a third C is of a fourth D, and let equimultiples EF, GH be taken of A, C;
I say that EF is the same multiple of B that GH is of D.

For, since EF is the same multiple of A that GH is of C, therefore, as many magnitudes as there are in EF equal to A, so many also are there in GH equal to C.

Let EF be divided into the magnitudes EK, KF equal to A, and GH into the magnitudes GL, LH equal to C;
then the multitude of the magnitudes EK, KF will be equal to the multitude of the magnitudes GL, LH.

And, since A is the same multiple of B that C is of D, while EK is equal to A, and GL to C, therefore EK is the same multiple of B that GL is of D.

For the same reason KF is the same multiple of B that LH is of D.

Since, then, a first magnitude EK is the same multiple of a second B that a third GL is of a fourth D,
and a fifth KF is also the same multiple of the second B that a sixth LH is of the fourth D,
therefore the sum of the first and fifth, EF, is also the same multiple of the second B that the sum of the third and sixth, GH, is of the fourth D. [v. 2]

Therefore etc. Q. E. D.

PROPOSITION 4

If a first magnitude have to a second the same ratio as a third to a fourth, any equimultiples whatever of the first and third will also have the same ratio to any equimultiples whatever of the second and fourth respectively, taken in corresponding order.

For let a first magnitude A have to a second B the same ratio as a third C to a fourth D; and let equimultiples E, F be taken of A, C, and G, H other, chance, equimultiples of B, D;

I say that, as E is to G, so is F to H.

For let equimultiples K, L be taken of E, F, and other, chance, equimultiples M, N of G, H.

Since E is the same multiple of A that F is of C, and equimultiples K, L of E, F have been taken, therefore K is the same multiple of A that L is of C.   [v. 3]

For the same reason M is the same multiple of B that N is of D.

And, since, as A is to B, so is C to D,

A ———
B ——
E ——+——
G ——+——+——
K ——————+———
M ——————+————+————
C ——
D ——
F ——+——
H ——+——+——
L ——————+——
N ————+————————+————————

and of A, C equimultiples K, L have been taken,
and of B, D other, chance, equimultiples M, N,
therefore, if K is in excess of M, L also is in excess of N,
if it is equal, equal, and if less, less.   [v. Def. 5]
And K, L are equimultiples of E, F,
and M, N other, chance, equimultiples of G, H;
therefore, as E is to G, so is F to H.   [v. Def. 5]

Therefore etc.   Q. E. D.

PROPOSITION 5

If a magnitude be the same multiple of a magnitude that a part subtracted is of a part subtracted, the remainder will also be the same multiple of the remainder that the whole is of the whole.

For let the magnitude AB be the same multiple of the magnitude CD that the part AE subtracted is of the part CF subtracted;

I say that the remainder EB is also the same multiple of the remainder FD that the whole AB is of the whole CD.

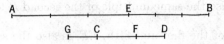

For, whatever multiple AE is of CF, let EB be made that multiple of CG.
Then, since AE is the same multiple of CF that EB is of GC,
therefore AE is the same multiple of CF that AB is of GF.   [v. 1]
But, by the assumption, AE is the same multiple of CF that AB is of CD.
Therefore AB is the same multiple of each of the magnitudes GF, CD;
therefore GF is equal to CD.
Let CF be subtracted from each;

therefore the remainder GC is equal to the remainder FD.

And, since AE is the same multiple of CF that EB is of GC,

and GC is equal to DF,

therefore AE is the same multiple of CF that EB is of FD.

But, by hypothesis,

AE is the same multiple of CF that AB is of CD;

therefore EB is the same multiple of FD that AB is of CD.

That is, the remainder EB will be the same multiple of the remainder FD that the whole AB is of the whole CD.

Therefore etc.   Q. E. D.

PROPOSITION 6

If two magnitudes be equimultiples of two magnitudes, and any magnitudes subtracted from them be equimultiples of the same, the remainders also are either equal to the same or equimultiples of them.

For let two magnitudes AB, CD be equimultiples of two magnitudes E, F, and let AG, CH subtracted from them be equimultiples of the same two E, F;

I say that the remainders also, GB, HD, are either equal to E, F or equimultiples of them.

For, first, let GB be equal to E;

I say that HD is also equal to F.

For let CK be made equal to F.

Since AG is the same multiple of E that CH is of F,

while GB is equal to E and KC to F,

therefore AB is the same multiple of E that KH is of F.   [v. 2]

But, by hypothesis, AB is the same multiple of E that CD is of F;

therefore KH is the same multiple of F that CD is of F.

Since then each of the magnitudes KH, CD is the same multiple of F,

therefore KH is equal to CD.

Let CH be subtracted from each;

therefore the remainder KC is equal to the remainder HD.

But F is equal to KC;

therefore HD is also equal to F.

Hence, if GB is equal to E, HD is also equal to F.

Similarly we can prove that, even if GB be a multiple of E, HD is also the same multiple of F.

Therefore etc.   Q. E. D.

PROPOSITION 7

Equal magnitudes have to the same the same ratio, as also has the same to equal magnitudes.

Let A, B be equal magnitudes and C any other, chance, magnitude;

I say that each of the magnitudes A, B has the same ratio to C, and C has the same ratio to each of the magnitudes A, B.

For let equimultiples D, E of A, B be taken, and of C another, chance, multiple F.

Then, since D is the same multiple of A that E is of B, while A is equal to B,

therefore D is equal to E.

But F is another, chance, magnitude.

If therefore D is in excess of F, E is also in excess of F, if equal to it, equal; and, if less, less.

And D, E are equimultiples of A, B, while F is another, chance, multiple of C; therefore, as A is to C, so is B to C.

[v. Def. 5]

I say next that C also has the same ratio to each of the magnitudes A, B.

For, with the same construction, we can prove similarly that D is equal to E; and F is some other magnitude.

If therefore F is in excess of D, it is also in excess of E, if equal, equal; and, if less, less.

And F is a multiple of C, while D, E are other, chance, equimultiples of A, B; therefore, as C is to A, so is C to B.   [v. Def. 5]

Therefore etc.

PORISM. From this it is manifest that, if any magnitudes are proportional, they will also be proportional inversely.   Q. E. D.

PROPOSITION 8

Of unequal magnitudes, the greater has to the same a greater ratio than the less has; and the same has to the less a greater ratio than it has to the greater.

Let AB, C be unequal magnitudes, and let AB be greater; let D be another, chance, magnitude;

I say that AB has to D a greater ratio than C has to D, and D has to C a greater ratio than it has to AB.

For, since AB is greater than C, let BE be made equal to C;

then the less of the magnitudes AE, EB, if multiplied, will sometime be greater than D.   [v. Def. 4]

First, let AE be less than EB; let AE be multiplied, and let FG be a multiple of it which is greater than D;

then, whatever multiple FG is of AE, let GH be made the same multiple of EB and K of C;

and let L be taken double of D, M triple of it, and successive multiples increasing by one, until what is taken is a multiple of D and the first that is greater than K. Let it be taken, and let it be N which is quadruple of D and the first multiple of it that is greater than K.

Then, since K is less than N first,
                    therefore K is not less than M.

And, since FG is the same multiple of AE that GH is of EB,
          therefore FG is the same multiple of AE that FH is of AB.   [v. 1]

But FG is the same multiple of AE that K is of C;
          therefore FH is the same multiple of AB that K is of C;
                    therefore FH, K are equimultiples of AB, C.

Again, since GH is the same multiple of EB that K is of C,
                    and EB is equal to C,

therefore GH is equal to K.

But K is not less than M;

therefore neither is GH less than M.

And FG is greater than D;

therefore the whole FH is greater than D, M together.

But D, M together are equal to N, inasmuch as M is triple of D, and M, D together are quadruple of D, while N is also quadruple of D; whence M, D together are equal to N.

But FH is greater than M, D;

therefore FH is in excess of N,

while K is not in excess of N.

And FH, K are equimultiples of AB, C, while N is another, chance, multiple of D;

therefore AB has to D a greater ratio than C has to D. [v. Def. 7]

I say next, that D also has to C a greater ratio than D has to AB.

For, with the same construction, we can prove similarly that N is in excess of K, while N is not in excess of FH.

And N is a multiple of D,

while FH, K are other, chance, equimultiples of AB, C;

therefore D has to C a greater ratio than D has to AB. [v. Def. 7]

Again, let AE be greater than EB.

Then the less, EB, if multiplied, will sometime be greater than D. [v. Def. 4]

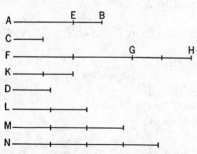

Let it be multiplied, and let GH be a multiple of EB and greater than D; and, whatever multiple GH is of EB, let FG be made the same multiple of AE, and K of C.

Then we can prove similarly that FH, K are equimultiples of AB, C; and, similarly, let N be taken a multiple of D but the first that is greater than FG, so that FG is again not less than M.

But GH is greater than D;

therefore the whole FH is in excess of D, M, that is, of N.

Now K is not in excess of N, inasmuch as FG also, which is greater than GH, that is, than K, is not in excess of N.

And in the same manner, by following the above argument, we complete the demonstration.

Therefore etc.

Q. E. D.

Proposition 9

Magnitudes which have the same ratio to the same are equal to one another; and magnitudes to which the same has the same ratio are equal.

For let each of the magnitudes A, B have the same ratio to C;

I say that A is equal to B.

For, otherwise, each of the magnitudes A, B would not have had the same ratio to C; but it has;   [v. 8]

therefore A is equal to B.

Again, let C have the same ratio to each of the magnitudes A, B;
I say that A is equal to B.

For, otherwise, C would not have had the same ratio to each of the magnitudes A, B;   [v. 8]
but it has;
therefore A is equal to B.

Therefore etc.   Q. E. D.

PROPOSITION 10

Of magnitudes which have a ratio to the same, that which has a greater ratio is greater; and that to which the same has a greater ratio is less.

For let A have to C a greater ratio than B has to C;
I say that A is greater than B.

A———————————————   B———————————————
C———————————————

For, if not, A is either equal to B or less.

Now A is not equal to B;

for in that case each of the magnitudes A, B would have had the same ratio to C;   [v. 7]
but they have not;
therefore A is not equal to B.

Nor again is A less than B;

for in that case A would have had to C a less ratio than B has to C;   [v. 8]
but it has not;
therefore A is not less than B.

But it was proved not to be equal either;
therefore A is greater than B.

Again, let C have to B a greater ratio than C has to A;
I say that B is less than A.

For, if not, it is either equal or greater.

Now B is not equal to A;

for in that case C would have had the same ratio to each of the magnitudes A, B;   [v. 7]
but it has not;
therefore A is not equal to B.

Nor again is B greater than A;

for in that case C would have had to B a less ratio than it has to A;   [v. 8]
but it has not;
therefore B is not greater than A.

But it was proved that it is not equal either;
therefore B is less than A.

Therefore etc.   Q. E. D.

PROPOSITION 11

Ratios which are the same with the same ratio are also the same with one another.

For, as A is to B, so let C be to D,
and, as C is to D, so let E be to F;

I say that, as A is to B, so is E to F.
For of A, C, E let equimultiples G, H, K be taken, and of B, D, F other,

```
A_____        C____        E___
B_____           D___         F__
G_____    H_____   K_____
L_____      M_____    N_____
```

chance, equimultiples L, M, N.
Then since, as A is to B, so is C to D,
            and of A, C equimultiples G, H have been taken,
            and of B, D other, chance, equimultiples L, M,
    therefore, if G is in excess of L, H is also in excess of M,
                    if equal, equal,
                    and if less, less.
Again, since, as C is to D, so is E to F,
            and of C, E equimultiples H, K have been taken,
            and of D, F other, chance, equimultiples M, N,
    therefore, if H is in excess of M, K is also in excess of N,
                    if equal, equal,
                    and if less, less.
But we saw that, if H was in excess of M, G was also in excess of L; if equal,
equal; and if less, less;
    so that, in addition, if G is in excess of L, K is also in excess of N,
                    if equal, equal,
                    and if less, less.
And G, K are equimultiples of A, E,
        while L, N are other, chance, equimultiples of B, F;
            therefore, as A is to B, so is E to F.
Therefore etc.   Q. E. D.

PROPOSITION 12

*If any number of magnitudes be proportional, as one of the antecedents is to one
of the consequents, so will all the antecedents be to all the consequents.*

Let any number of magnitudes A, B, C, D, E, F be proportional, so that, as
A is to B, so is C to D and E to F;
        I say that, as A is to B, so are A, C, E to B, D, F.

For of A, C, E let equimultiples G, H, K be taken,
and of B, D, F other, chance,
equimultiples L, M, N.

```
A_____     B_____     C____
D_____     E____      F__
G_____          L_____
H_____          M_____
K_____               N_____
```

Then since, as A is to B, so
is C to D, and E to F,
and of A, C, E equimultiples
G, H, K have been taken,
        and of B, D, F other, chance, equimultiples L, M, N,
    therefore, if G is in excess of L, H is also in excess of M, and K of N,
                    if equal, equal,

and if less, less;

so that, in addition,

if G is in excess of L, then G, H, K are in excess of L, M, N,

if equal, equal,

and if less, less.

Now G and G, H, K are equimultiples of A and A, C, E, since, if any number of magnitudes whatever are respectively equimultiples of any magnitudes equal in multitude, whatever multiple one of the magnitudes is of one, that multiple also will all be of all.   [v. 1]

For the same reason

L and L, M, N are also equimultiples of B and B, D, F;

therefore, as A is to B, so are A, C, E to B, D, F.   [v. Def. 5]

Therefore etc.   Q. E. D.

Proposition 13

If a first magnitude have to a second the same ratio as a third to a fourth, and the third have to the fourth a greater ratio than a fifth has to a sixth, the first will also have to the second a greater ratio than the fifth to the sixth.

For let a first magnitude A have to a second B the same ratio as a third C has to a fourth D,

and let the third C have to the fourth D a greater ratio than a fifth E has to a sixth F;

I say that the first A will also have to the second B a greater ratio than the fifth E to the sixth F.

For, since there are some equimultiples of C, E,

and of D, F other, chance, equimultiples, such that the multiple of C is in excess of the multiple of D,

while the multiple of E is not in excess of the multiple of F, [v. Def. 7]

let them be taken,

and let G, H be equimultiples of C, E,

and K, L other, chance, equimultiples of D, F,

so that G is in excess of K, but H is not in excess of L;

and, whatever multiple G is of C, let M be also that multiple of A,

and, whatever multiple K is of D, let N be also that multiple of B.

Now, since, as A is to B, so is C to D,

and of A, C equimultiples M, G have been taken,

and of B, D other, chance, equimultiples N, K,

therefore, if M is in excess of N, G is also in excess of K,

if equal, equal,

and if less, less.   [v. Def. 5]

But G is in excess of K;
                    therefore M is also in excess of N.
But H is not in excess of L;
                and M, H are equimultiples of A, E,
            and N, L other, chance, equimultiples of B, F;
        therefore A has to B a greater ratio than E has to F.   [v. Def. 7]
Therefore etc.   Q. E. D.

PROPOSITION 14

*If a first magnitude have to a second the same ratio as a third has to a fourth, and
the first be greater than the third, the second will also be greater than the fourth; if
equal, equal; and if less, less.*

For let a first magnitude A have the same ratio to a second B as a third C
has to a fourth D; and let A be greater than C;
                    I say that B is also greater than D.

                                For, since A is greater than C,
A————————   C—————   and B is another, chance, magnitude,
B——————   D———   therefore A has to B a greater ratio
                                than C has to B.   [v. 8]
But, as A is to B, so is C to D;
            therefore C has also to D a greater ratio than C has to B.   [v. 13]
But that to which the same has a greater ratio is less;   [v. 10]
                    therefore D is less than B;
                    so that B is greater than D.
Similarly we can prove that, if A be equal to C, B will also be equal to D;
        and, if A be less than C, B will also be less than D.
Therefore etc.   Q. E. D.

PROPOSITION 15

*Parts have the same ratio as the same multiples of them taken in corresponding
order.*

For let AB be the same multiple of C that DE is of F;
            I say that, as C is to F, so is AB to DE.

                                For, since AB is the same multiple
        G   H   of C that DE is of F, as many magni-
A├———————┼————————┤B   C├————————┤   tudes as there are in AB equal to C,
        K   L   so many are there also in DE equal
D├———————┼————┼———┤E   F├————┤   to F.
Let AB be divided into the magnitudes AG, GH, HB equal to C,
        and DE into the magnitudes DK, KL, LE equal to F;
then the multitude of the magnitudes AG, GH, HB will be equal to the multi-
tude of the magnitudes DK, KL, LE.
And, since AG, GH, HB are equal to one another,
            and DK, KL, LE are also equal to one another,
        therefore, as AG is to DK, so is GH to KL, and HB to LE.   [v. 7]
Therefore, as one of the antecedents is to one of the consequents, so will all
the antecedents be to all the consequents;   [v. 12]
                therefore, as AG is to DK, so is AB to DE.

But AG is equal to C and DK to F;
                    therefore, as C is to F, so is AB to DE.
Therefore etc.   Q. E. D.

PROPOSITION 16

If four magnitudes be proportional, they will also be proportional alternately.
    Let A, B, C, D be four proportional magnitudes,
                so that, as A is to B, so is C to D;
I say that they will also be so alternately, that is, as A is to C, so is B to D.

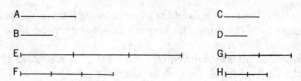

    For of A, B let equimultiples E, F be taken,
                and of C, D other, chance, equimultiples G, H.
    Then, since E is the same multiple of A that F is of B,
            and parts have the same ratio as the same multiples of them,   [v. 15]
                    therefore, as A is to B, so is E to F.
    But as A is to B, so is C to D;
                therefore also, as C is to D, so is E to F.   [v. 11]
    Again, since G, H are equimultiples of C, D,
                therefore, as C is to D, so is G to H.   [v. 15]
    But, as C is to D, so is E to F;
                therefore also, as E is to F, so is G to H.   [v. 11]
    But, if four magnitudes be proportional, and the first be greater than the
third,
                the second will also be greater than the fourth;
                            if equal, equal;
                            and if less, less.   [v. 14]
    Therefore, if E is in excess of G, F is also in excess of H,
                            if equal, equal,
                            and if less, less.
    Now E, F are equimultiples of A, B,
                and G, H other, chance, equimultiples of C, D;
                therefore, as A is to C, so is B to D.   [v. Def. 5]
    Therefore etc.   Q. E. D.

PROPOSITION 17

If magnitudes be proportional componendo, *they will also be proportional* separando.
    Let AB, BE, CD, DF be magnitudes proportional *componendo*, so that, as
AB is to BE, so is CD to DF;
    I say that they will also be proportional *separando*, that is, as AE is to EB,
so is CF to DF.
    For of AE, EB, CF, FD let equimultiples GH, HK, LM, MN be taken,
                and of EB, FD other, chance, equimultiples, KO, NP.

Then, since GH is the same multiple of AE that HK is of EB,
  therefore GH is the same multiple of AE that GK is of AB.   [v. 1]
But GH is the same multiple of AE that LM is of CF;
  therefore GK is the same multiple of AB that LM is of CF.

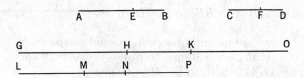

Again, since LM is the same multiple of CF that MN is of FD,
  therefore LM is the same multiple of CF that LN is of CD.   [v. 1]
But LM was the same multiple of CF that GK is of AB;
  therefore GK is the same multiple of AB that LN is of CD.
Therefore GK, LN are equimultiples of AB, CD.
Again, since HK is the same multiple of EB that MN is of FD,
  and KO is also the same multiple of EB that NP is of FD,
therefore the sum HO is also the same multiple of EB that MP is of FD.
                                                                    [v. 2]

And, since, as AB is to BE, so is CD to DF,
      and of AB, CD equimultiples GK, LN have been taken,
          and of EB, FD equimultiples HO, MP,
    therefore, if GK is in excess of HO, LN is also in excess of MP,
                  if equal, equal,
                  and if less, less.
Let GH be in excess of KO;
              then, if HK be added to each,
              GK is also in excess of HO.
But we saw that, if GK was in excess of HO, LN was also in excess of MP;
          therefore LN is also in excess of MP,
          and, if MN be subtracted from each,
              LM is also in excess of NP;
    so that, if GH is in excess of KO, LM is also in excess of NP.
Similarly we can prove that,
          if GH be equal to KO, LM will also be equal to NP,
                  and if less, less.
And GH, LM are equimultiples of AE, CF,
    while KO, NP are other, chance, equimultiples of EB, FD;
          therefore, as AE is to EB, so is CF to FD.
Therefore etc.   Q. E. D.

Proposition 18

If magnitudes be proportional separando, *they will also be proportional* componendo.

Let AE, EB, CF, FD be magnitudes proportional *separando*, so that, as AE is to EB, so is CF to FD;

I say that they will also be proportional *componendo*, that is, as AB is to BE, so is CD to FD.

For, if CD be not to DF as AB to BE,
then, as AB is to BE, so will CD be either to some magnitude less than DF or to a greater.

First, let it be in that ratio to a less magnitude DG.

Then, since, as AB is to BE, so is CD to DG,

> they are magnitudes proportional *componendo*;
> so that they will also be proportional *separando*. [v. 17]

Therefore, as AE is to EB, so is CG to GD.

But also, by hypothesis,

> as AE is to EB, so is CF to FD.

Therefore also, as CG is to GD, so is CF to FD. [v. 11]

But the first CG is greater than the third CF;

> therefore the second GD is also greater than the fourth FD. [v. 14]

But it is also less: which is impossible.

Therefore, as AB is to BE, so is not CD to a less magnitude than FD.

Similarly we can prove that neither is it in that ratio to a greater;

> it is therefore in that ratio to FD itself.

Therefore etc. Q. E. D.

Proposition 19

If, as a whole is to a whole, so is a part subtracted to a part subtracted, the remainder will also be to the remainder as whole to whole.

For, as the whole AB is to the whole CD, so let the part AE subtracted be to the part CF subtracted;

I say that the remainder EB will also be to the remainder FD as the whole AB to the whole CD.

For since, as AB is to CD, so is AE to CF,

> alternately also, as BA is to AE, so is DC to CF. [v. 16]

And, since the magnitudes are proportional *componendo*, they will also be proportional *separando*, [v. 17]

> that is, as BE is to EA, so is DF to CF,
> and, alternately,
> as BE is to DF, so is EA to FC. [v. 16]

But, as AE is to CF, so by hypothesis is the whole AB to the whole CD.

Therefore also the remainder EB will be to the remainder FD as the whole AB is to the whole CD. [v. 11]

Therefore etc.

[PORISM. From this it is manifest that, if magnitudes be proportional *componendo*, they will also be proportional *convertendo*.] Q. E. D.

Proposition 20

If there be three magnitudes, and others equal to them in multitude, which taken two and two are in the same ratio, and if ex aequali the first be greater than the third, the fourth will also be greater than the sixth; if equal, equal; and, if less, less.

Let there be three magnitudes A, B, C, and others D, E, F equal to them in multitude, which taken two and two are in the same ratio, so that,

> as A is to B, so is D to E,

and,   as B is to C, so is E to F;
                    and let A be greater than C *ex aequali*;
I say that D will also be greater than F; if A is equal to C, equal; and, if less, less.

For, since A is greater than C, and B is some other magnitude, and the greater has to the same a greater ratio than the less has, [v. 8] therefore A has to B a greater ratio than C has to B.

But, as A is to B, so is D to E,
            and, as C is to B, inversely, so is F to E;
        therefore D has also to E a greater ratio than F has to E.   [v. 13]
    But, of magnitudes which have a ratio to the same, that which has a greater ratio is greater;   [v. 10]
                    therefore D is greater than F.
Similarly we can prove that, if A be equal to C, D will also be equal to F; and if less, less.
    Therefore etc.   Q. E. D.

PROPOSITION 21

If there be three magnitudes, and others equal to them in multitude, which taken two and two together are in the same ratio, and the proportion of them be perturbed, then, if ex aequali the first magnitude is greater than the third, the fourth will also be greater than the sixth; if equal, equal; and if less, less.

Let there be three magnitudes A, B, C, and others D, E, F equal to them in multitude, which taken two and two are in the same ratio, and let the proportion of them be perturbed, so that,
                    as A is to B, so is E to F,
and,   as B is to C, so is D to E,
            and let A be greater than C ex aequali;
I say that D will also be greater than F; if A is equal to C, equal; and if less, less.

For, since A is greater than C, and B is some other magnitude, therefore A has to B a greater ratio than C has to B.   [v. 8]

But, as A is to B, so is E to F,
            and, as C is to B, inversely, so is E to D.
    Therefore also E has to F a greater ratio than E has to D.   [v. 13]
But that to which the same has a greater ratio is less;   [v. 10]
                    therefore F is less than D;
                    therefore D is greater than F.
Similarly we can prove that, if A be equal to C, D will also be equal to F; and if less, less.
    Therefore etc.   Q. E. D.

Proposition 22

If there be any number of magnitudes whatever, and others equal to them in multitude, which taken two and two together are in the same ratio, they will also be in the same ratio ex aequali.

Let there be any number of magnitudes A, B, C, and others D, E, F equal to them in multitude, which taken two and two together are in the same ratio, so that,

as A is to B, so is D to E,

and,   as B is to C, so is E to F;

I say that they will also be in the same ratio *ex aequali*,

<that is, as A is to C, so is D to F>.

For of A, D let equimultiples G, H be taken,

and of B, E other, chance, equimultiples K, L;

and, further, of C, F other, chance, equimultiples M, N.

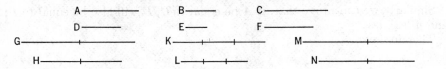

Then, since, as A is to B, so is D to E,

and of A, D equimultiples G, H have been taken,

and of B, E other, chance, equimultiples K, L,

therefore, as G is to K, so is H to L.   [v. 4]

For the same reason also,

as K is to M, so is L to N.

Since, then, there are three magnitudes G, K, M, and others H, L, N equal to them in multitude, which taken two and two together are in the same ratio,

therefore, *ex aequali*, if G is in excess of M, H is also in excess of N;

if equal, equal; and if less, less.   [v. 20]

And G, H are equimultiples of A, D,

and M, N other, chance, equimultiples of C, F.

Therefore, as A is to C, so is D to F.   [v. Def. 5]

Therefore etc.   Q. E. D.

Proposition 23

If there be three magnitudes, and others equal to them in multitude, which taken two and two together are in the same ratio, and the proportion of them be perturbed, they will also be in the same ratio ex aequali.

Let there be three magnitudes A, B, C, and others equal to them in multitude, which, taken two and two together, are in the same proportion, namely D, E, F; and let the proportion of them be perturbed, so that,

as A is to B, so is E to F,

and,   as B is to C, so is D to E;

I say that, as A is to C, so is D to F.

Of A, B, D let equimultiples G, H, K be taken,

and of C, E, F other, chance, equimultiples L, M, N.

Then, since G, H are equimultiples of A, B,

and parts have the same ratio as the same multiples of them,   [v. 15]
therefore, as A is to B, so is G to H.

For the same reason also,

A————   B——   C————
D——   E————   F——
G——+——+———— H—+—+——   L——+———
K——+——+——   M————+———— N——+——

as E is to F, so is M to N.

And, as A is to B, so is E to F;
therefore also, as G is to H, so is M to N.   [v. 11]

Next, since, as B is to C, so is D to E,
alternately, also, as B is to D, so is C to E.   [v. 16]

And, since H, K are equimultiples of B, D,
and parts have the same ratio as their equimultiples,
therefore, as B is to D, so is H to K.   [v. 15]

But, as B is to D, so is C to E;
therefore also, as H is to K, so is C to E.   [v. 11]

Again, since L, M are equimultiples of C, E,
therefore, as C is to E, so is L to M.   [v. 15]

But, as C is to E, so is H to K;
therefore also, as H is to K, so is L to M,   [v. 11]
and, alternately, as H is to L, so is K to M.   [v. 16]

But it was also proved that,
as G is to H, so is M to N.

Since, then, there are three magnitudes G, H, L, and others equal to them in
multitude K, M, N, which taken two and two together are in the same ratio,
and the proportion of them is perturbed,
therefore, *ex aequali*, if G is in excess of L, K is also in excess of N;
if equal, equal; and if less, less.   [v. 21]

And G, K are equimultiples of A, D,
and L N of C, F.

Therefore, as A is to C, so is D to F.

Therefore etc.   Q. E. D.

PROPOSITION 24

If a first magnitude have to a second the same ratio as a third has to a fourth, and
also a fifth have to the second the same ratio as a sixth to the fourth, the first and fifth
added together will have to the second the same ratio as the third and sixth have to
the fourth.

Let a first magnitude AB have to a second C the same ratio as a third DE
has to a fourth F;

A————————B————————G   and let also a fifth BG have to the second C
C————   the same ratio as a sixth EH has to the
D————————E————H   fourth F;
F————   I say that the first and fifth added together,
AG, will have to the second C the same ratio
as the third and sixth, DH, has to the fourth F.

For since, as BG is to C, so is EH to F,

inversely, as C is to BG, so is F to EH.

Since, then, as AB is to C, so is DE to F,

and, as C is to BG, so is F to EH,

therefore, *ex aequali*, as AB is to BG, so is DE to EH. [v. 22]

And, since the magnitudes are proportional *separando*, they will also be proportional *componendo*; [v. 18]

therefore, as AG is to GB, so is DH to HE.

But also, as BG is to C, so is EH to F;

therefore, *ex aequali*, as AG is to C, so is DH to F. [v. 22]

Therefore etc. Q. E. D.

PROPOSITION 25

If four magnitudes be proportional, the greatest and the least are greater than the remaining two.

Let the four magnitudes AB, CD, E, F be proportional so that, as AB is to CD, so is E to F, and let AB be the greatest of them and F the least;

I say that AB, F are greater than CD, E.

For let AG be made equal to E, and CH equal to F.

Since, as AB is to CD, so is E to F,

and E is equal to AG, and F to CH,

therefore, as AB is to CD, so is AG to CH.

And since, as the whole AB is to the whole CD, so is the part AG subtracted to the part CH subtracted,

the remainder GB will also be to the remainder HD as the whole AB is to the whole CD. [v. 19]

But AB is greater than CD;

therefore GB is also greater than HD.

And, since AG is equal to E, and CH to F,

therefore AG, F are equal to CH, E.

And if, GB, HD being unequal, and GB greater, AG, F be added to GB and CH, E be added to HD,

it follows that AB, F are greater than CD, E.

Therefore etc. Q. E. D.

BOOK SIX

DEFINITIONS

1. *Similar rectilineal figures* are such as have their angles severally equal and the sides about the equal angles proportional.

2. A straight line is said to have been *cut in extreme and mean ratio* when, as the whole line is to the greater segment, so is the greater to the less.

3. The *height* of any figure is the perpendicular drawn from the vertex to the base.

BOOK VI. PROPOSITIONS

PROPOSITION 1

Triangles and parallelograms which are under the same height are to one another as their bases.

Let ABC, ACD be triangles and EC, CF parallelograms under the same height;

I say that, as the base BC is to the base CD, so is the triangle ABC to the triangle ACD, and the parallelogram EC to the parallelogram CF.

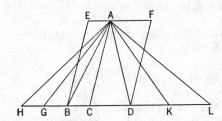

For let BD be produced in both directions to the points H, L and let [any number of straight lines] BG, GH be made equal to the base BC, and any number of straight lines DK, KL equal to the base CD;

let AG, AH, AK, AL be joined.

Then, since CB, BG, GH are equal to one another,

the triangles ABC, AGB, AHG are also equal to one another.   [I. 38]

Therefore, whatever multiple the base HC is of the base BC, that multiple also is the triangle AHC of the triangle ABC.

For the same reason,

whatever multiple the base LC is of the base CD, that multiple also is the triangle ALC of the triangle ACD;

and, if the base HC is equal to the base CL, the triangle AHC is also equal to the triangle ACL,   [I. 38]

if the base HC is in excess of the base CL, the triangle AHC is also in excess of the triangle ACL,

and, if less, less.

Thus, there being four magnitudes, two bases BC, CD and two triangles ABC, ACD, equimultiples have been taken of the base BC and the triangle ABC, namely the base HC and the triangle AHC,

and of the base CD and the triangle ADC other, chance, equimultiples, namely the base LC and the triangle ALC;

and it has been proved that,

if the base HC is in excess of the base CL, the triangle AHC is also in excess of the triangle ALC;

if equal, equal; and, if less, less.

Therefore, as the base BC is to the base CD, so is the triangle ABC to the triangle ACD. [v. Def. 5]

Next, since the parallelogram EC is double of the triangle ABC, [I. 41]

and the parallelogram FC is double of the triangle ACD,

while parts have the same ratio as the same multiples of them, [v. 15]

therefore, as the triangle ABC is to the triangle ACD, so is the parallelogram EC to the parallelogram FC.

Since, then, it was proved that, as the base BC is to CD, so is the triangle ABC to the triangle ACD,

and, as the triangle ABC is to the triangle ACD, so is the parallelogram EC to the parallelogram CF,

therefore also, as the base BC is to the base CD, so is the parallelogram EC to the parallelogram FC. [v. 11]

Therefore etc.

Q. E. D.

PROPOSITION 2

If a straight line be drawn parallel to one of the sides of a triangle, it will cut the sides of the triangle proportionally; and, if the sides of the triangle be cut proportionally, the line joining the points of section will be parallel to the remaining side of the triangle.

For let DE be drawn parallel to BC, one of the sides of the triangle ABC;

I say that, as BD is to DA, so is CE to EA.

For let BE, CD be joined.

Therefore the triangle BDE is equal to the triangle CDE;

for they are on the same base DE and in the same parallels DE, BC. [I. 38]

And the triangle ADE is another area.

But equals have the same ratio to the same; [v. 7]

therefore, as the triangle BDE is to the triangle ADE, so is the triangle CDE to the triangle ADE.

But, as the triangle BDE is to ADE, so is BD to DA;

for, being under the same height, the perpendicular drawn from E to AB, they are to one another as their bases. [VI. 1]

For the same reason also,

as the triangle CDE is to ADE, so is CE to EA.

Therefore also, as BD is to DA, so is CE to EA. [v. 11]

Again, let the sides AB, AC of the triangle ABC be cut proportionally, so that, as BD is to DA, so is CE to EA; and let DE be joined.

I say that DE is parallel to BC.

For, with the same construction,

since, as BD is to DA, so is CE to EA,

but, as BD is to DA, so is the triangle BDE to the triangle ADE,

and, as CE is to EA, so is the triangle CDE to the triangle ADE, [vi. 1]

therefore also,

as the triangle BDE is to the triangle ADE, so is the triangle CDE to the triangle ADE.   [v. 11]

Therefore each of the triangles BDE, CDE has the same ratio to ADE.

Therefore the triangle BDE is equal to the triangle CDE;   [v. 9]

and they are on the same base DE.

But equal triangles which are on the same base are also in the same parallels.

[i. 39]

Therefore DE is parallel to BC.

Therefore etc.   Q. E. D.

Proposition 3

If an angle of a triangle be bisected and the straight line cutting the angle cut the base also, the segments of the base will have the same ratio as the remaining sides of the triangle; and, if the segments of the base have the same ratio as the remaining sides of the triangle, the straight line joined from the vertex to the point of section will bisect the angle of the triangle.

Let ABC be a triangle, and let the angle BAC be bisected by the straight line AD;

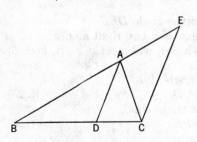

I say that, as BD is to CD, so is BA to AC.

For let CE be drawn through C parallel to DA, and let BA be carried through and meet it at E.

Then, since the straight line AC falls upon the parallels AD, EC,

the angle ACE is equal to the angle CAD.

[i. 29]

But the angle CAD is by hypothesis equal to the angle BAD;

therefore the angle BAD is also equal to the angle ACE.

Again, since the straight line BAE falls upon the parallels AD, EC,

the exterior angle BAD is equal to the interior angle AEC.   [i. 29]

But the angle ACE was also proved equal to the angle BAD;

therefore the angle ACE is also equal to the angle AEC,

so that the side AE is also equal to the side AC.   [i. 6]

And, since AD has been drawn parallel to EC, one of the sides of the triangle BCE,

therefore, proportionally, as BD is to DC, so is BA to AE.

But AE is equal to AC;   [vi. 2]

therefore, as BD is to DC, so is BA to AC.

Again, let BA be to AC as BD to DC, and let AD be joined;

I say that the angle BAC has been bisected by the straight line AD.

For, with the same construction,

since, as BD is to DC, so is BA to AC,

and also, as BD is to DC, so is BA to AE: for AD has been drawn parallel to

EC, one of the sides of the triangle BCE: [VI. 2]

       therefore also, as BA is to AC, so is BA to AE. [V. 11]

Therefore AC is equal to AE, [V. 9]

      so that the angle AEC is also equal to the angle ACE. [I. 5]

But the angle AEC is equal to the exterior angle BAD, [I. 29]

      and the angle ACE is equal to the alternate angle CAD; [*id.*]

    therefore the angle BAD is also equal to the angle CAD.

Therefore the angle BAC has been bisected by the straight line AD.

Therefore etc.   Q. E. D.

PROPOSITION 4

In equiangular triangles the sides about the equal angles are proportional, and those are corresponding sides which subtend the equal angles.

Let ABC, DCE be equiangular triangles having the angle ABC equal to the angle DCE, the angle BAC to the angle CDE, and further the angle ACB to the angle CED;

I say that in the triangles ABC, DCE the sides about the equal angles are proportional, and those are corresponding sides which subtend the equal angles.

For let BC be placed in a straight line with CE.

Then, since the angles ABC, ACB are less than two right angles,   [I. 17]

    and the angle ACB is equal to the angle DEC,

  therefore the angles ABC, DEC are less than two right angles;

    therefore BA, ED, when produced, will meet. [I. Post. 5]

Let them be produced and meet at F.

Now, since the angle DCE is equal to the angle ABC,

        BF is parallel to CD. [I. 28]

Again, since the angle ACB is equal to the angle DEC,

        AC is parallel to FE. [I. 28]

Therefore $FACD$ is a parallelogram;

    therefore FA is equal to DC, and AC to FD. [I. 34]

And, since AC has been drawn parallel to FE, one side of the triangle FBE,

    therefore, as BA is to AF, so is BC to CE. [VI. 2]

But AF is equal to CD;

    therefore, as BA is to CD, so is BC to CE,

  and alternately, as AB is to BC, so is DC to CE. [V. 16]

Again, since CD is parallel to BF,

    therefore, as BC is to CE, so is FD to DE. [VI. 2]

But FD is equal to AC;

    therefore, as BC is to CE, so is AC to DE,

  and alternately, as BC is to CA, so is CE to ED. [V. 16]

Since, then, it was proved that,

        as AB is to BC, so is DC to CE,

and,   as BC is to CA, so is CE to ED;

  therefore, *ex aequali*, as BA is to AC, so is CD to DE. [V. 22]

Therefore etc.   Q. E. D.

PROPOSITION 5

If two triangles have their sides proportional, the triangles will be equiangular and will have those angles equal which the corresponding sides subtend.

Let *ABC*, *DEF* be two triangles having their sides proportional, so that,

as *AB* is to *BC*, so is *DE* to *EF*,

as *BC* is to *CA*, so is *EF* to *FD*,

and further, as *BA* is to *AC*, so is *ED* to *DF*;

I say that the triangle *ABC* is equiangular with the triangle *DEF*, and they will have those angles equal which the corresponding sides subtend, namely the angle *ABC* to the angle *DEF*, the angle *BCA* to the angle *EFD*, and further the angle *BAC* to the angle *EDF*.

For on the straight line *EF*, and at the points *E*, *F* on it, let there be constructed the angle *FEG* equal to the angle *ABC*, and the angle *EFG* equal to the angle *ACB*;   [I. 23]

therefore the remaining angle at *A* is equal to the remaining angle at *G*.   [I. 32]

Therefore the triangle *ABC* is equiangular with the triangle *GEF*.

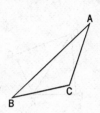

Therefore in the triangles *ABC*, *GEF* the sides about the equal angles are proportional, and those are corresponding sides which subtend the equal angles;   [VI. 4]
therefore, as *AB* is to *BC*, so is *GE* to *EF*.

But, as *AB* is to *BC*, so by hypothesis is *DE* to *EF*;

therefore, as *DE* is to *EF*, so is *GE* to *EF*.   [V. 11]

Therefore each of the straight lines *DE*, *GE* has the same ratio to *EF*;

therefore *DE* is equal to *GE*.   [V. 9]

For the same reason

DF is also equal to *GF*.

Since then *DE* is equal to *EG*,

and *EF* is common,

the two sides *DE*, *EF* are equal to the two sides *GE*, *EF*;

and the base *DF* is equal to the base *FG*;

therefore the angle *DEF* is equal to the angle *GEF*,   [I. 8]

and the triangle *DEF* is equal to the triangle *GEF*,

and the remaining angles are equal to the remaining angles, namely those which the equal sides subtend.   [I. 4]

Therefore the angle *DFE* is also equal to the angle *GFE*,

and the angle *EDF* to the angle *EGF*.

And, since the angle *FED* is equal to the angle *GEF*,

while the angle *GEF* is equal to the angle *ABC*,

therefore the angle *ABC* is also equal to the angle *DEF*.

For the same reason

the angle *ACB* is also equal to the angle *DFE*,

and further, the angle at *A* to the angle at *D*;

therefore the triangle *ABC* is equiangular with the triangle *DEF*.

Therefore etc.   Q. E. D.

Proposition 6

If two triangles have one angle equal to one angle and the sides about the equal angles proportional, the triangles will be equiangular and will have those angles equal which the corresponding sides subtend.

Let *ABC*, *DEF* be two triangles having one angle *BAC* equal to one angle *EDF* and the sides about the equal angles proportional, so that,

as *BA* is to *AC*, so is *ED* to *DF*;

I say that the triangle *ABC* is equiangular with the triangle *DEF*, and will have the angle *ABC* equal to the angle *DEF*, and the angle *ACB* to the angle *DFE*.

For on the straight line *DF*, and at the points *D*, *F* on it, let there be constructed the angle *FDG* equal to either of the angles *BAC*, *EDF*, and the angle *DFG* equal to the angle *ACB*;   [i. 23]
therefore the remaining angle at *B* is equal to the remaining angle at *G*. [i. 32]

Therefore the triangle *ABC* is equiangular with the triangle *DGF*.

Therefore, proportionally, as *BA* is to *AC*, so is *GD* to *DF*.   [vi. 4]

But, by hypothesis, as *BA* is to *AC*, so also is *ED* to *DF*;
therefore also, as *ED* is to *DF*, so is
GD to *DF*.   [v. 11]

Therefore *ED* is equal to *DG*; [v. 9]
                and *DF* is common;
therefore the two sides *ED*, *DF* are
equal to the two sides *GD*, *DF*; and
the angle *EDF* is equal to the angle
GDF;

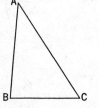

therefore the base *EF* is equal to the base *GF*,
          and the triangle *DEF* is equal to the triangle *DGF*,
and the remaining angles will be equal to the remaining angles, namely those which the equal sides subtend.   [i. 4]

Therefore the angle *DFG* is equal to the angle *DFE*,
          and the angle *DGF* to the angle *DEF*.

But the angle *DFG* is equal to the angle *ACB*;
          therefore the angle *ACB* is also equal to the angle *DFE*.

And, by hypothesis, the angle *BAC* is also equal to the angle *EDF*;
therefore the remaining angle at *B* is also equal to the remaining angle at *E*;
                                                                              [i. 32]

          therefore the triangle *ABC* is equiangular with the triangle *DEF*.

Therefore etc.   Q. E. D.

Proposition 7

If two triangles have one angle equal to one angle, the sides about other angles proportional, and the remaining angles either both less or both not less than a right angle, the triangles will be equiangular and will have those angles equal, the sides about which are proportional.

Let *ABC*, *DEF* be two triangles having one angle equal to one angle, the angle *BAC* to the angle *EDF*, the sides about other angles *ABC*, *DEF* proportional, so that, as *AB* is to *BC*, so is *DE* to *EF*, and, first, each of the remaining angles at *C*, *F* less than a right angle;

I say that the triangle ABC is equiangular with the triangle DEF, the angle ABC will be equal to the angle DEF, and the remaining angle, namely the angle at C, equal to the remaining angle, the angle at F.

For, if the angle ABC is unequal to the angle DEF, one of them is greater.

Let the angle ABC be greater; and on the straight line AB, and at the point B on it, let the angle ABG be constructed equal to the angle DEF.   [I. 23]

Then, since the angle A is equal to D, and the angle ABG to the angle DEF, therefore the remaining angle AGB is equal to the remaining angle DFE. [I. 32]

Therefore the triangle ABG is equiangular with the triangle DEF.

Therefore, as AB is to BG, so is DE to EF.   [VI. 4]

But, as DE is to EF, so by hypothesis is AB to BC;

therefore AB has the same ratio to each of the straight lines BC, BG;   [V. 11]

therefore BC is equal to BG,   [V. 9]

so that the angle at C is also equal to the angle BGC.   [I. 5]

But, by hypothesis, the angle at C is less than a right angle;

therefore the angle BGC is also less than a right angle;

so that the angle AGB adjacent to it is greater than a right angle. [I. 13]

And it was proved equal to the angle at F;

therefore the angle at F is also greater than a right angle.

But it is by hypothesis less than a right angle: which is absurd.

Therefore the angle ABC is not unequal to the angle DEF;

therefore it is equal to it.

But the angle at A is also equal to the angle at D;

therefore the remaining angle at C is equal to the remaining angle at F.   [I. 32]

Therefore the triangle ABC is equiangular with the triangle DEF.

But, again, let each of the angles at C, F be supposed not less than a right angle;

I say again that, in this case too, the triangle ABC is equiangular with the triangle DEF.

For, with the same construction, we can prove similarly that

BC is equal to BG;

so that the angle at C is also equal to the angle BGC.   [I. 5]

But the angle at C is not less than a right angle;

therefore neither is the angle BGC less than a right angle.

Thus in the triangle BGC the two angles are not less than two right angles: which is impossible.   [I. 17]

Therefore, once more, the angle ABC is not unequal to the angle DEF;

therefore it is equal to it.

But the angle at A is also equal to the angle at D;

therefore the remaining angle at C is equal to the remaining angle at F.   [I. 32]

Therefore the triangle ABC is equiangular with the triangle DEF.

Therefore etc.   Q. E. D.

PROPOSITION 8

If in a right-angled triangle a perpendicular be drawn from the right angle to the base, the triangles adjoining the perpendicular are similar both to the whole and to one another.

Let ABC be a right-angled triangle having the angle BAC right, and let AD be drawn from A perpendicular to BC;

I say that each of the triangles ABD, ADC is similar to the whole ABC and, further, they are similar to one another.

For, since the angle BAC is equal to the angle ADB, for each is right, and the angle at B is common to the two triangles ABC and ABD,

therefore the remaining angle ACB is equal to the remaining angle BAD;   [I. 32]
therefore the triangle ABC is equiangular with the triangle ABD.

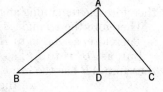

Therefore, as BC which subtends the right angle in the triangle ABC is to BA which subtends the right angle in the triangle ABD, so is AB itself which subtends the angle at C in the triangle ABC to BD which subtends the equal angle BAD in the triangle ABD, and so also is AC to AD which subtends the angle at B common to the two triangles.   [VI. 4]

Therefore the triangle ABC is both equiangular to the triangle ABD and has the sides about the equal angles proportional.

Therefore the triangle ABC is similar to the triangle ABD.   [VI. Def. 1]
Similarly we can prove that
        the triangle ABC is also similar to the triangle ADC;
therefore each of the triangles ABD, ADC is similar to the whole ABC.

I say next that the triangles ABD, ADC are also similar to one another.

For, since the right angle BDA is equal to the right angle ADC,
  and moreover the angle BAD was also proved equal to the angle at C,
therefore the remaining angle at B is also equal to the remaining angle DAC;
                                                                                          [I. 32]
        therefore the triangle ABD is equiangular with the triangle ADC.

Therefore, as BD which subtends the angle BAD in the triangle ABD is to DA which subtends the angle at C in the triangle ADC equal to the angle BAD, so is AD itself which subtends the angle at B in the triangle ABD to DC which subtends the angle DAC in the triangle ADC equal to the angle at B, and so also is BA to AC, these sides subtending the right angles;   [VI. 4]

        therefore the triangle ABD is similar to the triangle ADC.   [VI. Def. 1]
        Therefore etc.

PORISM. From this it is clear that, if in a right-angled triangle a perpendicular be drawn from the right angle to the base, the straight line so drawn is a mean proportional between the segments of the base.   Q. E. D.

PROPOSITION 9

From a given straight line to cut off a prescribed part.

        Let AB be the given straight line;
                thus it is required to cut off from AB a prescribed part.

Let the third part be that prescribed.

Let a straight line AC be drawn through from A containing with AB any angle;

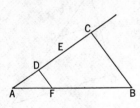

let a point D be taken at random on AC, and let DE, EC be made equal to AD. [I. 3]

Let BC be joined, and through D let DF be drawn parallel to it. [I. 31]

Then, since FD has been drawn parallel to BC, one of the sides of the triangle ABC,

therefore, proportionally, as CD is to DA, so is BF to FA. [VI. 2]

But CD is double of DA;

therefore BF is also double of FA;

therefore BA is triple of AF.

Therefore from the given straight line AB the prescribed third part AF has been cut off. Q. E. F.

PROPOSITION 10

To cut a given uncut straight line similarly to a given cut straight line.

Let AB be the given uncut straight line, and AC the straight line cut at the points D, E; and let them be so placed as to contain any angle;

let CB be joined, and through D, E let DF, EG be drawn parallel to BC, and through D let DHK be drawn parallel to AB. [I. 31]

Therefore each of the figures FH, HB is a parallelogram;

therefore DH is equal to FG and HK to GB. [I. 34]

Now, since the straight line HE has been drawn parallel to KC, one of the sides of the triangle DKC,

therefore, proportionally, as CE is to ED, so is KH to HD. [VI. 2]

But KH is equal to BG, and HD to GF;

therefore, as CE is to ED, so is BG to GF.

Again, since FD has been drawn parallel to GE, one of the sides of the triangle AGE,

therefore, proportionally, as ED is to DA, so is GF to FA. [VI. 2]

But it was also proved that,

as CE is to ED, so is BG to GF;

therefore, as CE is to ED, so is BG to GF,

and, as ED is to DA, so is GF to FA.

Therefore the given uncut straight line AB has been cut similarly to the given cut straight line AC. Q. E. F.

PROPOSITION 11

To two given straight lines to find a third proportional.

Let BA, AC be the two given straight lines, and let them be placed so as to contain any angle;

thus it is required to find a third proportional to BA, AC.

For let them be produced to the points D, E, and let BD be made equal to AC; [I. 3]

let BC be joined, and through D let DE be drawn parallel to it. [I. 31]

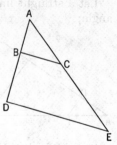

Since, then, BC has been drawn parallel to DE, one of the sides of the triangle ADE, proportionally, as AB is to BD, so is AC to CE. [VI. 2]

But BD is equal to AC;

therefore, as AB is to AC, so is AC to CE.

Therefore to two given straight lines AB, AC a third proportional to them, CE, has been found. Q. E. F.

PROPOSITION 12

To three given straight lines to find a fourth proportional.

Let A, B, C be the three given straight lines;

thus it is required to find a fourth proportional to A, B, C.

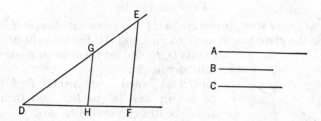

Let two straight lines DE, DF be set out containing any angle EDF;

let DG be made equal to A, GE equal to B, and further DH equal to C;

let GH be joined, and let EF be drawn through E parallel to it. [I. 31]

Since, then, GH has been drawn parallel to EF, one of the sides of the triangle DEF,

therefore, as DG is to GE, so is DH to HF. [VI. 2]

But DG is equal to A, GE to B, and DH to C;

therefore, as A is to B, so is C to HF.

Therefore to the three given straight lines A, B, C a fourth proportional HF has been found.

Q. E. F.

PROPOSITION 13

To two given straight lines to find a mean proportional.

Let AB, BC be the two given straight lines;

thus it is required to find a mean proportional to AB, BC.

Let them be placed in a straight line, and let the semicircle ADC be described on AC;

let BD be drawn from the point B at right angles to the straight line AC, and let AD, DC be joined.

Since the angle ADC is an angle in a semicircle, it is right. [III. 31]

And, since, in the right-angled triangle ADC, DB has been drawn from the right angle perpendicular to the base,

therefore *DB* is a mean proportional between the segments of the base, *AB*,
BC.   [VI. 8, Por.]

Therefore to the two given straight lines *AB*, *BC* a mean proportional *DB*
has been found.   Q. E. F.

PROPOSITION 14

*In equal and equiangular parallelograms the sides about the equal angles are re-
ciprocally proportional; and equiangular parallelograms in which the sides about
the equal angles are reciprocally proportional are equal.*

Let *AB*, *BC* be equal and equiangular parallelograms having the angles at
B equal, and let *DB*, *BE* be placed in a straight line;

therefore *FB*, *BG* are also in a straight line.

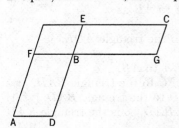

[I. 14]

I say that, in *AB*, *BC*, the sides about the
equal angles are reciprocally proportional, that
is to say, that, as *DB* is to *BE*, so is *GB* to
BF.

For let the parallelogram *FE* be completed.
Since, then, the parallelogram *AB* is equal
to the parallelogram *BC*,
and *FE* is another area,
therefore, as *AB* is to *FE*, so is *BC* to *FE*.   [V. 7]
But, as *AB* is to *FE*, so is *DB* to *BE*,   [VI. 1]
and, as *BC* is to *FE*, so is *GB* to *BF*.   [*id.*]
therefore also, as *DB* is to *BE*, so is *GB* to *BF*.   [V. 11]
Therefore in the parallelograms *AB*, *BC* the sides about the equal angles are
reciprocally proportional.

Next, let *GB* be to *BF* as *DB* to *BE*;
I say that the parallelogram *AB* is equal to the parallelogram *BC*.
For since, as *DB* is to *BE*, so is *GB* to *BF*,
while, as *DB* is to *BE*, so is the parallelogram *AB* to the parallelogram *FE*,
[VI. 1]
and, as *GB* is to *BF*, so is the parallelogram *BC* to the parallelogram *FE*, [VI. 1]
therefore also, as *AB* is to *FE*, so is *BC* to *FE*;   [V. 11]
therefore the parallelogram *AB* is equal to the parallelogram *BC*. [V. 9]
Therefore etc.   Q. E. D.

PROPOSITION 15

*In equal triangles which have one angle equal to one angle the sides about the equal
angles are reciprocally proportional; and those triangles which have one angle equal
to one angle, and in which the sides about the equal angles are reciprocally proportional, are equal.*

Let *ABC*, *ADE* be equal triangles having one angle equal to one angle,
namely the angle *BAC* to the angle *DAE*;

I say that in the triangles *ABC*, *ADE* the sides about the equal angles are
reciprocally proportional, that is to say, that,
as *CA* is to *AD*, so is *EA* to *AB*.

For let them be placed so that *CA* is in a straight line with *AD*;
therefore *EA* is also in a straight line with *AB*.   [I. 14]

Let *BD* be joined.

Since, then, the triangle *ABC* is equal to the triangle *ADE*, and *BAD* is another area,

therefore, as the triangle *CAB* is to the triangle *BAD*, so is
the triangle *EAD* to the triangle *BAD*.   [v. 7]

But, as *CAB* is to *BAD*, so is *CA* to *AD*,   [vi. 1]

and, as *EAD* is to *BAD*, so is *EA* to *AB*.   [*id.*]

Therefore also, as *CA* is to *AD*, so is *EA* to *AB*. [v. 11]

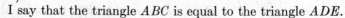

Therefore in the triangles *ABC*, *ADE* the sides about
the equal angles are reciprocally proportional.

Next, let the sides of the triangles *ABC*, *ADE* be reciprocally proportional, that is to say, let *EA* be to *AB* as
CA to *AD*;

I say that the triangle *ABC* is equal to the triangle *ADE*.

For, if *BD* be again joined,

since, as *CA* is to *AD*, so is *EA* to *AB*,

while, as *CA* is to *AD*, so is the triangle *ABC* to the triangle *BAD*,

and, as *EA* is to *AB*, so is the triangle *EAD* to the triangle *BAD*, [vi. 1]

therefore, as the triangle *ABC* is to the triangle *BAD*, so is the triangle *EAD*
to the triangle *BAD*.   [v. 11]

Therefore each of the triangles *ABC*, *EAD* has the same ratio to *BAD*.

Therefore the triangle *ABC* is equal to the triangle *EAD*.   [v. 9]

Therefore etc.   Q. E. D.

PROPOSITION 16

*If four straight lines be proportional, the rectangle contained by the extremes is
equal to the rectangle contained by the means; and, if the rectangle contained by the
extremes be equal to the rectangle contained by the means, the four straight lines
will be proportional.*

Let the four straight lines *AB*, *CD*, *E*, *F* be proportional, so that, as *AB* is to
CD, so is *E* to *F*;

I say that the rectangle contained by *AB*, *F* is equal to the rectangle contained by *CD*, *E*.

Let *AG*, *CH* be drawn from the points *A*, *C* at right angles to the straight
lines *AB*, *CD*, and let *AG* be made equal to *F*, and *CH* equal to *E*.

Let the parallelograms *BG*, *DH* be completed.

Then since, as *AB* is to *CD*, so is *E* to *F*,

while *E* is equal to *CH*, and *F* to *AG*,

therefore, as *AB* is to *CD*, so is *CH* to *AG*.

Therefore in the parallelograms *BG*, *DH* the sides about the equal angles
are reciprocally proportional.

But those equiangular parallelograms in which the sides about the equal
angles are reciprocally proportional are equal;   [vi. 14]

therefore the parallelogram BG is equal to the parallelogram DH.

And BG is the rectangle AB, F, for AG is equal to F;

and DH is the rectangle CD, E, for E is equal to CH;

therefore the rectangle contained by AB, F is equal to the rectangle contained by CD, E.

Next, let the rectangle contained by AB, F be equal to the rectangle contained by CD, E;

I say that the four straight lines will be proportional, so that, as AB is to CD, so is E to F.

For, with the same construction,

since the rectangle AB, F is equal to the rectangle CD, E,

and the rectangle AB, F is BG, for AG is equal to F,

and the rectangle CD, E is DH, for CH is equal to E,

therefore BG is equal to DH.

And they are equiangular.

But in equal and equiangular parallelograms the sides about the equal angles are reciprocally proportional.   [VI. 14]

Therefore, as AB is to CD, so is CH to AG.

But CH is equal to E, and AG to F;

therefore, as AB is to CD, so is E to F.

Therefore etc.   Q. E. D.

PROPOSITION 17

If three straight lines be proportional, the rectangle contained by the extremes is equal to the square on the mean; and, if the rectangle contained by the extremes be equal to the square on the mean, the three straight lines will be proportional.

Let the three straight lines A, B, C be proportional, so that, as A is to B, so is B to C;

I say that the rectangle contained by A, C is equal to the square on B.

Let D be made equal to B.

Then, since, as A is to B, so is B to C,

and B is equal to D,

therefore, as A is to B, so is D to C.

But, if four straight lines be proportional, the rectangle contained by the extremes is equal to the rectangle contained by the means.   [VI. 16]

Therefore the rectangle A, C is equal to the rectangle B, D.

But the rectangle B, D is the square on B, for B is equal to D;

therefore the rectangle contained by A, C is equal to the square on B.

Next, let the rectangle A, C be equal to the square on B; I say that, as A is to B, so is B to C.

For, with the same construction,

since the rectangle A, C is equal to the square on B,

while the square on B is the rectangle B, D, for B is equal to D,

therefore the rectangle A, C is equal to the rectangle B, D.

But, if the rectangle contained by the extremes be equal to that contained by the means, the four straight lines are proportional.   [VI. 16]

Therefore, as A is to B, so is D to C.

But B is equal to D;

therefore, as A is to B, so is B to C.

Therefore etc.   Q. E. D.

PROPOSITION 18

On a given straight line to describe a rectilineal figure similar and similarly situated to a given rectilineal figure.

Let AB be the given straight line and CE the given rectilineal figure; thus it is required to describe on the straight line AB a rectilineal figure similar and similarly situated to the rectilineal figure CE.

Let DF be joined, and on the straight line AB, and at the points A, B on it, let the angle GAB be constructed equal to the angle at C, and the angle ABG equal to the angle CDF.   [I. 23]

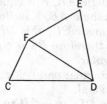

Therefore the remaining angle CFD is equal to the angle AGB;   [I. 32]

therefore the triangle FCD is equiangular with the triangle GAB.

Therefore, proportionally, as FD is to GB, so is FC to GA, and CD to AB.

Again, on the straight line BG, and at the points B, G on it, let the angle BGH be constructed equal to the angle DFE, and the angle GBH equal to the angle FDE.   [I. 23]

Therefore the remaining angle at E is equal to the remaining angle at H;   [I. 32]

therefore the triangle FDE is equiangular with the triangle GBH;

therefore, proportionally, as FD is to GB, so is FE to GH, and ED to HB.
                                                                         [VI. 4]

But it was also proved that, as FD is to GB, so is FC to GA, and CD to AB; therefore also, as FC is to AG, so is CD to AB, and FE to GH, and further ED to HB.

And, since the angle CFD is equal to the angle AGB,

and the angle DFE to the angle BGH,

therefore the whole angle CFE is equal to the whole angle AGH.

For the same reason

the angle CDE is also equal to the angle ABH.

And the angle at C is also equal to the angle at A,

and the angle at E to the angle at H.

Therefore AH is equiangular with CE;

and they have the sides about their equal angles proportional;

therefore the rectilineal figure AH is similar to the rectilineal figure CE.
                                                                 [VI. Def. 1]

Therefore on the given straight line AB the rectilineal figure AH has been described similar and similarly situated to the given rectilineal figure CE.

                                                                      Q. E. F.

PROPOSITION 19

Similar triangles are to one another in the duplicate ratio of the corresponding sides.

Let ABC, DEF be similar triangles having the angle at B equal to the angle

at E, and such that, as AB is to BC, so is DE to EF, so that BC corresponds
to EF;   [v. Def. 11]

I say that the triangle ABC has to the triangle DEF a ratio duplicate of
that which BC has to EF.

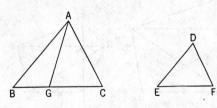

For let a third proportional BG be
taken to BC, EF, so that, as BC is to
EF, so is EF to BG;   [vi. 11]
and let AG be joined.

Since then, as AB is to BC, so is DE
to EF,

therefore, alternately, as AB is to DE,
so is BC to EF.   [v. 16]

But, as BC is to EF, so is EF to BG;

therefore also, as AB is to DE, so is EF to BG.   [v. 11]

Therefore in the triangles ABG, DEF the sides about the equal angles are
reciprocally proportional.

But those triangles which have one angle equal to one angle, and in which
the sides about the equal angles are reciprocally proportional, are equal;
                                                                            [vi. 15]

therefore the triangle ABG is equal to the triangle DEF.

Now since, as BC is to EF, so is EF to BG,
and, if three straight lines be proportional, the first has to the third a ratio
duplicate of that which it has to the second,   [v. Def. 9]

therefore BC has to BG a ratio duplicate of that which CB has to EF.

But, as CB is to BG, so is the triangle ABC to the triangle ABG;   [vi. 1]
therefore the triangle ABC also has to the triangle ABG a ratio duplicate of
that which BC has to EF.

But the triangle ABG is equal to the triangle DEF;
therefore the triangle ABC also has to the triangle DEF a ratio duplicate of
that which BC has to EF.

Therefore etc.

PORISM. From this it is manifest that, if three straight lines be proportional,
then, as the first is to the third, so is the figure described on the first to that
which is similar and similarly described on the second.   Q. E. D.

PROPOSITION 20

*Similar polygons are divided into similar triangles, and into triangles equal in
multitude and in the same ratio as the wholes, and the polygon has to the polygon
a ratio duplicate of that which the corresponding side has to the corresponding side.*

Let $ABCDE$, $FGHKL$ be similar polygons, and let AB correspond to FG;

I say that the polygons $ABCDE$, $FGHKL$ are divided into similar triangles,
and into triangles equal in multitude and in the same ratio as the wholes, and
the polygon $ABCDE$ has to the polygon $FGHKL$ a ratio duplicate of that
which AB has to FG.

Let BE, EC, GL, LH be joined.

Now, since the polygon $ABCDE$ is similar to the polygon $FGHKL$,
the angle BAE is equal to the angle GFL;
and, as BA is to AE, so is GF to FL.   [vi. Def. 1]

Since then ABE, FGL are two triangles having one angle equal to one angle and the sides about the equal angles proportional,

      therefore the triangle *ABE* is equiangular with the triangle *FGL*; [vi. 6]

                        so that it is also similar;   [vi. 4 and Def. 1]

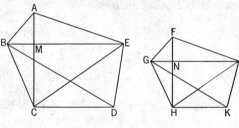

therefore the angle *ABE* is equal to the angle *FGL*.

  But the whole angle *ABC* is also equal to the whole angle *FGH* because of the similarity of the polygons;
therefore the remaining angle *EBC* is equal to the angle *LGH*.

    And, since, because of the similarity of the triangles *ABE*, *FGL*,

               as *EB* is to *BA*, so is *LG* to *GF*,

    and moreover also, because of the similarity of the polygons,

               as *AB* is to *BC*, so is *FG* to *GH*,

       therefore, *ex aequali*, as *EB* is to *BC*, so is *LG* to *GH*;   [v. 22]

  that is, the sides about the equal angles *EBC*, *LGH* are proportional;

    therefore the triangle *EBC* is equiangular with the triangle *LGH*, [vi. 6]
so that the triangle *EBC* is also similar to the triangle *LGH*.   [vi. 4 and Def. 1]

    For the same reason

          the triangle *ECD* is also similar to the triangle *LHK*.

    Therefore the similar polygons *ABCDE*, *FGHKL* have been divided into similar triangles, and into triangles equal in multitude.

    I say that they are also in the same ratio as the wholes, that is, in such manner that the triangles are proportional, and *ABE*, *EBC*, *ECD* are antecedents, while *FGL*, *LGH*, *LHK* are their consequents, and that the polygon *ABCDE* has to the polygon *FGHKL* a ratio duplicate of that which the corresponding side has to the corresponding side, that is *AB* to *FG*.

    For let *AC*, *FH* be joined.

    Then since, because of the similarity of the polygons,

           the angle *ABC* is equal to the angle *FGH*,

          and, as *AB* is to *BC*, so is *FG* to *GH*,

    the triangle *ABC* is equiangular with the triangle *FGH*;   [vi. 6]

         therefore the angle *BAC* is equal to the angle *GFH*,

           and the angle *BCA* to the angle *GHF*.

  And, since the angle *BAM* is equal to the angle *GFN*,

       and the angle *ABM* is also equal to the angle *FGN*,

therefore the remaining angle *AMB* is also equal to the remaining angle *FNG*;

                                         [i. 32]

    therefore the triangle *ABM* is equiangular with the triangle *FGN*.

  Similarly we can prove that

        the triangle *BMC* is also equiangular with the triangle *GNH*.

  Therefore, proportionally, as *AM* is to *MB*, so is *FN* to *NG*,
and,   as *BM* is to *MC*, so is *GN* to *NH*;
so that, in addition, *ex aequali*,

            as *AM* is to *MC*, so is *FN* to *NH*.

  But, as *AM* is to *MC*, so is the triangle *ABM* to *MBC*, and *AME* to *EMC*;
for they are to one another as their bases.   [vi. 1]

Therefore also, as one of the antecedents is to one of the consequents, so are all the antecedents to all the consequents;   [v. 12]

therefore, as the triangle AMB is to BMC, so is ABE to CBE.

But, as AMB is to BMC, so is AM to MC;

therefore also, as AM is to MC, so is the triangle ABE to the triangle EBC.

For the same reason also,

as FN is to NH, so is the triangle FGL to the triangle GLH.

And, as AM is to MC, so is FN to NH;

therefore also, as the triangle ABE is to the triangle BEC, so is the triangle FGL to the triangle GLH;

and, alternately, as the triangle ABE is to the triangle FGL, so is the triangle BEC to the triangle GLH.

Similarly we can prove, if BD, GK be joined, that, as the triangle BEC is to the triangle LGH, so also is the triangle ECD to the triangle LHK.

And since, as the triangle ABE is to the triangle FGL, so is EBC to LGH, and further ECD to LHK,

therefore also, as one of the antecedents is to one of the consequents, so are all the antecedents to all the consequents;   [v. 12]

therefore, as the triangle ABE is to the triangle FGL,

so is the polygon $ABCDE$ to the polygon $FGHKL$.

But the triangle ABE has to the triangle FGL a ratio duplicate of that which the corresponding side AB has to the corresponding side FG; for similar triangles are in the duplicate ratio of the corresponding sides.   [vi. 19]

Therefore the polygon $ABCDE$ also has to the polygon $FGHKL$ a ratio duplicate of that which the corresponding side AB has to the corresponding side FG.

Therefore etc.

PORISM. Similarly also it can be proved in the case of quadrilaterals that they are in the duplicate ratio of the corresponding sides. And it was also proved in the case of triangles; therefore also, generally, similar rectilineal figures are to one another in the duplicate ratio of the corresponding sides.

Q. E. D.

PROPOSITION 21

Figures which are similar to the same rectilineal figure are also similar to one another.

For let each of the rectilineal figures A, B be similar to C; I say that A is also similar to B.

For, since A is similar to C,

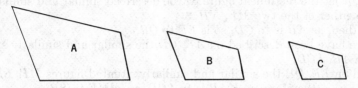

it is equiangular with it and has the sides about the equal angles proportional.

[vi. Def. 1]

Again, since B is similar to C,

it is equiangular with it and has the sides about the equal angles proportional.

Therefore each of the figures A, B is equiangular with C and with C has the sides about the equal angles proportional;

therefore A is similar to B.   Q. E. D.

PROPOSITION 22

If four straight lines be proportional, the rectilineal figures similar and similarly described upon them will also be proportional; and if the rectilineal figures similar and similarly described upon them be proportional, the straight lines will themselves also be proportional.

Let the four straight lines AB, CD, EF, GH be proportional,
so that, as AB is to CD, so is EF to GH,
and let there be described on AB, CD the similar and similarly situated rectilineal figures KAB, LCD,
and on EF, GH the similar and similarly situated rectilineal figures MF, NH;
I say that, as KAB is to LCD, so is MF to NH.

For let there be taken a third proportional O to AB, CD, and a third proportional P to EF, GH.   [VI. 11]

Then since, as AB is to CD, so is EF to GH,
and, as CD is to O, so is GH to P,
therefore, *ex aequali*, as AB is to O, so is EF to P.   [V. 22]

But, as AB is to O, so is KAB to LCD,   [VI. 19, Por.]
and, as EF is to P, so is MF to NH;
therefore also, as KAB is to LCD, so is MF to NH.   [V. 11]

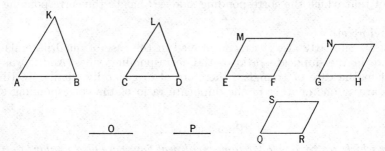

Next, let MF be to NH as KAB is to LCD;
I say also that, as AB is to CD, so is EF to GH.

For, if EF is not to GH as AB to CD,
let EF be to QR as AB to CD,   [VI. 12]
and on QR let the rectilineal figure SR be described similar and similarly situated to either of the two MF, NH.   [VI. 18]

Since then, as AB is to CD, so is EF to QR,
and there have been described on AB, CD the similar and similarly situated figures KAB, LCD,
and on EF, QR the similar and similarly situated figures MF, SR,
therefore, as KAB is to LCD, so is MF to SR.

But also, by hypothesis,
as KAB is to LCD, so is MF to NH;
therefore also, as MF is to SR, so is MF to NH.   [V. 11]

Therefore MF has the same ratio to each of the figures NH, SR;

therefore NH is equal to SR.   [v. 9]

But it is also similar and similarly situated to it;

therefore GH is equal to QR.

And, since, as AB is to CD, so is EF to QR,

while QR is equal to GH,

therefore, as AB is to CD, so is EF to GH.

Therefore etc.   Q. E. D.

PROPOSITION 23

Equiangular parallelograms have to one another the ratio compounded of the ratios of their sides.

Let AC, CF be equiangular parallelograms having the angle BCD equal to the angle ECG;

I say that the parallelogram AC has to the parallelogram CF the ratio compounded of the ratios of the sides.

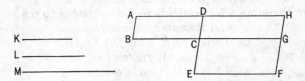

For let them be placed so that BC is in a straight line with CG;

therefore DC is also in a straight line with CE.

Let the parallelogram DG be completed;

let a straight line K be set out, and let it be contrived that,

as BC is to CG, so is K to L,

and,   as DC is to CE, so is L to M.   [vi. 12]

Then the ratios of K to L and of L to M are the same as the ratios of the sides, namely of BC to CG and of DC to CE.

But the ratio of K to M is compounded of the ratio of K to L and of that of L to M;

so that K has also to M the ratio compounded of the ratios of the sides.

Now since, as BC is to CG, so is the parallelogram AC to the parallelogram CH,   [vi. 1]

while, as BC is to CG, so is K to L,

therefore also, as K is to L, so is AC to CH.   [v. 11]

Again, since, as DC is to CE, so is the parallelogram CH to CF,   [vi. 1]

while, as DC is to CE, so is L to M,

therefore also, as L is to M, so is the parallelogram CH to the parallelogram CF.   [v. 11]

Since, then, it was proved that, as K is to L, so is the parallelogram AC to the parallelogram CH,

and, as L is to M, so is the parallelogram CH to the parallelogram CF,

therefore, *ex aequali*, as K is to M, so is AC to the parallelogram CF.

But K has to M the ratio compounded of the ratios of the sides;

therefore AC also has to CF the ratio compounded of the ratios of the sides.

Therefore etc.   Q. E. D.

Proposition 24

In any parallelogram the parallelograms about the diameter are similar both to the whole and to one another.

Let *ABCD* be a parallelogram, and *AC* its diameter, and let *EG, HK* be parallelograms about *AC*;

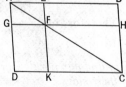

I say that each of the parallelograms *EG, HK* is similar both to the whole *ABCD* and to the other.

For, since *EF* has been drawn parallel to *BC*, one of the sides of the triangle *ABC*,

proportionally, as *BE* is to *EA*, so is *CF* to *FA*.

[vi. 2]

Again, since *FG* has been drawn parallel to *CD*, one of the sides of the triangle *ACD*,

proportionally, as *CF* is to *FA*, so is *DG* to *GA*.   [vi. 2]

But it was proved that,

as *CF* is to *FA*, so also is *BE* to *EA*;

therefore also, as *BE* is to *EA*, so is *DG* to *GA*,

and therefore, *componendo*,

as *BA* is to *AE*, so is *DA* to *AG*,   [v. 18]

and, alternately,

as *BA* is to *AD*, so is *EA* to *AG*.   [v. 16]

Therefore in the parallelograms *ABCD, EG*, the sides about the common angle *BAD* are proportional.

And, since *GF* is parallel to *DC*,

the angle *AFG* is equal to the angle *DCA*;

and the angle *DAC* is common to the two triangles *ADC, AGF*;

therefore the triangle *ADC* is equiangular with the triangle *AGF*.

For the same reason

the triangle *ACB* is also equiangular with the triangle *AFE*,

and the whole parallelogram *ABCD* is equiangular with the parallelogram *EG*.

Therefore, proportionally,

as *AD* is to *DC*, so is *AG* to *GF*,

as *DC* is to *CA*, so is *GF* to *FA*,

as *AC* is to *CB*, so is *AF* to *FE*,

and further, as *CB* is to *BA*, so is *FE* to *EA*.

And, since it was proved that,

as *DC* is to *CA*, so is *GF* to *FA*,

and,   as *AC* is to *CB*, so is *AF* to *FE*,

therefore, *ex aequali*, as *DC* is to *CB*, so is *GF* to *FE*.   [v. 22]

Therefore in the parallelograms *ABCD, EG* the sides about the equal angles are proportional;

therefore the parallelogram *ABCD* is similar to the parallelogram *EG*.

[vi. Def. 1]

For the same reason

the parallelogram *ABCD* is also similar to the parallelogram *KH*;

therefore each of the parallelograms *EG, HK* is similar to *ABCD*.

But figures similar to the same rectilineal figure are also similar to one another;   [vi. 21]

therefore the parallelogram EG is also similar to the parallelogram HK.
Therefore etc.   Q. E. D.

PROPOSITION 25

To construct one and the same figure similar to a given rectilineal figure and equal to another given rectilineal figure.

Let ABC be the given rectilineal figure to which the figure to be constructed must be similar, and D that to which it must be equal;
thus it is required to construct one and the same figure similar to ABC and equal to D.

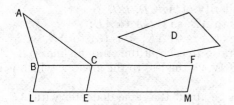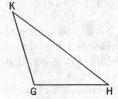

Let there be applied to BC the parallelogram BE equal to the triangle ABC [I. 44], and to CE the parallelogram CM equal to D in the angle FCE which is equal to the angle CBL.   [I. 45]

Therefore BC is in a straight line with CF, and LE with EM.

Now let GH be taken a mean proportional to BC, CF [VI. 13], and on GH let KGH be described similar and similarly situated to ABC.   [VI. 18]

Then, since, as BC is to GH, so is GH to CF,
and, if three straight lines be proportional, as the first is to the third, so is the figure on the first to the similar and similarly situated figure described on the second,   [VI. 19, Por.]

therefore, as BC is to CF, so is the triangle ABC to the triangle KGH.

But, as BC is to CF, so also is the parallelogram BE to the parallelogram EF.
                                                                   [VI. 1]

Therefore also, as the triangle ABC is to the triangle KGH, so is the parallelogram BE to the parallelogram EF;
therefore, alternately, as the triangle ABC is to the parallelogram BE, so is the triangle KGH to the parallelogram EF.   [V. 16]

But the triangle ABC is equal to the parallelogram BE;
   therefore the triangle KGH is also equal to the parallelogram EF.

But the parallelogram EF is equal to D;
               therefore KGH is also equal to D.

And KGH is also similar to ABC.

Therefore one and the same figure KGH has been constructed similar to the given rectilineal figure ABC and equal to the other given figure D.   Q. E. D.

PROPOSITION 26

If from a parallelogram there be taken away a parallelogram similar and similarly situated to the whole and having a common angle with it, it is about the same diameter with the whole.

For from the parallelogram $ABCD$ let there be taken away the parallelogram AF similar and similarly situated to $ABCD$, and having the angle DAB common with it;

I say that $ABCD$ is about the same diameter with AF.

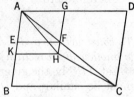

For suppose it is not, but, if possible, let AHC be the diameter < of $ABCD$>, let GF be produced and carried through to H, and let HK be drawn through H parallel to either of the straight lines AD, BC.
[i. 31]

Since, then, $ABCD$ is about the same diameter with KG, therefore, as DA is to AB, so is GA to AK. [vi. 24]

But also, because of the similarity of $ABCD$, EG,
as DA is to AB, so is GA to AE;
therefore also, as GA is to AK, so is GA to AE. [v. 11]
Therefore GA has the same ratio to each of the straight lines AK, AE.

Therefore AE is equal to AK [v. 9], the less to the greater: which is impossible.

Therefore $ABCD$ cannot but be about the same diameter with AF; therefore the parallelogram $ABCD$ is about the same diameter with the parallelogram AF.

Therefore etc. Q. E. D.

PROPOSITION 27

Of all the parallelograms applied to the same straight line and deficient by parallelogrammic figures similar and similarly situated to that described on the half of the straight line, that parallelogram is greatest which is applied to the half of the straight line and is similar to the defect.

Let AB be a straight line and let it be bisected at C; let there be applied to the straight line AB the parallelogram AD deficient by the parallelogrammic figure DB described on the half of AB, that is, CB;

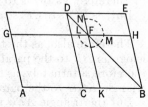

I say that, of the parallelograms applied to AB and deficient by parallelogrammic figures similar and similarly situated to DB, AD is greatest.

For let there be applied to the straight line AB the parallelogram AF deficient by the parallelogrammic figure FB similar and similarly situated to DB;

I say that AD is greater than AF.

For, since the parallelogram DB is similar to the parallelogram FB,
they are about the same diameter. [vi. 26]
Let their diameter DB be drawn, and let the figure be described.
Then, since CF is equal to FE, [i. 43]
and FB is common,
therefore the whole CH is equal to the whole KE.
But CH is equal to CG, since AC is also equal to CB. [i. 36]
Therefore GC is also equal to EK.
Let CF be added to each;
therefore the whole AF is equal to the gnomon LMN;

so that the parallelogram DB, that is, AD, is greater than the parallelogram AF.

Therefore etc.   Q. E. D.

PROPOSITION 28

To a given straight line to apply a parallelogram equal to a given rectilineal figure and deficient by a parallelogrammic figure similar to a given one: thus the given rectilineal figure must not be greater than the parallelogram described on the half of the straight line and similar to the defect.

Let AB be the given straight line, C the given rectilineal figure to which the figure to be applied to AB is required to be equal, not being greater than the parallelogram described on the half of AB and similar to the defect, and D the parallelogram to which the defect is required to be similar;

thus it is required to apply to the given straight line AB a parallelogram equal to the given rectilineal figure C and deficient by a parallelogrammic figure which is similar to D.

Let AB be bisected at the point E, and on EB let $EBFG$ be described similar and similarly situated to D;   [vi. 18]

let the parallelogram AG be completed.

If then AG is equal to C, that which was enjoined will have been done;

for there has been applied to the given straight line AB the parallelogram AG equal to the given rectilineal figure C and deficient by a parallelogrammic figure GB which is similar to D.

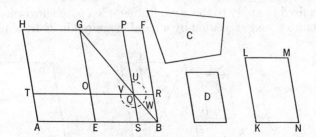

But, if not, let HE be greater than C.

Now HE is equal to GB;

therefore GB is also greater than C.

Let $KLMN$ be constructed at once equal to the excess by which GB is greater than C and similar and similarly situated to D.   [vi. 25]

But D is similar to GB;

therefore KM is also similar to GB.   [vi. 21]

Let, then, KL correspond to GE, and LM to GF.

Now, since GB is equal to C, KM,

therefore GB is greater than KM;

therefore also GE is greater than KL, and GF than LM.

Let GO be made equal to KL, and GP equal to LM; and let the parallelogram $OGPQ$ be completed;

therefore it is equal and similar to KM.

Therefore GQ is also similar to GB;   [vi. 21]

therefore GQ is about the same diameter with GB.   [VI. 26]
Let GQB be their diameter, and let the figure be described.
Then, since BG is equal to C, KM,
                    and in them GQ is equal to KM,
therefore the remainder, the gnomon UWV, is equal to the remainder C.
And, since PR is equal to OS,
                    let QB be added to each;
          therefore the whole PB is equal to the whole OB.
But OB is equal to TE, since the side AE is also equal to the side EB;   [I. 36]
                    therefore TE is also equal to PB.
Let OS be added to each;
    therefore the whole TS is equal to the whole, the gnomon VWU.
But the gnomon VWU was proved equal to C;
                    therefore TS is also equal to C.
Therefore to the given straight line AB there has been applied the parallelogram ST equal to the given rectilineal figure C and deficient by a parallelogrammic figure QB which is similar to D.   Q. E. F.

PROPOSITION 29

To a given straight line to apply a parallelogram equal to a given rectilineal figure and exceeding by a parallelogrammic figure similar to a given one.

Let AB be the given straight line, C the given rectilineal figure to which the figure to be applied to AB is required to be equal, and D that to which the excess is required to be similar;
thus it is required to apply to the straight line AB a parallelogram equal to the rectilineal figure C and exceeding by a parallelogrammic figure similar to D.

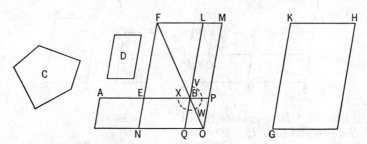

    Let AB be bisected at E;
let there be described on EB the parallelogram BF similar and similarly situated to D;
and let GH be constructed at once equal to the sum of BF, C and similar and similarly situated to D.   [VI. 25]
    Let KH correspond to FL and KG to FE.
    Now, since GH is greater than FB,
          therefore KH is also greater than FL, and KG than FE.
    Let FL, FE be produced,
                let FLM be equal to KH, and FEN to KG,
                    and let MN be completed;
          therefore MN is both equal and similar to GH.

But *GH* is similar to *EL*;

therefore *MN* is also similar to *EL*;   [VI. 21]

therefore *EL* is about the same diameter with *MN*.   [VI. 26]

Let their diameter *FO* be drawn, and let the figure be described.

Since *GH* is equal to *EL*, *C*,

while *GH* is equal to *MN*,

therefore *MN* is also equal to *EL*, *C*.

Let *EL* be subtracted from each;

therefore the remainder, the gnomon *XWV*, is equal to *C*.

Now, since *AE* is equal to *EB*,

AN is also equal to *NB* [I. 36], that is, to *LP*   [I. 43]

Let *EO* be added to each;

therefore the whole *AO* is equal to the gnomon *VWX*.

But the gnomon *VWX* is equal to *C*;

therefore *AO* is also equal to *C*.

Therefore to the given straight line *AB* there has been applied the parallelogram *AO* equal to the given rectilineal figure *C* and exceeding by a parallelogrammic figure *QP* which is similar to *D*, since *PQ* is also similar to *EL* [VI. 24].

Q. E. F.

PROPOSITION 30

To cut a given finite straight line in extreme and mean ratio.

Let *AB* be the given finite straight line;

thus it is required to cut *AB* in extreme and mean ratio.

On *AB* let the square *BC* be described; and let there be applied to *AC* the parallelogram *CD* equal to *BC* and exceeding by the figure *AD* similar to *BC*.   [VI. 29]

Now *BC* is a square;

therefore *AD* is also a square.

And, since *BC* is equal to *CD*,

let *CE* be subtracted from each;

therefore the remainder *BF* is equal to the remainder *AD*.

But it is also equiangular with it;

therefore in *BF*, *AD* the sides about the equal angles are reciprocally proportional;   [VI. 14]

therefore, as *FE* is to *ED*, so is *AE* to *EB*.

But *FE* is equal to *AB*, and *ED* to *AE*.

Therefore, as *BA* is to *AE*, so is *AE* to *EB*.

And *AB* is greater than *AE*;

therefore *AE* is also greater than *EB*.

Therefore the straight line *AB* has been cut in extreme and mean ratio at *E*, and the greater segment of it is *AE*.   Q. E. F.

PROPOSITION 31

In right-angled triangles the figure on the side subtending the right angle is equal to the similar and similarly described figures on the sides containing the right angle.

Let *ABC* be a right-angled triangle having the angle *BAC* right;

I say that the figure on *BC* is equal to the similar and similarly described figures on *BA*, *AC*.

Let AD be drawn perpendicular.

Then since, in the right-angled triangle ABC, AD has been drawn from the right angle at A perpendicular to the base BC, the triangles ABD, ADC adjoining the perpendicular are similar both to the whole ABC and to one another.   [VI. 8]

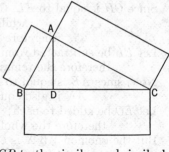

And, since ABC is similar to ABD, therefore, as CB is to BA, so is AB to BD.

[VI. Def. 1]

And, since three straight lines are proportional, as the first is to the third, so is the figure on the first to the similar and similarly described figure on the second. [VI. 19, Por.]

Therefore, as CB is to BD, so is the figure on CB to the similar and similarly described figure on BA.

For the same reason also,

as BC is to CD, so is the figure on BC to that on CA;

so that, in addition,

as BC is to BD, DC, so is the figure on BC to the similar and similarly described figures on BA, AC.

But BC is equal to BD, DC;

therefore the figure on BC is also equal to the similar and similarly described figures on BA, AC.

Therefore etc.   Q. E. D.

PROPOSITION 32

If two triangles having two sides proportional to two sides be placed together at one angle so that their corresponding sides are also parallel, the remaining sides of the triangles will be in a straight line.

Let ABC, DCE be two triangles having the two sides BA, AC proportional to the two sides DC, DE, so that, as AB is to AC, so is DC to DE, and AB parallel to DC, and AC to DE;

I say that BC is in a straight line with CE.

For, since AB is parallel to DC, and the straight line AC has fallen upon them, the alternate angles BAC, ACD are equal to one another.   [I. 29]

For the same reason the angle CDE is also equal to the angle ACD; so that the angle BAC is equal to the angle CDE.

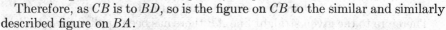

And, since ABC, DCE are two triangles having one angle, the angle at A, equal to one angle, the angle at D, and the sides about the equal angles proportional, so that, as BA is to AC, so is CD to DE, therefore the triangle ABC is equiangular with the triangle DCE;   [VI. 6]

therefore the angle *ABC* is equal to the angle *DCE*.
But the angle *ACD* was also proved equal to the angle *BAC*;
therefore the whole angle *ACE* is equal to the two angles *ABC*, *BAC*.
Let the angle *ACB* be added to each;
therefore the angles *ACE*, *ACB* are equal to the angles *BAC*, *ACB*, *CBA*.
But the angles *BAC*, *ABC*, *ACB* are equal to two right angles;   [I. 32]
therefore the angles *ACE*, *ACB* are also equal to two right angles.
Therefore with a straight line *AC*, and at the point *C* on it, the two straight lines *BC*, *CE* not lying on the same side make the adjacent angles *ACE*, *ACB* equal to two right angles;

therefore *BC* is in a straight line with *CE*.   [I. 14]
Therefore etc.   Q. E. D.

PROPOSITION 33

In equal circles angles have the same ratio as the circumferences on which they stand, whether they stand at the centres or at the circumferences.

Let *ABC*, *DEF* be equal circles, and let the angles *BGC*, *EHF* be angles at their centres *G*, *H*, and the angles *BAC*, *EDF* angles at the circumferences;

I say that, as the circumference *BC* is to the circumference *EF*, so is the angle *BGC* to the angle *EHF*, and the angle *BAC* to the angle *EDF*.

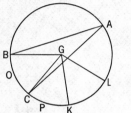 

For let any number of consecutive circumferences *CK*, *KL* be made equal to the circumference *BC*,
and any number of consecutive circumferences *FM*, *MN* equal to the circumference *EF*;
and let *GK*, *GL*, *HM*, *HN* be joined.

Then, since the circumferences *BC*, *CK*, *KL* are equal to one another,
the angles *BGC*, *CGK*, *KGL* are also equal to one another;   [III. 27]
therefore, whatever multiple the circumference *BL* is of *BC*, that multiple also is the angle *BGL* of the angle *BGC*.

For the same reason also,
whatever multiple the circumference *NE* is of *EF*, that multiple also is the angle *NHE* of the angle *EHF*.

If then the circumference *BL* is equal to the circumference *EN*, the angle *BGL* is also equal to the angle *EHN*;   [III. 27]
if the circumference *BL* is greater than the circumference *EN*, the angle *BGL* is also greater than the angle *EHN*;
and, if less, less.

There being then four magnitudes, two circumferences *BC*, *EF*, and two angles *BGC*, *EHF*,
there have been taken, of the circumference *BC* and the angle *BGC* equimultiples, namely the circumference *BL* and the angle *BGL*,
and of the circumference *EF* and the angle *EHF* equimultiples, namely the circumference *EN* and the angle *EHN*.

And it has been proved that,
if the circumference *BL* is in excess of the circumference *EN*,

the angle BGL is also in excess of the angle EHN;

if equal, equal;

and if less, less.

Therefore, as the circumference BC is to EF, so is the angle BGC to the angle EHF.   [v. Def. 5]

But, as the angle BGC is to the angle EHF, so is the angle BAC to the angle EDF; for they are doubles respectively.

Therefore also, as the circumference BC is to the circumference EF, so is the angle BGC to the angle EHF, and the angle BAC to the angle EDF.

Therefore etc.   Q. E. D.

BOOK SEVEN

DEFINITIONS

1. An *unit* is that by virtue of which each of the things that exist is called one.

2. A *number* is a multitude composed of units.

3. A number is *a part* of a number, the less of the greater, when it measures the greater;

4. but *parts* when it does not measure it.

5. The greater number is a *multiple* of the less when it is measured by the less.

6. An *even number* is that which is divisible into two equal parts.

7. An *odd number* is that which is not divisible into two equal parts, or that which differs by an unit from an even number.

8. An *even-times even number* is that which is measured by an even number according to an even number.

9. An *even-times odd number* is that which is measured by an even number according to an odd number.

10. An *odd-times odd number* is that which is measured by an odd number according to an odd number.

11. A *prime number* is that which is measured by an unit alone.

12. Numbers *prime to one another* are those which are measured by an unit alone as a common measure.

13. A *composite number* is that which is measured by some number.

14. Numbers *composite to one another* are those which are measured by some number as a common measure.

15. A number is said to *multiply* a number when that which is multiplied is added to itself as many times as there are units in the other, and thus some number is produced.

16. And, when two numbers having multiplied one another make some number, the number so produced is called *plane*, and its *sides* are the numbers which have multiplied one another.

17. And, when three numbers having multiplied one another make some number, the number so produced is *solid*, and its *sides* are the numbers which have multiplied one another.

18. A *square number* is equal multiplied by equal, or a number which is contained by two equal numbers.

19. And a *cube* is equal multiplied by equal and again by equal, or a number which is contained by three equal numbers.

20. Numbers are *proportional* when the first is the same multiple, or the same part, or the same parts, of the second that the third is of the fourth.

21. *Similar plane* and *solid* numbers are those which have their sides proportional.

22. A *perfect number* is that which is equal to its own parts.

BOOK VII. PROPOSITIONS

PROPOSITION 1

Two unequal numbers being set out, and the less being continually subtracted in turn from the greater, if the number which is left never measures the one before it until an unit is left, the original numbers will be prime to one another.

For, the less of two unequal numbers AB, CD being continually subtracted from the greater, let the number which is left never measure the one before it until an unit is left;

I say that AB, CD are prime to one another, that is, that an unit alone measures AB, CD.

For, if AB, CD are not prime to one another, some number will measure them.

Let a number measure them, and let it be E; let CD, measuring BF, leave FA less than itself,

  let AF, measuring DG, leave GC less than itself,

  and let GC, measuring FH, leave an unit HA.

Since, then, E measures CD, and CD measures BF,

  therefore E also measures BF.

But it also measures the whole BA;

  therefore it will also measure the remainder AF.

But AF measures DG;

  therefore E also measures DG.

But it also measures the whole DC;

  therefore it will also measure the remainder CG.

But CG measures FH;

  therefore E also measures FH.

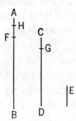

But it also measures the whole FA;

therefore it will also measure the remainder, the unit AH, though it is a number: which is impossible.

Therefore no number will measure the numbers AB, CD; therefore AB, CD are prime to one another.   [VII. Def. 12]

Q. E. D.

PROPOSITION 2

Given two numbers not prime to one another, to find their greatest common measure.

Let AB, CD be the two given numbers not prime to one another.

Thus it is required to find the greatest common measure of AB, CD.

If now CD measures AB—and it also measures itself—CD is a common measure of CD, AB.

And it is manifest that it is also the greatest; for no greater number than CD will measure CD.

But, if CD does not measure AB, then, the less of the numbers AB, CD being continually subtracted from the greater, some number will be left which will measure the one before it.

For an unit will not be left; otherwise AB, CD will be prime to one another [VII. 1], which is contrary to the hypothesis.

Therefore some number will be left which will measure the one before it.

Now let CD, measuring BE, leave EA less than itself,

let EA, measuring DF, leave FC less than itself,

and let CF measure AE.

Since then, CF measures AE, and AE measures DF,

therefore CF will also measure DF.

But it also measures itself;

therefore it will also measure the whole CD.

But CD measures BE;

therefore CF also measures BE.

But it also measures EA;

therefore it will also measure the whole BA.

But it also measures CD;

therefore CF measures AB, CD.

Therefore CF is a common measure of AB, CD.

I say next that it is also the greatest.

For, if CF is not the greatest common measure of AB, CD, some number which is greater than CF will measure the numbers AB, CD.

Let such a number measure them, and let it be G.

Now, since G measures CD, while CD measures BE, G also measures BE.

But it also measures the whole BA;

therefore it will also measure the remainder AE.

But AE measures DF;

therefore G will also measure DF.

But it also measures the whole DC;

therefore it will also measure the remainder CF, that is, the greater will measure the less: which is impossible.

Therefore no number which is greater than CF will measure the numbers AB, CD;

therefore CF is the greatest common measure of AB, CD.

PORISM. From this it is manifest that, if a number measure two numbers, it will also measure their greatest common measure.   Q. E. D.

PROPOSITION 3

Given three numbers not prime to one another, to find their greatest common measure.

Let A, B, C be the three given numbers not prime to one another;

thus it is required to find the greatest common measure of A, B, C.

For let the greatest common measure, D, of the two numbers A, B be taken;   [VII. 2]

then D either measures, or does not measure, C.

First, let it measure it.

But it measures A, B also;

therefore D measures A, B, C;

therefore D is a common measure of A, B, C.

I say that it is also the greatest.

For, if D is not the greatest common measure of A, B, C, some number which is greater than D will measure the numbers A, B, C.

Let such a number measure them, and let it be E.

Since then E measures A, B, C,

it will also measure A, B;

therefore it will also measure the greatest common measure of A, B.

[VII. 2, Por.]

But the greatest common measure of A, B is D;

therefore E measures D, the greater the less: which is impossible.

Therefore no number which is greater than D will measure the numbers A, B, C;

therefore D is the greatest common measure of A, B, C.

Next, let D not measure C;

I say first that C, D are not prime to one another.

For, since A, B, C are not prime to one another, some number will measure them.

Now that which measures A, B, C will also measure A, B, and will measure D, the greatest common measure of A, B. [VII. 2, Por.]

But it measures C also;

therefore some number will measure the numbers D, C;

therefore D, C are not prime to one another.

Let then their greatest common measure E be taken. [VII. 2]

Then, since E measures D,

and D measures A, B,

therefore E also measures A, B.

But it measures C also;

therefore E measures A, B, C;

therefore E is a common measure of A, B, C.

I say next that it is also the greatest.

For, if E is not the greatest common measure of A, B, C, some number which is greater than E will measure the numbers A, B, C.

Let such a number measure them, and let it be F.

Now, since F measures A, B, C,

it also measures A, B;

therefore it will also measure the greatest common measure of A, B.

[VII. 2, Por.]

But the greatest common measure of A, B is D;

therefore F measures D.

And it measures C also;

therefore F measures D, C;

therefore it will also measure the greatest common measure of D, C.

[VII. 2, Por.]

But the greatest common measure of D, C is E;

therefore F measures E, the greater the less: which is impossible

Therefore no number which is greater than E will measure the numbers A, B, C;

therefore E is the greatest common measure of A, B, C.

Q. E. D.

PROPOSITION 4

Any number is either a part or parts of any number, the less of the greater.

Let A, BC be two numbers, and let BC be the less;

I say that BC is either a part, or parts, of A.

For A, BC are either prime to one another or not.

First, let A, BC be prime to one another.

Then, if BC be divided into the units in it, each unit of those in BC will be some part of A; so that BC is parts of A.

Next let A, BC not be prime to one another; then BC either measures, or does not measure, A.

If now BC measures A, BC is a part of A.

But, if not, let the greatest common measure D of A, BC be taken;   [VII. 2] and let BC be divided into the numbers equal to D, namely BE, EF, FC.

Now, since D measures A, D is a part of A.

But D is equal to each of the numbers BE, EF, FC;

therefore each of the numbers BE, EF, FC is also a part of A; so that BC is parts of A.

Therefore etc.   Q. E. D.

PROPOSITION 5

If a number be a part of a number, and another be the same part of another, the sum will also be the same part of the sum that the one is of the one.

For let the number A be a part of BC,

and another, D, the same part of another EF that A is of BC;

I say that the sum of A, D is also the same part of the sum of BC, EF that A is of BC.

For since, whatever part A is of BC, D is also the same part of EF,

therefore, as many numbers as there are in BC equal to A, so many numbers are there also in EF equal to D.

Let BC be divided into the numbers equal to A, namely BG, GC,

and EF into the numbers equal to D, namely EH, HF;

then the multitude of BG, GC will be equal to the multitude of EH, HF.

And, since BG is equal to A, and EH to D,

therefore BG, EH are also equal to A, D.

For the same reason

GC, HF are also equal to A, D.

Therefore, as many numbers as there are in BC equal to A, so many are there also in BC, EF equal to A, D.

Therefore, whatever multiple BC is of A, the same multiple also is the sum of BC, EF of the sum of A, D.

Therefore, whatever part A is to BC, the same part also is the sum of A, D of the sum of BC, EF.   Q. E. D.

PROPOSITION 6

If a number be parts of a number, and another be the same parts of another, the sum will also be the same parts of the sum that the one is of the one.

For let the number AB be parts of the number C, and another, DE, the same parts of another, F, that AB is of C;

I say that the sum of AB, DE is also the same parts of the sum of C, F that AB is of C.

For since, whatever parts AB is of C, DE is also the same parts of F,
therefore, as many parts of C as there are in AB, so many parts of F are there also in DE.

Let AB be divided into the parts of C, namely AG, GB, and DE into the parts of F, namely DH, HE;
thus the multitude of AG, GB will be equal to the multitude of DH, HE.

And since, whatever part AG is of C, the same part is DH of F also,
therefore, whatever part AG is of C, the same part also is the sum of AG, DH of the sum of C, F.   [VII. 5]

For the same reason,
whatever part GB is of C, the same part also is the sum of GB, HE of the sum of C, F.

Therefore, whatever parts AB is of C, the same parts also is the sum of AB, DE of the sum of C, F.   Q. E. D.

PROPOSITION 7

If a number be that part of a number, which a number subtracted is of a number subtracted, the remainder will also be the same part of the remainder that the whole is of the whole.

For let the number AB be that part of the number CD which AE subtracted is of CF subtracted;

I say that the remainder EB is also the same part of the remainder FD that the whole AB is of the whole CD.

For, whatever part AE is of CF, the same part also let EB be of CG.

Now since, whatever part AE is of CF, the same part also is EB of CG,
therefore, whatever part AE is of CF, the same part also is AB of GF.   [VII. 5]

But, whatever part AE is of CF, the same part also, by hypothesis, is AB of CD;
therefore, whatever part AB is of GF, the same part is it of CD also;
therefore GF is equal to CD.

Let CF be subtracted from each;
therefore the remainder GC is equal to the remainder FD.

Now since, whatever part AE is of CF, the same part also is EB of GC,
while GC is equal to FD,
therefore, whatever part AE is of CF, the same part also is EB of FD.

But, whatever part AE is of CF, the same part also is AB of CD;
therefore also the remainder EB is the same part of the remainder FD that the whole AB is of the whole CD.   Q. E. D.

Proposition 8

If a number be the same parts of a number that a number subtracted is of a number subtracted, the remainder will also be the same parts of the remainder that the whole is of the whole.

For let the number *AB* be the same parts of the number *CD* that *AE* subtracted is of *CF* subtracted;

I say that the remainder *EB* is also the same parts of the remainder *FD* that the whole *AB* is of the whole *CD*.

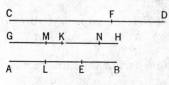

For let *GH* be made equal to *AB*.

Therefore, whatever parts *GH* is of *CD*, the same parts also is *AE* of *CF*.

Let *GH* be divided into the parts of *CD*, namely *GK*, *KH*, and *AE* into the parts of *CF*, namely *AL*, *LE*;

thus the multitude of *GK*, *KH* will be equal to the multitude of *AL*, *LE*.

Now since, whatever part *GK* is of *CD*, the same part also is *AL* of *CF*,

while *CD* is greater than *CF*,

therefore *GK* is also greater than *AL*.

Let *GM* be made equal to *AL*.

Therefore, whatever part *GK* is of *CD*, the same part also is *GM* of *CF*; therefore also the remainder *MK* is the same part of the remainder *FD* that the whole *GK* is of the whole *CD*.   [VII. 7]

Again, since, whatever part *KH* is of *CD*, the same part also is *EL* of *CF*,

while *CD* is greater than *CF*,

therefore *HK* is also greater than *EL*.

Let *KN* be made equal to *EL*.

Therefore, whatever part *KH* is of *CD*, the same part also is *KN* of *CF*; therefore also the remainder *NH* is the same part of the remainder *FD* that the whole *KH* is of the whole *CD*.   [VII. 7]

But the remainder *MK* was also proved to be the same part of the remainder *FD* that the whole *GK* is of the whole *CD*;

therefore also the sum of *MK*, *NH* is the same parts of *DF* that the whole *HG* is of the whole *CD*.

But the sum of *MK*, *NH* is equal to *EB*,

and *HG* is equal to *BA*;

therefore the remainder *EB* is the same parts of the remainder *FD* that the whole *AB* is of the whole *CD*.   Q. E. D.

Proposition 9

If a number be a part of a number, and another be the same part of another, alternately also, whatever part or parts the first is of the third, the same part, or the same parts, will the second also be of the fourth.

For let the number *A* be a part of the number *BC*, and another, *D*, the same part of another, *EF*, that *A* is of *BC*;

I say that, alternately also, whatever part or parts *A* is of *D*, the same part or parts is *BC* of *EF* also.

For since, whatever part *A* is of *BC*, the same part also is *D* of *EF*, therefore, as many numbers as there are in BC equal to A, so many also are there in EF equal to D.

Let BC be divided into the numbers equal to A, namely BG, GC,
and EF into those equal to D, namely EH, HF;
thus the multitude of BG, GC will be equal to the multitude of EH, HF.

Now, since the numbers BG, GC are equal to one another, and the numbers EH, HF are also equal to one another,
while the multitude of BG, GC is equal to the multitude of EH, HF,
therefore, whatever part or parts BG is of EH, the same part or the same parts is GC of HF also;
so that, in addition, whatever part or parts BG is of EH, the same part also, or the same parts, is the sum BC of the sum EF.   [VII. 5, 6]

But BG is equal to A, and EH to D;
therefore, whatever part or parts A is of D, the same part or the same parts is BC of EF also.   Q. E. D.

PROPOSITION 10

If a number be parts of a number, and another be the same parts of another, alternately also, whatever parts or part the first is of the third, the same parts or the same part will the second also be of the fourth.

For let the number AB be parts of the number C, and another, DE, the same parts of another, F;
I say that, alternately also, whatever parts or part AB is of DE, the same parts or the same part is C of F also.

For since, whatever parts AB is of C, the same parts also is DE of F,
therefore, as many parts of C as there are in AB, so many parts also of F are there in DE.

Let AB be divided into the parts of C, namely AG, GB, and DE into the parts of F, namely DH, HE;
thus the multitude of AG, GB will be equal to the multitude of DH, HE.

Now since, whatever part AG is of C, the same part also is DH of F,
alternately also, whatever part or parts AG is of DH,
the same part or the same parts is C of F also.   [VII. 9]

For the same reason also,
whatever part or parts GB is of HE, the same part or the same parts is C of F also;
so that, in addition, whatever parts or part AB is of DE, the same parts also, or the same part, is C of F.   [VII. 5, 6]

Q. E. D.

PROPOSITION 11

If, as whole is to whole, so is a number subtracted to a number subtracted, the remainder will also be to the remainder as whole to whole.

As the whole AB is to the whole CD, so let AE subtracted be to CF subtracted;
I say that the remainder EB is also to the remainder FD as the whole AB to the whole CD.

Since, as AB is to CD, so is AE to CF,

whatever part or parts AB is of CD, the same part or the same parts is AE of CF also;   [VII. Def. 20]

Therefore also the remainder EB is the same part or parts of FD that AB is of CD.   [VII. 7, 8]

Therefore, as EB is to FD, so is AB to CD.   [VII. Def. 20]

Q. E. D.

PROPOSITION 12

If there be as many numbers as we please in proportion, then, as one of the antecedents is to one of the consequents, so are all the antecedents to all the consequents.

Let A, B, C, D be as many numbers as we please in proportion, so that,

as A is to B, so is C to D;

I say that, as A is to B, so are A, C to B, D.

For since, as A is to B, so is C to D,

whatever part or parts A is of B, the same part or parts is C of D also.   [VII. Def. 20]

Therefore also the sum of A, C is the same part or the same parts of the sum of B, D that A is of B.   [VII. 5, 6]

Therefore, as A is to B, so are A, C to B, D.   [VII. Def. 20]

Q. E. D.

PROPOSITION 13

If four numbers be proportional, they will also be proportional alternately.

Let the four numbers A, B, C, D be proportional, so that,

as A is to B, so is C to D;

I say that they will also be proportional alternately, so that,

as A is to C, so will B be to D.

For since, as A is to B, so is C to D,

therefore, whatever part or parts A is of B, the same part or the same parts is C of D also.   [VII. Def. 20]

Therefore, alternately, whatever part or parts A is of C, the same part or the same parts is B of D also.   [VII. 10]

Therefore, as A is to C, so is B to D.   [VII. Def. 20]

Q. E. D.

PROPOSITION 14

If there be as many numbers as we please, and others equal to them in multitude, which taken two and two are in the same ratio, they will also be in the same ratio ex aequali.

Let there be as many numbers as we please A, B, C, and others equal to them in multitude D, E, F, which taken two and two are in the same ratio, so that,

as A is to B, so is D to E,

and, as B is to C, so is E to F;

I say that, *ex aequali*,

as A is to C, so also is D to F.

For, since, as A is to B, so is D to E,

therefore, alternately,

as A is to D, so is B to E.   [VII. 13]

Again, since, as B is to C, so is E to F,

therefore, alternately,

as B is to E, so is C to F.   [VII. 13]

But, as B is to E, so is A to D;

therefore also, as A is to D, so is C to F.

Therefore, alternately,

as A is to C, so is D to F.   [*id.*]

PROPOSITION 15

If an unit measure any number, and another number measure any other number the same number of times, alternately also, the unit will measure the third number the same number of times that the second measures the fourth.

For let the unit A measure any number BC, and let another number D measure any other number EF the same number of times;

I say that, alternately also, the unit A measures the number D the same number of times that BC measures EF.

For, since the unit A measures the number BC the same number of times that D measures EF,

therefore, as many units as there are in BC, so many numbers equal to D are there in EF also.

Let BC be divided into the units in it, BG, GH, HC,

and EF into the numbers EK, KL, LF equal to D.

Thus the multitude of BG, GH, HC will be equal to the multitude of EK, KL, LF.

And, since the units BG, GH, HC are equal to one another,

and the numbers EK, KL, LF are also equal to one another,

while the multitude of the units BG, GH, HC is equal to the multitude of the numbers EK, KL, LF,

therefore, as the unit BG is to the number EK, so will the unit GH be to the number KL, and the unit HC to the number LF.

Therefore also, as one of the antecedents is to one of the consequents, so will all the antecedents be to all the consequents;   [VII. 12]

therefore, as the unit BG is to the number EK, so is BC to EF.

But the unit BG is equal to the unit A,

and the number EK to the number D.

Therefore, as the unit A is to the number D, so is BC to EF.

Therefore the unit A measures the number D the same number of times that BC measures EF.   Q. E. D.

PROPOSITION 16

If two numbers by multiplying one another make certain numbers, the numbers so produced will be equal to one another.

Let A, B be two numbers, and let A by multiplying B make C, and B by multiplying A make D;

I say that C is equal to D.

For, since A by multiplying B has made C,

therefore B measures C according to the units in A.

But the unit E also measures the number A according to the units in it;
therefore the unit E measures A the same number of times that B measures C.

Therefore, alternately, the unit E measures the number B the same number of times that A measures C [VII. 15].

Again, since B by multiplying A has made D,

therefore A measures D according to the units in B.

But the unit E also measures B according to the units in it;
therefore the unit E measures the number B the same number of times that A measures D.

But the unit E measured the number B the same number of times that A measures C;
therefore A measures each of the numbers C, D the same number of times.

Therefore C is equal to D.   Q. E. D.

PROPOSITION 17

If a number by multiplying two numbers make certain numbers, the numbers so produced will have the same ratio as the numbers multiplied.

For let the number A be multiplying the two numbers B, C make D, E;
I say that, as B is to C, so is D to E.

For, since A by multiplying B has made D,
therefore B measures D according to the units in A.

But the unit F also measures the number A according to the units in it;
therefore the unit F measures the number A the same number of times that B measures D.

Therefore, as the unit F is to the number A, so is B to D.   [VII. Def. 20]
For the same reason,
as the unit F is to the number A, so also is C to E;
therefore also, as B is to D, so is C to E.

Therefore, alternately, as B is to C, so is D to E.   [VII. 13]

Q. E. D.

PROPOSITION 18

If two numbers by multiplying any number make certain numbers, the numbers so produced will have the same ratio as the multipliers.

For let two numbers A, B by multiplying any number C make D, E;
I say that, as A is to B, so is D to E.

For, since A by multiplying C has made D,
therefore also C by multiplying A has made D.   [VII. 16]

For the same reason also
C by multiplying B has made E.

Therefore the number C by multiplying the two numbers A, B has made D, E.
Therefore, as A is to B, so is D to E.   [VII. 17]

Q. E. D.

PROPOSITION 19

If four numbers be proportional, the number produced from the first and fourth will be equal to the number produced from the second and third; and, if the number produced from the first and fourth be equal to that produced from the second and third, the four numbers will be proportional.

Let A, B, C, D be four numbers in proportion, so that,

as A is to B, so is C to D;

and let A by multiplying D make E, and let B by multiplying C make F;

I say that E is equal to F.

For let A by multiplying C make G.

Since, then, A by multiplying C has made G, and by multiplying D has made E,

the number A by multiplying the two numbers C, D has made G, E.

Therefore, as C is to D, so is G to E.   [VII. 17]

But, as C is to D, so is A to B;

    therefore also, as A is to B, so is G to E.

Again, since A by multiplying C has made G,

but, further, B has also by multiplying C made F,

the two numbers A, B by multiplying a certain number C have made G, F.

Therefore, as A is to B, so is G to F.   [VII. 18]

But further, as A is to B, so is G to E also;

    therefore also, as G is to E, so is G to F.

Therefore G has to each of the numbers E, F the same ratio;

therefore E is equal to F.   [cf. V. 9]

Again, let E be equal to F;

I say that, as A is to B, so is C to D.

For, with the same construction,

since E is equal to F,

therefore, as G is to E, so is G to F.   [cf. V. 7]

But, as G is to E, so is C to D,   [VII. 17]

and, as G is to F, so is A to B.   [VII. 18]

Therefore also, as A is to B, so is C to D.   Q. E. D.

PROPOSITION 20

The least numbers of those which have the same ratio with them measure those which have the same ratio the same number of times, the greater the greater and the less the less.

For let CD, EF be the least numbers of those which have the same ratio with A, B;

I say that CD measures A the same number of times that EF measures B.

Now CD is not parts of A.

For, if possible, let it be so;

therefore EF is also the same parts of B that CD is of A.

[VII. 13 and Def. 20]

Therefore, as many parts of A as there are in CD, so many parts of B are there also in EF.

Let *CD* be divided into the parts of *A*, namely *CG*, *GD*, and *EF* into the parts of *B*, namely *EH*, *HF*;
thus the multitude of *CG*, *GD* will be equal to the multitude of *EH*, *HF*.

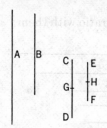

Now, since the numbers *CG*, *GD* are equal to one another, and the numbers *EH*, *HF* are also equal to one another, while the multitude of *CG*, *GD* is equal to the multitude of *EH*, *HF*,

therefore, as *CG* is to *EH*, so is *GD* to *HF*.

Therefore also, as one of the antecedents is to one of the consequents, so will all the antecedents be to all the consequents. [VII. 12]

Therefore, as *CG* is to *EH*, so is *CD* to *EF*.

Therefore *CG*, *EH* are in the same ratio with *CD*, *EF*, being less than they: which is impossible, for by hypothesis *CD*, *EF* are the least numbers of those which have the same ratio with them.

Therefore *CD* is not parts of *A*;

therefore it is a part of it. [VII. 4]

And *EF* is the same part of *B* that *CD* is of *A*; [VII. 13 and Def. 20]
therefore *CD* measures *A* the same number of times that *EF* measures *B*.

Q. E. D.

PROPOSITION 21

Numbers prime to one another are the least of those which have the same ratio with them.

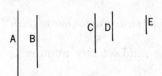

Let *A*, *B* be numbers prime to one another;
I say that *A*, *B* are the least of those which have the same ratio with them.

For, if not, there will be some numbers less than *A*, *B* which are in the same ratio with *A*, *B*.

Let them be *C*, *D*.

Since, then, the least numbers of those which have the same ratio measure those which have the same ratio the same number of times, the greater the greater and the less the less, that is, the antecedent the antecedent and the consequent the consequent, [VII. 20]

therefore *C* measures *A* the same number of times that *D* measures *B*.

Now, as many times as *C* measures *A*, so many units let there be in *E*.

Therefore *D* also measures *B* according to the units in *E*.

And, since *C* measures *A* according to the units in *E*,

therefore *E* also measures *A* according to the units in *C*. [VII. 16]

For the same reason

E also measures *B* according to the units in *D*. [VII. 16]

Therefore *E* measures *A*, *B* which are prime to one another: which is impossible. [VII. Def. 12]

Therefore there will be no numbers less than *A*, *B* which are in the same ratio with *A*, *B*.

Therefore *A*, *B* are the least of those which have the same ratio with them.

Q. E. D.

Proposition 22

The least numbers of those which have the same ratio with them are prime to one another.

Let *A*, *B* be the least numbers of those which have the same ratio with them;

I say that *A*, *B* are prime to one another.

For, if they are not prime to one another, some number will measure them.

Let some number measure them, and let it be *C*.

And, as many times as *C* measures *A*, so many units let there be in *D*,

and, as many times as *C* measures *B*, so many units let there be in *E*.

Since *C* measures *A* according to the units in *D*,

therefore *C* by multiplying *D* has made *A*.　　　[VII. Def. 15]

For the same reason also

C by multiplying *E* has made *B*.

Thus the number *C* by multiplying the two numbers *D*, *E* has made *A*, *B*;

therefore, as *D* is to *E*, so is *A* to *B*;　　　[VII. 17]

therefore *D*, *E* are in the same ratio with *A*, *B*, being less than they: which is impossible.

Therefore no number will measure the numbers *A*, *B*.

Therefore *A*, *B* are prime to one another.　　　Q. E. D.

Proposition 23

If two numbers be prime to one another, the number which measures the one of them will be prime to the remaining number.

Let *A*, *B* be two numbers prime to one another, and let any number *C* measure *A*;

I say that *C*, *B* are also prime to one another.

For, if *C*, *B* are not prime to one another,

some number will measure *C*, *B*.

Let a number measure them, and let it be *D*.

Since *D* measures *C*, and *C* measures *A*, therefore *D* also measures *A*.

But it also measures *B*;

therefore *D* measures *A*, *B* which are prime to one another: which is impossible.　　　[VII. Def. 12]

Therefore no number will measure the numbers *C*, *B*.

Therefore *C*, *B* are prime to one another.　　　Q. E. D.

Proposition 24

If two numbers be prime to any number, their product also will be prime to the same.

For let the two numbers *A*, *B* be prime to any number *C*, and let *A* by multiplying *B* make *D*;

I say that *C*, *D* are prime to one another.

For, if *C*, *D* are not prime to one another, some number will measure *C*, *D*.

Let a number measure them, and let it be *E*.

Now, since *C*, *A* are prime to one another,

and a certain number E measures C,

therefore A, E are prime to one another.   [VII. 23]

As many times, then, as E measures D, so many units let there be in F;

therefore F also measures D according to the units in E.   [VII. 16]

Therefore E by multiplying F has made D. [VII. Def. 15]

But, further, A by multiplying B has also made D; therefore the product of E, F is equal to the product of A, B.

But, if the product of the extremes be equal to that of the means, the four numbers are proportional;   [VII. 19] therefore, as E is to A, so is B to F.

But A, E are prime to one another,

numbers which are prime to one another are also the least of those which have the same ratio,   [VII. 21]

and the least numbers of those which have the same ratio with them measure those which have the same ratio the same number of times, the greater the greater and the less the less, that is, the antecedent the antecedent and the consequent the consequent;   [VII. 20]

therefore E measures B.

But it also measures C;

therefore E measures B, C which are prime to one another: which is impossible.
                    [VII. Def. 12]

Therefore no number will measure the numbers C, D.

Therefore C, D are prime to one another.   Q. E. D.

PROPOSITION 25

If two numbers be prime to one another, the product of one of them into itself will be prime to the remaining one.

Let A, B be two numbers prime to one another,

and let A by multiplying itself make C;

I say that B, C are prime to one another.

For let D be made equal to A.

Since A, B are prime to one another, and A is equal to D, therefore D, B are also prime to one another.

Therefore each of the two numbers D, A is prime to B;

therefore the product of D, A will also be prime to B. [VII. 24]

But the number which is the product of D, A is C.

Therefore C, B are prime to one another.   Q. E. D.

PROPOSITION 26

If two numbers be prime to two numbers, both to each, their products also will be prime to one another.

For let the two numbers A, B be prime to the two numbers C, D; both to each, and let A by multiplying B make E, and let C by multiplying D make F;

I say that E, F are prime to one another.

For, since each of the numbers A, B is prime to C,
        therefore the product of A, B will also be prime to C.   [VII. 24]
But the product of A, B is E;
        therefore E, C are prime to one another.
For the same reason
            E, D are also prime to one another.
Therefore each of the numbers C, D is prime to E.
Therefore the product of C, D will also be prime to E.   [VII. 24]
But the product of C, D is F.
Therefore E, F are prime to one another.   Q. E. D.

PROPOSITION 27

If two numbers be prime to one another, and each by multiplying itself make a certain number, the products will be prime to one another; and, if the original numbers by multiplying the products make certain numbers, the latter will also be prime to one another [and this is always the case with the extremes].

Let A, B be two numbers prime to one another,
let A by multiplying itself make C, and by multiplying C make D,
and let B by multiplying itself make E, and by multiplying E make F;
  I say that both C, E and D, F are prime to one another.
  For, since A, B are prime to one another, and A by
multiplying itself has made C,
        therefore C, B are prime to one another. [VII. 25]
Since, then, C, B are prime to one another,
     and B by multiplying itself has made E,
        therefore C, E are prime to one another.   [*id.*]
Again, since A, B are prime to one another,
       and B by multiplying itself has made E,
        therefore A, E are prime to one another.   [*id.*]
Since, then, the two numbers A, C are prime to the two numbers B, E, both
to each,
therefore also the product of A, C is prime to the product of B, E.   [VII. 26]
  And the product of A, C is D, and the product of B, E is F.
  Therefore D, F are prime to one another.   Q. E. D.

PROPOSITION 28

If two numbers be prime to one another, the sum will also be prime to each of them; and, if the sum of two numbers be prime to any one of them, the original numbers will also be prime to one another.

For let two numbers AB, BC prime to one another be added;
  I say that the sum AC is also prime to each of
the numbers AB, BC.
  For, if CA, AB are not prime to one another,
     some number will measure CA, AB.
Let a number measure them, and let it be D.
Since then D measures CA, AB,
       therefore it will also measure the remainder BC.

But it also measures BA;
therefore D measures AB, BC which are prime to one another: which is impossible.   [VII. Def. 12]

Therefore no number will measure the numbers CA, AB; therefore CA, AB are prime to one another.

For the same reason
$$AC, CB \text{ are also prime to one another.}$$
Therefore CA is prime to each of the numbers AB, BC.

Again, let CA, AB be prime to one another;
$$\text{I say that } AB, BC \text{ are also prime to one another.}$$
For, if AB, BC are not prime to one another,
$$\text{some number will measure } AB, BC.$$
Let a number measure them, and let it be D.

Now, since D measures each of the numbers AB, BC, it will also measure the whole CA.

But it also measures AB;
$$\text{therefore } D \text{ measures } CA, AB \text{ which are prime to one another:}$$
$$\text{which is impossible.} \qquad \text{[VII. Def. 12]}$$
Therefore no number will measure the numbers AB, BC.

Therefore AB, BC are prime to one another.   Q. E. D.

PROPOSITION 29

Any prime number is prime to any number which it does not measure.

Let A be a prime number, and let it not measure B;
$$\text{I say that } B, A \text{ are prime to one another.}$$
$$\text{For, if } B, A \text{ are not prime to one another,}$$
$$\text{some number will measure them.}$$
Let C measure them.

Since C measures B,
and A does not measure B,
$$\text{therefore } C \text{ is not the same with } A.$$
Now, since C measures B, A,
therefore it also measures A which is prime, though it is not the same with it:
$$\text{which is impossible.}$$
Therefore no number will measure B, A.

Therefore A, B are prime to one another.   Q. E. D.

PROPOSITION 30

If two numbers by multiplying one another make some number, and any prime number measure the product, it will also measure one of the original numbers.

For let the two numbers A, B by multiplying one another make C, and let any prime number D measure C;
$$\text{I say that } D \text{ measures one of the numbers } A, B.$$
For let it not measure A.

Now D is prime;
therefore A, D are prime to one another. [VII. 29]
And, as many times as D measures C, so many units let there be in E.

Since then D measures C according to the units in E,

therefore D by multiplying E has made C.   [VII. Def. 15]
Further, A by multiplying B has also made C;
    therefore the product of D, E is equal to the product of A, B.
Therefore, as D is to A, so is B to E.   [VII. 19]
But D, A are prime to one another,
                primes are also least,   [VII. 21]
and the least measure the numbers which have the same ratio the same number of times, the greater the greater and the less the less, that is, the antecedent the antecedent and the consequent the consequent;   [VII. 20]
                therefore D measures B.
Similarly we can also show that, if D does not measure B, it will measure A.
Therefore D measures one of the numbers A, B.   Q. E. D.

PROPOSITION 31

Any composite number is measured by some prime number.
    Let A be a composite number;
            I say that A is measured by some prime number.
    For, since A is composite,
            some number will measure it.
    Let a number measure it, and let it be B.
    Now, if B is prime, what was enjoined will have been done.
    But if it is composite, some number will measure it.
    Let a number measure it, and let it be C.
    Then, since C measures B,
            and B measures A,
            therefore C also measures A.
    And, if C is prime, what was enjoined will have been done.
    But if it is composite, some number will measure it.
    Thus, if the investigation be continued in this way, some prime number will be found which will measure the number before it, which will also measure A.
    For, if it is not found, an infinite series of numbers will measure the number A, each of which is less than the other:
            which is impossible in numbers.
    Therefore some prime number will be found which will measure the one before it, which will also measure A.
    Therefore any composite number is measured by some prime number.
                Q. E. D.

PROPOSITION 32

Any number either is prime or is measured by some prime number.
    Let A be a number;
    I say that A either is prime or is measured by some prime number.
    If now A is prime, that which was enjoined will have been done.
    But if it is composite, some prime number will measure it.   [VII. 31]
    Therefore any number either is prime or is measured by some prime number.
                Q. E. D.

Proposition 33

Given as many numbers as we please, to find the least of those which have the same ratio with them.

Let A, B, C be the given numbers, as many as we please;

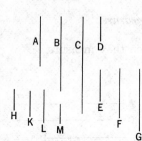

thus it is required to find the least of those which have the same ratio with A, B, C.

A, B, C are either prime to one another or not.

Now, if A, B, C are prime to one another, they are the least of those which have the same ratio with them. [VII. 21]

But, if not, let D the greatest common measure of A, B, C be taken, [VII. 3]

and, as many times as D measures the numbers A, B, C respectively, so many units let there be in the numbers E, F, G respectively.

Therefore the numbers E, F, G measure the numbers A, B, C respectively according to the units in D. [VII. 16]

Therefore E, F, G measure A, B, C the same number of times;

therefore E, F, G are in the same ratio with A, B, C. [VII. Def. 20]

I say next that they are the least that are in that ratio.

For, if E, F, G are not the least of those which have the same ratio with A, B, C,

there will be numbers less than E, F, G which are in the same ratio with A, B, C.

Let them be H, K, L;

therefore H measures A the same number of times that the numbers K, L measure the numbers B, C respectively.

Now, as many times as H measures A, so many units let there be in M;

therefore the numbers K, L also measure the numbers B, C respectively according to the units in M.

And, since H measures A according to the units in M,

therefore M also measures A according to the units in H. [VII. 16]

For the same reason

M also measures the numbers B, C according to the units in the numbers K, L respectively;

Therefore M measures A, B, C.

Now, since H measures A according to the units in M,

therefore H by multiplying M has made A. [VII. Def. 15]

For the same reason also

E by multiplying D has made A.

Therefore the product of E, D is equal to the product of H, M.

Therefore, as E is to H, so is M to D. [VII. 19]

But E is greater than H;

therefore M is also greater than D.

And it measures A, B, C:

which is impossible, for by hypothesis, D is the greatest common measure of A, B, C.

Therefore there cannot be any numbers less than E, F, G which are in the same ratio with A, B, C.

Therefore E, F, G are the least of those which have the same ratio with A, B, C.

Q. E. D.

PROPOSITION 34

Given two numbers, to find the least number which they measure.

Let A, B be the two given numbers;

thus it is required to find the least number which they measure.

Now A, B are either prime to one another or not.

First, let A, B be prime to one another, and let A by multiplying B make C;

therefore also B by multiplying A has made C.

Therefore A, B measure C.

I say next that it is also the least number they measure.

For, if not, A, B will measure some number which is less than C.

Let them measure D.

Then, as many times as A measures D, so many units let there be in E, and, as many times as B measures D, so many units let there be in F;

therefore A by multiplying E has made D,

and B by multiplying F has made D; [VII. Def. 15]

therefore the product of A, E is equal to the product of B, F.

Therefore, as A is to B, so is F to E. [VII. 19]

But A, B are prime,

primes are also least, [VII. 21]

and the least measure the numbers which have the same ratio the same number of times, the greater the greater and the less the less; [VII. 20]

therefore B measures E, as consequent consequent.

And, since A by multiplying B, E has made C, D,

therefore, as B is to E, so is C to D. [VII. 17]

But B measures E;

therefore C also measures D, the greater the less:

which is impossible.

Therefore A, B do not measure any number less than C;

therefore C is the least that is measured by A, B.

Next, let A, B not be prime to one another,

and let F, E, the least numbers of those which have the same ratio with A, B, be taken; [VII. 33]

therefore the product of A, E is equal to the product of B, F. [VII. 19]

And let A by multiplying E make C;

therefore also B by multiplying F has made C;

therefore A, B measure C.

I say next that it is also the least number that they measure.

For, if not, A, B will measure some number which is less than C.

Let them measure D.

And, as many times as A measures D, so many units let there be in G, and, as many times as B measures D, so many units let there be in H.

Therefore A by multiplying G has made D,
and B by multiplying H has made D.

Therefore the product of A, G is equal to the product of B, H;
therefore, as A is to B, so is H to G.   [VII. 19]

But, as A is to B, so is F to E.

Therefore also, as F is to E, so is H to G.

But F, E are least,
and the least measure the numbers which have the same ratio the same number of times, the greater the greater and the less the less;   [VII. 20]
therefore E measures G.

And, since A by multiplying E, G has made C, D,
therefore, as E is to G, so is C to D.   [VII. 17]

But E measures G;
therefore C also measures D, the greater the less:
which is impossible.

Therefore A, B will not measure any number which is less than C.

Therefore C is the least that is measured by A, B.   Q. E. D.

PROPOSITION 35

If two numbers measure any number, the least number measured by them will also measure the same.

For let the two numbers A, B measure any number CD,
and let E be the least that they measure;
I say that E also measures CD.

For, if E does not measure CD, let E, measuring DF, leave CF less than itself.

Now, since A, B measure E,
and E measures DF,
therefore A, B will also measure DF.
But they also measure the whole CD;
therefore they will also measure the remainder CF which is less than E:
which is impossible.

Therefore E cannot fail to measure CD;
therefore it measures it.   Q. E. D.

PROPOSITION 36

Given three numbers, to find the least number which they measure.

Let A, B, C be the three given numbers;
thus it is required to find the least number which they measure.

Let D, the least number measured by the two numbers A, B, be taken.   [VII. 34]

Then C either measures, or does not measure, D.

First, let it measure it.

But A, B also measure D;
therefore A, B, C measure D.

I say next that it is also the least that they measure.

For, if not, A, B, C will measure some number which is less than D.
Let them measure E.
Since A, B, C measure E,
therefore also A, B measure E.
Therefore the least number measured by A, B will also measure E. [VII. 35]
But D is the least number measured by A, B;
therefore D will measure E, the greater the less:
which is impossible.
Therefore A, B, C will not measure any number which is less than D;
therefore D is the least that A, B, C measure.
Again, let C not measure D,
and let E, the least number measured by C, D, be
taken.   [VII. 34]
Since A, B measure D,
and D measures E,
therefore also A, B measure E.
But C also measures E;
therefore also A, B, C measure E.
I say next that it is also the least that they measure.
For, if not, A, B, C will measure some number which is less than E.
Let them measure F.
Since A, B, C measure F,
therefore also A, B measure F;
therefore the least number measured by A, B will also measure F.   [VII. 35]
But D is the least number measured by A, B;
therefore D measures F.
But C also measures F;
therefore D, C measure F,
so that the least number measured by D, C will also measure F.
But E is the least number measured by C, D;
therefore E measures F, the greater the less:
which is impossible.
Therefore A, B, C will not measure any number which is less than E.
Therefore E is the least that is measured by A, B, C.   Q. E. D.

PROPOSITION 37

If a number be measured by any number, the number which is measured will have a part called by the same name as the measuring number.

For let the number A be measured by any number B;
I say that A has a part called by the same name as B.
For, as many times as B measures A, so many units let there be in C.
Since B measures A according to the units in C,
and the unit D also measures the number C according to the units in it,
therefore the unit D measures the number C the same number of times as B measures A.
Therefore, alternately, the unit D measures the number B the same number of times as C measures A;   [VII. 15]

therefore, whatever part the unit D is of the number B, the same part is C of A also.

But the unit D is a part of the number B called by the same name as it;

therefore C is also a part of A called by the same name as B,

so that A has a part C which is called by the same name as B.   Q. E. D.

PROPOSITION 38

If a number have any part whatever, it will be measured by a number called by the same name as the part.

For let the number A have any part whatever, B,

and let C be a number called by the same name as the part B;

I say that C measures A.

For, since B is a part of A called by the same name as C,

and the unit D is also a part of C called by the same name as it,

therefore, whatever part the unit D is of the number C,

the same part is B of A also;

therefore the unit D measures the number C the same number of times that B measures A.

Therefore, alternately, the unit D measures the number B the same number of times that C measures A.   [VII. 15]

Therefore C measures A.   Q. E. D.

PROPOSITION 39

To find the number which is the least that will have given parts.

Let A, B, C be the given parts;

thus it is required to find the number which is the least that will have the parts A, B, C.

Let D, E, F be numbers called by the same name as the parts A, B, C,

and let G, the least number measured by D, E, F, be taken.   [VII. 36]

Therefore G has parts called by the same name as D, E, F.   [VII. 37]

But A, B, C are parts called by the same name as D, E, F;

therefore G has the parts A, B, C.

I say next that it is also the least number that has.

For, if not, there will be some number less than G which will have the parts A, B, C.

Let it be H.

Since H has the parts A, B, C,

therefore H will be measured by numbers called by the same name as the parts A, B, C.   [VII. 38]

But D, E, F are numbers called by the same name as the parts A, B, C;

therefore H is measured by D, E, F.

And it is less than G: which is impossible.

Therefore there will be no number less than G that will have the parts A, B, C.   Q. E. D.

BOOK EIGHT

PROPOSITION 1

If there be as many numbers as we please in continued proportion, and the extremes of them be prime to one another, the numbers are the least of those which have the same ratio with them.

Let there be as many numbers as we please, A, B, C, D, in continued proportion,
and let the extremes of them A, D be prime to one another;
I say that A, B, C, D are the least of those which have the same ratio with them.

For, if not, let E, F, G, H be less than A, B, C, D, and in the same ratio with them.

Now, since A, B, C, D are in the same ratio with E, F, G, H,
and the multitude of the numbers A, B, C, D is equal to the multitude of the numbers E, F, G, H,

> therefore, *ex aequali*,
> as A is to D, so is E to H.   [VII. 14]

But A, D are prime,

> primes are also least,   [VII. 21]

and the least numbers measure those which have the same ratio the same number of times, the greater the greater and the less the less, that is, the antecedent the antecedent and the consequent the consequent.   [VII. 20]

Therefore A measures E, the greater the less:

> which is impossible.

Therefore E, F, G, H which are less than A, B, C, D are not in the same ratio with them.

Therefore A, B, C, D are the least of those which have the same ratio with them.   Q. E. D.

PROPOSITION 2

To find numbers in continued proportion, as many as may be prescribed, and the least that are in a given ratio.

Let the ratio of A to B be the given ratio in least numbers;
thus it is required to find numbers in continued proportion, as many as may be prescribed, and the least that are in the ratio of A to B.

Let four be prescribed;
let A by multiplying itself make C, and by multiplying B let it make D;
let B by multiplying itself make E;
further, let A by multiplying C, D, E make F, G, H.

and let B by multiplying E make K.

Now, since A by multiplying itself has made C,

and by multiplying B has made D,

therefore, as A is to B, so is C to D.

[VII. 17]

Again, since A by multiplying B has made D,

and B by multiplying itself has made E,

therefore the numbers A, B by multiplying B have made the numbers D, E respectively.

Therefore, as A is to B, so is D to E,   [VII. 18]

But, as A is to B, so is C to D;

therefore also, as C is to D, so is D to E.

And, since A by multiplying C, D has made F, G,

therefore, as C is to D, so is F to G.   [VII. 17]

But, as C is to D, so was A to B;

therefore also, as A is to B, so is F to G.

Again, since A by multiplying D, E has made G, H,

therefore, as D is to E, so is G to H.   [VII. 17]

But, as D is to E, so is A to B.

Therefore also, as A is to B, so is G to H.

And, since A, B by multiplying E have made H, K,

therefore, as A is to B, so is H to K.   [VII. 18]

But, as A is to B, so is F to G, and G to H.

Therefore also, as F is to G, so is G to H, and H to K;

therefore C, D, E, and F, G, H, K are proportional in the ratio of A to B.

I say next that they are the least numbers that are so.

For, since A, B are the least of those which have the same ratio with them, and the least of those which have the same ratio are prime to one another,

[VII. 22]

therefore A, B are prime to one another.

And the numbers A, B by multiplying themselves respectively have made the numbers C, E, and by multiplying the numbers C, E respectively have made the numbers F, K;

therefore C, E and F, K are prime to one another respectively.   [VII. 27]

But, if there be as many numbers as we please in continued proportion, and the extremes of them be prime to one another, they are the least of those which have the same ratio with them.   [VIII. 1]

Therefore C, D, E and F, G, H, K are the least of those which have the same ratio with A, B.   Q. E. D.

PORISM. From this it is manifest that, if three numbers in continued proportion be the least of those which have the same ratio with them, the extremes of them are squares, and, if four numbers, cubes.

PROPOSITION 3

If as many numbers as we please in continued proportion be the least of those which have the same ratio with them, the extremes of them are prime to one another.

Let as many numbers as we please, A, B, C, D, in continued proportion be the least of those which have the same ratio with them;

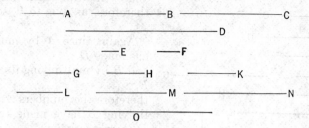

I say that the extremes of them A, D are prime to one another.

For let two numbers E, F, the least that are in the ratio of A, B, C, D, be taken,   [VII. 33]

then three others G, H, K with the same property;

and others, more by one continually,   [VIII. 2]

until the multitude taken becomes equal to the multitude of the numbers A, B, C, D.

Let them be taken, and let them be L, M, N, O.

Now, since E, F are the least of those which have the same ratio with them, they are prime to one another.   [VII. 22]

And, since the numbers E, F by multiplying themselves respectively have made the numbers G, K, and by multiplying the numbers G, K respectively have made the numbers L, O,   [VIII. 2, Por.]

therefore both G, K and L, O are prime to one another.   [VII. 27]

And, since A, B, C, D are the least of those which have the same ratio with them,

while L, M, N, O are the least that are in the same ratio with A, B, C, D,

and the multitude of the numbers A, B, C, D is equal to the multitude of the numbers L, M, N, O,

therefore the numbers A, B, C, D are equal to the numbers L, M, N, O respectively;

therefore A is equal to L, and D to O.

And L, O are prime to one another.

Therefore A, D are also prime to one another.   Q. E. D.

PROPOSITION 4

Given as many ratios as we please in least numbers, to find numbers in continued proportion which are the least in the given ratios.

Let the given ratios in least numbers be that of A to B, that of C to D, and that of E to F;

thus it is required to find numbers in continued proportion which are the least that are in the ratio of A to B, in the ratio of C to D, and in the ratio of E to F.

Let G, the least number measured by B, C, be taken.   [VII. 34]

And, as many times as B measures G, so many times also let A measure H, and, as many times as C measures G, so many times also let D measure K.

Now E either measures or does not measure K.

First, let it measure it.

And, as many times as E measures K, so many times let F measure L also.

Now, since A measures H the same number of times that B measures G, therefore, as A is to B, so is H to G.   [VII. Def. 20, VII. 13]

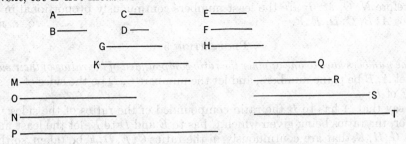

For the same reason also,

as C is to D, so is G to K,

and further, as E is to F, so is K to L;

therefore H, G, K, L are continuously proportional in the ratio of A to B, in the ratio of C to D, and in the ratio of E to F.

I say next that they are also the least that have this property.

For, if H, G, K, L are not the least numbers continuously proportional in the ratios of A to B, of C to D, and of E to F, let them be N, O, M, P.

Then since, as A is to B, so is N to O,

while A, B are least,

and the least numbers measure those which have the same ratio the same number of times, the greater the greater and the less the less, that is, the antecedent the antecedent and the consequent the consequent;

therefore B measures O.   [VII. 20]

For the same reason

C also measures O;

therefore B, C measure O;

therefore the least number measured by B, C will also measure O.   [VII. 35]

But G is the least number measured by B, C;

therefore G measures O, the greater the less:

which is impossible.

Therefore there will be no numbers less than H, G, K, L which are continuously in the ratio of A to B, of C to D, and of E to F.

Next, let E not measure K.

Let M, the least number measured by E, K, be taken.

And, as many times as K measures M, so many times let H, G measure N, O respectively,

and, as many times as E measures M, so many times let F measure P also.
Since H measures N the same number of times that G measures O,
therefore, as H is to G, so is N to O.   [VII. 13 and Def. 20]
But, as H is to G, so is A to B;
therefore also, as A is to B, so is N to O.
For the same reason also,
as C is to D, so is O to M.
Again, since E measures M the same number of times that F measures P,
therefore, as E is to F, so is M to P;   [VII. 13 and Def. 20]
therefore N, O, M, P are continuously proportional in the ratios of A to B, of
C to D, and of E to F.
I say next that they are also the least that are in the ratios $A:B$, $C:D$, $E:F$.
For, if not, there will be some numbers less than N, O, M, P continuously
proportional in the ratios $A:B$, $C:D$, $E:F$.
Let them be Q, R, S, T.
Now since, as Q is to R, so is A to B.
while A, B are least,
and the least numbers measure those which have the same ratio with them the
same number of times, the antecedent the antecedent and the consequent the
consequent,   [VII. 20]
therefore B measures R.
For the same reason C also measures R;
therefore B, C measure R.
Therefore the least number measured by B, C will also measure R.   [VII. 35]
But G is the least number measured by B, C;
therefore G measures R.
And, as G is to R, so is K to S: [VII. 13]
therefore K also measures S.
But E also measures S;
therefore E, K measure S.
Therefore the least number measured by E, K will also measure S.   [VII. 35]
But M is the least number measured by E, K;
therefore M measures S, the greater the less:
which is impossible.
Therefore there will not be any numbers less than N, O, M, P continuously
proportional in the ratios of A to B, of C to D, and of E to F;
therefore N, O, M, P are the least numbers continuously proportional in the
ratios $A:B$, $C:D$, $E:F$.   Q. E. D.

PROPOSITION 5

Plane numbers have to one another the ratio compounded of the ratios of their sides.
Let A, B be plane numbers, and let the numbers C, D be the sides of A, and
E, F of B;
I say that A has to B the ratio compounded of the ratios of the sides.
For, the ratios being given which C has to E and D to F, let the least numbers G, H, K that are continuously in the ratios $C:E$, $D:F$ be taken, so that,
as C is to E, so is G to H,
and,   as D is to F, so is H to K.   [VIII. 4]
And let D by multiplying E make L.

Now, since D by multiplying C has made A, and by multiplying E has made L,

therefore, as C is to E, so is A to L.   [VII. 17]

But, as C is to E, so is G to H;

therefore also, as G is to H, so is A to L.

Again, since E by multiplying D has made L, and further by multiplying F has made B,

therefore, as D is to F, so is L to B. [VII. 17]

But, as D is to F, so is H to K;

therefore also, as H is to K, so is L to B.

But it was also proved that,

as G is to H, so is A to L;

therefore, *ex aequali*,

as G is to K, so is A to B.   [VII. 14]

But G has to K the ratio compounded of the ratios of the sides;
therefore A also has to B the ratio compounded of the ratios of the sides.

Q. E. D.

PROPOSITION 6

If there be as many numbers as we please in continued proportion, and the first do not measure the second, neither will any other measure any other.

Let there be as many numbers as we please, A, B, C, D, E, in continued proportion, and let A not measure B;

I say that neither will any other measure any other.

Now it is manifest that A, B, C, D, E do not measure one another in order; for A does not even measure B.

I say, then, that neither will any other measure any other.

For, if possible, let A measure C.

And, however many A, B, C are, let as many numbers F, G, H, the least of those which have the same ratio with A, B, C, be taken.   [VII. 33]

Now, since F, G, H are in the same ratio with A, B, C, and the multitude of the numbers A, B, C is equal to the multitude of the numbers F, G, H,

therefore, *ex aequali*, as A is to C, so is F to H.   [VII. 14]

And since, as A is to B, so is F to G,

while A does not measure B,

therefore neither does F measure G;   [VII. Def. 20]

therefore F is not an unit, for the unit measures any number.

Now F, H are prime to one another.   [VIII. 3]

And, as F is to H, so is A to C;

therefore neither does A measure C.

Similarly we can prove that neither will any other measure any other.

Q. E. D.

Proposition 7

If there be as many numbers as we please in continued proportion, and the first measure the last, it will measure the second also.

Let there be as many numbers as we please, A, B, C, D, in continued proportion; and let A measure D;

I say that A also measures B.

For, if A does not measure B, neither will any other of the numbers measure any other.   [VIII. 6]

But A measures D.

Therefore A also measures B.

Q. E. D.

Proposition 8

If between two numbers there fall numbers in continued proportion with them, then, however many numbers fall between them in continued proportion, so many will also fall in continued proportion between the numbers which have the same ratio with the original numbers.

Let the numbers C, D fall between the two numbers A, B in continued proportion with them, and let E be made in the same ratio to F as A is to B;

I say that, as many numbers as have fallen between A, B in continued proportion, so many will also fall between E, F in continued proportion.

For, as many as A, B, C, D are in multitude, let so many numbers G, H, K, L, the least of those which have the same ratio with A, C, D, B, be taken;   [VII. 33] therefore the extremes of them G, L are prime to one another.   [VIII. 3]

Now, since A, C, D, B are in the same ratio with G, H, K, L, and the multitude of the numbers A, C, D, B is equal to the multitude of the numbers G, H, K, L,

therefore, *ex aequali*, as A is to B, so is G to L.   [VII. 14]

But, as A is to B, so is E to F;

therefore also, as G is to L, so is E to F.

But G, L are prime,

primes are also least,   [VII. 21]

and the least numbers measure those which have the same ratio the same number of times, the greater the greater and the less the less, that is, the antecedent the antecedent and the consequent the consequent.   [VII. 20]

Therefore G measures E the same number of times as L measures F.

Next, as many times as G measures E, so many times let H, K also measure M, N respectively;

therefore G, H, K, L measure E, M, N, F the same number of times.

Therefore G, H, K, L are in the same ratio with E, M, N, F.   [VII. Def. 20]

But G, H, K, L are in the same ratio with A, C, D, B;

therefore A, C, D, B are also in the same ratio with E, M, N, F.

But A, C, D, B are in continued proportion;

therefore E, M, N, F are also in continued proportion.

Therefore, as many numbers as have fallen between A, B in continued proportion with them, so many numbers have also fallen between E, F in continued proportion.   Q. E. D.

PROPOSITION 9

If two numbers be prime to one another, and numbers fall between them in continued proportion, then, however many numbers fall between them in continued proportion, so many will also fall between each of them and an unit in continued proportion.

Let A, B be two numbers prime to one another, and let C, D fall between them in continued proportion,

and let the unit E be set out;

I say that, as many numbers as fall between A, B in continued proportion, so many will also fall between either of the numbers A, B and the unit in continued proportion.

For let two numbers F, G, the least that are in the ratio of A, C, D, B, be taken,

three numbers H, K, L with the same property,

and others more by one continually, until their multitude is equal to the multitude of A, C, D, B.   [VIII. 2]

Let them be taken, and let them be M, N, O, P.

It is now manifest that F by multiplying itself has made H and by multiplying H has made M, while G by multiplying itself has made L and by multiplying L has made P.   [VIII. 2, Por.]

And, since M, N, O, P are the least of those which have the same ratio with F, G,

and A, C, D, B are also the least of those which have the same ratio with F, G,   [VIII. 1]

while the multitude of the numbers M, N, O, P is equal to the multitude of the numbers A, C, D, B,

therefore M, N, O, P are equal to A, C, D, B respectively;

therefore M is equal to A, and P to B.

Now, since F by multiplying itself has made H,

therefore F measures H according to the units in F.

But the unit E also measures F according to the units in it;

therefore the unit E measures the number F the same number of times as F measures H.

Therefore, as the unit E is to the number F, so is F to H.   [VII. Def. 20]

Again, since F by multiplying H has made M,

therefore H measures M according to the units in F.

But the unit E also measures the number F according to the units in it; therefore the unit E measures the number F the same number of times as H measures M.

Therefore, as the unit E is to the number F, so is H to M.

But it was also proved that, as the unit E is to the number F, so is F to H; therefore also, as the unit E is to the number F, so is F to H, and H to M.

But M is equal to A;

therefore, as the unit E is to the number F, so is F to H, and H to A.

For the same reason also,

as the unit E is to the number G, so is G to L and L to B.

Therefore, as many numbers as have fallen between A, B in continued proportion, so many numbers also have fallen between each of the numbers A, B and the unit E in continued proportion.   Q. E. D.

PROPOSITION 10

If numbers fall between each of two numbers and an unit in continued proportion however many numbers fall between each of them and an unit in continued proportion, so many also will fall between the numbers themselves in continued proportion.

For let the numbers D, E and F, G respectively fall between the two numbers A, B and the unit C in continued proportion;

I say that, as many numbers as have fallen between each of the numbers A, B and the unit C in continued proportion, so many numbers will also fall between A, B in continued proportion.

For let D by multiplying F make H, and let the numbers D, F by multiplying H make K, L respectively.

Now, since, as the unit C is to the number D, so is D to E, therefore the unit C measures the number D the same number of times as D measures E.   [VII. Def. 20]

But the unit C measures the number D according to the units in D;

therefore the number D also measures E according to the units in D;

therefore D by multiplying itself has made E.

Again, since, as C is to the number D, so is E to A, therefore the unit C measures the number D the same number of times as E measures A.

But the unit C measures the number D according to the units in D;

therefore E also measures A according to the units in D;

therefore D by multiplying E has made A.

For the same reason also

F by multiplying itself has made G, and by multiplying G has made B.

And, since D by multiplying itself has made E and by multiplying F has made H,

therefore, as D is to F, so is E to H. [VII. 17]

For the same reason also,

as D is to F, so is H to G. [VII. 18]

Therefore also, as E is to H, so is H to G.

Again, since D by multiplying the numbers E, H has made A, K respectively,

therefore, as E is to H, so is A to K. [VII. 17]

But, as E is to H, so is D to F;

therefore also, as D is to F, so is A to K.

Again, since the numbers D, F by multiplying H have made K, L respectively,

therefore, as D is to F, so is K to L. [VII. 18]

But, as D is to F, so is A to K;

therefore also, as A is to K, so is K to L.

Further, since F by multiplying the numbers H, G has made L, B respectively,

therefore, as H is to G, so is L to B, [VII. 17]

But, as H is to G, so is D to F;

therefore also, as D is to F, so is L to B.

But it was also proved that,

as D is to F, so is A to K and K to L;

therefore also, as A is to K, so is K to L and L to B.

Therefore A, K, L, B are in continued proportion.

Therefore, as many numbers as fall between each of the numbers A, B and the unit C in continued proportion, so many also will fall between A, B in continued proportion.   Q. E. D.

PROPOSITION 11

Between two square numbers there is one mean proportional number, and the square has to the square the ratio duplicate of that which the side has to the side.

Let A, B be square numbers,

and let C be the side of A, and D of B;

I say that between A, B there is one mean proportional number, and A has

to B the ratio duplicate of that which C has to D.

A————

B——————————

C——   D——

E——————————

For let C by multiplying D make E.

Now, since A is a square and C is its side,

therefore C by multiplying itself has made A.

For the same reason also,

D by multiplying itself has made B.

Since, then, C by multiplying the numbers C, D has made A, E respectively,

therefore, as C is to D, so is A to E. [VII. 17]

For the same reason also,

as C is to D, so is E to B. [VII. 18]

Therefore also, as A is to E, so is E to B.

Therefore between A, B there is one mean proportional number.

I say next that A also has to B the ratio duplicate of that which C has to D.

For, since A, E, B are three numbers in proportion,

therefore A has to B the ratio duplicate of that which A has to E.   [v. Def. 9]

But, as A is to E, so is C to D.

Therefore A has to B the ratio duplicate of that which the side C has to D.

Q. E. D.

PROPOSITION 12

Between two cube numbers there are two mean proportional numbers, and the cube has to the cube the ratio triplicate of that which the side has to the side.

Let A, B be cube numbers,

and let C be the side of A, and D of B;

I say that between A, B there are two mean proportional numbers, and A has to B the ratio triplicate of that which C has to D.

For let C by multiplying itself make E, and by multiplying D let it make F; let D by multiplying itself make G, and let the numbers C, D by multiplying F make H, K respectively.

Now, since A is a cube, and C its side,

and C by multiplying itself has made E,

therefore C by multiplying itself has made E and by multiplying E has made A.

For the same reason also

D by multiplying itself has made G and by multiplying G has made B.

And, since C by multiplying the numbers C, D has made E, F respectively,

therefore, as C is to D, so is E to F.   [VII. 17]

For the same reason also,

as C is to D, so is F to G.   [VII. 18]

Again, since C by multiplying the numbers E, F has made A, H respectively,

therefore, as E is to F, so is A to H.   [VII. 17]

But, as E is to F, so is C to D.

Therefore also, as C is to D, so is A to H.

Again, since the numbers C, D by multiplying F have made H, K respectively,

therefore, as C is to D, so is H to K.   [VII. 18]

Again, since D by multiplying each of the numbers F, G has made K, B respectively,

therefore, as F is to G, so is K to B.   [VII. 17]

But, as F is to G, so is C to D;

therefore also, as C is to D, so is A to H, H to K, and K to B.

Therefore H, K are two mean proportionals between A, B.

I say next that A also has to B the ratio triplicate of that which C has to D.

For, since A, H, K, B are four numbers in proportion,

therefore A has to B the ratio triplicate of that which A has to H.   [v. Def. 10]

But, as A is to H, so is C to D;

therefore A also has to B the ratio triplicate of that which C has to D.

Q. E. D.

Proposition 13

If there be as many numbers as we please in continued proportion, and each by multiplying itself make some number, the products will be proportional; and, if the original numbers by multiplying the products make certain numbers, the latter will also be proportional.

Let there be as many numbers as we please, A, B, C, in continued proportion, so that, as A is to B, so is B to C;
let A, B, C by multiplying themselves make D, E, F, and by multiplying D, E, F let them make G, H, K;

I say that D, E, F and G, H, K are in continued proportion.

```
A———              G——————————
B———              H————————————
C———              K——————————————
D————
E—————            M—————————
F——————           N———————————
L—————            P—————————————
O——————           Q———————————————
```

For let A by multiplying B make L,
and let the numbers A, B by multiplying L make M, N respectively.
And again let B by multiplying C make O,
and let the numbers B, C by multiplying O make P, Q respectively.

Then, in manner similar to the foregoing, we can prove that
D, L, E and G, M, N, H are continuously proportional in the ratio of A to B, and further E, O, F and H, P, Q, K are continuously proportional in the ratio of B to C.

Now, as A is to B, so is B to C;
therefore D, L, E are also in the same ratio with E, O, F,
and further G, M, N, H in the same ratio with H, P, Q, K.

And the multitude of D, L, E is equal to the multitude of E, O, F and that of G, M, N, H to that of H, P, Q, K;
therefore, *ex aequali*,
as D is to E, so is E to F,
and,   as G is to H, so is H to K.   [VII. 14]

Q. E. D.

Proposition 14

If a square measure a square, the side will also measure the side; and, if the side measure the side, the square will also measure the square.

Let A, B be square numbers, let C, D be their sides, and let A measure B;
I say that C also measures D.

```
A——
B————————
—C        ——D
E———
```

For let C by multiplying D make E;
therefore A, E, B are continuously proportional in the ratio of C to D.   [VIII. 11]
And, since A, E, B are continuously proportional, and A measures B,
therefore A also measures E.   [VIII. 7]

And, as A is to E, so is C to D;

therefore also C measures D.   [VII. Def. 20]

Again, let C measure D;

I say that A also measures B.

For, with the same construction, we can in a similar manner prove that A, E, B are continuously proportional in the ratio of C to D.

And since, as C is to D, so is A to E,

and C measures D,

therefore A also measures E.   [VII. Def. 20]

And A, E, B are continuously proportional;

therefore A also measures B.

Therefore etc.   Q. E. D.

PROPOSITION 15

If a cube number measure a cube number, the side will also measure the side; and, if the side measure the side, the cube will also measure the cube.

For let the cube number A measure the cube B,

and let C be the side of A and D of B;

I say that C measures D.

For let C by multiplying itself make E,

and let D by multiplying itself make G;

further, let C by multiplying D make F,

and let C, D by multiplying F make H, K respectively.

Now it is manifest that E, F, G and A, H, K, B are continuously proportional in the ratio of C to D.   [VIII. 11, 12]

And, since A, H, K, B are continuously proportional,

and A measures B,

therefore it also measures H.

[VIII. 7]

And, as A is to H, so is C to D;

therefore C also measures D.   [VII. Def. 20]

Next, let C measure D;

I say that A will also measure B.

For, with the same construction, we can prove in a similar manner that A, H, K, B are continuously proportional in the ratio of C to D.

And, since C measures D,

and, as C is to D, so is A to H,

therefore A also measures H,   [VII. Def. 20]

so that A measures B also.   Q. E. D.

PROPOSITION 16

If a square number do not measure a square number, neither will the side measure the side; and, if the side do not measure the side, neither will the square measure the square.

Let A, B be square numbers, and let C, D be their sides; and let A not measure B;

A————

B————————

C——

D———

I say that neither does C measure D.

For, if C measures D, A will also measure B. [VIII. 14]

But A does not measure B;

therefore neither will C measure D.

Again, let C not measure D;

I say that neither will A measure B.

For, if A measures B, C will also measure D.   [VIII. 14]

But C does not measure D;

therefore neither will A measure B.   Q. E. D.

PROPOSITION 17

If a cube number do not measure a cube number, neither will the side measure the side; and, if the side do not measure the side, neither will the cube measure the cube.

For let the cube number A not measure the cube number B,

and let C be the side of A, and D of B;

A————

B————————

C——

D——

I say that C will not measure D.

For if C measures D, A will also measure B.   [VIII. 15]

But A does not measure B;

therefore neither does C measure D.

Again, let C not measure D;

I say that neither will A measure B.

For, if A measures B, C will also measure D.   [VIII. 15]

But C does not measure D;

therefore neither will A measure B.   Q. E. D.

PROPOSITION 18

Between two similar plane numbers there is one mean proportional number; and the plane number has to the plane number the ratio duplicate of that which the corresponding side has to the corresponding side.

Let A, B be two similar plane numbers, and let the numbers C, D be the sides of A, and E, F of B.

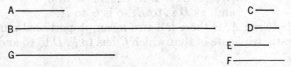

Now, since similar plane numbers are those which have their sides proportional,   [VII. Def. 21]

therefore, as C is to D, so is E to F.

I say then that between A, B there is one mean proportional number, and A has to B the ratio duplicate of that which C has to E, or D to F, that is, of that which the corresponding side has to the corresponding side.

Now since, as C is to D, so is E to F,

therefore, alternately, as C is to E, so is D to F.   [VII. 13]

And, since A is plane, and C, D are its sides,

therefore D by multiplying C has made A.

For the same reason also

E by multiplying F has made B.

Now let D by multiplying E make G.

Then, since D by multiplying C has made A, and by multiplying E has made G,

therefore, as C is to E, so is A to G.   [VII. 17]

But, as C is to E, so is D to F;

therefore also, as D is to F, so is A to G.

Again, since E by multiplying D has made G, and by multiplying F has made B,

therefore, as D is to F, so is G to B.   [VII. 17]

But it was also proved that,

as D is to F, so is A to G;

therefore also, as A is to G, so is G to B.

Therefore A, G, B are in continued proportion.

Therefore between A, B there is one mean proportional number.

I say next that A also has to B the ratio duplicate of that which the corresponding side has to the corresponding side, that is, of that which C has to E or D to F.

For, since A, G, B are in continued proportion,

A has to B the ratio duplicate of that which it has to G.   [V. Def. 9]

And, as A is to G, so is C to E, and so is D to F.

Therefore A also has to B the ratio duplicate of that which C has to E or D to F.   Q. E. D.

PROPOSITION 19

Between two similar solid numbers there fall two mean proportional numbers; and the solid number has to the similar solid number the ratio triplicate of that which the corresponding side has to the corresponding side.

Let A, B be two similar solid numbers, and let C, D, E be the sides of A, and F, G, H of B.

Now, since similar solid numbers are those which have their sides proportional,   [VII. Def. 21]

therefore, as C is to D, so is F to G,

and, as D is to E, so is G to H.

I say that between A, B there fall two mean proportional numbers, and A has to B the ratio triplicate of that which C has to F, D to G, and also E to H.

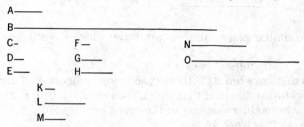

For let C by multiplying D make K, and let F by multiplying G make L.

Now, since C, D are in the same ratio with F, G,

and K is the product of C, D, and L the product of F, G, K, L are similar plane numbers;   [VII. Def. 21] therefore between K, L there is one mean proportional number.   [VIII. 18]

Let it be M.

Therefore M is the product of D, F, as was proved in the theorem preceding this.   [VIII. 18]

Now, since D by multiplying C has made K, and by multiplying F has made M,

therefore, as C is to F, so is K to M.   [VII. 17]

But, as K is to M, so is M to L.

Therefore K, M, L are continuously proportional in the ratio of C to F.

And since, as C is to D, so is F to G,

alternately therefore, as C is to F, so is D to G.   [VII. 13]

For the same reason also,

as D is to G, so is E to H.

Therefore K, M, L are continuously proportional in the ratio of C to F, in the ratio of D to G, and also in the ratio of E to H.

Next, let E, H by multiplying M make N, O respectively.

Now, since A is a solid number, and C, D, E are its sides,

therefore E by multiplying the product of C, D has made A.

But the product of C, D is K;

therefore E by multiplying K has made A.

For the same reason also

H by multiplying L has made B.

Now, since E by multiplying K has made A, and further also by multiplying M has made N,

therefore, as K is to M, so is A to N.   [VII. 17]

But, as K is to M, so is C to F, D to G, and also E to H;

therefore also, as C is to F, D to G, and E to H, so is A to N.

Again, since E, H by multiplying M have made N, O respectively,

therefore, as E is to H, so is N to O.   [VII. 18]

But, as E is to H, so is C to F and D to G;

therefore also, as C is to F, D to G, and E to H, so is A to N and N to O.

Again, since H by multiplying M has made O, and further also by multiplying L has made B,

therefore, as M is to L, so is O to B.   [VII. 17]

But, as M is to L, so is C to F, D to G, and E to H.

Therefore also, as C is to F, D to G, and E to H, so not only is O to B, but also A to N and N to O.

Therefore A, N, O, B are continuously proportional in the aforesaid ratios of the sides.

I say that A also has to B the ratio triplicate of that which the corresponding side has to the corresponding side, that is, of the ratio which the number C has to F, or D to G, and also E to H.

For, since A, N, O, B are four numbers in continued proportion,

therefore A has to B the ratio triplicate of that which A has to N.   [V. Def. 10]

But, as A is to N, so it was proved that C is to F, D to G, and also E to H.

Therefore A also has to B the ratio triplicate of that which the corresponding side has to the corresponding side, that is, of the ratio which the number C has to F, D to G, and also E to H.   Q. E. D.

PROPOSITION 20

If one mean proportional number fall between two numbers, the numbers will be similar plane numbers.

For let one mean proportional number C fall between the two numbers A, B;

I say that A, B are similar plane numbers.

Let D, E, the least numbers of those which have the same ratio with A, C, be taken;   [VII. 33]

therefore D measures A the same number of times that E measures C. [VII. 20]

Now, as many times as D measures A, so many units let there be in F;

therefore F by multiplying D has made A,

so that A is plane, and D, F are its sides.

Again, since D, E are the least of the numbers which have the same ratio with C, B,

therefore D measures C the same number of times that E measures B. [VII. 20]

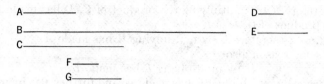

As many times, then, as E measures B, so many units let there be in G;

therefore E measures B according to the units in G;

therefore G by multiplying E has made B.

Therefore B is plane, and E, G are its sides.

Therefore A, B are plane numbers.

I say next that they are also similar.

For, since F by multiplying D has made A, and by multiplying E has made C,

therefore, as D is to E, so is A to C, that is, C to B.   [VII. 17]

Again, since E by multiplying F, G has made C, B respectively,

therefore, as F is to G, so is C to B.   [VII. 17]

But, as C is to B, so is D to E;

therefore also, as D is to E, so is F to G.

And alternately, as D is to F, so is E to G.   [VII. 13]

Therefore A, B are similar plane numbers; for their sides are proportional.

Q. E. D.

PROPOSITION 21

If two mean proportional numbers fall between two numbers, the numbers are similar solid numbers.

For let two mean proportional numbers C, D fall between the two numbers A, B;

I say that A, B are similar solid numbers.

For let three numbers E, F, G, the least of those which have the same ratio with A, C, D, be taken;   [VII. 33 or VIII. 2] therefore the extremes of them E, G are prime to one another.   [VIII. 3]

Now, since one mean proportional number F has fallen between E, G,
therefore E, G are similar plane numbers.   [VIII. 20]

Let, then, H, K be the sides of E, and L, M of G.

Therefore it is manifest from the theorem before this that E, F, G are continuously proportional in the ratio of H to L and that of K to M.

```
A———                                    E —
B——————————————————————                 F —
C————                                    G——
D——————————                              H–
       N—                                K —
       O——                               L —
                                         M——
```

Now, since E, F, G are the least of the numbers which have the same ratio with A, C, D,
and the multitude of the numbers E, F, G is equal to the multitude of the numbers A, C, D,
therefore, *ex aequali*, as E is to G, so is A to D.   [VII. 14]

But E, G are prime,
primes are also least,   [VII. 21]
and the least measure those which have the same ratio with them the same number of times, the greater the greater and the less the less, that is, the antecedent the antecedent and the consequent the consequent;   [VII. 20]
therefore E measures A the same number of times that G measures D.

Now, as many times as E measures A, so many units let there be in N.

Therefore N by multiplying E has made A.

But E is the product of H, K;
therefore N by multiplying the product of H, K has made A.

Therefore A is solid, and H, K, N are its sides.

Again, since E, F, G are the least of the numbers which have the same ratio as C, D, B,
therefore E measures C the same number of times that G measures B.

Now, as many times as E measures C, so many units let there be in O.

Therefore G measures B according to the units in O;
therefore O by multiplying G has made B.

But G is the product of L, M;
therefore O by multiplying the product of L, M has made B.

Therefore B is solid, and L, M, O are its sides;
therefore A, B are solid.

I say that they are also similar.

For, since N, O by multiplying E have made A, C,
therefore, as N is to O, so is A to C, that is, E to F.   [VII. 18]

But, as E is to F, so is H to L and K to M;
therefore also, as H is to L, so is K to M and N to O.

And H, K, N are the sides of A, and O, L, M the sides of B.

Therefore A, B are similar solid numbers.   Q. E. D.

PROPOSITION 22

If three numbers be in continued proportion, and the first be square, the third will also be square.

Let A, B, C be three numbers in continued proportion, and let A the first be square;

I say that C the third is also square.

For, since between A, C there is one mean proportional number, B,

therefore A, C are similar plane numbers. [VIII. 20]

But A is square;

therefore C is also square. Q. E. D.

PROPOSITION 23

If four numbers be in continued proportion, and the first be cube, the fourth will also be cube.

Let A, B, C, D be four numbers in continued proportion, and let A be cube;

I say that D is also cube.

For, since between A, D there are two mean proportional numbers B, C,

therefore A, D are similar solid numbers. [VIII. 21]

But A is cube;

therefore D is also cube. Q. E. D.

PROPOSITION 24

If two numbers have to one another the ratio which a square number has to a square number, and the first be square, the second will also be square.

For let the two numbers A, B have to one another the ratio which the square number C has to the square number D, and let A be square;

I say that B is also square.

For, since C, D are square,

C, D are similar plane numbers.

Therefore one mean proportional number falls between C, D. [VIII. 18]

And, as C is to D, so is A to B;

therefore one mean proportional number falls between A, B also. [VIII. 8]

And A is square;

therefore B is also square. [VIII. 22]

Q. E. D.

PROPOSITION 25

If two numbers have to one another the ratio which a cube number has to a cube number, and the first be cube, the second will also be cube.

For let the two numbers A, B have to one another the ratio which the cube number C has to the cube number D, and let A be cube;

I say that B is also cube.

For, since C, D are cube,

C, D are similar solid numbers.

Therefore two mean proportional numbers fall between C, D.   [VIII. 19]

And, as many numbers as fall between C, D in continued proportion, so many will also fall between those which have the same ratio with them;   [VIII. 8] so that two mean proportional numbers fall between A, B also.

A————
B——————————
C—————
D————————————

E————————
F————————

Let E, F so fall.

Since, then, the four numbers A, E, F, B are in continued proportion,

and A is cube,

therefore B is also cube.   [VIII. 23]

Q. E. D.

PROPOSITION 26

Similar plane numbers have to one another the ratio which a square number has to a square number.

Let A, B be similar plane numbers;

I say that A has to B the ratio which a square number has to a square number.

A————   B————————————————————————

C——————————————

D————   E————————   F——————————————

For, since A, B are similar plane numbers,

therefore one mean proportional number falls between A, B. [VIII. 18]

Let it so fall, and let it be C;

and let D, E, F, the least numbers of those which have the same ratio with A, C, B, be taken;   [VII. 33 or VIII. 2]

therefore the extremes of them D, F are square.   [VIII. 2, Por.]

And since, as D is to F, so is A to B,

and D, F are square,

therefore A has to B the ratio which a square number has to a square number.

Q. E. D.

PROPOSITION 27

Similar solid numbers have to one another the ratio which a cube number has to a cube number.

Let A, B be similar solid numbers;

I say that A has to B the ratio which a cube number has to a cube number.

A————   C——————————
B——————————————————————   D——————————————

E————   F————   G——————————   H——————————————.

For, since A, B are similar solid numbers,

therefore two mean proportional numbers fall between A, B.   [VIII. 19]

Let C, D so fall,
and let E, F, G, H, the least numbers of those which have the same ratio with
A, C, D, B, and equal with them in multitude, be taken;   [VII. 33 or VIII. 2]
therefore the extremes of them E, H are cube.   [VIII. 2, Por.]
And, as E is to H, so is A to B;
therefore A also has to B the ratio which a cube number has to a cube number.

Q. E. D.

BOOK NINE

PROPOSITION 1

If two similar plane numbers by multiplying one another make some number, the product will be square.

Let A, B be two similar plane numbers, and let A by multiplying B make C; I say that C is square.

For let A by multiplying itself make D.

Therefore D is square.

Since then A by multiplying itself has made D, and by multiplying B has made C,

therefore, as A is to B, so is D to C.   [VII. 17]

And, since A, B are similar plane numbers,

therefore one mean proportional number falls between A, B.   [VIII. 18]

But, if numbers fall between two numbers in continued proportion, as many as fall between them, so many also fall between those which have the same ratio;   [VIII. 8]

so that one mean proportional number falls between D, C also.

And D is square;

therefore C is also square.   [VIII. 22]

Q. E. D.

PROPOSITION 2

If two numbers by multiplying one another make a square number, they are similar plane numbers.

Let A, B be two numbers, and let A by multiplying B make the square number C;

I say that A, B are similar plane numbers.

For let A by multiplying itself make D;

therefore D is square.

Now, since A by multiplying itself has made D, and by multiplying B has made C,

therefore, as A is to B, so is D to C.   [VII. 17]

And, since D is square, and C is so also,

therefore D, C are similar plane numbers.

Therefore one mean proportional number falls between D, C.   [VIII. 18]

And, as D is to C, so is A to B;

therefore one mean proportional number falls between A, B also.   [VIII. 8]

But, if one mean proportional number fall between two numbers, they are similar plane numbers;   [VIII. 20]

therefore A, B are similar plane numbers.   Q. E. D.

171

PROPOSITION 3

If a cube number by multiplying itself make some number, the product will be cube.

For let the cube number A by multiplying itself make B;

I say that B is cube.

For let C, the side of A, be taken, and let C by multiplying itself make D.

It is then manifest that C by multiplying D has made A.

Now, since C by multiplying itself has made D,

therefore C measures D according to the units in itself.

But further the unit also measures C according to the units in it;

therefore, as the unit is to C, so is C to D.   [VII. Def. 20]

Again, since C by multiplying D has made A,

therefore D measures A according to the units in C.

But the unit also measures C according to the units in it;

therefore, as the unit is to C, so is D to A.

But, as the unit is to C, so is C to D;

therefore also, as the unit is to C, so is C to D, and D to A.

Therefore between the unit and the number A two mean proportional numbers C, D have fallen in continued proportion.

Again, since A by multiplying itself has made B,

therefore A measures B according to the units in itself.

But the unit also measures A according to the units in it;

therefore, as the unit is to A, so is A to B.   [VII. Def. 20]

But between the unit and A two mean proportional numbers have fallen;

therefore two mean proportional numbers will also fall between A, B.   [VIII. 8]

But, if two mean proportional numbers fall between two numbers, and the first be cube, the second will also be cube.   [VIII. 23]

And A is cube;

therefore B is also cube.   Q. E. D.

PROPOSITION 4

If a cube number by multiplying a cube number make some number, the product will be cube.

For let the cube number A by multiplying the cube number B make C;

I say that C is cube.

For let A by multiplying itself make D;

therefore D is cube.   [IX. 3]

And, since A by multiplying itself has made D, and by multiplying B has made C

therefore, as A is to B, so is D to C.   [VII. 17]

And, since A, B are cube numbers,

A, B are similar solid numbers.

Therefore two mean proportional numbers fall between A, B;   [VIII. 19]

so that two mean proportional numbers will fall between D, C also.   [VIII. 8]

And D is cube;

therefore C is also cube   [VIII. 23]

Q. E. D.

PROPOSITION 5

If a cube number by multiplying any number make a cube number, the multiplied number will also be cube.

For let the cube number A by multiplying any number B make the cube number C;

I say that B is cube.

A——————

B——————

C————————————————

D——————————

For let A by multiplying itself make D; therefore D is cube.   [IX. 3]

Now, since A by multiplying itself has made D, and by multiplying B has made C,

therefore, as A is to B, so is D to C.   [VII. 17]

And since D, C are cube,

they are similar solid numbers.

Therefore two mean proportional numbers fall between D, C.   [VIII. 19]

And, as D is to C, so is A to B;

therefore two mean proportional numbers fall between A, B also.   [VIII. 8]

And A is cube;

therefore B is also cube.   [VIII. 23]

PROPOSITION 6

If a number by multiplying itself make a cube number, it will itself also be cube.

For let the number A by multiplying itself make the cube number B;

I say that A is also cube.

A——————

B——————

C——————

For let A by multiplying B make C.

Since, then, A by multiplying itself has made B, and by multiplying B has made C,

therefore C is cube.

And, since A by multiplying itself has made B,

therefore A measures B according to the units in itself.

But the unit also measures A according to the units in it.

Therefore, as the unit is to A, so is A to B.   [VII. Def. 20]

And, since A by multiplying B has made C,

therefore B measures C according to the units in A.

But the unit also measures A according to the units in it.

Therefore, as the unit is to A, so is B to C.   [VII. Def. 20]

But, as the unit is to A, so is A to B;

therefore also, as A is to B, so is B to C.

And, since B, C are cube,

they are similar solid numbers.

Therefore there are two mean proportional numbers between B, C. [VIII. 19]

And, as B is to C, so is A to B.

Therefore there are two mean proportional numbers between A, B also.

[VIII. 8]

And B is cube;

therefore A is also cube.   [cf. VIII. 23]

Q. E. D.

PROPOSITION 7

If a composite number by multiplying any number make some number, the product will be solid.

For, let the composite number A by multiplying any number B make C;
  I say that C is solid.

For, since A is composite, it will be measured by some number.

A ─────────────────
B ───────
C ──────────────────────
D ─────   E ──────────────

[VII. Def. 13]

Let it be measured by D;
and, as many times as D measures A, so many units let there be in E.

Since, then, D measures A according to the units in E,
  therefore E by multiplying D has made A.   [VII. Def. 15]
And, since A by multiplying B has made C,
  and A is the product of D, E,
  therefore the product of D, E by multiplying B has made C.
Therefore C is solid, and D, E, B are its sides.   Q. E. D.

PROPOSITION 8

If as many numbers as we please beginning from an unit be in continued proportion, the third from the unit will be square, as will also those which successively leave out one; the fourth will be cube, as will also all those which leave out two; and the seventh will be at once cube and square, as will also those which leave out five.

Let there be as many numbers as we please, A, B, C, D, E, F, beginning from an unit and in continued proportion;

I say that B, the third from the unit, is square, as are also all those which leave out one; C, the fourth, is cube, as are also all those which leave out two; and F, the seventh, is at once cube and square, as are also all those which leave out five.

A ──────
B ──────
C ───────
D ─────────
E ──────────
F ────────────

For since, as the unit is to A, so is A to B,
therefore the unit measures the number A the same number of times that A measures B.   [VII. Def. 20]
But the unit measures the number A according to the units in it;
  therefore A also measures B according to the units in A.
Therefore A by multiplying itself has made B;
  therefore B is square.
And, since B, C, D are in continued proportion, and B is square,
  therefore D is also square.   [VIII. 22]
For the same reason
  F is also square.
Similarly we can prove that all those which leave out one are square.

I say next that C, the fourth from the unit, is cube, as are also all those which leave out two.

For since, as the unit is to A, so is B to C,
therefore the unit measures the number A the same number of times that B measures C.
But the unit measures the number A according to the units in A;

therefore B also measures C according to the units in A.

Therefore A by multiplying B has made C.

Since then A by multiplying itself has made B, and by multiplying B has made C,

therefore C is cube.

And, since C, D, E, F are in continued proportion, and C is cube,

therefore F is also cube.   [VIII. 23]

But it was also proved square;

therefore the seventh from the unit is both cube and square.

Similarly we can prove that all the numbers which leave out five are also both cube and square.   Q. E. D.

PROPOSITION 9

If as many numbers as we please beginning from an unit be in continued proportion, and the number after the unit be square, all the rest will also be square. And, if the number after the unit be cube, all the rest will also be cube.

Let there be as many numbers as we please, A, B, C, D, E, F, beginning from an unit and in continued proportion, and let A, the number after the unit, be square;

I say that all the rest will also be square.

Now it has been proved that B, the third from the unit, is square, as are also all those which leave out one;   [IX. 8]

I say that all the rest are also square.

For, since A, B, C are in continued proportion,

and A is square,

therefore C is also square.   [VIII. 22]

Again, since B, C, D are in continued proportion,

and B is square,

D is also square.   [VIII. 22]

Similarly we can prove that all the rest are also square.

Next, let A be cube;

I say that all the rest are also cube.

Now it has been proved that C, the fourth from the unit, is cube, as also are all those which leave out two;   [IX. 8]

I say that all the rest are also cube.

For, since, as the unit is to A, so is A to B,

therefore the unit measures A the same number of times as A measures B.

But the unit measures A according to the units in it;

therefore A also measures B according to the units in itself;

therefore A by multiplying itself has made B.

And A is cube.

But, if a cube number by multiplying itself make some number, the product is cube.   [IX. 3]

Therefore B is also cube.

And, since the four numbers A, B, C, D are in continued proportion,

and A is cube,

D also is cube.   [VIII. 23]

For the same reason

        E is also cube, and similarly all the rest are cube.   Q. E. D.

PROPOSITION 10

If as many numbers as we please beginning from an unit be in continued propor-
tion, and the number after the unit be not square, neither will any other be square
except the third from the unit and all those which leave out one. And, if the number
after the unit be not cube, neither will any other be cube except the fourth from the
unit and all those which leave out two.

Let there be as many numbers as we please, A, B, C, D, E, F, beginning from
an unit and in continued proportion,

        and let A, the number after the unit, not be square;

I say that neither will any other be square except the third from the unit
<and those which leave out one>.

    For, if possible, let C be square.

    But B is also square;   [IX. 8]
[therefore B, C have to one another the ratio
which a square number has to a square number].

    And, as B is to C, so is A to B;
therefore A, B have to one another the ratio
which a square number has to a square number;
[so that A, B are similar plane numbers].   [VIII. 26, converse]

    And B is square;

                  therefore A is also square:

              which is contrary to the hypothesis.

Therefore C is not square.

Similarly we can prove that neither is any other of the numbers square except the third from the unit and those which leave out one.

Next, let A not be cube.

I say that neither will any other be cube except the fourth from the unit and
those which leave out two.

    For, if possible, let D be cube.

    Now C is also cube; for it is fourth from the unit.   [IX. 8]

    And, as C is to D, so is B to C;

        therefore B also has to C the ratio which a cube has to a cube.

    And C is cube;

                therefore B is also cube.   [VIII. 25]

And since, as the unit is to A, so is A to B,

        and the unit measures A according to the units in it,

      therefore A also measures B according to the units in itself;

    therefore A by multiplying itself has made the cube number B.

    But, if a number by multiplying itself make a cube number, it is also itself
cube.   [IX. 6]

Therefore A is also cube:

              which is contrary to the hypothesis.

Therefore D is not cube.

Similarly we can prove that neither is any other of the numbers cube except
the fourth from the unit and those which leave out two.   Q. E. D.

PROPOSITION 11

If as many numbers as we please beginning from an unit be in continued proportion, the less measures the greater according to some one of the numbers which have place among the proportional numbers.

Let there be as many numbers as we please, B, C, D, E, beginning from the unit A and in continued proportion;

A——

B——

C———

D————

E—————

I say that B, the least of the numbers B, C, D, E, measures E according to some one of the numbers C, D.

For since, as the unit A is to B, so is D to E, therefore the unit A measures the number B the same number of times as D measures E;

therefore, alternately, the unit A measures D the same number of times as B measures E.   [VII. 15]

But the unit A measures D according to the units in it;

therefore B also measures E according to the units in D;

so that B the less measures E the greater according to some number of those which have place among the proportional numbers.—

PORISM. And it is manifest that, whatever place the measuring number has, reckoned from the unit, the same place also has the number according to which it measures, reckoned from the number measured, in the direction of the number before it.—   Q. E. D.

PROPOSITION 12

If as many numbers as we please beginning from an unit be in continued proportion, by however many prime numbers the last is measured, the next to the unit will also be measured by the same.

Let there be as many numbers as we please, A, B, C, D, beginning from an unit, and in continued proportion;

I say that, by however many prime numbers D is measured, A will also be measured by the same.

For let D be measured by any prime number E;

A——   F————————

B——   G—————

C———   H————

D————

E—

I say that E measures A.

For suppose it does not;

now E is prime, and any prime number is prime to any which it does not measure;   [VII. 29]

therefore E, A are prime to one another.

And, since E measures D, let it measure it according to F,

therefore E by multiplying F has made D.

Again, since A measures D according to the units in C,   [IX. 11 and Por.]

therefore A by multiplying C has made D.

But, further, E has also by multiplying F made D;

therefore the product of A, C is equal to the product of E, F.

Therefore, as A is to E, so is F to C.   [VII. 19]

But A, E are prime,

primes are also least,   [VII. 21]

and the least measure those which have the same ratio the same number of times, the antecedent the antecedent and the consequent the consequent;

[VII. 20]

therefore E measures C.

Let it measure it according to G;

therefore E by multiplying G has made C.

But, further, by the theorem before this,

A has also by multiplying B made C.   [IX. 11 and Por]

Therefore the product of A, B is equal to the product of E, G.

Therefore, as A is to E, so is G to B.   [VII. 19]

But A, E are prime,

primes are also least,   [VII. 21]

and the least numbers measure those which have the same ratio with them the same number of times, the antecedent the antecedent and the consequent the consequent: [VII. 20]

therefore E measures B.

Let it measure it according to H;

therefore E by multiplying H has made B.

But, further, A has also by multiplying itself made B;   [IX. 8]

therefore the product of E, H is equal to the square on A.

Therefore, as E is to A, so is A to H.   [VII. 19]

But A, E are prime,

primes are also least,   [VII. 21]

and the least measure those which have the same ratio the same number of times, the antecedent the antecedent and the consequent the consequent;   [VII. 20]

therefore E measures A, as antecedent antecedent.

But, again, it also does not measure it:

which is impossible.

Therefore E, A are not prime to one another.

Therefore they are composite to one another.

But numbers composite to one another are measured by some number.   [VII. Def. 14]

And, since E is by hypothesis prime,

and the prime is not measured by any number other than itself,

therefore E measures A, E,

so that E measures A.

[But it also measures D;

therefore E measures A, D.]

Similarly we can prove that, by however many prime numbers D is measured, A will also be measured by the same.   Q. E. D.

PROPOSITION 13

If as many numbers as we please beginning from an unit be in continued proportion, and the number after the unit be prime, the greatest will not be measured by any except those which have a place among the proportional numbers.

Let there be as many numbers as we please, A, B, C, D, beginning from an unit and in continued proportion, and let A, the number after the unit, be prime;

I say that D, the greatest of them, will not be measured by any other number except A, B, C.

For, if possible, let it be measured by E, and let E not be the same with any of the numbers A, B, C.

It is then manifest that E is not prime.

For, if E is prime and measures D,

it will also measure A [IX. 12], which is prime, though it is not the same with it:
which is impossible.

A————————   E——

B————————   F————————

C————————————   G——

D————————————————   H————

Therefore E is not prime.

Therefore it is composite.

But any composite number is measured by some prime number;   [VII. 31]

therefore E is measured by some prime number.

I say next that it will not be measured by any other prime except A.

For, if E is measured by another,

and E measures D,

that other will also measure D;

so that it will also measure A [IX. 12], which is prime, though it is not the same with it:

which is impossible.

Therefore A measures E.

And, since E measures D, let it measure it according to F.

I say that F is not the same with any of the numbers A, B, C.

For, if F is the same with one of the numbers A, B, C,

and measures D according to E,

therefore one of the numbers A, B, C also measures D according to E.

But one of the numbers A, B, C measures D according to some one of the numbers A, B, C;   [IX. 11]

therefore E is also the same with one of the numbers A, B, C:

which is contrary to the hypothesis.

Therefore F is not the same as any one of the numbers A, B, C.

Similarly we can prove that F is measured by A, by proving again that F is not prime.

For, if it is, and measures D,

it will also measure A [IX. 12], which is prime, though it is not the same with it:

which is impossible;

therefore F is not prime.

Therefore it is composite.

But any composite number is measured by some prime number;   [VII. 31]

therefore F is measured by some prime number.

I say next that it will not be measured by any other prime except A.

For, if any other prime number measures F,

and F measures D,

that other will also measure D;

so that it will also measure A [IX. 12], which is prime, though it is not the same with it:

which is impossible.

Therefore A measures F.

And, since E measures D according to F,

therefore E by multiplying F has made D.

But, further, A has also by multiplying C made D;   [IX. 11]

therefore the product of A, C is equal to the product of E, F.

Therefore, proportionally, as A is to E, so is F to C.   [VII. 19]
But A measures E;

therefore F also measures C.

Let it measure it according to G.

Similarly, then, we can prove that G is not the same with any of the numbers A, B, and that it is measured by A.

And, since F measures C according to G

therefore F by multiplying G has made C.

But, further, A has also by multiplying B made C;   [IX. 11]

therefore the product of A, B is equal to the product of F, G.

Therefore, proportionally, as A is to F, so is G to B.   [VII. 19]
But A measures F;

therefore G also measures B.

Let it measure it according to H.

Similarly then we can prove that H is not the same with A.

And, since G measures B according to H,

therefore G by multiplying H has made B.

But, further, A has also by multiplying itself made B;   [IX. 8]

therefore the product of H, G is equal to the square on A.

Therefore, as H is to A, so is A to G.   [VII. 19]
But A measures G;

therefore H also measures A, which is prime, though it is not the same with it:

which is absurd.

Therefore D the greatest will not be measured by any other number except A, B, C.   Q. E. D.

PROPOSITION 14

If a number be the least that is measured by prime numbers, it will not be measured by any other prime number except those originally measuring it.

For let the number A be the least that is measured by the prime numbers B, C, D;

I say that A will not be measured by any other prime number except B, C, D.

For, if possible, let it be measured by the prime number E, and let E not be the same with any one of the numbers B, C, D.

Now, since E measures A, let it measure it according to F;

therefore E by multiplying F has made A.

And A is measured by the prime numbers B, C, D.

But, if two numbers by multiplying one another make some number, and any prime number measure the product, it will also measure one of the original numbers;   [VII. 30]

therefore B, C, D will measure one of the numbers E, F.

Now they will not measure E;

for E is prime and not the same with any one of the numbers B, C, D.

Therefore they will measure F, which is less than A:

which is impossible, for A is by hypothesis the least number measured by B, C, D.

Therefore no prime number will measure A except B, C, D.   Q. E. D.

PROPOSITION 15

If three numbers in continued proportion be the least of those which have the same ratio with them, any two whatever added together will be prime to the remaining number.

Let A, B, C, three numbers in continued proportion, be the least of those which have the same ratio with them;

I say that any two of the numbers A, B, C whatever added together are prime to the remaining number, namely A, B to C; B, C to A; and further, A, C to B.

For let two numbers DE, EF, the least of those which have the same ratio with A, B, C, be taken.   [VIII. 2]

It is then manifest that DE by multiplying itself has made A, and by multiplying EF has made B, and, further, EF by multiplying itself has made C.

[VIII. 2]

Now, since DE, EF are least,

they are prime to one another.   [VII. 22]

But, if two numbers be prime to one another,

their sum is also prime to each;   [VII. 28]

therefore DF is also prime to each of the numbers DE, EF.

But, further, DE is also prime to EF;

therefore DF, DE are prime to EF.

But, if two numbers be prime to any number,

their product is also prime to the other;   [VII. 24]

so that the product of FD, DE is prime to EF;

hence the product of FD, DE is also prime to the square on EF.   [VII. 25]

But the product of FD, DE is the square on DE together with the product of DE, EF;   [II. 3]

therefore the square on DE together with the product of DE, EF is prime to the square on EF.

And the square on DE is A,

the product of DE, EF is B,

and the square on EF is C;

therefore A, B added together are prime to C.

Similarly we can prove that B, C added together are prime to A.

I say next that A, C added together are also prime to B.

For, since DF is prime to each of the numbers DE, EF,

the square on DF is also prime to the product of DE, EF.   [VII. 24, 25]

But the squares on DE, EF together with twice the product of DE, EF are equal to the square on DF;   [II. 4]

therefore the squares on DE, EF together with twice the product of DE, EF are prime to the product of DE, EF.

Separando, the squares on DE, EF together with once the product of DE, EF are prime to the product of DE, EF.

Therefore, *separando* again, the squares on DE, EF are prime to the product of DE, EF.

And the square on DE is A,

the product of DE, EF is B,

and the square on EF is C.

Therefore A, C added together are prime to B.   Q. E. D.

PROPOSITION 16

If two numbers be prime to one another, the second will not be to any other number as the first is to the second.

For let the two numbers A, B be prime to one another;

I say that B is not to any other number as A is to B.

For, if possible, as A is to B, so let B be to C.

Now A, B are prime,

primes are also least,   [VII. 21]

and the least numbers measure those which have the same ratio the same number of times, the antecedent the antecedent and the consequent the consequent;   [VII. 20]

therefore A measures B as antecedent antecedent.

But it also measures itself;

therefore A measures A, B which are prime to one another:

which is absurd.

Therefore B will not be to C, as A is to B.   Q. E. D.

PROPOSITION 17

If there be as many numbers as we please in continued proportion, and the extremes of them be prime to one another, the last will not be to any other number as the first to the second.

For let there be as many numbers as we please, A, B, C, D, in continued proportion,

and let the extremes of them, A, D, be prime to one another;

I say that D is not to any other number as A is to B.

For, if possible, as A is to B, so let D be to E;

therefore, alternately, as A is to D, so is B to E.   [VII. 13]

But A, D are prime,

primes are also least,   [VII. 21]

and the least numbers measure those which have the same ratio the same number of times, the antecedent the antecedent and the consequent the consequent.   [VII. 20]

Therefore A measures B.

And, as A is to B, so is B to C.

Therefore B also measures C;

so that A also measures C.

And since, as B is to C, so is C to D,

and B measures C,

therefore C also measures D.

But A measured C;

so that A also measures D.

But it also measures itself;

therefore A measures A, D which are prime to one another:

which is impossible.

Therefore D will not be to any other number as A is to B.   Q. E. D.

PROPOSITION 18

Given two numbers, to investigate whether it is possible to find a third proportional to them.

Let A, B be the given two numbers, and let it be required to investigate whether it is possible to find a third proportional to them.

Now A, B are either prime to one another or not.

And, if they are prime to one another, it has been proved that it is impossible to find a third proportional to them.   [IX. 16]

Next, let A, B not be prime to one another,

and let B by multiplying itself make C.

Then A either measures C or does not measure it.

First, let it measure it according to D;

therefore A by multiplying D has made C.

But, further, B has also by multiplying itself made C;

therefore the product of A, D is equal to the square on B.

Therefore, as A is to B, so is B to D;   [VII. 19]

therefore a third proportional number D has been found to A, B.

Next, let A not measure C;

A———
B———
                    D.———
        C.————————————

I say that it is impossible to find a third proportional number to A, B.

For, if possible, let D, such third proportional, have been found.

Therefore the product of A, D is equal to the square on B.

But the square on B is C;

therefore the product of A, D is equal to C.

Hence A by multiplying D has made C;

therefore A measures C according to D.

But, by hypothesis, it also does not measure it:

which is absurd.

Therefore it is not possible to find a third proportional number to A, B when A does not measure C.   Q. E. D.

PROPOSITION 19

Given three numbers, to investigate when it is possible to find a fourth proportional to them.

A———
B———
C————

Let A, B, C be the given three numbers, and let it be required to investigate when it is possible to find a fourth proportional to them.

[The Greek text of this proposition is corrupt. However, analagously to Proposition 18 the condition that a fourth proportional to A, B, C exists is that A measure the product of B and C.]

PROPOSITION 20

Prime numbers are more than any assigned multitude of prime numbers.

Let A, B, C be the assigned prime numbers;

I say that there are more prime numbers than A, B, C.

For let the least number measured by A, B, C be taken,
and let it be DE;
let the unit DF be added to DE.

Then EF is either prime or not.

First, let it be prime;
then the prime numbers A, B, C, EF have
been found which are more than A,B,C.

Next, let EF not be prime;
therefore it is measured by some prime number.   [VII. 31]

Let it be measured by the prime number G.

I say that G is not the same with any of the numbers A, B, C.

For, if possible, let it be so.

Now A, B, C measure DE;
therefore G also will measure DE.

But it also measures EF.

Therefore G, being a number, will measure the remainder, the unit DF:
which is absurd.

Therefore G is not the same with any one of the numbers A, B, C.

And by hypothesis it is prime.

Therefore the prime numbers A, B, C, G have been found which are more
than the assigned multitude of A, B, C.   Q. E. D.

Proposition 21

If as many even numbers as we please be added together, the whole is even.

For let as many even numbers as we please, AB, BC, CD, DE, be added together;

I say that the whole AE is even.

For, since each of the numbers AB,
BC, CD, DE is even, it has a half part;
[VII. Def. 6]
so that the whole AE also has a half part.

But an even number is that which is divisible into two equal parts;   [*id.*]
therefore AE is even.   Q. E. D.

Proposition 22

*If as many odd numbers as we please be added together, and their multitude be even,
the whole will be even.*

For let as many odd numbers as we please, AB, BC, CD, DE, even in multitude, be added together;

I say that the whole AE is even.

For, since each of the numbers
AB, BC, CD, DE is odd, if an unit
be subtracted from each, each of
the remainders will be even;   [VII. Def. 7]
so that the sum of them will be even.   [IX. 21]

But the multitude of the units is also even.

Therefore the whole AE is also even.   [IX. 21]

       Q. E. D.

PROPOSITION 23

If as many odd numbers as we please be added together, and their multitude be odd, the whole will also be odd.

For let as many odd numbers as we please, AB, BC, CD, the multitude of which is odd, be added together;

A———B———————C——E D   I say that the whole AD is also odd.

Let the unit DE be subtracted from CD;

therefore the remainder CE is even.   [VII. Def. 7]

But CA is also even;   [IX. 22]

therefore the whole AE is also even.   [IX. 21]

And DE is an unit.

Therefore AD is odd.   [VII. Def. 7]

Q. E. D.

PROPOSITION 24

If from an even number an even number be subtracted, the remainder will be even.

For from the even number AB let the even number BC be subtracted:

A————————C——B   I say that the remainder CA is even.

For, since AB is even, it has a half part. [VII. Def. 6]

For the same reason BC also has a half part;

so that the remainder [CA also has a half part, and] AC is therefore even.

Q. E. D.

PROPOSITION 25

If from an even number an odd number be subtracted, the remainder will be odd.

For from the even number AB let the odd number BC be subtracted;

A———————————C D B   I say that the remainder CA is odd.

For let the unit CD be subtracted from BC;

therefore DB is even.   [VII. Def. 7]

But AB is also even;

therefore the remainder AD is also even.   [IX. 24]

And CD is an unit;

therefore CA is odd.   [VII. Def. 7]

Q. E. D.

PROPOSITION 26

If from an odd number an odd number be subtracted, the remainder will be even.

For from the odd number AB let the odd number BC be subtracted;

A————————C—D B   I say that the remainder CA is even.

For, since AB is odd, let the unit BD be subtracted;

therefore the remainder AD is even.   [VII. Def. 7]

For the same reason CD is also even;   [VII. Def. 7]

so that the remainder CA is also even.   [IX. 24]

Q. E. D.

PROPOSITION 27

If from an odd number an even number be subtracted, the remainder will be odd.

For from the odd number AB let the even number BC be subtracted;

I say that the remainder CA is odd.

Let the unit AD be subtracted;

therefore DB is even. [VII. Def. 7]

A D C B

But BC is also even;

therefore the remainder CD is even. [IX. 24]

Therefore CA is odd. [VII. Def. 7]

Q. E. D.

PROPOSITION 28

If an odd number by multiplying an even number make some number, the product will be even.

. For let the odd number A by multiplying the even number B make C;

I say that C is even.

For, since A by multiplying B has made C,
therefore C is made up of as many numbers equal to B
as there are units in A. [VII. Def. 15]

A

B

C

And B is even;

therefore C is made up of even numbers.

But, if as many even numbers as we please be added together, the whole is even. [IX. 21]

Therefore C is even. Q. E. D.

PROPOSITION 29

If an odd number by multiplying an odd number make some number, the product will be odd.

For let the odd number A by multiplying the odd number B make C;

I say that C is odd.

For, since A by multiplying B has made C,
therefore C is made up of as many numbers equal to
B as there are units in A. [VII. Def. 15]

A

B

C

And each of the numbers A, B is odd;
therefore C is made up of odd numbers the multitude of which is odd.

Thus C is odd. [IX. 23]

Q. E. D.

PROPOSITION 30

If an odd number measure an even number, it will also measure the half of it.

For let the odd number A measure the even number B;

I say that it will also measure the half of it.

For, since A measures B,

let it measure it according to C;

I say that C is not odd.

A

B

C

For, if possible, let it be so.

Then, since A measures B according to C,

therefore A by multiplying C has made B.

Therefore B is made up of odd numbers the multitude of which is odd.

Therefore B is odd: [IX. 23]

which is absurd, for by hypothesis it is even.

Therefore C is not odd;

therefore C is even.

Thus A measures B an even number of times.

For this reason then it also measures the half of it.   Q. E. D.

Proposition 31

If an odd number be prime to any number, it will also be prime to the double of it.

For let the odd number A be prime to any number B,

and let C be double of B;

I say that A is prime to C.

A————

B—————————

C—————————————————

D——

For, if they are not prime to one another, some number will measure them.

Let a number measure them, and let it be D.

Now A is odd;

therefore D is also odd.

And since D which is odd measures C,

and C is even,

therefore $[D]$ will measure the half of C also.   [IX. 30]

But B is half of C;

therefore D measures B.

But it also measures A;

therefore D measures A, B which are prime to one another:

which is impossible.

Therefore A cannot but be prime to C.

Therefore A, C are prime to one another.   Q. E. D.

Proposition 32

Each of the numbers which are continually doubled beginning from a dyad is even-times even only.

For let as many numbers as we please, B, C, D, have been continually doubled beginning from the dyad A;

A——

B————

C——————————

D————————————————

I say that B, C, D are even-times even only.

Now that each of the numbers B, C, D is even-times even is manifest; for it is doubled from a dyad.

I say that it is also even-times even only.

For let an unit be set out.

Since then as many numbers as we please beginning from an unit are in continued proportion,

and the number A after the unit is prime,

therefore D, the greatest of the numbers A, B, C, D, will not be measured by any other number except A, B, C.   [IX. 13]

And each of the numbers A, B, C is even;

therefore D is even-times even only.   [VII. Def. 8]

Similarly we can prove that each of the numbers B, C is even-times even only.   Q. E. D.

Proposition 33

If a number have its half odd, it is even-times odd only.

For let the number A have its half odd;

I say that A is even-times odd only.

Now that it is even-times odd is manifest; for the half of it, being odd, measures it an even number of times. [VII. Def. 9]

I say next that it is also even-times odd only.

For, if A is even-times even also,

                                                                        A

it will be measured by an even number according to an even number;

[VII. Def. 8]

so that the half of it will also be measured by an even number though it is odd: which is absurd.

Therefore A is even-times odd only.   Q. E. D.

PROPOSITION 34

If a number neither be one of those which are continually doubled from a dyad, nor have its half odd, it is both even-times even and even-times odd.

For let the number A neither be one of those doubled from a dyad, nor have its half odd;

I say that A is both even-times even and even-times odd.   ———— A

Now that A is even-times even is manifest;

for it has not its half odd.   [VII. Def. 8]

I say next that it is also even-times odd.

For, if we bisect A, then bisect its half, and do this continually, we shall come upon some odd number which will measure A according to an even number.

For, if not, we shall come upon a dyad,

and A will be among those which are doubled from a dyad: which is contrary to the hypothesis.

Thus A is even-times odd.

But it was also proved even-times even.

Therefore A is both even-times even and even-times odd.   Q. E. D.

PROPOSITION 35

If as many numbers as we please be in continued proportion, and there be subtracted from the second and the last numbers equal to the first, then, as the excess of the second is to the first, so will the excess of the last be to all those before it.

Let there be as many numbers as we please in continued proportion, A, BC, D, EF, beginning from A as least,

and let there be subtracted from BC and
EF the numbers BG, FH, each equal
to A;

I say that, as GC is to A, so is EH
to A, BC, D.

For let FK be made equal to BC, and FL equal to D.

Then, since FK is equal to BC,

and of these the part FH is equal to the part BG,

therefore the remainder HK is equal to the remainder GC.

And since, as EF is to D, so is D to BC, and BC to A,

while D is equal to FL, BC to FK, and A to FH,

therefore, as EF is to FL, so is LF to FK, and FK to FH.

Separando, as EL is to LF, so is LK to FK, and KH to FH.   [VII. 11, 13]

Therefore also, as one of the antecedents is to one of the consequents, so are all the antecedents to all the consequents;   [VII. 12]
    therefore, as KH is to FH, so are EL, LK, KH to LF, FK, HF.
But KH is equal to CG, FH to A, and LF, FK, HF to D, BC, A;
        therefore, as CG is to A, so is EH to D, BC, A.
Therefore, as the excess of the second is to the first, so is the excess of the last to all those before it.   Q. E. D.

Proposition 36

If as many numbers as we please beginning from an unit be set out continuously in double proportion, until the sum of all becomes prime, and if the sum multiplied into the last make some number, the product will be perfect.

For let as many numbers as we please, A, B, C, D, beginning from an unit be set out in double proportion, until the sum of all becomes prime,
    let E be equal to the sum, and let E by multiplying D make FG;
                I say that FG is perfect.
For, however many A, B, C, D are in multitude, let so many E, HK, L, M be taken in double proportion beginning from E;
            therefore, *ex aequali*, as A is to D, so is E to M.   [VII. 14]
Therefore the product of E, D is equal to the product of A, M.   [VII. 19]
And the product of E, D is FG;
        therefore the product of A, M is also FG.
Therefore A by multiplying M has made FG;
        therefore M measures FG according to the units in A.
And A is a dyad;
            therefore FG is double of M.

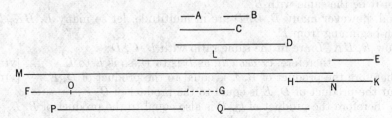

But M, L, HK, E are continuously double of each other;
therefore E, HK, L, M, FG are continuously proportional in double proportion.
Now let there be subtracted from the second HK and the last FG the numbers HN, FO, each equal to the first E;
therefore, as the excess of the second is to the first, so is the excess of the last to all those before it.   [IX. 35]
Therefore, as NK is to E, so is OG to M, L, KH, E.
And NK is equal to E;
        therefore OG is also equal to M, L, HK, E.
But FO is also equal to E,
        and E is equal to A, B, C, D and the unit.
Therefore the whole FG is equal to E, HK, L, M and A, B, C, D and the unit;
                and it is measured by them.

I say also that FG will not be measured by any other number except A, B, C, D, E, HK, L, M and the unit.

For, if possible, let some number P measure FG,
and let P not be the same with any of the numbers A, B, C, D, E, HK, L, M.

And, as many times as P measures FG, so many units let there be in Q;
               therefore Q by multiplying P has made FG.

But, further, E has also by multiplying D made FG;
              therefore, as E is to Q, so is P to D.   [VII. 19]

And, since A, B, C, D are continuously proportional beginning from an unit, therefore D will not be measured by any other number except A, B, C. [IX. 13]

And, by hypothesis, P is not the same with any of the numbers A, B, C;
               therefore P will not measure D.

But, as P is to D, so is E to Q;
             therefore neither does E measure Q.   [VII. Def. 20]

And E is prime;
and any prime number is prime to any number which it does not measure.
                                     [VII. 29]

Therefore E, Q are prime to one another.

But primes are also least,   [VII. 21]
and the least numbers measure those which have the same ratio the same number of times, the antecedent the antecedent and the consequent the consequent;   [VII. 20]
             and, as E is to Q, so is P to D;

therefore E measures P the same number of times that Q measures D.

But D is not measured by any other number except A, B, C;
             therefore Q is the same with one of the numbers A, B, C.

Let it be the same with B.

And, however many B, C, D are in multitude, let so many E, HK, L be taken beginning from E.

Now E, HK, L are in the same ratio with B, C, D;
          therefore, *ex aequali*, as B is to D, so is E to L.   [VII. 14]

Therefore the product of B, L is equal to the product of D, E.   [VII. 19]

But the product of D, E is equal to the product of Q, P;
        therefore the product of Q, P is also equal to the product of B, L.

Therefore, as Q is to B, so is L to P.   [VII. 19]

And Q is the same with B;
             therefore L is also the same with P:
which is impossible, for by hypothesis P is not the same with any of the numbers set out.

Therefore no number will measure FG except A, B, C, D, E, HK, L, M and the unit.

And FG was proved equal to A, B, C, D, E, HK, L, M and the unit;
and a perfect number is that which is equal to its own parts;   [VII. Def. 22]
              therefore FG is perfect.   Q. E. D.

BOOK TEN

DEFINITIONS I

1. Those magnitudes are said to be *commensurable* which are measured by the same measure, and those *incommensurable* which cannot have any common measure.

2. Straight lines are *commensurable in square* when the squares on them are measured by the same area, and *incommensurable in square* when the squares on them cannot possibly have any area as a common measure.

3. With these hypotheses, it is proved that there exist straight lines infinite in multitude which are commensurable and incommensurable respectively, some in length only, and others in square also, with an assigned straight line. Let then the assigned straight line be called *rational*, and those straight lines which are commensurable with it, whether in length and in square or in square only, *rational*, but those which are incommensurable with it *irrational*.

4. And let the square on the assigned straight line be called *rational* and those areas which are commensurable with it *rational*, but those which are incommensurable with it *irrational*, and the straight lines which produce them *irrational*, that is, in case the areas are squares, the sides themselves, but in case they are any other rectilineal figures, the straight lines on which are described squares equal to them.

BOOK X. PROPOSITIONS

PROPOSITION 1

Two unequal magnitudes being set out, if from the greater there be subtracted a magnitude greater than its half, and from that which is left a magnitude greater than its half, and if this process be repeated continually, there will be left some magnitude which will be less than the lesser magnitude set out.

Let *AB*, *C* be two unequal magnitudes of which *AB* is the greater:

I say that, if from *AB* there be subtracted a magnitude greater than its half, and from that which is left a magnitude greater than its half, and if this process be repeated continually, there will be left some magnitude which will be less than the magnitude *C*.

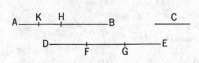

For *C* if multiplied will sometime be greater than *AB*.   [cf. v. Def. 4]

Let it be multiplied, and let *DE* be a multiple of *C*, and greater than *AB*;

let *DE* be divided into the parts *DF*, *FG*, *GE* equal to *C*,

from *AB* let there be subtracted *BH* greater than its half,

and, from *AH*, *HK* greater than its half,

and let this process be repeated continually until the divisions in AB are equal in multitude with the divisions in DE.

Let, then, AK, KH, HB be divisions which are equal in multitude with DF, FG, GE.

Now, since DE is greater than AB,
and from DE there has been subtracted EG less than its half,
and, from AB, BH greater than its half,
therefore the remainder GD is greater than the remainder HA.

And, since GD is greater than HA,
and there has been subtracted, from GD, the half GF,
and, from HA, HK greater than its half,
therefore the remainder DF is greater than the remainder AK.

But DF is equal to C;
therefore C is also greater than AK.

Therefore AK is less than C.

Therefore there is left of the magnitude AB the magnitude AK which is less than the lesser magnitude set out, namely C.   Q. E. D.

And the theorem can be similarly proved even if the parts subtracted be halves.

Proposition 2

If, when the less of two unequal magnitudes is continually subtracted in turn from the greater, that which is left never measures the one before it, the magnitudes will be incommensurable.

For, there being two unequal magnitudes AB, CD, and AB being the less, when the less is continually subtracted in turn from the greater, let that which is left over never measure the one before it;

I say that the magnitudes AB, CD are incommensurable.

For, if they are commensurable, some magnitude will measure them.

Let a magnitude measure them, if possible, and let it be E;
let AB, measuring FD, leave CF less than itself,
let CF measuring BG, leave AG less than itself,
and let this process be repeated continually, until there is left some magnitude which is less than E.

Suppose this done, and let there be left AG less than E.

Then, since E measures AB,
while AB measures DF,
therefore E will also measure FD.

But it measures the whole CD also;
therefore it will also measure the remainder CF.

But CF measures BG;
therefore E also measures BG.

But it measures the whole AB also;
therefore it will also measure the remainder AG, the greater the less:
which is impossible.

Therefore no magnitude will measure the magnitudes AB, CD;
    therefore the magnitudes AB, CD are incommensurable. [x. Def. 1]
Therefore etc.   Q. E. D.

PROPOSITION 3

Given two commensurable magnitudes, to find their greatest common measure.

Let the two given commensurable magnitudes be AB, CD of which AB is the less;
thus it is required to find the greatest common measure of AB, CD.

Now the magnitude AB either measures CD or it does not.

If then it measures it—and it measures itself also—AB is a common measure of AB, CD.

And it is manifest that it is also the greatest;
    for a greater magnitude than the magnitude AB will not measure AB.

Next, let AB not measure CD.

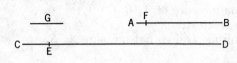

Then, if the less be continually subtracted in turn from the greater, that which is left over will sometime measure the one before it, because AB, CD are not incommensurable;
[cf. x. 2]

    let AB, measuring ED, leave EC less than itself,
    let EC, measuring FB, leave AF less than itself,
            and let AF measure CE.

Since, then, AF measures CE,
            while CE measures FB,
        therefore AF will also measure FB.

But it measures itself also;
        therefore AF will also measure the whole AB.

But AB measures DE;
        therefore AF will also measure ED.

But it measures CE also;
        therefore it also measures the whole CD.

Therefore AF is a common measure of AB, CD.

I say next that it is also the greatest.

For, if not, there will be some magnitude greater than AF which will measure AB, CD.

Let it be G.

Since then G measures AB,
            while AB measures ED,
        therefore G will also measure ED.

But it measures the whole CD also;
        therefore G will also measure the remainder CE.

But CE measures FB;
        therefore G will also measure FB.

But it measures the whole AB also,
and it will therefore measure the remainder AF, the greater the less:
            which is impossible.

Therefore no magnitude greater than AF will measure AB, CD;

therefore AF is the greatest common measure of AB, CD.

Therefore the greatest common measure of the two given commensurable magnitudes AB, CD has been found. Q. E. D.

PORISM. From this it is manifest that, if a magnitude measure two magnitudes, it will also measure their greatest common measure.

PROPOSITION 4

Given three commensurable magnitudes, to find their greatest common measure.

Let A, B, C be the three given commensurable magnitudes;
thus it is required to find the greatest common measure of A, B, C.

Let the greatest common measure of the two magnitudes A, B be taken, and let it be D; [x. 3] then D either measures C, or does not measure it.

First, let it measure it.

Since then D measures C,

while it also measures A, B,

therefore D is a common measure of A, B, C.

And it is manifest that it is also the greatest;
for a greater magnitude than the magnitude D does not measure A, B.

Next, let D not measure C.

I say first that C, D are commensurable.

For, since A, B, C are commensurable,

some magnitude will measure them,

and this will of course measure A, B also;

so that it will also measure the greatest common measure of A, B, namely D. [x. 3, Por.]

But it also measures C;

so that the said magnitude will measure C, D;

therefore C, D are commensurable.

Now let their greatest common measure be taken, and let it be E. [x. 3]

Since then E measures D,

while D measures A, B,

therefore E will also measure A, B.

But it measures C also;

therefore E measures A, B, C;

therefore E is a common measure of A, B, C.

I say next that it is also the greatest.

For, if possible, let there be some magnitude F greater than E, and let it measure A, B, C.

Now, since F measures A, B, C,

it will also measure A, B,

and will measure the greatest common measure of A, B. [x. 3, Por.]

But the greatest common measure of A, B is D;

therefore F measures D.

But it measures C also;

therefore F measures C, D;

therefore F will also measure the greatest common measure of C, D.

[x. 3, Por.]

But that is E;
                    therefore F will measure E, the greater the less:
                    which is impossible.
Therefore no magnitude greater than the magnitude E will measure A, B, C;
therefore E is the greatest common measure of A, B, C if D do not measure C,
        and, if it measure it, D is itself the greatest common measure.
Therefore the greatest common measure of the three given commensurable
magnitudes has been found.
PORISM. From this it is manifest that, if a magnitude measure three magnitudes, it will also measure their greatest common measure.
Similarly too, with more magnitudes, the greatest common measure can be
found, and the porism can be extended.   Q. E. D.

PROPOSITION 5

*Commensurable magnitudes have to one another the ratio which a number has to a
number.*
Let A, B be commensurable magnitudes;
I say that A has to B the ratio which a number has to a number.
For, since A, B are commensurable, some magnitude will measure them.
Let it measure them, and let it be C.

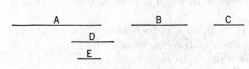

And, as many times as C measures A, so many units let there be
in D;
and, as many times as C measures B, so many units let there
be in E.
Since then C measures A according to the units in D,
        while the unit also measures D according to the units in it,
therefore the unit measures the number D the same number of times as the
magnitude C measures A;
                therefore as C, is to A, so is the unit to D;   [VII. Def. 20]
therefore, inversely, as A is to C, so is D to the unit.   [cf. V. 7, Por.]
Again, since C measures B according to the units in E,
        while the unit also measures E according to the units in it,
therefore the unit measures E the same number of times as C measures B;
                therefore, as C is to B, so is the unit to E.
But it was also proved that,
                as A is to C, so is D to the unit;
                therefore, *ex aequali,*
        as A is to B, so is the number D to E.   [V. 22]
Therefore the commensurable magnitudes A, B have to one another the
ratio which the number D has to the number E.   Q. E. D.

PROPOSITION 6

*If two magnitudes have to one another the ratio which a number has to a number,
the magnitudes will be commensurable.*
For let the two magnitudes A, B have to one another the ratio which the
number D has to the number E;
        I say that the magnitudes A, B are commensurable.

For let A be divided into as many equal parts as there are units in D,
and let C be equal to one of them;
and let F be made up of as
many magnitudes equal to C
as there are units in E.

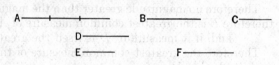

Since then there are in A
as many magnitudes equal to
C as there are units in D,

whatever part the unit is of D, the same part is C of A also;
therefore, as C is to A, so is the unit to D.   [VII. Def. 20]
But the unit measures the number D;
therefore C also measures A.

And since, as C is to A, so is the unit to D,
therefore, inversely, as A is to C, so is the number D to the unit.
[cf. v. 7, Por.]

Again, since there are in F as many magnitudes equal to C as there are units
in E,
therefore, as C is to F, so is the unit to E.   [VII. Def. 20]
But it was also proved that,
as A is to C, so is D to the unit;
therefore, *ex aequali*, as A is to F, so is D to E.   [v. 22]
But, as D is to E, so is A to B;
therefore also, as A is to B, so is it to F also.   [v. 11]
Therefore A has the same ratio to each of the magnitudes B, F;
therefore B is equal to F.   [v. 9]
But C measures F;
therefore it measures B also.
Further it measures A also;
therefore C measures A, B.
Therefore A is commensurable with B.
Therefore etc.

PORISM. From this it is manifest that, if there be two numbers, as D, E, and
a straight line, as A, it is possible to make a straight line $[F]$ such that the
given straight line is to it as the number D is to the number E.

And, if a mean proportional be also taken between A, F, as B,
as A is to F, so will the square on A be to the square on B, that is, as the first
is to the third, so is the figure on the first to that which is similar and similarly
described on the second.   [VI. 19, Por.]

But, as A is to F, so is the number D to the number E;
therefore it has been contrived that, as the number D is to the number E, so
also is the figure on the straight line A to the figure on the straight line B.

Q. E. D.

PROPOSITION 7

*Incommensurable magnitudes have not to one another the ratio which a number has
to a number.*

Let A, B be incommensurable magnitudes;
I say that A has not to B the ratio which a number has to a number.
For, if A has to B the ratio which a number has to a number, A will be com-

mensurable with B.   [x. 6]

But it is not;

$\underline{\quad A \quad}$ therefore A has not to B the ratio which a number has to a num-

$\underline{\quad B \quad}$ ber.

Therefore etc.   Q. E. D.

PROPOSITION 8

If two magnitudes have not to one another the ratio which a number has to a number, the magnitudes will be incommensurable.

For let the two magnitudes A, B not have to one another the ratio which a number has to a number;

$\underline{\qquad A \qquad}$ I say that the magnitudes A, B are incommensurable.

$\underline{\quad B \quad}$ For, if they are commensurable, A will have to B the ratio which a number has to a number.   [x. 5]

But it has not;

therefore the magnitudes A, B are incommensurable.

Therefore etc.   Q. E. D.

PROPOSITION 9

The squares on straight lines commensurable in length have to one another the ratio which a square number has to a square number; and squares which have to one another the ratio which a square number has to a square number will also have their sides commensurable in length. But the squares on straight lines incommensurable in length have not to one another the ratio which a square number has to a square number; and squares which have not to one another the ratio which a square number has to a square number will not have their sides commensurable in length either.

For let A, B be commensurable in length;

I say that the square on A has to the square on B the ratio which a square number has to a square number.

$\underline{\qquad A \qquad}$ $\underline{\qquad B \qquad}$

$\underline{\quad C \quad}$

$\underline{\quad D \quad}$ For, since A is commensurable in length with B,

therefore A has to B the ratio which a number has to a number.   [x. 5]

Let it have to it the ratio which C has to D.

Since then, as A is to B, so is C to D,

while the ratio of the square on A to the square on B is duplicate of the ratio of A to B,

for similar figures are in the duplicate ratio of their corresponding sides;

[vi. 20, Por.]

and the ratio of the square on C to the square on D is duplicate of the ratio of C to D,

for between two square numbers there is one mean proportional number, and the square number has to the square number the ratio duplicate of that which the side has to the side;   [viii. 11]

therefore also, as the square on A is to the square on B, so is the square on C to the square on D.

Next, as the square on A is to the square on B, so let the square on C be to the square on D;

I say that A is commensurable in length with B.

For since, as the square on A is to the square on B, so is the square on C to the square on D,

while the ratio of the square on A to the square on B is duplicate of the ratio of A to B,

and the ratio of the square on C to the square on D is duplicate of the ratio of C to D,

therefore also, as A is to B, so is C to D.

Therefore A has to B the ratio which the number C has to the number D;

therefore A is commensurable in length with B. [x. 6]

Next, let A be incommensurable in length with B;

I say that the square on A has not to the square on B the ratio which a square number has to a square number.

For, if the square on A has to the square on B the ratio which a square number has to a square number, A will be commensurable with B.

But it is not;

therefore the square on A has not to the square on B the ratio which a square number has to a square number.

Again, let the square on A not have to the square on B the ratio which a square number has to a square number;

I say that A is incommensurable in length with B.

For, if A is commensurable with B, the square on A will have to the square on B the ratio which a square number has to a square number.

But it has not;

therefore A is not commensurable in length with B.

Therefore etc.

PORISM. And it is manifest from what has been proved that straight lines commensurable in length are always commensurable in square also, but those commensurable in square are not always commensurable in length also.

[LEMMA. It has been proved in the arithmetical books that similar plane numbers have to one another the ratio which a square number has to a square number, [VIII. 26]

and that, if two numbers have to one another the ratio which a square number has to a square number, they are similar plane numbers. [Converse of VIII. 26]

And it is manifest from these propositions that numbers which are not similar plane numbers, that is, those which have not their sides proportional, have not to one another the ratio which a square number has to a square number.

For, if they have, they will be similar plane numbers: which is contrary to the hypothesis.

Therefore numbers which are not similar plane numbers have not to one another the ratio which a square number has to a square number.]

PROPOSITION 10

To find two straight lines incommensurable, the one in length only, and the other in square also, with an assigned straight line.

Let A be the assigned straight line;

thus it is required to find two straight lines incommensurable, the one in length only, and the other in square also, with A.

Let two numbers B, C be set out which have not to one another the ratio which a square number has to a square number, that is, which are not similar plane numbers;

and let it be contrived that,

A————————

as B is to C, so is the square on A to the square on D

D————————

—for we have learnt how to do this— [x. 6, Por.]

E————————

therefore the square on A is commensurable with the

B————

square on D.   [x. 6]

C————

And, since B has not to C the ratio which a square number has to a square number,

therefore neither has the square on A to the square on D the ratio which a square number has to a square number;

therefore A is incommensurable in length with D.   [x. 9]

Let E be taken a mean proportional between A, D;

therefore, as A is to D, so is the square on A to the square on E.   [v. Def. 9]

But A is incommensurable in length with D;

therefore the square on A is also incommensurable with the square on E;

[x. 11]

therefore A is incommensurable in square with E.

Therefore two straight lines D, E have been found incommensurable, D in length only, and E in square and of course in length also, with the assigned straight line A.   Q. E. D.

PROPOSITION 11

If four magnitudes be proportional, and the first be commensurable with the second, the third will also be commensurable with the fourth; and, if the first be incommensurable with the second, the third will also be incommensurable with the fourth.

Let A, B, C, D be four magnitudes in proportion, so that, as A is to B, so is C to D,

and let A be commensurable with B;

A————————   B————   I say that C will also be commensurable

C————————   D————   with D.

For, since A is commensurable with B,

therefore A has to B the ratio which a number has to a number.   [x. 5]

And, as A is to B, so is C to D;

therefore C also has to D the ratio which a number has to a number;

therefore C is commensurable with D.   [x. 6]

Next, let A be incommensurable with B;

I say that C will also be incommensurable with D.

For, since A is incommensurable with B,

therefore A has not to B the ratio which a number has to a number.   [x. 7]

And, as A is to B, so is C to D;

therefore neither has C to D the ratio which a number has to a number;

therefore C is incommensurable with D.   [x. 8]

Therefore etc.   Q. E. D.

PROPOSITION 12

Magnitudes commensurable with the same magnitude are commensurable with one another also.

For let each of the magnitudes A, B be commensurable with C;

I say that A is also commensurable with B.

For, since A is commensurable with C,
therefore A has to C the ratio
which a number has to a
number.   [x. 5]

Let it have the ratio which
D has to E.

Again, since C is commensurable with B,

therefore C has to B the ratio which a number has to a number.   [x. 5]

Let it have the ratio which F has to G.

And, given any number of ratios we please, namely the ratio which D has to E and that which F has to G,

let the numbers H, K, L be taken continuously in the given ratios;   [cf. VIII. 4]

so that, as D is to E, so is H to K,

and, as F is to G, so is K to L.

Since, then, as A is to C, so is D to E,

while, as D is to E, so is H to K,

therefore also, as A is to C, so is H to K.   [v. 11]

Again, since, as C is to B, so is F to G,

while, as F is to G, so is K to L,

therefore also, as C is to B, so is K to L.   [v. 11]

But also, as A is to C, so is H to K;

therefore, *ex aequali*, as A is to B, so is H to L.   [v. 22]

Therefore A has to B the ratio which a number has to a number;

therefore A is commensurable with B.   [x. 6]

Therefore etc.   Q. E. D.

Proposition 13

If two magnitudes be commensurable, and the one of them be incommensurable with any magnitude, the remaining one will also be incommensurable with the same.

Let A, B be two commensurable magnitudes, and let one of them, A, be incommensurable with any other magnitude C;

I say that the remaining one, B, will also be incommensurable with C.

For, if B is commensurable with C,

while A is also commensurable with B,

A is also commensurable with C.   [x. 12]

But it is also incommensurable with it:

which is impossible.

Therefore B is not commensurable with C;

therefore it is incommensurable with it.

Therefore etc.   Q. E. D.

Lemma

Given two unequal straight lines, to find by what square the square on the greater is greater than the square on the less.

Let AB, C be the given two unequal straight lines, and let AB be the greater of them;

thus it is required to find by what square the square on AB is greater than the square on C.

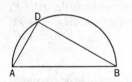

Let the semicircle ADB be described on AB, and let AD be fitted into it equal to C;   [IV. 1] let DB be joined.

It is then manifest that the angle ADB is right,   [III. 31]

and that the square on AB is greater than the square on AD, that is, C, by the square on DB.   [I. 47]

Similarly also, if two straight lines be given, the straight line the square on which is equal to the sum of the squares on them is found in this manner:

Let AD, DB be the given two straight lines, and let it be required to find the straight line the square on which is equal to the sum of the squares on them.

Let them be placed so as to contain a right angle, that formed by AD, DB; and let AB be joined.

It is again manifest that the straight line the square on which is equal to the sum of the squares on AD, DB is AB.   [I. 47]

                                                                                            Q. E. D.

PROPOSITION 14

If four straight lines be proportional, and the square on the first be greater than the square on the second by the square on a straight line commensurable with the first, the square on the third will also be greater than the square on the fourth by the square on a straight line commensurable with the third.

And, if the square on the first be greater than the square on the second by the square on a straight line incommensurable with the first, the square on the third will also be greater than the square on the fourth by the square on a straight line incommensurable with the third.

Let A, B, C, D be four straight lines in proportion, so that, as A is to B, so is C to D;

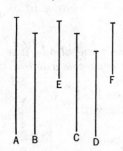

and let the square on A be greater than the square on B by the square on E, and let the square on C be greater than the square on D by the square on F;

I say that, if A is commensurable with E, C is also commensurable with F,

and, if A is incommensurable with E, C is also incommensurable with F.

For since, as A is to B, so is C to D,

therefore also, as the square on A is to the square on B, so is the square on C to the square on D.   [VI. 22]

But the squares on E, B are equal to the square on A,

and the squares on D, F are equal to the square on C.

Therefore, as the squares on E, B are to the square on B, so are the squares on D, F to the square on D;

therefore, *separando*, as the square on E is to the square on B, so is the square on F to the square on D;   [V. 17]

therefore also, as E is to B, so is F to D;   [VI. 22]

therefore, inversely, as B is to E, so is D to F.

But, as A is to B, so also is C to D;

therefore, *ex aequali*, as A is to E, so is C to F.   [v. 22]

Therefore, if A is commensurable with E, C is also commensurable with F, and, if A is incommensurable with E, C is also incommensurable with F. [x. 11]

Therefore etc.   Q. E. D.

PROPOSITION 15

If two commensurable magnitudes be added together, the whole will also be commensurable with each of them; and, if the whole be commensurable with one of them, the original magnitudes will also be commensurable.

For let the two commensurable magnitudes AB, BC be added together;

I say that the whole AC is also commensurable with each of the magnitudes AB, BC.

For, since AB, BC are commensurable, some magnitude will measure them.

Let it measure them, and let it be D.

Since then D measures AB, BC, it will also measure the whole AC.

But it measures AB, BC also;

therefore D measures AB, BC, AC;

therefore AC is commensurable with each of the magnitudes AB, BC.

[x. Def. 1]

Next, let AC be commensurable with AB;

I say that AB, BC are also commensurable.

For, since AC, AB are commensurable, some magnitude will measure them.

Let it measure them, and let it be D.

Since then D measures CA, AB, it will also measure the remainder BC.

But it measures AB also;

therefore D will measure AB, BC;

therefore AB, BC are commensurable.   [x. Def. 1]

Therefore etc.   Q. E. D.

PROPOSITION 16

If two incommensurable magnitudes be added together, the whole will also be incommensurable with each of them; and, if the whole be incommensurable with one of them, the original magnitudes will also be incommensurable.

For let the two incommensurable magnitudes AB, BC be added together; I say that the whole AC is also incommensurable with each of the magnitudes AB, BC.

For, if CA, AB are not incommensurable, some magnitude will measure them.

Let it measure them, if possible, and let it be D.

Since then D measures CA, AB,

therefore it will also measure the remainder BC.

But it measures AB also;

therefore D measures AB, BC.

Therefore AB, BC are commensurable;

but they were also, by hypothesis, incommensurable:

which is impossible.

Therefore no magnitude will measure CA, AB;

therefore CA, AB are incommensurable.   [x. Def. 1]

Similarly we can prove that AC, CB are also incommensurable.

Therefore AC is incommensurable with each of the magnitudes AB, BC.

Next, let AC be incommensurable with one of the magnitudes AB, BC.

First, let it be incommensurable with AB;

I say that AB, BC are also incommensurable.

For, if they are commensurable, some magnitude will measure them.

Let it measure them, and let it be D.

Since, then, D measures AB, BC,

therefore it will also measure the whole AC.

But it measures AB also;

therefore D measures CA, AB.

Therefore CA, AB are commensurable;

but they were also, by hypothesis, incommensurable:

which is impossible.

Therefore no magnitude will measure AB, BC;

therefore AB, BC are incommensurable.   [x. Def. 1]

Therefore etc.
                                                          Q. E. D.

LEMMA

If to any straight line there be applied a parallelogram deficient by a square figure, the applied parallelogram is equal to the rectangle contained by the segments of the straight line resulting from the application.

For let there be applied to the straight line AB the parallelogram AD deficient by the square figure DB;

I say that AD is equal to the rectangle contained by AC, CB.

This is indeed at once manifest;

for, since DB is a square,

DC is equal to CB;

and AD is the rectangle AC, CD, that is, the rectangle AC, CB.

Therefore etc.
                                                          Q. E. D.

PROPOSITION 17

If there be two unequal straight lines, and to the greater there be applied to a parallelogram equal to the fourth part of the square on the less and deficient by a square figure, and if it divide it into parts which are commensurable in length, then the square on the greater will be greater than the square on the less by the square on a straight line commensurable with the greater.

And, if the square on the greater be greater than the square on the less by the square on a straight line commensurable with the greater, and if there be applied to the greater a parallelogram equal to the fourth part of the square on the less and deficient by a square figure, it will divide it into parts which are commensurable in length.

Let A, BC be two unequal straight lines, of which BC is the greater, and let there be applied to BC a parallelogram equal to the fourth part of the square on the less, A, that is, equal to the square on the half of A, and deficient by a square figure. Let this be the rectangle BD, DC,   [cf. Lemma] and let BD be commensurable in length with DC;

I say that the square on BC is greater than the square on A by the square on a straight line commensurable with BC.

For let BC be bisected at the point E,

and let EF be made equal to DE.

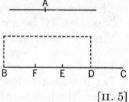

Therefore the remainder DC is equal to BF.

And, since the straight line BC has been cut into equal parts at E, and into unequal parts at D, therefore the rectangle contained by BD, DC, together with the square on ED, is equal to the square on EC;   [II. 5]

And the same is true of their quadruples;

therefore four times the rectangle BD, DC, together with four times the square on DE, is equal to four times the square on EC.

But the square on A is equal to four times the rectangle BD, DC;

and the square on DF is equal to four times the square on DE, for DF is double of DE.

And the square on BC is equal to four times the square on EC, for again BC is double of CE.

Therefore the squares on A, DF are equal to the square on BC,

so that the square on BC is greater than the square on A by the square on DF.

It is to be proved that BC is also commensurable with DF.

Since BD is commensurable in length with DC,

therefore BC is also commensurable in length with CD.   [x. 15]

But CD is commensurable in length with CD, BF, for CD is equal to BF.   [x. 6]

Therefore BC is also commensurable in length with BF, CD,   [x. 12]

so that BC is also commensurable in length with the remainder FD;   [x. 15]

therefore the square on BC is greater than the square on A by the square on a straight line commensurable with BC.

Next, let the square on BC be greater than the square on A by the square on a straight line commensurable with BC,

let a parallelogram be applied to BC equal to the fourth part of the square on A and deficient by a square figure, and let it be the rectangle BD, DC.

It is to be proved that BD is commensurable in length with DC.

With the same construction, we can prove similarly that the square on BC is greater than the square on A by the square on FD.

But the square on BC is greater than the square on A by the square on a straight line commensurable with BC.

Therefore BC is commensurable in length with FD,

so that BC is also commensurable in length with the remainder, the sum of BF, DC.   [x. 15]

But the sum of BF, DC is commensurable with DC,   [x. 6]

so that BC is also commensurable in length with CD;   [x. 12]

and therefore, *separando*, BD is commensurable in length with DC.   [x. 15]

Therefore etc.   Q. E. D.

PROPOSITION 18

If there be two unequal straight lines, and to the greater there be applied a parallelogram equal to the fourth part of the square on the less and deficient by a square figure, and if it divide it into parts which are incommensurable, the square on the greater will be greater than the square on the less by the square on a straight line incommensurable with the greater.

And, if the square on the greater be greater than the square on the less by the square on a straight line incommensurable with the greater, and if there be applied to the greater a parallelogram equal to the fourth part of the square on the less and deficient by a square figure, it divides it into parts which are incommensurable.

Let A, BC be two unequal straight lines, of which BC is the greater, and to BC let there be applied a parallelogram equal to the fourth part of the square on the less, A, and deficient by a square figure. Let this be the rectangle BD, DC,   [cf. Lemma before x. 17] and let BD be incommensurable in length with DC;

I say that the square on BC is greater than the square on A by the square on a straight line incommensurable with BC.

For, with the same construction as before, we can prove similarly that the square on BC is greater than the square on A by the square on FD.

It is to be proved that BC is incommensurable in length with DF.

Since BD is incommensurable in length with DC,

therefore BC is also incommensurable in length with CD.   [x. 16]

But DC is commensurable with the sum of BF, DC;   [x. 6]

therefore BC is also incommensurable with the sum of BF, DC;   [x. 13]

so that BC is also incommensurable in length with the remainder FD. [x. 16]

And the square on BC is greater than the square on A by the square on FD; therefore the square on BC is greater than the square on A by the square on a straight line incommensurable with BC.

Again, let the square on BC be greater than the square on A by the square on a straight line incommensurable with BC, and let there be applied to BC a parallelogram equal to the fourth part of the square on A and deficient by a square figure. Let this be the rectangle BD, DC.

It is to be proved that BD is incommensurable in length with DC.

For, with the same construction, we can prove similarly that the square on BC is greater than the square on A by the square on FD.

But the square on BC is greater than the square on A by the square on a straight line incommensurable with BC;

therefore BC is incommensurable in length with FD,

so that BC is also incommensurable with the remainder, the sum of BF, DC.   [x. 16]

But the sum of BF, DC is commensurable in length with DC;   [x. 6]

therefore BC is also incommensurable in length with DC,   [x. 13]

so that, *separando*, BD is also incommensurable in length with DC.   [x. 16]

Therefore etc.   Q. E. D.

Lemma

Since it has been proved that straight lines commensurable in length are always commensurable in square also, while those commensurable in square are not always commensurable in length also, but can of course be either commensurable or incommensurable in length, it is manifest that, if any straight line be commensurable in length with a given rational straight line, it is called rational and commensurable with the other not only in length but in square also, since straight lines commensurable in length are always commensurable in square also.

But, if any straight line be commensurable in square with a given rational straight line, then, if it is also commensurable in length with it, it is called in this case also rational and commensurable with it both in length and in square; but, if again any straight line, being commensurable in square with a given rational straight line, be incommensurable in length with it, it is called in this case also rational but commensurable in square only.

PROPOSITION 19

The rectangle contained by rational straight lines commensurable in length is rational.

For let the rectangle AC be contained by the rational straight lines AB, BC commensurable in length;

I say that AC is rational.

For on AB let the square AD be described;

therefore AD is rational.   [x. Def. 4]

And, since AB is commensurable in length with BC,

while AB is equal to BD,

therefore BD is commensurable in length with BC.

And, as BD is to BC, so is DA to AC.   [vi. 1]

Therefore DA is commensurable with AC.   [x. 11]

But DA is rational;

therefore AC is also rational.   [x. Def. 4]

Therefore etc.

Q. E. D.

PROPOSITION 20

If a rational area be applied to a rational straight line, it produces as breadth a straight line rational and commensurable in length with the straight line to which it is applied.

For let the rational area AC be applied to AB, a straight line once more rational in any of the aforesaid ways, producing BC as breadth;

I say that BC is rational and commensurable in length with BA.

For on AB let the square AD be described;

therefore AD is rational.   [x. Def. 4]

But AC is also rational;

therefore DA is commensurable with AC.

And, as DA is to AC, so is DB to BC.   [vi. 1]

Therefore DB is also commensurable with BC;   [x. 11]

and DB is equal to BA;

therefore AB is also commensurable with BC.

But AB is rational;

therefore BC is also rational and commensurable in length with AB.

Therefore etc.

Q. E. D.

PROPOSITION 21

The rectangle contained by rational straight lines commensurable in square only is irrational, and the side of the square equal to it is irrational. Let the latter be called medial.

For let the rectangle AC be contained by the rational straight lines AB, BC commensurable in square only;

I say that AC is irrational, and the side of the square equal to it is irrational; and let the latter be called *medial*.

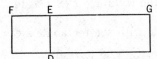

For on AB let the square AD be described;

therefore AD is rational.   [x. Def. 4]

And, since AB is incommensurable in length with BC,

for by hypothesis they are commensurable in square only,

while AB is equal to BD,

therefore DB is also incommensurable in length with BC.

And, as DB is to BC, so is AD to AC;   [vi. 1]

therefore DA is incommensurable with AC.   [x. 11]

But DA is rational;

therefore AC is irrational,

so that the side of the square equal to AC is also irrational.   [x. Def. 4]

And let the latter be called *medial*.   Q. E. D.

LEMMA

If there be two straight lines, then, as the first is to the second, so is the square on the first to the rectangle contained by the two straight lines.

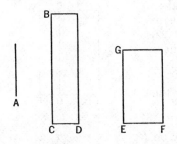

Let FE, EG be two straight lines.

I say that, as FE is to EG, so is the square on FE to the rectangle FE, EG.

For on FE let the square DF be described,

and let GD be completed.

Since then, as FE is to EG, so is FD to DG,   [vi. 1]

and FD is the square on FE,

and DG the rectangle DE, EG, that is, the rectangle FE, EG,

therefore, as FE is to EG, so is the square on FE to the rectangle FE, EG.

Similarly also, as the rectangle GE, EF is to the square on EF, that is, as GD is to FD, so is GE to EF.   Q. E. D.

PROPOSITION 22

The square on a medial straight line, if applied to a rational straight line, produces as breadth a straight line rational and incommensurable in length with that to which it is applied.

Let A be medial and CB rational, and let a rectangular area BD equal to the square on A be applied to BC, producing CD as breadth;

I say that CD is rational and incommensurable in length with CB.

For, since A is medial, the square on it is equal to a rectangular area contained by rational straight lines commensurable in square only.   [x. 21]

Let the square on it be equal to GF.

But the square on it is also equal to BD;

therefore BD is equal to GF.

But it is also equiangular with it;
and in equal and equiangular parallelograms the sides about the equal angles are reciprocally proportional;   [VI. 14]
        therefore, proportionally, as BC is to EG, so is EF to CD.

Therefore also, as the square on BC is to the square on EG, so is the square on EF to the square on CD.   [VI. 22]

But the square on CB is commensurable with the square on EG, for each of these straight lines is rational;
therefore the square on EF is also commensurable with the square on CD.
                                                                        [X. 11]

But the square on EF is rational;
        therefore the square on CD is also rational;   [X. Def. 4]
                therefore CD is rational.

And since EF is incommensurable in length with EG,
        for they are commensurable in square only,
and, as EF is to EG, so is the square on EF to the rectangle FE, EG,   [Lemma]
therefore the square on EF is incommensurable with the rectangle FE, EG.
                                                                        [X. 11]

But the square on CD is commensurable with the square on EF, for the straight lines are rational in square;
and the rectangle DC, CB is commensurable with the rectangle FE, EG, for they are equal to the square on A;
therefore the square on CD is also incommensurable with the rectangle DC, CB.   [X. 13]

But, as the square on CD is to the rectangle DC, CB, so is DC to CB;
                                                                        [Lemma]
        therefore DC is incommensurable in length with CB.   [X. 11]

Therefore CD is rational and incommensurable in length with CB.

                                                        Q. E. D.

PROPOSITION 23

A straight line commensurable with a medial straight line is medial.

        Let A be medial, and let B be commensurable with A;
                I say that B is also medial.

For let a rational straight line CD be set out,
and to CD let the rectangular area CE equal to the
square on A be applied, producing ED as breadth;
therefore ED is rational and incommensurable in
length with CD.   [X. 22]

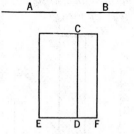

And let the rectangular area CF equal to the square on B be applied to CD, producing DF as breadth.

Since, then, A is commensurable with B,
the square on A is also commensurable with the square on B.

But EC is equal to the square on A,
        and CF is equal to the square on B;
                therefore EC is commensurable with CF.

And, as EC is to CF, so is ED to DF;   [VI. 1]
        therefore ED is commensurable in length with DF.   [X. 11]

But *ED* is rational and incommensurable in length with *DC*; therefore *DF* is also rational [x. Def. 3] and incommensurable in length with *DC*.   [x. 13]

Therefore *CD*, *DF* are rational and commensurable in square only.

But the straight line the square on which is equal to the rectangle contained by rational straight lines commensurable in square only is medial;   [x. 21] therefore the side of the square equal to the rectangle *CD*, *DF* is medial.

And *B* is the side of the square equal to the rectangle *CD*, *DF*;

therefore *B* is medial.   Q. E. D.

PORISM. From this it is manifest that an area commensurable with a medial area is medial.

[And in the same way as was explained in the case of rationals [Lemma following x. 18] it follows, as regards medials, that a straight line commensurable in length with a medial straight line is called *medial* and commensurable with it not only in length but in square also, since, in general, straight lines commensurable in length are always commensurable in square also.

But, if any straight line be commensurable in square with a medial straight line, then, if it is also commensurable in length with it, the straight lines are called, in this case too, medial and commensurable in length and in square, but, if in square only, they are called medial straight lines commensurable in square only.]

PROPOSITION 24

The rectangle contained by medial straight lines commensurable in length is medial.

For let the rectangle *AC* be contained by the medial straight lines *AB*, *BC* which are commensurable in length;

I say that *AC* is medial.

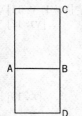

For on *AB* let the square *AD* be described;

therefore *AD* is medial.

And, since *AB* is commensurable in length with *BC*,

while *AB* is equal to *BD*,

therefore *DB* is also commensurable in length with *BC*;

so that *DA* is also commensurable with *AC*. [vi. 1, x. 11]

But *DA* is medial;

therefore *AC* is also medial.   [x. 23, Por.]

Q. E. D.

PROPOSITION 25

The rectangle contained by medial straight lines commensurable in square only is either rational or medial.

For let the rectangle *AC* be contained by the medial straight lines *AB*, *BC* which are commensurable in square only;

I say that *AC* is either rational or medial.

For on *AB*, *BC* let the squares *AD*, *BE* be described;

therefore each of the squares *AD*, *BE* is medial.

Let a rational straight line *FG* be set out,

to *FG* let there be applied the rectangular parallelogram *GH* equal to *AD*, producing *FH* as breadth,

to *HM* let there be applied the rectangular parallelogram *MK* equal to *AC*, producing *HK* as breadth, and further to KN let there be similarly applied NL equal to BE, producing KL as breadth;

therefore FH, HK, KL are in a straight line.

Since then each of the squares AD, BE is medial,

and AD is equal to GH, and BE to NL, therefore each of the rectangles GH, NL is also medial.

And they are applied to the rational straight line FG;

therefore each of the straight lines FH, KL is rational and incommensurable in length with FG.   [x. 22]

And, since AD is commensurable with BE,

therefore GH is also commensurable with NL.

And, as GH is to NL, so is FH to KL;   [vi. 1]

therefore FH is commensurable in length with KL.   [x. 11]

Therefore FH, KL are rational straight lines commensurable in length;

therefore the rectangle FH, KL is rational.   [x. 19]

And, since DB is equal to BA, and OB to BC,

therefore, as DB is to BC, so is AB to BO.

But, as DB is to BC, so is DA to AC,   [vi. 1]

and, as AB is to BO, so is AC to CO;   [id.]

therefore, as DA is to AC, so is AC to CO.

But AD is equal to GH, AC to MK and CO to NL;

therefore, as GH is to MK, so is MK to NL;

therefore also, as FH is to HK, so is HK to KL;   [vi. 1, v. 11]

therefore the rectangle FH, KL is equal to the square on HK.   [vi. 17]

But the rectangle FH, KL is rational;

therefore the square on HK is also rational.

Therefore HK is rational.

And, if it is commensurable in length with FG,

HN is rational;   [x. 19]

but, if it is incommensurable in length with FG,

KH, HM are rational straight lines commensurable in square only, and therefore HN is medial.   [x. 21]

Therefore HN is either rational or medial.

But HN is equal to AC;

therefore AC is either rational or medial.

Therefore etc.   Q. E. D.

PROPOSITION 26

A medial area does not exceed a medial area by a rational area.

For, if possible, let the medial area AB exceed the medial area AC by the rational area DB,

and let a rational straight line EF be set out;

to EF let there be applied the rectangular parallelogram FH equal to AB, producing EH as breadth,

and let the rectangle FG equal to AC be subtracted;

therefore the remainder *BD* is equal to the remainder *KH*.

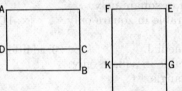

But *DB* is rational;

therefore *KH* is also rational.

Since, then, each of the rectangles *AB*, *AC* is medial,

and *AB* is equal to *FH*, and *AC* to *FG*, therefore each of the rectangles *FH*, *FG* is also medial.

And they are applied to the rational straight line *EF*;

therefore each of the straight lines *HE*, *EG* is rational and incommensurable in length with *EF*.   [x. 22]

And, since [*DB* is rational and is equal to *KH*,

therefore] *KH* is [also] rational;

and it is applied to the rational straight line *EF*;

therefore *GH* is rational and commensurable in length with *EF*.   [x. 20]

But *EG* is also rational, and is incommensurable in length with *EF*;

therefore *EG* is incommensurable in length with *GH*.   [x. 13]

And, as *EG* is to *GH*, so is the square on *EG* to the rectangle *EG*, *GH*;

therefore the square on *EG* is incommensurable with the rectangle *EG*, *GH*.

[x. 11]

But the squares on *EG*, *GH* are commensurable with the square on *EG*, for both are rational;

and twice the rectangle *EG*, *GH* is commensurable with the rectangle *EG*, *GH*, for it is double of it;   [x. 6]

therefore the squares on *EG*, *GH* are incommensurable with twice the rectangle *EG*, *GH*;   [x. 13]

therefore also the sum of the squares on *EG*, *GH* and twice the rectangle *EG*, *GH*, that is, the square on *EH* [ii. 4] is incommensurable with the squares on *EG*, *GH*.   [x. 16]

But the squares on *EG*, *GH* are rational;

therefore the square on *EH* is irrational.   [x. Def. 4]

Therefore *EH* is irrational.

But it is also rational:

which is impossible.

Therefore etc.   Q. E. D.

PROPOSITION 27

To find medial straight lines commensurable in square only which contain a rational rectangle.

Let two rational straight lines *A*, *B* commensurable in square only be set out;

let *C* be taken a mean proportional between *A*, *B*, [vi. 13] and let it be contrived that,

as *A* is to *B*, so is *C* to *D*.   [vi. 12]

Then, since *A*, *B* are rational and commensurable in square only,

the rectangle *A*, *B*, that is, the square on *C*

[vi. 17], is medial.   [x. 21]

Therefore C is medial.   [x. 21]
And since, as A is to B, so is C to D,
          and A, B are commensurable in square only,
     therefore C, D are also commensurable in square only.   [x. 11]
And C is medial;
                    therefore D is also medial.   [x. 23, addition]
Therefore C, D are medial and commensurable in square only.
I say that they also contain a rational rectangle.
For since, as A is to B, so is C to D,
          therefore, alternately, as A is to C, so is B to D.   [v. 16]
But, as A is to C, so is C to B;
                    therefore also, as C is to B, so is B to D;
          therefore the rectangle C, D is equal to the square on B.
But the square on B is rational;
                    therefore the rectangle C, D is also rational.
Therefore medial straight lines commensurable in square only have been
found which contain a rational rectangle.   Q. E. D.

PROPOSITION 28

To find medial straight lines commensurable in square only, which contain a medial
rectangle.

Let the rational straight lines A, B, C commensurable in square only be set
out;
          let D be taken a mean proportional between A, B,   [vi. 13]
                    and let it be contrived that,
               as B is to C, so is D to E.   [vi. 12]
Since A, B are rational straight
lines commensurable in square only,   A ————
therefore the rectangle A, B, that   B————————   D ————————
is, the square on D [vi. 17], is medi-   C————————   E ————————
al.   [x. 21]
Therefore D is medial.   [x. 21]
And since B, C are commensurable in square only,
               and, as B is to C, so is D to E,
     therefore D, E are also commensurable in square only.   [x. 11]
But D is medial;
                    therefore E is also medial.   [x. 23, addition]
Therefore D, E are medial straight lines commensurable in square only.
I say next that they also contain a medial rectangle.
For since, as B is to C, so is D to E,
          therefore, alternately, as B is to D, so is C to E.   [v. 16]
But, as B is to D, so is D to A;
               therefore also, as D is to A, so is C to E;
     therefore the rectangle A, C is equal to the rectangle D, E.   [vi. 16]
But the rectangle A, C is medial;   [x. 21]
                    therefore the rectangle D, E is also medial.
Therefore medial straight lines commensurable in square only have been
found which contain a medial rectangle.   Q. E. D.

Lemma 1

To find two square numbers such that their sum is also square.

Let two numbers AB, BC be set out, and let them be either both even or both odd.

Then since, whether an even number is subtracted from an even number, or an odd number from an odd number, the remainder is even, [IX. 24, 26] therefore the remainder AC is even.

Let AC be bisected at D.

Let AB, BC also be either similar plane numbers, or square numbers, which are themselves also similar plane numbers.

Now the product of AB, BC together with the square on CD is equal to the square on BD. [II. 6]

And the product of AB, BC is square, inasmuch as it was proved that, if two similar plane numbers by multiplying one another make some number, the product is square. [IX. 1]

Therefore two square numbers, the product of AB, BC, and the square on CD, have been found which, when added together, make the square on BD.

And it is manifest that two square numbers, the square on BD and the square on CD, have again been found such that their difference, the product of AB, BC, is a square, whenever AB, BC are similar plane numbers.

But when they are not similar plane numbers, two square numbers, the square on BD and the square on DC, have been found such that their difference, the product of AB, BC, is not square. Q. E. D.

Lemma 2

To find two square numbers such that their sum is not square.

For let the product of AB, BC, as we said, be square,
and CA even,
and let CA be bisected by D.

It is then manifest that the square product of AB, BC together with the square on CD is equal to the square on BD.

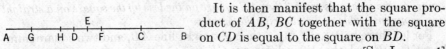

[See Lemma 1]

Let the unit DE be subtracted; therefore the product of AB, BC together with the square on CE is less than the square on BD.

I say then that the square product of AB, BC together with the square on CE will not be square.

For, if it is square, it is either equal to the square on BE, or less than the square on BE, but cannot any more be greater, lest the unit be divided.

First, if possible, let the product of AB, BC together with the square on CE be equal to the square on BE,
and let GA be double of the unit DE.

Since then the whole AC is double of the whole CD,
and in them AG is double of DE,
therefore the remainder GC is also double of the remainder EC;
therefore GC is bisected by E.

Therefore the product of *GB*, *BC* together with the square on *CE* is equal to the square on *BE*. [II. 6]

But the product of *AB*, *BC* together with the square on *CE* is also, by hypothesis, equal to the square on *BE*;

therefore the product of *GB*, *BC* together with the square on *CE* is equal to the product of *AB*, *BC* together with the square on *CE*.

And, if the common square on *CE* be subtracted,

it follows that *AB* is equal to *GB*:

which is absurd.

Therefore the product of *AB*, *BC* together with the square on *CE* is not equal to the square on *BE*.

I say next that neither is it less than the square on *BE*.

For, if possible, let it be equal to the square on *BF*,

and let *HA* be double of *DF*.

Now it will again follow that *HC* is double of *CF*;

so that *CH* has also been bisected at *F*,

and for this reason the product of *HB*, *BC* together with the square on *FC* is equal to the square on *BF*. [II. 6]

But, by hypothesis, the product of *AB*, *BC* together with the square on *CE* is also equal to the square on *BF*.

Thus the product of *HB*, *BC* together with the square on *CF* will also be equal to the product of *AB*, *BC* together with the square on *CE*:

which is absurd.

Therefore the product of *AB*, *BC* together with the square on *CE* is not less than the square on *BE*.

And it was proved that neither is it equal to the square on *BE*.

Therefore the product of *AB*, *BC* together with the square on *CE* is not square. Q. E. D.

PROPOSITION 29

To find two rational straight lines commensurable in square only and such that the square on the greater is greater than the square on the less by the square on a straight line commensurable in length with the greater.

For let there be set out any rational straight line *AB*, and two square numbers *CD*, *DE* such that their difference *CE* is not square; [Lemma 1]
let there be described on *AB* the semicircle *AFB*,
and let it be contrived that,
as *DC* is to *CE*, so is the square on *BA* to the square on *AF*. [x. 6, Por.]
Let *FB* be joined.

Since, as the square on *BA* is to the square on *AF*, so is *DC* to *CE*,
therefore the square on *BA* has to the square on *AF* the ratio which the number *DC* has to the number *CE*;
therefore the square on *BA* is commensurable with the square on *AF*. [x. 6]
But the square on *AB* is rational; [x. Def. 4]

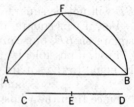

therefore the square on *AF* is also rational; [*id.*]
therefore *AF* is also rational.

And, since DC has not to CE the ratio which a square number has to a square number,
neither has the square on BA to the square on AF the ratio which a square number has to a square number;
therefore AB is incommensurable in length with AF.   [x. 9]
Therefore BA, AF are rational straight lines commensurable in square only.
And since, as DC is to CE, so is the square on BA to the square on AF,
therefore, *convertendo*, as CD is to DE, so is the square on AB to the square on BF.   [v. 19, Por., III. 31, I. 47]
But CD has to DE the ratio which a square number has to a square number:
therefore also the square on AB has to the square on BF the ratio which a square number has to a square number;
therefore AB is commensurable in length with BF.   [x. 9]
And the square on AB is equal to the squares on AF, FB;
therefore the square on AB is greater than the square on AF by the square on BF commensurable with AB.
Therefore there have been found two rational straight lines BA, AF commensurable in square only and such that the square on the greater AB is greater than the square on the less AF by the square on BF commensurable in length with AB.   Q. E. D.

PROPOSITION 30

To find two rational straight lines commensurable in square only and such that the square on the greater is greater than the square on the less by the square on a straight line incommensurable in length with the greater.

Let there be set out a rational straight line AB,

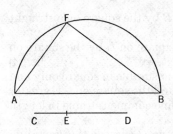

and two square numbers CE, ED such that their sum CD is not square;   [Lemma 2]
let there be described on AB the semicircle AFB,
let it be contrived that,
as DC is to CE, so is the square on BA to the square on AF.   [x. 6, Por.]
and let FB be joined.
Then, in a similar manner to the preceding, we can prove that BA, AF are rational straight lines commensurable in square only.
And since, as DC is to CE, so is the square on BA to the square on AF,
therefore, *convertendo*, as CD is to DE, so is the square on AB to the square on BF.   [v. 19, Por., III. 31, I. 47]
But CD has not to DE the ratio which a square number has to a square number;
therefore neither has the square on AB to the square on BF the ratio which a square number has to a square number;
therefore AB is incommensurable in length with BF.   [x. 9]
And the square on AB is greater than the square on AF by the square on FB incommensurable with AB.
Therefore AB, AF are rational straight lines commensurable in square only, and the square on AB is greater than the square on AF by the square on FB incommensurable in length with AB.   Q. E. D.

PROPOSITION 31

To find two medial straight lines commensurable in square only, containing a rational rectangle, and such that the square on the greater is greater than the square on the less by the square on a straight line commensurable in length with the greater.

Let there be set out two rational straight lines A, B commensurable in square only and such that the square on A, being the greater, is greater than the square on B the less by the square on a straight line commensurable in length with A.   [x. 29]

And let the square on C be equal to the rectangle A, B.

Now the rectangle A, B is medial;   [x. 21]

    therefore the square on C is also medial;

       therefore C is also medial.   [x. 21]

Let the rectangle C, D be equal to the square on B.

Now the square on B is rational;

       therefore the rectangle C, D is also rational.

And since, as A is to B, so is the rectangle A, B to the square on B,

    while the square on C is equal to the rectangle A, B,

      and the rectangle C, D is equal to the square on B,

therefore, as A is to B, so is the square on C to the rectangle C, D.

But, as the square on C is to the rectangle C, D, so is C to D;

      therefore also, as A is to B, so is C to D.

But A is commensurable with B in square only;

    therefore C is also commensurable with D in square only.   [x. 11]

And C is medial;

       therefore D is also medial.   [x. 23, addition]

And since, as A is to B, so is C to D,

and the square on A is greater than the square on B by the square on a straight line commensurable with A,

therefore also the square on C is greater than the square on D by the square on a straight line commensurable with C.   [x. 14]

Therefore two medial straight lines C, D, commensurable in square only and containing a rational rectangle, have been found, and the square on C is greater than the square on D by the square on a straight line commensurable in length with C.

Similarly also it can be proved that the square on C exceeds the square on D by the square on a straight line incommensurable with C, when the square on A is greater than the square on B by the square on a straight line incommensurable with A.   [x. 30]

PROPOSITION 32

To find two medial straight lines commensurable in square only, containing a medial rectangle, and such that the square on the greater is greater than the square on the less by the square on a straight line commensurable with the greater.

Let there be set out three rational straight lines A, B, C commensurable in square only, and such that the square on A is greater than the square on C by the square on a straight line commensurable with A,   [x. 29]

    and let the square on D be equal to the rectangle A, B.

Therefore the square on D is medial;

therefore D is also medial.   [x. 21]

Let the rectangle D, E be equal to the rectangle B, C.

A————————

D————————

B————————

E————————

C————————

Then since, as the rectangle A, B is to the rectangle B, C, so is A to C;

while the square on D is equal to the rectangle A, B,

and the rectangle D, E is equal to the rectangle B, C,

therefore, as A is to C, so is the square on D to the rectangle D, E.

But, as the square on D is to the rectangle D, E, so is D to E;

therefore also, as A is to C, so is D to E.

But A is commensurable with C in square only;

therefore D is also commensurable with E in square only.   [x. 11]

But D is medial;

therefore E is also medial.   [x. 23, addition]

And, since, as A is to C, so is D to E,

while the square on A is greater than the square on C by the square on a straight line commensurable with A,

therefore also the square on D will be greater than the square on E by the square on a straight line commensurable with D.   [x. 14]

I say next that the rectangle D, E is also medial.

For, since the rectangle B, C is equal to the rectangle D, E, while the rectangle B, C is medial,   [x. 21]

therefore the rectangle D, E is also medial.

Therefore two medial straight lines D, E, commensurable in square only, and containing a medial rectangle, have been found such that the square on the greater is greater than the square on the less by the square on a straight line commensurable with the greater.

Similarly again it can be proved that the square on D is greater than the square on E by the square on a straight line incommensurable with D, when the square on A is greater than the square on C by the square on a straight line incommensurable with A.   [x. 30]

LEMMA

Let ABC be a right-angled triangle having the angle A right, and let the perpendicular AD be drawn;

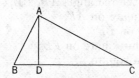

I say that the rectangle CB, BD is equal to the square on BA,

the rectangle BC, CD equal to the square on CA,

the rectangle BD, DC equal to the square on AD,

and, further, the rectangle BC, AD equal to the rectangle BA, AC.

And first that the rectangle CB, BD is equal to the square on BA.

For, since in a right-angled triangle AD has been drawn from the right angle perpendicular to the base,

therefore the triangles ABD, ADC are similar both to the whole ABC and to one another.   [vi. 8]

And since the triangle ABC is similar to the triangle ABD, therefore, as CB is to BA, so is BA to BD;   [vi. 4] therefore the rectangle CB, BD is equal to the square on AB.   [VI. 17]

For the same reason the rectangle BC, CD is also equal to the square on AC.

And since, if in a right-angled triangle a perpendicular be drawn from the right angle to the base, the perpendicular so drawn is a mean proportional between the segments of the base,   [VI. 8, Por.]

therefore, as BD is to DA, so is AD to DC;

therefore the rectangle BD, DC is equal to the square on AD.   [VI. 17]

I say that the rectangle BC, AD is also equal to the rectangle BA, AC.

For since, as we said, ABC is similar to ABD,

therefore, as BC is to CA, so is BA to AD.   [VI. 4]

Therefore the rectangle BC, AD is equal to the rectangle BA, AC.   [VI. 16]

Q. E. D.

PROPOSITION 33

To find two straight lines incommensurable in square which make the sum of the squares on them rational but the rectangle contained by them medial.

Let there be set out two rational straight lines AB, BC commensurable in square only and such that the square on the greater AB is greater than the square on the less BC by the square on a straight line incommensurable with AB,   [X. 30]

let BC be bisected at D,

let there be applied to AB a parallelogram equal to the square on either of the straight lines BD, DC and deficient by a square figure, and let it be the rectangle AE, EB;   [VI. 28]

let the semicircle AFB be described on AB,

let EF be drawn at right angles to AB,

and let AF, FB be joined.

Then, since AB, BC are unequal straight lines,

and the square on AB is greater than the square on BC by the square on a straight line incommensurable with AB,

while there has been applied to AB a parallelogram equal to the fourth part of the square on BC, that is, to the square on half of it, and deficient by a square figure, making the rectangle AE, EB,

therefore AE is incommensurable with EB.   [X. 18]

And, as AE is to EB, so is the rectangle BA, AE to the rectangle AB, BE,

while the rectangle BA, AE is equal to the square on AF,

and the rectangle AB, BE to the square on BF;

therefore the square on AF is incommensurable with the square on FB;

therefore AF, FB are incommensurable in square.

And, since AB is rational,

therefore the square on AB is also rational;

so that the sum of the squares on AF, FB is also rational.   [I. 47]

And since, again, the rectangle AE, EB is equal to the square on EF,

and, by hypothesis, the rectangle AE, EB is also equal to the square on BD,

therefore FE is equal to BD;

therefore BC is double of FE,

so that the rectangle AB, BC is also commensurable with the rectangle AB, EF.

But the rectangle AB, BC is medial;   [x. 21]
    therefore the rectangle AB, EF is also medial. [x. 23, Por.]
But the rectangle AB, EF is equal to the rectangle AF, FB; [Lemma]
    therefore the rectangle AF, FB is also medial.

But it was also proved that the sum of the squares on these straight lines is rational.

Therefore two straight lines AF, FB incommensurable in square have been found which make the sum of the squares on them rational, but the rectangle contained by them medial. Q. E. D.

PROPOSITION 34

To find two straight lines incommensurable in square which make the sum of the squares on them medial but the rectangle contained by them rational.

Let there be set out two medial straight lines AB, BC, commensurable in square only, such that the rectangle which they contain is rational, and the square on AB is greater than the square on BC by the square on a straight line incommensurable with AB; [x. 31, *ad fin.*]

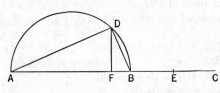

let the semicircle ADB be described on AB,
 let BC be bisected at E,
let there be applied to AB a parallelogram equal to the square on BE and deficient by a square figure, namely the rectangle AF, FB; [vi. 28]
  therefore AF is incommensurable in length with FB. [x. 18]

Let FD be drawn from F at right angles to AB,
   and let AD, DB be joined.

Since AF is incommensurable in length with FB,
therefore the rectangle BA, AF is also incommensurable with the rectangle AB, BF. [x. 11]

But the rectangle BA, AF is equal to the square on AD, and the rectangle AB, BF to the square on DB;
therefore the square on AD is also incommensurable with the square on DB.

And, since the square on AB is medial,
therefore the sum of the squares on AD, DB is also medial. [iii. 31, i. 47]

And, since BC is double of DF,
therefore the rectangle AB, BC is also double of the rectangle AB, FD.

But the rectangle AB, BC is rational;
  therefore the rectangle AB, FD is also rational. [x. 6]

But the rectangle AB, FD is equal to the rectangle AD, DB; [Lemma]
  so that the rectangle AD, DB is also rational.

Therefore two straight lines AD, DB incommensurable in square have been found which make the sum of the squares on them medial, but the rectangle contained by them rational. Q. E. D.

PROPOSITION 35

To find two straight lines incommensurable in square which make the sum of the squares on them medial and the rectangle contained by them medial and moreover incommensurable with the sum of the squares on them.

Let there be set out two medial straight lines AB, BC commensurable in square only, containing a medial rectangle, and such that the square on AB is greater than the square on BC by the square on a straight line incommensurable with AB;   [x. 32, *ad fin.*]

     let the semicircle ADB be described on AB,

      and let the rest of the construction be as above.

Then, since AF is incommensurable in length with FB,   [x. 18]
AD is also incommensurable in square
with DB.   [x. 11]

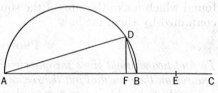

And, since the square on AB is
medial,
therefore the sum of the squares on
AD, DB is also medial. [iii. 31, i. 47]

And, since the rectangle AF, FB is equal to the square on each of the straight lines BE, DF,

      therefore BE is equal to DF;

     therefore BC is double of FD,

so that the rectangle AB, BC is also double of the rectangle AB, FD.

But the rectangle AB, BC is medial;

    therefore the rectangle AB, FD is also medial. [x. 32, Por.]

And it is equal to the rectangle AD, DB;   [Lemma after x. 32]

    therefore the rectangle AD, DB is also medial.

And, since AB is incommensurable in length with BC,

     while CB is commensurable with BE,

   therefore AB is also incommensurable in length with BE, [x. 13]

so that the square on AB is also incommensurable with the rectangle AB, BE.
                     [x. 11]

But the squares on AD, DB are equal to the square on AB, [i. 47]

and the rectangle AB, FD, that is, the rectangle AD, DB, is equal to the rectangle AB, BE;

therefore the sum of the squares on AD, DB is incommensurable with the rectangle AD, DB.

Therefore two straight lines AD, DB incommensurable in square have been found which make the sum of the squares on them medial and the rectangle contained by them medial and moreover incommensurable with the sum of the squares on them.   Q. E. D.

PROPOSITION 36

If two rational straight lines commensurable in square only be added together, the whole is irrational; and let it be called binomial.

For let two rational straight lines AB, BC commensurable in square only be added together;

   I say that the whole AC is irrational.

For, since AB is incommensurable in length with
BC—for they are commensurable in square only—

and, as AB is to BC, so is the rectangle AB, BC to the square on BC,

   therefore the rectangle AB, BC is incommensurable with the square
        on BC.   [x. 11]

But twice the rectangle AB, BC is commensurable with the rectangle AB, BC [x. 6], and the squares on AB, BC are commensurable with the square on BC—for AB, BC are rational straight lines commensurable in square only—

[x. 15]

therefore twice the rectangle AB, BC is incommensurable with the squares on AB, BC.   [x. 13]

And, *componendo*, twice the rectangle AB, BC together with the squares on AB, BC, that is, the square on AC [ii. 4], is incommensurable with the sum of the squares on AB, BC.   [x. 16]

But the sum of the squares on AB, BC is rational;
therefore the square on AC is irrational,
so that AC is also irrational.   [x. Def. 4]

And let it be called *binomial*.   Q. E. D.

PROPOSITION 37

If two medial straight lines commensurable in square only and containing a rational rectangle be added together, the whole is irrational; and let it be called a first bimedial *straight line.*

For let two medial straight lines AB, BC commensurable in square only and containing a rational rectangle be added together;

I say that the whole AC is irrational.

For, since AB is incommensurable in length with BC,

therefore the squares on AB, BC are also incommensurable with twice the rectangle AB, BC;   [cf. x. 36, ll. 9–20]

and, *componendo*, the squares on AB, BC together with twice the rectangle AB, BC, that is, the square on AC [ii. 4], is incommensurable with the rectangle AB, BC.   [x. 16]

But the rectangle AB, BC is rational, for, by hypothesis, AB, BC are straight lines containing a rational rectangle;

therefore the square on AC is irrational;
therefore AC is irrational.   [x. Def. 4]

And let it be called a *first bimedial* straight line.   Q. E. D.

PROPOSITION 38

If two medial straight lines commensurable in square only and containing a medial rectangle be added together, the whole is irrational; and let it be called a second bimedial *straight line.*

For let two medial straight lines AB, BC commensurable in square only and containing a medial rectangle be added together;

I say that AC is irrational.

For let a rational straight line DE be set out, and let the parallelogram DF equal to the square on AC be applied to DE, producing DG as breadth.   [i. 44]

Then, since the square on AC is equal to the squares on AB, BC and twice the rectangle AB, BC,   [ii. 4]

let EH, equal to the squares on AB, BC, be applied to DE;

therefore the remainder HF is equal to twice the rectangle AB, BC.

And, since each of the straight lines AB, BC is medial,
                therefore the squares on AB, BC are also medial.

But, by hypothesis, twice the rectangle AB, BC is also medial.

And EH is equal to the squares on AB, BC,
                while FH is equal to twice the rectangle AB, BC;
                therefore each of the rectangles EH, HF is medial.

And they are applied to the rational straight line DE;
therefore each of the straight lines DH, HG is rational and incommensurable
in length with DE.   [x. 22]

Since then AB is incommensurable in length with BC,
and, as AB is to BC, so is the square on AB to the rectangle AB, BC,
therefore the square on AB is incommensurable with the rectangle AB, BC.
                                                                        [x. 11]

But the sum of the squares on AB, BC is commensurable with the square on
AB,   [x. 15]
and twice the rectangle AB, BC is commensurable with the rectangle AB, BC.
                                                                        [x. 6]

Therefore the sum of the squares on AB, BC is incommensurable with twice
the rectangle AB, BC.   [x. 13]

But EH is equal to the squares on AB, BC,
                and HF is equal to twice the rectangle AB, BC.

Therefore EH is incommensurable with HF,
                so that DH is also incommensurable in length with HG. [vi. 1, x. 11]

Therefore DH, HG are rational straight lines commensurable in square only;
                so that DG is irrational.   [x. 36]

But DE is rational;
and the rectangle contained by an irrational and a rational straight line is irrational;   [cf. x. 20]
                therefore the area DF is irrational,
                and the side of the square equal to it is irrational. [x. Def. 4]

But AC is the side of the square equal to DF;
                therefore AC is irrational.

And let it be called a *second bimedial* straight line.   Q. E. D.

PROPOSITION 39

*If two straight lines incommensurable in square which make the sum of the squares
on them rational, but the rectangle contained by them medial, be added together, the
whole straight line is irrational: and let it be called* major.

For let two straight lines AB, BC incommensurable in square, and fulfilling
the given conditions [x. 33], be added together;
I say that AC is irrational.

For, since the rectangle AB, BC is medial,
                twice the rectangle AB, BC is also medial. [x. 6 and 23, Por.]

But the sum of the squares on AB, BC is rational;
therefore twice the rectangle AB, BC is incommensurable with the sum of the
squares on AB, BC,
so that the squares on AB, BC together with twice the rectangle AB, BC, that

is, the square on AC, is also incommensurable with the sum of the squares on AB, BC;   [x. 16]

therefore the square on AC is irrational,

so that AC is also irrational.   [x. Def. 4]

And let it be called *major*.   Q. E. D.

PROPOSITION 40

If two straight lines incommensurable in square which make the sum of the squares on them medial, but the rectangle contained by them rational, be added together, the whole straight line is irrational; and let it be called the side of a rational plus a medial area.

For let two straight lines AB, BC incommensurable in square, and fulfilling the given conditions [x. 34], be added together;

A   B   C

I say that AC is irrational.

For, since the sum of the squares on AB, BC is medial, while twice the rectangle AB, BC is rational,
therefore the sum of the squares on AB, BC is incommensurable with twice the rectangle AB, BC;
so that the square on AC is also incommensurable with twice the rectangle AB, BC.   [x. 16]

But twice the rectangle AB, BC is rational;

therefore the square on AC is irrational.

Therefore AC is irrational.   [x. Def. 4]

And let it be called the *side of a rational plus a medial area.*   Q. E. D.

PROPOSITION 41

If two straight lines incommensurable in square which make the sum of the squares on them medial, and the rectangle contained by them medial and also incommensurable with the sum of the squares on them, be added together, the whole straight line is irrational; and let it be called the side of the sum of two medial areas.

For let two straight lines AB, BC incommensurable in square and satisfying the given conditions [x. 35] be added together;

I say that AC is irrational.

Let a rational straight line DE be set out, and let there be applied to DE the rectangle DF equal to the squares on AB, BC, and the rectangle GH equal to twice the rectangle AB, BC;

therefore the whole DH is equal to the square on AC. [II. 4]

Now, since the sum of the squares on AB, BC is medial,

and is equal to DF,

therefore DF is also medial.

And it is applied to the rational straight line DE;
therefore DG is rational and incommensurable in length with DE.   [x. 22]

For the same reason GK is also rational and incommensurable in length with GF, that is, DE.

And, since the squares on AB, BC are incommensurable with twice the rectangle AB, BC,

DF is incommensurable with GH;

so that DG is also incommensurable with GK.   [VI. 1, X. 11]
And they are rational;
therefore DG, GK are rational straight lines commensurable in square only;
therefore DK is irrational and what is called binomial.   [X. 36]
But DE is rational;
therefore DH is irrational, and the side of the square which is equal to it is irrational.   [X. Def. 4]
But AC is the side of the square equal to HD;
therefore AC is irrational.
And let it be called the *side of the sum of two medial areas.*   Q. E. D.

LEMMA

And that the aforesaid irrational straight lines are divided only in one way into the straight lines of which they are the sum and which produce the types in question, we will now prove after premising the following lemma.
Let the straight line AB be set out, let the whole be cut into unequal parts at each of the points C, D,
and let AC be supposed greater than DB;
I say that the squares on AC, CB are greater than the squares on AD, DB.
For let AB be bisected at E.
Then, since AC is greater than DB,
let DC be subtracted from each;
therefore the remainder AD is greater than the remainder CB.
But AE is equal to EB;
therefore DE is less than EC;
therefore the points C, D are not equidistant from the point of bisection.
And, since the rectangle AC, CB together with the square on EC is equal to the square on EB,   [II. 5]
and, further, the rectangle AD, DB together with the square on DE is equal to the square on EB,   [*id.*]
therefore the rectangle AC, CB together with the square on EC is equal to the rectangle AD, DB together with the square on DE.
And of these the square on DE is less than the square on EC;
therefore the remainder, the rectangle AC, CB, is also less than the rectangle AD, DB,
so that twice the rectangle AC, CB is also less than twice the rectangle AD, DB.
Therefore also the remainder, the sum of the squares on AC, CB, is greater than the sum of the squares on AD, DB.   Q. E. D.

PROPOSITION 42

A binomial straight line is divided into its terms at one point only.
Let AB be a binomial straight line divided into its terms at C;
therefore AC, CB are rational straight lines commensurable in square only.
I say that AB is not divided at another point into two rational straight lines commensurable in square only.

For, if possible, let it be divided at D also, so that AD, DB are also rational straight lines commensurable in square only.

It is then manifest that AC is not the same with DB.

For, if possible, let it be so.

Then AD will also be the same as CB,

and, as AC is to CB, so will BD be to DA;

thus AB will be divided at D also in the same way as by the division at C:

which is contrary to the hypothesis.

Therefore AC is not the same with DB.

For this reason also the points C, D are not equidistant from the point of bisection.

Therefore that by which the squares on AC, CB differ from the squares on AD, DB is also that by which twice the rectangle AD, DB differs from twice the rectangle AC, CB,

because both the squares on AC, CB together with twice the rectangle AC, CB, and the squares on AD, DB together with twice the rectangle AD, DB, are equal to the square on AB.   [II. 4]

But the squares on AC, CB differ from the squares on AD, DB by a rational area,

for both are rational;

therefore twice the rectangle AD, DB also differs from twice the rectangle AC, CB by a rational area, though they are medial [x. 21]:

which is absurd, for a medial area does not exceed a medial by a rational area.
                                                                        [x. 26]

Therefore a binomial straight line is not divided at different points;

therefore it is divided at one point only.   Q. E. D.

PROPOSITION 43

A first bimedial straight line is divided at one point only.

Let AB be a first bimedial straight line divided at C, so that AC, CB are medial straight lines commensurable in square only and containing a rational rectangle; [x. 37]

A   D C   B

I say that AB is not so divided at another point.

For, if possible, let it be divided at D also, so that AD, DB are also medial straight lines commensurable in square only and containing a rational rectangle.

Since, then, that by which twice the rectangle AD, DB differs from twice the rectangle AC, CB is that by which the squares on AC, CB differ from the squares on AD, DB,

while twice the rectangle AD, DB differs from twice the rectangle AC, CB by a rational area—for both are rational—

therefore the squares on AC, CB also differ from the squares on AD, DB by a rational area, though they are medial:

which is absurd.   [x. 26]

Therefore a first bimedial straight line is not divided into its terms at different points;

therefore it is so divided at one point only.   Q. E. D.

PROPOSITION 44

A second bimedial straight line is divided at one point only.

Let AB be a second bimedial straight line divided at C, so that AC, CB are medial straight lines commensurable in square only and containing a medial rectangle;   [x. 38]
it is then manifest that C is not at the point of bisection, because the segments are not commensurable in length.

I say that AB is not so divided at another point.

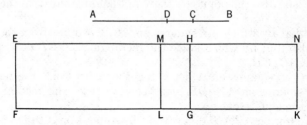

For, if possible, let it be divided at D also, so that AC is not the same with DB, but AC is supposed greater;
it is then clear that the squares on AD, DB are also, as we proved above [Lemma], less than the squares on AC, CB;
and suppose that AD, DB are medial straight lines commensurable in square only and containing a medial rectangle.

Now let a rational straight line EF be set out,
let there be applied to EF the rectangular parallelogram EK equal to the square on AB,
                    and let EG, equal to the squares on AC, CB, be subtracted;
therefore the remainder HK is equal to twice the rectangle AC, CB.   [ii. 4]

Again, let there be subtracted EL, equal to the squares on AD, DB, which were proved less than the squares on AC, CB [Lemma];
therefore the remainder MK is also equal to twice the rectangle AD, DB.

Now, since the squares on AC, CB are medial,
                    therefore EG is medial.

And it is applied to the rational straight line EF;
therefore EH is rational and incommensurable in length with EF.   [x. 22]

For the same reason
                    HN is also rational and incommensurable in length with EF.

And, since AC, CB are medial straight lines commensurable in square only,
                    therefore AC is incommensurable in length with CB.

But, as AC is to CB, so is the square on AC to the rectangle AC, CB;
therefore the square on AC is incommensurable with the rectangle AC, CB.

                                                                              [x. 11]

But the squares on AC, CB are commensurable with the square on AC; for AC, CB are commensurable in square.   [x. 15]

And twice the rectangle AC, CB is commensurable with the rectangle AC, CB.   [x. 6]

Therefore the squares on AC, CB are also incommensurable with twice the rectangle AC, CB.   [x. 13]

But *EG* is equal to the squares on *AC*, *CB*,
> and *HK* is equal to twice the rectangle *AC*, *CB*;
>> therefore *EG* is incommensurable with *HK*,
so that *EH* is also incommensurable in length with *HN*.   [VI. 1, X. 11]

And they are rational;
therefore *EH*, *HN* are rational straight lines commensurable in square only.

But, if two rational straight lines commensurable in square only be added
together, the whole is the irrational which is called binomial.   [X. 36]

Therefore *EN* is a binomial straight line divided at *H*.

In the same way *EM*, *MN* will also be proved to be rational straight lines
commensurable in square only;
and *EN* will be a binomial straight line divided at different points, *H* and *M*.

And *EH* is not the same with *MN*.

For the squares on *AC*, *CB* are greater than the squares on *AD*, *DB*.

But the squares on *AD*, *DB* are greater than twice the rectangle *AD*, *DB*;
therefore also the squares on *AC*, *CB*, that is, *EG*, are much greater than twice
the rectangle *AD*, *DB*, that is, *MK*,
> so that *EH* is also greater than *MN*.

Therefore *EH* is not the same with *MN*.   Q. E. D.

PROPOSITION 45

A major straight line is divided at one and the same point only.

Let *AB* be a major straight line divided at *C*, so that *AC*, *CB* are incommensurable in square and make the sum of the
squares on *AC*, *CB* rational, but the rectangle
AC, *CB* medial;

I say that *AB* is not so divided at another point.

For, if possible, let it be divided at *D* also, so that *AD*, *DB* are also incommensurable in square and make the sum of the squares on *AD*, *DB* rational,
but the rectangle contained by them medial.

Then, since that by which the squares on *AC*, *CB* differ from the squares on
AD, *DB* is also that by which twice the rectangle *AD*, *DB* differs from twice
the rectangle *AC*, *CB*,
while the squares on *AC*, *CB* exceed the squares on *AD*, *DB* by a rational area
—for both are rational—
therefore twice the rectangle *AD*, *DB* also exceeds twice the rectangle *AC*, *CB*
by a rational area, though they are medial:
> which is impossible.   [X. 26]

Therefore a major straight line is not divided at different points;
> therefore it is only divided at one and the same point.   Q. E. D.

PROPOSITION 46

The side of a rational plus a medial area is divided at one point only.

Let *AB* be the side of a rational plus a medial area divided at *C*, so that *AC*,
CB are incommensurable in square and make the
sum of the squares on *AC*, *CB* medial, but twice
the rectangle *AC*, *CB* rational;   [X. 40]

I say that *AB* is not so divided at another point.

For, if possible, let it be divided at *D* also, so that *AD*, *DB* are also incommensurable in square and make the sum of the squares on AD, DB medial, but twice the rectangle AD, DB rational.

Since, then, that by which twice the rectangle AC, CB differs from twice the rectangle AD, DB is also that by which the squares on AD, DB differ from the squares on AC, CB,
while twice the rectangle AC, CB exceeds twice the rectangle AD, DB by a rational area,
therefore the squares on AD, DB also exceed the squares on AC, CB by a rational area, though they are medial:
                              which is impossible.   [x. 26]
    Therefore the side of a rational plus a medial area is not divided at different points;
                    therefore it is divided at one point only.   Q. E. D.

Proposition 47

The side of the sum of two medial areas is divided at one point only.

    Let AB be divided at C, so that AC, CB are incommensurable in square and make the sum of the squares on AC, CB medial, and the rectangle AC, CB medial and also incommensurable with the sum of the squares on them;
    I say that AB is not divided at another point so as to fulfil the given conditions.

    For, if possible, let it be divided at D, so that again AC is of course not the same as BD, but AC is supposed greater;
let a rational straight line EF be set out,
and let there be applied to EF the rectangle EG equal to the squares on AC, CB,
and the rectangle HK equal to twice the rectangle AC, CB;
therefore the whole EK is equal to the square on AB.   [II. 4]

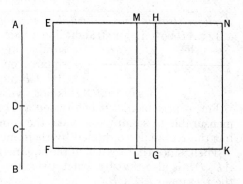

    Again, let EL, equal to the squares on AD, DB, be applied to EF;
therefore the remainder, twice the rectangle AD, DB, is equal to the remainder MK.
    And since, by hypothesis, the sum of the squares on AC, CB is medial,
                    therefore EG is also medial.
    And it is applied to the rational straight line EF;
therefore HE is rational and incommensurable in length with EF.   [x. 22]
    For the same reason
        HN is also rational and incommensurable in length with EF.
    And, since the sum of the squares on AC, CB is incommensurable with twice the rectangle AC, CB,
            therefore EG is also incommensurable with GN,
            so that EH is also incommensurable with HN.   [vi. 1, x. 11]
    And they are rational;
therefore EH, HN are rational straight lines commensurable in square only;
        therefore EN is a binomial straight line divided at H.   [x. 36]

Similarly we can prove that it is also divided at M.

And EH is not the same with MN;

therefore a binomial has been divided at different points:

which is absurd.   [x. 42]

Therefore a side of the sum of two medial areas is not divided at different points;

therefore it is divided at one point only.   Q. E. D.

DEFINITIONS II

1. Given a rational straight line and a binomial, divided into its terms, such that the square on the greater term is greater than the square on the lesser by the square on a straight line commensurable in length with the greater, then, if the greater term be commensurable in length with the rational straight line set out, let the whole be called a *first binomial* straight line;

2. but if the lesser term be commensurable in length with the rational straight line set out, let the whole be called a *second binomial*;

3. and if neither of the terms be commensurable in length with the rational straight line set out, let the whole be called a *third binomial*.

4. Again, if the square on the greater term be greater than the square on the lesser by the square on a straight line incommensurable in length with the greater, then, if the greater term be commensurable in length with the rational straight line set out, let the whole be called a *fourth binomial*;

5. if the lesser, a *fifth binomial*;

6. and if neither, a *sixth binomial*.

PROPOSITION 48

To find the first binomial straight line.

Let two numbers AC, CB be set out such that the sum of them AB has to BC the ratio which a square number has to a square number, but has not to CA the ratio which a square number has to a square number;   [Lemma 1 after x. 28]

let any rational straight line D be set out, and let EF be commensurable in length with D.

Therefore EF is also rational.

Let it be contrived that,

as the number BA is to AC, so is the square on EF to the square on FG.

[x. 6, Por.]

But AB has to AC the ratio which a number has to a number;

therefore the square on EF also has to the square on FG the ratio which a number has to a number,

so that the square on EF is commensurable with the square on FG.   [x. 6]

And EF is rational;

therefore FG is also rational.

And, since BA has not to AC the ratio which a square number has to a square number,

neither, therefore, has the square on EF to the square on FG the ratio which a square number has to a square number;

therefore EF is incommensurable in length with FG.   [x. 9]

Therefore EF, FG are rational straight lines commensurable in square only; therefore EG is binomial.   [x. 36]

I say that it is also a first binomial straight line.

For since, as the number BA is to AC, so is the square on EF to the square on FG,

while BA is greater than AC,

therefore the square on EF is also greater than the square on FG.

Let then the squares on FG, H be equal to the square on EF.

Now since, as BA is to AC, so is the square on EF to the square on FG, therefore, *convertendo*,

as AB is to BC, so is the square on EF to the square on H.   [v. 19, Por.]

But AB has to BC the ratio which a square number has to a square number; therefore the square on EF also has to the square on H the ratio which a square number has to a square number.

Therefore EF is commensurable in length with H;   [x. 9]
therefore the square on EF is greater than the square on FG by the square on a straight line commensurable with EF.

And EF, FG are rational, and EF is commensurable in length with D.

Therefore EF is a first binomial straight line.   Q. E. D.

Proposition 49

To find the second binomial straight line.

Let two numbers AC, CB be set out such that the sum of them AB has to BC the ratio which a square number has to a square number, but has not to AC the ratio which a square number has to a square number;

let a rational straight line D be set out, and let EF be commensurable in length with D;

therefore EF is rational.

Let it be contrived then that, as the number CA is to AB, so also is the square on EF to the square on FG;   [x. 6, Por.]

therefore the square on EF is commensurable with the square on FG.   [x. 6]

Therefore FG is also rational.

Now, since the number CA has not to AB the ratio which a square number has to a square number, neither has the square on EF to the square on FG the ratio which a square number has to a square number.

Therefore EF is incommensurable in length with FG;   [x. 9]
therefore EF, FG are rational straight lines commensurable in square only; therefore EG is binomial.   [x. 36]

It is next to be proved that it is also a second binomial straight line.

For since, inversely, as the number BA is to AC, so is the square on GF to the square on FE,

while BA is greater than AC,

therefore the square on GF is greater than the square on FE.

Let the squares on EF, H be equal to the square on GF;

therefore, *convertendo*, as AB is to BC, so is the square on FG to the square on H.   [v. 19, Por.]

But AB has to BC the ratio which a square number has to a square number;

therefore the square on FG also has to the square on H the ratio which a square number has to a square number.

Therefore FG is commensurable in length with H;   [x. 9]
so that the square on FG is greater than the square on FE by the square on a straight line commensurable with FG.

And FG, FE are rational straight lines commensurable in square only, and EF, the lesser term, is commensurable in length with the rational straight line D set out.

Therefore EG is a second binomial straight line.   Q. E. D.

PROPOSITION 50

To find the third binomial straight line.

Let two numbers AC, CB be set out such that the sum of them AB has to BC the ratio which a square number has to a square number, but has not to AC the ratio which a square number has to a square number.

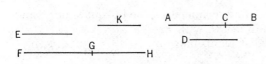

Let any other number D, not square, be set out also, and let it not have to either of the numbers BA, AC the ratio which a square number has to a square number.

Let any rational straight line E be set out,
and let it be contrived that, as D is to AB, so is the square on E to the square on FG;   [x. 6, Por.]
therefore the square on E is commensurable with the square on FG.   [x. 6]

And E is rational;
                therefore FG is also rational.

And, since D has not to AB the ratio which a square number has to a square number,
neither has the square on E to the square on FG the ratio which a square number has to a square number;
                therefore E is incommensurable in length with FG.   [x. 9]

Next let it be contrived that, as the number BA is to AC, so is the square on FG to the square on GH;   [x. 6, Por.]
therefore the square on FG is commensurable with the square on GH. [x. 6]

But FG is rational;
                therefore GH is also rational.

And, since BA has not to AC the ratio which a square number has to a square number,
neither has the square on FG to the square on HG the ratio which a square number has to a square number;
                therefore FG is incommensurable in length with GH.   [x. 9]

Therefore FG, GH are rational straight lines commensurable in square only;
                therefore FH is binomial.   [x. 36]

I say next that it is also a third binomial straight line.

For since, as D is to AB, so is the square on E to the square on FG,
    and, as BA is to AC, so is the square on FG to the square on GH,
therefore, *ex aequali*, as D is to AC, so is the square on E to the square on GH.
                [v. 22]

But D has not to AC the ratio which a square number has to a square number;
therefore neither has the square on E to the square on GH the ratio which a square number has to a square number;
therefore E is incommensurable in length with GH.   [x. 9]
And since, as BA is to AC, so is the square on FG to the square on GH,
therefore the square on FG is greater than the square on GH.
Let then the squares on GH, K be equal to the square on FG;
therefore, *convertendo*, as AB is to BC, so is the square on FG to the square on K.   [v. 19, Por.]
But AB has to BC the ratio which a square number has to a square number;
therefore the square on FG also has to the square on K the ratio which a square number has to a square number;
therefore FG is commensurable in length with K.   [x. 9]
Therefore the square on FG is greater than the square on GH by the square on a straight line commensurable with FG.

And FG, GH are rational straight lines commensurable in square only, and neither of them is commensurable in length with E.

Therefore FH is a third binomial straight line.   Q. E. D.

PROPOSITION 51

To find the fourth binomial straight line.

Let two numbers AC, CB be set out such that AB neither has to BC, nor yet to AC, the ratio which a square number has to a square number.

Let a rational straight line D be set out,
and let EF be commensurable in length with D;
therefore EF is also rational.
Let it be contrived that, as the number BA is to AC, so is the square on EF to the square on FG;   [x. 6, Por.]
therefore the square on EF is commensurable with the square on FG;   [x. 6]
therefore FG is also rational.
Now, since BA has not to AC the ratio which a square number has to a square number,
neither has the square on EF to the square on FG the ratio which a square number has to a square number;
therefore EF is incommensurable in length with FG.   [x. 9]
Therefore EF, FG are rational straight lines commensurable in square only;
so that EG is binomial.
I say next that it is also a fourth binomial straight line.

For since, as BA is to AC, so is the square on EF to the square on FG,
therefore the square on EF is greater than the square on FG.
Let then the squares on FG, H be equal to the square on EF;
therefore, *convertendo*, as the number AB is to BC, so is the square on EF to the square on H.   [v. 19, Por.]
But AB has not to BC the ratio which a square number has to a square number;
therefore neither has the square on EF to the square on H the ratio which a square number has to a square number.

Therefore EF is incommensurable in length with H; [x. 9]
therefore the square on EF is greater than the square on GF by the square on a straight line incommensurable with EF.

And EF, FG are rational straight lines commensurable in square only, and EF is commensurable in length with D.

Therefore EG is a fourth binomial straight line. Q. E. D.

PROPOSITION 52

To find the fifth binomial straight line.

Let two numbers AC, CB be set out such that AB has not to either of them the ratio which a square number has to a square number;
let any rational straight line D be set out,
and let EF be commensurable with D;
therefore EF is rational.

Let it be contrived that, as CA is to AB, so is the square on EF to the square on FG. [x. 6, Por.]

But CA has not to AB the ratio which a square number has to a square number;
therefore neither has the square on EF to the square on FG the ratio which a square number has to a square number.

Therefore EF, FG are rational straight lines commensurable in square only; [x. 9]
therefore EG is binomial. [x. 36]

I say next that it is also a fifth binomial straight line.

For since, as CA is to AB, so is the square on EF to the square on FG,
inversely, as BA is to AC, so is the square on FG to the square on FE;
therefore the square on GF is greater than the square on FE.

Let then the squares on EF, H be equal to the square on GF;
therefore, *convertendo*, as the number AB is to BC, so is the square on GF to the square on H. [v. 19, Por.]

But AB has not to BC the ratio which a square number has to a square number;
therefore neither has the square on FG to the square on H the ratio which a square number has to a square number.

Therefore FG is incommensurable in length with H; [x. 9]
so that the square on FG is greater than the square on FE by the square on a straight line incommensurable with FG.

And GF, FE are rational straight lines commensurable in square only, and the lesser term EF is commensurable in length with the rational straight line D set out.

Therefore EG is a fifth binomial straight line. Q. E. D.

PROPOSITION 53

To find the sixth binomial straight line.

Let two numbers AC, CB be set out such that AB has not to either of them the ratio which a square number has to a square number;
and let there also be another number D which is not square and which has not to either of the numbers BA, AC the ratio which a square number has to a square number.

Let any rational straight line E be set out,
and let it be contrived that, as D is to AB, so is the square on E to the square on FG; [x. 6, Por.]
therefore the square on E is commensurable with the square on FG. [x. 6]

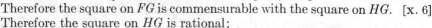

And E is rational;
   therefore FG is also rational.

Now, since D has not to AB the ratio which a square number has to a square number,
neither has the square on E to the square on FG the ratio which a square number has to a square number;
therefore E is incommensurable in length with FG. [x. 9]

Again, let it be contrived that, as BA is to AC, so is the square on FG to the square on GH. [x. 6, Por.]

Therefore the square on FG is commensurable with the square on HG. [x. 6]
Therefore the square on HG is rational;
   therefore HG is rational.

And, since BA has not to AC the ratio which a square number has to a square number,
neither has the square on FG to the square on GH the ratio which a square number has to a square number;
   therefore FG is incommensurable in length with GH. [x. 9]

Therefore FG, GH are rational straight lines commensurable in square only;
   therefore FH is binomial. [x. 36]

It is next to be proved that it is also a sixth binomial straight line.

For since, as D is to AB, so is the square on E to the square on FG,
and also, as BA is to AC, so is the square on FG to the square on GH,
therefore, *ex aequali*, as D is to AC, so is the square on E to the square on GH.
                   [v. 22]

But D has not to AC the ratio which a square number has to a square number;
   therefore neither has the square on E to the square on GH the ratio
      which a square number has to a square number;
   therefore E is incommensurable in length with GH. [x. 9]
But it was also proved incommensurable with FG;
  therefore each of the straight lines FG, GH is incommensurable
        in length with E.

And, since, as BA is to AC, so is the square on FG to the square on GH,
  therefore the square on FG is greater than the square on GH.

Let then the squares on GH, K be equal to the square on FG;
  therefore, *convertendo*, as AB is to BC, so is the square on FG
        to the square on K. [v. 19, Por.]

But AB has not to BC the ratio which a square number has to a square number;
so that neither has the square on FG to the square on K the ratio which a square number has to a square number.

Therefore FG is incommensurable in length with K; [x. 9]
therefore the square on FG is greater than the square on GH by the square on a straight line incommensurable with FG.

And *FG*, *GH* are rational straight lines commensurable in square only, and neither of them is commensurable in length with the rational straight line *E* set out.

Therefore *FH* is a sixth binomial straight line.   Q. E. D.

LEMMA

Let there be two squares *AB*, *BC*, and let them be placed so that *DB* is in a straight line with *BE*;

therefore *FB* is also in a straight line with *BG*.

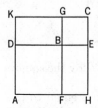

Let the parallelogram *AC* be completed;

I say that *AC* is a square, that *DG* is a mean proportional between *AB*, *BC*, and further that *DC* is a mean proportional between *AC*, *CB*.

For, since *DB* is equal to *BF*, and *BE* to *BG*,

therefore the whole *DE* is equal to the whole *FG*.

But *DE* is equal to each of the straight lines *AH*, *KC*,

and *FG* is equal to each of the straight lines *AK*, *HC* [I. 34];

therefore each of the straight lines *AH*, *KC* is also equal to each of the straight lines *AK*, *HC*.

Therefore the parallelogram *AC* is equilateral.

And it is also rectangular;

therefore *AC* is a square.

And since, as *FB* is to *BG*, so is *DB* to *BE*,

while, as *FB* is to *BG*, so is *AB* to *DG*,

and, as *DB* is to *BE*, so is *DG* to *BC*,   [VI. 1]

therefore also, as *AB* is to *DG*, so is *DG* to *BC*.   [V. 11]

Therefore *DG* is a mean proportional between *AB*, *BC*.

I say next that *DC* is also a mean proportional between *AC*, *CB*.

For since, as *AD* is to *DK*, so is *KG* to *GC*—

for they are equal respectively—

and, *componendo*, as *AK* is to *KD*, so is *KC* to *CG*,   [V. 18]

while, as *AK* is to *KD*, so is *AC* to *CD*,

and, as *KC* is to *CG*, so is *DC* to *CB*,   [VI. 1]

therefore also, as *AC* is to *DC*, so is *DC* to *BC*.   [V. 11]

Therefore *DC* is a mean proportional between *AC*, *CB*.

Being what it was proposed to prove.

PROPOSITION 54

If an area be contained by a rational straight line and the first binomial, the "side" of the area is the irrational straight line which is called binomial.

For let the area *AC* be contained by the rational straight line *AB* and the first binomial *AD*;

I say that the "side" of the area *AC* is the irrational straight line which is called binomial.

For, since *AD* is a first binomial straight line, let it be divided into its terms at *E*,

and let *AE* be the greater term.

It is then manifest that *AE*, *ED* are rational straight lines commensurable in square only,

the square on AE is greater than the square on ED by the square on a straight line commensurable with AE,
and AE is commensurable in length with the rational straight line AB set out.

[x. Deff. ii. 1]

Let ED be bisected at the point F.

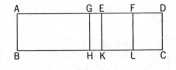
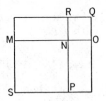

Then, since the square on AE is greater than the square on ED by the square on a straight line commensurable with AE,
therefore, if there be applied to the greater AE a parallelogram equal to the fourth part of the square on the less, that is, to the square on EF, and deficient by a square figure, it divides it into commensurable parts.　　　　[x. 17]

Let then the rectangle AG, GE equal to the square on EF be applied to AE;
therefore AG is commensurable in length with EG.

Let GH, EK, FL be drawn from G, E, F parallel to either of the straight lines AB, CD;
let the square SN be constructed equal to the parallelogram AH, and the square NQ equal to GK,　　　　[ii. 14]
　　and let them be placed so that MN is in a straight line with NO;
　　　　therefore RN is also in a straight line with NP.
And let the parallelogram SQ be completed;
　　　　　　therefore SQ is a square.　　　　[Lemma]
Now, since the rectangle AG, GE is equal to the square on EF,
　　　　therefore, as AG is to EF, so is FE to EG;　　　　[vi. 17]
　　　　therefore also, as AH is to EL, so is EL to KG;　　　　[vi. 1]
　　　therefore EL is a mean proportional between AH, GK.
But AH is equal to SN, and GK to NQ;
　　　therefore EL is a mean proportional between SN, NQ.
But MR is also a mean proportional between the same SN, NQ;　　[Lemma]
　　　　　therefore EL is equal to MR,
　　　　so that it is also equal to PO.
But AH, GK are also equal to SN, NQ;
therefore the whole AC is equal to the whole SQ, that is, to the square on MO;
　　　　　therefore MO is the "side" of AC.
I say next that MO is binomial.
For, since AG is commensurable with GE,
therefore AE is also commensurable with each of the straight lines AG, GE.

[x. 15]

But AE is also, by hypothesis, commensurable with AB;
　　　therefore AG, GE are also commensurable with AB.　　　　[x. 12]
And AB is rational;
　　　therefore each of the straight lines AG, GE is also rational;
　　　　therefore each of the rectangles AH, GK is rational,　　　　[x. 19]

and *AH* is commensurable with *GK*.

But *AH* is equal to *SN*, and *GK* to *NQ*;
therefore *SN*, *NQ*, that is, the squares on *MN*, *NO*, are rational and commensurable.

And, since *AE* is incommensurable in length with *ED*,
while *AE* is commensurable with *AG*, and *DE* is commensurable with *EF*,

therefore *AG* is also incommensurable with *EF*,   [x. 13]

so that *AH* is also incommensurable with *EL*.   [vi. 1, x. 11]

But *AH* is equal to *SN*, and *EL* to *MR*;

therefore *SN* is also incommensurable with *MR*.

But, as *SN* is to *MR*, so is *PN* to *NR*;   [vi. 1]

therefore *PN* is incommensurable with *NR*.   [x. 11]

But *PN* is equal to *MN*, and *NR* to *NO*;

therefore *MN* is incommensurable with *NO*.

And the square on *MN* is commensurable with the square on *NO*,

and each is rational;

therefore *MN*, *NO* are rational straight lines commensurable in square only.
Therefore *MO* is binomial [x. 36] and the "side" of *AC*.   Q. E. D.

PROPOSITION 55

If an area be contained by a rational straight line and the second binomial, the "side" of the area is the irrational straight line which is called a first bimedial.

For let the area *ABCD* be contained by the rational straight line *AB* and the second binomial *AD*;

I say that the "side" of the area *AC* is a first bimedial straight line.

For, since *AD* is a second binomial straight line, let it be divided into its terms at *E*, so that *AE* is the greater term;
therefore *AE*, *ED* are rational straight lines commensurable in square only,
the square on *AE* is greater than the square on *ED* by the square on a straight line commensurable with *AE*,
and the lesser term *ED* is commensurable in length with *AB*.   [x. Deff. ii. 2]

Let *ED* be bisected at *F*,
and let there be applied to *AE* the rectangle *AG*, *GE* equal to the square on *EF* and deficient by a square figure;

therefore *AG* is commensurable in length with *GE*.   [x. 17]

Through *G*, *E*, *F* let *GH*, *EK*, *FL* be drawn parallel to *AB*, *CD*,
let the square *SN* be constructed equal to the parallelogram *AH*, and the square *NQ* equal to *GK*,

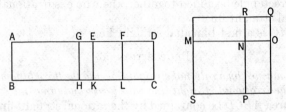

and let them be placed so that *MN* is in a straight line with *NO*;

therefore *RN* is also in a straight line with *NP*.

Let the square *SQ* be completed.

It is then manifest from what was proved before that MR is a mean proportional between SN, NQ and is equal to EL, and that MO is the "side" of the area AC.

It is now to be proved that MO is a first bimedial straight line.

Since AE is commensurable in length with ED,
                while ED is commensurable with AB,
                    therefore AE is incommensurable with AB.   [x. 13]

And, since AG is commensurable with EG,
AE is also commensurable with each of the straight lines AG, GE.   [x. 15]

But AE is incommensurable in length with AB;
                therefore AG, GE are also incommensurable with AB.   [x. 13]

Therefore BA, AG and BA, GE are pairs of rational straight lines commensurable in square only;
                so that each of the rectangles AH, GK is medial.   [x. 21]

Hence each of the squares SN, NQ is medial.

Therefore MN, NO are also medial.

And, since AG is commensurable in length with GE,
                AH is also commensurable with GK,   [vi. 1, x. 11]
                    that is, SN is commensurable with NQ,
                that is, the square on MN with the square on NO.

And, since AE is incommensurable in length with ED,
                while AE is commensurable with AG,
                and ED is commensurable with EF,
                    therefore AG is incommensurable with EF;   [x. 13]

so that AH is also incommensurable with EL,
                that is, SN is incommensurable with MR,
                    that is, PN with NR,   [vi. 1, x. 11]
                that is, MN is incommensurable in length with NO.

But MN, NO were proved to be both medial and commensurable in square; therefore MN, NO are medial straight lines commensurable in square only.

I say next that they also contain a rational rectangle.

For, since DE is, by hypothesis, commensurable with each of the straight lines AB, EF,
                therefore EF is also commensurable with EK.   [x. 12]

And each of them is rational;
                    therefore EL, that is, MR is rational,   [x. 19]
                and MR is the rectangle MN, NO.

But, if two medial straight lines commensurable in square only and containing a rational rectangle be added together, the whole is irrational and is called a first bimedial straight line.   [x. 37]

Therefore MO is a first bimedial straight line.   Q. E. D.

PROPOSITION 56

If an area be contained by a rational straight line and the third binomial, the "side" of the area is the irrational straight line called a second bimedial.

For let the area $ABCD$ be contained by the rational straight line AB and the third binomial AD divided into its terms at E, of which terms AE is the greater;

I say that the "side" of the area AC is the irrational straight line called a second bimedial.

For let the same construction be made as before.
Now, since AD is a third binomial straight line,

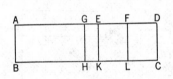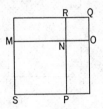

therefore AE, ED are rational straight lines commensurable in square only,
the square on AE is greater than the square on ED by the square on a straight
line commensurable with AE,
and neither of the terms AE, ED is commensurable in length with AB.

[x. Deff. II. 3]

Then, in manner similar to the foregoing, we shall prove that MO is the
"side" of the area AC,
and MN, NO are medial straight lines commensurable in square only;
so that MO is bimedial.
It is next to be proved that it is also a second bimedial straight line.
Since DE is incommensurable in length with AB, that is, with EK,
and DE is commensurable with EF,
therefore EF is incommensurable in length with EK.   [x. 13]
And they are rational;
therefore FE, EK are rational straight lines commensurable in square only.
Therefore EL, that is, MR, is medial.   [x. 21]
And it is contained by MN, NO;
therefore the rectangle MN, NO is medial.
Therefore MO is a second bimedial straight line.   [x. 38]

Q. E. D.

PROPOSITION 57

*If an area be contained by a rational straight line and the fourth binomial, the
"side" of the area is the irrational straight line called major.*

For let the area AC be contained by the rational straight line AB and the
fourth binomial AD divided into its terms at E, of which terms let AE be the
greater;
I say that the "side" of the area AC is the irrational straight line called major.
For, since AD is a fourth binomial straight line,
therefore AE, ED are rational straight lines commensurable in square only,
the square on AE is greater than the square on ED by the square on a straight
line incommensurable with AE,
and AE is commensurable in length with AB.   [x. Deff. II. 4]
Let DE be bisected at F,
and let there be applied to AE a parallelogram, the rectangle AG, GE, equal to
the square on EF;
therefore AG is incommensurable in length with GE.   [x. 18]
Let GH, EK, FL be drawn parallel to AB,

and let the rest of the construction be as before;
it is then manifest that MO is the "side" of the area AC.

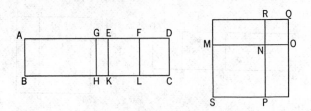

It is next to be proved that MO is the irrational straight line called major.
Since AG is incommensurable with EG,
AH is also incommensurable with GK, that is, SN with NQ;   [VI. 1, X. 11]
therefore MN, NO are incommensurable in square.
And, since AE is commensurable with AB,
AK is rational;   [X. 19]
and it is equal to the squares on MN, NO;
therefore the sum of the squares on MN, NO is also rational.
And, since DE is incommensurable in length with AB, that is, with EK,
while DE is commensurable with EF,
therefore EF is incommensurable in length with EK.   [X. 13]
Therefore EK, EF are rational straight lines commensurable in square only;
therefore LE, that is, MR, is medial.   [X. 21]
And it is contained by MN, NO;
therefore the rectangle MN, NO is medial.
And the [sum] of the squares on MN, NO is rational,
and MN, NO are incommensurable in square.
But, if two straight lines incommensurable in square and making the sum of
the squares on them rational, but the rectangle contained by them medial, be
added together, the whole is irrational and is called major.   [X. 39]
Therefore MO is the irrational straight line called major and is the "side" of
the area AC.   Q. E. D.

PROPOSITION 58

*If an area be contained by a rational straight line and the fifth binomial, the "side"
of the area is the irrational straight line called the side of a rational plus a medial
area.*

For let the area AC be contained by the rational straight line AB and the
fifth binomial AD divided into its terms at E, so that AE is the greater term;
I say that the "side" of the area AC is the irrational straight line called the
side of a rational plus a medial area.
For let the same construction be made as before shown;
it is then manifest that MO is the "side" of the area AC.
It is then to be proved that MO is the side of a rational plus a medial area.
For, since AG is incommensurable with GE,   [X. 18]
therefore AH is also commensurable with HE,   [VI. 1, X. 11]
that is, the square on MN with the square on NO;
therefore MN, NO are incommensurable in square.

And, since AD is a fifth binomial straight line, and ED the lesser segment, therefore ED is commensurable in length with AB. [x. Deff. ii. 5]

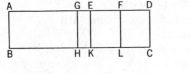 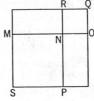

But AE is incommensurable with ED;

therefore AB is also incommensurable in length with AE.   [x. 13]

Therefore AK, that is, the sum of the squares on MN, NO, is medial. [x. 21]

And, since DE is commensurable in length with AB, that is, with EK,

while DE is commensurable with EF,

therefore EF is also commensurable with EK.   [x. 12]

And EK is rational;

therefore EL, that is, MR, that is, the rectangle MN, NO, is also rational.

[x. 19]

Therefore MN, NO are straight lines incommensurable in square which make the sum of the squares on them medial, but the rectangle contained by them rational.

Therefore MO is the side of a rational plus a medial area [x. 40] and is the "side" of the area AC.   Q. E. D.

PROPOSITION 59

If an area be contained by a rational straight line and the sixth binomial, the "side" of the area is the irrational straight line called the side of the sum of two medial areas.

For let the area $ABCD$ be contained by the rational straight line AB and the sixth binomial AD, divided into its terms at E, so that AE is the greater term;

I say that the "side" of AC is the side of the sum of two medial areas.

Let the same construction be made as before shown.

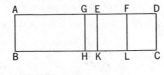 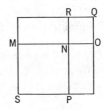

It is then manifest that MO is the "side" of AC, and that MN is incommensurable in square with NO.

Now, since EA is incommensurable in length with AB,

therefore EA, AB are rational straight lines commensurable in square only;

therefore AK, that is, the sum of the squares on MN, NO, is medial.   [x. 21]

Again, since ED is incommensurable in length with AB,

therefore FE is also incommensurable with EK;   [x. 13]

therefore FE, EK are rational straight lines commensurable in square only;

therefore EL, that is, MR, that is, the rectangle MN, NO, is medial. [x. 21]

And, since AE is incommensurable with EF,

AK is also incommensurable with EL.   [vi. 1, x. 11]

But AK is the sum of the squares on MN, NO,

and EL is the rectangle MN, NO;

therefore the sum of the squares on MN, NO is incommensurable with the rectangle MN, NO.

And each of them is medial, and MN, NO are incommensurable in square.

Therefore MO is the side of the sum of two medial areas [x. 41], and is the "side" of AC.   Q. E. D.

LEMMA

If a straight line be cut into unequal parts, the squares on the unequal parts are greater than twice the rectangle contained by the unequal parts.

Let AB be a straight line, and let it be cut into unequal parts at C, and let AC be the greater;

I say that the squares on AC, CB are greater than twice the rectangle AC, CB.

For let AB be bisected at D.

Since, then, a straight line has been cut into equal parts at D, and into unequal parts at C,

therefore the rectangle AC, CB together with the square on CD is equal to the square on AD,   [ii. 5]

so that the rectangle AC, CB is less than the square on AD;

therefore twice the rectangle AC, CB is less than double of the square on AD.

But the squares on AC, CB are double of the squares on AD, DC; [ii. 9]

therefore the squares on AC, CB are greater than twice the rectangle AC, CB.

Q. E. D.

PROPOSITION 60

The square on the binomial straight line applied to a rational straight line produces as breadth the first binomial.

Let AB be a binomial straight line divided into its terms at C, so that AC is the greater term;

let a rational straight line DE be set out,

and let $DEFG$ equal to the square on AB be applied to DE producing DG as its breadth;

I say that DG is a first binomial straight line.

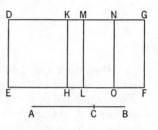

For let there be applied to DE the rectangle DH equal to the square on AC, and KL equal to the square on BC;

therefore the remainder, twice the rectangle AC, CB, is equal to MF.

Let MG be bisected at N, and let NO be drawn parallel [to ML or GF].

Therefore each of the rectangles MO, NF is equal to once the rectangle AC, CB.

Now, since AB is a binomial divided into its terms at C, therefore AC, CB are rational straight lines commensurable in square only;

[x. 36]

therefore the squares on AC, CB are rational and commensurable with one another,

so that the sum of the squares on AC, CB is also rational.   [x. 15]

And it is equal to DL;

therefore DL is rational.

And it is applied to the rational straight line DE;

therefore DM is rational and commensurable in length with DE. [x. 20]

Again, since AC, CB are rational straight lines commensurable in square only,

therefore twice the rectangle AC, CB, that is MF, is medial.   [x. 21]

And it is applied to the rational straight line ML;

therefore MG is also rational and incommensurable in length with ML, that is, DE.   [x. 22]

But MD is also rational and is commensurable in length with DE;

therefore DM is incommensurable in length with MG.   [x. 13]

And they are rational;

therefore DM, MG are rational straight lines commensurable in square only;

therefore DG is binomial.   [x. 36]

It is next to be proved that it is also a first binomial straight line.

Since the rectangle AC, CB is a mean proportional between the squares on AC, CB,   [cf. Lemma after x. 53]

therefore MO is also a mean proportional between DH, KL.

Therefore, as DH is to MO, so is MO to KL,

that is, as DK is to MN, so is MN to MK;   [vi. 1]

therefore the rectangle DK, KM is equal to the square on MN. [vi. 17]

And, since the square on AC is commensurable with the square on CB,

DH is also commensurable with KL,

so that DK is also commensurable with KM.   [vi. 1, x. 11]

And, since the squares on AC, CB are greater than twice the rectangle AC, CB,   [Lemma]

therefore DL is also greater than MF,

so that DM is also greater than MG.   [vi. 1]

And the rectangle DK, KM is equal to the square on MN, that is, to the fourth part of the square on MG,

and DK is commensurable with KM.

But, if there be two unequal straight lines, and to the greater there be applied a parallelogram equal to the fourth part of the square on the less and deficient by a square figure, and if it divide it into commensurable parts, the square on the greater is greater than the square on the less by the square on a straight line commensurable with the greater;   [x. 17]

therefore the square on DM is greater than the square on MG by the square on a straight line commensurable with DM.

And DM, MG are rational,

and DM, which is the greater term, is commensurable in length with the rational straight line DE set out.

Therefore DG is a first binomial straight line.   [x. Deff. ii. 1]

Q. E. D.

Proposition 61

The square on the first bimedial straight line applied to a rational straight line produces as breadth the second binomial.

Let AB be a first bimedial straight line divided into its medials at C, of which medials AC is the greater;
let a rational straight line DE be set out,
and let there be applied to DE the parallelogram DF equal to the square on AB, producing DG as its breadth;

I say that DG is a second binomial straight line.

For let the same construction as before be made.

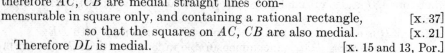

Then, since AB is a first bimedial divided at C, therefore AC, CB are medial straight lines commensurable in square only, and containing a rational rectangle, [x. 37]
                          so that the squares on AC, CB are also medial. [x. 21]
Therefore DL is medial.   [x. 15 and 13, Por.]
And it has been applied to the rational straight line DE;
therefore MD is rational and incommensurable in length with DE. [x. 22]
Again, since twice the rectangle AC, CB is rational, MF is also rational.
And it is applied to the rational straight line ML;
therefore MG is also rational and commensurable in length with ML, that is, DE;   [x. 20]
                  therefore DM is incommensurable in length with MG. [x. 13]
And they are rational;
therefore DM, MG are rational straight lines commensurable in square only;
                          therefore DG is binomial.   [x. 36]
It is next to be proved that it is also a second binomial straight line.

For, since the squares on AC, CB are greater than twice the rectangle AC, CB,
                          therefore DL is also greater than MF,
                          so that DM is also greater than MG.   [vi. 1]
And, since the square on AC is commensurable with the square on CB,
                          DH is also commensurable with KL,
                  so that DK is also commensurable with KM.   [vi. 1, x. 11]
And the rectangle DK, KM is equal to the square on MN;
therefore the square on DM is greater than the square on MG by the square on a straight line commensurable with DM.   [x. 17]
And MG is commensurable in length with DE.
Therefore DG is a second binomial straight line.   [x. Deff. ii. 2]

Proposition 62

The square on the second bimedial straight line applied to a rational straight line produces as breadth the third binomial.

Let AB be a second bimedial straight line divided into its medials at C, so that AC is the greater segment;
let DE be any rational straight line,
and to DE let there be applied the parallelogram DF equal to the square on AB and producing DG as its breadth;

I say that DG is a third binomial straight line.

Let the same construction be made as before shown.

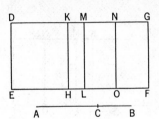

Then, since AB is a second bimedial divided at C,

therefore AC, CB are medial straight lines commensurable in square only and containing a medial rectangle,   [x. 38]

so that the sum of the squares on AC, CB is also medial.   [x. 15 and 23 Por.]

And it is equal to DL;

therefore DL is also medial.

And it is applied to the rational straight line DE;

therefore MD is also rational and incommensurable in length with DE. [x. 22]

For the same reason,

MG is also rational and incommensurable in length with ML, that is, with DE;

therefore each of the straight lines DM, MG is rational and incommensurable in length with DE.

And, since AC is incommensurable in length with CB,

and, as AC is to CB, so is the square on AC to the rectangle AC, CB,

therefore the square on AC is also incommensurable with the rectangle AC, CB.   [x. 11]

Hence the sum of the squares on AC, CB is incommensurable with twice the rectangle AC, CB,   [x. 12, 13]

that is, DL is incommensurable with MF,

so that DM is also incommensurable with MG.   [vi. 1, x. 11]

And they are rational;

therefore DG is binomial.   [x. 36]

It is to be proved that it is also a third binomial straight line.

In manner similar to the foregoing we may conclude that DM is greater than MG,

and that DK is commensurable with KM.

And the rectangle DK, KM is equal to the square on MN;

therefore the square on DM is greater than the square on MG by the square on a straight line commensurable with DM.

And neither of the straight lines DM, MG is commensurable in length with DE.

Therefore DG is a third binomial straight line.   [x. Deff. ii. 3]

Q. E. D.

PROPOSITION 63

The square on the major straight line applied to a rational straight line produces as breadth the fourth binomial.

Let AB be a major straight line divided at C, so that AC is greater than CB;

let DE be a rational straight line,

and to DE let there be applied the parallelogram DF equal to the square on AB and producing DG as its breadth;

I say that DG is a fourth binomial straight line.

Let the same construction be made as before shown.

Then, since AB is a major straight line divided at C,

AC, *CB* are straight lines incommensurable in square which make the sum of the squares on them rational, but the rectangle contained by them medial.
[x. 39]

Since, then, the sum of the squares on *AC*, *CB* is rational, therefore *DL* is rational;
therefore *DM* is also rational and commensurable in length with *DE*.   [x. 20]

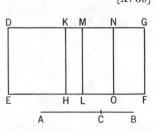

Again, since twice the rectangle *AC*, *CB*, that is, *MF*, is medial,
and it is applied to the rational straight line *ML*,
therefore *MG* is also rational and incommensurable in length with *DE*;   [x. 22]

therefore *DM* is also incommensurable in length with *MG*.   [x. 13]

Therefore *DM*, *MG* are rational straight lines commensurable in square only;

therefore *DG* is binomial.   [x. 36]

It is to be proved that it is also a fourth binomial straight line.

In manner similar to the foregoing we can prove that *DM* is greater than *MG*,

and that the rectangle *DK*, *KM* is equal to the square on *MN*.

Since then the square on *AC* is incommensurable with the square on *CB*,

therefore *DH* is also incommensurable with *KL*,

so that *DK* is also incommensurable with *KM*.   [vi. 1, x. 11]

But, if there be two unequal straight lines, and to the greater there be applied a parallelogram equal to the fourth part of the square on the less and deficient by a square figure, and if it divide it into incommensurable parts, then the square on the greater will be greater than the square on the less by the square on a straight line incommensurable in length with the greater;   [x. 18]
therefore the square on *DM* is greater than the square on *MG* by the square on a straight line incommensurable with *DM*.

And *DM*, *MG* are rational straight lines commensurable in square only, and *DM* is commensurable with the rational straight line *DE* set out.

Therefore *DG* is a fourth binomial straight line.   [x. Deff. ii. 4]

Q. E. D.

PROPOSITION 64

The square on the side of a rational plus a medial area applied to a rational straight line produces as breadth the fifth binomial.

Let *AB* be the side of a rational plus a medial area, divided into its straight lines at *C*, so that *AC* is the greater;
let a rational straight line *DE* be set out,
and let there be applied to *DE* the parallelogram *DF* equal to the square on *AB*, producing *DG* as its breadth;

I say that *DG* is a fifth binomial straight line.

Let the same construction as before be made.

Since then *AB* is the side of a rational plus a medial area, divided at *C*,
therefore *AC*, *CB* are straight lines incommensurable in square which make

the sum of the squares on them medial, but the rectangle contained by them
rational.   [x. 40]
   Since, then, the sum of the squares on AC, CB is medial,
therefore DL is medial,
so that DM is rational and incommensurable in length with DE.   [x. 22]
   Again, since twice the rectangle AC, CB, that is MF, is rational,
therefore MG is rational and commensurable with DE. [x. 20]
Therefore DM is incommensurable with MG;   [x. 13]
therefore DM, MG are rational straight lines commensurable in square only;
therefore DG is binomial.   [x. 36]
   I say next that it is also a fifth binomial straight line.
   For it can be proved similarly that the rectangle DK, KM is equal to the
square on MN,
and that DK is incommensurable in length with KM;
therefore the square on DM is greater than the square on MG by the square
on a straight line incommensurable with DM.   [x. 18]
   And DM, MG are commensurable in square only, and the less, MG, is commensurable in length with DE.
   Therefore DG is a fifth binomial.   Q. E. D.

PROPOSITION 65

The square on the side of the sum of two medial areas applied to a rational straight line produces as breadth the sixth binomial.

   Let AB be the side of the sum of two medial areas, divided at C,
let DE be a rational straight line,
and let there be applied to DE the parallelogram DF equal to the square on
AB, producing DG as its breadth;
I say that DG is a sixth binomial straight line.
   For let the same construction be made as before.

   Then, since AB is the side of the sum of two medial areas, divided at C,
therefore AC, CB are straight lines incommensurable in square which make the sum of the squares on them medial, the rectangle contained by them medial, and moreover the sum of the squares on them incommensurable with the rectangle contained by them,   [x. 41]
so that, in accordance with what was before proved, each of the rectangles DL, MF is medial.
   And they are applied to the rational straight line DE;
therefore each of the straight lines DM, MG is rational and incommensurable
in length with DE.   [x. 22]
   And, since the sum of the squares on AC, CB is incommensurable with twice
the rectangle AC, CB,
therefore DL is incommensurable with MF.
Therefore DM is also incommensurable with MG;   [vi. 1, x. 11]
therefore DM, MG are rational straight lines commensurable in square only;
therefore DG is binomial.   [x. 36]
   I say next that it is also a sixth binomial straight line.

Similarly again we can prove that the rectangle *DK*, *KM* is equal to the square on *MN*,

and that *DK* is incommensurable in length with *KM*;

and, for the same reason, the square on *DM* is greater than the square on *MG* by the square on a straight line incommensurable in length with *DM*.

And neither of the straight lines *DM*, *MG* is commensurable in length with the rational straight line *DE* set out.

Therefore *DG* is a sixth binomial straight line.   Q. E. D.

PROPOSITION 66

A straight line commensurable in length with a binomial straight line is itself also binomial and the same in order.

Let *AB* be binomial, and let *CD* be commensurable in length with *AB*;

I say that *CD* is binomial and the same in order with *AB*.

For, since *AB* is binomial, let it be divided into its terms at *E*,

and let *AE* be the greater term;

therefore *AE*, *EB* are rational straight lines commensurable in square only.

[x. 36]

Let it be contrived that,

as *AB* is to *CD*, so is *AE* to *CF*;   [VI. 12]

therefore also the remainder *EB* is to the remainder *FD* as *AB* is to *CD*. [v. 19]

But *AB* is commensurable in length with *CD*;

therefore *AE* is also commensurable with *CF*, and *EB* with *FD*.   [x. 11]

And *AE*, *EB* are rational;

therefore *CF*, *FD* are also rational.

And, as *AE* is to *CF*, so is *EB* to *FD*.   [v. 11]

Therefore, alternately, as *AE* is to *EB*, so is *CF* to *FD*.   [v. 16]

But *AE*, *EB* are commensurable in square only;

therefore *CF*, *FD* are also commensurable in square only.   [x. 11]

And they are rational;

therefore *CD* is binomial.   [x. 36]

I say next that it is the same in order with *AB*.

For the square on *AE* is greater than the square on *EB* either by the square on a straight line commensurable with *AE* or by the square on a straight line incommensurable with it.

If then the square on *AE* is greater than the square on *EB* by the square on a straight line commensurable with *AE*,

the square on *CF* will also be greater than the square on *FD* by the square on a straight line commensurable with *CF*.   [x. 14]

And, if *AE* is commensurable with the rational straight line set out, *CF* will also be commensurable with it,   [x. 12]

and for this reason each of the straight lines *AB*, *CD* is a first binomial, that is, the same in order.   [x. Deff. II. 1]

But, if *EB* is commensurable with the rational straight line set out, *FD* is also commensurable with it,   [x. 12]

and for this reason again *CD* will be the same in order with *AB*,

for each of them will be a second binomial.   [x. Deff. II. 2]

But, if neither of the straight lines AE, EB is commensurable with the rational straight line set out, neither of the straight lines CF, FD will be commensurable with it, [x. 13]
and each of the straight lines AB, CD is a third binomial. [x. Deff. II. 3]

But, if the square on AE is greater than the square on EB by the square on a straight line incommensurable with AE,
the square on CF is also greater than the square on FD by the square on a straight line incommensurable with CF. [x. 14]

And, if AE is commensurable with the rational straight line set out, CF is also commensurable with it,
and each of the straight lines AB, CD is a fourth binomial. [x. Deff. II. 4]

But, if EB is so commensurable, so is FD also,
and each of the straight lines AB, CD will be a fifth binomial. [x. Deff. II. 5]

But, if neither of the straight lines AE, EB is so commensurable, neither of the straight lines CF, FD is commensurable with the rational straight line set out,
and each of the straight lines AB, CD will be a sixth binomial. [x. Deff. II. 6]

Hence a straight line commensurable in length with a binomial straight line is binomial and the same in order. Q. E. D.

PROPOSITION 67

A straight line commensurable in length with a bimedial straight line is itself also bimedial and the same in order.

Let AB be bimedial, and let CD be commensurable in length with AB;
I say that CD is bimedial and the same in order with AB.
For, since AB is bimedial,
let it be divided into its medials at E;
therefore AE, EB are medial straight lines commensurable in square only.
[x. 37, 38]

And let it be contrived that,
as AB is to CD, so is AE to CF;
therefore also the remainder EB is to the remainder FD as AB is to CD. [v. 19]
But AB is commensurable in length with CD;
therefore AE, EB are also commensurable with CF, FD respectively. [x. 11]
But AE, EB are medial;
therefore CF, FD are also medial. [x. 23]
And since, as AE is to EB, so is CF to FD. [v. 11]
and AE, EB are commensurable in square only,
CF, FD are also commensurable in square only. [x. 11]
But they were also proved medial;
therefore CD is bimedial.
I say next that it is also the same in order with AB.
For since, as AE is to EB, so is CF to FD,
therefore also, as the square on AE is to the rectangle AE, EB, so is the square on CF to the rectangle CF, FD;
therefore, alternately,
as the square on AE is to the square on CF, so is the rectangle AE, EB to the rectangle CF, FD. [v. 16]
But the square on AE is commensurable with the square on CF;

therefore the rectangle AE, EB is also commensurable with the rectangle CF, FD.

If therefore the rectangle AE, EB is rational,
the rectangle CF, FD is also rational,
[and for this reason CD is a first bimedial];   [x. 37]
but if medial, medial,   [x. 23, Por.]
and each of the straight lines AB, CD is a second bimedial.   [x. 38]
And for this reason CD will be the same in order with AB.   Q. E. D.

PROPOSITION 68

A straight line commensurable with a major straight line is itself also major.

Let AB be major, and let CD be commensurable with AB;
I say that CD is major.

Let AB be divided at E;
therefore AE, EB are straight lines incommensurable in square which make the sum of the squares on them rational, but the rectangle contained by them medial.   [x. 39]

Let the same construction be made as before.

Then since, as AB is to CD, so is AE to CF, and EB to FD,
therefore also, as AE is to CF, so is EB to FD.   [v. 11]

But AB is commensurable with CD;
therefore AE, EB are also commensurable with CF, FD respectively.   [x. 11]

And since, as AE is to CF, so is EB to FD,
alternately also,
as AE is to EB, so is CF to FD;   [v. 16]
therefore also, *componendo*,
as AB is to BE, so is CD to DF;   [v. 18]
therefore also, as the square on AB is to the square on BE, so is the square on CD to the square on DF.   [vi. 20]

Similarly we can prove that, as the square on AB is to the square on AE, so also is the square on CD to the square on CF.

Therefore also, as the square on AB is to the squares on AE, EB, so is the square on CD to the squares on CF, FD;
therefore also, alternately,
as the square on AB is to the square on CD, so are the squares on AE, EB to the squares on CF, FD.   [v. 16]

But the square on AB is commensurable with the square on CD;
therefore the squares on AE, EB are also commensurable with the squares on CF, FD.

And the squares on AE, EB together are rational;
therefore the squares on CF, FD together are rational.

Similarly also twice the rectangle AE, EB is commensurable with twice the rectangle CF, FD.

And twice the rectangle AE, EB is medial;
therefore twice the rectangle CF, FD is also medial.   [x. 23, Por.]

Therefore CF, FD are straight lines incommensurable in square which make, at the same time, the sum of the squares on them rational, but the rectangle contained by them medial; therefore the whole CD is the irrational straight line called major.   [x. 39]

Therefore a straight line commensurable with the major straight line is major.   Q. E. D.

Proposition 69

A straight line commensurable with the side of a rational plus a medial area is itself also the side of a rational plus a medial area.

Let AB be the side of a rational plus a medial area, and let CD be commensurable with AB;

it is to be proved that CD is also the side of a rational plus a medial area.

Let AB be divided into its straight lines at E;

therefore AE, EB are straight lines incommensurable in square which make the sum of the squares on them medial, but the rectangle contained by them rational.   [x. 40]

Let the same construction be made as before.

We can then prove similarly that

    CF, FD are incommensurable in square,

and the sum of the squares on AE, EB is commensurable with the sum of the squares on CF, FD,

    and the rectangle AE, EB with the rectangle CF, FD;

so that the sum of the squares on CF, FD is also medial, and the rectangle CF, FD rational.

Therefore CD is the side of a rational plus a medial area.   Q. E. D.

Proposition 70

A straight line commensurable with the side of the sum of two medial areas is the side of the sum of two medial areas.

Let AB be the side of the sum of two medial areas, and CD commensurable with AB;

it is to be proved that CD is also the side of the sum of two medial areas.

For, since AB is the side of the sum of two medial areas,

let it be divided into its straight lines at E;

therefore AE, EB are straight lines incommensurable in square which make the sum of the squares on them medial, the rectangle contained by them medial, and furthermore the sum of the squares on AE, EB incommensurable with the rectangle AE, EB.

[x. 41]

Let the same construction be made as before.

We can then prove similarly that

    CF, FD are also incommensurable in square,

the sum of the squares on AE, EB is commensurable with the sum of the squares on CF, FD,

    and the rectangle AE, EB with the rectangle CF, FD;

so that the sum of the squares on CF, FD is also medial,

    the rectangle CF, FD is medial,

and moreover the sum of the squares on CF, FD is incommensurable with the rectangle CF, FD.

Therefore CD is the side of the sum of two medial areas.   Q. E. D.

Proposition 71

If a rational and a medial area be added together, four irrational straight lines arise, namely a binomial or a first bimedial or a major or a side of a rational plus a medial area.

Let AB be rational, and CD medial;

I say that the "side" of the area AD is a binomial or a first bimedial or a major or a side of a rational plus a medial area.

For AB is either greater or less than CD.

First, let it be greater;

let a rational straight line EF be set out,

let there be applied to EF the rectangle EG equal to AB, producing EH as breadth,

and let HI, equal to DC, be applied to EF, producing HK as breadth.

Then, since AB is rational
and is equal to EG,
therefore EG is also rational.

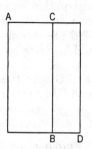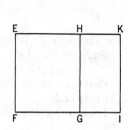

And it has been applied to EF, producing EH as breadth;
therefore EH is rational and commensurable in length with EF.   [x. 20]

Again, since CD is medial and is equal to HI,
therefore HI is also medial.

And it is applied to the rational straight line EF, producing HK as breadth;
therefore HK is rational and incommensurable in length with EF [x. 22]

And, since CD is medial,
while AB is rational,
therefore AB is incommensurable with CD,
so that EG is also incommensurable with HI.

But, as EG is to HI, so is EH to HK;   [vi. 1]
therefore EH is also incommensurable in length with HK.   [x. 11]

And both are rational;
therefore EH, HK are rational straight lines commensurable in square only;
therefore EK is a binomial straight line, divided at H.   [x. 36]

And, since AB is greater than CD,
while AB is equal to EG and CD to HI,
therefore EG is also greater than HI;
therefore EH is also greater than HK.

The square, then, on EH is greater than the square on HK either by the square on a straight line commensurable in length with EH or by the square on a straight line incommensurable with it.

First, let the square on it be greater by the square on a straight line commensurable with itself.

Now the greater straight line HE is commensurable in length with the rational straight line EF set out;

therefore EK is a first binomial.   [x. Deff. ii. 1]

But *EF* is rational;

and, if an area be contained by a rational straight line and the first binomial, the side of the square equal to the area is binomial.   [x. 54]

Therefore the "side" of *EI* is binomial;

so that the "side" of *AD* is also binomial.

Next, let the square on *EH* be greater than the square on *HK* by the square on a straight line incommensurable with *EH*.

Now the greater straight line *EH* is commensurable in length with the rational straight line *EF* set out;

therefore *EK* is a fourth binomial.   [x. Deff. ii. 4]

But *EF* is rational;

and, if an area be contained by a rational straight line and the fourth binomial, the "side" of the area is the irrational straight line called major.   [x. 57]

Therefore the "side" of the area *EI* is major;

so that the "side" of the area *AD* is also major.

Next, let *AB* be less than *CD*;

therefore *EG* is also less than *HI*,

so that *EH* is also less than *HK*.

Now the square on *HK* is greater than the square on *EH* either by the square on a straight line commensurable with *HK* or by the square on a straight line incommensurable with it.

First, let the square on it be greater by the square on a straight line commensurable in length with itself.

Now the lesser straight line *EH* is commensurable in length with the rational straight line *EF* set out;

therefore *EK* is a second binomial.   [x. Deff. ii. 2]

But *EF* is rational,

and, if an area be contained by a rational straight line and the second binomial, the side of the square equal to it is a first bimedial;   [x. 55]

therefore the "side" of the area *EI* is a first bimedial,

so that the "side" of *AD* is also a first bimedial.

Next, let the square on *HK* be greater than the square on *HE* by the square on a straight line incommensurable with *HK*.

Now the lesser straight line *EH* is commensurable with the rational straight line *EF* set out;

therefore *EK* is a fifth binomial.   [x. Deff. ii. 5]

But *EF* is rational;

and, if an area be contained by a rational straight line and the fifth binomial, the side of the square equal to the area is a side of a rational plus a medial area.   [x. 58]

Therefore the "side" of the area *EI* is a side of a rational plus a medial area, so that the "side" of the area *AD* is also a side of a rational plus a medial area.

Therefore etc.   Q. E. D.

PROPOSITION 72

If two medial areas incommensurable with one another be added together, the remaining two irrational straight lines arise, namely either a second bimedial or a side of the sum of two medial areas.

For let two medial areas *AB*, *CD* incommensurable with one another be added together;

I say that the "side" of the area *AD* is either a second bimedial or a side of the sum of two medial areas.

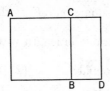

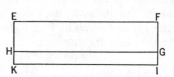

For *AB* is either greater or less than *CD*.

First, if it so chance, let *AB* be greater than *CD*.

Let the rational straight line *EF* be set out,

and to *EF* let there be applied the rectangle *EG* equal to *AB* and producing *EH* as breadth, and the rectangle *HI* equal to *CD* and producing *HK* as breadth.

Now, since each of the areas *AB*, *CD* is medial,

therefore each of the areas *EG*, *HI* is also medial.

And they are applied to the rational straight line *FE*, producing *EH*, *HK* as breadth;

therefore each of the straight lines *EH*, *HK* is rational and incommensurable in length with *EF*.   [x. 22]

And, since *AB* is incommensurable with *CD*,

and *AB* is equal to *EG*, and *CD* to *HI*,

therefore *EG* is also incommensurable with *HI*.

But, as *EG* is to *HI*, so is *EH* to *HK*;   [vi. 1]

therefore *EH* is incommensurable in length with *HK*.   [x. 11]

Therefore *EH*, *HK* are rational straight lines commensurable in square only;

therefore *EK* is binomial.   [x. 36]

But the square on *EH* is greater than the square on *HK* either by the square on a straight line commensurable with *EH* or by the square on a straight line incommensurable with it.

First, let the square on it be greater by the square on a straight line commensurable in length with itself.

Now neither of the straight lines *EH*, *HK* is commensurable in length with the rational straight line *EF* set out;

therefore *EK* is a third binomial.   [x. Deff. ii. 3]

But *EF* is rational;

and, if an area be contained by a rational straight line and the third binomial, the "side" of the area is a second bimedial;   [x. 56]

therefore the "side" of *EI*, that is, of *AD*, is a second bimedial.

Next, let the square on *EH* be greater than the square on *HK* by the square on a straight line incommensurable in length with *EH*.

Now each of the straight lines *EH*, *HK* is incommensurable in length with *EF*;

therefore *EK* is a sixth binomial.   [x. Deff. ii. 6]

But, if an area be contained by a rational straight line and the sixth binomial, the "side" of the area is the side of the sum of two medial areas; [x. 59] so that the "side" of the area AD is also the side of the sum of two medial areas.

Therefore etc.   Q. E. D.

The binomial straight line and the irrational straight lines after it are neither the same with the medial nor with one another.

For the square on a medial, if applied to a rational straight line, produces as breadth a straight line rational and incommensurable in length with that to which it is applied.   [x. 22]

But the square on the binomial, if applied to a rational straight line, produces as breadth the first binomial.   [x. 60]

The square on the first bimedial, if applied to a rational straight line, produces as breadth the second binomial.   [x. 61]

The square on the second bimedial, if applied to a rational straight line, produces as breadth the third binomial.   [x. 62]

The square on the major, if applied to a rational straight line, produces as breadth the fourth binomial.   [x. 63]

The square on the side of a rational plus a medial area, if applied to a rational straight line, produces as breadth the fifth binomial.   [x. 64]

The square on the side of the sum of two medial areas, if applied to a rational straight line, produces as breadth the sixth binomial.   [x. 65]

And the said breadths differ both from the first and from one another: from the first because it is rational, and from one another because they are not the same in order;

so that the irrational straight lines themselves also differ from one another.

PROPOSITION 73

If from a rational straight line there be subtracted a rational straight line commensurable with the whole in square only, the remainder is irrational; and let it be called an apotome.

For from the rational straight line AB let the rational straight line BC, commensurable with the whole in square only, be subtracted;

I say that the remainder AC is the irrational straight line called *apotome*.

A ——+———————— B

For, since AB is incommensurable in length with BC,
and, as AB is to BC, so is the square on AB to the rectangle AB, BC,
therefore the square on AB is incommensurable with the rectangle AB, BC.
                                                    [x. 11]

But the squares on AB, BC are commensurable with the square on AB,
                                                    [x. 15]
and twice the rectangle AB, BC is commensurable with the rectangle AB, BC.
                                                    [x. 6]

And, inasmuch as the squares on AB, BC are equal to twice the rectangle AB, BC together with the square on CA,   [ii. 7]
therefore the squares on AB, BC are also incommensurable with the remainder, the square on AC.   [x. 13, 16]

But the squares on AB, BC are rational;
                        therefore AC is irrational.   [x. Def. 4]

And let it be called an *apotome*.   Q. E. D.

PROPOSITION 74

If from a medial straight line there be subtracted a medial straight line which is commensurable with the whole in square only, and which contains with the whole a rational rectangle, the remainder is irrational. And let it be called a first apotome of a medial *straight line.*

For from the medial straight line AB let there be subtracted the medial straight line BC which is commensurable with AB in square only and with AB makes the rectangle AB, BC rational;

I say that the remainder AC is irrational; and let it be called a *first apotome of a medial* straight line.

A   C   B

For, since AB, BC are medial,
the squares on AB, BC are also medial.

But twice the rectangle AB, BC is rational;
therefore the squares on AB, BC are incommensurable with twice the rectangle AB, BC;
therefore twice the rectangle AB, BC is also incommensurable with the remainder, the square on AC,   [cf. II. 7]
since, if the whole is incommensurable with one of the magnitudes, the original magnitudes will also be incommensurable.   [x. 16]

But twice the rectangle AB, BC is rational;
therefore the square on AC is irrational;
therefore AC is irrational.   [x. Def. 4]

And let it be called a *first apotome of a medial* straight line.   Q. E. D.

PROPOSITION 75

If from a medial straight line there be subtracted a medial straight line which is commensurable with the whole in square only, and which contains with the whole a medial rectangle, the remainder is irrational; and let it be called a second apotome of a medial *straight line.*

For from the medial straight line AB let there be subtracted the medial straight line CB which is commensurable with the whole AB in square only and such that the rectangle AB, BC which it contains with the whole AB, is medial;   [x. 28]

I say that the remainder AC is irrational; and let it be called a *second apotome of a medial* straight line.

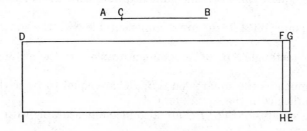

For let a rational straight line DI be set out,
let DE, equal to the squares on AB, BC, be applied to DI, producing DG as breadth,

and let DH equal to twice the rectangle AB, BC be applied to DI, producing DF as breadth;

therefore the remainder FE is equal to the square on AC.   [II. 7]

Now, since the squares on AB, BC are medial and commensurable,

therefore DE is also medial.   [x. 15 and 23, Por.]

And it is applied to the rational straight line DI, producing DG as breadth; therefore DG is rational and incommensurable in length with DI.   [x. 22]

Again, since the rectangle AB, BC is medial,

therefore twice the rectangle AB, BC is also medial. [x. 23, Por.]

And it is equal to DH;

therefore DH is also medial.

And it has been applied to the rational straight line DI, producing DF as breadth;

therefore DF is rational and incommensurable in length with DI. [x. 22]

And, since AB, BC are commensurable in square only,

therefore AB is incommensurable in length with BC;

therefore the square on AB is also incommensurable with the rectangle AB, BC.   [x. 11]

But the squares on AB, BC are commensurable with the square on AB,
        [x. 15]

and twice the rectangle AB, BC is commensurable with the rectangle AB, BC;
        [x. 6]

therefore twice the rectangle AB, BC is incommensurable with the squares on AB, BC.   [x. 13]

But DE is equal to the squares on AB, BC,

and DH to twice the rectangle AB, BC;

therefore DE is incommensurable with DH.

But, as DE is to DH, so is GD to DF;   [VI. 1]

therefore GD is incommensurable with DF.   [x. 11]

And both are rational;

therefore GD, DF are rational straight lines commensurable in square only;

therefore FG is an apotome.   [x. 73]

But DI is rational,

and the rectangle contained by a rational and an irrational straight line is irrational,   [deduction from x. 20]

and its "side" is irrational.

And AC is the "side" of FE;

therefore AC is irrational.

And let it be called a *second apotome of a medial* straight line.   Q. E. D.

PROPOSITION 76

If from a straight line there be subtracted a straight line which is incommensurable in square with the whole and which with the whole makes the squares on them added together rational, but the rectangle contained by them medial, the remainder is irrational; and let it be called minor.

For from the straight line AB let there be subtracted the straight line BC

A _____ C _____ B

which is incommensurable in square with the whole and fulfils the given conditions.   [x. 33]

I say that the remainder AC is the irrational straight line called *minor*.

For, since the sum of the squares on AB, BC is rational, while twice the rectangle AB, BC is medial,
therefore the squares on AB, BC are incommensurable with twice the rectangle AB, BC;
and, *convertendo*, the squares on AB, BC are incommensurable with the remainder, the square on AC.   [II. 7, X. 16]
But the squares on AB, BC are rational;
therefore the square on AC is irrational;
therefore AC is irrational.
And let it be called *minor*.   Q. E. D.

PROPOSITION 77

If from a straight line there be subtracted a straight line which is incommensurable in square with the whole, and which with the whole makes the sum of the squares on them medial, but twice the rectangle contained by them rational, the remainder is irrational; and let it be called that which produces with a rational area a medial whole.

For from the straight line AB let there be subtracted the straight line BC which is incommensurable in square with AB and fulfils the given conditions;   [X. 34]
I say that the remainder AC is the irrational straight line aforesaid.
For, since the sum of the squares on AB, BC is medial,
            while twice the rectangle AB, BC is rational,
therefore the squares on AB, BC are incommensurable with twice the rectangle AB, BC;
therefore the remainder also, the square on AC, is incommensurable with twice the rectangle AB, BC.   [II. 7, X. 16]
And twice the rectangle AB, BC is rational;
            therefore the square on AC is irrational;
                    therefore AC is irrational.
And let it be called *that which produces with a rational area a medial whole.*
                                                        Q. E. D.

PROPOSITION 78

If from a straight line there be subtracted a straight line which is incommensurable in square with the whole and which with the whole makes the sum of the squares on them medial, twice the rectangle contained by them medial, and further, the squares on them incommensurable with twice the rectangle contained by them, the remainder is irrational; and let it be called that which produces with a medial area a medial whole.

For from the straight line AB let there be subtracted the straight line BC incommensurable in square with AB and fulfilling the given conditions;   [X. 35]
I say that the remainder AC is the irrational straight line called *that which produces with a medial area a medial whole.*
For let a rational straight line DI be set out,
to DI let there be applied DE equal to the squares on AB, BC, producing DG as breadth,

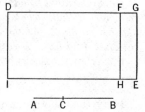

and let DH equal to twice the rectangle AB, BC be subtracted.

Therefore the remainder FE is equal to the square on AC,   [II. 7]

so that AC is the "side" of FE.

Now, since the sum of the squares on AB, BC is medial and is equal to DE, therefore DE is medial.

And it is applied to the rational straight line DI, producing DG as breadth; therefore DG is rational and incommensurable in length with DI.   [X. 22]

Again, since twice the rectangle AB, BC is medial and is equal to DH, therefore DH is medial.

And it is applied to the rational straight line DI, producing DF as breadth; therefore DF is also rational and incommensurable in length with DI.   [X. 22]

And, since the squares on AB, BC are incommensurable with twice the rectangle AB, BC,

therefore DE is also incommensurable with DH.

But, as DE is to DH, so also is DG to DF;   [VI. 1]

therefore DG is incommensurable with DF.   [X. 11]

And both are rational;

therefore GD, DF are rational straight lines commensurable in square only.

Therefore FG is an apotome.   [X. 73]

And FH is rational;

but the rectangle contained by a rational straight line and an apotome is irrational,   [deduction from X. 20]

and its "side" is irrational.

And AC is the "side" of FE;

therefore AC is irrational.

And let it be called *that which produces with a medial area a medial whole*.

Q. E. D.

PROPOSITION 79

To an apotome only one rational straight line can be annexed which is commensurable with the whole in square only.

Let AB be an apotome, and BC an annex to it;

therefore AC, CB are rational straight lines commensurable in square only.   [X. 73]

I say that no other rational straight line can be annexed to AB which is commensurable with the whole in square only.

For, if possible, let BD be so annexed;

therefore AD, DB are also rational straight lines commensurable in square only.   [X. 73]

Now, since the excess of the squares on AD, DB over twice the rectangle AD, DB is also the excess of the squares on AC, CB over twice the rectangle AC, CB,

for both exceed by the same, the square on AB,   [II. 7]

therefore, alternately, the excess of the squares on AD, DB over the squares on AC, CB is the excess of twice the rectangle AD, DB over twice the rectangle AC, CB.

But the squares on AD, DB exceed the squares on AC, CB by a rational area, for both are rational;

therefore twice the rectangle AD, DB also exceeds twice the rectangle AC, CB by a rational area:

which is impossible,
for both are medial [x. 21], and a medial area does not exceed a medial by a
rational area.						[x. 26]

Therefore no other rational straight line can be annexed to AB which is
commensurable with the whole in square only.

Therefore only one rational straight line can be annexed to an apotome
which is commensurable with the whole in square only.			Q. E. D.

PROPOSITION 80

*To a first apotome of a medial straight line only one medial straight line can be
annexed which is commensurable with the whole in square only and which contains
with the whole a rational rectangle.*

For let AB be a first apotome of a medial
straight line, and let BC be an annex to AB;
therefore AC, CB are medial straight lines commensurable in square only and
such that the rectangle AC, CB which they contain is rational;	[x. 74]

I say that no other medial straight line can be annexed to AB which is commensurable with the whole in square only and which contains with the whole
a rational area.

For, if possible, let DB also be so annexed;
therefore AD, DB are medial straight lines commensurable in square only and
such that the rectangle AD, DB which they contain is rational.	[x. 74]

Now, since the excess of the squares on AD, DB over twice the rectangle
AD, DB is also the excess of the squares on AC, CB over twice the rectangle
AC, CB,

for they exceed by the same, the square on AB,		[II. 7]
therefore, alternately, the excess of the squares on AD, DB over the squares
on AC, CB is also the excess of twice the rectangle AD, DB over twice the rectangle AC, CB.

But twice the rectangle AD, DB exceeds twice the rectangle AC, CB by a
rational area,

for both are rational.
Therefore the squares on AD, DB also exceed the squares on AC, CB by a
rational area:

which is impossible,
for both are medial [x. 15 and 23, Por.], and a medial area does not exceed a
medial by a rational area.						[x. 26]

Therefore etc.						Q. E. D.

PROPOSITION 81

*To a second apotome of a medial straight line only one medial straight line can be
annexed which is commensurable with the whole in square only and which contains
with the whole a medial rectangle.*

Let AB be a second apotome of a medial straight line and BC an annex to
AB;
therefore AC, CB are medial straight lines commensurable in square only and
such that the rectangle AC, CB which they contain is medial.	[x. 75]

I say that no other medial straight line can be annexed to AB which is com-

mensurable with the whole in square only and which contains with the whole
a medial rectangle.

For, if possible, let *BD* also be so annexed;

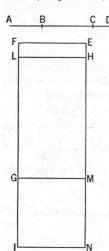

therefore *AD*, *DB* are also medial straight lines commensurable in square only and such that the rectangle
AD, *DB* which they contain is medial.   [x. 75]

Let a rational straight line *EF* be set out,
let *EG* equal to the squares on *AC*, *CB* be applied to
EF, producing *EM* as breadth,
and let *HG* equal to twice the rectangle *AC*, *CB* be subtracted, producing *HM* as breadth;

therefore the remainder *EL* is equal to the
square on *AB*,   [II. 7]
so that *AB* is the "side" of *EL*.

Again, let *EI* equal to the squares on *AD*, *DB* be applied to *EF*, producing *EN* as breadth.

But *EL* is also equal to the square on *AB*;
therefore the remainder *HI* is equal to twice the rectangle *AD*, *DB*.   [II. 7]

Now, since *AC*, *CB* are medial straight lines,
therefore the squares on *AC*, *CB* are also medial.

And they are equal to *EG*;
therefore *EG* is also medial.   [x. 15 and 23, Por.]

And it is applied to the rational straight line *EF*, producing *EM* as breadth;
therefore *EM* is rational and incommensurable in length with *EF*.   [x. 22]

Again, since the rectangle *AC*, *CB* is medial,
twice the rectangle *AC*, *CB* is also medial.   [x. 23, Por.]

And it is equal to *HG*;
therefore *HG* is also medial.

And it is applied to the rational straight line *EF*, producing *HM* as breadth;
therefore *HM* is also rational and incommensurable in length with *EF*.   [x. 22]

And, since *AC*, *CB* are commensurable in square only,
therefore *AC* is incommensurable in length with *CB*.

But, as *AC* is to *CB*, so is the square on *AC* to the rectangle *AC*, *CB*;
therefore the square on *AC* is incommensurable with the rectangle *AC*, *CB*.
[x. 11]

But the squares on *AC*, *CB* are commensurable with the square on *AC*,
while twice the rectangle *AC*, *CB* is commensurable with the rectangle *AC*,
CB;   [x. 6]
therefore the squares on *AC*, *CB* are incommensurable with twice the rectangle *AC*, *CB*.   [x. 13]

And *EG* is equal to the squares on *AC*, *CB*,
while *GH* is equal to twice the rectangle *AC*, *CB*;
therefore *EG* is incommensurable with *HG*.

But, as *EG* is to *HG*, so is *EM* to *HM*;   [VI. 1]
therefore *EM* is incommensurable in length with *MH*.   [x. 11]

And both are rational;
therefore *EM*, *MH* are rational straight lines commensurable in square only;
therefore *EH* is an apotome, and *HM* an annex to it.   [x. 73]

Similarly we can prove that HN is also an annex to it;
therefore to an apotome different straight lines are annexed which are commensurable with the wholes in square only:
                                      which is impossible.   [x. 79]
   Therefore etc.   Q. E. D.

PROPOSITION 82

To a minor straight line only one straight line can be annexed which is incommensurable in square with the whole and which makes, with the whole, the sum of the squares on them rational but twice the rectangle contained by them medial.

Let AB be the minor straight line, and let BC be an annex to AB;
therefore AC, CB are straight lines incommensurable in square which make
the sum of the squares on them rational, but twice
the rectangle contained by them medial.   [x. 76]
   I say that no other straight line can be annexed to AB fulfilling the same conditions.

   For, if possible, let BD be so annexed;
therefore AD, DB are also straight lines incommensurable in square which fulfil the aforesaid conditions.   [x. 76]
   Now, since the excess of the squares on AD, DB over the squares on AC, CB
is also the excess of twice the rectangle AD, DB over twice the rectangle AC,
CB,
while the squares on AD, DB exceed the squares on AC, CB by a rational area,
                              for both are rational,
therefore twice the rectangle AD, DB also exceeds twice the rectangle AC, CB
by a rational area:
                    which is impossible, for both are medial.   [x. 26]
   Therefore to a minor straight line only one straight line can be annexed
which is incommensurable in square with the whole and which makes the
squares on them added together rational, but twice the rectangle contained by
them medial.   Q. E. D.

PROPOSITION 83

To a straight line which produces with a rational area a medial whole only one straight line can be annexed which is incommensurable in square with the whole straight line and which with the whole straight line makes the sum of the squares on them medial, but twice the rectangle contained by them rational.

Let AB be the straight line which produces with a rational area a medial
whole,
and let BC be an annex to AB;
therefore AC, CB are straight lines incommensurable in square which fulfil the given conditions.   [x. 77]
   I say that no other straight line can be annexed to AB which fulfils the same conditions.

   For, if possible, let BD be so annexed;
therefore AD, DB are also straight lines incommensurable in square which fulfil the given conditions.   [x. 77]
   Since then, as in the preceding cases,
the excess of the squares on AD, DB over the squares on AC, CB is also the

excess of twice the rectangle AD, DB over twice the rectangle AC, CB,
while twice the rectangle AD, DB exceeds twice the rectangle AC, CB by a
rational area,

for both are rational,

therefore the squares on AD, DB also exceed the squares on AC, CB by a
rational area:

which is impossible, for both are medial.   [x. 26]

Therefore no other straight line can be annexed to AB which is incommensurable in square with the whole and which with the whole fulfils the aforesaid
conditions;

therefore only one straight line can be so annexed.   Q. E. D.

<h2>PROPOSITION 84</h2>

*To a straight line which produces with a medial area a medial whole only one
straight line can be annexed which is incommensurable in square with the whole
straight line and which with the whole straight line makes the sum of the squares
on them medial and twice the rectangle contained by them both medial and also incommensurable with the sum of the squares on them.*

Let AB be the straight line which produces with a medial area a medial
whole,

and BC an annex to it;

therefore AC, CB are straight lines incommensurable in square which fulfil the
aforesaid conditions.   [x. 78]

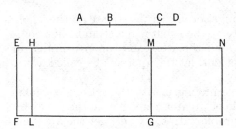

I say that no other straight line can
be annexed to AB which fulfils the
aforesaid conditions.

For, if possible, let BD be so annexed,

so that AD, DB are also straight lines
incommensurable in square which
make the squares on AD, DB added
together medial, twice the rectangle
AD, DB medial, and also the squares
on AD, DB incommensurable with twice the rectangle AD, DB.   [x. 78]

Let a rational straight line EF be set out,
let EG equal to the squares on AC, CB be applied to EF, producing EM as
breadth,
and let HG equal to twice the rectangle AC, CB be applied to EF, producing
HM as breadth;

therefore the remainder, the square on AB [II. 7], is equal to EL;

therefore AB is the "side" of EL.

Again, let EI equal to the squares on AD, DB be applied to EF, producing
EN as breadth.

But the square on AB is also equal to EL;

therefore the remainder, twice the rectangle AD, DB [II. 7], is equal to HI.

Now, since the sum of the squares on AC, CB is medial and is equal to EG,

therefore EG is also medial.

And it is applied to the rational straight line EF, producing EM as breadth;

therefore EM is rational and incommensurable in length with EF.   [x. 22]

Again, since twice the rectangle AC, CB is medial and is equal to HG,
therefore HG is also medial.

And it is applied to the rational straight line EF, producing HM as breadth;
therefore HM is rational and incommensurable in length with EF. [x. 22]

And, since the squares on AC, CB are incommensurable with twice the rectangle AC, CB,
$$EG \text{ is also incommensurable with } HG;$$
therefore EM is also incommensurable in length with MH. [vi. 1, x. 11]

And both are rational;

therefore EM, MH are rational straight lines commensurable in square only;
therefore EH is an apotome, and HM an annex to it.   [x. 73]

Similarly we can prove that EH is again an apotome and HN an annex to it.

Therefore to an apotome different rational straight lines are annexed which
are commensurable with the wholes in square only:
which was proved impossible.   [x. 79]

Therefore no other straight line can be so annexed to AB.

Therefore to AB only one straight line can be annexed which is incommensurable in square with the whole and which with the whole makes the squares on them added together medial, twice the rectangle contained by them medial, and also the squares on them incommensurable with twice the rectangle contained by them.   Q. E. D.

DEFINITIONS III

1. Given a rational straight line and an apotome, if the square on the whole be greater than the square on the annex by the square on a straight line commensurable in length with the whole, and the whole be commensurable in length with the rational straight line set out, let the apotome be called a *first apotome*.

2. But if the annex be commensurable in length with the rational straight line set out, and the square on the whole be greater than that on the annex by the square on a straight line commensurable with the whole, let the apotome be called a *second apotome*.

3. But if neither be commensurable in length with the rational straight line set out, and the square on the whole be greater than the square on the annex by the square on a straight line commensurable with the whole, let the apotome be called a *third apotome*.

4. Again, if the square on the whole be greater than the square on the annex by the square on a straight line incommensurable with the whole, then, if the whole be commensurable in length with the rational straight line set out, let the apotome be called a *fourth apotome*;

5. if the annex be so commensurable, a *fifth*;

6. and, if neither, a *sixth*.

PROPOSITION 85

To find the first apotome.

Let a rational straight line A be set out,
and let BG be commensurable in length with A;
therefore BG is also rational.

Let two square numbers DE, EF be set out, and let their difference FD not be square;

therefore neither has ED to DF the ratio which a square number has to a square number.

Let it be contrived that, as ED is to DF, so is the square on BG to the square on GC;   [x. 6, Por.]

therefore the square on BG is commensurable with the square on GC.   [x. 6]

But the square on BG is rational;

therefore the square on GC is also rational;

therefore GC is also rational.

And, since ED has not to DF the ratio which a square number has to a square number,

therefore neither has the square on BG to the square on GC the ratio which a square number has to a square number;

therefore BG is incommensurable in length with GC.   [x. 9]

And both are rational;

therefore BG, GC are rational straight lines commensurable in square only;

therefore BC is an apotome.   [x. 73]

I say next that it is also a first apotome.

For let the square on H be that by which the square on BG is greater than the square on GC.

Now since, as ED is to FD, so is the square on BG to the square on GC,

therefore also, *convertendo*,   [v. 19, Por.]

as DE is to EF, so is the square on GB to the square on H.

But DE has to EF the ratio which a square number has to a square number, for each is square;

therefore the square on GB also has to the square on H the ratio which a square number has to a square number;

therefore BG is commensurable in length with H.   [x. 9]

And the square on BG is greater than the square on GC by the square on H;

therefore the square on BG is greater than the square on GC by the square on a straight line commensurable in length with BG.

And the whole BG is commensurable in length with the rational straight line A set out.

Therefore BC is a first apotome.   [x. Deff. iii. 1]

Therefore the first apotome BC has been found.

(Being) that which it was required to find.   q. e. d.

Proposition 86

To find the second apotome.

Let a rational straight line A be set out, and GC commensurable in length with A;

therefore GC is rational.

Let two square numbers DE, EF be set out, and let their difference DF not be square.

Now let it be contrived that, as FD is to DE, so is the square on CG to the square on GB.   [x. 6, Por.]

Therefore the square on CG is commensurable with the square on GB.   [x. 6]

But the square on *CG* is rational;

therefore the square on *GB* is also rational;

therefore *BG* is rational.

And, since the square on *GC* has not to the square on *GB* the ratio which a square number has to a square number, *CG* is incommensurable in length with *GB*.

[x. 9]

And both are rational;

therefore *CG*, *GB* are rational straight lines commensurable in square only;

therefore *BC* is an apotome.   [x. 73]

I say next that it is also a second apotome.

For let the square on *H* be that by which the square on *BG* is greater than the square on *GC*.

Since then, as the square on *BG* is to the square on *GC*, so is the number *ED* to the number *DF*,

therefore, *convertendo*,

as the square on *BG* is to the square on *H*, so is *DE* to *EF*.   [v. 19, Por.]

And each of the numbers *DE*, *EF* is square;

therefore the square on *BG* has to the square on *H* the ratio which a square number has to a square number;

therefore *BG* is commensurable in length with *H*.   [x. 9]

And the square on *BG* is greater than the square on *GC* by the square on *H*;

therefore the square on *BG* is greater than the square on *GC* by the square on a straight line commensurable in length with *BG*.

And *CG*, the annex, is commensurable with the rational straight line *A* set out.

Therefore *BC* is a second apotome.   [x. Deff. iii. 2]

Therefore the second apotome *BC* has been found.   Q. E. D.

PROPOSITION 87

To find the third apotome.

Let a rational straight line *A* be set out, let three numbers *E*, *BC*, *CD* be set out which have not to one another the ratio which a square number has to a square number, but let *CB* have to *BD* the ratio which a square number has to a square number.

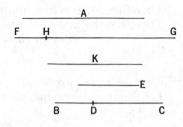

Let it be contrived that, as *E* is to *BC*, so is the square on *A* to the square on *FG*, and, as *BC* is to *CD*, so is the square on *FG* to the square on *GH*.   [x. 6, Por.]

Since then, as *E* is to *BC*, so is the square on *A* to the square on *FG*,

therefore the square on *A* is commensurable with the square on *FG*.   [x. 6]

But the square on *A* is rational;

therefore the square on *FG* is also rational;

therefore *FG* is rational.

And, since E has not to BC the ratio which a square number has to a square number,
therefore neither has the square on A to the square on FG the ratio which a square number has to a square number;
therefore A is incommensurable in length with FG.   [x. 9]
Again, since, as BC is to CD, so is the square on FG to the square on GH, therefore the square on FG is commensurable with the square on GH. [x. 6]
But the square on FG is rational;
therefore the square on GH is also rational;
therefore GH is rational.
And, since BC has not to CD the ratio which a square number has to a square number,
therefore neither has the square on FG to the square on GH the ratio which a square number has to a square number;
therefore FG is incommensurable in length with GH.   [x. 9]
And both are rational;
therefore FG, GH are rational straight lines commensurable in square only;
therefore FH is an apotome.   [x. 73]
I say next that it is also a third apotome.
For since, as E is to BC, so is the square on A to the square on FG,
and, as BC is to CD, so is the square on FG to the square on HG,
therefore, *ex aequali*, as E is to CD, so is the square on A to the square on HG.
[v. 22]
But E has not to CD the ratio which a square number has to a square number;
therefore neither has the square on A to the square on GH the ratio which a square number has to a square number;
therefore A is incommensurable in length with GH.   [x. 9]
Therefore neither of the straight lines FG, GH is commensurable in length with the rational straight line A set out.
Now let the square on K be that by which the square on FG is greater than the square on GH.
Since then, as BC is to CD, so is the square on FG to the square on GH,
therefore, *convertendo*, as BC is to BD, so is the square on FG to the square on K.   [v. 19, Por.]
But BC has to BD the ratio which a square number has to a square number;
therefore the square on FG also has to the square on K the ratio which a square number has to a square number.
Therefore FG is commensurable in length with K,   [x. 9]
and the square on FG is greater than the square on GH by the square on a straight line commensurable with FG.
And neither of the straight lines FG, GH is commensurable in length with the rational straight line A set out;
therefore FH is a third apotome.   [x. Deff. III. 3]
Therefore the third apotome FH has been found.   Q. E. D.

PROPOSITION 88

To find the fourth apotome.
Let a rational straight line A be set out, and BG commensurable in length with it;

therefore BG is also rational.

Let two numbers DF, FE be set out such that the whole DE has not to either of the numbers DF, EF the ratio which a square number has to a square number.

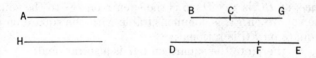

Let it be contrived that, as DE is to EF, so is the square on BG to the square on GC;　　　　　　　　　　　　　　　　　　　　　　　　[x. 6, Por.]
therefore the square on BG is commensurable with the square on GC.　[x. 6]

But the square on BG is rational;

therefore the square on GC is also rational;

therefore GC is rational.

Now, since DE has not to EF the ratio which a square number has to a square number,
therefore neither has the square on BG to the square on GC the ratio which a square number has to a square number;

therefore BG is incommensurable in length with GC.　　　[x. 9]

And both are rational;
therefore BG, GC are rational straight lines commensurable in square only;

therefore BC is an apotome.　　　　　　　　　　　[x. 73]

Now let the square on H be that by which the square on BG is greater than the square on GC.

Since then, as DE is to EF, so is the square on BG to the square on GC,
therefore also, *convertendo*, as ED is to DF, so is the square on GB to the square on H.　　　　　　　　　　　　　　　　　　　　　　　　[v. 19, Por.]

But ED has not to DF the ratio which a square number has to a square number;
therefore neither has the square on GB to the square on H the ratio which a square number has to a square number;

therefore BG is incommensurable in length with H.　　　[x. 9]

And the square on BG is greater than the square on GC by the square on H;
therefore the square on BG is greater than the square on GC by the square on a straight line incommensurable with BG.

And the whole BG is commensurable in length with the rational straight line A set out.

Therefore BC is a fourth apotome.　　　　　　　　　　[x. Deff. iii. 4]

Therefore the fourth apotome has been found.　　　　　　Q. E. D.

Proposition 89

To find the fifth apotome.

Let a rational straight line A be set out, and let CG be commensurable in length with A;

therefore CG is rational.

Let two numbers DF, FE be set out such that DE again has not to either of the numbers DF, FE the ratio which a square number has to a square number;

and let it be contrived that, as *FE* is to *ED*, so is the square on *CG* to the square on *GB*.

Therefore the square on *GB* is also rational;   [x. 6]
therefore *BG* is also rational.

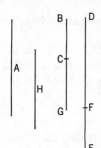

Now since, as *DE* is to *EF*, so is the square on *BG* to the square on *GC*,
while *DE* has not to *EF* the ratio which a square number has to a square number,
therefore neither has the square on *BG* to the square on *GC* the ratio which a square number has to a square number;
therefore *BG* is incommensurable in length with *GC*.   [x. 9]
And both are rational;
therefore *BG, GC* are rational straight lines commensurable in square only;
therefore *BC* is an apotome.   [x. 73]

I say next that it is also a fifth apotome.

For let the square on *H* be that by which the square on *BG* is greater than the square on *GC*.

Since then, as the square on *BG* is to the square on *GC*, so is *DE* to *EF*,
therefore, *convertendo*, as *ED* is to *DF*, so is the square on *BG* to the square on *H*.   [v. 19, Por.]

But *ED* has not to *DF* the ratio which a square number has to a square number;
therefore neither has the square on *BG* to the square on *H* the ratio which a square number has to a square number;
therefore *BG* is incommensurable in length with *H*.   [x. 9]

And the square on *BG* is greater than the square on *GC* by the square on *H*;
therefore the square on *GB* is greater than the square on *GC* by the square on a straight line incommensurable in length with *GB*.

And the annex *CG* is commensurable in length with the rational straight line *A* set out;
therefore *BC* is a fifth apotome.   [x. Deff. iii. 5]

Therefore the fifth apotome *BC* has been found.   Q. E. D.

PROPOSITION 90

To find the sixth apotome.

Let a rational straight line *A* be set out, and three numbers *E, BC, CD* not having to one another the ratio which a square number has to a square number; and further let *CB* also not have to *BD* the ratio which a square number has to a square number.

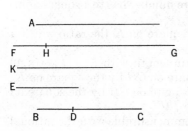

Let it be contrived that, as *E* is to *BC*, so is the square on *A* to the square on *FG*,
and, as *BC* is to *CD*, so is the square on *FG* to the square on *GH*.   [x. 6, Por.]

Now since, as *E* is to *BC*, so is the square on *A* to the square on *FG*,
therefore the square on *A* is commensurable with the square on *FG*.   [x. 6]
But the square on *A* is rational;

therefore the square on FG is also rational;

therefore FG is also rational.

And, since E has not to BC the ratio which a square number has to a square number,

therefore neither has the square on A to the square on FG the ratio which a square number has to a square number;

therefore A is incommensurable in length with FG.   [x. 9]

Again, since, as BC is to CD, so is the square on FG to the square on GH,

therefore the square on FG is commensurable with the square on GH. [x. 6]

But the square on FG is rational;

therefore the square on GH is also rational;

therefore GH is also rational.

And, since BC has not to CD the ratio which a square number has to a square number,

therefore neither has the square on FG to the square on GH the ratio which a square number has to a square number;

therefore FG is incommensurable in length with GH.   [x. 9]

And both are rational;

therefore FG, GH are rational straight lines commensurable in square only;

therefore FH is an apotome.   [x. 73]

I say next that it is also a sixth apotome.

For since, as E is to BC, so is the square on A to the square on FG,

    and, as BC is to CD, so is the square on FG to the square on GH,

therefore, *ex aequali*, as E is to CD, so is the square on A to the square on GH.

[v. 22]

But E has not to CD the ratio which a square number has to a square number;

therefore neither has the square on A to the square on GH the ratio which a square number has to a square number;

therefore A is incommensurable in length with GH;   [x. 9]

therefore neither of the straight lines FG, GH is commensurable in length with the rational straight line A.

Now let the square on K be that by which the square on FG is greater than the square on GH.

Since then, as BC is to CD, so is the square on FG to the square on GH,

therefore, *convertendo*, as CB is to BD, so is the square on FG to the square on K.   [v. 19, Por.]

But CB has not to BD the ratio which a square number has to a square number;

therefore neither has the square on FG to the square on K the ratio which a square number has to a square number;

therefore FG is incommensurable in length with K.   [x. 9]

And the square on FG is greater than the square on GH by the square on K;

therefore the square on FG is greater than the square on GH by the square on a straight line incommensurable in length with FG.

And neither of the straight lines FG, GH is commensurable with the rational straight line A set out.

Therefore FH is a sixth apotome.   [x. Deff. III. 6]

Therefore the sixth apotome FH has been found.   Q. E. D.

PROPOSITION 91

If an area be contained by a rational straight line and a first apotome, the "side"
of the area is an apotome.

For let the area AB be contained by the rational straight line AC and the
first apotome AD;

I say that the "side" of the area AB is an apotome.

For, since AD is a first apotome, let DG be its annex;
therefore AG, GD are rational straight lines commensurable in square only.
[x. 73]

And the whole AG is commensurable with the rational straight line AC set
out,

and the square on AG is greater than the square on GD by the square on a
straight line commensurable in length with AG; [x. Deff. III. 1]
if therefore there be applied to AG a parallelogram equal to the fourth part of
the square on DG and deficient by a square figure, it divides it into commensurable parts. [x. 17]

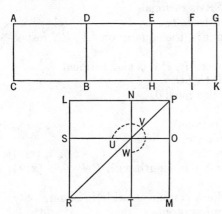

Let DG be bisected at E,
let there be applied to AG a parallelogram equal to the square on EG and
deficient by a square figure,
and let it be the rectangle AF, FG;
therefore AF is commensurable
with FG.

And through the points E, F, G let
EH, FI, GK be drawn parallel to AC.

Now, since AF is commensurable
in length with FG,
therefore AG is also commensurable
in length with each of the straight
lines AF, FG. [x. 15]

But AG is commensurable with AC;
therefore each of the straight lines AF, FG is commensurable in length with
AC. [x. 12]

And AC is rational;
therefore each of the straight lines AF, FG is also rational,
so that each of the rectangles AI, FK is also rational. [x. 19]

Now, since DE is commensurable in length with EG,
therefore DG is also commensurable in length with each of the straight lines
DE, EG. [x. 15]

But DG is rational and incommensurable in length with AC;
therefore each of the straight lines DE, EG is also rational and incommensurable in length with AC; [x. 13]
therefore each of the rectangles DH, EK is medial. [x. 21]

Now let the square LM be made equal to AI, and let there be subtracted
the square NO having a common angle with it, the angle LPM, and equal to
FK;

therefore the squares LM, NO are about the same diameter. [VI. 26]
Let PR be their diameter, and let the figure be drawn.

Since then the rectangle contained by AF, FG is equal to the square on EG,
therefore, as AF is to EG, so is EG to FG.   [VI. 17]
But, as AF is to EG, so is AI to EK,
and, as EG is to FG, so is EK to KF;   [VI. 1]
therefore EK is a mean proportional between AI, KF.   [V. 11]
But MN is also a mean proportional between LM, NO, as was before proved,
[Lemma after x. 53]
and AI is equal to the square LM, and KF to NO;
therefore MN is also equal to EK.
But EK is equal to DH, and MN to LO;
therefore DK is equal to the gnomon UVW and NO.
But AK is also equal to the squares LM, NO;
therefore the remainder AB is equal to ST.
But ST is the square on LN;
therefore the square on LN is equal to AB;
therefore LN is the "side" of AB.
I say next that LN is an apotome.
For, since each of the rectangles AI, FK is rational,
and they are equal to LM, NO,
therefore each of the squares LM, NO, that is, the squares on LP, PN respectively, is also rational;
therefore each of the straight lines LP, PN is also rational.
Again, since DH is medial and is equal to LO,
therefore LO is also medial.
Since, then, LO is medial,
while NO is rational,
therefore LO is incommensurable with NO.
But, as LO is to NO, so is LP to PN;   [VI. 1]
therefore LP is incommensurable in length with PN.   [X. 11]
And both are rational;
therefore LP, PN are rational straight lines commensurable in square only;
therefore LN is an apotome.   [X. 73]
And it is the "side" of the area AB;
therefore the "side" of the area AB is an apotome.
Therefore etc.   Q. E. D.

PROPOSITION 92

If an area be contained by a rational straight line and a second apotome, the "side"
of the area is a first apotome of a medial straight line.

For let the area AB be contained by the rational straight line AC and the
second apotome AD;
I say that the "side" of the area AB is a first apotome of a medial straight line.
For let DG be the annex to AD;
therefore AG, GD are rational straight lines commensurable in square only,
[X. 73]
and the annex DG is commensurable with the rational straight line AC set out,
while the square on the whole AG is greater than the square on the annex GD
by the square on a straight line commensurable in length with AG.
[X. Deff. III. 2]

Since, then, the square on AG is greater than the square on GD by the square on a straight line commensurable with AG,

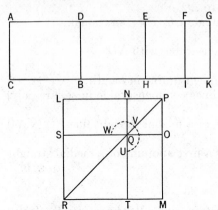

therefore, if there be applied to AG a parallelogram equal to the fourth part of the square on GD and deficient by a square figure, it divides it into commensurable parts.   [x. 17]

Let then DG be bisected at E, let there be applied to AG a parallelogram equal to the square on EG and deficient by a square figure, and let it be the rectangle AF, FG; therefore AF is commensurable in length with FG.

Therefore AG is also commensurable in length with each of the straight lines AF, FG.   [x. 15]

But AG is rational and incommensurable in length with AC; therefore each of the straight lines AF, FG is also rational and incommensurable in length with AC;   [x. 13]

therefore each of the rectangles AI, FK is medial.   [x. 21]

Again, since DE is commensurable with EG, therefore DG is also commensurable with each of the straight lines DE, EG.   [x. 15]

But DG is commensurable in length with AC.

Therefore each of the rectangles DH, EK is rational.   [x. 19]

Let then the square LM be constructed equal to AI, and let there be subtracted NO equal to FK and being about the same angle with LM, namely the angle LPM;

therefore the squares LM, NO are about the same diameter. [vi. 26]

Let PR be their diameter, and let the figure be drawn.

Since then AI, FK are medial and are equal to the squares on LP, PN,

the squares on LP, PN are also medial;

therefore LP, PN are also medial straight lines commensurable in square only.

And, since the rectangle AF, FG is equal to the square on EG,

therefore, as AF is to EG, so is EG to FG,   [vi. 17]

while, as AF is to EG, so is AI to EK,

and, as EG is to FG, so is EK to FK;   [vi. 1]

therefore EK is a mean proportional between AI, FK.   [v. 11]

But MN is also a mean proportional between the squares LM, NO,

and AI is equal to LM, and FK to NO;

therefore MN is also equal to EK.

But DH is equal to EK, and LO equal to MN;

therefore the whole DK is equal to the gnomon UVW and NO.

Since, then, the whole AK is equal to LM, NO,

and, in these, DK is equal to the gnomon UVW and NO,

therefore the remainder AB is equal to TS.

But TS is the square on LN;

therefore the square on LN is equal to the area AB;

therefore LN is the "side" of the area AB.

I say that LN is a first apotome of a medial straight line.

For, since EK is rational and is equal to LO,

therefore LO, that is, the rectangle LP, PN, is rational.

But NO was proved medial;

therefore LO is incommensurable with NO.

But, as LO is to NO, so is LP to PN;　　　　　　　　　　　[VI. 1]

therefore LP, PN are incommensurable in length.　　　　[X. 11]

Therefore LP, PN are medial straight lines commensurable in square only, which contain a rational rectangle;

therefore LN is a first apotome of a medial straight line.　　[X. 74]

And it is the "side" of the area AB.

Therefore the "side" of the area AB is a first apotome of a medial straight line.　　　　　　　　　　　　　　　　　　　　　Q. E. D.

PROPOSITION 93

If an area be contained by a rational straight line and a third apotome, the "side" of the area is a second apotome of a medial straight line.

For let the area AB be contained by the rational straight line AC and the third apotome AD;

I say that the "side" of the area AB is a second apotome of a medial straight line.

For let DG be the annex to AD;

therefore AG, GD are rational straight lines commensurable in square only, and neither of the straight lines AG, GD is commensurable in length with the rational straight line AC set out,

while the square on the whole AG is greater than the square on the annex DG by the square on a straight line commensurable with AG.　　[X. Deff. III. 3]

Since, then, the square on AG is greater than the square on GD by the square on a straight line commensurable with AG,

therefore, if there be applied to AG a parallelogram equal to the fourth part of the square on DG and deficient by a square figure, it will divide it into commensurable parts.　　　　[X. 17]

Let then DG be bisected at E, let there be applied to AG a parallelogram equal to the square on EG and deficient by a square figure, and let it be the rectangle AF, FG.

Let EH, FI, GK be drawn through the points E, F, G parallel to AC.

Therefore AF, FG are commensurable;

therefore AI is also commensurable with FK.　　　[VI. 1, X. 11]

And, since AF, FG are commensurable in length,

therefore AG is also commensurable in length with each of the straight lines AF, FG.　　　　　　　　　　　　　　　　　　　[X. 15]

But AG is rational and incommensurable in length with AC;

so that AF, FG are so also.   [x. 13]

Therefore each of the rectangles AI, FK is medial.   [x. 21]

Again, since DE is commensurable in length with EG,

therefore DG is also commensurable in length with each of the straight lines DE, EG.   [x. 15]

But GD is rational and incommensurable in length with AC;

therefore each of the straight lines DE, EG is also rational and incommensurable in length with AC;   [x. 13]

therefore each of the rectangles DH, EK is medial.   [x. 21]

And, since AG, GD are commensurable in square only,

therefore AG is incommensurable in length with GD.

But AG is commensurable in length with AF, and DG with EG;

therefore AF is incommensurable in length with EG.   [x. 13]

But, as AF is to EG, so is AI to EK;   [vi. 1]

therefore AI is incommensurable with EK.   [x. 11]

Now let the square LM be constructed equal to AI,

and let there be subtracted NO equal to FK and being about the same angle with LM;

therefore LM, NO are about the same diameter.   [vi. 26]

Let PR be their diameter, and let the figure be drawn.

Now, since the rectangle AF, FG is equal to the square on EG,

therefore, as AF is to EG, so is EG to FG.   [vi. 17]

But, as AF is to EG, so is AI to EK,

and, as EG is to FG, so is EK to FK;   [vi. 1]

therefore also, as AI is to EK, so is EK to FK;   [v. 11]

therefore EK is a mean proportional between AI, FK.

But MN is also a mean proportional between the squares LM, NO,

and AI is equal to LM, and FK to NO;

therefore EK is also equal to MN.

But MN is equal to LO, and EK equal to DH;

therefore the whole DK is also equal to the gnomon UVW and NO.

But AK is also equal to LM, NO;

therefore the remainder AB is equal to ST, that is, to the square on LN;

therefore LN is the "side" of the area AB.

I say that LN is a second apotome of a medial straight line.

For, since AI, FK were proved medial, and are equal to the squares on LP, PN,

therefore each of the squares on LP, PN is also medial;

therefore each of the straight lines LP, PN is medial.

And, since AI is commensurable with FK,   [vi. 1, x. 11]

therefore the square on LP is also commensurable with the square on PN.

Again, since AI was proved incommensurable with EK,

therefore LM is also incommensurable with MN,

that is, the square on LP with the rectangle LP, PN;

so that LP is also incommensurable in length with PN;   [vi. 1, x. 11]

therefore LP, PN are medial straight lines commensurable in square only.

I say next that they also contain a medial rectangle.

For, since EK was proved medial, and is equal to the rectangle LP, PN,

therefore the rectangle *LP*, *PN* is also medial,
so that *LP*, *PN* are medial straight lines commensurable in square only which
contain a medial rectangle.

Therefore *LN* is a second apotome of a medial straight line;   [x. 75]
and it is the "side" of the area *AB*.

Therefore the "side" of the area *AB* is a second apotome of a medial straight
line.   Q. E. D.

PROPOSITION 94

*If an area be contained by a rational straight line and a fourth apotome, the "side"
of the area is minor.*

For let the area *AB* be contained by the rational straight line *AC* and the
fourth apotome *AD*;

I say that the "side" of the area *AB* is minor.

For let *DG* be the annex to *AD*;
therefore *AG*, *GD* are rational straight lines commensurable in square only,
AG is commensurable in length with the rational straight line *AC* set out,
and the square on the whole *AG* is greater than the square on the annex *DG* by
the square on a straight line incommensurable in length with *AG*,

[x. Deff. III. 4]

Since, then, the square on *AG* is
greater than the square on *GD* by the
square on a straight line incommensurable in length with *AG*,
therefore, if there be applied to *AG* a
parallelogram equal to the fourth part
of the square on *DG* and deficient by
a square figure, it will divide it into
incommensurable parts.   [x. 18]

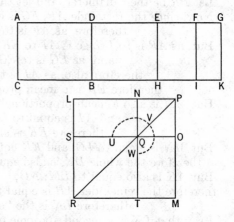

Let then *DG* be bisected at *E*,
let there be applied to *AG* a parallelogram equal to the square on *EG* and
deficient by a square figure,
and let it be the rectangle *AF*, *FG*;
therefore *AF* is incommensurable in
length with *FG*.

Let *EH*, *FI*, *GK* be drawn through *E*, *F*, *G* parallel to *AC*, *BD*.

Since, then, *AG* is rational and commensurable in length with *AC*,
therefore the whole *AK* is rational.   [x. 19]

Again, since *DG* is incommensurable in length with *AC*, and both are rational,

therefore *DK* is medial.   [x. 21]

Again, since *AF* is incommensurable in length with *FG*,
therefore *AI* is also incommensurable with *FK*.   [vi. 1, x. 11]

Now let the square *LM* be constructed equal to *AI*,
and let there be subtracted *NO* equal to *FK* and about the same angle, the
angle *LPM*.

Therefore the squares *LM*, *NO* are about the same diameter.   [vi. 26]

Let *PR* be their diameter, and let the figure be drawn.

Since, then, the rectangle AF, FG is equal to the square on EG,
therefore, proportionally, as AF is to EG, so is EG to FG.   [vi. 17]
But, as AF is to EG, so is AI to EK,
and, as EG is to FG, so is EK to FK;   [vi. 1]
therefore EK is a mean proportional between AI, FK.   [v. 11]
But MN is also a mean proportional between the squares LM, NO,
and AI is equal to LM, and FK to NO;
therefore EK is also equal to MN.
But DH is equal to EK, and LO is equal to MN;
therefore the whole DK is equal to the gnomon UVW and NO.
Since, then, the whole AK is equal to the squares LM, NO,
and, in these, DK is equal to the gnomon UVW and the square NO,
therefore the remainder AB is equal to ST, that is, to the square on LN;
therefore LN is the "side" of the area AB.
I say that LN is the irrational straight line called minor.
For, since AK is rational and is equal to the squares on LP, PN,
therefore the sum of the squares on LP, PN is rational.
Again, since DK is medial,
and DK is equal to twice the rectangle LP, PN,
therefore twice the rectangle LP, PN is medial.
And, since AI was proved incommensurable with FK,
therefore the square on LP is also incommensurable with the square on PN.
Therefore LP, PN are straight lines incommensurable in square which make
the sum of the squares on them rational, but twice the rectangle contained by
them medial.
Therefore LN is the irrational straight line called minor;   [x. 76]
and it is the "side" of the area AB.
Therefore the "side" of the area AB is minor.   Q. E. D.

PROPOSITION 95

*If an area be contained by a rational straight line and a fifth apotome, the "side"
of the area is a straight line which produces with a rational area a medial whole.*

For let the area AB be contained by the rational straight line AC and the
fifth apotome AD;
I say that the "side" of the area AB is a straight line which produces with
a rational area a medial whole.

For let DG be the annex to AD;
therefore AG, GD are rational straight lines commensurable in square only,
the annex GD is commensurable in length with the rational straight line AC
set out,
and the square on the whole AG is greater than the square on the annex DG by
the square on a straight line incommensurable with AG.   [x. Deff. iii. 5]

Therefore, if there be applied to AG a parallelogram equal to the fourth part
of the square on DG and deficient by a square figure, it will divide it into incommensurable parts.   [x. 18]

Let then DG be bisected at the point E,
let there be applied to AG a parallelogram equal to the square on EG and deficient by a square figure, and let it be the rectangle AF, FG;
therefore AF is incommensurable in length with FG.

Now, since AG is incommensurable in length with CA, and both are rational, therefore AK is medial.   [x. 21]

Again, since DG is rational and commensurable in length with AC,

DK is rational.   [x. 19]

Now let the square LM be constructed equal to AI, and let the square NO equal to FK and about the same angle, the angle LPM, be subtracted;

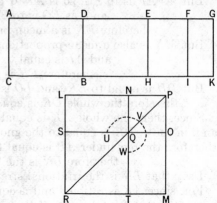

therefore the squares LM, NO are about the same diameter.   [vi. 26]

Let PR be their diameter, and let the figure be drawn.

Similarly then we can prove that LN is the "side" of the area AB.

I say that LN is the straight line which produces with a rational area a medial whole.

For, since AK was proved medial and is equal to the squares on LP, PN, therefore the sum of the squares on LP, PN is medial.

Again, since DK is rational and is equal to twice the rectangle LP, PN, the latter is itself also rational.

And, since AI is incommensurable with FK, therefore the square on LP is also incommensurable with the square on PN; therefore LP, PN are straight lines incommensurable in square which make the sum of the squares on them medial but twice the rectangle contained by them rational.

Therefore the remainder LN is the irrational straight line called that which produces with a rational area a medial whole;   [x. 77]

and it is the "side" of the area AB.

Therefore the "side" of the area AB is a straight line which produces with a rational area a medial whole.   Q. E. D.

PROPOSITION 96

If an area be contained by a rational straight line and a sixth apotome, the "side" of the area is a straight line which produces with a medial area a medial whole.

For let the area AB be contained by the rational straight line AC and the sixth apotome AD;

I say that the "side" of the area AB is a straight line which produces with a medial area a medial whole.

For let DG be the annex to AD;

therefore AG, GD are rational straight lines commensurable in square only, neither of them is commensurable in length with the rational straight line AC set out,

and the square on the whole AG is greater than the square on the annex DG by the square on a straight line incommensurable in length with AG.

[x. Deff. iii. 6]

Since, then, the square on AG is greater than the square on GD by the square on a straight line incommensurable in length with AG, therefore, if there be applied to AG a parallelogram equal to the fourth part of the square on DG and deficient by a square figure, it will divide it into incommensurable parts. [x. 18]

Let then DG be bisected at E, let there be applied to AG a parallelogram equal to the square on EG and deficient by a square figure, and let it be the rectangle AF, FG; therefore AF is incommensurable in length with FG.

But, as AF is to FG, so is AI to FK; [vi. 1] therefore AI is incommensurable with FK. [x. 11]

And, since AG, AC are rational straight lines commensurable in square only,

AK is medial. [x. 21]

Again, since AC, DG are rational straight lines and incommensurable in length,

DK is also medial. [x. 21]

Now, since AG, GD are commensurable in square only,

therefore AG is incommensurable in length with GD.

But, as AG is to GD, so is AK to KD; [vi. 1]

therefore AK is incommensurable with KD. [x. 11]

Now let the square LM be constructed equal to AI,

and let NO equal to FK, and about the same angle, be subtracted;

therefore the squares LM, NO are about the same diameter. [vi. 26]

Let PR be their diameter, and let the figure be drawn.

Then in manner similar to the above we can prove that LN is the "side" of the area AB.

I say that LN is a straight line which produces with a medial area a medial whole.

For, since AK was proved medial and is equal to the squares on LP, PN,

therefore the sum of the squares on LP, PN is medial.

Again, since DK was proved medial and is equal to twice the rectangle LP, PN,

twice the rectangle LP, PN is also medial.

And, since AK was proved incommensurable with DK,

the squares on LP, PN are also incommensurable with twice the rectangle LP, PN.

And, since AI is incommensurable with FK,

therefore the square on LP is also incommensurable with the square on PN; therefore LP, PN are straight lines incommensurable in square which make the sum of the squares on them medial, twice the rectangle contained by them medial, and further, the squares on them incommensurable with twice the rectangle contained by them.

Therefore LN is the irrational straight line called that which produces with a medial area a medial whole; [x. 78] and it is the "side" of the area AB.

Therefore the "side" of the area is a straight line which produces with a medial area a medial whole.   Q. E. D.

PROPOSITION 97

The square on an apotome applied to a rational straight line produces as breadth a first apotome.

Let AB be an apotome, and CD rational,
and to CD let there be applied CE equal to the square on AB and producing CF as breadth;

I say that CF is a first apotome.

For let BG be the annex to
AB;
therefore AG, GB are rational
straight lines commensurable
in square only.   [x. 73]

To CD let there be applied
CH equal to the square on AG,
and KL equal to the square on
BG.

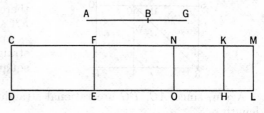

Therefore the whole CL is equal to the squares on AG, GB, and, in these, CE is equal to the square on AB;
therefore the remainder FL is equal to twice the rectangle AG, GB.   [II. 7]

Let FM be bisected at the point N,
and let NO be drawn through N parallel to CD;
therefore each of the rectangles FO, LN is equal to the rectangle AG, GB.

Now, since the squares on AG, GB are rational,
and DM is equal to the squares on AG, GB,
therefore DM is rational.

And it has been applied to the rational straight line CD, producing CM as breadth;
therefore CM is rational and commensurable in length with CD. [x. 20]

Again, since twice the rectangle AG, GB is medial, and FL is equal to twice the rectangle AG, GB,
therefore FL is medial.

And it is applied to the rational straight line CD, producing FM as breadth;
therefore FM is rational and incommensurable in length with CD. [x. 22]

And, since the squares on AG, GB are rational,
while twice the rectangle AG, GB is medial,
therefore the squares on AG, GB are incommensurable with twice the rectangle AG, GB.

And CL is equal to the squares on AG, GB,
and FL to twice the rectangle AG, GB,
therefore DM is incommensurable with FL.

But, as DM is to FL, so is CM to FM;   [VI. 1]
therefore CM is incommensurable in length with FM.   [x. 11]

And both are rational;
therefore CM, MF are rational straight lines commensurable in square only;
therefore CF is an apotome.   [x. 73]

I say next that it is also a first apotome.

For, since the rectangle AG, GB is a mean proportional between the squares on AG, GB,

and CH is equal to the square on AG,

KL equal to the square on BG,

and NL equal to the rectangle AG, GB,

therefore NL is also a mean proportional between CH, KL;

therefore, as CH is to NL, so is NL to KL.

But, as CH is to NL, so is CK to NM,

and, as NL is to KL, so is NM to KM;   [VI. 1]

therefore the rectangle CK, KM is equal to the square on NM [VI. 17], that is, to the fourth part of the square on FM.

And, since the square on AG is commensurable with the square on GB,

CH is also commensurable with KL.

But, as CH is to KL, so is CK to KM;   [VI. 1]

therefore CK is commensurable with KM.   [X. 11]

Since, then, CM, MF are two unequal straight lines,

and to CM there has been applied the rectangle CK, KM equal to the fourth part of the square on FM and deficient by a square figure,

while CK is commensurable with KM,

therefore the square on CM is greater than the square on MF by the square on a straight line commensurable in length with CM.   [X. 17]

And CM is commensurable in length with the rational straight line CD set out;

therefore CF is a first apotome.   [X. Deff. III. 1]

Therefore etc.   Q. E. D.

PROPOSITION 98

The square on a first apotome of a medial straight line applied to a rational straight line produces as breadth a second apotome.

Let AB be a first apotome of a medial straight line and CD a rational straight line,

and to CD let there be applied CE equal to the square on AB, producing CF as breadth;

I say that CF is a second apotome.

For let BG be the annex to AB;

therefore AG, GB are medial straight lines commensurable in square only which contain a rational rectangle.   [X. 74]

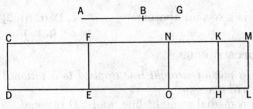

To CD let there be applied CH equal to the square on AG, producing CK as breadth, and KL equal to the square on GB, producing KM as breadth;

therefore the whole CL is equal to the squares on AG, GB;

therefore CL is also medial.   [X. 15 and 23, Por.]

And it is applied to the rational straight line CD, producing CM as breadth;

therefore CM is rational and incommensurable in length with CD.   [X. 22]

Now, since CL is equal to the squares on AG, GB,

and, in these, the square on AB is equal to CE,

therefore the remainder, twice the rectangle AG, GB, is equal to FL.   [II. 7]

But twice the rectangle AG, GB is rational;

therefore FL is rational.

And it is applied to the rational straight line FE, producing FM as breadth;

therefore FM is also rational and commensurable in length with CD.   [X. 20]

Now, since the sum of the squares on AG, GB, that is, CL, is medial, while twice the rectangle AG, GB, that is, FL, is rational,

therefore CL is incommensurable with FL.

But, as CL is to FL, so is CM to FM;   [VI. 1]

therefore CM is incommensurable in length with FM.   [X. 11]

And both are rational;

therefore CM, MF are rational straight lines commensurable in square only;

therefore CF is an apotome.   [X. 73]

I say next that it is also a second apotome.

For let FM be bisected at N,

and let NO be drawn through N parallel to CD;

therefore each of the rectangles FO, NL is equal to the rectangle AG, GB.

Now, since the rectangle AG, GB is a mean proportional between the squares on AG, GB,

and the square on AG is equal to CH,

the rectangle AG, GB to NL,

and the square on BG to KL,

therefore NL is also a mean proportional between CH, KL;

therefore, as CH is to NL, so is NL to KL.

But, as CH is to NL, so is CK to NM,

and, as NL is to KL, so is NM to MK;   [VI. 1]

therefore, as CK is to NM, so is NM to KM;   [V. 11]

therefore the rectangle CK, KM is equal to the square on NM [VI. 17], that is, to the fourth part of the square on FM.

Since, then, CM, MF are two unequal straight lines, and the rectangle CK, KM equal to the fourth part of the square on MF and deficient by a square figure has been applied to the greater, CM, and divides it into commensurable parts,

therefore the square on CM is greater than the square on MF by the square on a straight line commensurable in length with CM.   [X. 17]

And the annex FM is commensurable in length with the rational straight line CD set out;

therefore CF is a second apotome.   [X. Deff. III. 2]

Therefore etc.

                                                        Q. E. D.

PROPOSITION 99

The square on a second apotome of a medial straight line applied to a rational straight line produces as breadth a third apotome.

Let AB be a second apotome of a medial straight line, and CD rational, and to CD let there be applied CE equal to the square on AB, producing CF as breadth;

I say that CF is a third apotome.

For let *BG* be the annex to *AB*;
therefore *AG*, *GB* are medial straight lines commensurable in square only
which contain a medial rectangle.   [x. 75]

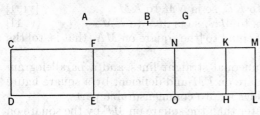

Let *CH* equal to the square
on *AG* be applied to *CD*, producing *CK* as breadth,
and let *KL* equal to the square
on *BG* be applied to *KH*, producing *KM* as breadth;
therefore the whole *CL* is equal
to the squares on *AG*, *GB*;

therefore *CL* is also medial.   [x. 15 and 23, Por.]

And it is applied to the rational straight line *CD*, producing *CM* as breadth;
therefore *CM* is rational and incommensurable in length with *CD*.   [x. 22]

Now, since the whole *CL* is equal to the squares on *AG*, *GB*, and, in these,
CE is equal to the square on *AB*,
therefore the remainder *LF* is equal to twice the rectangle *AG*, *GB*.   [ii. 7]

Let then *FM* be bisected at the point *N*,
and let *NO* be drawn parallel to *CD*;
therefore each of the rectangles *FO*, *NL* is equal to the rectangle *AG*, *GB*.

But the rectangle *AG*, *GB* is medial;
therefore *FL* is also medial.

And it is applied to the rational straight line *EF*, producing *FM* as breadth;
therefore *FM* is also rational and incommensurable in length with *CD*. [x. 22]

And, since *AG*, *GB* are commensurable in square only,
therefore *AG* is incommensurable in length with *GB*;
therefore the square on *AG* is also incommensurable with the rectangle *AG*,
GB.   [vi. 1, x. 11]

But the squares on *AG*, *GB* are commensurable with the square on *AG*,
and twice the rectangle *AG*, *GB* with the rectangle *AG*, *GB*;
therefore the squares on *AG*, *GB* are incommensurable with twice the rectangle
AG, *GB*.   [x. 13]

But *CL* is equal to the squares on *AG*, *GB*,
and *FL* is equal to twice the rectangle *AG*, *GB*;
therefore *CL* is also incommensurable with *FL*.

But, as *CL* is to *FL*, so is *CM* to *FM*;   [vi. 1]
therefore *CM* is incommensurable in length with *FM*.   [x. 11]

And both are rational;
therefore *CM*, *MF* are rational straight lines commensurable in square only;
therefore *CF* is an apotome.   [x. 73]

I say next that it is also a third apotome.

For, since the square on *AG* is commensurable with the square on *GB*,
therefore *CH* is also commensurable with *KL*,
so that *CK* is also commensurable with *KM*.   [vi. 1, x. 11]

And, since the rectangle *AG*, *GB* is a mean proportional between the squares
on *AG*, *GB*,
and *CH* is equal to the square on *AG*,
KL equal to the square on *GB*,
and *NL* equal to the rectangle *AG*, *GB*;

therefore NL is also a mean proportional between CH, KL;
therefore, as CH is to NL, so is NL to KL.
But, as CH is to NL, so is CK to NM,
and, as NL is to KL, so is NM to KM;   [VI. 1]
therefore, as CK is to MN, so is MN to KM;   [V. 11]
therefore the rectangle CK, KM is equal to [the square on MN, that is, to] the fourth part of the square on FM.

Since, then, CM, MF are two unequal straight lines, and a parallelogram equal to the fourth part of the square on FM and deficient by a square figure has been applied to CM, and divides it into commensurable parts,
therefore the square on CM is greater than the square on MF by the square on a straight line commensurable with CM.   [X. 17]

And neither of the straight lines CM, MF is commensurable in length with the rational straight line CD set out;
therefore CF is a third apotome.   [X. Deff. III. 3]
Therefore etc.   Q. E. D.

PROPOSITION 100

The square on a minor straight line applied to a rational straight line produces as breadth a fourth apotome.

Let AB be a minor and CD a rational straight line, and to the rational straight line CD let CE be applied equal to the square on AB and producing CF as breadth;
I say that CF is a fourth apotome.

For let BG be the annex to AB;
therefore AG, GB are straight lines incommensurable in square which make the sum of the squares on AG, GB rational, but twice the rectangle AG, GB medial.   [X. 76]

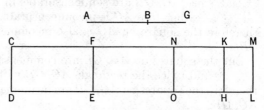

To CD let there be applied CH equal to the square on AG and producing CK as breadth,
and KL equal to the square on BG, producing KM as breadth;
therefore the whole CL is equal to the squares on AG, GB.

And the sum of the squares on AG, GB is rational;
therefore CL is also rational.

And it is applied to the rational straight line CD, producing CM as breadth;
therefore CM is also rational and commensurable in length with CD.   [X. 20]

And, since the whole CL is equal to the squares on AG, GB, and, in these, CE is equal to the square on AB,
therefore the remainder FL is equal to twice the rectangle AG, GB.   [II. 7]

Let then FM be bisected at the point N,
and let NO be drawn through N parallel to either of the straight lines CD, ML;
therefore each of the rectangles FO, NL is equal to the rectangle AG, GB.

And, since twice the rectangle AG, GB is medial and is equal to FL,
therefore FL is also medial.

And it is applied to the rational straight line FE, producing FM as breadth;

therefore FM is rational and incommensurable in length with CD.   [x. 22]

And, since the sum of the squares on AG, GB is rational,

while twice the rectangle AG, GB is medial,

the squares on AG, GB are incommensurable with twice the rectangle AG, GB.

But CL is equal to the squares on AG, GB,

and FL equal to twice the rectangle AG, GB;

therefore CL is incommensurable with FL.

But, as CL is to FL, so is CM to MF;   [vi. 1]

therefore CM is incommensurable in length with MF.   [x. 11]

And both are rational;

therefore CM, MF are rational straight lines commensurable in square only;

therefore CF is an apotome.   [x. 73]

I say that it is also a fourth apotome.

For, since AG, GB are incommensurable in square,

therefore the square on AG is also incommensurable with the square on GB.

And CH is equal to the square on AG,

and KL equal to the square on GB;

therefore CH is incommensurable with KL.

But, as CH is to KL, so is CK to KM;   [vi. 1]

therefore CK is incommensurable in length with KM.   [x. 11]

And, since the rectangle AG, GB is a mean proportional between the squares on AG, GB,

and the square on AG is equal to CH,

the square on GB to KL,

and the rectangle AG, GB to NL,

therefore NL is a mean proportional between CH, KL;

therefore, as CH is to NL, so is NL to KL.

But, as CH is to NL, so is CK to NM,

and, as NL is to KL, so is NM to KM;   [vi. 1]

therefore, as CK is to MN, so is MN to KM;   [v. 11]

therefore the rectangle CK, KM is equal to the square on MN [vi. 17], that is, to the fourth part of the square on FM.

Since then CM, MF are two unequal straight lines, and the rectangle CK, KM equal to the fourth part of the square on MF and deficient by a square figure has been applied to CM and divides it into incommensurable parts, therefore the square on CM is greater than the square on MF by the square on a straight line incommensurable with CM.   [x. 18]

And the whole CM is commensurable in length with the rational straight line CD set out;

therefore CF is a fourth apotome.   [x. Deff. iii. 4]

Therefore etc.   Q. E. D.

PROPOSITION 101

The square on the straight line which produces with a rational area a medial whole, if applied to a rational straight line, produces as breadth a fifth apotome.

Let AB be the straight line which produces with a rational area a medial whole, and CD a rational straight line, and to CD let CE be applied equal to the square on AB and producing CF as breadth;

I say that CF is a fifth apotome.

For let BG be the annex to AB;

therefore *AG*, *GB* are straight lines incommensurable in square which make the sum of the squares on them medial but twice the rectangle contained by them rational.   [x. 77]

To *CD* let there be applied *CH* equal to the square on *AG*, and *KL* equal to the square on *GB*;

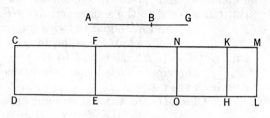

therefore the whole *CL* is equal to the squares on *AG*, *GB*.

But the sum of the squares on *AG*, *GB* together is medial; therefore *CL* is medial.

And it is applied to the rational straight line *CD*, producing *CM* as breadth; therefore *CM* is rational and incommensurable with *CD*.   [x. 22]

And, since the whole *CL* is equal to the squares on *AG*, *GB*, and, in these, *CE* is equal to the square on *AB*, therefore the remainder *FL* is equal to twice the rectangle *AG*, *GB*.   [II. 7]

Let then *FM* be bisected at *N*, and through *N* let *NO* be drawn parallel to either of the straight lines *CD*, *ML*; therefore each of the rectangles *FO*, *NL* is equal to the rectangle *AG*, *GB*.

And, since twice the rectangle *AG*, *GB* is rational and equal to *FL*, therefore *FL* is rational.

And it is applied to the rational straight line *EF*, producing *FM* as breadth; therefore *FM* is rational and commensurable in length with *CD*.   [x. 20]

Now, since *CL* is medial, and *FL* rational, therefore *CL* is incommensurable with *FL*.

But, as *CL* is to *FL*, so is *CM* to *MF*;   [vi. 1] therefore *CM* is incommensurable in length with *MF*.   [x. 11]

And both are rational; therefore *CM*, *MF* are rational straight lines commensurable in square only; therefore *CF* is an apotome.   [x. 73]

I say next that it is also a fifth apotome.

For we can prove similarly that the rectangle *CK*, *KM* is equal to the square on *NM*, that is, to the fourth part of the square on *FM*.

And, since the square on *AG* is incommensurable with the square on *GB*, while the square on *AG* is equal to *CH*, and the square on *GB* to *KL*, therefore *CH* is incommensurable with *KL*.

But, as *CH* is to *KL*, so is *CK* to *KM*;   [vi. 1] therefore *CK* is incommensurable in length with *KM*.   [x. 11]

Since then *CM*, *MF* are two unequal straight lines, and a parallelogram equal to the fourth part of the square on *FM* and deficient by a square figure has been applied to *CM*, and divides it into incommensurable parts, therefore the square on *CM* is greater than the square on *MF* by the square on a straight line incommensurable with *CM*.   [x. 18]

And the annex *FM* is commensurable with the rational straight line *CD* set out; therefore *CF* is a fifth apotome.   [x. Deff. III. 5]

Q. E. D.

Proposition 102

The square on the straight line which produces with a medial area a medial whole,
if applied to a rational straight line, produces as breadth a sixth apotome.

Let AB be the straight line which produces with a medial area a medial whole, and CD a rational straight line,
and to CD let CE be applied equal to the square on AB and producing CF as breadth;

I say that CF is a sixth apotome.

For let BG be the annex to AB;

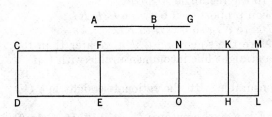

therefore AG, GB are straight lines incommensurable in square which make the sum of the squares on them medial, twice the rectangle AG, GB medial, and the squares on AG, GB incommensurable with twice the rectangle AG, GB.   [x. 78]

Now to CD let there be applied CH equal to the square on AG and producing CK as breadth,

and KL equal to the square on BG;
therefore the whole CL is equal to the squares on AG, GB;
therefore CL is also medial.

And it is applied to the rational straight line CD, producing CM as breadth;
therefore CM is rational and incommensurable in length with CD.   [x. 22]

Since now CL is equal to the squares on AG, GB,
and, in these, CE is equal to the square on AB,
therefore the remainder FL is equal to twice the rectangle AG, GB.   [II. 7]

And twice the rectangle AG, GB is medial;
therefore FL is also medial.

And it is applied to the rational straight line FE, producing FM as breadth;
therefore FM is rational and incommensurable in length with CD.   [x. 22]

And, since the squares on AG, GB are incommensurable with twice the rectangle AG, GB,
and CL is equal to the squares on AG, GB,
and FL equal to twice the rectangle AG, GB,
therefore CL is incommensurable with FL.

But, as CL is to FL, so is CM to MF;   [VI. 1]
therefore CM is incommensurable in length with MF.   [x. 11]

And both are rational.

Therefore CM, MF are rational straight lines commensurable in square only;
therefore CF is an apotome.   [x. 73]

I say next that it is also a sixth apotome.

For, since FL is equal to twice the rectangle AG, GB,
let FM be bisected at N,
and let NO be drawn through N parallel to CD;
therefore each of the rectangles FO, NL is equal to the rectangle AG, GB.

And, since AG, GB are incommensurable in square,

therefore the square on AG is incommensurable with the square on GB.
But CH is equal to the square on AG,
                    and KL is equal to the square on GB;
                therefore CH is incommensurable with KL.
But, as CH is to KL, so is CK to KM;   [vi. 1]
                therefore CK is incommensurable with KM.   [x. 11]
    And, since the rectangle AG, GB is a mean proportional between the squares
on AG, GB,

                    and CH is equal to the square on AG,
                        KL equal to the square on GB,
                    and NL equal to the rectangle AG, GB,
            therefore NL is also a mean proportional between CH, KL;
                therefore, as CH is to NL, so is NL to KL.
And for the same reason as before the square on CM is greater than the
square on MF by the square on a straight line incommensurable with CM.
                                                                                [x. 18]
    And neither of them is commensurable with the rational straight line CD
set out;
                    therefore CF is a sixth apotome.   [x. Deff. iii. 6]
                                                                                Q. E. D.

PROPOSITION 103

*A straight line commensurable in length with an apotome is an apotome and the
same in order.*

    Let AB be an apotome,
    and let CD be commensurable in length with AB;
    I say that CD is also an apotome and the same in
order with AB.
    For, since AB is an apotome, let BE be the annex to it;
therefore AE, EB are rational straight lines commensurable in square only.
                                                                                [x. 73]
    Let it be contrived that the ratio of BE to DF is the same as the ratio of AB
to CD;   [vi. 12]
                therefore also, as one is to one, so are all to all;   [v. 12]
    therefore also, as the whole AE is to the whole CF, so is AB to CD.
But AB is commensurable in length with CD.
Therefore AE is also commensurable with CF, and BE with DF.   [x. 11]
    And AE, EB are rational straight lines commensurable in square only;
therefore CF, FD are also rational straight lines commensurable in square only.
                                                                                [x. 13]
    Now since, as AE is to CF, so is BE to DF,
            alternately therefore, as AE is to EB, so is CF to FD.   [v. 16]
    And the square on AE is greater than the square on EB either by the square
on a straight line commensurable with AE or by the square on a straight line
incommensurable with it.
    If then the square on AE is greater than the square on EB by the square on
a straight line commensurable with AE, the square on CF will also be greater
than the square on FD by the square on a straight line commensurable with
CF.   [x. 14]

And, if AE is commensurable in length with the rational straight line set out,
CF is so also,   [x. 12]
if BE, then DF also,   [id.]
and, if neither of the straight lines AE, EB, then neither of the straight lines
CF, FD.   [x. 13]

But, if the square on AE is greater than the square on EB by the square on
a straight line incommensurable with AE,
the square on CF will also be greater than the square on FD by the square on
a straight line incommensurable with CF.   [x. 14]

And, if AE is commensurable in length with the rational straight line set out,
CF is so also,
if BE, then DF also,   [x. 12]
and, if neither of the straight lines AE, EB, then neither of the straight lines
CF, FD.   [x. 13]

Therefore CD is an apotome and the same in order with AB.   Q. E. D.

PROPOSITION 104

*A straight line commensurable with an apotome of a medial straight line is an
apotome of a medial straight line and the same in order.*

Let AB be an apotome of a medial straight line,
and let CD be commensurable in length with AB;

I say that CD is also an apotome of a medial straight
line and the same in order with AB.

For, since AB is an apotome of a medial straight
line, let EB be the annex to it.

Therefore AE, EB are medial straight lines commensurable in square only.
[x. 74, 75]

Let it be contrived that, as AB is to CD, so is BE to DF;   [vi. 12]
therefore AE is also commensurable with CF, and BE with DF.   [v. 12, x. 11]

But AE, EB are medial straight lines commensurable in square only;
therefore CF, FD are also medial straight lines [x. 23] commensurable in
square only;   [x. 13]
therefore CD is an apotome of a medial straight line.   [x. 74, 75]

I say next that it is also the same in order with AB.

Since, as AE is to EB, so is CF to FD,
therefore also, as the square on AE is to the rectangle AE, EB, so is the square
on CF to the rectangle CF, FD.

But the square on AE is commensurable with the square on CF;
therefore the rectangle AE, EB is also commensurable with the rectangle CF,
FD.   [v. 16, x. 11]

Therefore, if the rectangle AE, EB is rational, the rectangle CF, FD will
also be rational,   [x. Def. 4]
and if the rectangle AE, EB is medial, the rectangle CF, FD is also medial.
[x. 23, Por.]

Therefore CD is an apotome of a medial straight line and the same in order
with AB.   [x. 74, 75]

Q. E. D.

PROPOSITION 105

A straight line commensurable with a minor straight line is minor.

Let AB be a minor straight line, and CD commensurable with AB;
I say that CD is also minor.

Let the same construction be made as before;
then, since AE, EB are incommensurable in square, [x. 76]

therefore CF, FD are also incommensurable in square.   [x. 13]

Now since, as AE is to EB, so is CF to FD,   [v. 12, v. 16]
therefore also, as the square on AE is to the square on EB, so is the square on CF to the square on FD.   [vi. 22]

Therefore, *componendo*, as the squares on AE, EB are to the square on EB, so are the squares on CF, FD to the square on FD.   [v. 18]

But the square on BE is commensurable with the square on DF;
therefore the sum of the squares on AE, EB is also commensurable with the sum of the squares on CF, FD.   [v. 16, x. 11]

But the sum of the squares on AE, EB is rational;   [x. 76]
therefore the sum of the squares on CF, FD is also rational. [x. Def. 4]

Again, since, as the square on AE is to the rectangle AE, EB, so is the square on CF to the rectangle CF, FD,
while the square on AE is commensurable with the square on CF,
therefore the rectangle AE, EB is also commensurable with the rectangle CF, FD.

But the rectangle AE, EB is medial;   [x. 76]
therefore the rectangle CF, FD is also medial;   [x. 23, Por.]
therefore CF, FD are straight lines incommensurable in square which make the sum of the squares on them rational, but the rectangle contained by them medial.

Therefore CD is minor.   [x. 76]

Q. E. D.

PROPOSITION 106

A straight line commensurable with that which produces with a rational area a medial whole is a straight line which produces with a rational area a medial whole.

Let AB be a straight line which produces with a rational area a medial whole,
and CD commensurable with AB;
I say that CD is also a straight line which produces with a rational area a medial whole.

For let BE be the annex to AB;
therefore AE, EB are straight lines incommensurable in square which make the sum of the squares on AE, EB medial, but the rectangle contained by them rational.   [x. 77]

Let the same construction be made.

Then we can prove, in manner similar to the foregoing, that CF, FD are in the same ratio as AE, EB,
the sum of the squares on AE, EB is commensurable with the sum of the squares on CF, FD,
and the rectangle AE, EB with the rectangle CF, FD;

so that *CF*, *FD* are also straight lines incommensurable in square which make the sum of the squares on *CF*, *FD* medial, but the rectangle contained by them rational.

Therefore *CD* is a straight line which produces with a rational area a medial whole.   [x. 77]

Q. E. D.

PROPOSITION 107

A straight line commensurable with that which produces with a medial area a medial whole is itself also a straight line which produces with a medial area a medial whole.

Let *AB* be a straight line which produces with a medial area a medial whole, and let *CD* be commensurable with *AB*;

I say that *CD* is also a straight line which produces with a medial area a medial whole.

For let *BE* be the annex to *AB*,

and let the same construction be made;

therefore *AE*, *EB* are straight lines incommensurable in square which make the sum of the squares on them medial, the rectangle contained by them medial, and further, the sum of the squares on them incommensurable with the rectangle contained by them.   [x. 78]

Now, as was proved, *AE*, *EB* are commensurable with *CF*, *FD*, the sum of the squares on *AE*, *EB* with the sum of the squares on *CF*, *FD*, and the rectangle *AE*, *EB* with the rectangle *CF*, *FD*;

therefore *CF*, *FD* are also straight lines incommensurable in square which make the sum of the squares on them medial, the rectangle contained by them medial, and further, the sum of the squares on them incommensurable with the rectangle contained by them.

Therefore *CD* is a straight line which produces with a medial area a medial whole.   [x. 78]

Q. E. D.

PROPOSITION 108

If from a rational area a medial area be subtracted, the "side" of the remaining area becomes one of two irrational straight lines, either an apotome or a minor straight line.

For from the rational area *BC* let the medial area *BD* be subtracted;

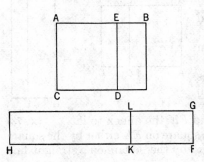

I say that the "side" of the remainder *EC* becomes one of two irrational straight lines, either an apotome or a minor straight line.

For let a rational straight line *FG* be set out,

to *FG* let there be applied the rectangular parallelogram *GH* equal to *BC*,

and let *GK* equal to *DB* be subtracted; therefore the remainder *EC* is equal to *LH*.

Since, then, *BC* is rational, and *BD* medial,

while *BC* is equal to *GH*, and *BD* to *GK*,
therefore *GH* is rational, and *GK* medial.

And they are applied to the rational straight line *FG*;
therefore *FH* is rational and commensurable in length with *FG*,   [x. 20]
while *FK* is rational and incommensurable in length with *FG*;   [x. 22]
therefore *FH* is incommensurable in length with *FK*.   [x. 13]

Therefore *FH*, *FK* are rational straight lines commensurable in square only;
therefore *KH* is an apotome [x. 73], and *KF* the annex to it.

Now the square on *HF* is greater than the square on *FK* by the square on a straight line either commensurable with *HF* or not commensurable.

First, let the square on it be greater by the square on a straight line commensurable with it.

Now the whole *HF* is commensurable in length with the rational straight line *FG* set out;
therefore *KH* is a first apotome.   [x. Deff. iii. 1]

But the "side" of the rectangle contained by a rational straight line and a first apotome is an apotome.   [x. 91]

Therefore the "side" of *LH*, that is, of *EC*, is an apotome.

But, if the square on *HF* is greater than the square on *FK* by the square on a straight line incommensurable with *HF*,
while the whole *FH* is commensurable in length with the rational straight line *FG* set out,
KH is a fourth apotome.   [x. Deff. iii. 4]

But the "side" of the rectangle contained by a rational straight line and a fourth apotome is minor.   [x. 94]

Q. E. D.

PROPOSITION 109

If from a medial area a rational area be subtracted, there arise two other irrational straight lines, either a first apotome of a medial straight line or a straight line which produces with a rational area a medial whole.

For from the medial area *BC* let the rational area *BD* be subtracted.

I say that the "side" of the remainder *EC* becomes one of two irrational straight lines, either a first apotome of a medial straight line or a straight line which produces with a rational area a medial whole.

For let a rational straight line *FG* be set out,
and let the areas be similarly applied.

It follows then that *FH* is rational and incommensurable in length with *FG*,
while *KF* is rational and commensurable in length with *FG*;
therefore *FH*, *FK* are rational straight lines commensurable in square only;   [x. 13]

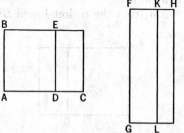

therefore *KH* is an apotome, and *FK* the annex to it.   [x. 73]

Now the square on *HF* is greater than the square on *FK* either by the square on a straight line commensurable with *HF* or by the square on a straight line incommensurable with it.

If then the square on HF is greater than the square on FK by the square on a straight line commensurable with HF,
while the annex FK is commensurable in length with the rational straight line FG set out,

KH is a second apotome.   [x. Deff. III. 2]

But FG is rational;
so that the "side" of LH, that is, of EC, is a first apotome of a medial straight line.   [x. 92]

But, if the square on HF is greater than the square on FK by the square on a straight line incommensurable with HF,
while the annex FK is commensurable in length with the rational straight line FG set out,

KH is a fifth apotome;   [x. Deff. III. 5]

so that the "side" of EC is a straight line which produces with a rational area a medial whole.   [x. 95]

Q. E. D.

PROPOSITION 110

If from a medial area there be subtracted a medial area incommensurable with the whole, the two remaining irrational straight lines arise, either a second apotome of a medial straight line or a straight line which produces with a medial area a medial whole.

For, as in the foregoing figures, let there be subtracted from the medial area BC the medial area BD incommensurable with the whole;

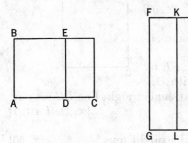

I say that the "side" of EC is one of two irrational straight lines, either a second apotome of a medial straight line or a straight line which produces with a medial area a medial whole.

For, since each of the rectangles BC, BD is medial,
and BC is incommensurable with BD,
it follows that each of the straight lines FH, FK will be rational and incommensurable in length with FG.   [x. 22]

And, since BC is incommensurable with BD,
that is, GH with GK,
HF is also incommensurable with FK;   [VI. 1, x. 11]
therefore FH, FK are rational straight lines commensurable in square only;
therefore KH is an apotome.   [x. 73]

If then the square on FH is greater than the square on FK by the square on a straight line commensurable with FH,
while neither of the straight lines FH, FK is commensurable in length with the rational straight line FG set out,

KH is a third apotome.   [x. Deff. III. 3]

But KL is rational,
and the rectangle contained by a rational straight line and a third apotome is irrational,

and the "side" of it is irrational, and is called a second apotome of a medial
straight line;   [x. 93]
so that the "side" of LH, that is, of EC, is a second apotome of a medial straight
line.

But, if the square on FH is greater than the square on FK by the square on
a straight line incommensurable with FH,
while neither of the straight lines HF, FK is commensurable in length with FG,
                    KH is a sixth apotome.   [x. Deff. III. 6]
But the "side" of the rectangle contained by a rational straight line and a
sixth apotome is a straight line which produces with a medial area a medial
whole.   [x. 96]

Therefore the "side" of LH, that is, of EC, is a straight line which produces
with a medial area a medial whole.   Q. E. D.

PROPOSITION 111

The apotome is not the same with the binomial straight line.

Let AB be an apotome;

I say that AB is not the same with the binomial
straight line.

For, if possible, let it be so;
let a rational straight line DC be set out, and to CD
let there be applied the rectangle CE equal to the
square on AB and producing DE as breadth.

Then, since AB is an apotome,
                    DE is a first apotome.   [x. 97]
Let EF be the annex to it;
therefore DF, FE are rational straight lines commensurable in square only,
the square on DF is greater than the square on FE by
the square on a straight line commensurable with DF,
and DF is commensurable in length with the rational straight line DC set out.
                                                          [x. Deff. III. 1]

Again, since AB is binomial,
                    therefore DE is a first binomial straight line.   [x. 60]
Let it be divided into its terms at G,
                    and let DG be the greater term;
therefore DG, GE are rational straight lines commensurable in square only,
the square on DG is greater than the square on GE by the square on a straight
line commensurable with DG, and the greater term DG is commensurable in
length with the rational straight line DC set out.   [x. Deff. II. 1]
Therefore DF is also commensurable in length with DG;   [x. 12]
therefore the remainder GF is also commensurable in length with DF.   [x. 15]
But DF is incommensurable in length with EF;
                    therefore FG is also incommensurable in length with EF.   [x. 13]
Therefore GF, FE are rational straight lines commensurable in square only;
                    therefore EG is an apotome.   [x. 73]
But it is also rational:

                    which is impossible.

Therefore the apotome is not the same with the binomial straight line.

Q. E. D.

The apotome and the irrational straight lines following it are neither the same with the medial straight line nor with one another.

For the square on a medial straight line, if applied to a rational straight line, produces as breadth a straight line rational and incommensurable in length with that to which it is applied,   [x. 22]
while the square on an apotome, if applied to a rational straight line, produces as breadth a first apotome,   [x. 97]
the square on a first apotome of a medial straight line, if applied to a rational straight line, produces as breadth a second apotome,   [x. 98]
the square on a second apotome of a medial straight line, if applied to a rational straight line, produces as breadth a third apotome,   [x. 99]
the square on a minor straight line, if applied to a rational straight line, produces as breadth a fourth apotome,   [x. 100]
the square on the straight line which produces with a rational area a medial whole, if applied to a rational straight line, produces as breadth a fifth apotome,   [x. 101]
and the square on the straight line which produces with a medial area a medial whole, if applied to a rational straight line, produces as breadth a sixth apotome.   [x. 102]
Since then the said breadths differ from the first and from one another, from the first because it is rational, and from one another since they are not the same in order,
it is clear that the irrational straight lines themselves also differ from one another.

And, since the apotome has been proved not to be the same as the binomial straight line,   [x. 111]
but, if applied to a rational straight line, the straight lines following the apotome produce, as breadths, each according to its own order, apotomes, and those following the binomial straight line themselves also, according to their order, produce the binomials as breadths,
therefore those following the apotome are different, and those following the binomial straight line are different, so that there are, in order, thirteen irrational straight lines in all,

Medial,
Binomial,
First bimedial,
Second bimedial,
Major,
"Side" of a rational plus a medial area,
"Side" of the sum of two medial areas,
Apotome,
First apotome of a medial straight line,
Second apotome of a medial straight line,
Minor,
Producing with a rational area a medial whole,
Producing with a medial area a medial whole.

PROPOSITION 112

The square on a rational straight line applied to the binomial straight line produces as breadth an apotome the terms of which are commensurable with the terms of the binomial and moreover in the same ratio; and further, the apotome so arising will have the same order as the binomial straight line.

Let *A* be a rational straight line,

     let *BC* be a binomial, and let *DC* be its greater term;

     let the rectangle *BC, EF* be equal to the square on *A*;

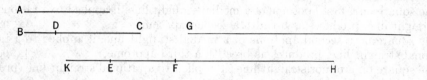

I say that *EF* is an apotome the terms of which are commensurable with *CD*, *DB*, and in the same ratio, and further, *EF* will have the same order as *BC*.

For again let the rectangle *BD, G* be equal to the square on *A*.

Since, then, the rectangle *BC, EF* is equal to the rectangle *BD, G*,

     therefore, as *CB* is to *BD*, so is *G* to *EF*.   [vi. 16]

But *CB* is greater than *BD*;

     therefore *G* is also greater than *EF*.   [v. 16, v. 14]

Let *EH* be equal to *G*;

     therefore, as *CB* is to *BD*, so is *HE* to *EF*;

     therefore, *separando*, as *CD* is to *BD*, so is *HF* to *FE*.   [v. 17]

Let it be contrived that, as *HF* is to *FE*, so is *FK* to *KE*;

therefore also the whole *HK* is to the whole *KF* as *FK* is to *KE*;

for, as one of the antecedents is to one of the consequents, so are all the antecedents to all the consequents.   [v. 12]

But, as *FK* is to *KE*, so is *CD* to *DB*;   [v. 11]

     therefore also, as *HK* is to *KF*, so is *CD* to *DB*.   [*id.*]

But the square on *CD* is commensurable with the square on *DB*;   [x. 36]

therefore the square on *HK* is also commensurable with the square on *KF*.

     [vi. 22, x. 11]

And, as the square on *HK* is to the square on *KF*, so is *HK* to *KE*, since the three straight lines *HK, KF, KE* are proportional.   [v. Def. 9]

Therefore *HK* is commensurable in length with *KE*,

     so that *HE* is also commensurable in length with *EK*.   [x. 15]

Now, since the square on *A* is equal to the rectangle *EH, BD*,

     while the square on *A* is rational,

     therefore the rectangle *EH, BD* is also rational.

And it is applied to the rational straight line *BD*;

     therefore *EH* is rational and commensurable in length with *BD*; [x. 20]

so that *EK*, being commensurable with it, is also rational and commensurable in length with *BD*.

Since, then, as *CD* is to *DB*, so is *FK* to *KE*,

     while *CD, DB* are straight lines commensurable in square only,

     therefore *FK, KE* are also commensurable in square only.   [x. 11]

But KE is rational;
therefore FK is also rational.
Therefore FK, KE are rational straight lines commensurable in square only;
therefore EF is an apotome.   [x. 73]
Now the square on CD is greater than the square on DB either by the square on a straight line commensurable with CD or by the square on a straight line incommensurable with it.

If then the square on CD is greater than the square on DB by the square on a straight line commensurable with CD, the square on FK is also greater than the square on KE by the square on a straight line commensurable with FK.
[x. 14]
And, if CD is commensurable in length with the rational straight line set out,
so also is FK;   [x. 11, 12]
if BD is so commensurable,
so also is KE;   [x. 12]
but, if neither of the straight lines CD, DB is so commensurable,
neither of the straight lines FK, KE is so.
But, if the square on CD is greater than the square on DB by the square on a straight line incommensurable with CD,
the square on FK is also greater than the square on KE by the square on a straight line incommensurable with FK.   [x. 14]
And, if CD is commensurable with the rational straight line set out,
so also is FK;
if BD is so commensurable,
so also is KE;
but, if neither of the straight lines CD, DB is so commensurable,
neither of the straight lines FK, KE is so;
so that FE is an apotome, the terms of which, FK, KE are commensurable with the terms CD, DB of the binomial straight line and in the same ratio, and it has the same order as BC.   Q. E. D.

PROPOSITION 113

The square on a rational straight line, if applied to an apotome, produces as breadth the binomial straight line the terms of which are commensurable with the terms of the apotome and in the same ratio; and further, the binomial so arising has the same order as the apotome.

Let A be a rational straight line and BD an apotome, and let the rectangle BD, KH be equal to the square on A, so that the square on the rational straight line A when applied to the apotome BD produces KH as breadth;

I say that KH is a binomial straight line the terms of which are commensurable with the terms of BD and in the same ratio; and further, KH has the same order as BD.

For let DC be the annex to BD;

therefore BC, CD are rational straight lines commensurable in square only.   [x. 73]

Let the rectangle BC, G be also equal to the square on A.

But the square on A is rational;

therefore the rectangle BC, G is also rational.

And it has been applied to the rational straight line BC;

therefore G is rational and commensurable in length with BC.   [x. 20]

Since now the rectangle BC, G is equal to the rectangle BD, KH,

therefore, proportionally, as CB is to BD, so is KH to G.   [vi. 16]

But BC is greater than BD;

therefore KH is also greater than G.   [v. 16, v. 14]

Let KE be made equal to G;

therefore KE is commensurable in length with BC.

And since, as CB is to BD, so is HK to KE,

therefore, *convertendo*, as BC is to CD, so is KH to HE.   [v. 19, Por.]

Let it be contrived that, as KH is to HE, so is HF to FE;

therefore also the remainder KF is to FH as KH is to HE, that is, as BC is to CD.   [v. 19]

But BC, CD are commensurable in square only;

therefore KF, FH are also commensurable in square only.   [x. 11]

And since, as KH is to HE, so is KF to FH,

while, as KH is to HE, so is HF to FE,

therefore also, as KF is to FH, so is HF to FE,   [v. 11]

so that also, as the first is to the third, so is the square on the first to the square on the second;   [v. Def. 9]

therefore also, as KF is to FE, so is the square on KF to the square on FH.

But the square on KF is commensurable with the square on FH,

for KF, FH are commensurable in square;

therefore KF is also commensurable in length with FE,   [x. 11]

so that KF is also commensurable in length with KE.   [x. 15]

But KE is rational and commensurable in length with BC;

therefore KF is also rational and commensurable in length with BC.   [x. 12]

And, since, as BC is to CD, so is KF to FH,

alternately, as BC is to KF, so is DC to FH.   [v. 16]

But BC is commensurable with KF;

therefore FH is also commensurable in length with CD.   [x. 11]

But BC, CD are rational straight lines commensurable in square only;

therefore KF, FH are also rational straight lines [x. Def. 3] commensurable in square only;

therefore KH is binomial.   [x. 36]

If now the square on BC is greater than the square on CD by the square on a straight line commensurable with BC,

the square on KF will also be greater than the square on FH by the square on a straight line commensurable with KF.   [x. 14]

And, if BC is commensurable in length with the rational straight line set out,

so also is KF;

if CD is commensurable in length with the rational straight line set out,

so also is FH,

but, if neither of the straight lines BC, CD,

then neither of the straight lines KF, FH.

But, if the square on BC is greater than the square on CD by the square on a straight line incommensurable with BC,

the square on KF is also greater than the square on FH by the square on a

straight line incommensurable with KF.   [x. 14]
And, if BC is commensurable with the rational straight line set out,
so also is KF;
if CD is so commensurable,
so also is FH;
but, if neither of the straight lines BC, CD,
then neither of the straight lines KF, FH.
Therefore KH is a binomial straight line, the terms of which KF, FH are commensurable with the terms BC, CD of the apotome and in the same ratio, and further, KH has the same order as BD.   Q. E. D.

PROPOSITION 114

If an area be contained by an apotome and the binomial straight line the terms of which are commensurable with the terms of the apotome and in the same ratio, the "side" of the area is rational.

For let an area, the rectangle AB, CD, be contained by the apotome AB and the binomial straight line CD,
and let CE be the greater term of the latter; let the terms CE, ED of the binomial straight line be commensurable with the terms AF, FB of the apotome and in the same ratio;
and let the "side" of the rectangle AB, CD be G;
I say that G is rational.
For let a rational straight line H be set out, and to CD let there be applied a rectangle equal to the square on H and producing KL as breadth,
Therefore KL is an apotome.
Let its terms be KM, ML commensurable with the terms CE, ED of the binomial straight line and in the same ratio.   [x. 112]
But CE, ED are also commensurable with AF, FB and in the same ratio; therefore, as AF is to FB, so is KM to ML.
Therefore, alternately, as AF is to KM, so is BF to LM; therefore also the remainder AB is to the remainder KL as AF is to KM. [v. 19]
But AF is commensurable with KM;   [x. 12]
therefore AB is also commensurable with KL.   [x. 11]
And, as AB is to KL, so is the rectangle CD, AB to the rectangle CD, KL;
[vi. 1]
therefore the rectangle CD, AB is also commensurable with the rectangle CD, KL.   [x. 11]
But the rectangle CD, KL is equal to the square on H;
therefore the rectangle CD, AB is commensurable with the square on H.
But the square on G is equal to the rectangle CD, AB;
therefore the square on G is commensurable with the square on H.
But the square on H is rational;
therefore the square on G is also rational;
therefore G is rational.
And it is the "side" of the rectangle CD, AB.
Therefore etc.

PORISM. And it is made manifest to us by this also that it is possible for a rational area to be contained by irrational straight lines. Q. E. D.

PROPOSITION 115

From a medial straight line there arise irrational straight lines infinite in number, and none of them is the same as any of the preceding.

Let A be a medial straight line;

I say that from A there arise irrational straight lines infinite in number, and none of them is the same as any of the preceding.

Let a rational straight line B be set out, and let the square on C be equal to the rectangle B, A;

therefore C is irrational; [x. Def. 4] for that which is contained by an irrational and a rational straight line is irrational. [deduction from x. 20]

And it is not the same with any of the preceding; for the square on none of the preceding, if applied to a rational straight line produces as breadth a medial straight line.

Again, let the square on D be equal to the rectangle B, C; therefore the square on D is irrational. [deduction from x. 20]

Therefore D is irrational; [x. Def. 4] and it is not the same with any of the preceding, for the square on none of the preceding, if applied to a rational straight line, produces C as breadth.

Similarly, if this arrangement proceeds *ad infinitum*, it is manifest that from the medial straight line there arise irrational straight lines infinite in number, and none is the same with any of the preceding. Q. E. D.

BOOK ELEVEN

DEFINITIONS

1. A *solid* is that which has length, breadth, and depth.

2. An extremity of a solid is a surface.

3. A *straight line* is *at right angles to a plane*, when it makes right angles with all the straight lines which meet it and are in the plane.

4. A *plane* is *at right angles to a plane* when the straight lines drawn, in one of the planes, at right angles to the common section of the planes are at right angles to the remaining plane.

5. The *inclination of a straight line to a plane* is, assuming a perpendicular drawn from the extremity of the straight line which is elevated above the plane to the plane, and a straight line joined from the point thus arising to the extremity of the straight line which is in the plane, the angle contained by the straight line so drawn and the straight line standing up.

6. The *inclination of a plane to a plane* is the acute angle contained by the straight lines drawn at right angles to the common section at the same point, one in each of the planes.

7. A plane is said to be *similarly inclined* to a plane as another is to another when the said angles of the inclinations are equal to one another.

8. *Parallel planes* are those which do not meet.

9. *Similar solid figures* are those contained by similar planes equal in multitude.

10. *Equal and similar solid figures* are those contained by similar planes equal in multitude and in magnitude.

11. A *solid angle* is the inclination constituted by more than two lines which meet one another and are not in the same surface, towards all the lines.

Otherwise: A *solid angle* is that which is contained by more than two plane angles which are not in the same plane and are constructed to one point.

12. A *pyramid* is a solid figure, contained by planes, which is constructed from one plane to one point.

13. A *prism* is a solid figure contained by planes two of which, namely those which are opposite, are equal, similar and parallel, while the rest are parallelograms.

14. When, the diameter of a semicircle remaining fixed, the semicircle is carried round and restored again to the same position from which it began to be moved, the figure so comprehended is a *sphere*.

15. The *axis of the sphere* is the straight line which remains fixed and about which the semicircle is turned.

16. The *centre of the sphere* is the same as that of the semicircle.

17. A *diameter of the sphere* is any straight line drawn through the centre and

terminated in both directions by the surface of the sphere.

18. When, one side of those about the right angle in a right-angled triangle remaining fixed, the triangle is carried round and restored again to the same position from which it began to be moved, the figure so comprehended is a *cone.*

And, if the straight line which remains fixed be equal to the remaining side about the right angle which is carried round, the cone will be *right-angled*; if less, *obtuse-angled*; and if greater, *acute-angled.*

19. The *axis of the cone* is the straight line which remains fixed and about which the triangle is turned.

20. And the *base* is the circle described by the straight line which is carried round.

21. When, one side of those about the right angle in a rectangular parallelogram remaining fixed, the parallelogram is carried round and restored again to the same position from which it began to be moved, the figure so comprehended is a *cylinder.*

22. The *axis of the cylinder* is the straight line which remains fixed and about which the parallelogram is turned.

23. And the *bases* are the circles described by the two sides opposite to one another which are carried round.

24. *Similar cones and cylinders* are those in which the axes and the diameters of the bases are proportional.

25. A *cube* is a solid figure contained by six equal squares.

26. An *octahedron* is a solid figure contained by eight equal and equilateral triangles.

27. An *icosahedron* is a solid figure contained by twenty equal and equilateral triangles.

28. A *dodecahedron* is a solid figure contained by twelve equal, equilateral, and equiangular pentagons.

BOOK XI.   PROPOSITIONS

PROPOSITION 1

A part of a straight line cannot be in the plane of reference and a part in a plane more elevated.

For, if possible, let a part AB of the straight line ABC be in the plane of reference, and a part BC in a plane more elevated.

There will then be in the plane of reference some straight line continuous with AB in a straight line.

Let it be BD;

therefore AB is a common segment of the two straight lines ABC, ABD:

which is impossible, inasmuch as, if we describe a circle with centre B and distance AB, the diameters will cut off unequal circumferences of the circle.

Therefore a part of a straight line cannot be in the plane of reference, and a part in a plane more elevated.

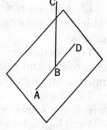

Q. E. D.

Proposition 2

If two straight lines cut one another, they are in one plane, and every triangle is in one plane.

For let the two straight lines *AB*, *CD* cut one another at the point *E*;

I say that *AB*, *CD* are in one plane, and every triangle is in one plane.

For let points *F*, *G* be taken at random on *EC*, *EB*,

let *CB*, *FG* be joined,

and let *FH*, *GK* be drawn across;

I say first that the triangle *ECB* is in one plane.

For, if part of the triangle *ECB*, either *FHC* or *GBK*, is in the plane of reference, and the rest in another,

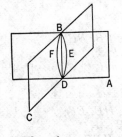

a part also of one of the straight lines *EC*, *EB* will be in the plane of reference, and a part in another.

But, if the part *FCBG* of the triangle *ECB* be in the plane of reference, and the rest in another,

a part also of both the straight lines *EC*, *EB* will be in the plane of reference and a part in another:

which was proved absurd.   [XI. 1]

Therefore the triangle *ECB* is in one plane.

But, in whatever plane the triangle *ECB* is, in that plane also is each of the straight lines *EC*, *EB*,

and, in whatever plane each of the straight lines *EC*, *EB* is, in that plane are *AB*, *CD* also.   [XI. 1]

Therefore the straight lines *AB*, *CD* are in one plane,

and every triangle is in one plane.   Q. E. D.

Proposition 3

If two planes cut one another, their common section is a straight line.

For let the two planes *AB*, *BC* cut one another,

and let the line *DB* be their common section;

I say that the line *DB* is a straight line.

For, if not, from *D* to *B* let the straight line *DEB* be joined in the plane *AB*,

and in the plane *BC* the straight line *DFB*.

Then the two straight lines *DEB*, *DFB* will have the same extremities, and will clearly enclose an area:

which is absurd.

Therefore *DEB*, *DFB* are not straight lines.

Similarly we can prove that neither will there be any other straight line joined from *D* to *B* except *DB* the common section of the planes *AB*, *BC*.

Therefore etc.   Q. E. D.

Proposition 4

If a straight line be set up at right angles to two straight lines which cut one another, at their common point of section, it will also be at right angles to the plane through them.

For let a straight line EF be set up at right angles to the two straight lines AB, CD, which cut one another at the point E, from E;

I say that EF is also at right angles to the plane through AB, CD.

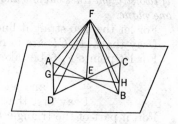

For let AE, EB, CE, ED be cut off equal to one another,

and let any straight line GEH be drawn across through E, at random;

let AD, CB be joined,

and further, let FA, FG, FD, FC, FH, FB be joined from the point F taken at random <on EF>.

Now, since the two straight lines AE, ED are equal to the two straight lines CE, EB, and contain equal angles,   [I. 15]

therefore the base AD is equal to the base CB,

and the triangle AED will be equal to the triangle CEB;   [I. 4]

so that the angle DAE is also equal to the angle EBC.

But the angle AEG is also equal to the angle BEH;   [I. 15]

therefore AGE, BEH are two triangles which have two angles equal to two angles respectively, and one side equal to one side, namely that adjacent to the equal angles, that is to say, AE to EB;

therefore they will also have the remaining sides equal to the remaining sides.

[I. 26]

Therefore GE is equal to EH, and AG to BH.

And, since AE is equal to EB,

while FE is common and at right angles,

therefore the base FA is equal to the base FB.   [I. 4]

For the same reason

FC is also equal to FD.

And, since AD is equal to CB,

and FA is also equal to FB,

the two sides FA, AD are equal to the two sides FB, BC respectively;

and the base FD was proved equal to the base FC;

therefore the angle FAD is also equal to the angle FBC.   [I. 8]

And since, again, AG was proved equal to BH,

and further, FA also equal to FB,

the two sides FA, AG are equal to the two sides FB, BH.

And the angle FAG was proved equal to the angle FBH;

therefore the base FG is equal to the base FH.   [I. 4]

Now since, again, GE was proved equal to EH,

and EF is common,

the two sides GE, EF are equal to the two sides HE, EF;

and the base FG is equal to the base FH;

therefore the angle GEF is equal to the angle HEF.   [I. 8]

Therefore each of the angles GEF, HEF is right.

Therefore FE is at right angles to GH drawn at random through E.

Similarly we can prove that FE will also make right angles with all the straight lines which meet it and are in the plane of reference.

But a straight line is at right angles to a plane when it makes right angles

with all the straight lines which meet it and are in that same plane; [xi. Def. 3]
therefore FE is at right angles to the plane of reference.

But the plane of reference is the plane through the straight lines AB, CD.

Therefore FE is at right angles to the plane through AB, CD.

Therefore etc.   Q. E. D.

PROPOSITION 5

If a straight line be set up at right angles to three straight lines which meet one an-other, at their common point of section, the three straight lines are in one plane.

For let a straight line AB be set up at right angles to the three straight lines BC, BD, BE, at their point of meeting at B;

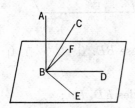

I say that BC, BD, BE are in one plane.

For suppose they are not, but, if possible, let BD, BE be in the plane of reference and BC in one more elevated;

let the plane through AB, BC be produced;
it will thus make, as common section in the plane of reference, a straight line.   [xi. 3]

Let it make BF.

Therefore the three straight lines AB, BC, BF are in one plane, namely that drawn through AB, BC.

Now, since AB is at right angles to each of the straight lines BD, BE, therefore AB is also at right angles to the plane through BD, BE.   [xi. 4]

But the plane through BD, BE is the plane of reference;
therefore AB is at right angles to the plane of reference.

Thus AB will also make right angles with all the straight lines which meet it and are in the plane of reference.   [xi. Def. 3]

But BF which is in the plane of reference meets it;
therefore the angle ABF is right.

But, by hypothesis, the angle ABC is also right;
therefore the angle ABF is equal to the angle ABC.

And they are in one plane:
which is impossible.

Therefore the straight line BC is not in a more elevated plane;
therefore the three straight lines BC, BD, BE are in one plane.

Therefore, if a straight line be set up at right angles to three straight lines, at their point of meeting, the three straight lines are in one plane.   Q. E. D.

PROPOSITION 6

If two straight lines be at right angles to the same plane, the straight lines will be parallel.

For let the two straight lines AB, CD be at right angles to the plane of reference;

I say that AB is parallel to CD.

For let them meet the plane of reference at the points B, D,
let the straight line BD be joined,
let DE be drawn, in the plane of reference, at right angles to BD,
let DE be made equal to AB,

and let *BE, AE, AD* be joined.

Now, since *AB* is at right angles to the plane of reference, it will also make right angles with all the straight lines which meet it and are in the plane of reference.   [XI. Def. 3]

But each of the straight lines *BD, BE* is in the plane of reference and meets *AB*;
therefore each of the angles *ABD, ABE* is right.

For the same reason
each of the angles *CDB, CDE* is also right.

And, since *AB* is equal to *DE*,
and *BD* is common,
the two sides *AB, BD* are equal to the two sides *ED, DB*;

and they include right angles;
therefore the base *AD* is equal to the base *BE*.   [I. 4]

And, since *AB* is equal to *DE*,
while *AD* is also equal to *BE*,
the two sides *AB, BE* are equal to the two sides *ED, DA*;
and *AE* is their common base;
therefore the angle *ABE* is equal to the angle *EDA*.   [I. 8]

But the angle *ABE* is right;
therefore the angle *EDA* is also right;
therefore *ED* is at right angles to *DA*.

But it is also at right angles to each of the straight lines *BD, DC*;
therefore *ED* is set up at right angles to the three straight lines *BD, DA, DC* at their point of meeting;
therefore the three straight lines *BD, DA, DC* are in one plane.   [XI. 5]

But, in whatever plane *DB, DA* are, in that plane is *AB* also,
for every triangle is in one plane;   [XI. 2]
therefore the straight lines *AB, BD, DC* are in one plane.

And each of the angles *ABD, BDC* is right;
therefore *AB* is parallel to *CD*.   [I. 28]

Therefore etc.
                                                                                                 Q. E. D.

PROPOSITION 7

If two straight lines be parallel and points be taken at random on each of them, the straight line joining the points is in the same plane with the parallel straight lines.

Let *AB, CD* be two parallel straight lines,
and let points *E, F* be taken at random on them respectively;

I say that the straight line joining the points *E, F* is in the same plane with the parallel straight lines.

For suppose it is not, but, if possible, let it be in a more elevated plane as *EGF*,
and let a plane be drawn through *EGF*;
it will then make, as section in the plane of reference, a straight line.   [XI. 3]

Let it make it, as *EF*;
therefore the two straight lines *EGF, EF* will enclose an area:
which is impossible.

Therefore the straight line joined from E to F is not in a plane more elevated; therefore the straight line joined from E to F is in the plane through the parallel straight lines AB, CD.

Therefore etc.   Q. E. D.

PROPOSITION 8

If two straight lines be parallel, and one of them be at right angles to any plane, the remaining one will also be at right angles to the same plane.

Let AB, CD be two parallel straight lines,

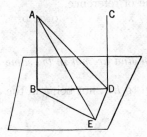

and let one of them, AB, be at right angles to the plane of reference;

I say that the remaining one, CD, will also be at right angles to the same plane.

For let AB, CD meet the plane of reference at the points B, D,

and let BD be joined;

therefore AB, CD, BD are in one plane.   [XI. 7]

Let DE be drawn, in the plane of reference, at right angles to BD,

let DE be made equal to AB,

and let BE, AE, AD be joined.

Now, since AB is at right angles to the plane of reference, therefore AB is also at right angles to all the straight lines which meet it and are in the plane of reference;   [XI. Def. 3]

therefore each of the angles ABD, ABE is right.

And, since the straight line BD has fallen on the parallels AB, CD,

therefore the angles ABD, CDB are equal to two right angles.   [I. 29]

But the angle ABD is right;

therefore the angle CDB is also right;

therefore CD is at right angles to BD.

And, since AB is equal to DE,

and BD is common,

the two sides AB, BD are equal to the two sides ED, DB;

and the angle ABD is equal to the angle EDB,

for each is right;

therefore the base AD is equal to the base BE.

And, since AB is equal to DE,

and BE to AD,

the two sides AB, BE are equal to the two sides ED, DA respectively,

and AE is their common base;

therefore the angle ABE is equal to the angle EDA.

But the angle ABE is right;

therefore the angle EDA is also right;

therefore ED is at right angles to AD.

But it is also at right angles to DB;

therefore ED is also at right angles to the plane through BD, DA.   [XI. 4]

Therefore ED will also make right angles with all the straight lines which meet it and are in the plane through BD, DA.

But DC is in the plane through BD, DA, inasmuch as AB, BD are in the

plane through *BD, DA,*   [XI. 2]
        and *DC* is also in the plane in which *AB, BD* are.
    Therefore *ED* is at right angles to *DC,*
        so that *CD* is also at right angles to *DE.*
    But *CD* is also at right angles to *BD.*
    Therefore *CD* is set up at right angles to the two straight lines *DE, DB*
which cut one another, from the point of section at *D;*
so that *CD* is also at right angles to the plane through *DE, DB.*   [XI. 4]
    But the plane through *DE, DB* is the plane of reference;
       therefore *CD* is at right angles to the plane of reference.
    Therefore etc.
                                       Q. E. D.

PROPOSITION 9

Straight lines which are parallel to the same straight line and are not in the same plane with it are also parallel to one another.

    For let each of the straight lines *AB, CD* be parallel to *EF,* not being in the same plane with it;
    I say that *AB* is parallel to *CD.*
    For let a point *G* be taken at random on *EF,*
and from it let there be drawn *GH,* in the plane through *EF, AB,* at right angles to *EF,* and *GK* in the plane through *FE, CD* again at right angles to *EF.*
    Now, since *EF* is at right angles to each of the straight lines *GH, GK,*
therefore *EF* is also at right angles to the plane through *GH, GK.*   [XI. 4]
    And *EF* is parallel to *AB;*
therefore *AB* is also at right angles to the plane through *HG, GK.*   [XI. 8]
    For the same reason
        CD is also at right angles to the plane through *HG, GK;*
therefore each of the straight lines *AB, CD* is at right angles to the plane through *HG, GK.*
    But, if two straight lines be at right angles to the same plane, the straight lines are parallel;   [XI. 6]
        therefore *AB* is parallel to *CD.*   Q. E. D.

PROPOSITION 10

If two straight lines meeting one another be parallel to two straight lines meeting one another not in the same plane, they will contain equal angles.

    For let the two straight lines *AB, BC* meeting one another be parallel to the two straight lines *DE, EF* meeting one another, not in the same plane;
       I say that the angle *ABC* is equal to the angle *DEF.*
    For let *BA, BC, ED, EF* be cut off equal to one another, and let *AD, CF, BE, AC, DF* be joined.
    Now, since *BA* is equal and parallel to *ED,*
        therefore *AD* is also equal and parallel to *BE.*   [I. 33]
    For the same reason
        CF is also equal and parallel to *BE.*

Therefore each of the straight lines AD, CF is equal and parallel to BE.

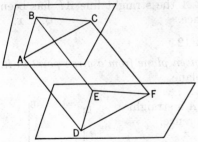

But straight lines which are parallel to the same straight line and are not in the same plane with it are parallel to one another;   [XI. 9]

therefore AD is parallel and equal to CF.

And AC, DF join them;

therefore AC is also equal and parallel to DF.   [I. 33]

Now, since the two sides AB, BC are equal to the two sides DE, EF,

and the base AC is equal to the base DF,

therefore the angle ABC is equal to the angle DEF.   [I. 8]

Therefore etc.   Q. E. D.

PROPOSITION 11

From a given elevated point to draw a straight line perpendicular to a given plane.

Let A be the given elevated point, and the plane of reference the given plane; thus it is required to draw from the point A a straight line perpendicular to the plane of reference.

Let any straight line BC be drawn, at random, in the plane of reference,

and let AD be drawn from the point A perpendicular to BC.   [I. 12]

If then AD is also perpendicular to the plane of reference, that which was enjoined will have been done.

But, if not, let DE be drawn from the point D at right angles to BC and in the plane of reference, [I. 11]

let AF be drawn from A perpendicular to DE,   [I. 12]

and let GH be drawn through the point F parallel to BC.   [I. 31]

Now, since BC is at right angles to each of the straight lines DA, DE, therefore BC is also at right angles to the plane through ED, DA.   [XI. 4]

And GH is parallel to it;

but, if two straight lines be parallel, and one of them be at right angles to any plane, the remaining one will also be at right angles to the same plane; [XI. 8] therefore GH is also at right angles to the plane through ED, DA.

Therefore GH is also at right angles to all the straight lines which meet it and are in the plane through ED, DA.   [XI. Def. 3]

But AF meets it and is in the plane through ED, DA;

therefore GH is at right angles to FA,

so that FA is also at right angles to GH.

But AF is also at right angles to DE;

therefore AF is at right angles to each of the straight lines GH, DE.

But, if a straight line be set up at right angles to two straight lines which cut one another, at the point of section, it will also be at right angles to the plane through them;   [XI. 4]

therefore FA is at right angles to the plane through ED, GH.

But the plane through ED, GH is the plane of reference;

therefore *AF* is at right angles to the plane of reference.

Therefore from the given elevated point *A* the straight line *AF* has been drawn perpendicular to the plane of reference.

Q. E. F.

PROPOSITION 12

To set up a straight line at right angles to a given plane from a given point in it.

Let the plane of reference be the given plane,
and *A* the point in it;
thus it is required to set up from the point *A* a straight line at right angles to the plane of reference.

Let any elevated point *B* be conceived,
from *B* let *BC* be drawn perpendicular to
the plane of reference, [XI. 11]
and through the point *A* let *AD* be drawn
parallel to *BC*. [I. 31]

Then, since *AD*, *CB* are two parallel straight lines, while one of them, *BC*, is at right angles to the plane of reference, therefore the remaining one, *AD*, is also at right angles to the plane of reference. [XI. 8]

Therefore *AD* has been set up at right angles to the given plane from the point *A* in it.

Q. E. F.

PROPOSITION 13

From the same point two straight lines cannot be set up at right angles to the same plane on the same side.

For, if possible, from the same point *A* let the two straight lines *AB*, *AC* be set up at right angles to the plane of reference and on the same side,
and let a plane be drawn through *BA*, *AC*;
it will then make, as section through *A* in the plane of reference, a straight line. [XI. 3]

Let it make *DAE*;
therefore the straight lines *AB*, *AC*,
DAE are in one plane.

And, since *CA* is at right angles to the plane of reference, it will also make right angles with all the straight lines which meet it and are in the plane of reference. [XI. Def. 3]

But *DAE* meets it and is in the plane of reference;
therefore the angle *CAE* is right.

For the same reason
the angle *BAE* is also right;
therefore the angle *CAE* is equal to the angle *BAE*.

And they are in one plane:
which is impossible.

Therefore etc.

Q. E. D.

PROPOSITION 14

Planes to which the same straight line is at right angles will be parallel.

For let any straight line *AB* be at right angles to each of the planes *CD*, *EF*;

I say that the planes are parallel.

For, if not, they will meet when produced.

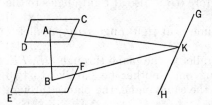

Let them meet;

they will then make, as common section, a straight line.   [xi. 3]

Let them make *GH*;

let a point *K* be taken at random on *GH*, and let *AK, BK* be joined.

Now, since *AB* is at right angles to the plane *EF*,

therefore *AB* is also at right angles to *BK* which is a straight line in the plane *EF* produced;   [xi. Def. 3]

therefore the angle *ABK* is right.

For the same reason

the angle *BAK* is also right.

Thus, in the triangle *ABK*, the two angles *ABK, BAK* are equal to two right angles:

which is impossible.   [i. 17]

Therefore the planes *CD, EF* will not meet when produced;

therefore the planes *CD, EF* are parallel.   [xi. Def. 8]

Therefore planes to which the same straight line is at right angles are parallel.   Q. E. D.

PROPOSITION 15

If two straight lines meeting one another be parallel to two straight lines meeting one another, not being in the same plane, the planes through them are parallel.

For let the two straight lines *AB, BC* meeting one another be parallel to the

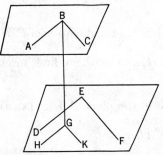

two straight lines *DE, EF* meeting one another, not being in the same plane; I say that the planes produced through *AB, BC* and *DE, EF* will not meet one another.

For let *BG* be drawn from the point *B* perpendicular to the plane through *DE, EF* [xi. 11],

and let it meet the plane at the point *G*;

through *G* let *GH* be drawn parallel to *ED*, and *GK* parallel to *EF*.   [i. 31]

Now, since *BG* is at right angles to the plane through *DE, EF*,

therefore it will also make right angles with all the straight lines which meet it and are in the plane through *DE, EF*.   [xi. Def. 3]

But each of the straight lines *GH, GK* meets it and is in the plane through *DE, EF*;

therefore each of the angles *BGH, BGK* is right.

And, since *BA* is parallel to *GH*,   [xi. 9]

therefore the angles *GBA, BGH* are equal to two right angles.   [i. 29]

But the angle *BGH* is right;

therefore the angle *GBA* is also right;

therefore *GB* is at right angles to *BA*.

For the same reason

GB is also at right angles to *BC*.

Since then the straight line *GB* is set up at right angles to the two straight lines *BA*, *BC* which cut one another, therefore *GB* is also at right angles to the plane through *BA*, *BC*.   [XI. 4]

But planes to which the same straight line is at right angles are parallel;

[XI. 14]

therefore the plane through *AB*, *BC* is parallel to the plane through *DE*, *EF*.

Therefore, if two straight lines meeting one another be parallel to two straight lines meeting one another, not in the same plane, the planes through them are parallel.   Q. E. D.

PROPOSITION 16

If two parallel planes be cut by any plane, their common sections are parallel.

For let the two parallel planes *AB*, *CD* be cut by the plane *EFGH*, and let *EF*, *GH* be their common sections;

I say that *EF* is parallel to *GH*.

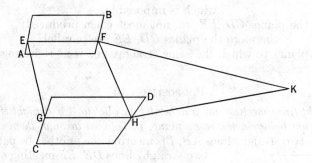

For, if not, *EF*, *GH* will, when produced, meet either in the direction of *F*, *H* or of *E*, *G*.

Let them be produced, as in the direction of *F*, *H*, and let them, first, meet at *K*.

Now, since *EFK* is in the plane *AB*,

therefore all the points on *EFK* are also in the plane *AB*.   [XI. 1]

But *K* is one of the points on the straight line *EFK*;

therefore *K* is in the plane *AB*.

For the same reason

K is also in the plane *CD*;

therefore the planes *AB*, *CD* will meet when produced.

But they do not meet, because they are, by hypothesis, parallel;

therefore the straight lines *EF*, *GH* will not meet when produced in the direction of *F*, *H*.

Similarly we can prove that neither will the straight lines *EF*, *GH* meet when produced in the direction of *E*, *G*.

But straight lines which do not meet in either direction are parallel.

[I. Def. 23]

Therefore *EF* is parallel to *GH*.

Therefore etc.   Q. E. D.

PROPOSITION 17

If two straight lines be cut by parallel planes, they will be cut in the same ratios.

For let the two straight lines AB, CD be cut by the parallel planes GH, KL, MN at the points A, E, B and C, F, D;

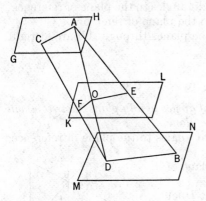

I say that, as the straight line AE is to EB, so is CF to FD.

For let AC, BD, AD be joined, let AD meet the plane KL at the point O, and let EO, OF be joined.

Now, since the two parallel planes KL, MN are cut by the plane $EBDO$, their common sections EO, BD are parallel. [XI. 16]

For the same reason, since the two parallel planes GH, KL are cut by the plane $AOFC$, their common sections AC, OF are parallel. [id.]

And, since the straight line EO has been drawn parallel to BD, one of the sides of the triangle ABD,

therefore, proportionally, as AE is to EB, so is AO to OD.   [VI. 2]

Again, since the straight line OF has been drawn parallel to AC, one of the sides of the triangle ADC,

proportionally, as AO is to OD, so is CF to FD.   [id.]

But it was also proved that, as AO is to OD, so is AE to EB;

therefore also, as AE is to EB, so is CF to FD.   [V. 11]

Therefore etc.   Q. E. D.

PROPOSITION 18

If a straight line be at right angles to any plane, all the planes through it will also be at right angles to the same plane.

For let any straight line AB be at right angles to the plane of reference;

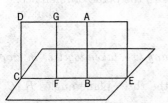

I say that all the planes through AB are also at right angles to the plane of reference.

For let the plane DE be drawn through AB, let CE be the common section of the plane DE and the plane of reference,

let a point F be taken at random on CE, and from F let FG be drawn in the plane DE at right angles to CE.   [I. 11]

Now, since AB is at right angles to the plane of reference, AB is also at right angles to all the straight lines which meet it and are in the plane of reference;   [XI. Def. 3]

so that it is also at right angles to CE;

therefore the angle ABF is right.

But the angle GFB is also right;

therefore AB is parallel to FG.   [I. 28]

But AB is at right angles to the plane of reference;

therefore FG is also at right angles to the plane of reference.   [xi. 8]

Now a plane is at right angles to a plane, when the straight lines drawn, in one of the planes, at right angles to the common section of the planes are at right angles to the remaining plane.   [xi. Def. 4]

And FG, drawn in one of the planes DE at right angles to CE, the common section of the planes, was proved to be at right angles to the plane of reference; therefore the plane DE is at right angles to the plane of reference.

Similarly also it can be proved that all the planes through AB are at right angles to the plane of reference.

Therefore etc.   Q. E. D.

PROPOSITION 19

If two planes which cut one another be at right angles to any plane, their common section will also be at right angles to the same plane.

For let the two planes AB, BC be at right angles to the plane of reference,
         and let BD be their common section;

I say that BD is at right angles to the plane of reference.

For suppose it is not, and from the point D let DE be drawn in the plane AB at right angles to the straight line AD, and DF in the plane BC at right angles to CD.

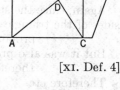

Now, since the plane AB is at right angles to the plane of reference,
and DE has been drawn in the plane AB at right angles to AD, their common section,
therefore DE is at right angles to the plane of reference.   [xi. Def. 4]

Similarly we can prove that
         DF is also at right angles to the plane of reference.

Therefore from the same point D two straight lines have been set up at right angles to the plane of reference on the same side:
                    which is impossible.   [xi. 13]

Therefore no straight line except the common section DB of the planes AB, BC can be set up from the point D at right angles to the plane of reference.

Therefore etc.   Q. E. D.

PROPOSITION 20

If a solid angle be contained by three plane angles, any two, taken together in any manner, are greater than the remaining one.

For let the solid angle at A be contained by the three plane angles BAC, CAD, DAB;

I say that any two of the angles BAC, CAD, DAB, taken together in any manner, are greater than the remaining one.

If now the angles BAC, CAD, DAB are equal to one another, it is manifest that any two are greater than the remaining one.

But, if not, let BAC be greater,
and on the straight line AB, and at the point A on it, let the angle BAE be

constructed, in the plane through BA, AC, equal to the angle DAB;

let AE be made equal to AD,

and let BEC, drawn across through the point E, cut the straight lines AB, AC at the points B, C;

let DB, DC be joined.

Now, since DA is equal to AE,

and AB is common,

two sides are equal to two sides;

and the angle DAB is equal to the angle BAE;

therefore the base DB is equal to the base BE.   [I. 4]

And, since the two sides BD, DC are greater than BC,   [I. 20]

and of these DB was proved equal to BE,

therefore the remainder DC is greater than the remainder EC.

Now, since DA is equal to AE,

and AC is common,

and the base DC is greater than the base EC,

therefore the angle DAC is greater than the angle EAC.   [I. 25]

But the angle DAB was made equal to the angle BAE;

therefore the angles DAB, DAC are greater than the angle BAC.

Similarly we can prove that the remaining angles also, taken together two and two, are greater than the remaining one.

Therefore etc.   Q. E. D.

PROPOSITION 21

Any solid angle is contained by plane angles less than four right angles.

Let the angle at A be a solid angle contained by the plane angles BAC, CAD, DAB;

I say that the angles BAC, CAD, DAB are less than four right angles.

For let points B, C, D be taken at random on the straight lines AB, AC, AD respectively,

and let BC, CD, DB be joined.

Now, since the solid angle at B is contained by the three plane angles CBA, ABD, CBD,

any two are greater than the remaining one;

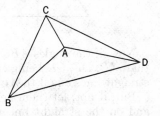

[XI. 20]

therefore the angles CBA, ABD are greater than the angle CBD.

For the same reason

the angles BCA, ACD are also greater than the angle BCD, and the angles CDA, ADB are greater than the angle CDB;

therefore the six angles CBA, ABD, BCA, ACD, CDA, ADB are greater than the three angles CBD, BCD, CDB.

But the three angles CBD, BDC, BCD are equal to two right angles;   [I. 32]

therefore the six angles CBA, ABD, BCA, ACD, CDA, ADB are greater than two right angles.

And, since the three angles of each of the triangles ABC, ACD, ADB are equal to two right angles,

therefore the nine angles of the three triangles, the angles CBA, ACB, BAC, ACD, CDA, CAD, ADB, DBA, BAD are equal to six right angles;

and of them the six angles ABC, BCA, ACD, CDA, ADB, DBA are greater than two right angles;
therefore the remaining three angles BAC, CAD, DAB containing the solid angle are less than four right angles.

Therefore etc.   Q. E. D.

PROPOSITION 22

If there be three plane angles of which two, taken together in any manner, are greater than the remaining one, and they are contained by equal straight lines, it is possible to construct a triangle out of the straight lines joining the extremities of the equal straight lines.

Let there be three plane angles ABC, DEF, GHK, of which two, taken together in any manner, are greater than the remaining one, namely

the angles ABC, DEF greater than the angle GHK,

the angles DEF, GHK greater than the angle ABC,

and, further, the angles GHK, ABC greater than the angle DEF;

let the straight lines AB, BC, DE, EF, GH, HK be equal,

and let AC, DF, GK be joined;

I say that it is possible to construct a triangle out of straight lines equal to AC, DF, GK, that is, that any two of the straight lines AC, DF, GK are greater than the remaining one.

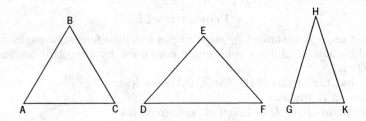

Now, if the angles ABC, DEF, GHK are equal to one another, it is manifest that, AC, DF, GK being equal also, it is possible to construct a triangle out of straight lines equal to AC, DF, GK.

But, if not, let them be unequal,
and on the straight line HK, and at the point H on it, let the angle KHL be constructed equal to the angle ABC;
let HL be made equal to one of the straight lines AB, BC, DE, EF, GH, HK,
                            and let KL, GL be joined.

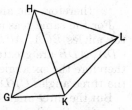

Now, since the two sides AB, BC are equal to the two sides KH, HL,
        and the angle at B is equal to the angle KHL,
                therefore the base AC is equal to the base KL.   [I. 4]
And, since the angles ABC, GHK are greater than the angle DEF,
            while the angle ABC is equal to the angle KHL,
            therefore the angle GHL is greater than the angle DEF.
And, since the two sides GH, HL are equal to the two sides DE, EF,

and the angle *GHL* is greater than the angle *DEF*,
therefore the base *GL* is greater than the base *DF*.   [I. 24]
But *GK*, *KL* are greater than *GL*.
Therefore *GK*, *KL* are much greater than *DF*.
But *KL* is equal to *AC*;
therefore *AC*, *GK* are greater than the remaining straight line *DF*.
Similarly we can prove that
AC, DF are greater than GK,
and further, DF, GK are greater than AC.
Therefore it is possible to construct a triangle out of straight lines equal to
AC, *DF*, *GK*.   Q. E. D.

PROPOSITION 23

*To construct a solid angle out of three plane angles two of which, taken together in
any manner, are greater than the remaining one: thus the three angles must be less
than four right angles.*

Let the angles *ABC*, *DEF*, *GHK* be the three given plane angles, and let two
of these, taken together in any manner, be greater than the remaining one,
while, further, the three are less than four right angles;
thus it is required to construct a solid angle out of angles equal to the angles
ABC, *DEF*, *GHK*.

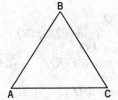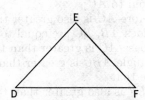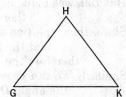

Let *AB*, *BC*, *DE*, *EF*, *GH*, *HK* be cut off equal to one another,
and let *AC*, *DF*, *GK* be joined;
it is therefore possible to construct a triangle out of straight lines equal to *AC*,
DF, *GK*.   [XI. 22]

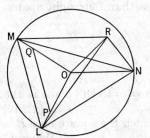

Let *LMN* be so constructed that *AC* is equal to
LM, *DF* to *MN*, and further, *GK* to *NL*,
let the circle *LMN* be described about the triangle
LMN,
let its centre be taken, and let it be *O*;
let *LO*, *MO*, *NO* be joined;
I say that *AB* is greater than *LO*.
For, if not, *AB* is either equal to *LO*, or less.
First, let it be equal.
Then, since *AB* is equal to *LO*,
while *AB* is equal to *BC*, and *OL* to *OM*,
the two sides *AB*, *BC* are equal to the two sides *LO*, *OM* respectively;
and, by hypothesis, the base *AC* is equal to the base *LM*;
therefore the angle *ABC* is equal to the angle *LOM*.   [I. 8]
For the same reason

the angle *DEF* is also equal to the angle *MON*,
and further the angle *GHK* to the angle *NOL*;
therefore the three angles *ABC*, *DEF*, *GHK* are equal to the three angles *LOM*, *MON*, *NOL*.

But the three angles *LOM*, *MON*, *NOL* are equal to four right angles;
therefore the angles *ABC*, *DEF*, *GKH* are equal to four right angles.

But they are also, by hypothesis, less than four right angles:
which is absurd.

Therefore *AB* is not equal to *LO*.

I say next that neither is *AB* less than *LO*.

For, if possible, let it be so,
and let *OP* be made equal to *AB*, and *OQ* equal to *BC*,
and let *PQ* be joined.

Then, since *AB* is equal to *BC*,
OP is also equal to *OQ*,
so that the remainder *LP* is equal to *QM*.

Therefore *LM* is parallel to *PQ*,   [VI. 2]
and *LMO* is equiangular with *PQO*;   [I. 29]
therefore, as *OL* is to *LM*, so is *OP* to *PQ*;   [VI. 4]
and alternately, as *LO* is to *OP*, so is *LM* to *PQ*.   [V. 16]

But *LO* is greater than *OP*;
therefore *LM* is also greater than *PQ*.

But *LM* was made equal to *AC*;
therefore *AC* is also greater than *PQ*.

Since, then, the two sides *AB*, *BC* are equal to the two sides *PO*, *OQ*,
and the base *AC* is greater than the base *PQ*,
therefore the angle *ABC* is greater than the angle *POQ*.   [I. 25]

Similarly we can prove that
the angle *DEF* is also greater than the angle *MON*,
and the angle *GHK* greater than the angle *NOL*.

Therefore the three angles *ABC*, *DEF*, *GHK* are greater than the three angles *LOM*, *MON*, *NOL*.

But, by hypothesis, the angles *ABC*, *DEF*, *GHK* are less than four right angles;
therefore the angles *LOM*, *MON*, *NOL* are much less than four right angles.

But they are also equal to four right angles:
which is absurd.

Therefore *AB* is not less than *LO*.

And it was proved that neither is it equal;
therefore *AB* is greater than *LO*.

Let then *OR* be set up from the point *O* at right angles to the plane of the circle *LMN*,   [XI. 12]
and let the square on *OR* be equal to that area by which the square on *AB* is greater than the square on *LO*;   [Lemma]
let *RL*, *RM*, *RN* be joined.

Then, since *RO* is at right angles to the plane of the circle *LMN*,
therefore *RO* is also at right angles to each of the straight lines *LO*, *MO*, *NO*.

And, since *LO* is equal to *OM*,
while *OR* is common and at right angles,

therefore the base RL is equal to the base RM.   [I. 4]

For the same reason

RN is also equal to each of the straight lines RL, RM;

therefore the three straight lines RL, RM, RN are equal to one another.

Next, since by hypothesis the square on OR is equal to that area by which the square on AB is greater than the square on LO,

therefore the square on AB is equal to the squares on LO, OR.

But the square on LR is equal to the squares on LO, OR, for the angle LOR is right;   [I. 47]

therefore the square on AB is equal to the square on RL;

therefore AB is equal to RL.

But each of the straight lines BC, DE, EF, GH, HK is equal to AB,

while each of the straight lines RM, RN is equal to RL;

therefore each of the straight lines AB, BC, DE, EF, GH, HK

is equal to each of the straight lines RL, RM, RN.

And, since the two sides LR, RM are equal to the two sides AB, BC,

and the base LM is by hypothesis equal to the base AC,

therefore the angle LRM is equal to the angle ABC.   [I. 8]

For the same reason

the angle MRN is also equal to the angle DEF,

and the angle LRN to the angle GHK.

Therefore, out of the three plane angles LRM, MRN, LRN, which are equal to the three given angles ABC, DEF, GHK, the solid angle at R has been constructed, which is contained by the angles LRM, MRN, LRN.   Q. E. F.

LEMMA

But how it is possible to take the square on OR equal to that area by which the square on AB is greater than the square on LO, we can show as follows.

Let the straight lines AB, LO be set out,

and let AB be the greater;

let the semicircle ABC be described on AB,

and into the semicircle ABC let AC be fitted equal to the straight line LO, not being greater than the diameter AB;   [IV. 1]

let CB be joined

Since then the angle ACB is an angle in the semicircle ACB,

therefore the angle ACB is right.   [III. 31]

Therefore the square on AB is equal to the squares on AC, CB.   [I. 47]

Hence the square on AB is greater than the square on AC by the square on CB.

But AC is equal to LO.

Therefore the square on AB is greater than the square on LO by the square on CB.

If then we cut off OR equal to BC, the square on AB will be greater than the square on LO by the square on OR.   Q. E. F.

PROPOSITION 24

If a solid be contained by parallel planes, the opposite planes in it are equal and parallelogrammic.

For let the solid *CDHG* be contained by the parallel planes *AC*, *GF*, *AH*, *DF*, *BF*, *AE*;

I say that the opposite planes in it are equal and parallelogrammic.

For, since the two parallel planes *BG*, *CE* are cut by the plane *AC*,

their common sections are parallel.   [XI. 16]

Therefore *AB* is parallel to *DC*.

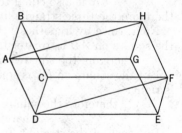

Again, since the two parallel planes *BF*, *AE* are cut by the plane *AC*,

their common sections are parallel.   [XI. 16]

Therefore *BC* is parallel to *AD*.

But *AB* was also proved parallel to *DC*;

therefore *AC* is a parallelogram.

Similarly we can prove that each of the planes *DF*, *FG*, *GB*, *BF*, *AE* is a parallelogram.

Let *AH*, *DF* be joined.

Then, since *AB* is parallel to *DC*, and *BH* to *CF*, the two straight lines *AB*, *BH* which meet one another are parallel to the two straight lines *DC*, *CF* which meet one another, not in the same plane;

therefore they will contain equal angles;   [XI. 10]

therefore the angle *ABH* is equal to the angle *DCF*.

And, since the two sides *AB*, *BH* are equal to the two sides *DC*, *CF*,

[I. 34]

and the angle *ABH* is equal to the angle *DCF*,

therefore the base *AH* is equal to the base *DF*,

and the triangle *ABH* is equal to the triangle *DCF*.   [I. 4]

And the parallelogram *BG* is double of the triangle *ABH*, and the parallelogram *CE* double of the triangle *DCF*;   [I. 34]

therefore the parallelogram *BG* is equal to the parallelogram *CE*.

Similarly we can prove that

AC is also equal to *GF*,

and *AE* to *BF*.

Therefore etc.   Q. E. D.

PROPOSITION 25

If a parallelepipedal solid be cut by a plane which is parallel to the opposite planes, then, as the base is to the base, so will the solid be to the solid.

For let the parallelepipedal solid *ABCD* be cut by the plane *FG* which is parallel to the opposite planes *RA*, *DH*;

I say that, as the base *AEFV* is to the base *EHCF*, so is the solid *ABFU* to the solid *EGCD*.

For let *AH* be produced in each direction,

let any number of straight lines whatever, *AK*, *KL*, be made equal to *AE*,

and any number whatever, *HM*, *MN*, equal to *EH*;

and let the parallelograms *LP*, *KV*, *HW*, *MS* and the solids *LQ*, *KR*, *DM*, *MT* be completed.

Then, since the straight lines *LK*, *KA*, *AE* are equal to one another,

the parallelograms *LP*, *KV*, *AF* are also equal to one another,

KO, *KB*, *AG* are equal to one another,
and further, *LX*, *KQ*, *AR* are equal to one another, for they are opposite.

[XI. 24]

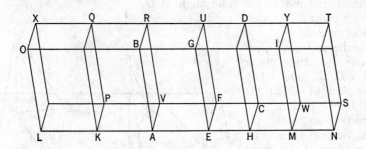

For the same reason
  the parallelograms *EC*, *HW*, *MS* are also equal to one another,
    HG, *HI*, *IN* are equal to one another,
   and further, *DH*, *MY*, *NT* are equal to one another.
Therefore in the solids *LQ*, *KR*, *AU* three planes are equal to three planes.
But the three planes are equal to the three opposite;
  therefore the three solids *LQ*, *KR*, *AU* are equal to one another.
For the same reason
  the three solids *ED*, *DM*, *MT* are also equal to one another.
Therefore, whatever multiple the base *LF* is of the base *AF*, the same multiple also is the solid *LU* of the solid *AU*.
For the same reason,
whatever multiple the base *NF* is of the base *FH*, the same multiple also is the solid *NU* of the solid *HU*.
And, if the base *LF* is equal to the base *NF*, the solid *LU* is also equal to the solid *NU*;
if the base *LF* exceeds the base *NF*, the solid *LU* also exceeds the solid *NU*;
   and, if one falls short, the other falls short.
Therefore, there being four magnitudes, the two bases *AF*, *FH*, and the two solids *AU*, *UH*,
equimultiples have been taken of the base *AF* and the solid *AU*, namely the base *LF* and the solid *LU*,
and equimultiples of the base *HF* and the solid *HU*, namely the base *NF* and the solid *NU*,
and it has been proved that, if the base *LF* exceeds the base *FN*, the solid *LU* also exceeds the solid *NU*,
   if the bases are equal, the solids are equal,
  and if the base falls short, the solid falls short,
Therefore, as the base *AF* is to the base *FH*, so is the solid *AU* to the solid *UH*.
                  [v. Def. 5]

                     Q. E. D.

PROPOSITION 26

On a given straight line, and at a given point on it, to construct a solid angle equal to a given solid angle.

Let AB be the given straight line, A the given point on it, and the angle at D, contained by the angles EDC, EDF, FDC, the given solid angle; thus it is required to construct on the straight line AB, and at the point A on it, a solid angle equal to the solid angle at D.

For let a point F be taken at random on DF, let FG be drawn from F perpendicular to the plane through ED, DC, and let it meet the plane at G, [XI. 11]

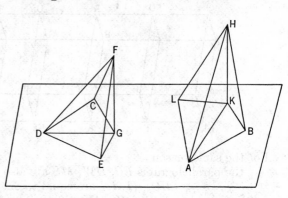

let DG be joined, let there be constructed on the straight line AB and at the point A on it the angle BAL equal to the angle EDC, and the angle BAK equal to the angle EDG, [I. 23]

let AK be made equal to DG,
let KH be set up from the point K at right angles to the plane through BA, AL, [XI. 12]

let KH be made equal to GF,
and let HA be joined;

I say that the solid angle at A, contained by the angles BAL, BAH, HAL is equal to the solid angle at D contained by the angles EDC, EDF, FDC.

For let AB, DE be cut off equal to one another,
and let HB, KB, FE, GE be joined.

Then, since FG is at right angles to the plane of reference, it will also make right angles with all the straight lines which meet it and are in the plane of reference; [XI. Def. 3]

therefore each of the angles FGD, FGE is right.

For the same reason
each of the angles HKA, HKB is also right.

And, since the two sides KA, AB are equal to the two sides GD, DE respectively,
and they contain equal angles,
therefore the base KB is equal to the base GE.   [I. 4]

But KH is also equal to GF,
and they contain right angles;
therefore HB is also equal to FE.   [I. 4]

Again, since the two sides AK, KH are equal to the two sides DG, GF,
and they contain right angles,
therefore the base AH is equal to the base FD.   [I. 4]

But AB is also equal to DE;
therefore the two sides HA, AB are equal to the two sides DF, DE.

And the base HB is equal to the base FE;
therefore the angle BAH is equal to the angle EDF.   [I. 8]

For the same reason
the angle HAL is also equal to the angle FDC.

And the angle BAL is also equal to the angle EDC.

Therefore on the straight line AB, and at the point A on it, a solid angle has been constructed equal to the given solid angle at D.   Q. E. F.

PROPOSITION 27

On a given straight line to describe a parallelepipedal solid similar and similarly situated to a given parallelepipedal solid.

Let AB be the given straight line and CD the given parallelepipedal solid; thus it is required to describe on the given straight line AB a parallelepipedal solid similar and similarly situated to the given parallelepipedal solid CD.

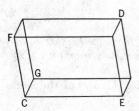 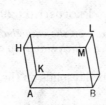

For on the straight line AB and at the point A on it let the solid angle, contained by the angles BAH, HAK, KAB, be constructed equal to the solid angle at C, so that the angle BAH is equal to the angle ECF, the angle BAK equal to the angle ECG, and the angle KAH to the angle GCF;

and let it be contrived that,
> as EC is to CG, so is BA to AK,
and, as GC is to CF, so is KA to AH.   [vi. 12]
Therefore also, *ex aequali,*
> as EC is to CF, so is BA to AH.   [v. 22]
Let the parallelogram HB and the solid AL be completed.

Now since, as EC is to CG, so is BA to AK,
and the sides about the equal angles ECG, BAK are thus proportional,
> therefore the parallelogram GE is similar to the parallelogram KB.

For the same reason
the parallelogram KH is also similar to the parallelogram GF, and further, FE to HB;
therefore three parallelograms of the solid CD are similar to three parallelograms of the solid AL.

But the former three are both equal and similar to the three opposite parallelograms,
and the latter three are both equal and similar to the three opposite parallelograms;
therefore the whole solid CD is similar to the whole solid AL.   [xi. Def. 9]

Therefore on the given straight line AB there has been described AL similar and similarly situated to the given parallelepipedal solid CD.   Q. E. F.

PROPOSITION 28

If a parallelepipedal solid be cut by a plane through the diagonals of the opposite planes, the solid will be bisected by the plane.

For let the parallelepipedal solid AB be cut by the plane $CDEF$ through the diagonals CF, DE of opposite planes;
> I say that the solid AB will be bisected by the plane $CDEF$.

For, since the triangle CGF is equal to the triangle CFB,   [i. 34] and *ADE* to *DEH*,

while the parallelogram *CA* is also equal to the parallelogram *EB*, for they are opposite, and *GE* to *CH*, therefore the prism contained by the two triangles *CGF*, *ADE* and the three parallelograms *GE*, *AC*, *CE* is also equal to the prism contained by the two triangles *CFB*, *DEH* and the three parallelograms *CH*, *BE*, *CE*; for they are contained by planes equal both in multitude and in magnitude.   [XI. Def. 10]

Hence the whole solid *AB* is bisected by the plane *CDEF*.   Q. E. D.

PROPOSITION 29

Parallelepipedal solids which are on the same base and of the same height, and in which the extremities of the sides which stand up are on the same straight lines, are equal to one another.

Let *CM*, *CN* be parallelepipedal solids on the same base *AB* and of the same height,

and let the extremities of their sides which stand up, namely *AG*, *AF*, *LM*, *LN*, *CD*, *CE*, *BH*, *BK*, be on the same straight lines *FN*, *DK*;

I say that the solid *CM* is equal to the solid *CN*.

For, since each of the figures *CH*, *CK* is a parallelogram, *CB* is equal to each of the straight lines *DH*, *EK*,   [I. 34]
          hence *DH* is also equal to *EK*.

Let *EH* be subtracted from each;

          therefore the remainder *DE* is equal to the remainder *HK*.

Hence the triangle *DCE* is also equal to the triangle *HBK*,   [I. 8, 4]
          and the parallelogram *DG* to the parallelogram *HN*.   [I. 36]

For the same reason
          the triangle *AFG* is also equal to the triangle *MLN*.

But the parallelogram *CF* is equal to the parallelogram *BM*, and *CG* to *BN*, for they are opposite;

therefore the prism contained by the two triangles *AFG*, *DCE* and the three parallelograms *AD*, *DG*, *CG* is equal to the prism contained by the two triangles *MLN*, *HBK* and the three parallelograms *BM*, *HN*, *BN*.

Let there be added to each the solid of which the parallelogram *AB* is the base and *GEHM* its opposite;

therefore the whole parallelepipedal solid *CM* is equal to the whole parallelepipedal solid *CN*.

Therefore etc.   Q. E. D.

PROPOSITION 30

Parallelepipedal solids which are on the same base and of the same height, and in which the extremities of the sides which stand up are not on the same straight lines, are equal to one another.

Let CM, CN be parallelepipedal solids on the same base AB and of the same height,

and let the extremities of their sides which stand up, namely AF, AG, LM, LN, CD, CE, BH, BK, not be on the same straight lines;

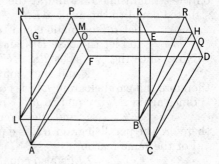

I say that the solid CM is equal to the solid CN.

For let NK, DH be produced and meet one another at R,

and further, let FM, GE be produced to P, Q;

let AO, LP, CQ, BR be joined.

Then the solid CM, of which the parallelogram $ACBL$ is the base, and $FDHM$ its opposite, is equal to the solid CP, of which the parallelogram $ACBL$ is the base, and $OQRP$ its opposite;

for they are on the same base $ACBL$ and of the same height, and the extremities of their sides which stand up, namely AF, AO, LM, LP, CD, CQ, BH, BR, are on the same straight lines FP, DR.   [XI. 29]

But the solid CP, of which the parallelogram $ACBL$ is the base, and $OQRP$ its opposite, is equal to the solid CN, of which the parallelogram $ACBL$ is the base and $GEKN$ its opposite;

for they are again on the same base $ACBL$ and of the same height, and the extremities of their sides which stand up, namely AG, AO, CE, CQ, LN, LP, BK, BR, are on the same straight lines GQ, NR.

Hence the solid CM is also equal to the solid CN.

Therefore etc.   Q. E. D.

PROPOSITION 31

Parallelepipedal solids which are on equal bases and of the same height are equal to one another.

Let the parallelepipedal solids AE, CF, of the same height, be on equal bases AB, CD.

I say that the solid AE is equal to the solid CF.

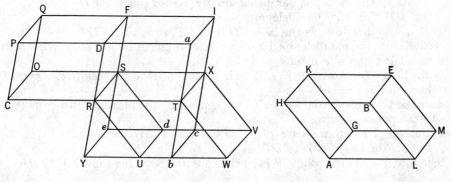

First, let the sides which stand up, HK, BE, AG, LM, PQ, DF, CO, RS, be at right angles to the bases AB, CD;

let the straight line RT be produced in a straight line with CR;
on the straight line RT, and at the point R on it, let the angle TRU be constructed equal to the angle ALB,   [I. 23]

let RT be made equal to AL, and RU equal to LB,
and let the base RW and the solid XU be completed.

Now, since the two sides TR, RU are equal to the two sides AL, LB,
and they contain equal angles,
therefore the parallelogram RW is equal and similar to the parallelogram HL.

Since again AL is equal to RT, and LM to RS,
and they contain right angles,
therefore the parallelogram RX is equal and similar to the parallelogram AM.

For the same reason

LE is also equal and similar to SU;
therefore three parallelograms of the solid AE are equal and similar to three parallelograms of the solid XU.

But the former three are equal and similar to the three opposite, and the latter three to the three opposite;   [XI. 24]
therefore the whole parallelepipedal solid AE is equal to the whole parallelepipedal solid XU.   [XI. Def. 10]

Let DR, WU be drawn through and meet one another at Y,
let aTb be drawn through T parallel to DY,
let PD be produced to a,
and let the solids YX, RI be completed.

Then the solid XY, of which the parallelogram RX is the base and Yc its opposite, is equal to the solid XU of which the parallelogram RX is the base and UV its opposite,
for they are on the same base RX and of the same height, and the extremities of their sides which stand up, namely RY, RU, Tb, TW, Se, Sd, Xc, XV, are on the same straight lines YW, eV.   [XI. 29]

But the solid XU is equal to AE;
therefore the solid XY is also equal to the solid AE.

And, since the parallelogram $RUWT$ is equal to the parallelogram YT,
for they are on the same base RT and in the same parallels RT, YW,   [I. 35]
while $RUWT$ is equal to CD, since it is also equal to AB,
therefore the parallelogram YT is also equal to CD.

But DT is another parallelogram;
therefore, as the base CD is to DT, so is YT to DT.   [V. 7]

And, since the parallelepipedal solid CI has been cut by the plane RF which is parallel to opposite planes,
as the base CD is to the base DT, so is the solid CF to the solid RI.   [XI. 25]

For the same reason,
since the parallelepipedal solid YI has been cut by the plane RX which is parallel to opposite planes,
as the base YT is to the base TD, so is the solid YX to the solid RI.   [XI. 25]

But, as the base CD is to DT, so is YT to DT;
therefore also, as the solid CF is to the solid RI, so is the solid YX to RI.

[V. 11]

Therefore each of the solids CF, YX has to RI the same ratio;
therefore the solid CF is equal to the solid YX.   [V. 9]

But YX was proved equal to AE;
        therefore AE is also equal to CF.

Next, let the sides standing up, AG, HK, BE, LM, CN, PQ, DF, RS, not be at right angles to the bases AB, CD;
        I say again that the solid AE is equal to the solid CF.

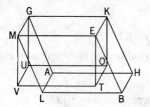 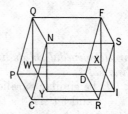

For from the points K, E, G, M, Q, F, N, S let KO, ET, GU, MV, QW, FX, NY, SI be drawn perpendicular to the plane of reference, and let them meet the plane at the points O, T, U, V, W, X, Y, I,
        and let OT, OU, UV, TV, WX, WY, YI, IX be joined.

Then the solid KV is equal to the solid QI,
for they are on the equal bases KM, QS and of the same height, and their sides which stand up are at right angles to their bases.   [First part of this Prop.]

But the solid KV is equal to the solid AE,
        and QI to CF;
for they are on the same base and of the same height, while the extremities of their sides which stand up are not on the same straight lines.   [xi. 30]

Therefore the solid AE is also equal to the solid CF.

Therefore etc.   Q. E. D.

PROPOSITION 32

Parallelepipedal solids which are of the same height are to one another as their bases.

Let AB, CD be parallelepipedal solids of the same height;

I say that the parallelepipedal solids AB, CD are to one another as their bases, that is, that, as the base AE is to the base CF, so is the solid AB to the solid CD.

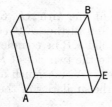 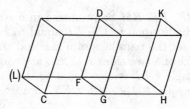

For let FH equal to AE be applied to FG,   [i. 45]
and, on FH as base, and with the same height as that of CD, let the parallelepipedal solid GK be completed.

Then the solid AB is equal to the solid GK;
for they are on equal bases AE, FH and of the same height.   [xi. 31]

And, since the parallelepipedal solid CK is cut by the plane DG which is parallel to opposite planes, therefore, as the base CF is to the base FH, so is the solid CD to the solid DH.

[XI. 25]

But the base FH is equal to the base AE,
and the solid GK to the solid AB;
therefore also, as the base AE is to the base CF, so is the solid AB to the solid CD.

Therefore etc.   Q. E. D.

PROPOSITION 33

Similar parallelepipedal solids are to one another in the triplicate ratio of their corresponding sides.

Let AB, CD be similar parallelepipedal solids,
and let AE be the side corresponding to CF;
I say that the solid AB has to the solid CD the ratio triplicate of that which AE has to CF.

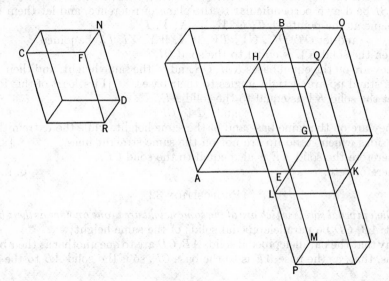

For let EK, EL, EM be produced in a straight line with AE, GE, HE,
let EK be made equal to CF, EL equal to FN, and further, EM equal to FR,
and let the parallelogram KL and the solid KP be completed.

Now, since the two sides KE, EL are equal to the two sides CF, FN,
while the angle KEL is also equal to the angle CFN, inasmuch as the angle AEG is also equal to the angle CFN because of the similarity of the solids AB, CD,
therefore the parallelogram KL is equal <and similar> to the parallelogram CN.

For the same reason
the parallelogram KM is also equal and similar to CR,
and further, EP to DF;
therefore three parallelograms of the solid KP are equal and similar to three parallelograms of the solid CD.

But the former three parallelograms are equal and similar to their opposites, and the latter three to their opposites;   [xi. 24]
therefore the whole solid KP is equal and similar to the whole solid CD.
[xi. Def. 10]

Let the parallelogram GK be completed,
and on the parallelograms GK, KL as bases, and with the same height as that of AB, let the solids EO, LQ be completed.
Then since owing to the similarity of the solids AB, CD,
as AE is to CF, so is EG to FN, and EH to FR,
while CF is equal to EK, FN to EL, and FR to EM,
therefore, as AE is to EK, so is GE to EL, and HE to EM.
But, as AE is to EK, so is AG to the parallelogram GK,
as GE is to EL, so is GK to KL,
and, as HE is to EM, so is QE to KM;   [vi. 1]
therefore also, as the parallelogram AG is to GK, so is GK to KL, and QE to KM.
But, as AG is to GK, so is the solid AB to the solid EO,
as GK is to KL, so is the solid OE to the solid QL,
and, as QE is to KM, so is the solid QL to the solid KP;   [xi. 32]
therefore also, as the solid AB is to EO, so is EO to QL, and QL to KP.
But, if four magnitudes be continuously proportional, the first has to the fourth the ratio triplicate of that which it has to the second;   [v. Def. 10]
therefore the solid AB has to KP the ratio triplicate of that which AB has to EO.
But, as AB is to EO, so is the parallelogram AG to GK, and the straight line AE to EK [vi. 1];
hence the solid AB has also to KP the ratio triplicate of that which AE has to EK.
But the solid KP is equal to the solid CD,
and the straight line EK to CF;
therefore the solid AB has also to the solid CD the ratio triplicate of that which the corresponding side of it, AE, has to the corresponding side CF.
Therefore etc.   Q. E. D.

PORISM. From this it is manifest that, if four straight lines be <continuously> proportional, as the first is to the fourth, so will a parallelepipedal solid on the first be to the similar and similarly described parallelepipedal solid on the second, inasmuch as the first has to the fourth the ratio triplicate of that which it has to the second.

PROPOSITION 34

In equal parallelepipedal solids the bases are reciprocally proportional to the heights; and those parallelepipedal solids in which the bases are reciprocally proportional to the heights are equal.

Let AB, CD be equal parallelepipedal solids;
I say that in the parallelepipedal solids AB, CD the bases are reciprocally proportional to the heights,
that is, as the base EH is to the base NQ, so is the height of the solid CD to the height of the solid AB.
First, let the sides which stand up, namely AG, EF, LB, HK, CM, NO, PD,

QR, be at right angles to their bases;

> I say that, as the base *EH* is to the base *NQ*, so is *CM* to *AG*.

If now the base *EH* is equal to the base *NQ*,

> > while the solid *AB* is also equal to the solid *CD*,
> >
> > > *CM* will also be equal to *AG*.

For parallelepipedal solids of the same height are to one another as the bases;   [XI. 32]

> > and, as the base *EH* is to *NQ*, so will *CM* be to *AG*,

and it is manifest that in the parallelepipedal solids *AB*, *CD* the bases are reciprocally proportional to the heights.

Next, let the base *EH* not be equal to the base *NQ*,

> > but let *EH* be greater.

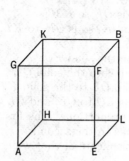
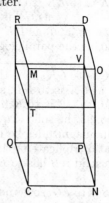

Now the solid *AB* is equal to the solid *CD*;

> > therefore *CM* is also greater than *AG*.

Let then *CT* be made equal to *AG*,
and let the parallelepipedal solid *VC* be completed on *NQ* as base and with *CT* as height.

Now, since the solid *AB* is equal to the solid *CD*,

> > and *CV* is outside them,

> > > while equals have to the same the same ratio,   [V. 7]

therefore, as the solid *AB* is to the solid *CV*, so is the solid *CD* to the solid *CV*.

But, as the solid *AB* is to the solid *CV*, so is the base *EH* to the base *NQ*,

> > for the solids *AB*, *CV* are of equal height;   [XI. 32]

and, as the solid *CD* is to the solid *CV*, so is the base *MQ* to the base *TQ* [XI. 25] and *CM* to *CT* [VI. 1];

> > therefore also, as the base *EH* is to the base *NQ*, so is *MC* to *CT*.

But *CT* is equal to *AG*;

> > therefore also, as the base *EH* is to the base *NQ*, so is *MC* to *AG*.

Therefore in the parallelepipedal solids *AB*, *CD* the bases are reciprocally proportional to the heights.

Again, in the parallelepipedal solids *AB*, *CD* let the bases be reciprocally proportional to the heights, that is, as the base *EH* is to the base *NQ*, so let the height of the solid *CD* be to the height of the solid *AB*;

> > I say that the solid *AB* is equal to the solid *CD*.

Let the sides which stand up be again at right angles to the bases.

Now, if the base *EH* is equal to the base *NQ*,

and, as the base EH is to the base NQ, so is the height of the solid CD to the height of the solid AB,
therefore the height of the solid CD is also equal to the height of the solid AB.
But parallelepipedal solids on equal bases and of the same height are equal to one another;   [XI. 31]
therefore the solid AB is equal to the solid CD.
Next, let the base EH not be equal to the base NQ,
but let EH be greater;
therefore the height of the solid CD is also greater than the height of the solid AB,
that is, CM is greater than AG.
Let CT be again made equal to AG,
and let the solid CV be similarly completed.
Since, as the base EH is to the base NQ, so is MC to AG,
while AG is equal to CT,
therefore, as the base EH is to the base NQ, so is CM to CT.
But, as the base EH is to the base NQ, so is the solid AB to the solid CV,
for the solids AB, CV are of equal height;   [XI. 32]
and, as CM is to CT, so is the base MQ to the base QT [VI. 1]
and the solid CD to the solid CV.   [XI. 25]
Therefore also, as the solid AB is to the solid CV, so is the solid CD to the solid CV;
therefore each of the solids AB, CD has to CV the same ratio.
Therefore the solid AB is equal to the solid CD.   [V. 9]
Now let the sides which stand up, FE, BL, GA, HK, ON, DP, MC, RQ, not be at right angles to their bases;
let perpendiculars be drawn from the points F, G, B, K, O, M, D, R to the planes through EH, NQ,
and let them meet the planes at S, T, U, V, W, X, Y, a,
and let the solids FV, Oa be completed;
I say that, in this case too, if the solids AB, CD are equal, the bases are reciprocally proportional to the heights, that is, as the base EH is to the base NQ, so is the height of the solid CD to the height of the solid AB.
Since the solid AB is equal to the solid CD,

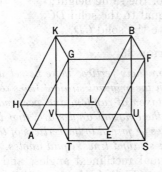
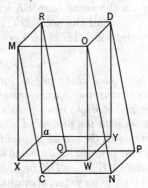

while AB is equal to BT,
for they are on the same base FK and of the same height;   [XI. 29, 30]

and the solid CD is equal to DX,

for they are again on the same base RO and of the same height;   [*id.*]

therefore the solid BT is also equal to the solid DX.

Therefore, as the base FK is to the base OR, so is the height of the solid DX to the height of the solid BT.   [Part I.]

But the base FK is equal to the base EH,

and the base OR to the base NQ;

therefore, as the base EH is to the base NQ, so is the height of the solid DX to the height of the solid BT.

But the solids DX, BT and the solids DC, BA have the same heights respectively;

therefore, as the base EH is to the base NQ, so is the height of the solid DC to the height of the solid AB.

Therefore in the parallelepipedal solids AB, CD the bases are reciprocally proportional to the heights.

Again, in the parallelepipedal solids AB, CD let the bases be reciprocally proportional to the heights,

that is, as the base EH is to the base NQ, so let the height of the solid CD be to the height of the solid AB;

I say that the solid AB is equal to the solid CD.

For, with the same construction,

since, as the base EH is to the base NQ, so is the height of the solid CD to the height of the solid AB,

while the base EH is equal to the base FK,

and NQ to OR,

therefore, as the base FK is to the base OR, so is the height of the solid CD to the height of the solid AB.

But the solids AB, CD and BT, DX have the same heights respectively;

therefore, as the base FK is to the base OR, so is the height of the solid DX to the height of the solid BT.

Therefore in the parallelepipedal solids BT, DX the bases are reciprocally proportional to the heights;

therefore the solid BT is equal to the solid DX.   [Part I.]

But BT is equal to BA,

for they are on the same base FK and of the same height;   [XI. 29, 30]

and the solid DX is equal to the solid DC.   [*id.*]

Therefore the solid AB is also equal to the solid CD.   Q. E. D.

PROPOSITION 35

If there be two equal plane angles, and on their vertices there be set up elevated straight lines containing equal angles with the original straight lines respectively, if on the elevated straight lines points be taken at random and perpendiculars be drawn from them to the planes in which the original angles are, and if from the points so arising in the planes straight lines be joined to the vertices of the original angles, they will contain, with the elevated straight lines, equal angles.

Let the angles BAC, EDF be two equal rectilineal angles, and from the points A, D let the elevated straight lines AG, DM be set up containing, with the original straight lines, equal angles respectively, namely, the angle MDE to the angle GAB and the angle MDF to the angle GAC,

let points G, M be taken at random on AG, DM,
let GL, MN be drawn from the points G, M perpendicular to the planes through
BA, AC and ED, DF, and let them meet the planes at L, N,

and let LA, ND be joined;

I say that the angle GAL is equal to the angle MDN.

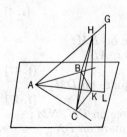
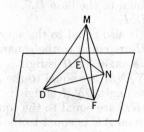

Let AH be made equal to DM,

and let HK be drawn through the point H parallel to GL.

But GL is perpendicular to the plane through BA, AC;

therefore HK is also perpendicular to the plane through BA, AC.   [XI. 8]

From the points K, N let KC, NF, KB, NE be drawn perpendicular to the
straight lines AC, DF, AB, DE,

and let HC, CB, MF, FE be joined.

Since the square on HA is equal to the squares on HK, KA,

and the squares on KC, CA are equal to the square on KA,   [I. 47]
therefore the square on HA is also equal to the squares on HK, KC, CA.

But the square on HC is equal to the squares on HK, KC;   [I. 47]

therefore the square on HA is equal to the squares on HC, CA.

Therefore the angle HCA is right.   [I. 48]

For the same reason

the angle DFM is also right.

Therefore the angle ACH is equal to the angle DFM.

But the angle HAC is also equal to the angle MDF.

Therefore MDF, HAC are two triangles which have two angles equal to two
angles respectively, and one side equal to one side, namely, that subtending
one of the equal angles, that is, HA equal to MD;
therefore they will also have the remaining sides equal to the remaining sides
respectively.   [I. 26]

Therefore AC is equal to DF.

Similarly we can prove that AB is also equal to DE.

Since then AC is equal to DF, and AB to DE,

the two sides CA, AB are equal to the two sides FD, DE.

But the angle CAB is also equal to the angle FDE;
therefore the base BC is equal to the base EF, the triangle to the triangle, and
the remaining angles to the remaining angles;   [I. 4]

therefore the angle ACB is equal to the angle DFE.

But the right angle ACK is also equal to the right angle DFN;
therefore the remaining angle BCK is also equal to the remaining angle EFN.

For the same reason

the angle CBK is also equal to the angle FEN.

Therefore BCK, EFN are two triangles which have two angles equal to two
angles respectively, and one side equal to one side, namely, that adjacent to
the equal angles, that is, BC equal to EF;

therefore they will also have the remaining sides equal to the remaining sides.
[I. 26]

Therefore CK is equal to FN.

But AC is also equal to DF;

therefore the two sides AC, CK are equal to the two sides DF, FN;
and they contain right angles.

Therefore the base AK is equal to the base DN. [I. 4]

And, since AH is equal to DM,

the square on AH is also equal to the square on DM.

But the squares on AK, KH are equal to the square on AH,
for the angle AKH is right; [I. 47]

and the squares on DN, NM are equal to the square on DM,
for the angle DNM is right; [I. 47]

therefore the squares on AK, KH are equal to the squares on DN, NM;

and of these the square on AK is equal to the square on DN;

therefore the remaining square on KH is equal to the square on NM;
therefore HK is equal to MN.

And, since the two sides HA, AK are equal to the two sides MD, DN respectively,

and the base HK was proved equal to the base MN,
therefore the angle HAK is equal to the angle MDN. [I. 8]

Therefore etc.

PORISM. From this it is manifest that, if there be two equal plane angles, and if there be set up on them elevated straight lines which are equal and contain equal angles with the original straight lines respectively, the perpendiculars drawn from their extremities to the planes in which are the original angles are equal to one another. Q. E. D.

PROPOSITION 36

If three straight lines be proportional, the parallelepipedal solid formed out of the three is equal to the parallelepipedal solid on the mean which is equilateral, but equiangular with the aforesaid solid.

Let A, B, C be three straight lines in proportion, so that, as A is to B, so is B to C;

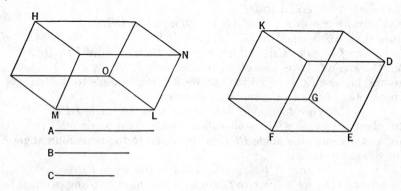

I say that the solid formed out of A, B, C is equal to the solid on B which is equilateral, but equiangular with the aforesaid solid.

Let there be set out the solid angle at E contained by the angles DEG, GEF, FED,

let each of the straight lines DE, GE, EF be made equal to B, and let the parallelepipedal solid EK be completed,

let LM be made equal to A,

and on the straight line LM, and at the point L on it, let there be constructed a solid angle equal to the solid angle at E, namely that contained by NLO, OLM, MLN;

let LO be made equal to B, and LN equal to C.

Now, since, as A is to B, so is B to C,

while A is equal to LM, B to each of the straight lines LO, ED, and C to LN,

therefore, as LM is to EF, so is DE to LN.

Thus the sides about the equal angles NLM, DEF are reciprocally proportional;

therefore the parallelogram MN is equal to the parallelogram DF.   [VI. 14]

And, since the angles DEF, NLM are two plane rectilineal angles, and on them the elevated straight lines LO, EG are set up which are equal to one another and contain equal angles with the original straight lines respectively,

therefore the perpendiculars drawn from the points G, O to the planes through NL, LM and DE, EF are equal to one another;   [XI. 35, Por.]

hence the solids LH, EK are of the same height.

But parallelepipedal solids on equal bases and of the same height are equal to one another;   [XI. 31]

therefore the solid HL is equal to the solid EK.

And LH is the solid formed out of A, B, C, and EK the solid on B;

therefore the parallelepipedal solid formed out of A, B, C is equal to the solid on B which is equilateral, but equiangular with the aforesaid solid.

Q. E. D.

PROPOSITION 37

If four straight lines be proportional, the parallelepipedal solids on them which are similar and similarly described will also be proportional; and, if the parallelepipedal solids on them which are similar and similarly described be proportional, the straight lines will themselves also be proportional.

Let AB, CD, EF, GH be four straight lines in proportion, so that, as AB is to CD, so is EF to GH;

and let there be described on AB, CD, EF, GH the similar and similarly situ-

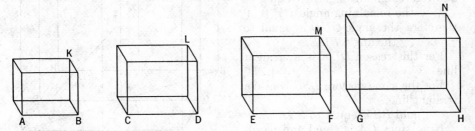

ated parallelepipedal solids KA, LC, ME, NG;

I say that, as KA is to LC, so is ME to NG.

For, since the parallelepipedal solid KA is similar to LC, therefore KA has to LC the ratio triplicate of that which AB has to CD.

[XI. 33]

For the same reason

ME also has to NG the ratio triplicate of that which EF has to GH.   [*id.*]

And, as AB is to CD, so is EF to GH.

Therefore also, as AK is to LC, so is ME to NG.

Next, as the solid AK is to the solid LC, so let the solid ME be to the solid NG;

I say that, as the straight line AB is to CD, so is EF to GH.

For since, again, KA has to LC the ratio triplicate of that which AB has to CD,

[XI. 33]

and ME also has to NG the ratio triplicate of that which EF has to GH, [*id.*]

and, as KA is to LC, so is ME to NG,

therefore also, as AB is to CD, so is EF to GH.

Therefore etc.

Q. E. D.

PROPOSITION 38

If the sides of the opposite planes of a cube be bisected, and planes be carried through the points of section, the common section of the planes and the diameter of the cube bisect one another.

For let the sides of the opposite planes CF, AH of the cube AF be bisected at the points K, L, M, N, O, Q, P, R, and through the points of section let the planes KN, OR be carried;

let US be the common section of the planes, and DG the diameter of the cube AF.

I say that UT is equal to TS, and DT to TG.

For let DU, UE, BS, SG be joined.

Then, since DO is parallel to PE,

the alternate angles DOU, UPE are equal to one another.   [I. 29]

And, since DO is equal to PE, and OU to UP,

and they contain equal angles,

therefore the base DU is equal to the base UE,

the triangle DOU is equal to the triangle PUE,

and the remaining angles are equal to the remaining angles;   [I. 4]

therefore the angle OUD is equal to the angle PUE.

For this reason DUE is a straight line.   [I. 14]

For the same reason, BSG is also a straight line,

and BS is equal to SG.

Now, since CA is equal and parallel to DB,

while CA is also equal and parallel to EG,

therefore DB is also equal and parallel to EG.   [XI. 9]
And the straight lines DE, BG join their extremities;
therefore DE is parallel to BG.   [I. 33]
Therefore the angle EDT is equal to the angle BGT,
for they are alternate;   [I. 29]
and the angle DTU is equal to the angle GTS.   [I. 15]

Therefore DTU, GTS are two triangles which have two angles equal to two angles, and one side equal to one side, namely that subtending one of the equal angles, that is, DU equal to GS,
for they are the halves of DE, BG;
therefore they will also have the remaining sides equal to the remaining sides.   [I. 26]

Therefore DT is equal to TG, and UT to TS.
Therefore etc.   Q. E. D.

PROPOSITION 39

If there be two prisms of equal height, and one have a parallelogram as base and the other a triangle, and if the parallelogram be double of the triangle, the prisms will be equal.

Let $ABCDEF$, $GHKLMN$ be two prisms of equal height,
let one have the parallelogram AF as base, and the other the triangle GHK,
and let the parallelogram AF be double of the triangle GHK;
I say that the prism $ABCDEF$ is equal to the prism $GHKLMN$.

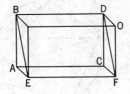 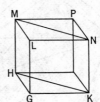

For let the solids AO, GP be completed.
Since the parallelogram AF is double of the triangle GHK,
while the parallelogram HK is also double of the triangle GHK,   [I. 34]
therefore the parallelogram AF is equal to the parallelogram HK.

But parallelepipedal solids which are on equal bases and of the same height are equal to one another;   [XI. 31]
therefore the solid AO is equal to the solid GP.
And the prism $ABCDEF$ is half of the solid AO,
and the prism $GHKLMN$ is half of the solid GP;   [XI. 28]
therefore the prism $ABCDEF$ is equal to the prism $GHKLMN$.
Therefore etc.   Q. E. D.

BOOK TWELVE

PROPOSITIONS

PROPOSITION 1

Similar polygons inscribed in circles are to one another as the squares on the diameters.

Let *ABC*, *FGH* be circles,
let *ABCDE*, *FGHKL* be similar polygons inscribed in them, and let *BM*, *GN* be diameters of the circles;

I say that, as the square on *BM* is to the square on *GN*, so is the polygon *ABCDE* to the polygon *FGHKL*.

For let *BE*, *AM*, *GL*, *FN* be joined.

Now, since the polygon *ABCDE* is similar to the polygon *FGHKL*,

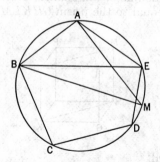 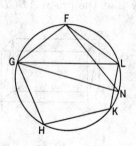

the angle *BAE* is equal to the angle *GFL*,
and, as *BA* is to *AE*, so is *GF* to *FL*.　　　　　[VI. Def. 1]

Thus *BAE*, *GFL* are two triangles which have one angle equal to one angle, namely the angle *BAE* to the angle *GFL*, and the sides about the equal angles proportional;

therefore the triangle *ABE* is equiangular with the triangle *FGL*.　　　[VI. 6]

Therefore the angle *AEB* is equal to the angle *FLG*.

But the angle *AEB* is equal to the angle *AMB*,
for they stand on the same circumference;　　　　　[III. 27]
and the angle *FLG* to the angle *FNG*;

therefore the angle *AMB* is also equal to the angle *FNG*.

But the right angle *BAM* is also equal to the right angle *GFN*;　　[III. 31]
therefore the remaining angle is equal to the remaining angle.　　[I. 32]

Therefore the triangle *ABM* is equiangular with the triangle *FGN*.

Therefore, proportionally, as *BM* is to *GN*, so is *BA* to *GF*.　　　　[VI. 4]

But the ratio of the square on *BM* to the square on *GN* is duplicate of the ratio of *BM* to *GN*,

and the ratio of the polygon *ABCDE* to the polygon *FGHKL* is duplicate of the ratio of *BA* to *GF*;   [VI. 20]

therefore also, as the square on *BM* is to the square on *GN*, so is the polygon *ABCDE* to the polygon *FGHKL*.

Therefore etc.   Q. E. D.

PROPOSITION 2

Circles are to one another as the squares on the diameters.

Let *ABCD, EFGH* be circles, and *BD, FH* their diameters;

I say that, as the circle *ABCD* is to the circle *EFGH*, so is the square on *BD* to the square on *FH*.

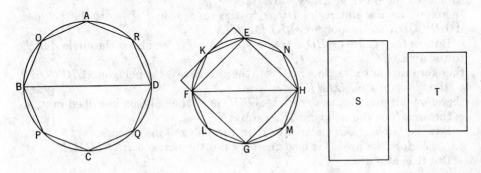

For, if the square on *BD* is not to the square on *FH* as the circle *ABCD* is to the circle *EFGH*,

then, as the square on *BD* is to the square on *FH*, so will the circle *ABCD* be either to some less area than the circle *EFGH*, or to a greater.

First, let it be in that ratio to a less area *S*.

Let the square *EFGH* be inscribed in the circle *EFGH*; then the inscribed square is greater than the half of the circle *EFGH*, inasmuch as, if through the points *E, F, G, H* we draw tangents to the circle, the square *EFGH* is half the square circumscribed about the circle, and the circle is less than the circumscribed square;

hence the inscribed square *EFGH* is greater than the half of the circle *EFGH*.

Let the circumferences *EF, FG, GH, HE* be bisected at the points *K, L, M, N*,

and let *EK, KF, FL, LG, GM, MH, HN, NE* be joined;

therefore each of the triangles *EKF, FLG, GMH, HNE* is also greater than the half of the segment of the circle about it, inasmuch as, if through the points *K, L, M, N* we draw tangents to the circle and complete the parallelograms on the straight lines *EF, FG, GH, HE*, each of the triangles *EKF, FLG, GMH, HNE* will be half of the parallelogram about it,

while the segment about it is less than the parallelogram;

hence each of the triangles *EKF, FLG, GMH, HNE* is greater than the half of the segment of the circle about it.

Thus, by bisecting the remaining circumferences and joining straight lines, and by doing this continually, we shall leave some segments of the circle which will be less than the excess by which the circle $EFGH$ exceeds the area S.

For it was proved in the first theorem of the tenth book that, if two unequal magnitudes be set out, and if from the greater there be subtracted a magnitude greater than the half, and from that which is left a greater than the half, and if this be done continually, there will be left some magnitude which will be less than the lesser magnitude set out.

Let segments be left such as described, and let the segments of the circle $EFGH$ on $EK, KF, FL, LG, GM, MH, HN, NE$ be less than the excess by which the circle $EFGH$ exceeds the area S.

Therefore the remainder, the polygon $EKFLGMHN$, is greater than the area S.

Let there be inscribed, also, in the circle $ABCD$ the polygon $AOBPCQDR$ similar to the polygon $EKFLGMHN$;
therefore, as the square on BD is to the square on FH, so is the polygon $AOBPCQDR$ to the polygon $EKFLGMHN$.   [XII. 1]

But, as the square on BD is to the square on FH, so also is the circle $ABCD$ to the area S;
therefore also, as the circle $ABCD$ is to the area S, so is the polygon $AOBPCQDR$ to the polygon $EKFLGMHN$;   [v. 11]
therefore, alternately, as the circle $ABCD$ is to the polygon inscribed in it, so is the area S to the polygon $EKFLGMHN$.   [v. 16]

But the circle $ABCD$ is greater than the polygon inscribed in it;
therefore the area S is also greater than the polygon $EKFLGMHN$.
But it is also less:

which is impossible.

Therefore, as the square on BD is to the square on FH, so is not the circle $ABCD$ to any area less than the circle $EFGH$.

Similarly we can prove that neither is the circle $EFGH$ to any area less than the circle $ABCD$ as the square on FH is to the square on BD.

I say next that neither is the circle $ABCD$ to any area greater than the circle $EFGH$ as the square on BD is to the square on FH.

For, if possible, let it be in that ratio to a greater area S.

Therefore, inversely, as the square on FH is to the square on DB, so is the area S to the circle $ABCD$.

But, as the area S is to the circle $ABCD$, so is the circle $EFGH$ to some area less than the circle $ABCD$;
therefore also, as the square on FH is to the square on BD, so is the circle $EFGH$ to some area less than the circle $ABCD$:   [v. 11]
which was proved impossible.

Therefore, as the square on BD is to the square on FH, so is not the circle $ABCD$ to any area greater than the circle $EFGH$.

And it was proved that neither is it in that ratio to any area less than the circle $EFGH$;
therefore, as the square on BD is to the square on FH, so is the circle $ABCD$ to the circle $EFGH$.

Therefore etc.   Q. E. D.

LEMMA

I say that, the area S being greater than the circle $EFGH$, as the area S is to the circle $ABCD$, so is the circle $EFGH$ to some area less than the circle $ABCD$.

For let it be contrived that, as the area S is to the circle $ABCD$, so is the circle $EFGH$ to the area T.

I say that the area T is less than the circle $ABCD$.

For since, as the area S is to the circle $ABCD$, so is the circle $EFGH$ to the area T,

therefore, alternately, as the area S is to the circle $EFGH$, so is the circle $ABCD$ to the area T.   [v. 16]

But the area S is greater than the circle $EFGH$;

therefore the circle $ABCD$ is also greater than the area T.

Hence, as the area S is to the circle $ABCD$, so is the circle $EFGH$ to some area less than the circle $ABCD$.   Q. E. D.

PROPOSITION 3

Any pyramid which has a triangular base is divided into two pyramids equal and similar to one another, similar to the whole and having triangular bases, and into two equal prisms; and the two prisms are greater than the half of the whole pyramid.

Let there be a pyramid of which the triangle ABC is the base and the point D the vertex;

I say that the pyramid $ABCD$ is divided into two pyramids equal to one another, having triangular bases and similar to the whole pyramid, and into two equal prisms; and the two prisms are greater than the half of the whole pyramid.

For let AB, BC, CA, AD, DB, DC be bisected at the points E, F, G, H, K, L, and let HE, EG, GH, HK, KL, LH, KF, FG be joined.

Since AE is equal to EB, and AH to DH,

therefore EH is parallel to DB.   [vi. 2]

For the same reason

HK is also parallel to AB.

Therefore $HEBK$ is a parallelogram;

therefore HK is equal to EB.   [i. 34]

But EB is equal to EA;

therefore AE is also equal to HK.

But AH is also equal to HD;

therefore the two sides EA, AH are equal to the two sides KH, HD respectively,

and the angle EAH is equal to the angle KHD;

therefore the base EH is equal to the base KD.   [i. 4]

Therefore the triangle AEH is equal and similar to the triangle HKD.

For the same reason

the triangle AHG is also equal and similar to the triangle HLD.

Now, since two straight lines EH, HG meeting one another are parallel to two straight lines KD, DL meeting one another, and are not in the same plane, they will contain equal angles.   [xi. 10]

Therefore the angle EHG is equal to the angle KDL.

And, since the two straight lines EH, HG are equal to the two KD, DL respectively,

and the angle EHG is equal to the angle KDL,

therefore the base EG is equal to the base KL;   [I. 4]

therefore the triangle EHG is equal and similar to the triangle KDL.

For the same reason

the triangle AEG is also equal and similar to the triangle HKL.

Therefore the pyramid of which the triangle AEG is the base and the point H the vertex is equal and similar to the pyramid of which the triangle HKL is the base and the point D the vertex.   [XI. Def. 10]

And, since HK has been drawn parallel to AB, one of the sides of the triangle ADB,

the triangle ADB is equiangular to the triangle DHK,   [I. 29]

and they have their sides proportional;

therefore the triangle ADB is similar to the triangle DHK.   [VI. Def. 1]

For the same reason

the triangle DBC is also similar to the triangle DKL, and the triangle ADC to the triangle DLH.

Now, since the two straight lines BA, AC meeting one another are parallel to the two straight lines KH, HL meeting one another, not in the same plane, they will contain equal angles.   [XI. 10]

Therefore the angle BAC is equal to the angle KHL.

And, as BA is to AC, so is KH to HL;

therefore the triangle ABC is similar to the triangle HKL.

Therefore also the pyramid of which the triangle ABC is the base and the point D the vertex is similar to the pyramid of which the triangle HKL is the base and the point D the vertex.

But the pyramid of which the triangle HKL is the base and the point D the vertex was proved similar to the pyramid of which the triangle AEG is the base and the point H the vertex.

Therefore each of the pyramids $AEGH$, $HKLD$ is similar to the whole pyramid $ABCD$.

Next, since BF is equal to FC,

the parallelogram $EBFG$ is double of the triangle GFC.

And since, if there be two prisms of equal height, and one have a parallelogram as base, and the other a triangle, and if the parallelogram be double of the triangle, the prisms are equal,   [XI. 39]

therefore the prism contained by the two triangles BKF, EHG, and the three parallelograms $EBFG$, $EBKH$, $HKFG$ is equal to the prism contained by the two triangles GFC, HKL and the three parallelograms $KFCL$, $LCGH$, $HKFG$.

And it is manifest that each of the prisms, namely that in which the parallelogram $EBFG$ is the base and the straight line HK is its opposite, and that in which the triangle GFC is the base and the triangle HKL its opposite, is greater than each of the pyramids of which the triangles AEG, HKL are the bases and the points H, D the vertices,

inasmuch as, if we join the straight lines EF, EK, the prism in which the parallelogram $EBFG$ is the base and the straight line HK its opposite is greater than the pyramid of which the triangle EBF is the base and the point K the vertex.

But the pyramid of which the triangle EBF is the base and the point K the vertex is equal to the pyramid of which the triangle AEG is the base and the point H the vertex;

for they are contained by equal and similar planes.

Hence also the prism in which the parallelogram $EBFG$ is the base and the straight line HK its opposite is greater than the pyramid of which the triangle AEG is the base and the point H the vertex.

But the prism in which the parallelogram $EBFG$ is the base and the straight line HK its opposite is equal to the prism in which the triangle GFC is the base and the triangle HKL its opposite,

and the pyramid of which the triangle AEG is the base and the point H the vertex is equal to the pyramid of which the triangle HKL is the base and the point D the vertex.

Therefore the said two prisms are greater than the said two pyramids of which the triangles AEG, HKL are the bases and the points H, D the vertices.

Therefore the whole pyramid, of which the triangle ABC is the base and the point D the vertex, has been divided into two pyramids equal to one another and into two equal prisms, and the two prisms are greater than the half of the whole pyramid.   Q. E. D.

PROPOSITION 4

If there be two pyramids of the same height which have triangular bases, and each of them be divided into two pyramids equal to one another and similar to the whole, and into two equal prisms, then, as the base of the one pyramid is to the base of the other pyramid, so will all the prisms in the one pyramid be to all the prisms, being equal in multitude, in the other pyramid.

Let there be two pyramids of the same height which have the triangular bases ABC, DEF, and vertices the points G, H,

and let each of them be divided into two pyramids equal to one another and similar to the whole and into two equal prisms;   [XII. 3]

I say that, as the base ABC is to the base DEF, so are all the prisms in the pyramid $ABCG$ to all the prisms, being equal in multitude, in the pyramid $DEFH$,

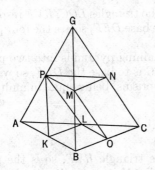
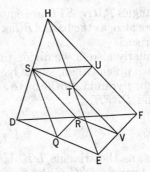

For, since BO is equal to OC, and AL to LC,
therefore LO is parallel to AB,
and the triangle ABC is similar to the triangle LOC.

For the same reason

the triangle DEF is also similar to the triangle RVF.

And, since BC is double of CO, and EF of FV,

therefore, as BC is to CO, so is EF to FV.

And on BC, CO are described the similar and similarly situated rectilineal figures ABC, LOC,

and on EF, FV the similar and similarly situated figures DEF, RVF;

therefore, as the triangle ABC is to the triangle LOC, so is the triangle DEF to the triangle RVF;   [VI. 22]

therefore, alternately, as the triangle ABC is to the triangle DEF, so is the triangle LOC to the triangle RVF.   [V. 16]

But, as the triangle LOC is to the triangle RVF, so is the prism in which the triangle LOC is the base and PMN its opposite, to the prism in which the triangle RVF is the base and STU its opposite;   [Lemma following]

therefore also, as the triangle ABC is to the triangle DEF, so is the prism in which the triangle LOC is the base and PMN its opposite, to the prism in which the triangle RVF is the base and STU its opposite.

But, as the said prisms are to one another, so is the prism in which the parallelogram $KBOL$ is the base and the straight line PM its opposite, to the prism in which the parallelogram $QEVR$ is the base and the straight line ST its opposite.   [XI. 39; cf. XII. 3]

Therefore also the two prisms, that in which the parallelogram $KBOL$ is the base and PM its opposite, and that in which the triangle LOC is the base and PMN its opposite, are to the prisms in which $QEVR$ is the base and the straight line ST its opposite and in which the triangle RVF is the base and STU its opposite in the same ratio.   [V. 12]

Therefore also, as the base ABC is to the base DEF, so are the said two prisms to the said two prisms.

And similarly, if the pyramids $PMNG$, $STUH$ be divided into two prisms and two pyramids,

as the base PMN is to the base STU, so will the two prisms in the pyramid $PMNG$ be to the two prisms in the pyramid $STUH$.

But, as the base PMN is to the base STU, so is the base ABC to the base DEF;

for the triangles PMN, STU are equal to the triangles LOC, RVF respectively.

Therefore also, as the base ABC is to the base DEF, so are the four prisms to the four prisms.

And similarly also, if we divide the remaining pyramids into two pyramids and into two prisms, then, as the base ABC is to base the DEF, so will all the prisms in the pyramid $ABCG$ be to all the prisms, being equal in multitude, in the pyramid $DEFH$.   Q. E. D.

LEMMA

But that, as the triangle LOC is to the triangle RVF, so is the prism in which the triangle LOC is the base and PMN its opposite, to the prism in which the triangle RVF is the base and STU its opposite, we must prove as follows.

For in the same figure let perpendiculars be conceived drawn from G, H to the planes ABC, DEF; these are of course equal because, by hypothesis, the pyramids are of equal height.

Now, since the two straight lines GC and the perpendicular from G are cut by the parallel planes ABC, PMN;

they will be cut in the same ratios.   [XI. 17]

And GC is bisected by the plane PMN at N;
therefore the perpendicular from G to the plane ABC will also be bisected by the plane PMN.

For the same reason
the perpendicular from H to the plane DEF will also be bisected by the plane STU.

And the perpendiculars from G, H to the planes ABC, DEF are equal;
therefore the perpendiculars from the triangles PMN, STU to the planes ABC, DEF are also equal.

Therefore the prisms in which the triangles LOC, RVF are bases, and PMN, STU their opposites, are of equal height.

Hence also the parallelepipedal solids described from the said prisms are of equal height and are to one another as their bases;   [XI. 32]
therefore their halves, namely the said prisms, are to one another as the base LOC is to the base RVF.   Q. E. D.

Proposition 5

Pyramids which are of the same height and have triangular bases are to one another as the bases.

Let there by pyramids of the same height, of which the triangles ABC, DEF are the bases and the points G, H the vertices;

I say that, as the base ABC is to the base DEF, so is the pyramid $ABCG$ to the pyramid $DEFH$.

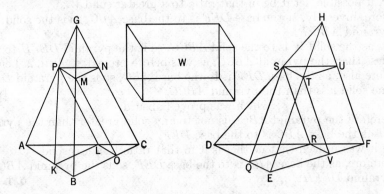

For, if the pyramid $ABCG$ is not to the pyramid $DEFH$ as the base ABC is to the base DEF,
then, as the base ABC is to the base DEF, so will the pyramid $ABCG$ be either to some solid less than the pyramid $DEFH$ or to a greater.

Let it, first, be in that ratio to a less solid W, and let the pyramid $DEFH$ be divided into two pyramids equal to one another and similar to the whole and into two equal prisms;

then the two prisms are greater than the half of the whole pyramid.   [XII. 3]

Again, let the pyramids arising from the division be similarly divided, and let this be done continually until there are left over from the pyramid *DEFH* some pyramids which are less than the excess by which the pyramid *DEFH* exceeds the solid *W*.   [X. 1]

Let such be left, and let them be, for the sake of argument, *DQRS*, *STUH*; therefore the remainders, the prisms in the pyramid *DEFH*, are greater than the solid *W*.

Let the pyramid *ABCG* also be divided similarly, and a similar number of times, with the pyramid *DEFH*;

therefore, as the base *ABC* is to the base *DEF*, so are the prisms in the pyramid *ABCG* to the prisms in the pyramid *DEFH*.   [XII. 4]

But, as the base *ABC* is to the base *DEF*, so also is the pyramid *ABCG* to the solid *W*;

therefore also, as the pyramid *ABCG* is to the solid *W*, so are the prisms in the pyramid *ABCG* to the prisms in the pyramid *DEFH*;   [v. 11]
therefore, alternately, as the pyramid *ABCG* is to the prisms in it, so is the solid *W* to the prisms in the pyramid *DEFH*.   [v. 16]

But the pyramid *ABCG* is greater than the prisms in it;
therefore the solid *W* is also greater than the prisms in the pyramid *DEFH*.

But it is also less:

which is impossible.

Therefore the prism *ABCG* is not to any solid less than the pyramid *DEFH* as the base *ABC* is to the base *DEF*.

Similarly it can be proved that neither is the pyramid *DEFH* to any solid less than the pyramid *ABCG* as the base *DEF* is to the base *ABC*.

I say next that neither is the pyramid *ABCG* to any solid greater than the pyramid *DEFH* as the base *ABC* is to the base *DEF*.

For, if possible, let it be in that ratio to a greater solid *W*;
therefore, inversely, as the base *DEF* is to the base *ABC*, so is the solid *W* to the pyramid *ABCG*.

But, as the solid *W* is to the solid *ABCG*, so is the pyramid *DEFH* to some solid less than the pyramid *ABCG*, as was before proved;   [XII. 2, Lemma]
therefore also, as the base *DEF* is to the base *ABC*, so is the pyramid *DEFH* to some solid less than the pyramid *ABCG*:   [v. 11]

which was proved absurd.

Therefore the pyramid *ABCG* is not to any solid greater than the pyramid *DEFH* as the base *ABC* is to the base *DEF*.

But it was proved that neither is it in that ratio to a less solid.

Therefore, as the base *ABC* is to the base *DEF*, so is the pyramid *ABCG* to the pyramid *DEFH*.   Q. E. D.

PROPOSITION 6

Pyramids which are of the same height and have polygonal bases are to one another as the bases.

Let there be pyramids of the same height of which the polygons *ABCDE*, *FGHKL* are the bases and the points *M*, *N* the vertices;

I say that, as the base *ABCDE* is to the base *FGHKL*, so is the pyramid *ABCDEM* to the pyramid *FGHKLN*.

For let AC, AD, FH, FK be joined.

Since then $ABCM$, $ACDM$ are two pyramids which have triangular bases and equal height,

they are to one another as the bases;   [XII. 5]

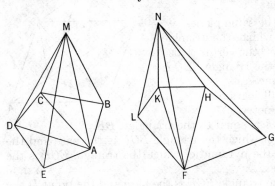

therefore, as the base ABC is to the base ACD, so is the pyramid $ABCM$ to the pyramid $ACDM$.

And, *componendo*, as the base $ABCD$ is to the base ACD, so is the pyramid $ABCDM$ to the pyramid $ACDM$.   [v. 18]

But also, as the base ACD is to the base ADE, so is the pyramid $ACDM$ to the pyramid $ADEM$.   [XII. 5]

Therefore, *ex aequali*, as the base $ABCD$ is to the base ADE, so is the pyramid $ABCDM$ to the pyramid $ADEM$.   [v. 22]

And again, *componendo*, as the base $ABCDE$ is to the base ADE, so is the pyramid $ABCDEM$ to the pyramid $ADEM$.   [v. 18]

Similarly also it can be proved that, as the base $FGHKL$ is to the base FGH, so is the pyramid $FGHKLN$ to the pyramid $FGHN$.

And, since $ADEM$, $FGHN$ are two pyramids which have triangular bases and equal height,

therefore, as the base ADE is to the base FGH, so is the pyramid $ADEM$ to the pyramid $FGHN$.   [XII. 5]

But, as the base ADE is to the base $ABCDE$, so was the pyramid $ADEM$ to the pyramid $ABCDEM$.

Therefore also, *ex aequali*, as the base $ABCDE$ is to the base FGH, so is the pyramid $ABCDEM$ to the pyramid $FGHN$.   [v. 22]

But further, as the base FGH is to the base $FGHKL$, so also was the pyramid $FGHN$ to the pyramid $FGHKLN$.

Therefore also, *ex aequali*, as the base $ABCDE$ is to the base $FGHKL$, so is the pyramid $ABCDEM$ to the pyramid $FGHKLN$.   [v. 22]

Q. E. D.

PROPOSITION 7

Any prism which has a triangular base is divided into three pyramids equal to one another which have triangular bases.

Let there be a prism in which the triangle ABC is the base and DEF its opposite;

I say that the prism $ABCDEF$ is divided into three pyramids equal to one another, which have triangular bases.

For let BD, EC, CD be joined.

Since $ABED$ is a parallelogram, and BD is its diameter,

therefore the triangle ABD is equal to the triangle EBD;   [I. 34]

therefore also the pyramid of which the triangle ABD is the base and the point C the vertex is equal to the pyramid of which the triangle DEB is the base and the point C the vertex.   [XII. 5]

But the pyramid of which the triangle DEB is the base and the point C the
vertex is the same with the pyramid of which the
triangle EBC is the base and the point D the
vertex;

for they are contained by the same planes.

Therefore the pyramid of which the triangle
ABD is the base and the point C the vertex is also
equal to the pyramid of which the triangle EBC is
the base and the point D the vertex.

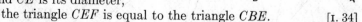

Again, since $FCBE$ is a parallelogram,
and CE is its diameter,
the triangle CEF is equal to the triangle CBE.   [I. 34]

Therefore also the pyramid of which the triangle BCE is the base and the
point D the vertex is equal to the pyramid of which the triangle ECF is the
base and the point D the vertex.   [XII. 5]

But the pyramid of which the triangle BCE is the base and the point D the
vertex was proved equal to the pyramid of which the triangle ABD is the base
and the point C the vertex;

therefore also the pyramid of which the triangle CEF is the base and the point
D the vertex is equal to the pyramid of which the triangle ABD is the base and
the point C the vertex;

therefore the prism $ABCDEF$ has been divided into three pyramids equal to
one another which have triangular bases.

And, since the pyramid of which the triangle ABD is the base and the point
C the vertex is the same with the pyramid of which the triangle CAB is the
base and the point D the vertex,

for they are contained by the same planes,

while the pyramid of which the triangle ABD is the base and the point C the
vertex was proved to be a third of the prism in which the triangle ABC is the
base and DEF its opposite,

therefore also the pyramid of which the triangle ABC is the base and the point
D the vertex is a third of the prism which has the same base, the triangle ABC,
and DEF as its opposite.

PORISM. From this it is manifest that any pyramid is a third part of the
prism which has the same base with it and equal height.   Q. E. D.

PROPOSITION 8

*Similar pyramids which have triangular bases are in the triplicate ratio of their
corresponding sides.*

Let there be similar and similarly situated pyramids of which the triangles
ABC, DEF are the bases and the points G, H the vertices;

I say that the pyramid $ABCG$ has to the pyramid $DEFH$ the ratio triplicate
of that which BC has to EF.

For let the parallelepipedal solids $BGML$, $EHQP$ be completed.

Now, since the pyramid $ABCG$ is similar to the pyramid $DEFH$,

therefore the angle ABC is equal to the angle DEF,
the angle GBC to the angle HEF,
and the angle ABG to the angle DEH;

and, as AB is to DE, so is BC to EF, and BG to EH.

And since, as AB is to DE, so is BC to EF,
        and the sides are proportional about equal angles,

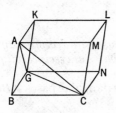
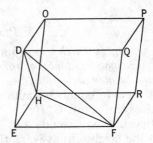

therefore the parallelogram BM is similar to the parallelogram EQ.

For the same reason
            BN is also similar to ER, and BK to EO;
therefore the three parallelograms MB, BK, BN are similar to the three EQ, EO, ER.

But the three parallelograms MB, BK, BN are equal and similar to their three opposites,
and the three EQ, EO, ER are equal and similar to their three opposites.

[XI. 24]

Therefore the solids $BGML$, $EHQP$ are contained by similar planes equal in multitude.

Therefore the solid $BGML$ is similar to the solid $EHQP$.

But similar parallelepipedal solids are in the triplicate ratio of their corresponding sides.   [XI. 33]

Therefore the solid $BGML$ has to the solid $EHQP$ the ratio triplicate of that which the corresponding side BC has to the corresponding side EF.

But, as the solid $BGML$ is to the solid $EHQP$, so is the pyramid $ABCG$ to the pyramid $DEFH$,
inasmuch as the pyramid is a sixth part of the solid, because the prism which is half of the parallelepipedal solid [XI. 28] is also triple of the pyramid. [XII. 7]

Therefore the pyramid $ABCG$ also has to the pyramid $DEFH$ the ratio triplicate of that which BC has to EF.   Q. E. D.

PORISM. From this it is manifest that similar pyramids which have polygonal bases are also to one another in the triplicate ratio of their corresponding sides.

For, if they are divided into the pyramids contained in them which have triangular bases, by virtue of the fact that the similar polygons forming their bases are also divided into similar triangles equal in multitude and corresponding to the wholes,   [VI. 20]
then, as the one pyramid which has a triangular base in the one complete pyramid is to the one pyramid which has a triangular base in the other complete pyramid, so also will all the pyramids which have triangular bases contained in the one pyramid be to all the pyramids which have triangular bases contained in the other pyramid [V. 12], that is, the pyramid itself which has a polygonal base, to the pyramid which has a polygonal base.

But the pyramid which has a triangular base is to the pyramid which has a triangular base in the triplicate ratio of the corresponding sides; therefore also the pyramid which has a polygonal base has to the pyramid which has a similar base the ratio triplicate of that which the side has to the side.

PROPOSITION 9

In equal pyramids which have triangular bases the bases are reciprocally proportional to the heights; and those pyramids in which the bases are reciprocally proportional to the heights are equal.

For let there be equal pyramids which have the triangular bases ABC, DEF and vertices the points G, H;

I say that in the pyramids $ABCG$, $DEFH$ the bases are reciprocally proportional to the heights, that is, as the base ABC is to the base DEF, so is the height of the pyramid $DEFH$ to the height of the pyramid $ABCG$.

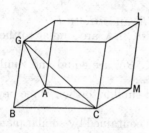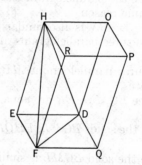

For let the parallelepipedal solids $BGML$, $EHQP$ be completed.

Now, since the pyramid $ABCG$ is equal to the pyramid $DEFH$,
        and the solid $BGML$ is six times the pyramid $ABCG$,
        and the solid $EHQP$ six times the pyramid $DEFH$,
        therefore the solid $BGML$ is equal to the solid $EHQP$.

But in equal parallelepipedal solids the bases are reciprocally proportional to the heights;   [XI. 34]
therefore, as the base BM is to the base EQ, so is the height of the solid $EHQP$ to the height of the solid $BGML$.

But, as the base BM is to EQ, so is the triangle ABC to the triangle DEF.
                                                                        [I. 34]
Therefore also, as the triangle ABC is to the triangle DEF, so is the height of the solid $EHQP$ to the height of the solid $BGML$.   [V. 11]

But the height of the solid $EHQP$ is the same with the height of the pyramid $DEFH$,
and the height of the solid $BGML$ is the same with the height of the pyramid $ABCG$,
therefore, as the base ABC is to the base DEF, so is the height of the pyramid $DEFH$ to the height of the pyramid $ABCG$.

Therefore in the pyramids $ABCG$, $DEFH$ the bases are reciprocally proportional to the heights.

Next, in the pyramids $ABCG$, $DEFH$ let the bases be reciprocally proportional to the heights;

that is, as the base ABC is to the base DEF, so let the height of the pyramid $DEFH$ be to the height of the pyramid $ABCG$;

I say that the pyramid $ABCG$ is equal to the pyramid $DEFH$.

For, with the same construction,

since, as the base ABC is to the base DEF, so is the height of the pyramid $DEFH$ to the height of the pyramid $ABCG$,

while, as the base ABC is to the base DEF, so is the parallelogram BM to the parallelogram EQ,

therefore also, as the parallelogram BM is to the parallelogram EQ, so is the height of the pyramid $DEFH$ to the height of the pyramid $ABCG$.   [v. 11]

But the height of the pyramid $DEFH$ is the same with the height of the parallelepiped $EHQP$,

and the height of the pyramid $ABCG$ is the same with the height of the parallelepiped $BGML$;

therefore, as the base BM is to the base EQ, so is the height of the parallelepiped $EHQP$ to the height of the parallelepiped $BGML$.

But those parallelepipedal solids in which the bases are reciprocally proportional to the heights are equal;   [xi. 34]

therefore the parallelepipedal solid $BGML$ is equal to the parallelepipedal solid $EHQP$.

And the pyramid $ABCG$ is a sixth part of $BGML$, and the pyramid $DEFH$ a sixth part of the parallelepiped $EHQP$;

therefore the pyramid $ABCG$ is equal to the pyramid $DEFH$.

Therefore etc.   Q. E. D.

PROPOSITION 10

Any cone is a third part of the cylinder which has the same base with it and equal height.

For let a cone have the same base, namely the circle $ABCD$, with a cylinder and equal height;

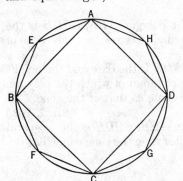

I say that the cone is a third part of the cylinder, that is, that the cylinder is triple of the cone.

For if the cylinder is not triple of the cone, the cylinder will be either greater than triple or less than triple of the cone.

First let it be greater than triple, and let the square $ABCD$ be inscribed in the circle $ABCD$;   [iv. 6] then the square $ABCD$ is greater than the half of the circle $ABCD$.

From the square $ABCD$ let there be set up a prism of equal height with the cylinder.

Then the prism so set up is greater than the half of the cylinder, inasmuch as, if we also circumscribe a square about the circle $ABCD$ [iv. 7], the square inscribed in the circle $ABCD$ is half of that circumscribed about it, and the solids set up from them are parallelepipedal prisms of equal height,

while parallelepipedal solids which are of the same height are to one another as their bases;   [XI. 32]
therefore also the prism set up on the square $ABCD$ is half of the prism set up from the square circumscribed about the circle $ABCD$;

[cf. XI. 28, or XII. 6 and 7, Por.]
and the cylinder is less than the prism set up from the square circumscribed about the circle $ABCD$;
therefore the prism set up from the square $ABCD$ and of equal height with the cylinder is greater than the half of the cylinder.

Let the circumferences AB, BC, CD, DA be bisected at the points E, F, G, H,

and let AE, EB, BF, FC, CG, GD, DH, HA be joined;
then each of the triangles AEB, BFC, CGD, DHA is greater than the half of that segment of the circle $ABCD$ which is about it, as we proved before.

[XII. 2]
On each of the triangles AEB, BFC, CGD, DHA let prisms be set up of equal height with the cylinder;
then each of the prisms so set up is greater than the half part of that segment of the cylinder which is about it,
inasmuch as, if we draw through the points E, F, G, H parallels to AB, BC, CD, DA, complete the parallelograms on AB, BC, CD, DA, and set up from them parallelepipedal solids of equal height with the cylinder, the prisms on the triangles AEB, BFC, CGD, DHA are halves of the several solids set up;
and the segments of the cylinder are less than the parallelepipedal solids set up;
hence also the prisms on the triangles AEB, BFC, CGD, DHA are greater than the half of the segments of the cylinder about them.

Thus, bisecting the circumferences that are left, joining straight lines, setting up on each of the triangles prisms of equal height with the cylinder,
and doing this continually,
we shall leave some segments of the cylinder which will be less than the excess by which the cylinder exceeds the triple of the cone.   [X. 1]

Let such segments be left, and let them be AE, EB, BF, FC, CG, GD, DH, HA;
therefore the remainder, the prism of which the polygon $AEBFCGDH$ is the base and the height is the same as that of the cylinder, is greater than triple of the cone.

But the prism of which the polygon $AEBFCGDH$ is the base and the height the same as that of the cylinder is triple of the pyramid of which the polygon $AEBFCGDH$ is the base and the vertex is the same as that of the cone;

[XII. 7, Por.]
therefore also the pyramid of which the polygon $AEBFCGDH$ is the base and the vertex is the same as that of the cone is greater than the cone which has the circle $ABCD$ as base.

But it is also less, for it is enclosed by it:
which is impossible.
Therefore the cylinder is not greater than triple of the cone.
I say next that neither is the cylinder less than triple of the cone,
For, if possible, let the cylinder be less than triple of the cone,
therefore, inversely, the cone is greater than a third part of the cylinder.

Let the square $ABCD$ be inscribed in the circle $ABCD$;
therefore the square $ABCD$ is greater than the half of the circle $ABCD$.

Now let there be set up from the square $ABCD$ a pyramid having the same vertex with the cone;
therefore the pyramid so set up is greater than the half part of the cone, seeing that, as we proved before, if we circumscribe a square about the circle, the square $ABCD$ will be half of the square circumscribed about the circle, and if we set up from the squares parallelepipedal solids of equal height with the cone, which are also called prisms, the solid set up from the square $ABCD$ will be half of that set up from the square circumscribed about the circle;
for they are to one another as their bases.   [XI. 32]

Hence also the thirds of them are in that ratio;
therefore also the pyramid of which the square $ABCD$ is the base is half of the pyramid set up from the square circumscribed about the circle.

And the pyramid set up from the square about the circle is greater than the cone,
for it encloses it.

Therefore the pyramid of which the square $ABCD$ is the base and the vertex is the same with that of the cone is greater than the half of the cone.

Let the circumferences AB, BC, CD, DA be bisected at the points E, F, G, H,
and let AE, EB, BF, FC, CG, GD, DH, HA be joined;
therefore also each of the triangles AEB, BFC, CGD, DHA is greater than the half part of that segment of the circle $ABCD$ which is about it.

Now, on each of the triangles AEB, BFC, CGD, DHA let pyramids be set up which have the same vertex as the cone;
therefore also each of the pyramids so set up is, in the same manner, greater than the half part of that segment of the cone which is about it.

Thus, by bisecting the circumferences that are left, joining straight lines, setting up on each of the triangles a pyramid which has the same vertex as the cone,
and doing this continually,
we shall leave some segments of the cone which will be less than the excess by which the cone exceeds the third part of the cylinder.   [X. 1]

Let such be left, and let them be the segments on AE, EB, BF, FC, CG, GD, DH, HA;
therefore the remainder, the pyramid of which the polygon $AEBFCGDH$ is the base and the vertex the same with that of the cone, is greater than a third part of the cylinder.

But the pyramid of which the polygon $AEBFCGDH$ is the base and the vertex the same with that of the cone is a third part of the prism of which the polygon $AEBFCGDH$ is the base and the height is the same with that of the cylinder;
therefore the prism of which the polygon $AEBFCGDH$ is the base and the height is the same with that of the cylinder is greater than the cylinder of which the circle $ABCD$ is the base.

But it is also less, for it is enclosed by it:
which is impossible.

Therefore the cylinder is not less than triple of the cone.

But it was proved that neither is it greater than triple;
therefore the cylinder is triple of the cone;
hence the cone is a third part of the cylinder.

Therefore etc.

Q. E. D.

PROPOSITION 11

Cones and cylinders which are of the same height are to one another as their bases.

Let there be cones and cylinders of the same height,
let the circles *ABCD*, *EFGH* be their bases, *KL, MN* their axes and *AC, EG* the diameters of their bases;

I say that, as the circle *ABCD* is to the circle *EFGH*, so is the cone *AL* to the cone *EN*.

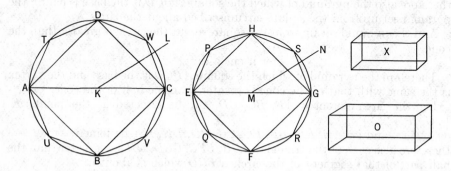

For, if not, then, as the circle *ABCD* is to the circle *EFGH*, so will the cone *AL* be either to some solid less than the cone *EN* or to a greater.

First, let it be in that ratio to a less solid *O*, and let the solid *X* be equal to that by which the solid *O* is less than the cone *EN*;

therefore the cone *EN* is equal to the solids *O, X*.

Let the square *EFGH* be inscribed in the circle *EFGH*;

therefore the square is greater than the half of the circle.

Let there be set up from the square *EFGH* a pyramid of equal height with the cone;

therefore the pyramid so set up is greater than the half of the cone, inasmuch as, if we circumscribe a square about the circle, and set up from it a pyramid of equal height with the cone, the inscribed pyramid is half of the circumscribed pyramid,

for they are to one another as their bases,   [XII. 6]
while the cone is less than the circumscribed pyramid.

Let the circumferences *EF, FG, GH, HE* be bisected at the points *P, Q, R, S,* and let *HP, PE, EQ, QF, FR, RG, GS, SH* be joined.

Therefore each of the triangles *HPE, EQF, FRG, GSH* is greater than the half of that segment of the circle which is about it.

On each of the triangles *HPE, EQF, FRG, GSH* let there be set up a pyramid of equal height with the cone;

therefore, also, each of the pyramids so set up is greater than the half of that segment of the cone which is about it.

Thus, bisecting the circumferences which are left, joining straight lines, set-

ting up on each of the triangles pyramids of equal height with the cone,
and doing this continually,
we shall leave some segments of the cone which will be less than the solid X.
[x. 1]

Let such be left, and let them be the segments on HP, PE, EQ, QF, FR, RG, GS, SH;
therefore the remainder, the pyramid of which the polygon $HPEQFRGS$ is the base and the height the same with that of the cone, is greater than the solid O.

Let there also be inscribed in the circle $ABCD$ the polygon $DTAUBVCW$ similar and similarly situated to the polygon $HPEQFRGS$,
and on it let a pyramid be set up of equal height with the cone AL.

Since then, as the square on AC is to the square on EG, so is the polygon $DTAUBVCW$ to the polygon $HPEQFRGS$, [xii. 1]
while, as the square on AC is to the square on EG, so is the circle $ABCD$ to the circle $EFGH$, [xii. 2]
therefore also, as the circle $ABCD$ is to the circle $EFGH$, so is the polygon $DTAUBVCW$ to the polygon $HPEQFRGS$.

But, as the circle $ABCD$ is to the circle $EFGH$, so is the cone AL to the solid O,
and, as the polygon $DTAUBVCW$ is to the polygon $HPEQFRGS$, so is the pyramid of which the polygon $DTAUBVCW$ is the base and the point L the vertex to the pyramid of which the polygon $HPEQFRGS$ is the base and the point N the vertex. [xii. 6]

Therefore also, as the cone AL is to the solid O, so is the pyramid of which the polygon $DTAUBVCW$ is the base and the point L the vertex to the pyramid of which the polygon $HPEQFRGS$ is the base and the point N the vertex; [v. 11]
therefore, alternately, as the cone AL is to the pyramid in it, so is the solid O to the pyramid in the cone EN. [v. 16]

But the cone AL is greater than the pyramid in it;
therefore the solid O is also greater than the pyramid in the cone EN.

But it is also less:
which is absurd.

Therefore the cone AL is not to any solid less than the cone EN as the circle $ABCD$ is to the circle $EFGH$.

Similarly we can prove that neither is the cone EN to any solid less than the cone AL as the circle $EFGH$ is to the circle $ABCD$.

I say next that neither is the cone AL to any solid greater than the cone EN as the circle $ABCD$ is to the circle $EFGH$.

For, if possible, let it be in that ratio to a greater solid O;
therefore, inversely, as the circle $EFGH$ is to the circle $ABCD$, so is the solid O to the cone AL.

But, as the solid O is to the cone AL, so is the cone EN to some solid less than the cone AL;
therefore also, as the circle $EFGH$ is to the circle $ABCD$, so is the cone EN to some solid less than the cone AL:
which was proved impossible.

Therefore the cone AL is not to any solid greater than the cone EN as the circle $ABCD$ is to the circle $EFGH$.

But it was proved that neither is it in this ratio to a less solid;
therefore, as the circle *ABCD* is to the circle *EFGH*, so is the cone *AL* to the
cone *EN*.

But, as the cone is to the cone, so is the cylinder to the cylinder,
for each is triple of each;   [XII. 10]
Therefore also, as the circle *ABCD* is to the circle *EFGH*, so are the cylinders on them which are of equal height.

Therefore etc.
                                                                        Q. E. D.

PROPOSITION 12

*Similar cones and cylinders are to one another in the triplicate ratio of the diameters
in their bases.*

Let there be similar cones and cylinders,
let the circles *ABCD*, *EFGH* be their bases, *BD*, *FH* the diameters of the bases,
and *KL*, *MN* the axes of the cones and cylinders;

I say that the cone of which the circle *ABCD* is the base and the point *L* the
vertex has to the cone of which the circle *EFGH* is the base and the point *N*
the vertex the ratio triplicate of that which *BD* has to *FH*.

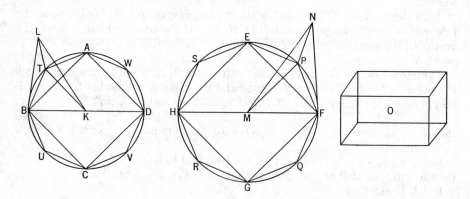

For, if the cone *ABCDL* has not to the cone *EFGHN* the ratio triplicate of
that which *BD* has to *FH*,
the cone *ABCDL* will have that triplicate ratio either to some solid less than
the cone *EFGHN* or to a greater.

First, let it have that triplicate ratio to a less solid *O*.

Let the square *EFGH* be inscribed in the circle *EFGH*;   [IV. 6]
therefore the square *EFGH* is greater than the half of the circle *EFGH*.

Now let there be set up on the square *EFGH* a pyramid having the same
vertex with the cone;
therefore the pyramid so set up is greater than the half part of the cone.

Let the circumferences *EF*, *FG*, *GH*, *HE* be bisected at the points *P*, *Q*, *R*, *S*,
and let *EP*, *PF*, *FQ*, *QG*, *GR*, *RH*, *HS*, *SE* be joined.

Therefore each of the triangles *EPF*, *FQG*, *GRH*, *HSE* is also greater than
the half part of that segment of the circle *EFGH* which is about it.

Now on each of the triangles *EPF*, *FQG*, *GRH*, *HSE* let a pyramid be set up
having the same vertex with the cone;

therefore each of the pyramids so set up is also greater than the half part of that segment of the cone which is about it.

Thus, bisecting the circumferences so left, joining straight lines, setting up on each of the triangles pyramids having the same vertex with the cone,

and doing this continually,

we shall leave some segments of the cone which will be less than the excess by which the cone *EFGHN* exceeds the solid *O*.   [x. 1]

Let such be left, and let them be the segments on *EP*, *PF*, *FQ*, *QG*, *GR*, *RH*, *HS*, *SE*;

therefore the remainder, the pyramid of which the polygon *EPFQGRHS* is the base and the point *N* the vertex, is greater than the solid *O*.

Let there be also inscribed in the circle *ABCD* the polygon *ATBUCVDW* similar and similarly situated to the polygon *EPFQGRHS*,

and let there be set up on the polygon *ATBUCVDW* a pyramid having the same vertex with the cone;

of the triangles containing the pyramid of which the polygon *ATBUCVDW* is the base and the point *L* the vertex let *LBT* be one,

and of the triangles containing the pyramid of which the polygon *EPFQGRHS* is the base and the point *N* the vertex let *NFP* be one;

and let *KT*, *MP* be joined.

Now, since the cone *ABCDL* is similar to the cone *EFGHN*,

therefore, as *BD* is to *FH*, so is the axis *KL* to the axis *MN*.   [xi. Def. 24]

But, as *BD* is to *FH*, so is *BK* to *FM*;

therefore also, as *BK* is to *FM*, so is *KL* to *MN*.

And, alternately, as *BK* is to *KL*, so is *FM* to *MN*.   [v. 16]

And the sides are proportional about equal angles, namely the angles *BKL*, *FMN*;

therefore the triangle *BKL* is similar to the triangle *FMN*.   [vi. 6]

Again, since, as *BK* is to *KT*, so is *FM* to *MP*,

and they are about equal angles, namely the angles *BKT*, *FMP*,

inasmuch as, whatever part the angle *BKT* is of the four right angles at the centre *K*, the same part also is the angle *FMP* of the four right angles at the centre *M*;

since then the sides are proportional about equal angles,

therefore the triangle *BKT* is similar to the triangle *FMP*.   [vi. 6]

Again, since it was proved that, as *BK* is to *KL*, so is *FM* to *MN*,

while *BK* is equal to *KT*, and *FM* to *PM*,

therefore, as *TK* is to *KL*, so is *PM* to *MN*;

and the sides are proportional about equal angles, namely the angles *TKL*, *PMN*, for they are right;

therefore the triangle *LKT* is similar to the triangle *NMP*.   [vi. 6]

And since, owing to the similarity of the triangles *LKB*, *NMF*,

as *LB* is to *BK*, so is *NF* to *FM*,

and, owing to the similarity of the triangles *BKT*, *FMP*,

as *KB* is to *BT*, so is *MF* to *FP*,

therefore, *ex aequali*, as *LB* is to *BT*, so is *NF* to *FP*.   [v. 22]

Again, since, owing to the similarity of the triangles *LTK*, *NPM*,

as *LT* is to *TK*, so is *NP* to *PM*,

and, owing to the similarity of the triangles *TKB*, *PMF*,

as KT is to TB, so is MP to PF;

therefore, *ex aequali*, as LT is to TB, so is NP to PF.   [v. 22]

But it was also proved that, as TB is to BL, so is PF to FN.

Therefore, *ex aequali*, as TL is to LB, so is PN to NF.   [v. 22]

Therefore in the triangles LTB, NPF the sides are proportional;

therefore the triangles LTB, NPF are equiangular;   [vi. 5]

hence they are also similar.   [vi. Def. 1]

Therefore the pyramid of which the triangle BKT is the base and the point L the vertex is also similar to the pyramid of which the triangle FMP is the base and the point N the vertex,

for they are contained by similar planes equal in multitude.   [xi. Def. 9]

But similar pyramids which have triangular bases are to one another in the triplicate ratio of their corresponding sides.   [xii. 8]

Therefore the pyramid $BKTL$ has to the pyramid $FMPN$ the ratio triplicate of that which BK has to FM.

Similarly, by joining straight lines from A, W, D, V, C, U to K, and from E, S, H, R, G, Q to M, and setting up on each of the triangles pyramids which have the same vertex with the cones,

we can prove that each of the similarly arranged pyramids will also have to each similarly arranged pyramid the ratio triplicate of that which the corresponding side BK has to the corresponding side FM, that is, which BD has to FH.

And, as one of the antecedents is to one of the consequents, so are all the antecedents to all the consequents;   [v. 12]

therefore also, as the pyramid $BKTL$ is to the pyramid $FMPN$, so is the whole pyramid of which the polygon $ATBUCVDW$ is the base and the point L the vertex to the whole pyramid of which the polygon $EPFQGRHS$ is the base and the point N the vertex;

hence also the pyramid of which $ATBUCVDW$ is the base and the point L the vertex has to the pyramid of which the polygon $EPFQGRHS$ is the base and the point N the vertex the ratio triplicate of that which BD has to FH.

But, by hypothesis, the cone of which the circle $ABCD$ is the base and the point L the vertex has also to the solid O the ratio triplicate of that which BD has to FH;

therefore, as the cone of which the circle $ABCD$ is the base and the point L the vertex is to the solid O, so is the pyramid of which the polygon $ATBUCVDW$ is the base and L the vertex to the pyramid of which the polygon $EPFQGRHS$ is the base and the point N the vertex;

therefore, alternately, as the cone of which the circle $ABCD$ is the base and L the vertex is to the pyramid contained in it of which the polygon $ATBUCVDW$ is the base and L the vertex, so is the solid O to the pyramid of which the polygon $EPFQGRHS$ is the base and N the vertex.   [v. 16]

But the said cone is greater than the pyramid in it;

for it encloses it.

Therefore the solid O is also greater than the pyramid of which the polygon $EPFQGRHS$ is the base and N the vertex.

But it is also less:

which is impossible.

Therefore the cone of which the circle $ABCD$ is the base and L the vertex has not to any solid less than the cone of which the circle *EFGH* is the base and the point *N* the vertex the ratio triplicate of that which *BD* has to *FH*.

Similarly we can prove that neither has the cone *EFGHN* to any solid less than the cone *ABCDL* the ratio triplicate of that which *FH* has to *BD*.

I say next that neither has the cone *ABCDL* to any solid greater than the cone *EFGHN* the ratio triplicate of that which *BD* has to *FH*.

For, if possible, let it have that ratio to a greater solid *O*.

Therefore, inversely, the solid *O* has to the cone *ABCDL* the ratio triplicate of that which *FH* has to *BD*.

But, as the solid *O* is to the cone *ABCDL*, so is the cone *EFGHN* to some solid less than the cone *ABCDL*.

Therefore the cone *EFGHN* also has to some solid less than the cone *ABCDL* the ratio triplicate of that which *FH* has to *BD*:
which was proved impossible.

Therefore the cone *ABCDL* has not to any solid greater than the cone *EFGHN* the ratio triplicate of that which *BD* has to *FH*.

But it was proved that neither has it this ratio to a less solid than the cone *EFGHN*.

Therefore the cone *ABCDL* has to the cone *EFGHN* the ratio triplicate of that which *BD* has to *FH*.

But, as the cone is to the cone, so is the cylinder to the cylinder,
for the cylinder which is on the same base as the cone and of equal height with it is triple of the cone;   [XII. 10]
therefore the cylinder also has to the cylinder the ratio triplicate of that which *BD* has to *FH*.

Therefore etc.   Q. E. D.

Proposition 13

If a cylinder be cut by a plane which is parallel to its opposite planes, then, as the cylinder is to the cylinder, so will the axis be to the axis.

For let the cylinder *AD* be cut by the plane *GH* which is parallel to the opposite planes *AB*, *CD*,
and let the plane *GH* meet the axis at the point *K*;
I say that, as the cylinder *BG* is to the cylinder *GD*, so is the axis *EK* to the axis *KF*.

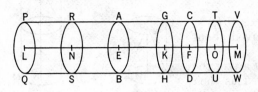

For let the axis *EF* be produced in both directions to the points *L, M*,
and let there be set out any number whatever of axes *EN*, *NL* equal to the axis *EK*, and any number whatever *FO*, *OM* equal to *FK*;
and let the cylinder *PW* on the axis *LM* be conceived of which the circles *PQ*, *VW* are the bases.

Let planes be carried through the points *N, O* parallel to *AB*, *CD* and to the bases of the cylinder *PW*,
and let them produce the circles *RS*, *TU* about the centres *N, O*.
Then, since the axes *LN*, *NE*, *EK* are equal to one another,

therefore the cylinders *QR*, *RB*, *BG* are to one another as their bases. [XII. 11]

But the bases are equal;

therefore the cylinders *QR*, *RB*, *BG* are also equal to one another.

Since then the axes *LN*, *NE*, *EK* are equal to one another,

and the cylinders *QR*, *RB*, *BG* are also equal to one another,

and the multitude of the former is equal to the multitude of the latter,

therefore, whatever multiple the axis *KL* is of the axis *EK*, the same multiple also will the cylinder *QG* be of the cylinder *GB*.

For the same reason, whatever multiple the axis *MK* is of the axis *KF*, the same multiple also is the cylinder *WG* of the cylinder *GD*.

And, if the axis *KL* is equal to the axis *KM*, the cylinder *QG* will also be equal to the cylinder *GW*,

if the axis is greater than the axis, the cylinder will also be greater than the cylinder,

and if less, less.

Thus, there being four magnitudes, the axes *EK*, *KF* and the cylinders *BG*, *GD*,

there have been taken equimultiples of the axis *EK* and of the cylinder *BG*, namely the axis *LK* and the cylinder *QG*,

and equimultiples of the axis *KF* and of the cylinder *GD*, namely the axis *KM* and the cylinder *GW*;

and it has been proved that,

if the axis *KL* is in excess of the axis *KM*, the cylinder *QG* is also in excess of the cylinder *GW*,

if equal, equal,

and if less, less.

Therefore, as the axis *EK* is to the axis *KF*, so is the cylinder *BG* to the cylinder *GD*. [V. Def. 5]

Q. E. D.

PROPOSITION 14

Cones and cylinders which are on equal bases are to one another as their heights.

For let *EB*, *FD* be cylinders on equal bases, the circles *AB*, *CD*;

I say that, as the cylinder *EB* is to the cylinder *FD*, so is the axis *GH* to the axis *KL*.

For let the axis *KL* be produced to the point *N*,

let *LN* be made equal to the axis *GH*, and let the cylinder *CM* be conceived about *LN* as axis.

Since then the cylinders *EB*, *CM* are of the same height, they are to one another as their bases [XII. 11]

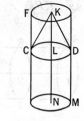

But the bases are equal to one another:

therefore the cylinders *EB*, *CM* are also equal.

And, since the cylinder *FM* has been cut by the plane *CD* which is parallel to its opposite planes,

therefore, as the cylinder *CM* is to the cylinder *FD*, so is the axis *LN* to the axis *KL*. [XII. 13]

But the cylinder *CM* is equal to the cylinder *EB*,
and the axis *LN* to the axis *GH*;
therefore, as the cylinder *EB* is to the cylinder *FD*, so is the axis *GH* to the axis *KL*.

But, as the cylinder *EB* is to the cylinder *FD*, so is the cone *ABG* to the cone *CDK*.   [XII. 10]

Therefore also, as the axis *GH* is to the axis *KL*, so is the cone *ABG* to the cone *CDK* and the cylinder *EB* to the cylinder *FD*.   Q. E. D.

PROPOSITION 15

In equal cones and cylinders the bases are reciprocally proportional to the heights; and those cones and cylinders in which the bases are reciprocally proportional to the heights are equal.

Let there be equal cones and cylinders of which the circles *ABCD*, *EFGH* are the bases;
let *AC*, *EG* be the diameters of the bases,
and *KL*, *MN* the axes, which are also the heights of the cones or cylinders;
let the cylinders *AO*, *EP* be completed.

I say that in the cylinders *AO*, *EP* the bases are reciprocally proportional to the heights,
that is, as the base *ABCD* is to the base *EFGH*, so is the height *MN* to the height *KL*.

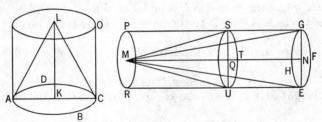

For the height *LK* is either equal to the height *MN* or not equal.
First, let it be equal.
Now the cylinder *AO* is also equal to the cylinder *EP*.

But cones and cylinders which are of the same height are to one another as their bases;   [XII. 11]
therefore the base *ABCD* is also equal to the base *EFGH*.

Hence also, reciprocally, as the base *ABCD* is to the base *EFGH*, so is the height *MN* to the height *KL*.

Next, let the height *LK* not be equal to *MN*,
but let *MN* be greater;
from the height *MN* let *QN* be cut off equal to *KL*,
through the point *Q* let the cylinder *EP* be cut by the plane *TUS* parallel to the planes of the circles *EFGH*, *RP*,
and let the cylinder *ES* be conceived erected from the circle *EFGH* as base and with height *NQ*.

Now, since the cylinder *AO* is equal to the cylinder *EP*,
therefore, as the cylinder *AO* is to the cylinder *ES*, so is the cylinder *EP* to the cylinder *ES*.   [V. 7]

But, as the cylinder AO is to the cylinder ES, so is the base $ABCD$ to the base $EFGH$,

for the cylinders AO, ES are of the same height;   [XII. 11]
and, as the cylinder EP is to the cylinder ES, so is the height MN to the height QN,

for the cylinder EP has been cut by a plane which is parallel to its opposite planes.   [XII. 13]

Therefore also, as the base $ABCD$ is to the base $EFGH$, so is the height MN to the height QN.   [v. 11]

But the height QN is equal to the height KL;

therefore, as the base $ABCD$ is to the base $EFGH$, so is the height MN to the height KL.

Therefore in the cylinders AO, EP the bases are reciprocally proportional to the heights.

Next, in the cylinders AO, EP let the bases be reciprocally proportional to the heights,

that is, as the base $ABCD$ is to the base $EFGH$, so let the height MN be to the height KL;

I say that the cylinder AO is equal to the cylinder EP.

For, with the same construction,

since, as the base $ABCD$ is to the base $EFGH$, so is the height MN to the height KL,

while the height KL is equal to the height QN,

therefore, as the base $ABCD$ is to the base $EFGH$, so is the height MN to the height QN.

But, as the base $ABCD$ is to the base $EFGH$, so is the cylinder AO to the cylinder ES,

for they are of the same height;   [XII. 11]
and, as the height MN is to QN, so is the cylinder EP to the cylinder ES;

[XII. 13]

therefore, as the cylinder AO is to the cylinder ES, so is the cylinder EP to the cylinder ES.   [v. 11]

Therefore the cylinder AO is equal to the cylinder EP.   [v. 9]

And the same is true for the cones also.   Q. E. D.

PROPOSITION 16

Given two circles about the same centre, to inscribe in the greater circle an equilateral polygon with an even number of sides which does not touch the lesser circle.

Let $ABCD$, $EFGH$ be the two given circles about the same centre K;

thus it is required to inscribe in the greater circle $ABCD$ an equilateral polygon with an even number of sides which does not touch the circle $EFGH$.

For let the straight line BKD be drawn through the centre K,

and from the point G let GA be drawn at right angles to the straight line BD and carried through to C;

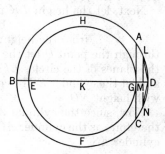

therefore AC touches the circle $EFGH$.   [III. 16, Por.]

Then, bisecting the circumference BAD, bisecting the half of it, and doing this continually, we shall leave a circumference less than AD.   [x. 1]

Let such be left, and let it be LD;

from L let LM be drawn perpendicular to BD and carried through to N,

and let LD, DN be joined;

therefore LD is equal to DN.   [III. 3, I. 4]

Now, since LN is parallel to AC,

and AC touches the circle $EFGH$,

therefore LN does not touch the circle $EFGH$;

therefore LD, DN are far from touching the circle $EFGH$.

If then we fit into the circle $ABCD$ straight lines equal to the straight line LD and placed continuously, there will be inscribed in the circle $ABCD$ an equilateral polygon with an even number of sides which does not touch the lesser circle $EFGH$.   Q. E. F.

PROPOSITION 17

Given two spheres about the same centre, to inscribe in the greater sphere a polyhedral solid which does not touch the lesser sphere at its surface.

Let two spheres be conceived about the same centre A;

thus it is required to inscribe in the greater sphere a polyhedral solid which does not touch the lesser sphere at its surface.

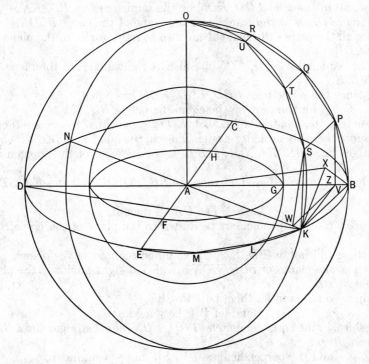

Let the spheres be cut by any plane through the centre;

then the sections will be circles,

inasmuch as the sphere was produced by the diameter remaining fixed and the semicircle being carried round it;   [XI. Def. 14] hence, in whatever position we conceive the semicircle to be, the plane carried through it will produce a circle on the circumference of the sphere.

And it is manifest that this circle is the greatest possible, inasmuch as the diameter of the sphere, which is of course the diameter both of the semicircle and of the circle, is greater than all the straight lines drawn across in the circle or the sphere.

Let then $BCDE$ be the circle in the greater sphere,
                   and FGH the circle in the lesser sphere;
let two diameters in them, BD, CE, be drawn at right angles to one another; then, given the two circles $BCDE$, FGH about the same centre, let there be inscribed in the greater circle $BCDE$ an equilateral polygon with an even number of sides which does not touch the lesser circle FGH,
        let BK, KL, LM, ME be its sides in the quadrant BE,
                let KA be joined and carried through to N,
let AO be set up from the point A at right angles to the plane of the circle $BCDE$, and let it meet the surface of the sphere at O, and through AO and each of the straight lines BD, KN let planes be carried; they will then make greatest circles on the surface of the sphere, for the reason stated.

Let them make such,
        and in them let BOD, KON be the semicircles on BD, KN.

Now, since OA is at right angles to the plane of the circle $BCDE$, therefore all the planes through OA are also at right angles to the plane of the circle $BCDE$;   [XI. 18] hence the semicircles BOD, KON are also at right angles to the plane of the circle $BCDE$.

And, since the semicircles BED, BOD, KON are equal,
                for they are on the equal diameters BD, KN,
        therefore the quadrants BE, BO, KO are also equal to one another.

Therefore there are as many straight lines in the quadrants BO, KO equal to the straight lines BK, KL, LM, ME as there are sides of the polygon in the quadrant BE.

Let them be inscribed, and let them be BP, PQ, QR, RO and KS, ST, TU, UO,
                let SP, TQ, UR be joined,
and from P, S let perpendiculars be drawn to the plane of the circle $BCDE$;
                                                                [XI. 11]
        these will fall on BD, KN, the common sections of the planes, inasmuch as the planes of BOD, KON are also at right angles to the plane of the circle $BCDE$.   [cf. XI. Def. 4]

Let them so fall, and let them be PV, SW,
                and let WV be joined.

Now since, in the equal semicircles BOD, KON, equal straight lines BP, KS have been cut off,
        and the perpendiculars PV, SW have been drawn,
                therefore PV is equal to SW, and BV to KW.   [III. 27, I. 26]
But the whole BA is also equal to the whole KA;

therefore the remainder VA is also equal to the remainder WA;

therefore, as BV is to VA, so is KW to WA;

therefore WV is parallel to KB.   [VI. 2]

And, since each of the straight lines PV, SW is at right angles to the plane of the circle $BCDE$,

therefore PV is parallel to SW.   [XI. 6]

But it was also proved equal to it;

therefore WV, SP are also equal and parallel.   [I. 33]

And, since WV is parallel to SP,

while WV is parallel to KB,

therefore SP is also parallel to KB.   [XI. 9]

And BP, KS join their extremities;

therefore the quadrilateral $KBPS$ is in one plane,

inasmuch as, if two straight lines be parallel, and points be taken at random on each of them, the straight line joining the points is in the same plane with the parallels.   [XI. 7]

For the same reason

each of the quadrilaterals $SPQT$, $TQRU$ is also in one plane.

But the triangle URO is also in one plane.   [XI. 2]

If then we conceive straight lines joined from the points P, S, Q, T, R, U to A, there will be constructed a certain polyhedral solid figure between the circumferences BO, KO, consisting of pyramids of which the quadrilaterals $KBPS$, $SPQT$, $TQRU$ and the triangle URO are the bases and the point A the vertex.

And, if we make the same construction in the case of each of the sides KL, LM, ME as in the case of BK, and further, in the case of the remaining three quadrants,

there will be constructed a certain polyhedral figure inscribed in the sphere and contained by pyramids, of which the said quadrilaterals and the triangle URO, and the others corresponding to them, are the bases and the point A the vertex.

I say that the said polyhedron will not touch the lesser sphere at the surface on which the circle FGH is.

Let AX be drawn from the point A perpendicular to the plane of the quadrilateral $KBPS$, and let it meet the plane at the point X;   [XI. 11]

let XB, XK be joined.

Then, since AX is at right angles to the plane of the quadrilateral $KBPS$, therefore it is also at right angles to all the straight lines which meet it and are in the plane of the quadrilateral.   [XI. Def. 3]

Therefore AX is at right angles to each of the straight lines BX, XK.

And, since AB is equal to AK,

the square on AB is also equal to the square on AK.

And the squares on AX, XB are equal to the square on AB,

for the angle at X is right;   [I. 47]

and the squares on AX, XK are equal to the square on AK.   [$id.$]

Therefore the squares on AX, XB are equal to the squares on AX, XK.

Let the square on AX be subtracted from each;

therefore the remainder, the square on BX, is equal to the remainder, the square on XK;

therefore BX is equal to XK.

Similarly we can prove that the straight lines joined from X to P, S are equal to each of the straight lines BX, XK.

Therefore the circle described with centre X and distance one of the straight lines XB, XK will pass through P, S also,

and $KBPS$ will be a quadrilateral in a circle.

Now, since KB is greater than WV,

while WV is equal to SP,

therefore KB is greater than SP.

But KB is equal to each of the straight lines KS, BP;

therefore each of the straight lines KS, BP is greater than SP.

And, since $KBPS$ is a quadrilateral in a circle,

and KB, BP, KS are equal, and PS less,

and BX is the radius of the circle,

therefore the square on KB is greater than double of the square on BX.

Let KZ be drawn from K perpendicular to BV.

Then, since BD is less than double of DZ,

and, as BD is to DZ, so is the rectangle DB, BZ to the rectangle DZ, ZB,

if a square be described upon BZ and the parallelogram on ZD be completed,

then the rectangle DB, BZ is also less than double of the rectangle DZ, ZB.

And, if KD be joined,

the rectangle DB, BZ is equal to the square on BK,

and the rectangle DZ, ZB equal to the square on KZ; [III. 31, VI. 8 and Por.]

therefore the square on KB is less than double of the square on KZ.

But the square on KB is greater than double of the square on BX;

therefore the square on KZ is greater than the square on BX.

And, since BA is equal to KA,

the square on BA is equal to the square on AK.

And the squares on BX, XA are equal to the square on BA,

and the squares on KZ, ZA equal to the square on KA; [I. 47]

therefore the squares on BX, XA are equal to the squares on KZ, ZA.

and of these the square on KZ is greater than the square on BX;

therefore the remainder, the square on ZA, is less than the square on XA.

Therefore AX is greater than AZ;

therefore AX is much greater than AG.

And AX is the perpendicular on one base of the polyhedron,

and AG on the surface of the lesser sphere;

hence the polyhedron will not touch the lesser sphere on its surface.

Therefore, given two spheres about the same centre, a polyhedral solid has been inscribed in the greater sphere which does not touch the lesser sphere at its surface. Q. E. F.

PORISM. But if in another sphere also a polyhedral solid be inscribed similar to the solid in the sphere $BCDE$,

the polyhedral solid in the sphere $BCDE$ has to the polyhedral solid in the other sphere the ratio triplicate of that which the diameter of the sphere $BCDE$ has to the diameter of the other sphere.

For, the solids being divided into their pyramids similar in multitude and arrangement, the pyramids will be similar.

But similar pyramids are to one another in the triplicate ratio of their corresponding sides; [XII. 8, Por.]

therefore the pyramid of which the quadrilateral $KBPS$ is the base, and the point A the vertex, has to the similarly arranged pyramid in the other sphere the ratio triplicate of that which the corresponding side has to the corresponding side, that is, of that which the radius AB of the sphere about A as centre has to the radius of the other sphere.

Similarly also each pyramid of those in the sphere about A as centre has to each similarly arranged pyramid of those in the other sphere the ratio triplicate of that which AB has to the radius of the other sphere.

And, as one of the antecedents is to one of the consequents, so are all the antecedents to all the consequents;   [v. 12]
hence the whole polyhedral solid in the sphere about A as centre has to the whole polyhedral solid in the other sphere the ratio triplicate of that which AB has to the radius of the other sphere, that is, of that which the diameter BD has to the diameter of the other sphere.   Q. E. D.

PROPOSITION 18

Spheres are to one another in the triplicate ratio of their respective diameters.

Let the spheres ABC, DEF be conceived,
                    and let BC, EF be their diameters;
I say that the sphere ABC has to the sphere DEF the ratio triplicate of that which BC has to EF.

For, if the sphere ABC has not to the sphere DEF the ratio triplicate of that which BC has to EF,
then the sphere ABC will have either to some less sphere than the sphere DEF, or to a greater, the ratio triplicate of that which BC has to EF.

First, let it have that ratio to a less sphere GHK,

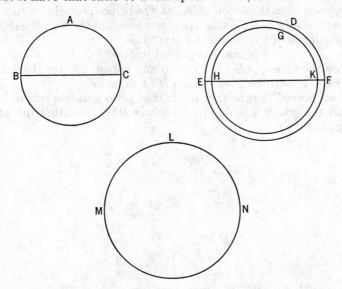

let DEF be conceived about the same centre with GHK,
let there be inscribed in the greater sphere DEF a polyhedral solid which does not touch the lesser sphere GHK at its surface,   [XII. 17]

and let there also be inscribed in the sphere ABC a polyhedral solid similar to the polyhedral solid in the sphere DEF;
therefore the polyhedral solid in ABC has to the polyhedral solid in DEF the ratio triplicate of that which BC has to EF.   [XII. 17, Por.]

But the sphere ABC also has to the sphere GHK the ratio triplicate of that which BC has to EF;
therefore, as the sphere ABC is to the sphere GHK, so is the polyhedral solid in the sphere ABC to the polyhedral solid in the sphere DEF;
and, alternately, as the sphere ABC is to the polyhedron in it, so is the sphere GHK to the polyhedral solid in the sphere DEF.   [v. 16]

But the sphere ABC is greater than the polyhedron in it;
therefore the sphere GHK is also greater than the polyhedron in the sphere DEF.

But it is also less,
                        for it is enclosed by it.

Therefore the sphere ABC has not to a less sphere than the sphere DEF the ratio triplicate of that which the diameter BC has to EF.

Similarly we can prove that neither has the sphere DEF to a less sphere than the sphere ABC the ratio triplicate of that which EF has to BC.

I say next that neither has the sphere ABC to any greater sphere than the sphere DEF the ratio triplicate of that which BC has to EF.

For, if possible, let it have that ratio to a greater, LMN;
therefore, inversely, the sphere LMN has to the sphere ABC the ratio triplicate of that which the diameter EF has to the diameter BC.

But, inasmuch as LMN is greater than DEF,
therefore, as the sphere LMN is to the sphere ABC, so is the sphere DEF to some less sphere than the sphere ABC, as was before proved.   [XII. 2, Lemma]

Therefore the sphere DEF also has to some less sphere than the sphere ABC the ratio triplicate of that which EF has to BC:
                        which was proved impossible.

Therefore the sphere ABC has not to any sphere greater than the sphere DEF the ratio triplicate of that which BC has to EF.

But it was proved that neither has it that ratio to a less sphere.

Therefore the sphere ABC has to the sphere DEF the ratio triplicate of that which BC has to EF.   Q. E. D.

BOOK THIRTEEN

PROPOSITIONS

PROPOSITION 1

If a straight line be cut in extreme and mean ratio, the square on the greater segment added to the half of the whole is five times the square on the half.

For let the straight line AB be cut in extreme and mean ratio at the point C, and let AC be the greater segment;

let the straight line AD be produced in a straight line with CA,

and let AD be made half of AB;

I say that the square on CD is five times the square on AD.

For let the squares AE, DF be described on AB, DC,

and let the figure in DF be drawn;

let FC be carried through to G.

Now, since AB has been cut in extreme and mean ratio at C,

therefore the rectangle AB, BC is equal to the square on AC. [VI. Def. 3, VI. 17]

And CE is the rectangle AB, BC, and FH the square on AC;

therefore CE is equal to FH.

And, since BA is double of AD,

while BA is equal to KA, and AD to AH,

therefore KA is also double of AH.

But, as KA is to AH, so is CK to CH; [VI. 1]

therefore CK is double of CH.

But LH, HC are also double of CH.

Therefore KC is equal to LH, HC.

But CE was also proved equal to HF;

therefore the whole square AE is equal to the gnomon MNO.

And, since BA is double of AD,

the square on BA is quadruple of the square on AD,

that is, AE is quadruple of DH.

But AE is equal to the gnomon MNO;

therefore the gnomon MNO is also quadruple of AP;

therefore the whole DF is five times AP.

And DF is the square on DC, and AP the square on DA;

therefore the square on CD is five times the square on DA.

Therefore etc. Q. E. D.

PROPOSITION 2

If the square on a straight line be five times the square on a segment of it, then, when the double of the said segment is cut in extreme and mean ratio, the greater segment is the remaining part of the original straight line.

For let the square on the straight line AB be five times the square on the segment AC of it,

and let CD be double of AC;

I say that, when CD is cut in extreme and mean ratio, the greater segment is CB.

Let the squares AF, CG be described on AB, CD respectively,

let the figure in AF be drawn,
and let BE be drawn through.

Now, since the square on BA is five times the square on AC,

AF is five times AH.

Therefore the gnomon MNO is quadruple of AH.

And, since DC is double of CA,
therefore the square on DC is quadruple of the square on CA, that is, CG is quadruple of AH.

But the gnomon MNO was also proved quadruple of AH;

therefore the gnomon MNO is equal to CG.

And, since DC is double of CA,

while DC is equal to CK, and AC to CH,
therefore KB is also double of BH. [VI. 1]

But LH, HB are also double of HB;

therefore KB is equal to LH, HB.

But the whole gnomon MNO was also proved equal to the whole CG;

therefore the remainder HF is equal to BG.

And BG is the rectangle CD, DB,

for CD is equal to DG;
and HF is the square on CB;

therefore the rectangle CD, DB is equal to the square on CB.

Therefore, as DC is to CB, so is CB to BD.

But DC is greater than CB;

therefore CB is also greater than BD.

Therefore, when the straight line CD is cut in extreme and mean ratio, CB is the greater segment.

Therefore etc.

Q. E. D.

LEMMA

That the double of AC is greater than BC is to be proved thus.

If not, let BC be, if possible, double of CA.

Therefore the square on BC is quadruple of the square on CA;

therefore the squares on BC, CA are five times the square on CA.

But, by hypothesis, the square on BA is also five times the square on CA;

therefore the square on BA is equal to the squares on BC, CA:

which is impossible.   [II. 4]

Therefore CB is not double of AC.

Similarly we can prove that neither is a straight line less than CB double of CA;

for the absurdity is much greater.

Therefore the double of AC is greater than CB.   Q. E. D.

PROPOSITION 3

If a straight line be cut in extreme and mean ratio, the square on the lesser segment added to the half of the greater segment is five times the square on the half of the greater segment.

For let any straight line AB be cut in extreme and mean ratio at the point C,

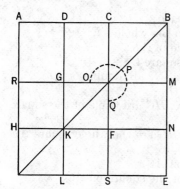

let AC be the greater segment,

and let AC be bisected at D;

I say that the square on BD is five times the square on DC.

For let the square AE be described on AB,

and let the figure be drawn double.

Since AC is double of DC,

therefore the square on AC is quadruple of the square on DC,

that is, RS is quadruple of FG.

And, since the rectangle AB, BC is equal to the square on AC,

and CE is the rectangle AB, BC,

therefore CE is equal to RS.

But RS is quadruple of FG;

therefore CE is also quadruple of FG.

Again, since AD is equal to DC,

HK is also equal to KF.

Hence the square GF is also equal to the square HL.

Therefore GK is equal to KL, that is MN to NE;

hence MF is also equal to FE.

But MF is equal to CG;

therefore CG is also equal to FE.

Let CN be added to each;

therefore the gnomon OPQ is equal to CE.

But CE was proved quadruple of GF;

therefore the gnomon OPQ is also quadruple of the square FG.

Therefore the gnomon OPQ and the square FG are five times FG.

But the gnomon OPQ and the square FG are the square DN.

And DN is the square on DB, and GF the square on DC.

Therefore the square on DB is five times the square on DC.   Q. E. D.

PROPOSITION 4

If a straight line be cut in extreme and mean ratio, the square on the whole and the square on the lesser segment together are triple of the square on the greater segment.

Let AB be a straight line,

let it be cut in extreme and mean ratio at C, and let AC be the greater segment;

I say that the squares on AB, BC are triple of the square on CA.

For let the square $ADEB$ be described on AB,
and let the figure be drawn.

Since, then, AB has been cut in extreme and mean ratio at C,
and AC is the greater segment,
therefore the rectangle AB, BC is equal to the square on AC.   [VI. Def. 3, VI. 17]

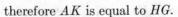

And AK is the rectangle AB, BC, and HG the square on AC;

therefore AK is equal to HG.

And, since AF is equal to FE,
let CK be added to each;
therefore the whole AK is equal to the whole CE;
therefore AK, CE are double of AK.

But AK, CE are the gnomon LMN and the square CK;
therefore the gnomon LMN and the square CK are double of AK.

But, further, AK was also proved equal to HG;
therefore the gnomon LMN and the squares CK, HG are triple of the square HG.

And the gnomon LMN and the squares CK, HG are the whole square AE and CK, which are the squares on AB, BC,
while HG is the square on AC.

Therefore the squares on AB, BC are triple of the square on AC.

                                                                 Q. E. D.

PROPOSITION 5

If a straight line be cut in extreme and mean ratio, and there be added to it a straight line equal to the greater segment, the whole straight line has been cut in extreme and mean ratio, and the original straight line is the greater segment.

For let the straight line AB be cut in extreme and mean ratio at the point C, let AC be the greater segment, and let AD be equal to AC.

I say that the straight line DB has been cut in extreme and mean ratio at A, and the original straight line AB is the greater segment.

For let the square AE be described on AB, and let the figure be drawn.

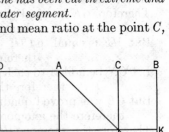

Since AB has been cut in extreme and mean ratio at C,
therefore the rectangle AB, BC is equal to the square on AC.   [VI. Def. 3, VI. 17]

And CE is the rectangle AB, BC, and CH the square on AC;
therefore CE is equal to HC.

But HE is equal to CE,

and *DH* is equal to *HC*;
therefore *DH* is also equal to *HE*.
Therefore the whole *DK* is equal to the whole *AE*.
And *DK* is the rectangle *BD*, *DA*,
for *AD* is equal to *DL*;
and *AE* is the square on *AB*;
therefore the rectangle *BD*, *DA* is equal to the square on *AB*.
Therefore, as *DB* is to *BA*, so is *BA* to *AD*.   [VI. 17]
And *DB* is greater than *BA*;
therefore *BA* is also greater than *AD*.   [V. 14]
Therefore *DB* has been cut in extreme and mean ratio at *A*, and *AB* is the
greater segment.   Q. E. D.

PROPOSITION 6

If a rational straight line be cut in extreme and mean ratio, each of the segments is
the irrational straight line called apotome.

Let *AB* be a rational straight line,
let it be cut in extreme and mean ratio at *C*,
and let *AC* be the greater segment;
I say that each of the straight lines *AC*, *CB*
is the irrational straight line called apotome.
For let *BA* be produced, and let *AD* be made half of *BA*.
Since, then, the straight line *AB* has been cut in extreme and mean ratio,
and to the greater segment *AC* is added *AD* which is half of *AB*,
therefore the square on *CD* is five times the square on *DA*. [XIII. 1]
Therefore the square on *CD* has to the square on *DA* the ratio which a number has to a number;
therefore the square on *CD* is commensurable with the square on *DA*. [X. 6]
But the square on *DA* is rational,
for *DA* is rational, being half of *AB* which is rational;
therefore the square on *CD* is also rational;   [X. Def. 4]
therefore *CD* is also rational.
And, since the square on *CD* has not to the square on *DA* the ratio which a
square number has to a square number,
therefore *CD* is incommensurable in length with *DA*;   [X. 9]
therefore *CD*, *DA* are rational straight lines commensurable in square only;
therefore *AC* is an apotome.   [X. 73]
Again, since *AB* has been cut in extreme and mean ratio,
and *AC* is the greater segment,
therefore the rectangle *AB*, *BC* is equal to the square on *AC*. [VI. Def. 3, VI. 17]
Therefore the square on the apotome *AC*, if applied to the rational straight
line *AB*, produces *BC* as breadth.
But the square on an apotome, if applied to a rational straight line, produces
as breadth a first apotome;   [X. 97]
therefore *CB* is a first apotome.
And *CA* was also proved to be an apotome.
Therefore etc.   Q. E. D.

Proposition 7

If three angles of an equilateral pentagon, taken either in order or not in order, be equal, the pentagon will be equiangular.

For in the equilateral pentagon *ABCDE* let, first, three angles taken in order, those at *A*, *B*, *C*, be equal to one another;

I say that the pentagon *ABCDE* is equiangular.

For let *AC*, *BE*, *FD* be joined.

Now, since the two sides *CB*, *BA* are equal to the two sides *BA*, *AE* respectively,

and the angle *CBA* is equal to the angle *BAE*,

therefore the base *AC* is equal to the base *BE*,

the triangle *ABC* is equal to the triangle *ABE*,

and the remaining angles will be equal to the remaining angles, namely those which the equal sides subtend, [I. 4]

that is, the angle *BCA* to the angle *BEA*, and the angle *ABE* to the angle *CAB*;

hence the side *AF* is also equal to the side *BF*.   [I. 6]

But the whole *AC* was also proved equal to the whole *BE*;

therefore the remainder *FC* is also equal to the remainder *FE*.

But *CD* is also equal to *DE*.

Therefore the two sides *FC*, *CD* are equal to the two sides *FE*, *ED*;

and the base *FD* is common to them;

therefore the angle *FCD* is equal to the angle *FED*.   [I. 8]

But the angle *BCA* was also proved equal to the angle *AEB*;

therefore the whole angle *BCD* is also equal to the whole angle *AED*.

But, by hypothesis, the angle *BCD* is equal to the angles at *A*, *B*;

therefore the angle *AED* is also equal to the angles at *A*, *B*.

Similarly we can prove that the angle *CDE* is also equal to the angles at *A*, *B*, *C*;

therefore the pentagon *ABCDE* is equiangular.

Next, let the given equal angles not be angles taken in order, but let the angles at the points *A*, *C*, *D* be equal;

I say that in this case too the pentagon *ABCDE* is equiangular.

For let *BD* be joined.

Then, since the two sides *BA*, *AE* are equal to the two sides *BC*, *CD*,

and they contain equal angles,

therefore the base *BE* is equal to the base *BD*,

the triangle *ABE* is equal to the triangle *BCD*,

and the remaining angles will be equal to the remaining angles,

namely those which the equal sides subtend;   [I. 4]

therefore the angle *AEB* is equal to the angle *CDB*.

But the angle *BED* is also equal to the angle *BDE*,

since the side *BE* is also equal to the side *BD*.   [I. 5]

Therefore the whole angle *AED* is equal to the whole angle *CDE*.

But the angle *CDE* is, by hypothesis, equal to the angles at *A*, *C*;

therefore the angle *AED* is also equal to the angles at *A*, *C*.

For the same reason

the angle *ABC* is also equal to the angles at *A*, *C*, *D*.

Therefore the pentagon *ABCDE* is equiangular.   Q. E. D.

PROPOSITION 8

If in an equilateral and equiangular pentagon straight lines subtend two angles taken in order, they cut one another in extreme and mean ratio, and their greater segments are equal to the side of the pentagon.

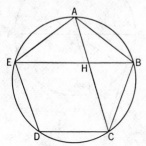

For in the equilateral and equiangular pentagon $ABCDE$ let the straight lines AC, BE, cutting one another at the point H, subtend two angles taken in order, the angles at A, B;

I say that each of them has been cut in extreme and mean ratio at the point H, and their greater segments are equal to the side of the pentagon.

For let the circle $ABCDE$ be circumscribed about the pentagon $ABCDE$.   [IV. 14]

Then, since the two straight lines EA, AB are equal to the two AB, BC,

and they contain equal angles,

therefore the base BE is equal to the base AC,

the triangle ABE is equal to the triangle ABC,

and the remaining angles will be equal to the remaining angles respectively, namely those which the equal sides subtend.   [I. 4]

Therefore the angle BAC is equal to the angle ABE;

therefore the angle AHE is double of the angle BAH.   [I. 32]

But the angle EAC is also double of the angle BAC,

inasmuch as the circumference EDC is also double of the circumference CB;   [III. 28, VI. 33]

therefore the angle HAE is equal to the angle AHE;

hence the straight line HE is also equal to EA, that is, to AB.   [I. 6]

And, since the straight line BA is equal to AE,

the angle ABE is also equal to the angle AEB.   [I. 5]

But the angle ABE was proved equal to the angle BAH;

therefore the angle BEA is also equal to the angle BAH.

And the angle ABE is common to the two triangles ABE and ABH;

therefore the remaining angle BAE is equal to the remaining angle AHB; [I. 32]

therefore the triangle ABE is equiangular with the triangle ABH;

therefore, proportionally, as EB is to BA, so is AB to BH.   [VI. 4]

But BA is equal to EH;

therefore, as BE is to EH, so is EH to HB.

And BE is greater than EH;

therefore EH is also greater than HB.   [V. 14]

Therefore BE has been cut in extreme and mean ratio at H, and the greater segment HE is equal to the side of the pentagon.

Similarly we can prove that AC has also been cut in extreme and mean ratio at H, and its greater segment CH is equal to the side of the pentagon.   Q. E. D.

PROPOSITION 9

If the side of the hexagon and that of the decagon inscribed in the same circle be added together, the whole straight line has been cut in extreme and mean ratio, and its greater segment is the side of the hexagon.

Let ABC be a circle;
of the figures inscribed in the circle ABC let BC be the side of a decagon, CD that of a hexagon,
and let them be in a straight line;
I say that the whole straight line BD has been cut in extreme and mean ratio, and CD is its greater segment.

For let the centre of the circle, the point E, be taken,
let EB, EC, ED be joined,
and let BE be carried through to A.

Since BC is the side of an equilateral decagon, therefore the circumference ACB is five times the circumference BC;
therefore the circumference AC is quadruple of CB.

But, as the circumference AC is to CB, so is the angle AEC to the angle CEB;　　　[VI. 33]
therefore the angle AEC is quadruple of the angle CEB.

And, since the angle EBC is equal to the angle ECB,　　　　　　[I. 5]
therefore the angle AEC is double of the angle ECB.　　[I. 32]

And, since the straight line EC is equal to CD,
for each of them is equal to the side of the hexagon inscribed in the circle ABC,
[IV. 15, Por.]
the angle CED is also equal to the angle CDE;　　　[I. 5]
therefore the angle ECB is double of the angle EDC.　　[I. 32]

But the angle AEC was proved double of the angle ECB;
therefore the angle AEC is quadruple of the angle EDC.

But the angle AEC was also proved quadruple of the angle BEC;
therefore the angle EDC is equal to the angle BEC.

But the angle EBD is common to the two triangles BEC and BED;
therefore the remaining angle BED is also equal to the remaining angle ECB;
[I. 32]

therefore the triangle EBD is equiangular with the triangle EBC.
Therefore, proportionally, as DB is to BE, so is EB to BC.　　[VI. 4]
But EB is equal to CD.
Therefore, as BD is to DC, so is DC to CB.
And BD is greater than DC;
therefore DC is also greater than CB.

Therefore the straight line BD has been cut in extreme and mean ratio, and DC is its greater segment.　　　　　　　　　Q. E. D.

PROPOSITION 10

If an equilateral pentagon be inscribed in a circle, the square on the side of the pentagon is equal to the squares on the side of the hexagon and on that of the decagon inscribed in the same circle.

Let $ABCDE$ be a circle,
and let the equilateral pentagon $ABCDE$ be inscribed in the circle $ABCDE$.
I say that the square on the side of the pentagon $ABCDE$ is equal to the

squares on the side of the hexagon and on that of the decagon inscribed in the circle $ABCDE$.

For let the centre of the circle, the point F, be taken,
let AF be joined and carried through to the point G,
let FB be joined,
let FH be drawn from F perpendicular to AB and be carried through to K,
let AK, KB be joined,
let FL be again drawn from F perpendicular to AK, and be carried through to M,

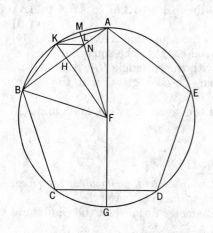

and let KN be joined.
Since the circumference $ABCG$ is equal to the circumference $AEDG$,
and in them ABC is equal to AED,
therefore the remainder, the circumference CG, is equal to the remainder GD.
But CD belongs to a pentagon;
therefore CG belongs to a decagon.
And, since FA is equal to FB,
and FH is perpendicular,
therefore the angle AFK is also equal to the angle KFB.   [I. 5, I. 26]
Hence the circumference AK is also equal to KB;   [III. 26]
therefore the circumference AB is double of the circumference BK;

therefore the straight line AK is a side of a decagon.
For the same reason

AK is also double of KM.

Now, since the circumference AB is double of the circumference BK,
while the circumference CD is equal to the circumference AB,
therefore the circumference CD is also double of the circumference BK.
But the circumference CD is also double of CG;
therefore the circumference CG is equal to the circumference BK.
But BK is double of KM, since KA is so also;
therefore CG is also double of KM.
But, further, the circumference CB is also double of the circumference BK,
for the circumference CB is equal to BA.
Therefore the whole circumference GB is also double of BM;
hence the angle GFB is also double of the angle BFM.   [VI. 33]
But the angle GFB is also double of the angle FAB,
for the angle FAB is equal to the angle ABF.
Therefore the angle BFN is also equal to the angle FAB.
But the angle ABF is common to the two triangles ABF and BFN;
therefore the remaining angle AFB is equal to the remaining angle BNF; [I. 32]
therefore the triangle ABF is equiangular with the triangle BFN.
Therefore, proportionally, as the straight line AB is to BF, so is FB to BN;
                                    [VI. 4]
therefore the rectangle AB, BN is equal to the square on BF. [VI. 17]
Again, since AL is equal to LK,

while LN is common and at right angles,
therefore the base KN is equal to the base AN;   [I. 4]
therefore the angle LKN is also equal to the angle LAN.
But the angle LAN is equal to the angle KBN;
therefore the angle LKN is also equal to the angle KBN.
And the angle at A is common to the two triangles AKB and AKN.
Therefore the remaining angle AKB is equal to the remaining angle KNA;
[I. 32]
therefore the triangle KBA is equiangular with the triangle KNA.
Therefore, proportionally, as the straight line BA is to AK, so is KA to AN;
[VI. 4]
therefore the rectangle BA, AN is equal to the square on AK.   [VI. 17]

But the rectangle AB, BN was also proved equal to the square on BF;
therefore the rectangle AB, BN together with the rectangle BA, AN, that is,
the square on BA [II. 2], is equal to the square on BF together with the square
on AK.

And BA is a side of the pentagon, BF of the hexagon [IV. 15, Por.], and AK
of the decagon.

Therefore etc.   Q. E. D.

PROPOSITION 11

*If in a circle which has its diameter rational an equilateral pentagon be inscribed,
the side of the pentagon is the irrational straight line called minor.*

For in the circle $ABCDE$ which has its diameter rational let the equilateral
pentagon $ABCDE$ be inscribed;
I say that the side of the pentagon is the irrational straight line called minor.

For let the centre of the circle, the point F, be taken,
let AF, FB be joined and carried
through to the points, G, H,
let AC be joined,
and let FK be made a fourth
part of AF.
Now AF is rational;
therefore FK is also rational.
But BF is also rational;
therefore the whole BK is rational.
And, since the circumference
ACG is equal to the circumference ADG,
and in them ABC is equal to
AED,
therefore the remainder CG is
equal to the remainder GD.

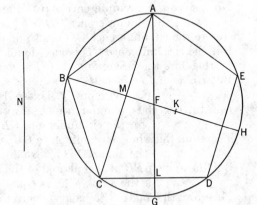

And, if we join AD, we conclude that the angles at L are right,
and CD is double of CL.
For the same reason
the angles at M are also right,
and AC is double of CM.
Since then the angle ALC is equal to the angle AMF,

and the angle LAC is common to the two triangles ACL and AMF,
therefore the remaining angle ACL is equal to the remaining angle MFA;
[I. 32]
therefore the triangle ACL is equiangular with the triangle AMF;
therefore, proportionally, as LC is to CA, so is MF to FA.
And the doubles of the antecedents may be taken;
therefore, as the double of LC is to CA, so is the double of MF to FA.
But, as the double of MF is to FA, so is MF to the half of FA;
therefore also, as the double of LC is to CA, so is MF to the half of FA.
And the halves of the consequents may be taken;
therefore, as the double of LC is to the half of CA, so is MF to the fourth of FA.
And DC is double of LC, CM is half of CA, and FK a fourth part of FA;
therefore, as DC is to CM, so is MF to FK.
Componendo also, as the sum of DC, CM is to CM, so is MK to KF;   [v. 18]
therefore also, as the square on the sum of DC, CM is to the square on CM, so
is the square on MK to the square on KF.
And since, when the straight line subtending two sides of the pentagon, as
AC, is cut in extreme and mean ratio, the greater segment is equal to the side
of the pentagon, that is, to DC,   [XIII. 8]
while the square on the greater segment added to the half of the whole is five
times the square on the half of the whole,   [XIII. 1]
and CM is half of the whole AC,
therefore the square on DC, CM taken as one straight line is five times the
square on CM.
But it was proved that, as the square on DC, CM taken as one straight line is
to the square on CM, so is the square on MK to the square on KF;
therefore the square on MK is five times the square on KF.
But the square on KF is rational,
for the diameter is rational;
therefore the square on MK is also rational;
therefore MK is rational.
And, since BF is quadruple of FK,
therefore BK is five times KF;
therefore the square on BK is twenty-five times the square on KF.
But the square on MK is five times the square on KF;
therefore the square on BK is five times the square on KM;
therefore the square on BK has not to the square on KM the ratio which a
square number has to a square number;
therefore BK is incommensurable in length with KM.   [x. 9]
And each of them is rational.
Therefore BK, KM are rational straight lines commensurable in square only.
But, if from a rational straight line there be subtracted a rational straight
line which is commensurable with the whole in square only, the remainder is
irrational, namely an apotome;
therefore MB is an apotome and MK the annex to it.   [x. 73]
I say next that MB is also a fourth apotome.
Let the square on N be equal to that by which the square on BK is greater
than the square on KM;
therefore the square on BK is greater than the square on KM by the square on N.

And, since KF is commensurable with FB,

        componendo also, KB is commensurable with FB.   [x. 15]

But BF is commensurable with BH;

        therefore BK is also commensurable with BH.   [x. 12]

And, since the square on BK is five times the square on KM,
therefore the square on BK has to the square on KM the ratio which 5 has to 1.

Therefore, *convertendo*, the square on BK has to the square on N the ratio which 5 has to 4 [v. 19, Por.], and this is not the ratio which a square number has to a square number;

        therefore BK is incommensurable with N;   [x. 9]
therefore the square on BK is greater than the square on KM by the square on a straight line incommensurable with BK.

Since then the square on the whole BK is greater than the square on the annex KM by the square on a straight line incommensurable with BK,
and the whole BK is commensurable with the rational straight line, BH, set out,

        therefore MB is a fourth apotome.   [x. Deff. III. 4]

But the rectangle contained by a rational straight line and a fourth apotome is irrational,

        and its square root is irrational, and is called minor.   [x. 94]

But the square on AB is equal to the rectangle HB, BM,
because, when AH is joined, the triangle ABH is equiangular with the triangle ABM, and, as HB is to BA, so is AB to BM.

Therefore the side AB of the pentagon is the irrational straight line called minor.   Q. E. D.

Proposition 12

If an equilateral triangle be inscribed in a circle, the square on the side of the triangle is triple of the square on the radius of the circle.

Let ABC be a circle,
and let the equilateral triangle ABC be inscribed in it;
I say that the square on one side of the triangle ABC is triple of the square on the radius of the circle.

For let the centre D of the circle ABC be taken,
    let AD be joined and carried through to E,
        and let BE be joined.

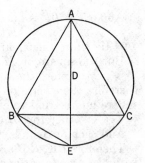

Then, since the triangle ABC is equilateral,
therefore the circumference BEC is a third part of the circumference of the circle ABC.

Therefore the circumference BE is a sixth part of the circumference of the circle;
therefore the straight line BE belongs to a hexagon;
        therefore it is equal to the radius DE.   [iv. 15, Por.]

And, since AE is double of DE,
the square on AE is quadruple of the square on ED, that is, of the square on BE.

But the square on AE is equal to the squares on AB, BE;   [III. 31, I. 47]
therefore the squares on AB, BE are quadruple of the square on BE.

Therefore, *separando*, the square on AB is triple of the square on BE.

But BE is equal to DE;
therefore the square on AB is triple of the square on DE.
Therefore the square on the side of the triangle is triple of the square on the radius.

Q. E. D.

PROPOSITION 13

To construct a pyramid, to comprehend it in a given sphere, and to prove that the square on the diameter of the sphere is one and a half times the square on the side of the pyramid.

Let the diameter AB of the given sphere be set out,
and let it be cut at the point C so that AC is double of CB;
let the semicircle ADB be described on AB,
let CD be drawn from the point C at right angles to AB,
and let DA be joined;
let the circle EFG which has its radius equal to DC be set out,
let the equilateral triangle EFG be inscribed in the circle EFG,   [IV. 2]
let the centre of the circle, the point H, be taken,   [III. 1]
let EH, HF, HG be joined;
from the point H let HK be set up at right angles to the plane of the circle EFG,   [XI. 12]
let HK equal to the straight line AC be cut off from HK,
and let KE, KF, KG be joined.

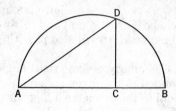
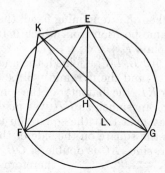

Now, since KH is at right angles to the plane of the circle EFG,
therefore it will also make right angles with all the straight lines which meet it and are in the plane of the circle EFG.   [XI. Def. 3]
But each of the straight lines HE, HF, HG meets it:
therefore HK is at right angles to each of the straight lines HE, HF, HG.
And, since AC is equal to HK, and CD to HE,
and they contain right angles,
therefore the base DA is equal to the base KE.   [I. 4]
For the same reason
each of the straight lines KF, KG is also equal to DA;
therefore the three straight lines KE, KF, KG are equal to one another.
And, since AC is double of CB,
therefore AB is triple of BC.

But, as AB is to BC, so is the square on AD to the square on DC, as will be proved afterwards.

Therefore the square on AD is triple of the square on DC.

But the square on FE is also triple of the square on EH,   [XIII. 12]
                    and DC is equal to EH;
                    therefore DA is also equal to EF.

But DA was proved equal to each of the straight lines KE, KF, KG; therefore each of the straight lines EF, FG, GE is also equal to each of the straight lines KE, KF, KG;
        therefore the four triangles EFG, KEF, KFG, KEG are equilateral.

Therefore a pyramid has been constructed out of four equilateral triangles, the triangle EFG being its base and the point K its vertex.

It is next required to comprehend it in the given sphere and to prove that the square on the diameter of the sphere is one and a half times the square on the side of the pyramid.

For let the straight line HL be produced in a straight line with KH,
                    and let HL be made equal to CB.

Now, since, as AC is to CD, so is CD to CB,   [VI. 8, Por.]
        while AC is equal to KH, CD to HE, and CB to HL,
            therefore, as KH is to HE, so is EH to HL;
therefore the rectangle KH, HL is equal to the square on EH.   [VI. 17]

And each of the angles KHE, EHL is right;
therefore the semicircle described on KL will pass through E also.
                                                    [cf. VI. 8, III. 31]

If then, KL remaining fixed, the semicircle be carried round and restored to the same position from which it began to be moved, it will also pass through the points F, G,
since, if FL, LG be joined, the angles at F, G similarly become right angles;
            and the pyramid will be comprehended in the given sphere.

For KL, the diameter of the sphere, is equal to the diameter AB of the given sphere, inasmuch as KH was made equal to AC, and HL to CB.

I say next that the square on the diameter of the sphere is one and a half times the square on the side of the pyramid.

For, since AC is double of CB,
                    therefore AB is triple of BC;
                and, *convertendo*, BA is one and a half times AC.

But, as BA is to AC, so is the square on BA to the square on AD.

Therefore the square on BA is also one and a half times the square on AD.

And BA is the diameter of the given sphere, and AD is equal to the side of the pyramid.

Therefore the square on the diameter of the sphere is one and a half times the square on the side of the pyramid.   Q. E. D.

LEMMA

It is to be proved that, as AB is to BC, so is the square on AD to the square on DC.

For let the figure of the semicircle be set out,
                    let DB be joined,
            let the square EC be described on AC,

and let the parallelogram FB be completed.

Since then, because the triangle DAB is equiangular with the triangle DAC,

as BA is to AD, so is DA to AC, [VI. 8, VI. 4]

therefore the rectangle BA, AC is equal to the square on AD. [VI. 17]

And since, as AB is to BC, so is EB to BF, [VI. 1]

and EB is the rectangle BA, AC, for EA is equal to AC,

and BF is the rectangle AC, CB,

therefore, as AB is to BC, so is the rectangle BA, AC to the rectangle AC, CB.

And the rectangle BA, AC is equal to the square on AD, and the rectangle AC, CB to the square on DC,

for the perpendicular DC is a mean proportional between the segments AC, CB of the base, because the angle ADB is right. [VI. 8, Por.]

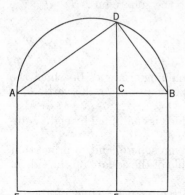

Therefore, as AB is to BC, so is the square on AD to the square on DC.

Q. E. D.

PROPOSITION 14

To construct an octahedron and comprehend it in a sphere, as in the preceding case; and to prove that the square on the diameter of the sphere is double of the square on the side of the octahedron.

Let the diameter AB of the given sphere be set out,

and let it be bisected at C;

let the semicircle ADB be described on AB,

let CD be drawn from C at right angles to AB,

let DB be joined;

let the square $EFGH$, having each of its sides equal to DB, be set out,

let HF, EG be joined,

from the point K let the straight line KL be set up at right angles to the plane of the square $EFGH$ [XI. 12], and let it be carried through to the other side of the plane, as KM;

from the straight lines KL, KM let KL, KM be respectively cut off equal to one of the straight lines EK, FK, GK, HK,

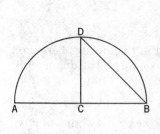

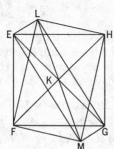

and let LE, LF, LG, LH, ME, MF, MG, MH be joined.

Then, since KE is equal to KH,

and the angle EKH is right, therefore the square on HE is double of the square on EK. [I. 47]

Again, since LK is equal to KE,

and the angle LKE is right,

therefore the square on *EL* is double of the square on *EK*.   [*id.*]

But the square on *HE* was also proved double of the square on *EK*;

therefore the square on *LE* is equal to the square on *EH*;

therefore *LE* is equal to *EH*.

For the same reason

LH is also equal to *HE*;

therefore the triangle *LEH* is equilateral.

Similarly we can prove that each of the remaining triangles of which the sides of the square *EFGH* are the bases, and the points *L*, *M* the vertices, is equilateral;

therefore an octahedron has been constructed which is contained by eight equilateral triangles.

It is next required to comprehend it in the given sphere, and to prove that the square on the diameter of the sphere is double of the square on the side of the octahedron.

For, since the three straight lines *LK*, *KM*, *KE* are equal to one another,

therefore the semicircle described on *LM* will also pass through *E*.

And for the same reason,

if, *LM* remaining fixed, the semicircle be carried round and restored to the same position from which it began to be moved,

it will also pass through the points *F*, *G*, *H*,

and the octahedron will have been comprehended in a sphere.

I say next that it is also comprehended in the given sphere.

For, since *LK* is equal to *KM*,

while *KE* is common,

and they contain right angles,

therefore the base *LE* is equal to the base *EM*.   [I. 4]

And, since the angle *LEM* is right, for it is in a semicircle,   [III. 31]

therefore the square on *LM* is double of the square on *LE*.   [I. 47]

Again, since *AC* is equal to *CB*,

AB is double of *BC*.

But, as *AB* is to *BC*, so is the square on *AB* to the square on *BD*;

therefore the square on *AB* is double of the square on *BD*.

But the square on *LM* was also proved double of the square on *LE*.

And the square on *DB* is equal to the square on *LE*, for *EH* was made equal to *DB*.

Therefore the square on *AB* is also equal to the square on *LM*;

therefore *AB* is equal to *LM*.

And *AB* is the diameter of the given sphere;

therefore *LM* is equal to the diameter of the given sphere.

Therefore the octahedron has been comprehended in the given sphere, and it has been demonstrated at the same time that the square on the diameter of the sphere is double of the square on the side of the octahedron.   Q. E. D.

PROPOSITION 15

To construct a cube and comprehend it in a sphere, like the pyramid; and to prove that the square on the diameter of the sphere is triple of the square on the side of the cube.

Let the diameter *AB* of the given sphere be set out,

and let it be cut at C so that AC is double of CB;
let the semicircle ADB be described on AB,
let CD be drawn from C at right angles to AB,
and let DB be joined;
let the square $EFGH$ having its side equal to DB be set out,
from E, F, G, H let EK, FL, GM, HN be drawn at right angles to the plane of the square $EFGH$,
from EK, FL, GM, HN let EK, FL, GM, HN respectively be cut off equal to one of the straight lines EF, FG, GH, HE,
and let KL, LM, MN, NK be joined;
therefore the cube FN has been constructed which is contained by six equal squares.

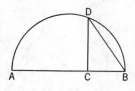
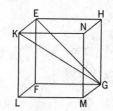

It is then required to comprehend it in the given sphere, and to prove that the square on the diameter of the sphere is triple of the square on the side of the cube.

For let KG, EG be joined.
Then, since the angle KEG is right, because KE is also at right angles to the plane EG and of course to the straight line EG also,   [XI. Def. 3]
therefore the semicircle described on KG will also pass through the point E.
Again, since GF is at right angles to each of the straight lines FL, FE,
GF is also at right angles to the plane FK;
hence also, if we join FK, GF will be at right angles to FK;
and for this reason again the semicircle described on GK will also pass through F.
Similarly it will also pass through the remaining angular points of the cube.
If then, KG remaining fixed, the semicircle be carried round and restored to the same position from which it began to be moved,
the cube will be comprehended in a sphere.
I say next that it is also comprehended in the given sphere.
For, since GF is equal to FE,
and the angle at F is right,
therefore the square on EG is double of the square on EF.
But EF is equal to EK;
therefore the square on EG is double of the square on EK;
hence the squares on GE, EK, that is the square on GK [I. 47], is triple of the square on EK.
And, since AB is triple of BC,
while, as AB is to BC, so is the square on AB to the square on BD.
therefore the square on AB is triple of the square on BD.
But the square on GK was also proved triple of the square on KE.
And KE was made equal to DB;
therefore KG is also equal to AB.
And AB is the diameter of the given sphere;
therefore KG is also equal to the diameter of the given sphere.

Therefore the cube has been comprehended in the given sphere; and it has been demonstrated at the same time that the square on the diameter of the sphere is triple of the square on the side of the cube.   Q. E. D.

PROPOSITION 16

To construct an icosahedron and comprehend it in a sphere, like the aforesaid figures; and to prove that the side of the icosahedron is the irrational straight line called minor.

Let the diameter *AB* of the given sphere be set out,
            and let it be cut at *C* so that *AC* is quadruple of *CB*,
                  let the semicircle *ADB* be described on *AB*,
      let the straight line *CD* be drawn from *C* at right angles to *AB*,
                        and let *DB* be joined;

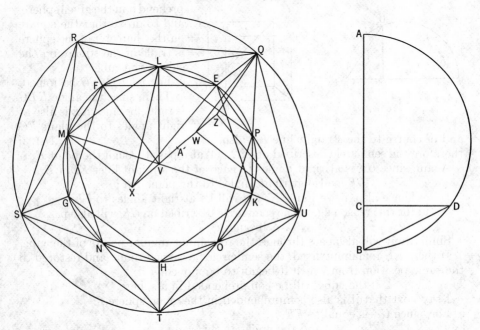

      let the circle *EFGHK* be set out and let its radius be equal to *DB*,
let the equilateral and equiangular pentagon *EFGHK* be inscribed in the circle *EFGHK*,
let the circumferences *EF*, *FG*, *GH*, *HK*, *KE* be bisected at the points *L*, *M*, *N*, *O*, *P*,
                  and let *LM*, *MN*, *NO*, *OP*, *PL*, *EP* be joined.
      Therefore the pentagon *LMNOP* is also equilateral,
                  and the straight line *EP* belongs to a decagon.
      Now from the points *E*, *F*, *G*, *H*, *K* let the straight lines *EQ*, *FR*, *GS*, *HT*, *KU* be set up at right angles to the plane of the circle, and let them be equal to the radius of the circle *EFGHK*,
let *QR*, *RS*, *ST*, *TU*, *UQ*, *QL*, *LR*, *RM*, *MS*, *SN*, *NT*, *TO*, *OU*, *UP*, *PQ* be joined.

Now, since each of the straight lines EQ, KU is at right angles to the same plane,

therefore EQ is parallel to KU.   [XI. 6]

But it is also equal to it;

and the straight lines joining those extremities of equal and parallel straight lines which are in the same direction are equal and parallel.   [I. 33]

Therefore QU is equal and parallel to EK.

But EK belongs to an equilateral pentagon;

therefore QU also belongs to the equilateral pentagon inscribed in the circle $EFGHK$.

For the same reason

each of the straight lines QR, RS, ST, TU also belongs to the equilateral pentagon inscribed in the circle $EFGHK$;

therefore the pentagon $QRSTU$ is equilateral.

And, since QE belongs to a hexagon,

and EP to a decagon,

and the angle QEP is right,

therefore QP belongs to a pentagon;

for the square on the side of the pentagon is equal to the square on the side of the hexagon and the square on the side of the decagon inscribed in the same circle.   [XIII. 10]

For the same reason

PU is also a side of a pentagon.

But QU also belongs to a pentagon;

therefore the triangle QPU is equilateral.

For the same reason

each of the triangles QLR, RMS, SNT, TOU is also equilateral.

And, since each of the straight lines QL, QP was proved to belong to a pentagon,

and LP also belongs to a pentagon,

therefore the triangle QLP is equilateral.

For the same reason

each of the triangles LRM, MSN, NTO, OUP is also equilateral.

Let the centre of the circle $EFGHK$, the point V, be taken;

from V let VZ be set up at right angles to the plane of the circle,

let it be produced in the other direction, as VX,

let there be cut off VW, the side of a hexagon, and each of the straight lines VX, WZ, being sides of a decagon,

and let QZ, QW, UZ, EV, LV, LX, XM be joined.

Now, since each of the straight lines VW, QE is at right angles to the plane of the circle,

therefore VW is parallel to QE.   [XI. 6]

But they are also equal;

therefore EV, QW are also equal and parallel.   [I. 33]

But EV belongs to a hexagon;

therefore QW also belongs to a hexagon.

And, since QW belongs to a hexagon,

and WZ to a decagon,

and the angle QWZ is right,

therefore QZ belongs to a pentagon.   [XIII. 10]

For the same reason

UZ also belongs to a pentagon,

inasmuch as, if we join VK, WU, they will be equal and opposite, and VK, being a radius, belongs to a hexagon;   [IV. 15, Por.]

therefore WU also belongs to a hexagon.

But WZ belongs to a decagon,

and the angle UWZ is right;

therefore UZ belongs to a pentagon.   [XIII. 10]

But QU also belongs to a pentagon;

therefore the triangle QUZ is equilateral.

For the same reason

each of the remaining triangles of which the straight lines QR, RS, ST, TU are the bases, and the point Z the vertex, is also equilateral.

Again, since VL belongs to a hexagon,

and VX to a decagon,

and the angle LVX is right,

therefore LX belongs to a pentagon.   [XIII. 10]

For the same reason,

if we join MV, which belongs to a hexagon,

MX is also inferred to belong to a pentagon.

But LM also belongs to a pentagon;

therefore the triangle LMX is equilateral.

Similarly it can be proved that each of the remaining triangles of which MN, NO, OP, PL are the bases, and the point X the vertex, is also equilateral.

Therefore an icosahedron has been constructed which is contained by twenty equilateral triangles.

It is next required to comprehend it in the given sphere, and to prove that the side of the icosahedron is the irrational straight line called minor.

For, since VW belongs to a hexagon,

and WZ to a decagon,

therefore VZ has been cut in extreme and mean ratio at W,

and VW is its greater segment;   [XIII. 9]

therefore as ZV is to VW, so is VW to WZ.

But VW is equal to VE, and WZ to VX;

therefore, as ZV is to VE, so is EV to VX.

And the angles ZVE, EVX are right;

therefore, if we join the straight line EZ, the angle XEZ will be right because of the similarity of the triangles XEZ, VEZ.

For the same reason,

since, as ZV is to VW, so is VW to WZ,

and ZV is equal to XW, and VW to WQ,

therefore, as XW is to WQ, so is QW to WZ.

And for this reason again,

if we join QX, the angle at Q will be right;   [VI. 8]

therefore the semicircle described on XZ will also pass through Q.   [III. 31]

And if, XZ remaining fixed, the semicircle be carried round and restored to the same position from which it began to be moved, it will also pass through Q and the remaining angular points of the icosahedron, and the icosahedron will have been comprehended in a sphere.

I say next that it is also comprehended in the given sphere.

For let VW be bisected at A'.

Then, since the straight line VZ has been cut in extreme and mean ratio at W,

and ZW is its lesser segment,

therefore the square on ZW added to the half of the greater segment, that is WA', is five times the square on the half of the greater segment;   [XIII. 3]

therefore the square on ZA' is five times the square on $A'W$.

And ZX is double of ZA', and VW double of $A'W$;

therefore the square on ZX is five times the square on WV.

And, since AC is quadruple of CB,

therefore AB is five times BC.

But, as AB is to BC, so is the square on AB to the square on BD;

[VI. 8, V. Def. 9]

therefore the square on AB is five times the square on BD.

But the square on ZX was also proved to be five times the square on VW.

And DB is equal to VW,

for each of them is equal to the radius of the circle $EFGHK$;

therefore AB is also equal to XZ.

And AB is the diameter of the given sphere;

therefore XZ is also equal to the diameter of the given sphere.

Therefore the icosahedron has been comprehended in the given sphere.

I say next that the side of the icosahedron is the irrational straight line called minor.

For, since the diameter of the sphere is rational,

and the square on it is five times the square on the radius of the circle $EFGHK$,

therefore the radius of the circle $EFGHK$ is also rational;

hence its diameter is also rational.

But, if an equilateral pentagon be inscribed in a circle which has its diameter rational, the side of the pentagon is the irrational straight line called minor.

[XIII. 11]

And the side of the pentagon $EFGHK$ is the side of the icosahedron.

Therefore the side of the icosahedron is the irrational straight line called minor.

PORISM. From this it is manifest that the square on the diameter of the sphere is five times the square on the radius of the circle from which the icosahedron has been described, and that the diameter of the sphere is composed of the side of the hexagon and two of the sides of the decagon inscribed in the same circle.   Q. E. D.

PROPOSITION 17

To construct a dodecahedron and comprehend it in a sphere, like the aforesaid figures, and to prove that the side of the dodecahedron is the irrational straight line called apotome.

Let $ABCD$, $CBEF$, two planes of the aforesaid cube at right angles to one another, be set out,

let the sides AB, BC, CD, DA, EF, EB, FC be bisected at G, H, K, L, M, N, O respectively, let *GK*, *HL*, *MH*, *NO* be joined.

let the straight lines *NP*, *PO*, *HQ* be cut in extreme and mean ratio at the points *R*, *S*, *T* respectively,

and let *RP*, *PS*, *TQ* be their greater segments;

from the points *R*, *S*, *T* let *RU*, *SV*, *TW* be set up at right angles to the planes of the cube towards the outside of the cube,

let them be made equal to *RP*, *PS*, *TQ*,

and let *UB*, *BW*, *WC*, *CV*, *VU* be joined.

I say that the pentagon *UBWCV* is equilateral, and in one plane, and is further equiangular.

For let *RB*, *SB*, *VB* be joined.

Then, since the straight line *NP* has been cut in extreme and mean ratio at *R*,

and *RP* is the greater segment, therefore the squares on *PN*, *NR* are triple of the square on *RP*.   [XIII. 4]

But *PN* is equal to *NB*, and *PR* to *RU*;

therefore the squares on *BN*, *NR* are triple of the square on *RU*.

But the square on *BR* is equal to the squares on *BN*, *NR*;   [I. 47]

therefore the square on *BR* is triple of the square on *RU*;

hence the squares on *BR*, *RU* are quadruple of the square on *RU*.

But the square on *BU* is equal to the squares on *BR*, *RU*;

therefore the square on *BU* is quadruple of the square on *RU*;

therefore *BU* is double of *RU*.

But *VU* is also double of *UR*,

inasmuch as *SR* is also double of *PR*, that is, of *RU*;

therefore *BU* is equal to *UV*.

Similarly it can be proved that each of the straight lines *BW*, *WC*, *CV* is also equal to each of the straight lines *BU*, *UV*.

Therefore the pentagon *BUVCW* is equilateral.

I say next that it is also in one plane.

For let *PX* be drawn from *P* parallel to each of the straight lines *RU*, *SV* and towards the outside of the cube, and let *XH*, *HW* be joined;

I say that *XHW* is a straight line.

For, since *HQ* has been cut in extreme and mean ratio at *T*, and *QT* is its greater segment,

therefore, as *HQ* is to *QT*, so is *QT* to *TH*.

But *HQ* is equal to *HP*, and *QT* to each of the straight lines *TW*, *PX*;

therefore, as *HP* is to *PX*, so is *WT* to *TH*.

And *HP* is parallel to *TW*,

for each of them is at right angles to the plane *BD*;   [XI. 6]

and *TH* is parallel to *PX*,

for each of them is at right angles to the plane BF.   [*id.*]

But if two triangles, as XPH, HTW, which have two sides proportional to two sides be placed together at one angle so that their corresponding sides are also parallel,

the remaining straight lines will be in a straight line;   [VI. 32]

therefore XH is in a straight line with HW.

But every straight line is in one plane;   [XI. 1]

therefore the pentagon $UBWCV$ is in one plane.

I say next that it is also equiangular.

For, since the straight line NP has been cut in extreme and mean ratio at R, and PR is the greater segment,

while PR is equal to PS,

therefore NS has also been cut in extreme and mean ratio at P,

and NP is the greater segment;   [XIII. 5]

therefore the squares on NS, SP are triple of the square on NP.   [XIII. 4]

But NP is equal to NB, and PS to SV;

therefore the squares on NS, SV are triple of the square on NB;

hence the squares on VS, SN, NB are quadruple of the square on NB.

But the square on SB is equal to the squares on SN, NB;

therefore the squares on BS, SV, that is, the square on BV—for the angle VSB is right—is quadruple of the square on NB;

therefore VB is double of BN.

But BC is also double of BN;

therefore BV is equal to BC.

And, since the two sides BU, UV are equal to the two sides BW, WC,

and the base BV is equal to the base BC,

therefore the angle BUV is equal to the angle BWC.   [I. 8]

Similarly we can prove that the angle UVC is also equal to the angle BWC;

therefore the three angles BWC, BUV, UVC are equal to one another.

But if in an equilateral pentagon three angles are equal to one another, the pentagon will be equiangular,   [XIII. 7]

therefore the pentagon $BUVCW$ is equiangular.

And it was also proved equilateral;

therefore the pentagon $BUVCW$ is equilateral and equiangular, and it is on one side BC of the cube.

Therefore, if we make the same construction in the case of each of the twelve sides of the cube,

a solid figure will have been constructed which is contained by twelve equilateral and equiangular pentagons, and which is called a dodecahedron.

It is then required to comprehend it in the given sphere, and to prove that the side of the dodecahedron is the irrational straight line called apotome.

For let XP be produced, and let the produced straight line be XZ;

therefore PZ meets the diameter of the cube, and they bisect one another, for this has been proved in the last theorem but one of the eleventh book.

[XI. 38]

Let them cut at Z;

therefore Z is the centre of the sphere which comprehends the cube,

and ZP is half of the side of the cube.

Let UZ be joined.

Now, since the straight line NS has been cut in extreme and mean ratio at P,

and NP is its greater segment,

therefore the squares on NS, SP are triple of the square on NP.   [XIII. 4]

But NS is equal to XZ,

inasmuch as NP is also equal to PZ, and XP to PS.

But further, PS is also equal to XU,

since it is also equal to RP;

therefore the squares on ZX, XU are triple of the square on NP.

But the square on UZ is equal to the squares on ZX, XU;

therefore the square on UZ is triple of the square on NP.

But the square on the radius of the sphere which comprehends the cube is also triple of the square on the half of the side of the cube,

for it has previously been shown how to construct a cube and comprehend it in a sphere, and to prove that the square on the diameter of the sphere is triple of the square on the side of the cube.   [XIII. 15]

But, if whole is so related to whole, so is half to half also;

and NP is half of the side of the cube;

therefore UZ is equal to the radius of the sphere which comprehends the cube.

And Z is the centre of the sphere which comprehends the cube;

therefore the point U is on the surface of the sphere.

Similarly we can prove that each of the remaining angles of the dodecahedron is also on the surface of the sphere;

therefore the dodecahedron has been comprehended in the given sphere.

I say next that the side of the dodecahedron is the irrational straight line called apotome.

For since, when NP has been cut in extreme and mean ratio, RP is the greater segment,

and, when PO has been cut in extreme and mean ratio, PS is the greater segment,

therefore, when the whole NO is cut in extreme and mean ratio, RS is the greater segment.

[Thus, since, as NP is to PR, so is PR to RN,

the same is true of the doubles also,

for parts have the same ratio as their equimultiples;   [V. 15]

therefore as NO is to RS, so is RS to the sum of NR, SO.

But NO is greater than RS;

therefore RS is also greater than the sum of NR, SO;

therefore NO has been cut in extreme and mean ratio,

and RS is its greater segment.]

But RS is equal to UV;

therefore, when NO is cut in extreme and mean ratio, UV is the greater segment.

And, since the diameter of the sphere is rational,

and the square on it is triple of the square on the side of the cube,

therefore NO, being a side of the cube, is rational.

[But if a rational line be cut in extreme and mean ratio, each of the segments is an irrational apotome.]

Therefore UV, being a side of the dodecahedron, is an irrational apotome.

[XIII. 6]

PORISM. From this it is manifest that, when the side of the cube is cut in extreme and mean ratio, the greater segment is the side of the dodecahedron.

Q. E. D.

PROPOSITION 18

To set out the sides of the five figures and to compare them with one another.

Let AB, the diameter of the given sphere, be set out, and let it be cut at C so that AC is equal to CB, and at D so that AD is double of DB; let the semicircle AEB be described on AB, from C, D let CE, DF be drawn at right angles to AB,

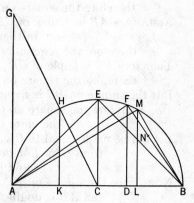

and let AF, FB, EB be joined.

Then, since AD is double of DB,
therefore AB is triple of BD.

Convertendo, therefore, BA is one and a half times AD.

But, as BA is to AD, so is the square on BA to the square on AF,   [v. Def. 9, vi. 8] for the triangle AFB is equiangular with the triangle AFD;

therefore the square on BA is one and a half times the square on AF.

But the square on the diameter of the sphere is also one and a half times the square on the side of the pyramid.   [XIII. 13]

And AB is the diameter of the sphere;
therefore AF is equal to the side of the pyramid.

Again, since AD is double of DB,
therefore AB is triple of BD.

But, as AB is to BD, so is the square on AB to the square on BF;
[vi. 8, v. Def. 9]

therefore the square on AB is triple of the square on BF.

But the square on the diameter of the sphere is also triple of the square on the side of the cube.   [XIII. 15]

And AB is the diameter of the sphere;
therefore BF is the side of the cube.

And, since AC is equal to CB,
therefore AB is double of BC.

But, as AB is to BC, so is the square on AB to the square on BE;
therefore the square on AB is double of the square on BE.

But the square on the diameter of the sphere is also double of the square on the side of the octahedron.   [XIII. 14]

And AB is the diameter of the given sphere;
therefore BE is the side of the octahedron.

Next, let AG be drawn from the point A at right angles to the straight line AB,
let AG be made equal to AB,
let GC be joined,
and from H let HK be drawn perpendicular to AB.

Then, since GA is double of AC,

for GA is equal to AB,

and, as GA is to AC, so is HK to KC,

therefore HK is also double of KC.

Therefore the square on HK is quadruple of the square on KC; therefore the squares on HK, KC, that is, the square on HC, is five times the square on KC.

But HC is equal to CB;

therefore the square on BC is five times the square on CK.

And, since AB is double of CB,

and, in them, AD is double of DB,

therefore the remainder BD is double of the remainder DC.

Therefore BC is triple of CD;

therefore the square on BC is nine times the square on CD.

But the square on BC is five times the square on CK;

therefore the square on CK is greater than the square on CD;

therefore CK is greater than CD.

Let CL be made equal to CK,

from L let LM be drawn at right angles to AB,

and let MB be joined.

Now, since the square on BC is five times the square on CK,

and AB is double of BC, and KL double of CK,

therefore the square on AB is five times the square on KL.

But the square on the diameter of the sphere is also five times the square on the radius of the circle from which the icosahedron has been described.

[XIII. 16, Por.]

And AB is the diameter of the sphere;

therefore KL is the radius of the circle from which the icosahedron has been described;

therefore KL is a side of the hexagon in the said circle.   [IV. 15, Por.]

And, since the diameter of the sphere is made up of the side of the hexagon and two of the sides of the decagon inscribed in the same circle,

[XIII. 16, Por.]

and AB is the diameter of the sphere,

while KL is a side of the hexagon,

and AK is equal to LB,

therefore each of the straight lines AK, LB is a side of the decagon inscribed in the circle from which the icosahedron has been described.

And, since LB belongs to a decagon, and ML to a hexagon,

for ML is equal to KL, since it is also equal to HK, being the same distance from the centre, and each of the straight lines HK, KL is double of KC,

therefore MB belongs to a pentagon.   [XIII. 10]

But the side of the pentagon is the side of the icosahedron;   [XIII. 16]

therefore MB belongs to the icosahedron.

Now, since FB is a side of the cube,

let it be cut in extreme and mean ratio at N,

and let NB be the greater segment;

therefore NB is a side of the dodecahedron.   [XIII. 17, Por.]

And, since the square on the diameter of the sphere was proved to be one and a half times the square on the side AF of the pyramid, double of the square on

the side BE of the octahedron and triple of the side FB of the cube,
therefore, of parts of which the square on the diameter of the sphere contains
six, the square on the side of the pyramid contains four, the square on the side
of the octahedron three, and the square on the side of the cube two.

Therefore the square on the side of the pyramid is four-thirds of the square
on the side of the octahedron, and double of the square on the side of the cube;
and the square on the side of the octahedron is one and a half times the square
on the side of the cube.

The said sides, therefore, of the three figures, I mean the pyramid, the octahedron and the cube, are to one another in rational ratios.

But the remaining two, I mean the side of the icosahedron and the side of
the dodecahedron, are not in rational ratios either to one another or to the
aforesaid sides;
for they are irrational, the one being minor [XIII. 16] and the other an apotome
[XIII. 17].

That the side MB of the icosahedron is greater than the side NB of the dodecahedron we can prove thus.

For, since the triangle FDB is equiangular with the triangle FAB,   [VI. 8]
            proportionally, as DB is to BF, so is BF to BA.   [VI. 4]
And, since the three straight lines are proportional,
as the first is to the third, so is the square on the first to the square on the
second;   [V. Def. 9, VI. 20, Por.]
therefore, as DB is to BA, so is the square on DB to the square on BF;
therefore, inversely, as AB is to BD, so is the square on FB to the square on
BD.

But AB is triple of BD;
            therefore the square on FB is triple of the square on BD.
But the square on AD is also quadruple of the square on DB,
                  for AD is double of DB;
      therefore the square on AD is greater than the square on FB;
                  therefore AD is greater than FB;
            therefore AL is by far greater than FB.
And, when AL is cut in extreme and mean ratio,
                  KL is the greater segment,
inasmuch as LK belongs to a hexagon, and KA to a decagon;   [XIII. 9]
and, when FB is cut in extreme and mean ratio, NB is the greater segment;
                  therefore KL is greater than NB.
But KL is equal to LM;
                  therefore LM is greater than NB.
Therefore MB, which is a side of the icosahedron, is by far greater than NB
which is a side of the dodecahedron.   Q. E. D.

I say next that *no other figure, besides the said five figures, can be constructed
which is contained by equilateral and equiangular figures equal to one another.*

For a solid angle cannot be constructed with two triangles, or indeed planes.

With three triangles the angle of the pyramid is constructed, with four the
angle of the octahedron, and with five the angle of the icosahedron;

but a solid angle cannot be formed by six equilateral and equiangular triangles placed together at one point,

for, the angle of the equilateral triangle being two-thirds of a right angle, the six will be equal to four right angles:

which is impossible, for any solid angle is contained by angles less than four right angles. [XI. 21]

For the same reason, neither can a solid angle be constructed by more than six plane angles.

By three squares the angle of the cube is contained, but by four it is impossible for a solid angle to be contained,

for they will again be four right angles.

By three equilateral and equiangular pentagons the angle of the dodecahedron is contained;

but by four such it is impossible for any solid angle to be contained,

for, the angle of the equilateral pentagon being a right angle and a fifth, the four angles will be greater than four right angles:

which is impossible.

Neither again will a solid angle be contained by other polygonal figures by reason of the same absurdity.

Therefore etc.

Q. E. D.

Lemma

But that *the angle of the equilateral and equiangular pentagon is a right angle and a fifth* we must prove thus.

Let *ABCDE* be an equilateral and equiangular pentagon,
let the circle *ABCDE* be circumscribed about it,

let its centre *F* be taken,

and let *FA, FB, FC, FD, FE* be joined.

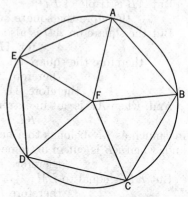

Therefore they bisect the angles of the pentagon at *A, B, C, D, E.*

And, since the angles at *F* are equal to four right angles and are equal,

therefore one of them, as the angle *AFB,* is one right angle less a fifth;

therefore the remaining angles *FAB, ABF* consist of one right angle and a fifth.

But the angle *FAB* is equal to the angle *FBC*;

therefore the whole angle *ABC* of the pentagon consists of one right angle and a fifth.

Q. E. D.

THE WORKS OF ARCHIMEDES
INCLUDING THE METHOD

BIOGRAPHICAL NOTE
ARCHIMEDES, *c.* 287–212 B.C.

ARCHIMEDES was a citizen of Syracuse, in Sicily, where he was born around the year 287 B.C. He was intimate with Hiero, King of Syracuse, and with his son, Gelo, and Plutarch says that he was related to them. In his *Sand-Reckoner*, which was dedicated to Gelo, Archimedes speaks of his father, Pheidias, as an astronomer who investigated the sizes and distances of the sun and moon.

As a young man Archimedes seems to have spent some time in Egypt, where he invented the water-screw as a means of drawing water out of the Nile for irrigating the fields, though it is also said that he invented this machine to drain bilge water from a huge ship built for King Hiero. He may have studied with the pupils of Euclid in Alexandria. It was probably there that he made the friendship of Conon of Samos and Eratosthenes. To Conon he was in the habit of communicating his discoveries before their publication, and it was for Eratosthenes that he wrote the *Method* and through him that he addressed the famous *Cattle-Problem* to the mathematicians of Alexandria—if the tradition is to be credited that associates Archimedes with this problem. After the death of Conon, Archimedes sent his discoveries to Conon's friend and pupil, Dositheus of Pelusium, to whom four of the extant treatises are dedicated.

His mechanical inventions won great fame for Archimedes and figure largely in the traditions about him. After discovering the solution of the problem *To move a given weight by a given force*, he boasted to King Hiero: "Give me a place to stand on and I can move the earth." Asked for a practical demonstration, he contrived a machine by which with the use of only one arm he drew out of the dock a large ship, laden with passengers and goods, which the combined strength of the Syracusans could scarcely move. From that day Hiero ordered that "Archimedes was to be believed in everything he might say." At the king's request Archimedes then made for him catapults, battering rams, cranes, and many other engines of war, which were later used with such success in the defense of Syracuse against the Romans that they were unable to take the city except by treachery. There is also a story in Lucian that Archimedes set fire to the Roman ships by an arrangement of burning glasses.

Although Archimedes acquired by his mechanical inventions "the renown of more than human sagacity," according to Plutarch, he "would not deign to leave behind him any commentary or writing on such subjects," since he considered them "sordid and ignoble." He did, however, write a description, now lost, of an apparatus, composed of concentric glass spheres moved by water power, representing the Eudoxian system of the world. This astronomical machine, which survived to be seen and described by Cicero in his *Republic*, was sufficiently accurate to show the eclipses of the sun and the moon. Except for this lost work *On Sphere-making*, Archimedes wrote only on strictly mathematical subjects. He took all the mathematical sciences for his province: arithmetic, geometry, astronomy, mechanics, and hydrostatics. Unlike Euclid and Apollonius he wrote no textbooks. Of his writings, although some have been lost, the most important have survived.

The absorption of Archimedes in his mathematical investigations was so great that he forgot his food and neglected his person, and when carried by force to the bath, Plutarch records, "he used to trace geometrical figures in the ashes of the fire and diagrams in the oil on his body." Asked by Hiero to discover whether a goldsmith had alloyed with silver the gold of his crown, Archimedes found the answer while bathing by considering the water displaced by his body, whereupon he is reported to have run home in his excitement without his clothes, shouting, "Eureka" (I have found it).

Archimedes' preoccupation with mathematics is even said to have been the cause of his death. In the general massacre which followed the capture of Syracuse by Marcellus in 212 B.C., Archimedes was so intent upon a mathematical diagram that he took no notice, and when ordered by a soldier to attend the victorious general, he refused until he should have solved his problem, whereupon he was slain by the enraged soldier. No blame attaches to the Roman general, Marcellus, since he had given orders to spare the house and person of the mathematician, and in the midst of his triumph he lamented the death of Archimedes, provided him with an honorable burial, and befriended his surviving relatives. In accordance with the expressed desire of Archimedes, his family and friends inscribed on his tomb the figure of his favorite theorem, on the sphere and the circumscribed cylinder, and the ratio of the containing solid to the contained. When Cicero was in Sicily as quaestor in 75 B.C., he discovered the neglected and forgotten tomb of Archimedes near the Agrigentine Gate and piously restored it.

CONTENTS

ON THE SPHERE AND CYLINDER

BOOK ONE

ARCHIMEDES to DOSITHEUS greeting

"On a former occasion I sent you the investigations which I had up to that time completed, including the proofs, showing that any segment bounded by a straight line and a section of a right-angled cone [a parabola] is four-thirds of the triangle which has the same base with the segment and equal height. Since then certain theorems not hitherto demonstrated have occurred to me, and I have worked out the proofs of them. They are these: first, that the surface of any sphere is four times its greatest circle; next, that the surface of any segment of a sphere is equal to a circle whose radius is equal to the straight line drawn from the vertex of the segment to the circumference of the circle which is the base of the segment; and, further, that any cylinder having its base equal to the greatest circle of those in the sphere, and height equal to the diameter of the sphere, is itself [*i.e.* in content] half as large again as the sphere, and its surface also [including its bases] is half as large again as the surface of the sphere. Now these properties were all along naturally inherent in the figures referred to, but remained unknown to those who were before my time engaged in the study of geometry. Having, however, now discovered that the properties are true of these figures, I cannot feel any hesitation in setting them side by side both with my former investigations and with those of the theorems of Eudoxus on solids which are held to be most irrefragably established, namely, that any pyramid is one third part of the prism which has the same base with the pyramid and equal height, and that any cone is one third part of the cylinder which has the same base with the cone and equal height. For, though these properties also were naturally inherent in the figures all along, yet they were in fact unknown to all the many able geometers who lived before Eudoxus, and had not been observed by any one. Now, however, it will be open to those who possess the requisite ability to examine these discoveries of mine. They ought to have been published while Conon was still alive, for I should conceive that he would best have been able to grasp them and to pronounce upon them the appropriate verdict; but, as I judge it well to communicate them to those who are conversant with mathematics, I send them to you with the proofs written out, which it will be open to mathematicians to examine. Farewell.

"I first set out the axioms and the assumptions which I have used for the proofs of my propositions."

DEFINITIONS

1. "There are in a plane certain terminated bent lines, which either lie wholly on the same side of the straight lines joining their extremities, or have no part of them on the other side."

2. "I apply the term *concave in the same direction* to a line such that, if any two points on it are taken, either all the straight lines connecting the points fall on the same side of the line, or some fall on one and the same side while others fall on the line itself, but none on the other side."

3. "Similarly also there are certain terminated surfaces, not themselves being in a plane but having their extremities in a plane, and such that they will either be wholly on the same side of the plane containing their extremities, or have no part of them on the other side."

4. "I apply the term *concave in the same direction* to surfaces such that, if any two points on them are taken, the straight lines connecting the points either all fall on the same side of the surface, or some fall on one and the same side of it while some fall upon it, but none on the other side."

5. "I use the term *solid sector,* when a cone cuts a sphere, and has its apex at the centre of the sphere, to denote the figure comprehended by the surface of the cone and the surface of the sphere included within the cone."

6. "I apply the term *solid rhombus,* when two cones with the same base have their apices on opposite sides of the plane of the base in such a position that their axes lie in a straight line, to denote the solid figure made up of both the cones."

ASSUMPTIONS

1. "*Of all lines which have the same extremities the straight line is the least.*"

2. "Of other lines in a plane and having the same extremities, [any two] such are unequal whenever both are concave in the same direction and one of them is either wholly included between the other and the straight line which has the same extremities with it, or is partly included by, and is partly common with, the other; and that [line] which is included is the lesser [of the two]."

3. "Similarly, of surfaces which have the same extremities, if those extremities are in a plane, the plane is the least [in area]."

4. "Of other surfaces with the same extremities, the extremities being in a plane, [any two] such are unequal whenever both are concave in the same direction and one surface is either wholly included between the other and the plane which has the same extremities with it, or is partly included by, and partly common with, the other; and that [surface] which is included is the lesser [of the two in area]."

5. "Further, of unequal lines, unequal surfaces, and unequal solids, the greater exceeds the less by such a magnitude as, when added to itself, can be made to exceed any assigned magnitude among those which are comparable with [it and with] one another.

"These things being premised, *if a polygon be inscribed in a circle, it is plain that the perimeter of the inscribed polygon is less than the circumference of the circle;* for each of the sides of the polygon is less than that part of the circumference of the circle which is cut off by it."

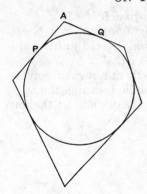

PROPOSITION 1

If a polygon be circumscribed about a circle, the perimeter of the circumscribed polygon is greater than the perimeter of the circle.

Let any two adjacent sides, meeting in A, touch the circle at P, Q respectively.

Then [*Assumptions*, 2]

$$PA + AQ > (\text{arc } PQ).$$

A similar inequality holds for each angle of the polygon; and, by addition, the required result follows.

PROPOSITION 2

Given two unequal magnitudes, it is possible to find two unequal straight lines such that the greater straight line has to the less a ratio less than the greater magnitude has to the less.

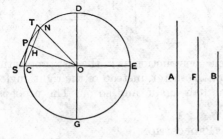

Let AB, D represent the two unequal magnitudes, AB being the greater.

Suppose BC measured along BA equal to D, and let GH be any straight line.

Then, if CA be added to itself a sufficient number of times, the sum will exceed D. Let AF be this sum, and take E on GH produced such that GH is the same multiple of HE that AF is of AC.

Thus $EH : HG = AC : AF.$

But, since $AF > D$ (or CB),

$$AC : AF < AC : CB.$$

Therefore, *componendo*,

$$EG : GH < AB : D.$$

Hence EG, GH are two lines satisfying the given condition.

PROPOSITION 3

Given two unequal magnitudes and a circle, it is possible to inscribe a polygon in the circle and to describe another about it so that the side of the circumscribed polygon may have to the side of the inscribed polygon a ratio less than that of the greater magnitude to the less.

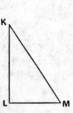

Let A, B represent the given magnitudes, A being the greater.

Find [Prop. 2] two straight lines F, KL, of which F is the greater, such that

$$F : KL < A : B. \qquad\qquad (1).$$

Draw LM perpendicular to LK and of such length that $KM = F$.

In the given circle let CE, DG be two diameters at right angles. Then, bisecting the angle DOC, bisecting the half again, and so on, we shall arrive ultimately at an angle (as NOC) less than twice the angle LKM.

Join NC, which (by the construction) will be the side of a regular polygon inscribed in the circle. Let OP be the radius of the circle bisecting the angle NOC (and therefore bisecting NC at right angles, in H, say), and let the tangent at P meet OC, ON produced in S, T respectively.

Now, since
$$\angle CON < 2\angle LKM,$$
$$\angle HOC < \angle LKM,$$
and the angles at H, L are right;

therefore $MK : LK > OC : OH$
$$> OP : OH.$$

Hence
$$ST : CN < MK : LK$$
$$< F : LK;$$

therefore, *a fortiori*, by (1),
$$ST : CN < A : B.$$

Thus two polygons are found satisfying the given condition.

PROPOSITION 4

Again, given two unequal magnitudes and a sector, it is possible to describe a polygon about the sector and to inscribe another in it so that the side of the circumscribed polygon may have to the side of the inscribed polygon a ratio less than the greater magnitude has to the less.

[The "inscribed polygon" found in this proposition is one which has for two sides the two radii bounding the sector, while the remaining sides (the number of which is, by construction, some power of 2) subtend equal parts of the arc of the sector; the "circumscribed polygon" is formed by the tangents parallel to the sides of the inscribed polygon and by the two bounding radii produced.]

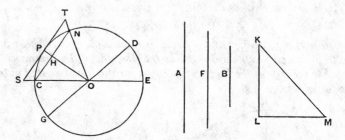

In this case we make the same construction as in the last proposition except that we bisect the angle COD of the sector, instead of the right angle between two diameters, then bisect the half again, and so on. The proof is exactly similar to the preceding one.

PROPOSITION 5

Given a circle and two unequal magnitudes, to describe a polygon about the circle and inscribe another in it, so that the circumscribed polygon may have to the inscribed a ratio less than the greater magnitude has to the less.

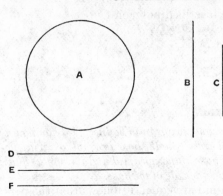

Let A be the given circle and B, C the given magnitudes, B being the greater.

Take two unequal straight lines D, E, of which D is the greater, such that $D : E < B : C$ [Prop. 2], and let F be a mean proportional between D, E so that D is also greater than F.

Describe (in the manner of Prop. 3) one polygon about the circle, and inscribe another in it, so that the side of the former has to the side of the latter a ratio less than the ratio $D : F$.

Thus the duplicate ratio of the side of the former polygon to the side of the latter is less than the ratio $D^2 : F^2$.

But the said duplicate ratio of the sides is equal to the ratio of the areas of the polygons, since they are similar;

therefore the area of the circumscribed polygon has to the area of the inscribed polygon a ratio less than the ratio $D^2 : F^2$, or $D : E$, and *a fortiori* less than the ratio $B : C$.

Proposition 6

"Similarly we can show that, *given two unequal magnitudes and a sector, it is possible to circumscribe a polygon about the sector and inscribe in it another similar one so that the circumscribed may have to the inscribed a ratio less than the greater magnitude has to the less.*

"And it is likewise clear that, *if a circle or a sector, as well as a certain area, be given, it is possible, by inscribing regular polygons in the circle or sector, and by continually inscribing such in the remaining segments, to leave segments of the circle or sector which are [together] less than the given area.* For this is proved in the *Elements* [Eucl. xii. 2].

"But it is yet to be proved that, *given a circle or sector and an area, it is possible to describe a polygon about the circle or sector, such that the area remaining between the circumference and the circumscribed figure is less than the given area.*"

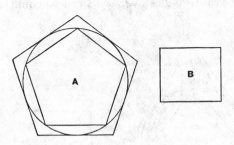

The proof for the circle (which, as Archimedes says, can be equally applied to a sector) is as follows.

Let A be the given circle and B the given area.

Now, there being two unequal magnitudes $A + B$ and A, let a polygon (C) be circumscribed about the circle and a polygon (I) inscribed in it [as in Prop. 5],

so that

$$C : I < A + B : A. \tag{1}.$$

The circumscribed polygon (C) shall be that required.

For the circle (A) is greater than the inscribed polygon (I).

Therefore, from (1), *a fortiori*,

$$C : A < A + B : A,$$

whence

$$C < A + B,$$

or

$$C - A < B.$$

Proposition 7

If in an isosceles cone [i.e. *a right circular cone*] *a pyramid be inscribed having an equilateral base, the surface of the pyramid excluding the base is equal to a triangle having its base equal to the perimeter of the base of the pyramid and its height equal to the perpendicular drawn from the apex on one side of the base.*

Since the sides of the base of the pyramid are equal, it follows that the perpendiculars from the apex to all the sides of the base are equal; and the proof of the proposition is obvious.

Proposition 8

If a pyramid be circumscribed about an isosceles cone, the surface of the pyramid excluding its base is equal to a triangle having its base equal to the perimeter of the base of the pyramid and its height equal to the side [i.e. *a generator*] *of the cone.*

The base of the pyramid is a polygon circumscribed about the circular base of the cone, and the line joining the apex of the cone or pyramid to the point of contact of any side of the polygon is perpendicular to that side. Also all these perpendiculars, being generators of the cone, are equal; whence the proposition follows immediately.

Proposition 9

If in the circular base of an isosceles cone a chord be placed, and from its extremities straight lines be drawn to the apex of the cone, the triangle so formed will be less than the portion of the surface of the cone intercepted between the lines drawn to the apex.

Let ABC be the circular base of the cone, and O its apex.

Draw a chord AB in the circle, and join OA, OB. Bisect the arc ACB in C, and join AC, BC, OC.

Then

$$\triangle OAC + \triangle OBC > \triangle OAB.$$

Let the excess of the sum of the first two triangles over the third be equal to the area D.

Then D is either less than the sum of the segments AEC, CFB, or not less.

I. Let D be not less than the sum of the segments referred to.

We have now two surfaces

(1) that consisting of the portion $OAEC$ of the surface of the cone together with the segment AEC, and

(2) the triangle OAC;

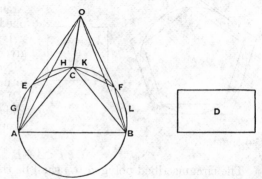

and, since the two surfaces have the same extremities (the perimeter of the triangle OAC), the former surface is greater than the latter, which is *included* by it [*Assumptions*, 3 or 4].

Hence   (surface $OAEC$)+(segment AEC) > △OAC.
Similarly   (surface $OCFB$)+(segment CFB) > △OBC.

Therefore, since D is not less than the sum of the segments, we have, by addition,

$$(\text{surface } OAECFB)+D > △OAC+△OBC$$
$$> △OAB+D, \text{ by hypothesis.}$$

Taking away the common part D, we have the required result.

II. Let D be less than the sum of the segments AEC, CFB.

If now we bisect the arcs AC, CB, then bisect the halves, and so on, we shall ultimately leave segments which are together less than D.   [Prop. 6]

Let AGE, EHC, CKF, FLB be those segments, and join OE, OF.

Then, as before,

$$(\text{surface } OAGE)+(\text{segment } AGE) > △OAE$$
and $$(\text{surface } OEHC)+(\text{segment } EHC) > △OEC.$$

Therefore (surface $OAGHC$)+(segments AGE, EHC)
$$> △OAE+△OEC$$
$$> △OAC, \text{ a fortiori.}$$

Similarly for the part of the surface of the cone bounded by OC, OB and the arc CFB.

Hence, by addition,

(surface $OAGEHCKFLB$)+(segments AGE, EHC, CKF, FLB)
$$> △OAC+△OBC$$
$$> △OAB+D, \text{ by hypothesis.}$$

But the sum of the segments is less than D, and the required result follows.

PROPOSITION 10

If in the plane of the circular base of an isosceles cone two tangents be drawn to the circle meeting in a point, and the points of contact and the point of concourse of the tangents be respectively joined to the apex of the cone, the sum of the two triangles formed by the joining lines and the two tangents are together greater than the included portion of the surface of the cone.

Let ABC be the circular base of the cone, O its apex, AD, BD the two tangents to the circle meeting in D. Join OA, OB, OD.

Let ECF be drawn touching the circle at C, the middle point of the arc ACB, and therefore parallel to AB. Join OE, OF.

Then $ED+DF > EF$,
and, adding $AE+FB$ to each side,
$$AD+DB > AE+EF+FB.$$

Now OA, OC, OB, being generators of the cone, are equal, and they are respectively perpendicular to the tangents at A, C, B.

It follows that
$$△OAD+△ODB > △OAE+△OEF+△OFB.$$

Let the area G be equal to the excess of the first sum over the second.

G is then either less, or not less, than the sum of the spaces $EAHC$, $FCKB$ remaining between the circle and the tangents, which sum we will call L.

I. Let G be not less than L.

We have now two surfaces

(1) that of the pyramid with apex O and base $AEFB$, excluding the face OAB,

(2) that consisting of the part $OACB$ of the surface of the cone together with the segment ACB.

These two surfaces have the same extremities, viz. the perimeter of the triangle OAB, and, since the former *includes* the latter, the former is the greater [*Assumptions*, 4].

That is, the surface of the pyramid exclusive of the face OAB is greater than the sum of the surface $OACB$ and the segment ACB.

Taking away the segment from each sum, we have

$$\triangle OAE + \triangle OEF + \triangle OFB + L > \text{the surface } OAHCKB.$$

And G is not less than L.

It follows that

$$\triangle OAE + \triangle OEF + \triangle OFB + G,$$

which is by hypothesis equal to $\triangle OAD + \triangle ODB$, is greater than the same surface.

II. Let G be less than L.

If we bisect the arcs AC, CB and draw tangents at their middle points, then bisect the halves and draw tangents, and so on, we shall lastly arrive at a polygon such that the sum of the parts remaining between the sides of the polygon and the circumference of the segment is less than G.

Let the remainders be those between the segment and the polygon $APQRSB$, and let their sum be M. Join OP, OQ, etc.

Then, as before,

$$\triangle OAE + \triangle OEF + \triangle OFB > \triangle OAP + \triangle OPQ + \cdots + \triangle OSB.$$

Also, as before,

(surface of pyramid $OAPQRSB$ excluding the face OAB) > the part $OACB$ of the surface of the cone together with the segment ACB.

Taking away the segment from each sum,

$$\triangle OAP + \triangle OPQ + \cdots + M > \text{the part } OACB \text{ of the surface of the cone.}$$

Hence, *a fortiori*,

$$\triangle OAE + \triangle OEF + \triangle OFB + G,$$

which is by hypothesis equal to

$$\triangle OAD + \triangle ODB,$$

is greater than the part $OACB$ of the surface of the cone.

Proposition 11

If a plane parallel to the axis of a right cylinder cut the cylinder, the part of the surface of the cylinder cut off by the plane is greater than the area of the parallelogram in which the plane cuts it.

PROPOSITION 12

If at the extremities of two generators of any right cylinder tangents be drawn to the circular bases in the planes of those bases respectively, and if the pairs of tangents meet, the parallelograms formed by each generator and the two corresponding tangents respectively are together greater than the included portion of the surface of the cylinder between the two generators.

[The proofs of these two propositions follow exactly the methods of Props. 9, 10 respectively, and it is therefore unnecessary to reproduce them.]

"From the properties thus proved it is clear (1) that, *if a pyramid be inscribed in an isosceles cone, the surface of the pyramid excluding the base is less than the surface of the cone [excluding the base]*, and (2) that, *if a pyramid be circumscribed about an isosceles cone, the surface of the pyramid excluding the base is greater than the surface of the cone excluding the base.*

"It is also clear from what has been proved both (1) that, *if a prism be inscribed in a right cylinder, the surface of the prism made up of its parallelograms* [i.e. *excluding its bases*] *is less than the surface of the cylinder excluding its bases,* and (2) that, *if a prism be circumscribed about a right cylinder, the surface of the prism made up of its parallelograms is greater than the surface of the cylinder excluding its bases.*"

PROPOSITION 13

The surface of any right cylinder excluding the bases is equal to a circle whose radius is a mean proportional between the side [i.e. *a generator*] *of the cylinder and the diameter of its base.*

Let the base of the cylinder be the circle A, and make CD equal to the diameter of this circle, and EF equal to the height of the cylinder.

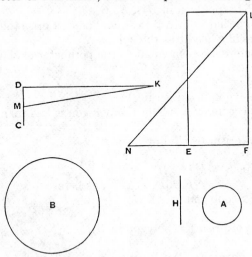

Let H be a mean proportional between CD, EF, and B a circle with radius equal to H.

Then the circle B shall be equal to the surface of the cylinder (excluding the bases), which we will call S.

For, if not, B must be either greater or less than S.

I. Suppose $B < S$.

Then it is possible to circumscribe a regular polygon about B, and to inscribe another in it, such that the ratio of the former to the latter is less than the ratio $S : B$.

Suppose this done, and circumscribe about A a polygon similar to that described about B; then erect on the polygon about A a prism of the same height as the cylinder. The prism will therefore be circumscribed to the cylinder.

Let KD, perpendicular to CD, and FL, perpendicular to EF, be each equal to the perimeter of the polygon about A. Bisect CD in M, and join MK.

Then $\triangle KDM$ = the polygon about A.

Also $\square EL$ = surface of prism (excluding bases).

Produce FE to N so that $FE = EN$, and join NL.

Now the polygons about A, B, being similar, are in the duplicate ratio of the radii of A, B.

Thus

$$\triangle KDM : (\text{polygon about } B) = MD^2 : H^2$$
$$= MD^2 : CD \cdot EF$$
$$= MD : NF$$
$$= \triangle KDM : \triangle LFN$$

(since $DK = FL$).

Therefore (polygon about B) $= \triangle LFN$
$$= \square EL$$
$$= (\text{surface of prism about } A),$$

from above.

But   (polygon about B) : (polygon in B) $< S : B$.

Therefore

(surface of prism about A) : (polygon in B) $< S : B$,

and, alternately,

(surface of prism about A) : $S <$ (polygon in B) : B;

which is impossible, since the surface of the prism is greater than S, while the polygon inscribed in B is less than B.

Therefore $B \not< S$.

II. Suppose $B > S$.

Let a regular polygon be circumscribed about B and another inscribed in it so that

(polygon about B) : (polygon in B) $< B : S$.

Inscribe in A a polygon similar to that inscribed in B, and erect a prism on the polygon inscribed in A of the same height as the cylinder.

Again, let DK, FL, drawn as before, be each equal to the perimeter of the polygon inscribed in A.

Then, in this case,

$$\triangle KDM > (\text{polygon inscribed in } A)$$

(since the perpendicular from the centre on a side of the polygon is less than the radius of A).

Also $\triangle LFN = \square EL$ = surface of prism (excluding bases).

Now

(polygon in A) : (polygon in B) $= MD^2 : H^2$,
$$= \triangle KDM : \triangle LFN, \text{ as before.}$$

And $\triangle KDM > (\text{polygon in } A)$.

Therefore

$\triangle LFN$, or (surface of prism) $>$ (polygon in B).

But this is impossible, because

(polygon about B) : (polygon in B) $< B : S$,
$$< (\text{polygon about } B) : S, \textit{ a fortiori,}$$

so that   (polygon in B) $> S$,
$$> (\text{surface of prism}), \textit{ a fortiori.}$$

Hence B is neither greater nor less than S, and therefore
$$B = S.$$

Proposition 14

The surface of any isosceles cone excluding the base is equal to a circle whose radius is a mean proportional between the side of the cone [a generator] and the radius of the circle which is the base of the cone.

Let the circle A be the base of the cone; draw C equal to the radius of the circle, and D equal to the side of the cone, and let E be a mean proportional between C, D.

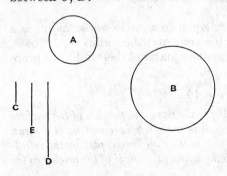

Draw a circle B with radius equal to E.

Then shall B be equal to the surface of the cone (excluding the base), which we will call S.

If not, B must be either greater or less than S.

I. Suppose $B < S$.

Let a regular polygon be described about B and a similar one inscribed in it such that the former has to the latter a ratio less than the ratio $S : B$.

Describe about A another similar polygon, and on it set up a pyramid with apex the same as that of the cone.

Then   (polygon about A) : (polygon about B)

$\quad = C^2 : E^2$

$\quad = C : D$

$\quad =$ (polygon about A) : (surface of pyramid excluding base).

Therefore

(surface of pyramid $=$ (polygon about B).

Now   (polygon about B) : (polygon in B) $< S : B$.

Therefore

(surface of pyramid) : (polygon in B) $< S : B$,

which is impossible, (because the surface of the pyramid is greater than S, while the polygon in B is less than B).

Hence $B \not< S$.

II. Suppose $B > S$.

Take regular polygons circumscribed and inscribed to B such that the ratio of the former to the latter is less than the ratio $B : S$.

Inscribe in A a similar polygon to that inscribed in B, and erect a pyramid on the polygon inscribed in A with apex the same as that of the cone.

In this case

(polygon in A) : (polygon in B) $= C^2 : E^2$

$\quad\quad\quad = C : D$

$>$ (polygon in A) : (surface of pyramid excluding base).

This is clear because the ratio of C to D is greater than the ratio of the perpendicular from the centre of A on a side of the polygon to the perpendicular from the apex of the cone on the same side.

Therefore

(surface of pyramid) $>$ (polygon in B).

But   (polygon about B) : (polygon in B) $< B : S$.

Therefore, *a fortiori*,

(polygon about B) : (surface of pyramid) $< B : S$;

which is impossible.

Since therefore B is neither greater nor less than S,

$$B = S.$$

PROPOSITION 15

The surface of any isosceles cone has the same ratio to its base as the side of the cone has to the radius of the base.

By Prop. 14, the surface of the cone is equal to a circle whose radius is a mean proportional between the side of the cone and the radius of the base.

Hence, since circles are to one another as the squares of their radii, the proposition follows.

PROPOSITION 16

If an isosceles cone be cut by a plane parallel to the base, the portion of the surface of the cone between the parallel planes is equal to a circle whose radius is a mean proportional between (1) the portion of the side of the cone intercepted by the parallel planes and (2) the line which is equal to the sum of the radii of the circles in the parallel planes.

Let OAB be a triangle through the axis of a cone, DE its intersection with the plane cutting off the frustum, and OFC the axis of the cone.

Then the surface of the cone OAB is equal to a circle whose radius is equal to $\sqrt{OA \cdot AC}$.   [Prop. 14.]

Similarly the surface of the cone ODE is equal to a circle whose radius is equal to $\sqrt{OD \cdot DF}$.

And the surface of the frustum is equal to the difference between the two circles.

Now

$$OA \cdot AC - OD \cdot DF = DA \cdot AC + OD \cdot AC - OD \cdot DF.$$

But $OD \cdot AC = OA \cdot DF$,

since $OA : AC = OD : DF.$

Hence $OA \cdot AC - OD \cdot DF = DA \cdot AC + DA \cdot DF$

$$= DA \cdot (AC + DF).$$

And, since circles are to one another as the squares of their radii, it follows that the difference between the circles whose radii are $\sqrt{OA \cdot AC}$, $\sqrt{OD \cdot DF}$ respectively is equal to a circle whose radius is $\sqrt{DA \cdot (AC + DF)}$.

Therefore the surface of the frustum is equal to this circle.

LEMMAS

"1. *Cones having equal height have the same ratio as their bases; and those having equal bases have the same ratio as their heights*[1].

2. *If a cylinder be cut by a plane parallel to the base, then, as the cylinder is to the cylinder, so is the axis to the axis*[2].

[1]Euclid XII. 11. "Cones and cylinders of equal height are to one another as their bases." Euclid XII. 14. "Cones and cylinders on equal bases are to one another as their heights."

[2]Euclid XII. 13. "If a cylinder be cut by a plane parallel to the opposite planes [the bases], then, as the cylinder is to the cylinder, so will the axis be to the axis."

3. *The cones which have the same bases as the cylinders [and equal height] are in the same ratio as the cylinders.*

4. *Also the bases of equal cones are reciprocally proportional to their heights; and those cones whose bases are reciprocally proportional to their heights are equal.*[1]

5. *Also the cones, the diameters of whose bases have the same ratio as their axes, are to one another in the triplicate ratio of the diameters of the bases.*[2]

And all these propositions have been proved by earlier geometers."

PROPOSITION 17

If there be two isosceles cones, and the surface of one cone be equal to the base of the other, while the perpendicular from the centre of the base [of the first cone] on the side of that cone is equal to the height [of the second], the cones will be equal.

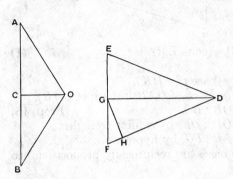

Let OAB, DEF be triangles through the axes of two cones respectively, C, G the centres of the respective bases, GH the perpendicular from G on FD; and suppose that the base of the cone OAB is equal to the surface of the cone DEF, and that $OC = GH$.

Then, since the base of OAB is equal to the surface of DEF,

(base of cone OAB) : (base of cone DEF)

= (surface of DEF) : (base of DEF)

= $DF : FG$ [Prop. 15]

= $DG : GH$, by similar triangles,

= $DG : OC$.

Therefore the bases of the cones are reciprocally proportional to their heights; whence the cones are equal. [*Lemma* 4.]

PROPOSITION 18

Any solid rhombus consisting of isosceles cones is equal to the cone which has its base equal to the surface of one of the cones composing the rhombus and its height equal to the perpendicular drawn from the apex of the second cone to one side of the first cone.

Let the rhombus be $OABD$ consisting of two cones with apices O, D and with a common base (the circle about AB as diameter).

Let FHK be another cone with base equal to the surface of the cone OAB and height FG equal to DE, the perpendicular from D on OB.

Then shall the cone FHK be equal to the rhombus.

Construct a third cone LMN with base (the circle about MN) equal to the base of OAB and height LP equal to OD.

[1]Euclid xii. 15. "The bases of equal cones and cylinders are reciprocally proportional to their heights; and those cones and cylinders whose bases are reciprocally proportional to their heights are equal."

[2]Euclid xii. 12. "Similar cones and cylinders are to one another in the triplicate ratio of the diameters of their bases."

Then, since $\qquad\qquad LP = OD,$
$$LP : CD = OD : CD.$$
But   [Lemma 1] $OD : CD = $ (rhombus $OADB$) : (cone DAB),
and $\qquad\qquad LP : CD = $ (cone LMN) : (cone DAB).
It follows that

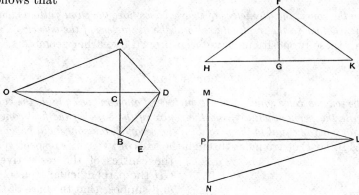

$$\text{(rhombus } OADB) = \text{(cone } LMN). \qquad\qquad (1)$$
Again, since $AB = MN$, and
$$\text{(surface of } OAB) = \text{(base of } FHK),$$
(base of FHK) : (base of LMN) = (surface of OAB) : (base of OAB)
$$= OB : BC \qquad\qquad [\text{Prop. } 15]$$
$$= OD : DE, \text{ by similar triangles,}$$
$$= LP : FG, \text{ by hypothesis.}$$
Thus, in the cones FHK, LMN, the bases are reciprocally proportional to the heights.

Therefore the cones FHK, LMN are equal,
and hence, by (1) the cone FHK is equal to the given solid rhombus.

PROPOSITION 19

If an isosceles cone be cut by a plane parallel to the base, and on the resulting circular section a cone be described having as its apex the centre of the base [of the first cone], and if the rhombus so formed be taken away from the whole cone, the part remaining will be equal to the cone with base equal to the surface of the portion of the first cone between the parallel planes and with height equal to the perpendicular drawn from the centre of the base of the first cone on one side of that cone.

Let the cone OAB be cut by a plane parallel to the base in the circle on DE as diameter. Let C be the centre of the base of the cone, and with C as apex and the circle about DE as base describe a cone, making with the cone ODE the rhombus $ODCE$.

Take a cone FGH with base equal to the surface of the frustum $DABE$ and height equal to the perpendicular (CK) from C on AO.

Then shall the cone FGH be equal to the difference between the cone OAB and the rhombus $ODCE$.

Take (1) a cone LMN with base equal to the surface of the cone OAB, and height equal to CK,

(2) a cone PQR with base equal to the surface of the cone ODE and height equal to CK.

Now, since the surface of the cone OAB is equal to the surface of the cone ODE together with that of the frustum $DABE$, we have, by the construction,

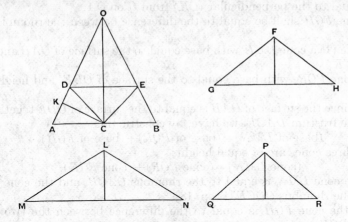

$$\text{(base of } LMN) = \text{(base of } FGH) + \text{(base of } PQR)$$

and, since the heights of the three cones are equal,

$$\text{(cone } LMN) = \text{(cone } FGH) + \text{(cone } PQR).$$

But the cone LMN is equal to the cone OAB [Prop. 17], and the cone PQR is equal to the rhombus $ODCE$ [Prop. 18].

Therefore (cone OAB) = (cone FGH) + (rhombus $ODCE$), and the proposition is proved.

PROPOSITION 20

If one of the two isosceles cones forming a rhombus be cut by a plane parallel to the base and on the resulting circular section a cone be described having the same apex as the second cone, and if the resulting rhombus be taken from the whole rhombus, the remainder will be equal to the cone with base equal to the surface of the portion of the cone between the parallel planes and with height equal to the perpendicular drawn from the apex of the second cone to the side of the first cone.

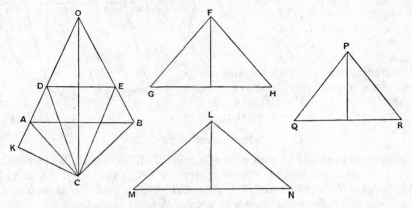

Let the rhombus be $OACB$, and let the cone OAB be cut by a plane parallel to its base in the circle about DE as diameter. With this circle as base and C

as apex describe a cone, which therefore with *ODE* forms the rhombus *ODCE*.

Take a cone *FGH* with base equal to the surface of the frustum *DABE* and height equal to the perpendicular (*CK*) from *C* on *OA*.

The cone *FGH* shall be equal to the difference between the rhombi *OACB*, *ODCE*.

For take (1) a cone *LMN* with base equal to the surface of *OAB* and height equal to *CK*,

(2) a cone *PQR*, with base equal to the surface of *ODE*, and height equal to *CK*.

Then, since the surface of *OAB* is equal to the surface of *ODE* together with that of the frustum *DABE*, we have, by construction,

$$\text{(base of } LMN) = \text{(base of } PQR) + \text{(base of } FGH),$$

and the three cones are of equal height;

therefore $\quad\quad\text{(cone } LMN) = \text{(cone } PQR) + \text{(cone } FGH).$

But the cone *LMN* is equal to the rhombus *OACB*, and the cone *PQR* is equal to the rhombus *ODCE* [Prop. 18].

Hence the cone *FGH* is equal to the difference between the two rhombi *OACB*, *ODCE*.

PROPOSITION 21

A regular polygon of an even number of sides being inscribed in a circle, as ABC···A'···C'B'A, so that AA' is a diameter, if two angular points next but one to each other, as B, B', be joined, and the other lines parallel to BB' and joining pairs of angular points be drawn, as CC', DD'···, then

$$(BB' + CC' + \cdots) : AA' = A'B : BA.$$

Let *BB'*, *CC'*, *DD'*, ··· meet *AA'* in *F*, *G*, *H*, ···; and let *CB'*, *DC'*, ··· be joined meeting *AA'* in *K*, *L*, ··· respectively.

Then clearly *CB'*, *DC'*, ··· are parallel to one another and to *AB*.

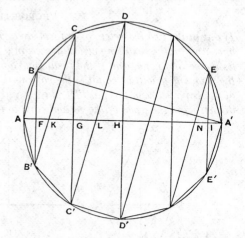

Hence, by similar triangles,

$$BF : FA = B'F : FK$$
$$= CG : GK$$
$$= C'G : GL$$
$$\cdots\cdots\cdots\cdots$$
$$= E'I : IA';$$

and, summing the antecedents and consequents respectively, we have

$$(BB' + CC' + \cdots) : AA' = BF : FA$$
$$= A'B : BA.$$

PROPOSITION 22

If a polygon be inscribed in a segment of a circle LAL' so that all its sides excluding the base are equal and their number even, as LK···A···K'L', A being the middle point of the segment, and if the lines BB', CC', ··· parallel to the base LL' and joining pairs of angular points be drawn, then

$$(BB' + CC' + \cdots + LM) : AM = A'B : BA,$$

where M is the middle point of LL' and AA' is the diameter through M.

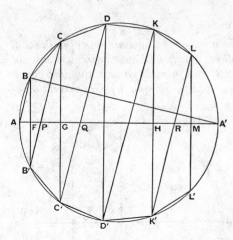

Joining CB', DC', $\cdots LK'$, as in the last proposition, and supposing that they meet AM in P, Q, $\cdots R$, while BB', CC', $\cdots$, KK' meet AM in F, G, $\cdots H$, we have, by similar triangles,

$$BF : FA = B'F : FP$$
$$= CG : PG$$
$$= C'G : GQ$$
$$\cdots\cdots\cdots\cdots$$
$$= LM : RM;$$

and, summing the antecedents and consequents, we obtain
$$(BB'+CC'+\cdots+LM) : AM$$
$$= BF : FA$$
$$= A'B : BA.$$

PROPOSITION 23

Take a great circle $ABC \cdots$ of a sphere, and inscribe in it a regular polygon whose sides are a multiple of four in number. Let AA', MM' be diameters at right angles and joining opposite angular points of the polygon.

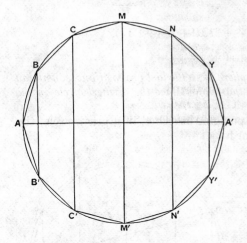

Then, if the polygon and great circle revolve together about the diameter AA', the angular points of the polygon, except A, A', will describe circles on the surface of the sphere at right angles to the diameter AA'. Also the sides of the polygon will describe portions of conical surfaces, e.g. BC will describe a surface forming part of a cone whose base is a circle about CC' as diameter and whose apex is the point in which CB, $C'B'$ produced meet each other and the diameter AA'.

Comparing the hemisphere MAM' and that half of the figure described by the revolution of the polygon which is included in the hemisphere, we see that the surface of the hemisphere and the surface of the inscribed figure have the same boundaries in one plane (viz. the circle on MM' as diameter), the former surface entirely includes the latter, and they are both concave in the same direction.

Therefore [*Assumptions*, 4] the surface of the hemisphere is greater than that of the inscribed figure; and the same is true of the other halves of the figures.

Hence *the surface of the sphere is greater than the surface described by the revolution of the polygon inscribed in the great circle about the diameter of the great circle.*

PROPOSITION 24

If a regular polygon $AB \cdots A' \cdots B'A$, the number of whose sides is a multiple of four, be inscribed in a great circle of a sphere, and if BB' subtending two sides be joined, and all the other lines parallel to BB' and joining pairs of angular points be drawn, then the surface of the figure inscribed in the sphere by the revolution of the polygon about the diameter AA' is equal to a circle the square of whose radius is equal to the rectangle

$$BA(BB'+CC'+ \cdots).$$

The surface of the figure is made up of the surfaces of parts of different cones.

Now the surface of the cone ABB' is equal to a circle whose radius is $\sqrt{BA \cdot \frac{1}{2}BB'}$.   [Prop. 14]

The surface of the frustum $BB'C'C$ is equal to a circle of radius $\sqrt{BC \cdot \frac{1}{2}(BB'+CC')}$,   [Prop. 16] and so on.

It follows, since $BA = BC = \cdots$, that the whole surface is equal to a circle whose radius is equal to

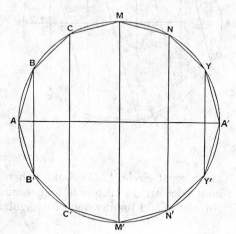

$$\sqrt{BA(BB'+CC'+ \cdots +MM'+ \cdots +YY')}.$$

PROPOSITION 25

The surface of the figure inscribed in a sphere as in the last propositions, consisting of portions of conical surfaces, is less than four times the greatest circle in the sphere.

Let $AB \cdots A' \cdots B'A$ be a regular polygon inscribed in a great circle, the number of its sides being a multiple of four.

As before, let BB' be drawn subtending two sides, and $CC', \cdots YY'$ parallel to BB'.

Let R be a circle such that the square of its radius is equal to

$$AB(BB'+CC'+ \cdots +YY'),$$

so that the surface of the figure inscribed in the sphere is equal to R.
                               [Prop. 24]

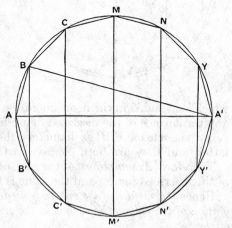

Now
$$(BB'+CC'+ \cdots +YY') : AA'$$
$$= A'B : AB, \quad \text{[Prop. 21]}$$
whence $\quad AB(BB'+CC'+ \cdots +YY')$
$$= AA' \cdot A'B.$$

Hence   (radius of R)$^2 = AA' \cdot A'B$
$$< AA'^2.$$

Therefore the surface of the inscribed figure, or the circle R, is less than four times the circle $AMA'M'$.

PROPOSITION 26

The figure inscribed as above in a sphere is equal [in volume] to a cone whose base is a circle equal to the surface of the figure inscribed in the sphere and whose height is equal to the perpendicular drawn from the centre of the sphere to one side of the polygon.

Suppose, as before, that $AB \cdots A' \cdots B'A$ is the regular polygon inscribed in a great circle, and let BB', CC', $\cdots$ be joined.

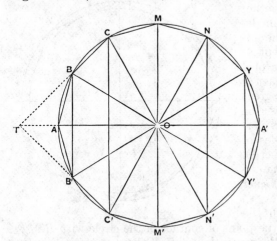

With apex O construct cones whose bases are the circles on BB', CC', $\cdots$ as diameters in planes perpendicular to AA'.

Then $OBAB'$ is a solid rhombus, and its volume is equal to a cone whose base is equal to the surface of the cone ABB' and whose height is equal to the perpendicular from O on AB [Prop. 18]. Let the length of the perpendicular be p.

Again, if CB, $C'B'$ produced meet in T, the portion of the solid figure which is described by the revolution of the triangle BOC about AA' is equal to the difference between the rhombi $OCTC'$ and $OBTB'$, i.e. to a cone whose base is equal to the surface of the frustum $BB'C'C$ and whose height is p [Prop. 20].

Proceeding in this manner, and adding, we prove that, since cones of equal height are to one another as their bases, the volume of the solid of revolution is equal to a cone with height p and base equal to the sum of the surfaces of the cone BAB', the frustum $BB'C'C$, etc., i.e. a cone with height p and base equal to the surface of the solid.

PROPOSITION 27

The figure inscribed in the sphere as before is less than four times the cone whose base is equal to a great circle of the sphere and whose height is equal to the radius of the sphere.

By Prop. 26 the volume of the solid figure is equal to a cone whose base is equal to the surface of the solid and whose height is p, the perpendicular from O on any side of the polygon. Let R be such a cone.

Take also a cone S with base equal to the great circle, and height equal to the radius, of the sphere.

Now, since the surface of the inscribed solid is less than four times the great circle [Prop. 25], the base of the cone R is less than four times the base of the cone S.

Also the height (p) of R is less than the height of S.

Therefore the volume of R is less than four times that of S; and the proposition is proved.

Proposition 28

Let a regular polygon, whose sides are a multiple of four in number, be circumscribed about a great circle of a given sphere, as $AB \cdots A' \cdots B'A$; and about the polygon describe another circle, which will therefore have the same centre as the great circle of the sphere. Let AA' bisect the polygon and cut the sphere in a, a'.

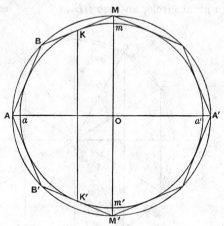

If the great circle and the circumscribed polygon revolve together about AA', the great circle will describe the surface of a sphere, the angular points of the polygon except A, A' will move round the surface of a larger sphere, the points of contact of the sides of the polygon with the great circle of the inner sphere will describe circles on that sphere in planes perpendicular to AA', and the sides of the polygon themselves will describe portions of conical surfaces. *The circumscribed figure will thus be greater than the sphere itself.*

Let any side, as BM, touch the inner circle in K, and let K' be the point of contact of the circle with $B'M'$.

Then the circle described by the revolution of KK' about AA' is the boundary in one plane of two surfaces

(1) the surface formed by the revolution of the circular segment KaK', and

(2) the surface formed by the revolution of the part $KB \cdots A \cdots B'K'$ of the polygon.

Now the second surface entirely includes the first, and they are both concave in the same direction;

therefore [*Assumptions*, 4] the second surface is greater than the first.

The same is true of the portion of the surface on the opposite side of the circle on KK' as diameter.

Hence, adding, we see that *the surface of the figure circumscribed to the given sphere is greater than that of the sphere itself.*

Proposition 29

In a figure circumscribed to a sphere in the manner shown in the previous proposition the surface is equal to a circle the square on whose radius is equal to
$$AB(BB' + CC' + \cdots).$$

For the figure circumscribed to the sphere is inscribed in a larger sphere, and the proof of Prop. 24 applies.

Proposition 30

The surface of a figure circumscribed as before about a sphere is greater than four times the great circle of the sphere.

Let $AB \cdots A' \cdots B'A$ be the regular polygon of $4n$ sides which by its revolution about AA' describes the figure circumscribing the sphere of which $ama'm'$ is a great circle. Suppose aa', AA' to be in one straight line.

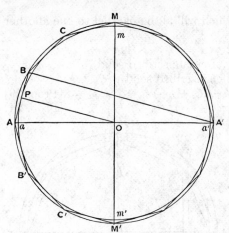

Let R be a circle equal to the surface of the circumscribed solid.

Now

$$(BB'+CC'+\cdots):AA'=A'B:BA,$$
$$\text{[as in Prop. 21]}$$

so that

$$AB(BB'+CC'+\cdots)=AA'\cdot A'B.$$

Hence $(\text{radius of } R)=\sqrt{AA'\cdot A'B}$
$$\text{[Prop. 29]}$$
$$>A'B.$$

But $A'B=2OP$, where P is the point in which AB touches the circle $ama'm'$.

Therefore $(\text{radius of } R)>(\text{diameter of circle } ama'm')$;

whence R, and therefore the surface of the circumscribed solid, is greater than four times the great circle of the given sphere.

PROPOSITION 31

The solid of revolution circumscribed as before about a sphere is equal to a cone whose base is equal to the surface of the solid and whose height is equal to the radius of the sphere.

The solid is, as before, a solid inscribed in a larger sphere; and, since the perpendicular on any side of the revolving polygon is equal to the radius of the inner sphere, the proposition is identical with Prop. 26.

COR. *The solid circumscribed about the smaller sphere is greater than four times the cone whose base is a great circle of the sphere and whose height is equal to the radius of the sphere.*

For, since the surface of the solid is greater than four times the great circle of the inner sphere [Prop. 30], the cone whose base is equal to the surface of the solid and whose height is the radius of the sphere is greater than four times the cone of the same height which has the great circle for base. [*Lemma* 1.]

Hence, by the proposition, the volume of the solid is greater than four times the latter cone.

PROPOSITION 32

If a regular polygon with $4n$ sides be inscribed in a great circle of a sphere, as $ab\cdots a'\cdots b'a$, and a similar polygon $AB\cdots A'\cdots B'A$ be described about the great circle, and if the polygons revolve with the great circle about the diameters aa', AA' respectively, so that they describe the surfaces of solid figures inscribed in and circumscribed to the sphere respectively, then

(1) *the surfaces of the circumscribed and inscribed figures are to one another in the duplicate ratio of their sides, and*

(2) *the figures themselves [i.e. their volumes] are in the triplicate ratio of their sides.*

(1) Let AA', aa' be in the same straight line, and let $MmOm'M'$ be a diameter at right angles to them.

Join BB', CC', $\cdots$ and bb', cc', $\cdots$ which will all be parallel to one another and MM'.

Suppose R, S to be circles such that

$$R = (\text{surface of circumscribed solid}),$$
$$S = (\text{surface of inscribed solid}).$$

Then 　　　(radius of R)$^2 = AB(BB' + CC' + \cdots)$ 　　　　[Prop. 29]
　　　　　　(radius of S)$^2 = ab(bb' + cc' + \cdots)$. 　　　　[Prop. 24]

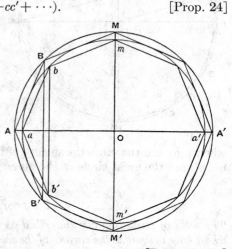

And, since the polygons are similar, the rectangles in these two equations are similar, and are therefore in the ratio of

$$AB^2 : ab^2.$$

Hence
(surface of circumscribed solid) : (surface of inscribed solid) $= AB^2 : ab^2$.

(2) Take a cone V whose base is the circle R and whose height is equal to Oa, and a cone W whose base is the circle S and whose height is equal to the perpendicular from O on ab, which we will call p.

Then V, W are respectively equal to the volumes of the circumscribed and inscribed figures. 　　　　[Props. 31, 26]

Now, since the polygons are similar,

$$AB : ab = Oa : p$$
$$= (\text{height of cone } V) : (\text{height of cone } W);$$

and, as shown above, the bases of the cones (the circles R, S) are in the ratio of AB^2 to ab^2.

Therefore 　　　　　　　　　$V : W = AB^3 : ab^3$.

PROPOSITION 33

The surface of any sphere is equal to four times the greatest circle in it.

Let C be a circle equal to four times the great circle.

Then, if C is not equal to the surface of the sphere, it must either be less or greater.

I. Suppose C less than the surface of the sphere.

It is then possible to find two lines β, γ, of which β is the greater, such that

$$\beta : \gamma < (\text{surface of sphere}) : C.$$ 　　　　[Prop. 2]

Take such lines, and let δ be a mean proportional between them.

Suppose similar regular polygons with $4n$ sides circumscribed about and inscribed in a great circle such that the ratio of their sides is less than the ratio $\beta : \delta$. 　　　　[Prop. 3]

Let the polygons with the circle revolve together about a diameter common to all, describing solids of revolution as before.

Then   (surface of outer solid) : (surface of inner solid)
                = (side of outer)^2 : (side of inner)^2 [Prop. 32]
                $< \beta^2 : \delta^2$, or $\beta : \gamma$
                $<$ (surface of sphere) : C, *a fortiori.*

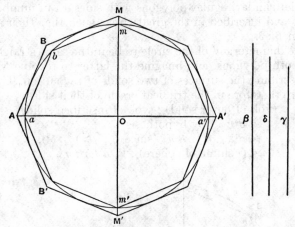

But this is impossible, since the surface of the circumscribed solid is greater than that of the sphere [Prop. 28], while the surface of the inscribed solid is less than C [Prop. 25].

Therefore C is not less than the surface of the sphere.

II. Suppose C greater than the surface of the sphere.

Take lines β, γ, of which β is the greater, such that
$$\beta : \gamma < C : \text{(surface of sphere)}.$$

Circumscribe and inscribe to the great circle similar regular polygons, as before, such that their sides are in a ratio less than that of β to δ, and suppose solids of revolution generated in the usual manner.

Then, in this case,
            (surface of circumscribed solid) : (surface of inscribed solid)
                $< C :$ (surface of sphere).

But this is impossible, because the surface of the circumscribed solid is greater than C [Prop. 30], while the surface of the inscribed solid is less than that of the sphere [Prop. 23].

Thus C is not greater than the surface of the sphere.

Therefore, since it is neither greater nor less, C is equal to the surface of the sphere.

PROPOSITION 34

Any sphere is equal to four times the cone which has its base equal to the greatest circle in the sphere and its height equal to the radius of the sphere.

Let the sphere be that of which $ama'm'$ is a great circle.

If now the sphere is not equal to four times the cone described, it is either greater or less.

I. If possible, let the sphere be greater than four times the cone.

Suppose V to be a cone whose base is equal to four times the great circle and whose height is equal to the radius of the sphere.

Then, by hypothesis, the sphere is greater than V; and two lines β, γ can be found (of which β is the greater) such that

$$\beta : \gamma < (\text{volume of sphere}) : V.$$

Between β and γ place two arithmetic means δ, ϵ.

As before, let similar regular polygons with sides $4n$ in number be circumscribed about and inscribed in the great circle, such that their sides are in a ratio less than $\beta : \delta$.

Imagine the diameter aa' of the circle to be in the same straight line with a diameter of both polygons, and imagine the latter to revolve with the circle about aa', describing the surfaces of two solids of revolution. The volumes of these solids are therefore in the triplicate ratio of their sides.   [Prop. 32]

Thus   (vol. of outer solid) : (vol. of inscribed solid)

$< \beta^3 : \delta^3$, by hypothesis,

$< \beta : \gamma$, *a fortiori* (since $\beta : \gamma > \beta^3 : \delta^3$),

$< (\text{volume of sphere}) : V$, *a fortiori*.

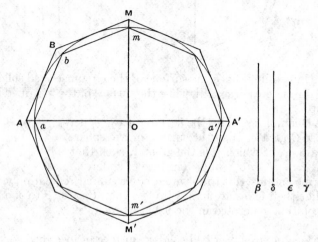

But this is impossible, since the volume of the circumscribed solid is greater than that of the sphere [Prop. 28], while the volume of the inscribed solid is less than V [Prop. 27].

Hence the sphere is not greater than V, or four times the cone described in the enunciation.

II. If possible, let the sphere be less than V.

In this case we take β, γ (β being the greater) such that

$$\beta : \gamma < V : (\text{volume of sphere}).$$

The rest of the construction and proof proceeding as before, we have finally

(volume of outer solid) : (volume of inscribed solid)

$< V : (\text{volume of sphere}).$

But this is impossible, because the volume of the outer solid is greater than V [Prop. 31, Cor.], and the volume of the inscribed solid is less than the volume of the sphere.

Hence the sphere is not less than V.

Since then the sphere is neither less nor greater than V, it is equal to V, or to four times the cone described in the enunciation.

Cor. From what has been proved it follows that *every cylinder whose base is the greatest circle in a sphere and whose height is equal to the diameter of the sphere is $\frac{3}{2}$ of the sphere, and its surface together with its bases is $\frac{3}{2}$ of the surface of the sphere.*

For the cylinder is three times the cone with the same base and height [Eucl. XII. 10], i.e. six times the cone with the same base and with height equal to the radius of the sphere.

But the sphere is four times the latter cone [Prop. 34]. Therefore the cylinder is $\frac{3}{2}$ of the sphere.

Again, the surface of a cylinder (excluding the bases) is equal to a circle whose radius is a mean proportional between the height of the cylinder and the diameter of its base [Prop. 13].

In this case the height is equal to the diameter of the base and therefore the circle is that whose radius is the diameter of the sphere, or a circle equal to four times the great circle of the sphere.

Therefore the surface of the cylinder with the bases is equal to six times the great circle.

And the surface of the sphere is four times the great circle [Prop. 33]; whence

(surface of cylinder with bases) $= \frac{3}{2} \cdot$ (surface of sphere).

PROPOSITION 35

If in a segment of a circle LAL' (where A is the middle point of the arc) a polygon $LK \cdots A \cdots K'L'$ be inscribed of which LL' is one side, while the other sides are $2n$ in number and all equal, and if the polygon revolve with the segment about the diameter AM, generating a solid figure inscribed in a segment of a sphere, then the surface of the inscribed solid is equal to a circle the square on whose radius is equal to the rectangle

$$AB\left(BB' + CC' + \cdots + KK' + \frac{LL'}{2}\right).$$

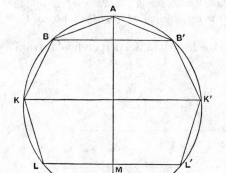

The surface of the inscribed figure is made up of portions of surfaces of cones.

If we take these successively, the surface of the cone BAB' is equal to a circle whose radius is

$\sqrt{AB \cdot \frac{1}{2}BB'}$.   [Prop. 14]

The surface of the frustum of a cone $BCC'B'$ is equal to a circle whose radius is

$$\sqrt{AB \cdot \frac{BB' + CC'}{2}};\quad [\text{Prop. 16}]$$

and so on.

Proceeding in this way and adding, we find, since circles are to one another as the squares of their radii, that the surface of the inscribed figure is equal to a circle whose radius is

$$\sqrt{AB\left(BB' + CC' + \ldots + KK' + \frac{LL'}{2}\right)}.$$

PROPOSITION 36

The surface of the figure inscribed as before in the segment of a sphere is less than that of the segment of the sphere.

This is clear, because the circular base of the segment is a common boundary of each of two surfaces, of which one, the segment, includes the other, the solid, while both are concave in the same direction [*Assumptions*, 4].

PROPOSITION 37

The surface of the solid figure inscribed in the segment of the sphere by the revolution of $LK \cdots A \cdots K'L'$ about AM is less than a circle with radius equal to AL.

Let the diameter AM meet the circle of which LAL' is a segment again in A'. Join $A'B$.

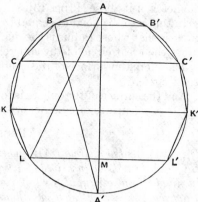

As in Prop. 35, the surface of the inscribed solid is equal to a circle the square on whose radius is

$$AB(BB'+CC'+ \cdots +KK'+LM).$$

But this rectangle

$$= A'B \cdot AM \quad [\text{Prop. 22}]$$
$$< A'A \cdot AM$$
$$< AL^2.$$

Hence the surface of the inscribed solid is less than the circle whose radius is AL.

PROPOSITION 38

The solid figure described as before in a segment of a sphere less than a hemisphere, together with the cone whose base is the base of the segment and whose apex is the centre of the sphere, is equal to a cone whose base is equal to the surface of the inscribed solid and whose height is equal to the perpendicular from the centre of the sphere on any side of the polygon.

Let O be the centre of the sphere, and p the length of the perpendicular from O on AB.

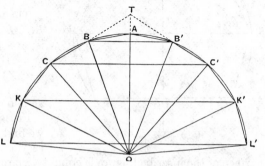

Suppose cones described with O as apex, and with the circles on BB', CC', $\cdots$ as diameters as bases.

Then the rhombus $OBAB'$ is equal to a cone whose base is equal to the surface of the cone BAB', and whose height is p. [Prop. 18]

Again, if CB, $C'B'$ meet in T, the solid described by the triangle BOC as the polygon revolves about AO is the difference between the rhombi $OCTC'$ and $OBTB'$, and is therefore equal to a cone whose base is equal to the surface of the frustum $BCC'B'$ and whose height is p. [Prop. 20]

Similarly for the part of the solid described by the triangle COD as the polygon revolves; and so on.

Hence, by addition, the solid figure inscribed in the segment together with the cone OLL' is equal to a cone whose base is the surface of the inscribed solid and whose height is p.

COR. *The cone whose base is a circle with radius equal to AL and whose height is equal to the radius of the sphere is greater than the sum of the inscribed solid and the cone OLL'.*

For, by the proposition, the inscribed solid together with the cone OLL' is equal to a cone with base equal to the surface of the solid and with height p.

This latter cone is less than a cone with height equal to OA and with base equal to the circle whose radius is AL, because the height p is less than OA, while the surface of the solid is less than a circle with radius AL. [Prop. 37]

PROPOSITION 39

Let lal' be a segment of a great circle of a sphere, being less than a semicircle. Let O be the centre of the sphere, and join Ol, Ol'. Suppose a polygon circumscribed about the sector $Olal'$ such that its sides, excluding the two radii, are $2n$ in number and all equal, as $LK, \cdots BA, AB', \cdots K'L'$; and let OA be that radius of the great circle which bisects the segment lal'.

The circle circumscribing the polygon will then have the same centre O as the given great circle.

Now suppose the polygon and the two circles to revolve together about OA. The two circles will describe spheres, the angular points except A will describe

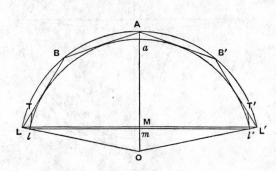

circles on the outer sphere, with diameters BB' etc., the points of contact of the sides with the inner segment will describe circles on the inner sphere, the sides themselves will describe the surfaces of cones or frusta of cones, and the whole figure circumscribed to the segment of the inner sphere by the revolution of the equal sides of the polygon will have for its base the circle on LL' as diameter.

The surface of the solid figure so circumscribed about the sector of the sphere [excluding its base] will be greater than that of the segment of the sphere whose base is the circle on ll' as diameter.

For draw the tangents lT, $l'T'$ to the inner segment at l, l'. These with the sides of the polygon will describe by their revolution a solid whose surface is greater than that of the segment [*Assumptions*, 4].

But the surface described by the revolution of lT is less than that described by the revolution of LT, since the angle TlL is a right angle, and therefore $LT > lT$.

Hence, *a fortiori*, the surface described by $LK \cdots A \cdots K'L'$ is greater than that of the segment.

Cor. *The surface of the figure so described about the sector of the sphere is equal to a circle the square on whose radius is equal to the rectangle*

$$AB\ (BB'+CC'+\cdots+KK'+\tfrac{1}{2}LL').$$

For the circumscribed figure is inscribed in the outer sphere, and the proof of Prop. 35 therefore applies.

PROPOSITION 40

The surface of the figure circumscribed to the sector as before is greater than a circle whose radius is equal to al.

Let the diameter AaO meet the great circle and the circle circumscribing the revolving polygon again in a', A'. Join $A'B$, and let ON be drawn to N, the point of contact of AB with the inner circle.

Now, by Prop. 39, Cor., the surface of the solid figure circumscribed to the sector $OlAl'$ is equal to a circle the square on whose radius is equal to the rectangle

$$AB\left(BB'+CC'+\cdots+KK'+\frac{LL'}{2}\right).$$

But this rectangle is equal to $A'B\cdot AM$ [as in Prop. 22].

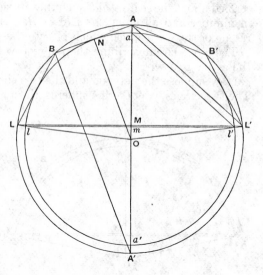

Next, since AL', al' are parallel, the triangles AML', aml' are similar. And $AL'>al'$; therefore $AM>am$.

Also $\quad A'B=2ON=aa'$.

Therefore $\quad A'B\cdot AM>am\cdot aa'$
$$>al'^2.$$

Hence the surface of the solid figure circumscribed to the sector is greater than a circle whose radius is equal to al', or al.

Cor. 1. *The volume of the figure circumscribed about the sector together with the cone whose apex is O and base the circle on LL' as diameter, is equal to the volume of a cone whose base is equal to the surface of the circumscribed figure and whose height is ON.*

For the figure is inscribed in the outer sphere which has the same centre as the inner. Hence the proof of Prop. 38 applies.

Cor. 2. *The volume of the circumscribed figure with the cone OLL' is greater than the cone whose base is a circle with radius equal to al and whose height is equal to the radius (Oa) of the inner sphere.*

For the volume of the figure with the cone OLL' is equal to a cone whose base is equal to the surface of the figure and whose height is equal to ON.

And the surface of the figure is greater than a circle with radius equal to al [Prop. 40], while the heights Oa, ON are equal.

PROPOSITION 41

Let *lal'* be a segment of a great circle of a sphere which is less than a semicircle.

Suppose a polygon inscribed in the sector *Olal'* such that the sides *lk*, · · ·*ba*, *ab'*, · · ·*k'l'* are 2*n* in number and all equal. Let a similar polygon be circumscribed about the sector so that its sides are parallel to those of the first polygon; and draw the circle circumscribing the outer polygon.

Now let the polygons and circles revolve together about *OaA*, the radius bisecting the segment *lal'*.

Then (1) *the surfaces of the outer and inner solids of revolution so described are in the ratio of AB^2 to ab^2, and* (2) *their volumes together with the corresponding cones with the same base and with apex O in each case are as AB^3 to ab^3.*

(1) For the surfaces are equal to circles the squares on whose radii are equal respectively to

$$AB\left(BB'+CC'+\cdots+KK'+\frac{LL'}{2}\right),\qquad \text{[Prop. 39, Cor.]}$$

and

$$ab\left(bb'+cc'+\cdots+kk'+\frac{ll'}{2}\right).\qquad \text{[Prop. 35]}$$

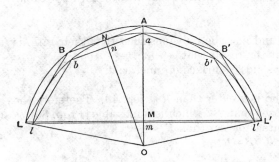

But these rectangles are in the ratio of AB^2 to ab^2. Therefore so are the surfaces.

(2) Let *OnN* be drawn perpendicular to *ab* and *AB*; and suppose the circles which are equal to the surfaces of the outer and inner solids of revolution to be denoted by *S*, *s* respectively.

Now the volume of the circumscribed solid together with the cone *OLL'* is equal to a cone whose base is *S* and whose height is *ON* [Prop. 40, Cor. 1].

And the volume of the inscribed figure with the cone *Oll'* is equal to a cone with base *s* and height *On* [Prop. 38].

But $S:s=AB^2:ab^2$,

and $ON:On=AB:ab$.

Therefore the volume of the circumscribed solid together with the cone *OLL'* is to the volume of the inscribed solid together with the cone *Oll'* as AB^3 is to ab^3 [*Lemma* 5].

PROPOSITION 42

If lal' be a segment of a sphere less than a hemisphere and Oa the radius perpendicular to the base of the segment, the surface of the segment is equal to a circle whose radius is equal to al.

Let *R* be a circle whose radius is equal to *al*. Then the surface of the segment, which we will call *S*, must, if it be not equal to *R*, be either greater or less than *R*.

I. Suppose, if possible, $S > R$.

Let lal' be a segment of a great circle which is less than a semicircle. Join Ol, Ol', and let similar polygons with $2n$ equal sides be circumscribed and inscribed to the sector, as in the previous propositions, but such that

(circumscribed polygon) : (inscribed polygon) $< S : R$.

[Prop. 6]

Let the polygons now revolve with the segment about OaA, generating solids of revolution circumscribed and inscribed to the segment of the sphere.

Then

(surface of outer solid) : (surface of inner solid)
$= AB^2 : ab^2$ [Prop. 41]
$=$ (circumscribed polygon) : (inscribed polygon)
$< S : R$, by hypothesis.

But the surface of the outer solid is greater than S [Prop. 39].

Therefore the surface of the inner solid is greater than R; which is impossible, by Prop. 37.

II. Suppose, if possible, $S < R$.

In this case we circumscribe and inscribe polygons such that their ratio is less than $R : S$; and we arrive at the result that

(surface of outer solid) : (surface of inner solid)
$< R : S$.

But the surface of the outer solid is greater than R [Prop. 40]. Therefore the surface of the inner solid is greater than S : which is impossible [Prop. 36].

Hence, since S is neither greater nor less than R,

$$S = R.$$

PROPOSITION 43

Even if the segment of the sphere is greater than a hemisphere, its surface is still equal to a circle whose radius is equal to al.

For let $lal'a'$ be a great circle of the sphere, aa' being the diameter perpendicular to ll'; and let $la'l'$ be a segment less than a semicircle.

Then, by Prop. 42, the surface of the segment $la'l'$ of the sphere is equal to a circle with radius equal to $a'l$.

Also the surface of the whole sphere is equal to a circle with radius equal to aa' [Prop. 33].

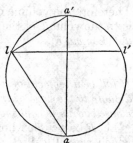

But $aa'^2 - a'l^2 = al^2$, and circles are to one another as the squares on their radii.

Therefore the surface of the segment lal', being the difference between the surfaces of the sphere and of $la'l'$, is equal to a circle with radius equal to al.

PROPOSITION 44

The volume of any sector of a sphere is equal to a cone whose base is equal to the surface of the segment of the sphere included in the sector, and whose height is equal to the radius of the sphere.

Let R be a cone whose base is equal to the surface of the segment lal' of a sphere and whose height is equal to the radius of the sphere; and let S be the volume of the sector $Olal'$.

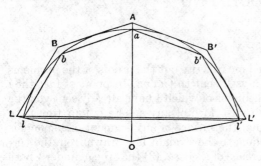

Then, if S is not equal to R, it must be either greater or less.

I. Suppose, if possible, that $S > R$.

Find two straight lines β, γ, of which β is the greater, such that

$$\beta : \gamma < S : R;$$

and let δ, ϵ be two arithmetic means between β, γ.

Let lal' be a segment of a great circle of the sphere. Join Ol, Ol', and let similar polygons with $2n$ equal sides be circumscribed and inscribed to the sector of the circle as before, but such that their sides are in a ratio less than $\beta : \delta$. [Prop. 4].

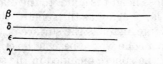

Then let the two polygons revolve with the segment about OaA, generating two solids of revolution.

Denoting the volumes of these solids by V, v respectively, we have

$$(V + \text{cone } OLL') : (v + \text{cone } Oll') = AB^3 : ab^3 \qquad \text{[Prop. 41]}$$
$$< \beta^3 : \delta^3$$
$$< \beta : \gamma, \text{ a fortiori,}$$
$$< S : R, \text{ by hypothesis.}$$

Now $(V + \text{cone } OLL') > S$.

Therefore also $(v + \text{cone } Oll') > R$.

But this is impossible, by Prop. 38, Cor. combined with Props. 42, 43.

Hence $S \not> R$.

II. Suppose, if possible, that $S < R$.

In this case we take β, γ such that

$$\beta : \gamma < R : S,$$

and the rest of the construction proceeds as before.

We thus obtain the relation

$$(V + \text{cone } OLL') : (v + \text{cone } Oll') < R : S.$$

Now $(v + \text{cone } Oll') < S.$

Therefore $(V + \text{cone } OLL') < R;$

which is impossible, by Prop. 40, Cor. 2 combined with Props. 42, 43.

Since then S is neither greater nor less than R,

$$S = R.$$

ON THE SPHERE AND CYLINDER

BOOK TWO

ARCHIMEDES to Dositheus greeting.

"On a former occasion you asked me to write out the proofs of the problems the enunciations of which I had myself sent to Conon. In point of fact they depend for the most part on the theorems of which I have already sent you the demonstrations, namely (1) that the surface of any sphere is four times the greatest circle in the sphere, (2) that the surface of any segment of a sphere is equal to a circle whose radius is equal to the straight line drawn from the vertex of the segment to the circumference of its base, (3) that the cylinder whose base is the greatest circle in any sphere and whose height is equal to the diameter of the sphere is itself in magnitude half as large again as the sphere, while its surface [including the two bases] is half as large again as the surface of the sphere, and (4) that any solid sector is equal to a cone whose base is the circle which is equal to the surface of the segment of the sphere included in the sector, and whose height is equal to the radius of the sphere. Such then of the theorems and problems as depend on these theorems I have written out in the book which I send herewith; those which are discovered by means of a different sort of investigation, those namely which relate to spirals and the conoids, I will endeavour to send you soon.

"The first of the problems was as follows: *Given a sphere, to find a plane area equal to the surface of the sphere.*

"The solution of this is obvious from the theorems aforesaid. For four times the greatest circle in the sphere is both a plane area and equal to the surface of the sphere.

"The second problem was the following."

PROPOSITION 1 (PROBLEM)

Given a cone or a cylinder, to find a sphere equal to the cone or to the cylinder.

If V be the given cone or cylinder, we can make a cylinder equal to $\frac{3}{2}V$. Let this cylinder be the cylinder whose base is the circle on AB as diameter and whose height is OD.

Now, if we could make another cylinder, equal to the cylinder (OD) but such that its height is equal to the diameter of its base, the problem would be solved, because this latter cylinder would be equal to $\frac{3}{2}V$, and the sphere whose diameter is equal to the height (or to the diameter of the base) of the same cylinder would then be the sphere required [I. 34, Cor.].

Suppose the problem solved, and let the cylinder (CG) be equal to the cylinder (OD), while EF, the diameter of the base, is equal to the height CG.

434

Then, since in equal cylinders the heights and bases are reciprocally proportional,

$$AB^2 : EF^2 = CG : OD$$
$$= EF : OD. \tag{1}$$

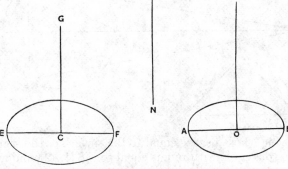

Suppose MN to be such a line that
$$EF^2 = AB \cdot MN. \tag{2}$$

Hence $AB : EF = EF : MN,$

and, combining (1) and (2), we have
$$AB : MN = EF : OD,$$

or $AB : EF = MN : OD.$

Therefore $AB : EF = EF : MN = MN : OD,$

and *EF, MN are two mean proportionals between AB, OD.*

The synthesis of the problem is therefore as follows. Take two mean proportionals EF, MN between AB and OD, and describe a cylinder whose base is a circle on EF as diameter and whose height CG is equal to EF.

Then, since
$$AB : EF = EF : MN = MN : OD,$$
$$EF^2 = AB \cdot MN,$$

and therefore $AB^2 : EF^2 = AB : MN$
$$= EF : OD$$
$$= CG : OD;$$

whence the bases of the two cylinders (OD), (CG) are reciprocally proportional to their heights.

Therefore the cylinders are equal, and it follows that
$$\text{cylinder } (CG) = \tfrac{3}{2}V.$$

The sphere on EF as diameter is therefore the sphere required, being equal to V.

PROPOSITION 2

If BAB' be a segment of a sphere, BB' a diameter of the base of the segment, and O the centre of the sphere, and if AA' be the diameter of the sphere bisecting BB' in M, then the volume of the segment is equal to that of a cone whose base is the same as that of the segment and whose height is h, where
$$h : AM = OA' + A'M : A'M.$$

Measure MH along MA equal to h, and MH' along MA' equal to h', where
$$h' : A'M = OA + AM : AM.$$

Suppose the three cones constructed which have O, H, H' for their apices and the base (BB') of the segment for their common base. Join AB, $A'B$.

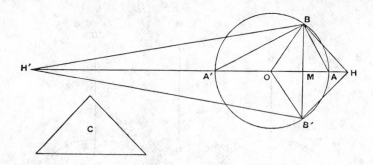

Let C be a cone whose base is equal to the surface of the segment BAB' of the sphere, i.e. to a circle with radius equal to AB [I. 42], and whose height is equal to OA.

Then the cone C is equal to the solid sector $OBAB'$ [I. 44].

Now, since $HM : MA = OA' + A'M : A'M$,

dividendo, $HA : AM = OA : A'M$,

and, alternately, $HA : AO = AM : MA'$,

so that

$$HO : OA = AA' : A'M$$
$$= AB^2 : BM^2$$
$$= \text{(base of cone } C\text{)} : \text{(circle on } BB' \text{ as diameter)}.$$

But OA is equal to the height of the cone C; therefore, since cones are equal if their bases and heights are reciprocally proportional, it follows that the cone C (or the solid sector $OBAB'$) is equal to a cone whose base is the circle on BB' as diameter and whose height is equal to OH.

And this latter cone is equal to the sum of two others having the same base and with heights OM, MH, i.e. to the solid rhombus $OBHB'$.

Hence the sector $OBAB'$ is equal to the rhombus $OBHB'$.

Taking away the common part, the cone OBB',

the segment $BAB' =$ the cone HBB'.

Similarly, by the same method, we can prove that

the segment $BA'B' =$ the cone $H'BB'$.

Alternative proof of the latter property.

Suppose D to be a cone whose base is equal to the surface of the whole sphere and whose height is equal to OA.

Thus D is equal to the volume of the sphere.   [I. 33, 34]

Now, since $OA' + A'M : A'M = HM : MA$,

dividendo and *alternando*, as before,

$$OA : AH = A'M : MA.$$

Again, since $H'M : MA' = OA + AM : AM$,

$$H'A' : OA = A'M : MA$$
$$= OA : AH, \text{ from above.}$$

Componendo, $H'O : OA = OH : HA$,   (1)

Alternately, $H'O : OH = OA : AH$,   (2)

and, *componendo*, $\qquad HH' : HO = OH : HA,$
$$= H'O : OA, \text{ from } (1),$$
whence $\qquad\qquad\qquad HH' \cdot OA = H'O \cdot OH.$ $\qquad\qquad$ (3)

Next, since $\qquad\qquad\quad H'O : OH = OA : AH, \text{ by } (2),$
$$= A'M : MA,$$
$$(H'O + OH)^2 : H'O \cdot OH = (A'M + MA)^2 : A'M \cdot MA,$$
whence, by means of (3),
$$HH'^2 : HH' \cdot OA = AA'^2 : A'M \cdot MA,$$
or $\qquad\qquad\qquad\qquad HH' : OA = AA'^2 : BM^2.$

Now the cone D, which is equal to the sphere, has for its base a circle whose radius is equal to AA', and for its height a line equal to OA.

Hence this cone D is equal to a cone whose base is the circle on BB' as diameter and whose height is equal to HH';

therefore $\qquad\qquad\qquad$ the cone D = the rhombus $HBH'B'$,

or $\qquad\qquad\qquad$ the rhombus $HBH'B'$ = the sphere.

But $\qquad\qquad\qquad$ the segment BAB' = the cone HBB';

therefore the remaining segment $BA'B'$ = the cone $H'BB'$.

COR. *The segment BAB' is to a cone with the same base and equal height in the ratio of $OA' + A'M$ to $A'M$.*

PROPOSITION 3 (PROBLEM)

To cut a given sphere by a plane so that the surfaces of the segments may have to one another a given ratio.

Suppose the problem solved. Let AA' be a diameter of a great circle of the

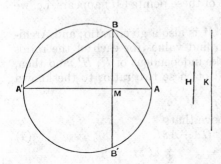

sphere, and suppose that a plane perpendicular to AA' cuts the plane of the great circle in the straight line BB', and AA' in M, and that it divides the sphere so that the surface of the segment BAB' has to the surface of the segment $BA'B'$ the given ratio.

Now these surfaces are respectively equal to circles with radii equal to AB, $A'B$ [I. 42, 43].

Hence the ratio $AB^2 : A'B^2$ is equal to the given ratio, i.e. AM is to MA' in the given ratio.

Accordingly the synthesis proceeds as follows.

If $H : K$ be the given ratio, divide AA' in M so that
$$AM : MA' = H : K.$$
Then $AM : MA' = AB^2 : A'B^2$
$$= \text{(circle with radius } AB) : \text{(circle with radius } A'B)$$
$$= \text{(surface of segment } BAB') : \text{(surface of segment } BA'B').$$
Thus the ratio of the surfaces of the segments is equal to the ratio $H : K$.

PROPOSITION 4 (PROBLEM)

To cut a given sphere by a plane so that the volumes of the segments are to one another in a given ratio.

Suppose the problem solved, and let the required plane cut the great circle

438 ARCHIMEDES

ABA' at right angles in the line BB'. Let AA' be that diameter of the great circle which bisects BB' at right angles (in M), and let O be the centre of the sphere.

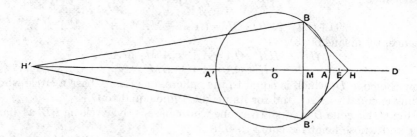

Take H on OA produced, and H' on OA' produced, such that
$$OA'+A'M : A'M = HM : MA, \qquad (1)$$
and
$$OA+AM : AM = H'M : MA'. \qquad (2)$$
Join BH, $B'H$, BH', $B'H'$.

Then the cones HBB', $H'BB'$ are respectively equal to the segments BAB', $BA'B'$ of the sphere [Prop. 2].

Hence the ratio of the cones, and therefore of their altitudes, is given, i.e.
$$HM : H'M = \text{the given ratio.} \qquad (3)$$

We have now three equations (1), (2), (3), in which there appear three as yet undetermined points M, H, H'; and it is first necessary to find, by means of them, another equation in which only one of these points (M) appears, i.e. we have, so to speak, to *eliminate* H, H'.

Now, from (3), it is clear that $HH' : H'M$ is also a given ratio; and Archimedes' method of elimination is, *first*, to find values for each of the ratios $A'H' : H'M$ and $HH' : H'A'$ which are alike independent of H, H', and then, *secondly*, to equate the ratio compounded of these two ratios to the known value of the ratio $HH' : H'M$.

(*a*) To find such a value for $A'H' : H'M$.

It is at once clear from equation (2) above that
$$A'H' : H'M = OA : OA+AM. \qquad (4)$$

(*b*) To find such a value for $HH' : A'H'$.

From (1) we derive
$$A'M : MA = OA'+A'M : HM$$
$$= OA' : AH; \qquad (5)$$
and, from (2), $\quad A'M : MA = H'M : OA+AM$
$$= A'H' : OA. \qquad (6)$$

Thus $\qquad\qquad HA : AO = OA' : A'H'$,
whence $\qquad OH : OA' = OH' : A'H'$,
or $\qquad\qquad OH : OH' = OA' : A'H'$.

It follows that
$$HH' : OH' = OH' : A'H',$$
or $\qquad\qquad HH' \cdot H'A' = OH'^2.$
Therefore $\quad HH' : H'A' = OH'^2 : H'A'^2$
$$= AA'^2 : A'M^2, \text{ by means of (6)}$$

(*c*) To express the ratios $A'H' : H'M$ and $HH' : H'M$ more simply we make the following construction. Produce OA to D so that $OA = AD$. (D will lie beyond H, for $A'M > MA$, and therefore, by (5), $OA > AH$.)

Then $\qquad\qquad\qquad A'H' : H'M = OA : OA + AM$
$$= AD : DM. \tag{7}$$

Now divide AD at E so that
$$HH' : H'M = AD : DE. \tag{8}$$
Thus, using equations (8), (7) and the value of $HH' : H'A'$ above found, we have
$$AD : DE = HH' : H'M$$
$$= (HH' : H'A') \cdot (A'H' : H'M)$$
$$= (AA'^2 : A'M^2) \cdot (AD : DM).$$
But $\qquad\qquad\qquad AD : DE = (DM : DE) \cdot (AD : DM).$

Therefore $\qquad\qquad MD : DE = AA'^2 : A'M^2. \tag{9}$

And D is given, since $AD = OA$. Also $AD : DE$ (being equal to $HH' : H'M$) is a given ratio. Therefore DE is given.

Hence the problem reduces itself to the problem of dividing $A'D$ into two parts at M so that
$$MD : \text{(a given length)} = \text{(a given area)} : A'M^2.$$

Archimedes adds: "If the problem is propounded in this general form, it requires a διορισμός [i.e. it is necessary to investigate the limits of possibility], but, if there be added the conditions subsisting in the present case, it does not require a διορισμός."

In the present case the problem is:

Given a straight line $A'A$ produced to D so that $A'A = 2AD$, and given a point E on AD, to cut AA' in a point M so that
$$AA'^2 : A'M^2 = MD : DE.$$

"And the analysis and synthesis of both problems will be given at the end."[1]

The synthesis of the main problem will be as follows. Let $R : S$ be the given ratio, R being less than S. AA' being a diameter of a great circle, and O the centre, produce OA to D so that $OA = AD$, and divide AD in E so that
$$AE : ED = R : S.$$

Then cut AA' in M so that
$$MD : DE = AA'^2 : A'M^2.$$

Through M erect a plane perpendicular to AA'; this plane will then divide the sphere into segments which will be to one another as R to S.

Take H on $A'A$ produced, and H' on AA' produced, so that
$$OA' + A'M : A'M = HM : MA, \tag{1}$$
$$OA + AM : AM = H'M : MA'. \tag{2}$$
We have then to show that
$$HM : MH' = R : S, \text{ or } AE : ED.$$
(a) We first find the value of $HH' : H'A'$ as follows.

As was shown in the analysis (b),
$$HH' \cdot H'A' = OH'^2,$$
or $\qquad\qquad HH' : H'A' = OH'^2 : H'A'^2$
$$= AA'^2 : A'M^2$$
$$= MD : DE, \text{ by construction.}$$

---

[1]As Archimedes' commentator, Eutocius, notes: ". . . we do not find the promise kept in any of the copies." Sir Thomas Heath's translation of Eutocius' note on the matter, along with the solutions of Dionysodorus and Diocles, is omitted from this edition.—ED.

(β) Next we have

$$H'A' : H'M = OA : OA + AM$$
$$= AD : DM.$$

Therefore $HH' : H'M = (HH' : H'A') \cdot (H'A' : H'M)$
$$= (MD : DE) \cdot (AD : DM)$$
$$= AD : DE,$$

whence $HM : MH' = AE : ED$
$$= R : S.$$

Q. E. D.

PROPOSITION 5 (PROBLEM)

To construct a segment of a sphere similar to one segment and equal in volume to another.

Let ABB' be one segment whose vertex is A and whose base is the circle on BB' as diameter; and let DEF be another segment whose vertex is D and whose base is the circle on EF as diameter. Let AA', DD' be diameters of the great circles passing through BB', EF respectively, and let O, C be the respective centres of the spheres.

Suppose it required to draw a segment similar to DEF and equal in volume to ABB'.

Analysis. Suppose the problem solved, and let def be the required segment, d being the vertex and ef the diameter of the base. Let dd' be the diameter of the sphere which bisects ef at right angles, c the centre of the sphere.

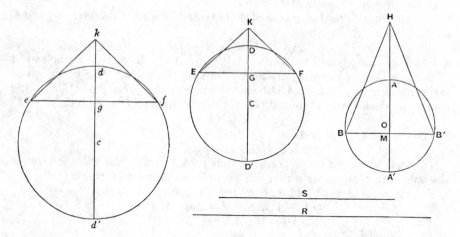

Let M, G, g be the points where BB', EF, ef are bisected at right angles by AA', DD', dd' respectively, and produce OA, CD, cd respectively to H, K, k, so that

$$\left.\begin{array}{l} OA' + A'M : A'M = HM : MA \\ CD' + D'G : D'G = KG : GD \\ cd' + d'g : d'g = kg : gd \end{array}\right\},$$

and suppose cones formed with vertices H, K, k and with the same bases as the respective segments. The cones will then be equal to the segments respectively [Prop. 2].

Therefore, by hypothesis,

the cone HBB' = the cone kef.

Hence

(circle on diameter BB') : (circle on diameter ef) = $kg : HM$,

so that $$BB'^2 : ef^2 = kg : HM \qquad\qquad (1)$$

But, since the segments DEF, def are similar, so are the cones KEF, kef.

Therefore $$KG : EF = kg : ef.$$

And the ratio $KG : EF$ is given. Therefore the ratio $kg : ef$ is given.

Suppose a length R taken such that
$$kg : ef = HM : R. \qquad\qquad (2)$$

Thus R is given.

Again, since $kg : HM = BB'^2 : ef^2 = ef : R$, by (1) and (2), suppose a length S taken such that
$$ef^2 = BB' \cdot S,$$
or $$BB'^2 : ef^2 = BB' : S.$$
Thus $$BB' : ef = ef : S = S : R,$$
and ef, S are two mean proportionals in continued proportion between BB', R.

Synthesis. Let ABB', DEF be great circles, AA', DD' the diameters bisecting BB', EF at right angles in M, G respectively, and O, C the centres.

Take H, K in the same way as before, and construct the cones HBB', KEF, which are therefore equal to the respective segments ABB', DEF.

Let R be a straight line such that
$$KG : EF = HM : R,$$
and between BB', R take two mean proportionals ef, S.

On ef as base describe a segment of a circle with vertex d and similar to the segment of a circle DEF. Complete the circle, and let dd' be the diameter through d, and c the centre. Conceive a sphere constructed of which def is a great circle, and through ef draw a plane at right angles to dd'.

Then shall def be the required segment of a sphere.

For the segments DEF, def of the spheres are similar, like the circular segments DEF, def.

Produce cd to k so that
$$cd' + d'g : d'g = kg : gd.$$
The cones KEF, kef are then similar.

Therefore $$kg : ef = KG : EF = HM : R,$$
whence $$kg : HM = ef : R.$$

But, since BB', ef, S, R are in continued proportion,
$$BB'^2 : ef^2 = BB' : S$$
$$= ef : R$$
$$= kg : HM.$$

Thus the bases of the cones HBB', kef are reciprocally proportional to their heights. The cones are therefore equal, and def is the segment required, being equal in volume to the cone kef.   [Prop. 2]

PROPOSITION 6 (PROBLEM)

Given two segments of spheres, to find a third segment of a sphere similar to one of the given segments and having its surface equal to that of the other.

Let ABB' be the segment to whose surface the surface of the required segment is to be equal, $ABA'B'$ the great circle whose plane cuts the plane of the base of the segment ABB' at right angles in BB'. Let AA' be the diameter which bisects BB' at right angles.

Let DEF be the segment to which the required segment is to be similar, $DED'F$ the great circle cutting the base of the segment at right angles in EF. Let DD' be the diameter bisecting EF at right angles in G.

Suppose the problem solved, def being a segment similar to DEF and having its surface equal to that of ABB'; and complete the figure for def as for DEF, corresponding points being denoted by small and capital letters respectively.

Join AB, DF, df.

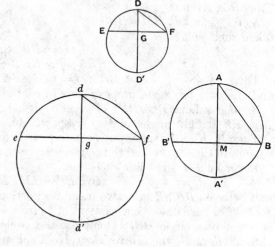

Now, since the surfaces of the segments def, ABB' are equal, so are the circles on df, AB as diameters;

[I. 42, 43]

that is, $df = AB$.

From the similarity of the segments DEF, def we obtain

$$d'd : dg = D'D : DG,$$

and $dg : df = DG : DF$;

whence $d'd : df = D'D : DF$,

or $d'd : AB = D'D : DF$.

But AB, $D'D$, DF are all given;

therefore $d'd$ is given.

Accordingly the synthesis is as follows.

Take $d'd$ such that

$$d'd : AB = D'D : DF. \tag{1}$$

Describe a circle on $d'd$ as diameter, and conceive a sphere constructed of which this circle is a great circle.

Divide $d'd$ at g so that

$$d'g : gd = D'G : GD,$$

and draw through g a plane perpendicular to $d'd$ cutting off the segment def of the sphere and intersecting the plane of the great circle in ef. The segments def, DEF are thus similar, and

$$dg : df = DG : DF.$$

But from above, *componendo*,

$$d'd : dg = D'D : DG.$$

Therefore, *ex aequali*, $d'd : df = D'D : DF$,

whence, by (1), $df = AB$.

Therefore the segment def has its surface equal to the surface of the segment ABB' [I. 42, 43], while it is also similar to the segment DEF.

PROPOSITION 7 (PROBLEM)

From a given sphere to cut off a segment by a plane so that the segment may have a given ratio to the cone which has the same base as the segment and equal height.

Let AA' be the diameter of a great circle of the sphere. It is required to draw a plane at right angles to AA' cutting off a segment, as ABB', such that the segment ABB' has to the cone ABB' a given ratio.

Analysis.

Suppose the problem solved, and let the plane of section cut the plane of the great circle in BB', and the diameter AA' in M. Let O be the centre of the sphere.

Produce OA to H so that

$$OA' + A'M : A'M = HM : MA. \tag{1}$$

Thus the cone HBB' is equal to the segment ABB'.

[Prop. 2]

Therefore the given ratio must be equal to the ratio of the cone HBB' to the cone ABB', *i.e.* to the ratio $HM : MA$.

Hence the ratio $OA' + A'M : A'M$ is given; and therefore $A'M$ is given.

διορισμός.

Now $OA' : A'M > OA' : A'A,$

so that $OA' + A'M : A'M > OA' + A'A : A'A$
$$> 3 : 2.$$

Thus, *in order that a solution may be possible, it is a necessary condition that the given ratio must be greater than* $3 : 2$.

The *synthesis* proceeds thus.

Let AA' be a diameter of a great circle of the sphere, O the centre.

Take a line DE, and a point F on it, such that $DE : EF$ is equal to the given ratio, being greater than $3 : 2$.

Now, since $OA' + A'A : A'A = 3 : 2,$
$$DE : EF > OA' + A'A : A'A,$$
so that $DF : FE > OA' : A'A.$

Hence a point M can be found on AA' such that

$$DF : FE = OA' : A'M. \tag{2}$$

Through M draw a plane at right angles to AA' intersecting the plane of the great circle in BB', and cutting off from the sphere the segment ABB'.

As before, take H on OA produced such that

$$OA' + A'M : A'M = HM : MA.$$

Therefore $HM : MA = DE : EF$, by means of (2).

It follows that the cone HBB', or the segment ABB', is to the cone ABB' in the given ratio $DE : EF$.

Proposition 8

If a sphere be cut by a plane not passing through the centre into two segments $A'BB'$, ABB', *of which* $A'BB'$ *is the greater, then the ratio*
$(segmt.\ A'BB') : (segmt.\ ABB')$
$$< (surface\ of\ A'BB')^2 : (surface\ of\ ABB')$$
$$but > (surface\ of\ A'BB')^{\frac{3}{2}} : (surface\ of\ ABB')^{\frac{3}{2}}.$$

Let the plane of section cut a great circle $A'BAB'$ at right angles in BB', and let AA' be the diameter bisecting BB' at right angles in M.

Let O be the centre of the sphere.

Join $A'B$, AB.

As usual, take H on OA produced, and H' on OA' produced, so that

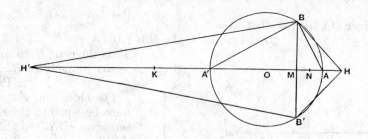

$$OA' + A'M : A'M = HM : MA, \qquad (1)$$
$$OA + AM : AM = H'M : MA', \qquad (2)$$

and conceive cones drawn each with the same base as the two segments and with apices H, H' respectively. The cones are then respectively equal to the segments [Prop. 2], and they are in the ratio of their heights HM, $H'M$.

Also

$$\text{(surface of } A'BB') : \text{(surface of } ABB') = A'B^2 : AB^2 \qquad \text{[I. 42, 43]}$$
$$= A'M : AM.$$

We have therefore to prove

(a) that $\qquad\qquad H'M : MH < A'M^2 : MA^2,$

(b) that $\qquad\qquad H'M : MH > A'M^3 : MA^3.$

(a) From (2) above,

$$A'M : AM = H'M : OA + AM$$
$$= H'A' : OA', \text{ since } OA = OA'.$$

Since $A'M > AM$, $H'A' > OA'$; therefore, if we take K on $H'A'$ so that $OA' = A'K$, K will fall between H' and A'.

And, by (1), $\qquad\qquad A'M : AM = KM : MH.$

Thus $\qquad\qquad KM : MH = H'A' : A'K, \text{ since } A'K = OA',$
$$> H'M : MK.$$

Therefore $\qquad\qquad H'M \cdot MH < KM^2.$

It follows that

$$H'M \cdot MH : MH^2 < KM^2 : MH^2,$$

or $\qquad\qquad H'M : MH < KM^2 : MH^2$
$$< A'M^2 : AM^2, \text{ by (1)}.$$

(b) Since $\qquad\qquad OA' = OA,$
$$A'M \cdot MA < A'O \cdot OA,$$

or $\qquad\qquad A'M : OA' < OA : AM$
$$< H'A' : A'M, \text{ by means of (2)}.$$

Therefore $\qquad\qquad A'M^2 < H'A' \cdot OA'$
$$< H'A' \cdot A'K.$$

Take a point N on $A'A$ such that

$$A'N^2 = H'A' \cdot A'K.$$

Thus $\qquad\qquad H'A' : A'K = A'N^2 : A'K^2. \qquad (3)$

Also $\qquad\qquad H'A' : A'N = A'N : A'K,$

and, componendo,

$$H'N : A'N = NK : A'K,$$

whence $\qquad\qquad A'N^2 : A'K^2 = H'N^2 : NK^2.$

Therefore, by (3),

$$H'A' : A'K = H'N^2 : NK^2.$$

Now $\qquad\qquad H'M : MK > H'N : NK.$

Therefore $\quad H'M^2 : MK^2 > H'A' : A'K$
$$> H'A' : OA'$$
$$> A'M : MA, \text{ by (2), as above,}$$
$$> OA' + A'M : MH, \text{ by (1),}$$
$$> KM : MH.$$

Hence $\qquad H'M^2 : MH^2 = (H'M^2 : MK^2) \cdot (KM^2 : MH^2)$
$$> (KM : MH) \cdot (KM^2 : MH^2).$$

It follows that

$$H'M : MH > KM^{\frac{3}{2}} : MH^{\frac{3}{2}}$$
$$> A'M^{\frac{3}{2}} : AM^{\frac{3}{2}}, \text{ by (1)}.$$

PROPOSITION 9

Of all segments of spheres which have equal surfaces the hemisphere is the greatest in volume.

Let $ABA'B'$ be a great circle of a sphere, AA' being a diameter, and O the centre. Let the sphere be cut by a plane, not passing through O, perpendicular to AA' (at M), and intersecting the plane of the great circle in BB'. The segment ABB' may then be either less than a hemisphere as in Fig. 1, or greater than a hemisphere as in Fig. 2.

Let $DED'E'$ be a great circle of another sphere, DD' being a diameter and C the centre. Let the sphere be cut by a plane through C perpendicular to DD' and intersecting the plane of the great circle in the diameter EE'.

Suppose the surfaces of the segment ABB' and of the hemisphere DEE' to be equal.

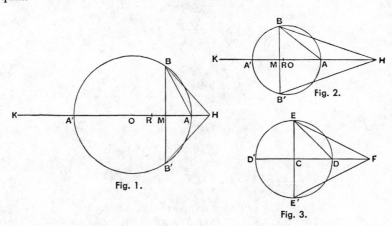

Fig. 1.

Fig. 2.

Fig. 3.

Since the surfaces are equal, $AB = DE$. $\qquad\qquad$ [I. 42, 43]

Now, in Fig. 1, $\qquad AB^2 > 2AM^2$ and $< 2AO^2,$

and, in Fig. 2, $\qquad AB^2 < 2AM^2$ and $> 2AO^2.$

Hence, if R be taken on AA' such that

$$AR^2 = \tfrac{1}{2} AB^2,$$

R will fall between O and M.

Also, since $AB^2 = DE^2$, $AR = CD$.

Produce OA' to K so that $OA' = A'K$, and produce $A'A$ to H so that
$$A'K : A'M = HA : AM,$$
or, *componendo*, $\qquad A'K + A'M : A'M = HM : MA.$ \hfill (1)

Thus the cone HBB' is equal to the segment ABB'. \hfill [Prop. 2]

Again, produce CD to F so that $CD = DF$, and the cone FEE' will be equal to the hemisphere DEE'. \hfill [Prop. 2]

Now $\qquad\qquad\qquad AR \cdot RA' > AM \cdot MA',$

and $\qquad\qquad AR^2 = \tfrac{1}{2}AB^2 = \tfrac{1}{2}AM \cdot AA' = AM \cdot A'K.$

Hence
$$AR \cdot RA' + RA^2 > AM \cdot MA' + AM \cdot A'K,$$
or $\qquad\qquad\qquad AA' \cdot AR > AM \cdot MK$
$$> HM \cdot A'M, \text{ by (1)}.$$

Therefore $\qquad\qquad AA' : A'M > HM : AR,$

or $\qquad\qquad\qquad AB^2 : BM^2 > HM : AR,$

i.e. $\qquad\qquad AR^2 : BM^2 > HM : 2AR$, since $AB^2 = 2AR^2$,
$$> HM : CF.$$

Thus, since $AR = CD$, or CE,

(circle on diam. EE') : (circle on diam. BB') $> HM : CF$.

It follows that
$$\text{(the cone } FEE') > \text{(the cone } HBB'),$$
and therefore the hemisphere DEE' is greater in volume than the segment ABB'.

MEASUREMENT OF A CIRCLE

PROPOSITION 1

The area of any circle is equal to a right-angled triangle in which one of the sides about the right angle is equal to the radius, and the other to the circumference, of the circle.

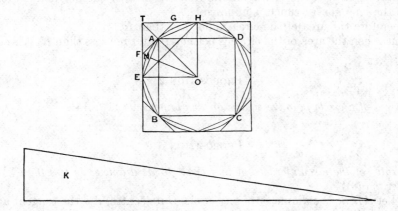

Let $ABCD$ be the given circle, K the triangle described.

Then, if the circle is not equal to K, it must be either greater or less.

I. If possible, let the circle be greater than K.

Inscribe a square $ABCD$, bisect the arcs AB, BC, CD, DA, then bisect (if necessary) the halves, and so on, until the sides of the inscribed polygon whose angular points are the points of division subtend segments whose sum is less than the excess of the area of the circle over K.

Thus the area of the polygon is greater than K.

Let AE be any side of it, and ON the perpendicular on AE from the centre O.

Then ON is less than the radius of the circle and therefore less than one of the sides about the right angle in K. Also the perimeter of the polygon is less than the circumference of the circle, i.e. less than the other side about the right angle in K.

Therefore the area of the polygon is less than K; which is inconsistent with the hypothesis.

Thus the area of the circle is not greater than K.

II. If possible, let the circle be less than K.

Circumscribe a square, and let two adjacent sides, touching the circle in E, H, meet in T. Bisect the arcs between adjacent points of contact and draw the

447

tangents at the points of bisection. Let A be the middle point of the arc EH, and FAG the tangent at A.

Then the angle TAG is a right angle.

Therefore $$TG > GA$$
$$> GH.$$

It follows that the triangle FTG is greater than half the area $TEAH$.

Similarly, if the arc AH be bisected and the tangent at the point of bisection be drawn, it will cut off from the area GAH more than one-half.

Thus, by continuing the process, we shall ultimately arrive at a circumscribed polygon such that the spaces intercepted between it and the circle are together less than the excess of K over the area of the circle.

Thus the area of the polygon will be less than K.

Now, since the perpendicular from O on any side of the polygon is equal to the radius of the circle, while the perimeter of the polygon is greater than the circumference of the circle, it follows that the area of the polygon is greater than the triangle K; which is impossible.

Therefore the area of the circle is not less than K.

Since then the area of the circle is neither greater nor less than K, it is equal to it.

PROPOSITION 2

The area of a circle is to the square on its diameter as 11 *to* 14[1].

PROPOSITION 3

The ratio of the circumference of any circle to its diameter is less than $3\frac{1}{7}$ *but greater than* $3\frac{10}{71}$ [2].

I. Let AB be the diameter of any circle, O its centre, AC the tangent at A; and let the angle AOC be one-third of a right angle.

Then $$OA : AC [= \sqrt{3} : 1] > 265 : 153, \tag{1}$$
and $$OC : CA [= 2 : 1] = 306 : 153. \tag{2}$$

First, draw OD bisecting the angle AOC and meeting AC in D.

Now $$CO : OA = CD : DA, \qquad\qquad \text{[Eucl. VI. 3]}$$
so that $$[CO + OA : OA = CA : DA, \text{ or}]$$
$$CO + OA : CA = OA : AD.$$

Therefore [by (1) and (2)]
$$OA : AD > 571 : 153. \tag{3}$$

---

[1]The text of this proposition is not satisfactory, and Archimedes cannot have placed it before Proposition 3, as the approximation depends upon the result of that proposition.

[2]In view of the interesting questions arising out of the arithmetical content of this proposition of Archimedes, it is necessary, in reproducing it, to distinguish carefully the actual steps set out in the text as we have it from the intermediate steps (mostly supplied by Eutocius) which it is convenient to put in for the purpose of making the proof easier to follow. Accordingly all the steps not actually appearing in the text have been enclosed in square brackets, in order that it may be clearly seen how far Archimedes omits actual calculations and only gives results. It will be observed that he gives two fractional approximations to $\sqrt{3}$ (one being less and the other greater than the real value) without any explanation as to how he arrived at them; and in like manner approximations to the square roots of several large numbers which are not complete squares are merely stated.

Hence $OD^2 : AD^2 [= (OA^2 + AD^2) : AD^2$
$> (571^2 + 153^2) : 153^2]$
$> 349450 : 23409,$

so that $OD : DA > 591\frac{1}{8} : 153.$ (4)

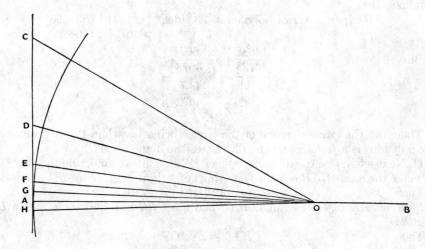

Secondly, let OE bisect the angle AOD, meeting AD in E.
[Then $DO : OA = DE : EA,$
so that $DO + OA : DA = OA : AE.$]
Therefore $OA : AE \,[> (591\frac{1}{8} + 571) : 153,$ by (3) and (4)]
$> 1162\frac{1}{8} : 153.$ (5)
[It follows that
$OE^2 : EA^2 > \{(1162\frac{1}{8})^2 + 153^2\} : 153^2$
$> (1350534\frac{33}{64} + 23409) : 23409$
$> 1373943\frac{33}{64} : 23409.]$
Thus $OE : EA > 1172\frac{1}{8} : 153.$ (6)
Thirdly, let OF bisect the angle AOE and meet AE in F.
We thus obtain the result [corresponding to (3) and (5) above] that
$OA : AF \,[> (1162\frac{1}{8} + 1172\frac{1}{8}) : 153]$
$> 2334\frac{1}{4} : 153.$ (7)
[Therefore $OF^2 : FA^2 > \{(2334\frac{1}{4})^2 + 153^2\} : 153^2$
$> 5472132\frac{1}{16} : 23409.]$
Thus $OF : FA > 2339\frac{1}{4} : 153.$ (8)
Fourthly, let OG bisect the angle AOF, meeting AF in G.
We have then
$OA : AG \,[> (2334\frac{1}{4} + 2339\frac{1}{4}) : 153,$ by means of (7) and (8)]
$> 4673\frac{1}{2} : 153.$
Now the angle AOC, which is one-third of a right angle, has been bisected
four times, and it follows that
$\angle AOG = \frac{1}{48}$ (a right angle).
Make the angle AOH on the other side of OA equal to the angle AOG, and
let GA produced meet OH in H.
Then $\angle GOH = \frac{1}{24}$ (a right angle).

Thus GH is one side of a regular polygon of 96 sides circumscribed to the given circle.

And, since
$$OA : AG > 4673\tfrac{1}{2} : 153,$$
while
$$AB = 2OA,\ GH = 2AG,$$
it follows that
$$AB : \text{(perimeter of polygon of 96 sides)}[>4673\tfrac{1}{2} : 153 \times 96]$$
$$>4673\tfrac{1}{2} : 14688.$$

But
$$\frac{14688}{4673\tfrac{1}{2}} = 3 + \frac{667\tfrac{1}{2}}{4673\tfrac{1}{2}}$$
$$\left[<3 + \frac{667\tfrac{1}{2}}{4672\tfrac{1}{2}} \right]$$
$$<3\tfrac{1}{7}.$$

Therefore the circumference of the circle (being less than the perimeter of the polygon) is *a fortiori* less than $3\tfrac{1}{7}$ times the diameter AB.

II. Next let AB be the diameter of a circle, and let AC, meeting the circle in C, make the angle CAB equal to one-third of a right angle. Join BC.

Then
$$AC : CB[=\sqrt{3} : 1] < 1351 : 780.$$

First, let AD bisect the angle BAC and meet BC in d and the circle in D. Join BD.

Then
$$\angle BAD = \angle dAC$$
$$= \angle dBD,$$
and the angles at D, C are both right angles.

It follows that the triangles ADB, $[ACd]$, BDd are similar.

Therefore
$$AD : DB = BD : Dd$$
$$[= AC : Cd]$$
$$= AB : Bd \qquad\qquad \text{[Eucl. vi. 3]}$$
$$= AB + AC : Bd + Cd$$
$$= AB + AC : BC$$
or
$$BA + AC : BC = AD : DB.$$
[But
$$AC : CB < 1351 : 780, \text{ from above,}$$
while
$$BA : BC = 2 : 1$$
$$= 1560 : 780.]$$
Therefore
$$AD : DB < 2911 : 780. \qquad\qquad (1)$$
[Hence
$$AB^2 : BD^2 < (2911^2 + 780^2) : 780^2$$
$$< 9082321 : 608400.]$$
Thus
$$AB : BD < 3013\tfrac{3}{4} : 780. \qquad\qquad (2)$$

Secondly, let AE bisect the angle BAD, meeting the circle in E; and let BE be joined.

Then we prove, in the same way as before, that
$$AE : EB [= BA + AD : BD$$
$$< (3013\tfrac{3}{4} + 2911) : 780, \text{ by (1) and (2)}]$$
$$< 5924\tfrac{3}{4} : 780$$
$$< 5924\tfrac{3}{4} \times \tfrac{4}{13} : 780 \times \tfrac{4}{13}$$
$$< 1823 : 240. \qquad\qquad (3)$$
[Hence
$$AB^2 : BE^2 < (1823^2 + 240^2) : 240^2$$
$$< 3380929 : 57600.]$$
Therefore
$$AB : BE < 1838\tfrac{9}{11} : 240. \qquad\qquad (4)$$

Thirdly, let AF bisect the angle BAE, meeting the circle in F.

Thus $\qquad AF : FB \,[=BA+AE : BE$
$$< 3661\tfrac{9}{11} : 240, \text{ by (3) and (4)}]$$
$$< 3661\tfrac{9}{11} \times \tfrac{11}{40} : 240 \times \tfrac{11}{40}$$
$$< 1007 : 66. \tag{5}$$

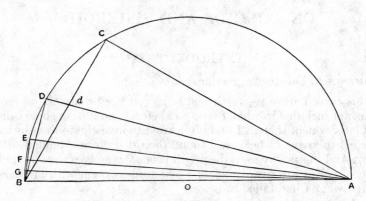

[It follows that
$$AB^2 : BF^2 < (1007^2 + 66^2) : 66^2$$
$$< 1018405 : 4356.]$$

Therefore $\qquad AB : BF < 1009\tfrac{1}{6} : 66.$ $\qquad\qquad$ (6)

Fourthly, let the angle BAF be bisected by AG meeting the circle in G.

Then $\qquad AG : GB \,[=BA+AF : BF]$
$$< 2016\tfrac{1}{6} : 66, \text{ by (5) and (6).}$$

[And $\qquad AB^2 : BG^2 < \{(2016\tfrac{1}{6})^2 + 66^2\} : 66^2$
$$< 4069284\tfrac{1}{36} : 4356.]$$

Therefore $\qquad AB : BG < 2017\tfrac{1}{4} : 66,$

whence $\qquad BG : AB > 66 : 2017\tfrac{1}{4}.$ $\qquad\qquad$ (7)

[Now the angle BAG which is the result of the fourth bisection of the angle BAC, or of one-third of a right angle, is equal to one-fortyeighth of a right angle.

Thus the angle subtended by BG at the centre is
$$\tfrac{1}{24} \text{ (a right angle).]}$$

Therefore BG is a side of a regular inscribed polygon of 96 sides.

It follows from (7) that
$$\text{(perimeter of polygon)} : AB \,[> 96 \times 66 : 2017\tfrac{1}{4}]$$
$$> 6336 : 2017\tfrac{1}{4}.$$

And $\qquad\qquad \dfrac{6336}{2017\tfrac{1}{4}} > 3\tfrac{10}{71}.$

Much more then is the circumference of the circle greater than $3\tfrac{10}{71}$ times the diameter.

Thus the ratio of the circumference to the diameter
$$< 3\tfrac{1}{7} \text{ but } > 3\tfrac{10}{71}.$$

ON CONOIDS AND SPHEROIDS

INTRODUCTION[1]

"ARCHIMEDES to Dositheus greeting.

"In this book I have set forth and send you the proofs of the remaining theorems not included in what I sent you before, and also of some others discovered later which, though I had often tried to investigate them previously, I had failed to arrive at because I found their discovery attended with some difficulty. And this is why even the propositions themselves were not published with the rest. But afterwards, when I had studied them with greater care, I discovered what I had failed in before.

"Now the remainder of the earlier theorems were propositions concerning the right-angled conoid [paraboloid of revolution]; but the discoveries which I have now added relate to an obtuse-angled conoid [hyperboloid of revolution] and to spheroidal figures, some of which I call *oblong* and others *flat*."

I. "Concerning the *right-angled conoid* it was laid down that, if a section of a right-angled cone [a parabola] be made to revolve about the diameter [axis] which remains fixed and return to the position from which it started, the figure comprehended by the section of the right-angled cone is called a *right-angled conoid*, and the diameter which has remained fixed is called its *axis*, while its *vertex* is the point in which the axis meets the surface of the conoid. And if a plane touch the right-angled conoid, and another plane drawn parallel to the tangent plane cut off a segment of the conoid, the *base* of the segment cut off is defined as the portion intercepted by the section of the conoid on the cutting plane, the *vertex* [of the segment] as the point in which the first plane touches the conoid, and the *axis* [of the segment] as the portion cut off within the segment from the line drawn through the vertex of the segment parallel to the axis of the conoid.

"The questions propounded for consideration were"

(1) "why, if a segment of the right-angled conoid be cut off by a plane at right angles to the axis, will the segment so cut off be half as large again as the cone which has the same base as the segment and the same axis, and"

(2) "why, if two segments be cut off from the right-angled conoid by planes drawn in any manner, will the segments so cut off have to one another the duplicate ratio of their axes."

II. "Respecting the *obtuse-angled conoid* we lay down the following premisses. If there be in a plane a section of an obtuse-angled cone [a hyperbola], its

---

[1]The whole of this introductory matter, including the definitions, is translated literally from the Greek text in order that the terminology of Archimedes may be faithfully represented. When this has once been set out, nothing will be lost by returning to modern phraseology and notation. These will accordingly be employed, as usual, when we come to the actual propositions of the treatise.

diameter [axis], and the nearest lines to the section of the obtuse-angled cone [*i.e.* the asymptotes of the hyperbola], and if, the diameter [axis] remaining fixed, the plane containing the aforesaid lines be made to revolve about it and return to the position from which it started, the nearest lines to the section of the obtuse-angled cone [the asymptotes] will clearly comprehend an isosceles cone whose vertex will be the point of concourse of the nearest lines and whose axis will be the diameter [axis] which has remained fixed. The figure comprehended by the section of the obtuse-angled cone is called an *obtuse-angled conoid* [hyperboloid of revolution], its *axis* is the diameter which has remained fixed, and its *vertex* the point in which the axis meets the surface of the conoid. The cone comprehended by the nearest lines to the section of the obtuse-angled cone is called [the cone] *enveloping the conoid,* and the straight line between the vertex of the conoid and the vertex of the cone enveloping the conoid is called [the line] *adjacent to the axis.* And if a plane touch the obtuse-angled conoid, and another plane drawn parallel to the tangent plane cut off a segment of the conoid, the *base* of the segment so cut off is defined as the portion intercepted by the section of the conoid on the cutting plane, the *vertex* [of the segment] as the point of contact of the plane which touches the conoid, the *axis* [of the segment] as the portion cut off within the segment from the line drawn through the vertex of the segment and the vertex of the cone enveloping the conoid; and the straight line between the said vertices is called *adjacent to the axis.*

"Right-angled conoids are all similar; but of obtuse-angled conoids let those be called similar in which the cones enveloping the conoids are similar.

"The following questions are propounded for consideration":

(1) "why, if a segment be cut off from the obtuse-angled conoid by a plane at right angles to the axis, the segment so cut off has to the cone which has the same base as the segment and the same axis the ratio which the line equal to the sum of the axis of the segment and three times the line adjacent to the axis bears to the line equal to the sum of the axis of the segment and twice the line adjacent to the axis, and"

(2) "why, if a segment of the obtuse-angled conoid be cut off by a plane not at right angles to the axis, the segment so cut off will bear to the figure which has the same base as the segment and the same axis, being a segment of a cone, the ratio which the line equal to the sum of the axis of the segment and three times the line adjacent to the axis bears to the line equal to the sum of the axis of the segment and twice the line adjacent to the axis."

III. "Concerning spheroidal figures we lay down the following premisses. If a section of an acute-angled cone [ellipse] be made to revolve about the greater diameter [major axis] which remains fixed and return to the position from which it started, the figure comprehended by the section of the acute-angled cone is called an *oblong spheroid.* But if the section of the acute-angled cone revolve about the lesser diameter [minor axis] which remains fixed and return to the position from which it started, the figure comprehended by the section of the acute-angled cone is called a *flat spheroid.* In either of the spheroids the *axis* is defined as the diameter [axis] which has remained fixed, the *vertex* as the point in which the axis meets the surface of the spheroid, the *centre* as the middle point of the axis, and the *diameter* as the line drawn through the centre at right angles to the axis. And, if parallel planes touch, without cutting, either of the spheroidal figures, and if another plane be drawn parallel to the tangent planes and cutting the spheroid, the *base* of the resulting segments is defined as the portion intercepted by the section of the spheroid on the cutting plane, their *vertices* as the points in which the parallel planes touch the spheroid, and their *axes* as the portions cut off within the segments from the straight line joining their vertices. And that the planes touching the spheroid meet its surface at one point only, and that the straight line joining the points of contact passes through the centre of the spheroid, we shall prove. Those spheroidal figures are called *similar* in which the axes have the same ratio to the 'diameters.' And let segments of spheroidal figures and conoids be called *similar* if they are cut off from similar figures and have their bases similar, while their axes, being either at right angles to the planes of the bases or making equal angles with the corresponding diameters [axes] of the bases, have the same ratio to one another as the corresponding diameters [axes] of the bases.

"The following questions about spheroids are propounded for consideration,"

(1) "why, if one of the spheroidal figures be cut by a plane through the centre at right angles to the axis, each of the resulting segments will be double of the cone having the same base as the segment and the same axis; while, if the plane of section be at right angles to the axis without passing through the centre, (*a*) the greater of the resulting segments will bear to the cone which has the same base as the segment and the same axis the ratio which the line equal to the sum of half the straight line which is the axis of the spheroid and the axis of the lesser segment bears to the axis of the lesser segment, and (*b*) the lesser segment bears to the cone which has the same base as the segment and the same axis the ratio which the line equal to the sum of half the straight line which is the axis of the spheroid and the axis of the greater segment bears to the axis of the greater segment";

(2) "why, if one of the spheroids be cut by a plane passing through the centre but not at right angles to the axis, each of the resulting segments will be double of the figure having the same base as the segment and the same axis and consisting of a segment of a cone.

(3) "But, if the plane cutting the spheroid be neither through the centre nor at right angles to the axis, (*a*) the greater of the resulting segments will have to the figure which has the same base as the segment and the same axis the ratio which the line equal to the sum of half the line joining the vertices of the segments and the axis of the lesser segment bears to the axis of the lesser segment, and (*b*) the lesser segment will have to the figure with the same base as the segment and the same axis the ratio which the line equal to the sum of half the line joining the vertices of the segments and the axis of the greater segment bears to the axis of the greater segment. And the figure referred to is in these cases also a segment of a cone.

"When the aforesaid theorems are proved, there are discovered by means of them many theorems and problems.

"Such, for example, are the theorems":

(1) "that similar spheroids and similar segments both of spheroidal figures and conoids have to one another the triplicate ratio of their axes, and"

(2) "that in equal spheroidal figures the squares on the 'diameters' are reciprocally proportional to the axes, and, if in spheroidal figures the squares on

the 'diameters' are reciprocally proportional to the axes, the spheroids are equal.

"Such also is the problem, From a given spheroidal figure or conoid to cut off a segment by a plane drawn parallel to a given plane so that the segment cut off is equal to a given cone or cylinder or to a given sphere.

"After prefixing therefore the theorems and directions which are necessary for the proof of them, I will then proceed to expound the propositions themselves to you. Farewell."

DEFINITIONS

"If a cone be cut by a plane meeting all the sides [generators] of the cone, the section will be either a circle or a section of an acute-angled cone [an ellipse]. If then the section be a circle, it is clear that the segment cut off from the cone towards the same parts as the vertex of the cone will be a cone. But, if the section be a section of an acute-angled cone [an ellipse], let the figure cut off from the cone towards the same parts as the vertex of the cone be called a *segment of a cone*. Let the *base* of the segment be defined as the plane comprehended by the section of the acute-angled cone, its *vertex* as the point which is also the vertex of the cone, and its *axis* as the straight line joining the vertex of the cone to the centre of the section of the acute-angled cone.

"And if a cylinder be cut by two parallel planes meeting all the sides [generators] of the cylinder, the sections will be either circles or sections of acute-angled cones [ellipses] equal and similar to one another. If then the sections be circles, it is clear that the figure cut off from the cylinder between the parallel planes will be a cylinder. But, if the sections be sections of acute-angled cones [ellipses], let the figure cut off from the cylinder between the parallel planes be called a *frustum of a cylinder*. And let the *bases* of the frustum be defined as the planes comprehended by the sections of the acute-angled cones [ellipses], and the *axis* as the straight line joining the centres of the sections of the acute-angled cones, so that the axis will be in the same straight line with the axis of the cylinder."

Lemma

If in an ascending arithmetical progression consisting of the magnitudes A_1, A_2, $\cdots A_n$ the common difference be equal to the least term A_1, then

$$n \cdot A_n < 2(A_1 + A_2 + \cdots + A_n),$$

and
$$> 2(A_1 + A_2 + \cdots + A_{n-1}).$$

[The proof of this is given incidentally in the treatise *On Spirals*, Prop. 11. By placing lines side by side to represent the terms of the progression and then producing each so as to make it equal to the greatest term, Archimedes gives the equivalent of the following proof.

If $\qquad S_n = A_1 + A_2 + \cdots + A_{n-1} + A_n,$
we have also $\qquad S_n = A_n + A_{n-1} + A_{n-2} + \cdots + A_1.$
And $\qquad A_1 + A_{n-1} = A_2 + A_{n-2} = \cdots = A_n.$

Therefore $\qquad 2S_n = (n+1)A_n,$
whence $\qquad n \cdot A_n < 2S_n,$
and $\qquad n \cdot A_n > 2S_{n-1}.$

Thus, if the progression is $a, 2a, \cdots na,$

$$S_n = \frac{n(n+1)}{2}a,$$

and $\qquad\qquad\qquad n^2a < 2S_n,$
but $\qquad\qquad\qquad\qquad > 2S_{n-1}.]$

Proposition 1

If A_1, B_1, C_1, $\cdots K_1$ and A_2, B_2, C_2, $\cdots K_2$ be two series of magnitudes such that

$$\left.\begin{array}{l} A_1 : B_1 = A_2 : B_2, \\ B_1 : C_1 = B_2 : C_2, \text{ and so on,} \end{array}\right\} \qquad (\alpha)$$

and if A_3, B_3, C_3, $\cdots K_3$ and A_4, B_4, C_4, $\cdots K_4$ be two other series such that

$$\left.\begin{array}{l} A_1 : A_3 = A_2 : A_4, \\ B_1 : B_3 = B_2 : B_4, \text{ and so on,} \end{array}\right\} \qquad (\beta)$$

then $\qquad (A_1+B_1+C_1+\cdots+K_1) : (A_3+B_3+C_3+\cdots+K_3)$
$$= (A_2+B_2+C_2+\cdots+K_2) : (A_4+B_4+\cdots+K_4).$$

The proof is as follows.
Since $\qquad\qquad\qquad A_3 : A_1 = A_4 : A_2,$
and $\qquad\qquad\qquad A_1 : B_1 = A_2 : B_2,$
while $\qquad\qquad\qquad B_1 : B_3 = B_2 : B_4,$
we have, *ex aequali*, $\qquad A_3 : B_3 = A_4 : B_4.$
Similarly $\qquad\qquad B_3 : C_3 = B_4 : C_4,$ and so on. $\left.\right\}$ $\qquad (\gamma)$

Again, it follows from equations (α) that
$$A_1 : A_2 = B_1 : B_2 = C_1 : C_2 = \cdots$$

Therefore
$$A_1 : A_2 = (A_1+B_1+C_1+\cdots+K_1) : (A_2+B_2+\cdots+K_2),$$
or $\qquad (A_1+B_1+C_1+\cdots+K_1) : A_1 = (A_2+B_2+C_2+\cdots+K_2) : A_2;$
and $\qquad\qquad\qquad\qquad A_1 : A_3 = A_2 : A_4,$
while from equations (γ) it follows in like manner that
$$A_3 : (A_3+B_3+C_3+\cdots+K_3) = A_4 : (A_4+B_4+C_4+\cdots+K_4).$$
By the last three equations, *ex aequali*,
$$(A_1+B_1+C_1+\cdots+K_1) : (A_3+B_3+C_3+\cdots+K_3)$$
$$= (A_2+B_2+C_2+\cdots+K_2) : (A_4+B_4+C_4+\cdots+K_4).$$

Cor. If any terms in the third and fourth series corresponding to terms in the first and second be left out, the result is the same. For example, if the last terms K_3, K_4 are absent,
$$(A_1+B_1+C_1+\cdots+K_1) : (A_3+B_3+C_3+\cdots+I_3)$$
$$= (A_2+B_2+C_2+\cdots+K_2) : (A_4+B_4+C_4+\cdots+I_4),$$
where I immediately precedes K in each series.

Lemma to Proposition 2
[*On Spirals*, Prop. 10.]

If A_1, A_2, A_3, $\cdots A_n$ be n lines forming an ascending arithmetical progression in which the common difference is equal to the least term A_1, then
$$(n+1)A_n{}^2 + A_1(A_1+A_2+A_3+\cdots+A_n) = 3(A_1{}^2+A_2{}^2+A_3{}^2+\cdots+A_n{}^2).$$

Let the lines A_n, A_{n-1}, A_{n-2}, $\ldots A_1$ be placed in a row from left to right. Produce A_{n-1}, A_{n-2}, $\ldots A_1$ until they are each equal to A_n, so that the parts produced are respectively equal to A_1, A_2, $\ldots A_{n-1}$.

Taking each line successively, we have
$$2A_n{}^2 = 2A_n{}^2,$$
$$(A_1+A_{n-1})^2 = A_1{}^2 + A^2{}_{n-1} + 2A_1 \cdot A_{n-1},$$
$$(A_2+A_{n-2})^2 = A_2{}^2 + A^2{}_{n-2} + 2A_2 \cdot A_{n-2},$$

$$\cdots\cdots\cdots\cdots\cdots\cdots\cdots\cdots\cdots\cdots\cdots$$
$$(A_{n-1}+A_1)^2 = A^2{}_{n-1}+A_1{}^2+2A_{n-1}\cdot A_1.$$

And, by addition,
$$(n+1)A_n{}^2 = 2(A_1{}^2+A_2{}^2+\cdots+A_n{}^2)$$
$$+2A_1\cdot A_{n-1}+2A_2\cdot A_{n-2}+\cdots+2A_{n-1}\cdot A_1.$$

Therefore, in order to obtain the required result, we have to prove that
$$2(A_1\cdot A_{n-1}+A_2\cdot A_{n-2}+\cdots+A_{n-1}\cdot A_1)+$$
$$A_1(A_1+A_2+A_3+\cdots+A_n)$$
$$=A_1{}^2+A_2{}^2+\cdots+A_n{}^2. \qquad (\alpha)$$

Now
$$2A_2\cdot A_{n-2}=A_1\cdot 4A_{n-2}, \text{ because } A_2=2A_1,$$
$$2A_3\cdot A_{n-3}=A_1\cdot 6A_{n-3}, \text{ because } A_3=3A_1,$$
$$\cdots\cdots\cdots\cdots\cdots\cdots\cdots$$
$$2A_{n-1}\cdot A_1=A_1\cdot 2(n-1)A_1.$$

It follows that
$$2(A_1\cdot A_{n-1}+A_2\cdot A_{n-2}+\cdots+A_{n-1}\cdot A_1)+$$
$$A_1(A_1+A_2+\cdots+A_n)=A_1\{A_n+3A_{n-1}+$$
$$5A_{n-2}+\cdots+(2n-1)A_1\}.$$

And this last expression can be proved to be equal to
$$A_1{}^2+A_2{}^2+\cdots+A_n{}^2.$$

For
$$A_n{}^2 = A_1(n\cdot A_n)$$
$$= A_1\{A_n+(n-1)A_n\}$$
$$= A_1\{A_n+2(A_{n-1}+A_{n-2}+\cdots+A_1)\},$$
because $(n-1)A_n = A_{n-1}+A_1$
$$+A_{n-2}+A_2$$
$$+\cdots\cdots\cdots$$
$$+A_1+A_{n-1}.$$

Similarly $\quad A^2{}_{n-1}=A_1\{A_{n-1}+2(A_{n-2}+A_{n-3}+\cdots+A_1)\},$
$$\cdots\cdots\cdots\cdots\cdots$$
$$A_2{}^2 = A_1(A_2+2A_1),$$
$$A_1{}^2 = A_1\cdot A_1;$$

whence, by addition,
$$A_1{}^2+A_2{}^2+A_3{}^2+\cdots+A_n{}^2=A_1\{A_n+3A_{n-1}+5A_{n-2}+\cdots+(2n-1)A_1\}.$$

Thus the equation marked (α) above is true; and it follows that
$$(n+1)A_n{}^2+A_1(A_1+A_2+A_3+\cdots+A_n)=3(A_1{}^2+A_2{}^2+\cdots+A_n{}^2).$$

Cor. 1. *From this it is evident that*
$$n\cdot A_n{}^2 < 3(A_1{}^2+A_2{}^2+\cdots+A_n{}^2). \qquad (1)$$

Also $\qquad A_n{}^2 = A_1\{A_n+2(A_{n-1}+A_{n-2}+\cdots+A_1)\}$, as above,

so that $\qquad A_n{}^2 > A_1(A_n+A_{n-1}+\cdots+A_1),$

and therefore
$$A_n{}^2+A_1(A_1+A_2+\cdots+A_n)<2A_n{}^2.$$

It follows from the proposition that
$$n\cdot A_n{}^2 > 3(A_1{}^2+A_2{}^2+\cdots+A^2{}_{n-1}). \qquad (2)$$

Cor. 2. All these results will hold if we substitute *similar figures* for squares on all the lines; for similar figures are in the duplicate ratio of their sides.

Proposition 2

If A_1, $A_2 \cdots A_n$ be any number of areas such that

$$A_1 = ax + x^2,$$
$$A_2 = a \cdot 2x + (2x)^2,$$
$$A_3 = a \cdot 3x + (3x)^2,$$
$$\cdots\cdots\cdots\cdots$$
$$A_n = a \cdot nx + (nx)^2,$$

then

$$n \cdot A_n : (A_1 + A_2 + \cdots + A_n) < (a+nx) : \left(\frac{a}{2} + \frac{nx}{3}\right),$$

and

$$n \cdot A_n : (A_1 + A_2 + \cdots + A_{n-1}) > (a+nx) : \left(\frac{a}{2} + \frac{nx}{3}\right).$$

For, by the Lemma immediately preceding Prop. 1,

$$n \cdot anx < (ax + a \cdot 2x + \cdots + a \cdot nx),$$

and

$$> 2(ax + a \cdot 2x + \cdots + a \cdot \overline{n-1}x).$$

Also, by the Lemma preceding this proposition,

$$n \cdot (nx)^2 < 3\{x^2 + (2x)^2 + (3x)^2 + \cdots + (nx)^2\}$$

and

$$> 3\{x^2 + (2x)^2 + \cdots + (\overline{n-1}x)^2\}.$$

Hence

$$\frac{an^2x}{2} + \frac{n(nx)^2}{3} < [(ax+x^2) + \{a \cdot 2x + (2x)^2\} + \cdots + \{a \cdot nx + (nx)^2\}],$$

and

$$> [(ax+x^2) + \{a \cdot 2x + (2x)^2\} + \cdots + \{a \cdot \overline{n-1}x + (\overline{n-1}x)^2\}],$$

or

$$\frac{an^2x}{2} + \frac{n(nx)^2}{3} < A_1 + A_2 + \cdots + A_n,$$

and

$$> A_1 + A_2 + \cdots + A_{n-1}.$$

It follows that

$$n \cdot A_n : (A_1 + A_2 + \cdots + A_n) < n\{a \cdot nx + (nx)^2\} : \left\{\frac{an^2x}{2} + \frac{n(nx)^2}{3}\right\},$$

or

$$n \cdot A_n : (A_1 + A_2 + \cdots + A_n) < (a+nx) : \left(\frac{a}{2} + \frac{nx}{3}\right);$$

also

$$n \cdot A_n : (A_1 + A_2 + \cdots + A_{n-1}) > (a+nx) : \left(\frac{a}{2} + \frac{nx}{3}\right).$$

Proposition 3

(1) *If TP, TP′ be two tangents to any conic meeting in T, and if Qq, Q′q′ be any two chords parallel respectively to TP, TP′ and meeting in O, then*

$$QO \cdot Oq : Q'O \cdot Oq' = TP^2 : TP'^2.$$

"And this is proved in the elements of conics."[1]

(2) *If QQ′ be a chord of a parabola bisected in V by the diameter PV, and if PV be of constant length, then the areas of the triangle PQQ′ and of the segment PQQ′ are both constant whatever be the direction of QQ′.*

Let *ABB′* be the particular segment of the parabola whose vertex is *A*, so that *BB′* is bisected perpendicularly by the axis at the point *H*, where *AH = PV*.

Draw *QD* perpendicular to *PV*.

[1] In the treatises on conics by Aristaeus and Euclid.

Let p_a be the parameter of the principal ordinates, and let p be another line of such length that

$$QV^2 : QD^2 = p : p_a;$$

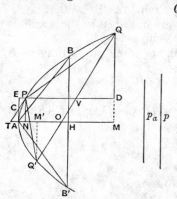

it will then follow that p is equal to the parameter of the ordinates to the diameter PV, i.e. those which are parallel to QV.

"For this is proved in the conics."[1]

Thus $QV^2 = p \cdot PV$.

And $BH^2 = p_a \cdot AH$, while $AH = PV$.

Therefore $QV^2 : BH^2 = p : p_a$.

But $QV^2 : QD^2 = p : p_a;$

hence $BH = QD$.

Thus $BH \cdot AH = QD \cdot PV$,

and therefore $\triangle ABB' = \triangle PQQ'$;

that is, the area of the triangle PQQ' is constant so long as PV is of constant length.

Hence also the area of the segment PQQ' is constant under the same conditions; for the segment is equal to $\frac{4}{3}\triangle PQQ'$. [*Quadrature of the Parabola*, Prop. 17 or 24.]

PROPOSITION 4

The area of any ellipse is to that of the auxiliary circle as the minor axis to the major.

Let AA' be the major and BB' the minor axis of the ellipse, and let BB' meet the auxiliary circle in b, b'.

Suppose O to be such a circle that

$$(\text{circle } AbA'b') : O = CA : CB.$$

Then shall O be equal to the area of the ellipse.

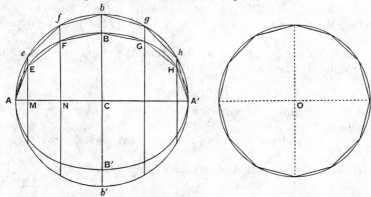

For, if not, O must be either greater or less than the ellipse.

I. If possible, let O be greater than the ellipse.

We can then inscribe in the circle O an equilateral polygon of $4n$ sides such that its area is greater than that of the ellipse. [cf. *On the Sphere and Cylinder,* I. 6.]

[1]The theorem which is here assumed by Archimedes as known . . . is easily deduced from Apollonius I. 49. . . .

Let this be done, and inscribe in the auxiliary circle of the ellipse the polygon $AefbghA'\ldots$ similar to that inscribed in O. Let the perpendiculars $eM, fN, \ldots$ on AA' meet the ellipse in $E, F, \ldots$ respectively. Join $AE, EF, FB, \ldots$

Suppose that P' denotes the area of the polygon inscribed in the auxiliary circle, and P that of the polygon inscribed in the ellipse.

Then, since all the lines $eM, fN, \cdots$ are cut in the same proportions at E, $F, \ldots$,

i.e. $eM : EM = fN : FN = \cdots = bC : BC,$

the pairs of triangles, as eAM, EAM, and the pairs of trapeziums, as $eMNf$, $EMNF$, are all in the same ratio to one another as bC to BC, or as CA to CB.

Therefore, by addition,
$$P' : P = CA : CB.$$

Now P' : (polygon inscribed in O)
$$= (\text{circle } AbA'b') : O$$
$$= CA : CB, \text{ by hypothesis.}$$

Therefore P is equal to the polygon inscribed in O.

But this is impossible, because the latter polygon is by hypothesis greater than the ellipse, and *a fortiori* greater than P.

Hence O is not greater than the ellipse.

II. If possible, let O be less than the ellipse.

In this case we inscribe in the *ellipse* a polygon P with $4n$ equal sides such that $P > O$.

Let the perpendiculars from the angular points on the axis AA' be produced to meet the auxiliary circle, and let the corresponding polygon (P') in the circle be formed.

Inscribe in O a polygon similar to P'.

Then $P' : P = CA : CB$
$$= (\text{circle } AbA'b') : O, \text{ by hypothesis,}$$
$$= P' : (\text{polygon inscribed in } O).$$

Therefore the polygon inscribed in O is equal to the polygon P; which is impossible, because $P > O$.

Hence O, being neither greater nor less than the ellipse, is equal to it; and the required result follows.

PROPOSITION 5

If AA', BB' be the major and minor axis of an ellipse respectively, and if d be the diameter of any circle, then
$$(\text{area of ellipse}) : (\text{area of circle}) = AA' \cdot BB' : d^2.$$

For
(area of ellipse) : (area of auxiliary circle) $= BB' : AA'$ [Prop. 4]
$$= AA' \cdot BB' : AA'^2.$$

And
(area of aux. circle) : (area of circle with diam. d) $= AA'^2 : d^2.$

Therefore the required result follows *ex aequali*.

PROPOSITION 6

The areas of ellipses are as the rectangles under their axes.

This follows at once from Props. 4, 5.

COR. *The areas of similar ellipses are as the squares of corresponding axes.*

PROPOSITION 7

Given an ellipse with centre C, and a line CO drawn perpendicular to its plane, it is possible to find a circular cone with vertex O and such that the given ellipse is a section of it [or, in other words, to find the circular sections of the cone with vertex O passing through the circumference of the ellipse].

Conceive an ellipse with BB' as its minor axis and lying in a plane perpendicular to that of the paper. Let CO be drawn perpendicular to the plane of the ellipse, and let O be the vertex of the required cone. Produce OB, OC, OB', and in the same plane with them draw BED meeting OC, OB' produced in E, D respectively and in such a direction that

$$BE \cdot ED : EO^2 = CA^2 : CO^2,$$

where CA is half the major axis of the ellipse.

"And this is possible, since

$$BE \cdot ED : EO^2 > BC \cdot CB' : CO^2.$$"

[Both the construction and this proposition are assumed as known.]

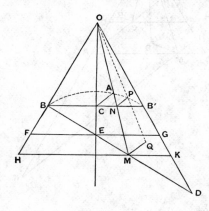

Now conceive a circle with BD as diameter lying in a plane at right angles to that of the paper, and describe a cone with this circle for its base and with vertex O.

We have therefore to prove that the given ellipse is a section of the cone, or, if P be any point on the ellipse, that P lies on the surface of the cone.

Draw PN perpendicular to BB'. Join ON and produce it to meet BD in M, and let MQ be drawn in the plane of the circle on BD as diameter perpendicular to BD and meeting the circle in Q. Also let FG, HK be drawn through E, M respectively parallel to BB'.

We have then

$$QM^2 : HM \cdot MK = BM \cdot MD : HM \cdot MK$$
$$= BE \cdot ED : FE \cdot EG$$
$$= (BE \cdot ED : EO^2) \cdot (EO^2 : FE \cdot EG)$$
$$= (CA^2 : CO^2) \cdot (CO^2 : BC \cdot CB')$$
$$= CA^2 : CB^2$$
$$= PN^2 : BN \cdot NB'.$$

Therefore $\qquad QM^2 : PN^2 = HM \cdot MK : BN \cdot NB'$
$$= OM^2 : ON^2;$$

whence, since PN, QM are parallel, OPQ is a straight line.

But Q is on the circumference of the circle on BD as diameter; therefore OQ is a generator of the cone, and hence P lies on the cone.

Thus the cone passes through all points on the ellipse.

PROPOSITION 8

Given an ellipse, a plane through one of its axes AA' and perpendicular to the plane of the ellipse, and a line CO drawn from C, the centre, in the given plane through AA' but not perpendicular to AA', it is possible to find a cone with vertex

O such that the given ellipse is a section of it [or, in other words, to find the circular sections of the cone with vertex O whose surface passes through the circumference of the ellipse].

By hypothesis, OA, OA' are unequal. Produce OA' to D so that $OA = OD$. Join AD, and draw FG through C parallel to it.

The given ellipse is to be supposed to lie in a plane perpendicular to the plane of the paper. Let BB' be the other axis of the ellipse.

Conceive a plane through AD perpendicular to the plane of the paper, and in it describe either (a), if $CB^2 = FC \cdot CG$, a circle with diameter AD, or (b), if not, an ellipse on AD as axis such that, if d be the other axis,

$$d^2 : AD^2 = CB^2 : FC \cdot CG.$$

Take a cone with vertex O whose surface passes through the circle or ellipse just drawn. This is possible even when the curve is an ellipse, because the line from O to the middle point of AD is perpendicular to the plane of the ellipse, and the construction is effected by means of Prop. 7.

Let P be any point on the given ellipse, and we have only to prove that P lies on the surface of the cone so described.

Draw PN perpendicular to AA'. Join ON, and produce it to meet AD in M. Through M draw HK parallel to $A'A$.

Lastly, draw MQ perpendicular to the plane of the paper (and therefore perpendicular to both HK and AD) meeting the ellipse or circle about AD (and therefore the surface of the cone) in Q.

Then

$$QM^2 : HM \cdot MK = (QM^2 : DM \cdot MA) \cdot (DM \cdot MA : HM \cdot MK)$$
$$= (d^2 : AD^2) \cdot (FC \cdot CG : A'C \cdot CA)$$
$$= (CB^2 : FC \cdot CG) \cdot (FC \cdot CG : A'C \cdot CA)$$
$$= CB^2 : CA^2$$
$$= PN^2 : A'N \cdot NA.$$

Therefore, alternately,

$$QM^2 : PN^2 = HM \cdot MK : A'N \cdot NA$$
$$= OM^2 : ON^2.$$

Thus, since PN, QM are parallel, OPQ is a straight line; and, Q being on the surface of the cone, it follows that P is also on the surface of the cone.

Similarly all points on the ellipse are also on the cone, and the ellipse is therefore a section of the cone.

PROPOSITION 9

Given an ellipse, a plane through one of its axes and perpendicular to that of the ellipse, and a straight line CO drawn from the centre C of the ellipse in the given plane through the axis but not perpendicular to that axis, it is possible to find a

*cylinder with axis OC such that the ellipse is a section of it [or, in other words, to
find the circular sections of the cylinder with axis OC whose surface passes through
the circumference of the given ellipse].*

Let AA' be an axis of the ellipse, and suppose the plane of the ellipse to be
perpendicular to that of the paper, so that OC lies in the plane of the paper.

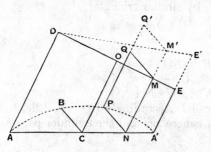

Draw AD, $A'E$ parallel to CO, and let
DE be the line through O perpendicular
to both AD and $A'E$.

We have now three different cases
according as the other axis BB' of the
ellipse is (1) equal to, (2) greater than,
or (3) less than, DE.

(1) Suppose $BB' = DE$.

Draw a plane through DE at right
angles to OC, and in this plane describe
a circle on DE as diameter. Through
this circle describe a cylinder with axis OC.

This cylinder shall be the cylinder required, or its surface shall pass through
every point P of the ellipse.

For, if P be any point on the ellipse, draw PN perpendicular to AA';
through N draw NM parallel to CO meeting DE in M, and through M, in the
plane of the circle on DE as diameter, draw MQ perpendicular to DE, meeting
the circle in Q.

Then, since $$DE = BB',$$
$$PN^2 : AN \cdot NA' = DO^2 : AC \cdot CA'.$$

And $$DM \cdot ME : AN \cdot NA' = DO^2 : AC^2,$$
since AD, NM, CO, $A'E$ are parallel.

Therefore $$PN^2 = DM \cdot ME$$
$$= QM^2,$$
by the property of the circle.

Hence, since PN, QM are equal as well as parallel, PQ is parallel to MN and
therefore to CO. It follows that PQ is a generator of the cylinder, whose surface
accordingly passes through P.

(2) If $BB' > DE$, we take E' on $A'E$ such that $DE' = BB'$ and describe a
circle on DE' as diameter in a plane perpendicular to that of the paper; and the
rest of the construction and proof is exactly similar to those given for case (1).

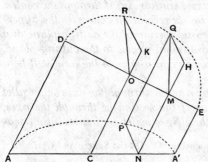

(3) Suppose $BB' < DE$.

Take a point K on CO produced such
that
$$DO^2 - CB^2 = OK^2.$$

From K draw KR perpendicular to
the plane of the paper and equal to CB.

Thus $OR^2 = OK^2 + CB^2 = OD^2$.

In the plane containing DE, OR describe a circle on DE as diameter.
Through this circle (which must pass
through R) draw a cylinder with axis OC.

We have then to prove that, if P be
any point on the given ellipse, P lies on the cylinder so described.

Draw PN perpendicular to AA', and through N draw NM parallel to CO meeting DE in M. In the plane of the circle on DE as diameter draw MQ perpendicular to DE and meeting the circle in Q.

Lastly, draw QH perpendicular to NM produced. QH will then be perpendicular to the plane containing AC, DE, i.e. the plane of the paper.

Now $\qquad QH^2 : QM^2 = KR^2 : OR^2$, by similar triangles.

And $\qquad QM^2 : AN \cdot NA' = DM \cdot ME : AN \cdot NA'$
$$= OD^2 : CA^2.$$

Hence, *ex aequali*, since $\qquad OR = OD$,
$$QH^2 : AN \cdot NA' = KR^2 : CA^2$$
$$= CB^2 : CA^2$$
$$= PN^2 : AN \cdot NA'.$$

Thus $QH = PN$. And QH, PN are also parallel. Accordingly PQ is parallel to MN, and therefore to CO, so that PQ is a generator, and the cylinder passes through P.

PROPOSITION 10

It was proved by the earlier geometers that *any two cones have to one another the ratio compounded of the ratios of their bases and of their heights.*[1] The same method of proof will show that *any segments of cones have to one another the ratio compounded of the ratios of their bases and of their heights.*

The proposition that *any 'frustum' of a cylinder is triple of the conical segment which has the same base as the frustum and equal height* is also proved in the same manner as the proposition that *the cylinder is triple of the cone which has the same base as the cylinder and equal height.*[2]

PROPOSITION 11

(1) *If a paraboloid of revolution be cut by a plane through, or parallel to, the axis, the section will be a parabola equal to the original parabola which by its revolution generates the paraboloid. And the axis of the section will be the intersection between the cutting plane and the plane through the axis of the paraboloid at right angles to the cutting plane.*

If the paraboloid be cut by a plane at right angles to its axis, the section will be a circle whose centre is on the axis.

(2) *If a hyperboloid of revolution be cut by a plane through the axis, parallel to the axis, or through the centre, the section will be a hyperbola, (a) if the section be through the axis, equal, (b) if parallel to the axis, similar, (c) if through the centre, not similar, to the original hyperbola which by its revolution generates the hyperboloid. And the axis of the section will be the intersection of the cutting plane and the plane through the axis of the hyperboloid at right angles to the cutting plane.*

Any section of the hyperboloid by a plane at right angles to the axis will be a circle whose centre is on the axis.

(3) *If any of the spheroidal figures be cut by a plane through the axis or parallel to the axis, the section will be an ellipse, (a) if the section be through the axis, equal, (b) if parallel to the axis, similar, to the ellipse which by its revolution gen-*

---

[1] This follows from Eucl. XII. 11 and 14 taken together. Cf. *On the Sphere and Cylinder* I, Lemma 1.

[2] This proposition was proved by Eudoxus, as stated in the preface to *On the Sphere and Cylinder* I. Cf. Eucl. XII. 10.

erates the figure. And the axis of the section will be the intersection of the cutting plane and the plane through the axis of the spheroid at right angles to the cutting plane.

If the section be by a plane at right angles to the axis of the spheroid, it will be a circle whose centre is on the axis.

(4) *If any of the said figures be cut by a plane through the axis, and if a perpendicular be drawn to the plane of section from any point on the surface of the figure but not on the section, that perpendicular will fall within the section.*

"And the proofs of all these propositions are evident."

PROPOSITION 12

If a paraboloid of revolution be cut by a plane neither parallel nor pendicular to the axis, and if the plane through the axis perpendicular to the cutting plane intersect it in a straight line of which the portion intercepted within the paraboloid is RR′, the section of the paraboloid will be an ellipse whose major axis is RR′ and whose minor axis is equal to the perpendicular distance between the lines through R, R′ parallel to the axis of the paraboloid.

Suppose the cutting plane to be perpendicular to the plane of the paper, and let the latter be the plane through the axis ANF of the paraboloid which intersects the cutting plane at right angles in RR'. Let RH be parallel to the axis of the paraboloid, and $R'H$ perpendicular to RH.

Let Q be any point on the section made by the cutting plane, and from Q draw QM perpendicular to RR'. QM will therefore be perpendicular to the plane of the paper.

Through M draw $DMFE$ perpendicular to the axis ANF meeting the parabolic section made by the plane of the paper in D, E. Then QM is perpendicular to DE, and, if a plane be drawn through DE, QM, it will be perpendicular to the axis and will cut the paraboloid in a circular section.

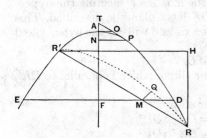

Since Q is on this circle,

$$QM^2 = DM \cdot ME.$$

Again, if PT be that tangent to the parabolic section in the plane of the paper which is parallel to RR', and if the tangent at A meet PT in O, then, from the property of the parabola,

$$DM \cdot ME : RM \cdot MR' = AO^2 : OP^2 \qquad \text{[Prop. 3 (1)]}$$
$$= AO^2 : OT^2, \text{ since } AN = AT.$$

Therefore $\qquad QM^2 : RM \cdot MR' = AO^2 : OT^2$
$$= R'H^2 : RR'^2,$$

by similar triangles.

Hence Q lies on an ellipse whose major axis is RR' and whose minor axis is equal to $R'H$.

PROPOSITIONS 13, 14

If a hyperboloid of revolution be cut by a plane meeting all the generators of the enveloping cone, or if an 'oblong' spheroid be cut by a plane not perpendicular to the axis,[1] *and if a plane through the axis intersect the cutting plane at right angles in a straight line on which the hyperboloid or spheroid intercepts a length RR', then the section by the cutting plane will be an ellipse whose major axis is RR'.*

Suppose the cutting plane to be at right angles to the plane of the paper, and suppose the latter plane to be that through the axis ANF which intersects the

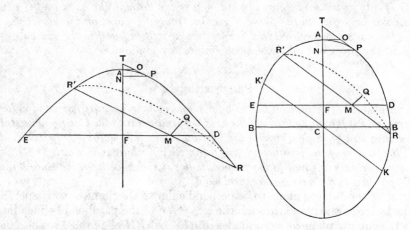

cutting plane at right angles in RR'. The section of the hyperboloid or spheroid by the plane of the paper is thus a hyperbola or ellipse having ANF for its transverse or major axis.

Take any point on the section made by the cutting plane, as Q, and draw QM perpendicular to RR'. QM will then be perpendicular to the plane of the paper.

Through M draw DFE at right angles to the axis ANF meeting the hyperbola or ellipse in D, E; and through QM, DE let a plane be described. This plane will accordingly be perpendicular to the axis and will cut the hyperboloid or spheroid in a circular section.

Thus
$$QM^2 = DM \cdot ME.$$

Let PT be that tangent to the hyperbola or ellipse which is parallel to RR', and let the tangent at A meet PT in O.

Then, by the property of the hyperbola or ellipse,
$$DM \cdot ME : RM \cdot MR' = OA^2 : OP^2,$$
or
$$QM^2 : RM \cdot MR' = OA^2 : OP^2.$$

Now (1) in the hyperbola $OA < OP$, because $AT < AN$, and accordingly
$$OT < OP, \text{ while } OA < OT,$$

(2) in the ellipse, if KK' be the diameter parallel to RR', and BB' the minor axis,
$$BC \cdot CB' : KC \cdot CK' = OA^2 : OP^2;$$
$$\text{and } BC \cdot CB' < KC \cdot CK', \text{ so that } OA < OP.$$

Hence in both cases the locus of Q is an ellipse whose major axis is RR'.

Cor. 1. If the spheroid be a 'flat' spheroid, the section will be an ellipse, and everything will proceed as before except that RR' will in this case be the *minor* axis.

---

[1]Archimedes begins Prop. 14 for the *spheroid* with the remark that, when the cutting plane passes through or is parallel to the axis, the case is clear. Cf. Prop. 11 (3).

Cor 2. In all conoids or spheroids parallel sections will be similar, since the ratio $OA^2 : OP^2$ is the same for all the parallel sections.

PROPOSITION 15

(1) *If from any point on the surface of a conoid a line be drawn, in the case of the paraboloid, parallel to the axis, and, in the case of the hyperboloid, parallel to any line passing through the vertex of the enveloping cone, the part of the straight line which is in the same direction as the convexity of the surface will fall without it, and the part which is in the other direction within it.*

For, if a plane be drawn, in the case of the paraboloid, through the axis and the point, and, in the case of the hyperboloid, through the given point and through the given straight line drawn through the vertex of the enveloping cone, the section by the plane will be (*a*) in the paraboloid a parabola whose axis is the axis of the paraboloid, (*b*) in the hyperboloid a hyperbola in which the given line through the vertex of the enveloping cone is a diameter.[1]

[Prop. 11]

Hence the property follows from the plane properties of the conics.

(2) *If a plane touch a conoid without cutting it, it will touch it at one point only, and the plane drawn through the point of contact and the axis of the conoid will be at right angles to the plane which touches it.*

For, if possible, let the plane touch at two points. Draw through each point a parallel to the axis. The plane passing through both parallels will therefore either pass through, or be parallel to, the axis. Hence the section of the conoid made by this plane will be a conic [Prop. 11 (1), (2)], the two points will lie on this conic, and the line joining them will lie within the conic and therefore within the conoid. But this line will be in the tangent plane, since the two points are in it. Therefore some portion of the tangent plane will be within the conoid; which is impossible, since the plane does not cut it.

Therefore the tangent plane touches in one point only.

That the plane through the point of contact and the axis is perpendicular to the tangent plane is evident in the particular case where the point of contact is the vertex of the conoid. For, if two planes through the axis cut it in two conics, the tangents at the vertex in both conics will be perpendicular to the axis of the conoid. And all such tangents will be in the tangent plane, which must therefore be perpendicular to the axis and to any plane through the axis.

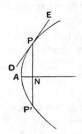

If the point of contact P is not the vertex, draw the plane passing through the axis AN and the point P. It will cut the conoid in a conic whose axis is AN and the tangent plane in a line DPE touching the conic at P. Draw PNP' perpendicular to the axis, and draw a plane through it also perpendicular to the axis. This plane will make a circular section and meet the tangent plane in a tangent to the circle, which will therefore be at right angles to PN. Hence the tangent to the circle will be at right angles to the plane containing PN, AN; and it follows that this last plane is perpendicular to the tangent plane.

---

[1] There seems to be some error in the text here, which says that "the *diameter*" (i.e. axis) of the hyperbola is "the straight line drawn in the conoid from the vertex of the cone." But this straight line is not, in general, the *axis* of the section.

Proposition 16

(1) *If a plane touch any of the spheroidal figures without cutting it, it will touch at one point only, and the plane through the point of contact and the axis will be at right angles to the tangent plane.*

This is proved by the same method as the last proposition.

(2) *If any conoid or spheroid be cut by a plane through the axis, and if through any tangent to the resulting conic a plane be erected at right angles to the plane of section, the plane so erected will touch the conoid or spheroid in the same point as that in which the line touches the conic.*

For it cannot meet the surface at any other point. If it did, the perpendicular from the second point on the cutting plane would be perpendicular also to the tangent to the conic and would therefore fall outside the surface. But it must fall within it. [Prop. 11 (4)]

(3) *If two parallel planes touch any of the spheroidal figures, the line joining the points of contact will pass through the centre of the spheroid.*

If the planes are at right angles to the axis, the proposition is obvious. If not, the plane through the axis and one point of contact is at right angles to the tangent plane at that point. It is therefore at right angles to the parallel tangent plane, and therefore passes through the second point of contact. Hence both points of contact lie on one plane through the axis, and the proposition is reduced to a plane one.

Proposition 17

If two parallel planes touch any of the spheroidal figures, and another plane be drawn parallel to the tangent planes and passing through the centre, the line drawn through any point of the circumference of the resulting section parallel to the chord of contact of the tangent planes will fall outside the spheroid.

This is proved at once by reduction to a plane proposition.

Archimedes adds that it is evident that, if the plane parallel to the tangent planes does not pass through the centre, a straight line drawn in the manner described will fall without the spheroid in the direction of the smaller segment but within it in the other direction.

Proposition 18

Any spheroidal figure which is cut by a plane through the centre is divided, both as regards its surface and its volume, into two equal parts by that plane.

To prove this, Archimedes takes another equal and similar spheroid, divides it similarly by a plane through the centre, and then uses the method of application.

Propositions 19, 20

Given a segment cut off by a plane from a paraboloid or hyperboloid of revolution, or a segment of a spheroid less than half the spheroid also cut off by a plane, it is possible to inscribe in the segment one solid figure and to circumscribe about it another solid figure, each made up of cylinders or "frusta" of cylinders of equal height, and such that the circumscribed figure exceeds the inscribed figure by a volume less than that of any given solid.

Let the plane base of the segment be perpendicular to the plane of the paper, and let the plane of the paper be the plane through the axis of the conoid or spheroid which cuts the base of the segment at right angles in *BC*. The section in the plane of the paper is then a conic *BAC*.   [Prop. 11]

Let *EAF* be that tangent to the conic which is parallel to *BC*, and let *A* be the point of contact. Through *EAF* draw a plane parallel to the plane through *BC* bounding the segment. The plane so drawn will then touch the conoid or spheroid at *A*.   [Prop. 16]

(1) If the base of the segment is at right angles to the axis of the conoid or spheroid, *A* will be the vertex of the conoid or spheroid, and its axis *AD* will bisect *BC* at right angles.

(2) If the base of the segment is not at right angles to the axis of the conoid or spheroid, we draw *AD*

(*a*) in the paraboloid, parallel to the axis,

(*b*) in the hyperboloid, through the centre (or the vertex of the enveloping cone),

(*c*) in the spheroid, through the centre,

and in all the cases it will follow that *AD* bisects *BC* in *D*.

Then *A* will be the vertex of the segment, and *AD* will be its axis.

Further, the base of the segment will be a circle or an ellipse with *BC* as diameter or as an axis respectively, and with centre *D*. We can therefore describe through this circle or ellipse a cylinder or a 'frustum' of a cylinder whose axis is *AD*.   [Prop. 9]

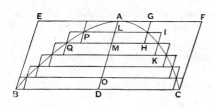

Dividing this cylinder or frustum continually into equal parts by planes parallel to the base, we shall at length arrive at a cylinder or frustum less in volume than any given solid.

Let this cylinder or frustum be that whose axis is *OD*, and let *AD* be divided into parts equal to *OD*, at *L*, *M*,....

Through *L*, *M*, ... draw lines parallel to *BC* meeting the conic in *P*, *Q*,..., and through these lines draw planes parallel to the base of the segment. These will cut the conoid or spheroid in circles or similar ellipses. On each of these circles or ellipses describe two cylinders or frusta of cylinders each with axis equal to *OD*, one of them lying in the direction of *A* and the other in the direction of *D*, as shown in the figure.

Then the cylinders or frusta of cylinders drawn in the direction of *A* make up a circumscribed figure, and those in the direction of *D* an inscribed figure, in relation to the segment.

Also the cylinder or frustum *PG* in the circumscribed figure is equal to the cylinder or frustum *PH* in the inscribed figure, *QI* in the circumscribed figure is equal to *QK* in the inscribed figure, and so on.

Therefore, by addition,

(circumscribed fig.) = (inscr. fig.) + (cylinder or frustum whose axis is *OD*).

But the cylinder or frustum whose axis is *OD* is less than the given solid figure; whence the proposition follows.

"Having set out these preliminary propositions, let us proceed to demonstrate the theorems propounded with reference to the figures."

PROPOSITIONS 21, 22

Any segment of a paraboloid of revolution is half as large again as the cone or segment of a cone which has the same base and the same axis.

Let the base of the segment be perpendicular to the plane of the paper, and let the plane of the paper be the plane through the axis of the paraboloid which cuts the base of the segment at right angles in BC and makes the parabolic section BAC.

Let EF be that tangent to the parabola which is parallel to BC, and let A be the point of contact.

Then (1), if the plane of the base of the segment is perpendicular to the axis of the paraboloid, that axis is the line AD bisecting BC at right angles in D.

(2) If the plane of the base is not perpendicular to the axis of the paraboloid, draw AD parallel to the axis of the paraboloid. AD will then bisect BC, but not at right angles.

Draw through EF a plane parallel to the base of the segment. This will touch the paraboloid at A, and A will be the vertex of the segment, AD its axis.

The base of the segment will be a circle with diameter BC or an ellipse with BC as major axis.

Accordingly a cylinder or a frustum of a cylinder can be found passing through the circle or ellipse and having AD for its axis [Prop. 9]; and likewise a cone or a segment of a cone can be drawn passing through the circle or ellipse and having A for vertex and AD for axis. [Prop. 8]

Suppose X to be a cone equal to $\frac{3}{2}$ (cone or segment of cone ABC). The cone X is therefore equal to half the cylinder or frustum of a cylinder EC.

[Cf. Prop. 10]

We shall prove that the volume of the segment of the paraboloid is equal to X.

If not, the segment must be either greater or less than X.

I. If possible, let the segment be greater than X.

We can then inscribe and circumscribe, as in the last proposition, figures made up of cylinders or frusta of cylinders with equal height and such that

(circumscribed fig.) − (inscribed fig.) < (segment) − X.

Let the greatest of the cylinders or frusta forming the circumscribed figure be that whose base is the circle or ellipse about BC and whose axis is OD, and let the smallest of them be that whose base is the circle or ellipse about PP' and whose axis is AL.

Let the greatest of the cylinders forming the inscribed figure be that whose base is the circle or ellipse about RR' and whose axis is OD, and let the smallest be that whose base is the circle or ellipse about PP' and whose axis is LM.

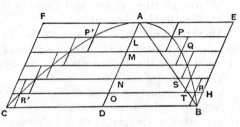

Produce all the plane bases of the cylinders or frusta to meet the surface of the complete cylinder or frustum EC.

Now, since

(circumscribed fig.) − (inscr. fig.) < (segment) − X,

it follows that   (inscribed figure) $> X$.   (α)

Next, comparing successively the cylinders or frusta with heights equal to OD and respectively forming parts of the complete cylinder or frustum EC and of the inscribed figure, we have

(first cylinder or frustum in EC) : (first in inscr. fig.)

$$= BD^2 : RO^2$$
$$= AD : AO$$
$$= BD : TO, \text{ where } AB \text{ meets } OR \text{ in } T.$$

And   (second cylinder or frustum in EC) : (second in inscr. fig.)

$$= HO : SN, \text{ in like manner,}$$

and so on.

Hence [Prop. 1]   (cylinder or frustum EC) : (inscribed figure)

$$= (BD + HO + \cdots) : (TO + SN + \cdots),$$

where $BD, HO, \ldots$ are all equal, and $BD, TO, SN, \ldots$ diminish in arithmetical progression.

But [Lemma preceding Prop. 1]

$$BD + HO + \cdots > 2(TO + SN + \cdots).$$

Therefore   (cylinder or frustum EC) > 2 (inscribed fig.),

or $X >$ (inscribed fig.);

which is impossible, by (α) above.

II. If possible, let the segment be less than X.

In this case we inscribe and circumscribe figures as before, but such that

(circumscr. fig.) $-$ (inscr. fig.) $< X -$ (segment),

whence it follows that

(circumscribed figure) $< X$.   (β)

And, comparing the cylinders or frusta making up the complete cylinder or frustum CE and the *circumscribed* figure respectively, we have

(first cylinder or frustum in CE) : (first in circumscr. fig.)

$$= BD^2 : BD^2$$
$$= BD : BD.$$

(second in CE) : (second in circumscr. fig.)

$$= HO^2 : RO^2$$
$$= AD : AO$$
$$= HO : TO,$$

and so on.

Hence [Prop. 1]

(cylinder or frustum CE) : (circumscribed fig.)

$$= (BD + HO + \cdots) : (BD + TO + \cdots),$$

$$< 2 : 1, \hspace{3cm} \text{[Lemma preceding Prop. 1]}$$

and it follows that

$$X < \text{(circumscribed fig.)};$$

which is impossible, by (β).

Thus the segment, being neither greater nor less than X, is equal to it, and therefore to $\frac{3}{2}$ (cone or segment of cone ABC).

PROPOSITION 23

If from a paraboloid of revolution two segments be cut off, one by a plane perpendicular to the axis, the other by a plane not perpendicular to the axis, and if the axes of the segments are equal, the segments will be equal in volume.

Let the two planes be supposed perpendicular to the plane of the paper, and let the latter plane be the plane through the axis of the paraboloid cutting the other two planes at right angles in BB', QQ' respectively and the paraboloid itself in the parabola $QPQ'B'$.

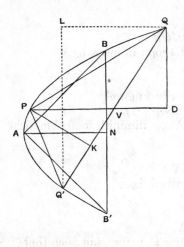

Let AN, PV be the equal axes of the segments, and A, P their respective vertices.

Draw QL parallel to AN or PV and $Q'L$ perpendicular to QL.

Now, since the segments of the parabolic section cut off by BB', QQ' have equal axes, the triangles ABB', PQQ' are equal [Prop. 3]. Also, if QD be perpendicular to PV, $QD = BN$ (as in the same Prop. 3).

Conceive two cones drawn with the same bases as the segments and with A, P as vertices respectively. The height of the cone PQQ' is then PK, where PK is perpendicular to QQ'.

Now the cones are in the ratio compounded of the ratios of their bases and of their heights, i.e. the ratio compounded of (1) the ratio of the circle about BB' to the ellipse about QQ', and (2) the ratio of AN to PK.

That is to say, we have, by means of Props. 5, 12,

$$\text{(cone } ABB') : \text{(cone } PQQ') = (BB'^2 : QQ' \cdot Q'L) \cdot (AN : PK).$$

And $BB' = 2BN = 2QD = Q'L$, while $QQ' = 2QV$.

Therefore

$$\text{(cone } ABB') : \text{(cone } PQQ') = (QD : QV) \cdot (AN : PK)$$
$$= (PK : PV) \cdot (AN : PK)$$
$$= AN : PV.$$

Since $AN = PV$, the ratio of the cones is a ratio of equality; and it follows that the segments, being each half as large again as the respective cones [Prop. 22], are equal.

PROPOSITION 24

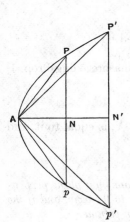

If from a paraboloid of revolution two segments be cut off by planes drawn in any manner, the segments will be to one another as the squares on their axes.

For let the paraboloid be cut by a plane through the axis in the parabolic section $P'PApp'$, and let the axis of the parabola and paraboloid be ANN'.

Measure along ANN' the lengths AN, AN' equal to the respective axes of the given segments, and through N, N' draw planes perpendicular to the axis, making circular sections on Pp, $P'p'$ as diameters respectively. With these circles as bases and with the common vertex A let two cones be described.

Now the segments of the paraboloid whose bases are the circles about Pp, $P'p'$ are equal to the given segments respectively, since their respective axes are equal [Prop. 23]; and, since the segments APp, $AP'p'$ are half as large again as the cones APp, $AP'p'$ respectively, we have only to show that the cones are in the ratio of AN^2 to AN'^2.

But

$$\text{(cone } APp) : \text{(cone } AP'p') = (PN^2 : P'N'^2) \cdot (AN : AN')$$
$$= (AN : AN') \cdot (AN : AN')$$
$$= AN^2 : AN'^2;$$

thus the proposition is proved.

PROPOSITIONS 25, 26

In any hyperboloid of revolution, if A be the vertex and AD the axis of any segment cut off by a plane, and if CA be the semidiameter of the hyperboloid through A (CA being of course in the same straight line with AD), then

(segment) : (cone with same base and axis)
$$= (AD+3CA) : (AD+2CA).$$

Let the plane cutting off the segment be perpendicular to the plane of the paper, and let the latter plane be the plane through the axis of the hyperboloid which intersects the cutting plane at right angles in BB', and makes the hyperbolic segment BAB'. Let C be the centre of the hyperboloid (or the vertex of the enveloping cone).

Let EF be that tangent to the hyperbolic section which is parallel to BB'. Let EF touch at A, and join CA. Then CA produced will bisect BB' at D, CA will be a semi-diameter of the hyperboloid, A will be the vertex of the segment, and AD its axis. Produce AC to A' and H, so that $AC = CA' = A'H$.

Through EF draw a plane parallel to the base of the segment. This plane will touch the hyperboloid at A.

Then (1), if the base of the segment is at right angles to the axis of the hyperboloid, A will be the vertex, and AD the axis, of the hyperboloid as well as of the segment, and the base of the segment will be a circle on BB' as diameter.

(2) If the base of the segment is not perpendicular to the axis of the hyperboloid, the base will be an ellipse on BB' as major axis. [Prop. 13]

Then we can draw a cylinder or a frustum of a cylinder $EBB'F$ passing through the circle or ellipse about BB' and having AD for its axis; also we can describe a cone or a segment of a cone through the circle or ellipse and having A for its vertex.

We have to prove that

(segment ABB') : (cone or segment of cone ABB') $= HD : A'D$.

Let V be a cone such that

$$V : \text{(cone or segment of cone } ABB') = HD : A'D, \qquad (\alpha)$$

and we have to prove that V is equal to the segment.

Now

(cylinder or frustum EB') : (cone or segmt. of cone ABB') $= 3 : 1$.

Therefore, by means of (α), (cylinder or frustum EB') : $V = A'D : \dfrac{HD}{3}$. (β)

If the segment is not equal to V, it must either be greater or less.

I. If possible, let the segment be greater than V.

Inscribe and circumscribe to the segment figures made up of cylinders or frusta of cylinders, with axes along AD and all equal to one another, such that

$$\text{(circumscribed fig.)} - \text{(inscr. fig.)} < \text{(segmt.)} - V,$$

whence   (inscribed figure) $> V$.   (γ)

Produce all the planes forming the bases of the cylinders or frusta of cylinders to meet the surface of the complete cylinder or frustum EB'.

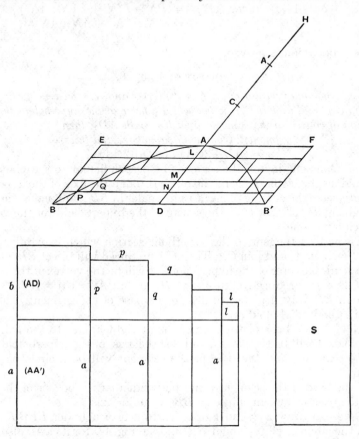

Then, if ND be the axis of the greatest cylinder or frustum in the circumscribed figure, the complete cylinder will be divided into cylinders or frusta each equal to this greatest cylinder or frustum.

Let there be a number of straight lines a equal to AA' and as many in number as the parts into which AD is divided by the bases of the cylinders or frusta. To each line a apply a rectangle which shall overlap it by a square, and let the greatest of the rectangles be equal to the rectangle $AD \cdot A'D$ and the least equal to the rectangle $AL \cdot A'L$; also let the sides of the overlapping squares $b, p, q, \ldots l$ be in descending arithmetical progression. Thus $b, p, q, \ldots l$ will be respectively equal to $AD, AN, AM, \ldots AL$, and the rectangles $(ab + b^2)$, $(ap + p^2), \ldots (al + l^2)$ will be respectively equal to $AD \cdot A'D, AN \cdot A'N, \ldots AL \cdot A'L$.

Suppose, further, that we have a series of spaces S each equal to the largest rectangle $AD \cdot A'D$ and as many in number as the diminishing rectangles.

Comparing now the successive cylinders or frusta (1) in the complete cylinder or frustum EB' and (2) in the inscribed figure, beginning from the base of the segment, we have

(first cylinder or frustum in EB') : (first in inscr. figure)

$$= BD^2 : PN^2$$
$$= AD \cdot A'D : AN \cdot A'N, \text{ from the hyperbola,}$$
$$= S : (ap+p^2).$$

Again

(second cylinder or frustum in EB') : (second in inscr. fig.)

$$= BD^2 : QM^2$$
$$= AD \cdot A'D : AM \cdot A'M$$
$$= S : (aq+q^2),$$

and so on.

The last cylinder or frustum in the complete cylinder or frustum EB' has no cylinder or frustum corresponding to it in the inscribed figure.

Combining the proportions, we have   [Prop. 1]

(cylinder or frustum EB') : (inscribed figure)

$$= (\text{sum of all the spaces } S) : (ap+p^2)+(aq+q^2)+ \cdots$$

$$> (a+b) : \left(\frac{a}{2}+\frac{b}{3}\right)$$ [Prop. 2]

$$> A'D : \frac{HD}{3}, \text{ since } a=AA', \; b=AD,$$

$$> (EB') : V, \text{ by } (\beta) \text{ above.}$$

Hence   (inscribed figure) $< V$.

But this is impossible, because, by (γ) above, the inscribed figure is greater than V.

II. Next suppose, if possible, that the segment is less than V.

In this case we circumscribe and inscribe figures such that

(circumscribed fig.) $-$ (inscribed fig.) $< V -$ (segment),

whence we derive

$$V > (\text{circumscribed figure}). \tag{δ}$$

We now compare successive cylinders or frusta in the complete cylinder or frustum and in the *circumscribed* figure; and we have

(first cylinder or frustum in EB') : (first in circumscribed fig.)

$$= S : S$$
$$= S : (ab+b^2),$$

(second in EB') : (second in circumscribed fig.)

$$= S : (ap+p^2),$$

and so on.

Hence [Prop. 1]

(cylinder or frustum EB') : (circumscribed fig.)

$$= (\text{sum of all spaces } S) : (ab+b^2)+(ap+p^2)+ \cdots$$

$$< (a+b) : \left(\frac{a}{2}+\frac{b}{3}\right)$$ [Prop. 2]

$$< A'D : \frac{HD}{3}$$

$$< (EB') : V, \text{ by } (\beta) \text{ above.}$$

Hence the circumscribed figure is greater than V; which is impossible, by (δ) above.

Thus the segment is neither greater nor less than V, and is therefore equal to it.

Therefore, by (α),

(segment ABB') : (cone or segment of cone ABB')

$$= (AD+3CA) : (AD+2CA).$$

Propositions 27, 28, 29, 30

(1) *In any spheroid whose centre is C, if a plane meeting the axis cut off a segment not greater than half the spheroid and having A for its vertex and AD for its axis, and if $A'D$ be the axis of the remaining segment of the spheroid, then*

(first segmt.) : (cone or segmt. of cone with same base and axis)

$$= CA+A'D : A'D$$
$$[= 3CA-AD : 2CA-AD].$$

(2) *As a particular case, if the plane passes through the centre, so that the segment is half the spheroid, half the spheroid is double of the cone or segment of a cone which has the same vertex and axis.*

Let the plane cutting off the segment be at right angles to the plane of the paper, and let the latter plane be the plane through the axis of the spheroid which intersects the cutting plane in BB' and makes the elliptic section $ABA'B'$.

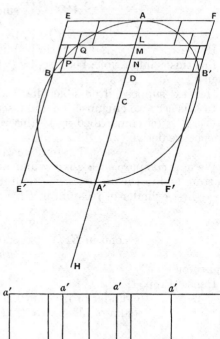

Let EF, $E'F'$ be the two tangents to the ellipse which are parallel to BB', let them touch it in A, A', and through the tangents draw planes parallel to the base of the segment. These planes will touch the spheroid at A, A', which will be the vertices of the two segments into which it is divided. Also AA' will pass through the centre C and bisect BB' in D.

Then (1) if the base of the segments be perpendicular to the axis of the spheroid, A, A' will be the vertices of the spheroid as well as of the segments, AA' will be the axis of the spheroid, and the base of the segments will be a circle on BB' as diameter;

(2) if the base of the segments be not perpendicular to the axis of the spheroid, the base of the segments will be an ellipse of which BB' is one axis, and AD, $A'D$ will be the axes of the segments respectively.

We can now draw a cylinder or a frustum of a cylinder $EBB'F$ through the circle or ellipse about BB' and having AD for its axis; and we can also draw a cone or a segment of a cone passing through the circle or ellipse about BB' and having A for its vertex.

We have then to show that, if CA' be produced to H so that $CA'=A'H$,

(segment ABB') : (cone or segment of cone ABB') $=HD : A'D$.

Let V be such a cone that

$$V : \text{(cone or segment of cone } ABB') = HD : A'D; \qquad (\alpha)$$

and we have to show that the segment ABB' is equal to V.

But, since

(cylinder or frustum EB') : (cone or segment of cone ABB') $=3 : 1$,

we have, by the aid of (α),

$$\text{(cylinder or frustum } EB') : V = A'D : \frac{HD}{3} \qquad (\beta)$$

Now, if the segment ABB' is not equal to V, it must be either greater or less.

I. Suppose, if possible, that the segment is greater than V.

Let figures be inscribed and circumscribed to the segment consisting of cylinders or frusta of cylinders, with axes along AD and all equal to one another, such that

(circumscribed fig.) $-$ (inscribed fig.) $<$ (segment) $-V$,

whence it follows that

$$\text{(inscribed fig.)} > V. \qquad (\gamma)$$

Produce all the planes forming the bases of the cylinders or frusta to meet the surface of the complete cylinder or frustum EB'. Thus, if ND be the axis of the greatest cylinder or frustum of a cylinder in the circumscribed figure, the complete cylinder or frustum EB' will be divided into cylinders or frusta of cylinders each equal to the greatest of those in the circumscribed figure.

Take straight lines da' each equal to $A'D$ and as many in number as the parts into which AD is divided by the bases of the cylinders or frusta, and measure da along da' equal to AD. It follows that $aa'=2CD$.

Apply to each of the lines $a'd$ rectangles with height equal to ad, and draw the squares on each of the lines ad as in the figure. Let S denote the area of each complete rectangle.

From the first rectangle take away a gnomon with breadth equal to AN (i.e. with each end of a length equal to AN); take away from the second rectangle a gnomon with breadth equal to AM, and so on, the last rectangle having no gnomon taken from it.

Then

$$\text{the first gnomon} = A'D \cdot AD - ND \cdot (A'D - AN)$$
$$= A'D \cdot AN + ND \cdot AN$$
$$= AN \cdot A'N.$$

Similarly,

$$\text{the second gnomon} = AM \cdot A'M,$$

and so on.

And the last gnomon (that in the last rectangle but one) is equal to $AL \cdot A'L$.

Also, after the gnomons are taken away from the successive rectangles, the remainders (which we will call $R_1, R_2, \cdots R_n$, where n is the number of rectangles and accordingly $R_n=S$) are rectangles applied to straight lines each of length aa' and "exceeding by squares" whose sides are respectively equal to $DN, DM, \ldots DA$.

For brevity, let DN be denoted by x, and aa' or $2CD$ by c, so that
$$R_1 = cx + x^2, \; R_2 = c \cdot 2x + (2x)^2, \; \cdots$$

Then, comparing successively the cylinders or frusta of cylinders (1) in the complete cylinder or frustum EB' and (2) in the inscribed figure, we have

(first cylinder or frustum in EB') : (first in inscribed fig.)
$$= BD^2 : PN^2$$
$$= AD \cdot A'D : AN \cdot A'N$$
$$= S : \text{(first gnomon)};$$

(second cylinder or frustum in EB') : (second in inscribed fig.)
$$= S : \text{(second gnomon)},$$

and so on.

The last of the cylinders or frusta in the cylinder or frustum EB' has none corresponding to it in the inscribed figure, and there is no corresponding gnomon.

Combining the proportions, we have [by Prop. 1]

(cylinder or frustum EB') : (inscribed fig.)
$$= \text{(sum of all spaces } S) : \text{(sum of gnomons)}.$$

Now the differences between S and the successive gnomons are $R_1, R_2, \ldots R_n$, while
$$R_1 = cx + x^2,$$
$$R_2 = c \cdot 2x + (2x)^2,$$
$$\cdots\cdots\cdots\cdots\cdots$$
$$R_n = cb + b^2 = S,$$

where $b = nx = AD$.

Hence [Prop. 2]

(sum of all spaces S) : $(R_1 + R_2 + \cdots + R_n) < (c+b) : \left(\dfrac{c}{2} + \dfrac{b}{3}\right)$.

It follows that

(sum of all spaces S) : (sum of gnomons) $> (c+b) : \left(\dfrac{c}{2} + \dfrac{2b}{3}\right)$
$$> A'D : \frac{HD}{3}.$$

Thus (cylinder or frustum EB') : (inscribed fig.)
$$> A'D : \frac{HD}{3}$$
$$> \text{(cylinder or frustum } EB') : V,$$

from (β) above.

Therefore (inscribed fig.) $< V$;

which is impossible, by (γ) above.

Hence the segment ABB' is not greater than V.

II. If possible, let the segment ABB' be less than V.

We then inscribe and circumscribe figures such that

(circumscribed fig.) $-$ (inscribed fig.) $< V -$ (segment),

whence $\qquad V >$ (circumscribed fig.). $\qquad\qquad (\delta)$

In this case we compare the cylinders or frusta in (EB') with those in the *circumscribed* figure.

Thus

(first cylinder or frustum in EB') : (first in circumscribed fig.)
$$= S : S;$$
(second in EB') : (second in circumscribed fig.)
$$= S : \text{(first gnomon)},$$

and so on.

Lastly

(last in EB') : (last in circumscribed fig.)
$$= S : \text{(last gnomon)}.$$

Now

$$\{S + \text{(all the gnomons)}\} = nS - (R_1 + R_2 + \cdots + R_{n-1}).$$

And

$$nS : R_1 + R_2 + \cdots + R_{n-1} > (c+b) : \left(\frac{c}{2} + \frac{b}{3}\right), \qquad \text{[Prop. 2]}$$

so that

$$nS : \{S + \text{(all the gnomons)}\} < (c+b) : \left(\frac{c}{2} + \frac{2b}{3}\right).$$

It follows that, if we combine the above proportions as in Prop. 1, we obtain

(cylinder or frustum EB') : (circumscribed fig.)

$$< (c+b) : \left(\frac{c}{2} + \frac{2b}{3}\right)$$

$$< A'D : \frac{HD}{3}$$

$$< (EB') : V, \text{ by } (\beta) \text{ above}.$$

Hence the circumscribed figure is greater than V; which is impossible, by (δ) above.

Thus, since the segment ABB' is neither greater nor less than V, it is equal to it; and the proposition is proved.

(2) The particular case [Props. 27, 28] where the segment is half the spheroid differs from the above in that the distance CD or $c/2$ vanishes, and the rectangles $cb + b^2$ are simply squares (b^2), so that the gnomons are simply the differences between b^2 and x^2, b^2 and $(2x)^2$, and so on.

Instead therefore of Prop. 2 we use the *Lemma to Prop.* 2, *Cor.* 1, given above [*On Spirals*, Prop. 10], and instead of the ratio $(c+b) : \left(\frac{c}{2} + \frac{2b}{3}\right)$ we obtain the ratio $3 : 2$, whence (segment ABB') : (cone or segment of cone ABB') $= 2 : 1$.

PROPOSITIONS 31, 32

If a plane divide a spheroid into two unequal segments, and if AN, $A'N$ be the axes of the lesser and greater segments respectively, while C is the centre of the spheroid, then

(greater segmt.) : (cone or segmt. of cone with same base and axis)
$$= CA + AN : AN.$$

Let the plane dividing the spheroid be that through PP' perpendicular to the plane of the paper, and let the latter plane be that through the axis of the spheroid which intersects the cutting plane in PP' and makes the elliptic section $PAP'A'$.

Draw the tangents to the ellipse which are parallel to PP'; let them touch the ellipse at A, A', and through the tangents draw planes parallel to the base of the segments. These planes will touch the spheroid at A, A', the line AA'

will pass through the centre C and bisect PP' in N, while AN, $A'N$ will be the axes of the segments.

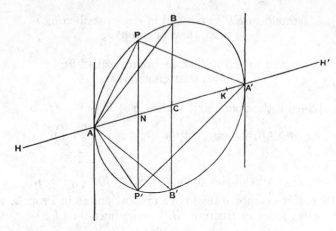

Then (1) if the cutting plane be perpendicular to the axis of the spheroid, AA' will be that axis, and A, A' will be the vertices of the spheroid as well as of the segments. Also the sections of the spheroid by the cutting plane and all planes parallel to it will be circles.

(2) If the cutting plane be not perpendicular to the axis, the base of the segments will be an ellipse of which PP' is an axis, and the sections of the spheroid by all planes parallel to the cutting plane will be similar ellipses.

Draw a plane through C parallel to the base of the segments and meeting the plane of the paper in BB'.

Construct three cones or segments of cones, two having A for their common vertex and the plane sections through PP', BB' for their respective bases, and a third having the plane section through PP' for its base and A' for its vertex.

Produce CA to H and CA' to H' so that
$$AH = A'H' = CA.$$
We have then to prove that
$$\text{(segment } A'PP') : \text{(cone or segment of cone } A'PP')$$
$$= CA + AN : AN$$
$$= NH : AN.$$
Now half the spheroid is double of the cone or segment of a cone ABB' [Props. 27, 28]. Therefore
$$\text{(the spheroid)} = 4\text{(cone or segment of cone } ABB').$$
But
$$\text{(cone or segmt. of cone } ABB') : \text{(cone or segmt. of cone } APP')$$
$$= (CA : AN) \cdot (BC^2 : PN^2)$$
$$= (CA : AN) \cdot (CA \cdot CA' : AN \cdot A'N). \qquad\qquad (\alpha)$$
If we measure AK along AA' so that
$$AK : AC = AC : AN,$$
we have $\qquad\qquad AK \cdot A'N : AC \cdot A'N = CA : AN,$
and the compound ratio in (α) becomes
$$(AK \cdot A'N : CA \cdot A'N) \cdot (CA \cdot CA' : AN \cdot A'N),$$
i.e. $\qquad\qquad\qquad AK \cdot CA' : AN \cdot A'N.$

Thus

$$(\text{cone or segmt. of cone } ABB') : (\text{cone or segmt. of cone } APP')$$
$$= AK \cdot CA' : AN \cdot A'N.$$

But $\quad$ (cone or segment of cone APP') : (segment APP')
$$= A'N : NH' \qquad\qquad \text{[Props. 29, 30]}$$
$$= AN \cdot A'N : AN \cdot NH'.$$

Therefore, *ex aequali*,

$$(\text{cone or segment of cone } ABB') : (\text{segment } APP')$$
$$= AK \cdot CA' : AN \cdot NH',$$

so that $\quad\quad\quad$ (spheroid) : (segment APP')
$$= HH' \cdot AK : AN \cdot NH',$$

since $\qquad\qquad\qquad HH' = 4CA'.$

Hence $\qquad\qquad$ (segment $A'PP'$) : (segment APP')
$$= (HH' \cdot AK - AN \cdot NH') : AN \cdot NH'$$
$$= (AK \cdot NH + NH' \cdot NK) : AN \cdot NH'.$$

Further,

$$(\text{segment } APP') : (\text{cone or segment of cone } APP')$$
$$= NH' : A'N$$
$$= AN \cdot NH' : AN \cdot A'N,$$

and

$$(\text{cone or segmt. of cone } APP') : (\text{cone or segmt. of cone } A'PP')$$
$$= AN : A'N$$
$$= AN \cdot A'N : A'N^2.$$

From the last three proportions we obtain, *ex aequali*,

$$(\text{segment } A'PP') : (\text{cone or segment of cone } A'PP')$$
$$= (AK \cdot NH + NH' \cdot NK) : A'N^2$$
$$= (AK \cdot NH + NH' \cdot NK) : (CA^2 + NH' \cdot CN)$$
$$= (AK \cdot NH + NH' \cdot NK) : (AK \cdot AN + NH' \cdot CN). \qquad (\beta)$$

But

$$AK \cdot NH : AK \cdot AN = NH : AN$$
$$= CA + AN : AN$$
$$= AK + CA : CA \text{ (since } AK : AC = AC : AN)$$
$$= HK : CA$$
$$= HK - NH : CA - AN$$
$$= NK : CN$$
$$= NH' \cdot NK : NH' \cdot CN.$$

Hence the ratio in (β) is equal to the ratio
$$AK \cdot NH : AK \cdot AN, \text{ or } NH : AN.$$

Therefore

$$(\text{segment } A'PP') : (\text{cone or segment of cone } A'PP')$$
$$= NH : AN$$
$$= CA + AN : AN.$$

ON SPIRALS

"ARCHIMEDES to Dositheus greeting.

"Of most of the theorems which I sent to Conon, and of which you ask me from time to time to send you the proofs, the demonstrations are already before you in the books brought to you by Heracleides; and some more are also contained in that which I now send you. Do not be surprised at my taking a considerable time before publishing these proofs. This has been owing to my desire to communicate them first to persons engaged in mathematical studies and anxious to investigate them. In fact, how many theorems in geometry which have seemed at first impracticable are in time successfully worked out! Now Conon died before he had sufficient time to investigate the theorems referred to; otherwise he would have discovered and made manifest all these things, and would have enriched geometry by many other discoveries besides. For I know well that it was no common ability that he brought to bear on mathematics, and that his industry was extraordinary. But, though many years have elapsed since Conon's death, I do not find that any one of the problems has been stirred by a single person. I wish now to put them in review one by one, particularly as it happens that there are two included among them which are impossible of realisation [and which may serve as a warning] how those who claim to discover everything but produce no proofs of the same may be confuted as having actually pretended to discover the impossible.

"What are the problems I mean, and what are those of which you have already received the proofs, and those of which the proofs are contained in this book respectively, I think it proper to specify. The first of the problems was, Given a sphere, to find a plane area equal to the surface of the sphere; and this was first made manifest on the publication of the book concerning the sphere, for, when it is once proved that the surface of any sphere is four times the greatest circle in the sphere, it is clear that it is possible to find a plane area equal to the surface of the sphere. The second was, Given a cone or a cylinder, to find a sphere equal to the cone or cylinder; the third, To cut a given sphere by a plane so that the segments of it have to one another an assigned ratio; the fourth, To cut a given sphere by a plane so that the segments of the surface have to one another an assigned ratio; the fifth, To make a given segment of a sphere similar to a given segment of a sphere;[1] the sixth, Given two segments of either the same or different spheres, to find a segment of a sphere which shall be similar to one of the segments and have its surface equal to the surface of the other segment. The seventh was, From a given sphere to cut off a segment by a plane so that the segment bears to the cone which has the same base

[1] Cf. *On the Sphere and Cylinder*, II. 5.

482

as the segment and equal height an assigned ratio greater than that of three to two. Of all the propositions just enumerated Heracleides brought you the proofs. The proposition stated next after these was wrong, viz. that, if a sphere be cut by a plane into unequal parts, the greater segment will have to the less the duplicate ratio of that which the greater surface has to the less. That this is wrong is obvious by what I sent you before; for it included this proposition: If a sphere be cut into unequal parts by a plane at right angles to any diameter in the sphere, the greater segment of the surface will have to the less the same ratio as the greater segment of the diameter has to the less, while the greater segment of the sphere has to the less a ratio less than the duplicate ratio of that which the greater surface has to the less, but greater than the sesqui-alterate[1] of that ratio. The last of the problems was also wrong, viz. that, if the diameter of any sphere be cut so that the square on the greater segment is triple of the square on the lesser segment, and if through the point thus arrived at, a plane be drawn at right angles to the diameter and cutting the sphere, the figure in such a form as is the greater segment of the sphere is the greatest of all the segments which have an equal surface. That this is wrong is also clear from the theorems which I before sent you. For it was there proved that the hemisphere is the greatest of all the segments of a sphere bounded by an equal surface.

"After these theorems the following were propounded concerning the cone.[2] If a section of a right-angled cone [a parabola], in which the diameter [axis] remains fixed, be made to revolve so that the diameter [axis] is the axis [of revolution], let the figure described by the section of the right-angled cone be called a *conoid*. And if a plane touch the conoidal figure and another plane drawn parallel to the tangent plane cut off a segment of the conoid, let the *base* of the segment cut off be defined as the cutting plane, and the *vertex* as the point in which the other plane touches the conoid. Now, if the said figure be cut by a plane at right angles to the axis, it is clear that the section will be a circle; but it needs to be proved that the segment cut off will be half as large again as the cone which has the same base as the segment and equal height. And if two segments be cut off from the conoid by planes drawn in any manner, it is clear that the sections will be sections of acute-angled cones [ellipses] if the cutting planes be not at right angles to the axis; but it needs to be proved that the segments will bear to one another the ratio of the squares on the lines drawn from their vertices parallel to the axis to meet the cutting planes. The proofs of these propositions are not yet sent to you.

"After these came the following propositions about the *spiral*, which are as it were another sort of problem having nothing in common with the foregoing; and I have written out the proofs of them for you in this book. They are as follows. If a straight line of which one extremity remains fixed be made to revolve at a uniform rate in a plane until it returns to the position from which it started, and if, at the same time as the straight line revolves, a point move at a uniform rate along the straight line, starting from the fixed extremity, the point will describe a spiral in the plane. I say then that the area bounded by the spiral and the straight line which has returned to the position from which it started is a third part of the circle described with the fixed point as centre and with radius the length traversed by the point along the straight line during

[1]See *On the Sphere and Cylinder*, II. 8.
[2]This should be presumably "the *conoid*," not "the *cone*."

the one revolution. And, if a straight line touch the spiral at the extreme end of the spiral, and another straight line be drawn at right angles to the line which has revolved and resumed its position from the fixed extremity of it, so as to meet the tangent, I say that the straight line so drawn to meet it is equal to the circumference of the circle. Again, if the revolving line and the point moving along it make several revolutions and return to the position from which the straight line started, I say that the area added by the spiral in the third revolution will be double of that added in the second, that in the fourth three times, that in the fifth four times, and generally the areas added in the later revolutions will be multiples of that added in the second revolution according to the successive numbers, while the area bounded by the spiral in the first revolution is a sixth part of that added in the second revolution. Also, if on the spiral described in one revolution two points be taken and straight lines be drawn joining them to the fixed extremity of the revolving line, and if two circles be drawn with the fixed point as centre and radii the lines drawn to the fixed extremity of the straight line, and the shorter of the two lines be produced, I say that (1) the area bounded by the circumference of the greater circle in the direction of (the part of) the spiral included between the straight lines, the spiral (itself) and the produced straight line will bear to (2) the area bounded by the circumference of the lesser circle, the same (part of the) spiral and the straight line joining their extremities the ratio which (3) the radius of the lesser circle together with two thirds of the excess of the radius of the greater circle over the radius of the lesser bears to (4) the radius of the lesser circle together with one third of the said excess.

"The proofs then of these theorems and others relating to the spiral are given in the present book. Prefixed to them, after the manner usual in other geometrical works, are the propositions necessary to the proofs of them. And here too, as in the books previously published, I assume the following lemma, that, if there be (two) unequal lines or (two) unequal areas, the excess by which the greater exceeds the less can, by being [continually] added to itself, be made to exceed any given magnitude among those which are comparable with [it and with] one another."

PROPOSITION 1

If a point move at a uniform rate along any line, and two lengths be taken on it, they will be proportional to the times of describing them.

Two unequal lengths are taken on a straight line, and two lengths on another straight line representing the times; and they are proved to be proportional by taking equimultiples of each length and the corresponding time after the manner of Eucl. V, Def. 5.

PROPOSITION 2

If each of two points on different lines respectively move along them each at a uniform rate, and if lengths be taken, one on each line, forming pairs, such that each pair are described in equal times, the lengths will be porportionals.

This is proved at once by equating the ratio of the lengths taken on one line to that of the times of description, which must also be equal to the ratio of the lengths taken on the other line.

Proposition 3

Given any number of circles, it is possible to find a straight line greater than the sum of all their circumferences.

For we have only to describe polygons about each and then take a straight line equal to the sum of the perimeters of the polygons.

Proposition 4

Given two unequal lines, viz. a straight line and the circumference of a circle, it is possible to find a straight line less than the greater of the two lines and greater than the less.

For, by the Lemma, the excess can, by being added a sufficient number of times to itself, be made to exceed the lesser line.

Thus e.g., if $c > l$ (where c is the circumference of the circle and l the length of the straight line), we can find a number n such that

$$n(c-l) > l.$$

Therefore

$$c - l > \frac{l}{n},$$

and

$$c > l + \frac{l}{n} > l.$$

Hence we have only to divide l into n equal parts and add one of them to l. The resulting line will satisfy the condition.

Proposition 5

Given a circle with centre O, and the tangent to it at a point A, it is possible to draw from O a straight line OPF, meeting the circle in P and the tangent in F, such that, if c be the circumference of any given circle whatever,

$$FP : OP < (\text{arc } AP) : c.$$

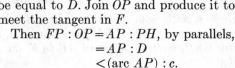

Take a straight line, as D, greater than the circumference c. [Prop. 3]

Through O draw OH parallel to the given tangent, and draw through A a line APH, meeting the circle in P and OH in H, such that the portion PH intercepted between the circle and the line OH may be equal to D. Join OP and produce it to meet the tangent in F.

Then $FP : OP = AP : PH$, by parallels,

$$= AP : D$$
$$< (\text{arc } AP) : c.$$

Proposition 6

Given a circle with centre O, a chord AB less than the diameter, and OM the perpendicular on AB from O, it is possible to draw a straight line OFP, meeting the chord AB in F and the circle in P, such that

$$FP : PB = D : E,$$

where $D : E$ is any given ratio less than $BM : MO$.

Draw OH parallel to AB, and BT perpendicular to BO meeting OH in T.

Then the triangles BMO, OBT are similar, and therefore
$$BM : MO = OB : BT,$$
whence $\qquad\qquad\qquad D : E < OB : BT.$

Suppose that a line PH (greater
than BT) is taken such that
$$D : E = OB : PH,$$
and let PH be so placed that it
passes through B and P lies on the
circumference of the circle, while
H is on the line OH. (PH will fall
outside BT, because $PH > BT$.)
Join OP meeting AB in F.

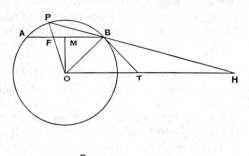

We now have
$$FP : PB = OP : PH$$
$$= OB : PH$$
$$= D : E.$$

PROPOSITION 7

Given a circle with centre O, a chord AB less than the diameter, and OM the per-
pendicular on it from O, it is possible to draw from O a straight line OPF, meeting
the circle in P and AB produced in F, such that
$$FP : PB = D : E,$$
where $D : E$ is any given ratio greater than $BM : MO$.

Draw OT parallel to AB, and BT perpendicular to BO meeting OT in T.
In this case,
$$D : E > BM : MO$$
$$> OB : BT, \text{ by similar triangles.}$$
Take a line PH (less than BT) such that
$$D : E = OB : PH,$$
and place PH so that P, H are on the circle and
on OT respectively, while HP produced passes
through B.

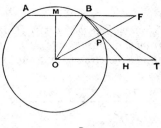

Then $\qquad\qquad FP : PB = OP : PH$
$$= D : E.$$

PROPOSITION 8

Given a circle with centre O, a chord AB less than the diameter, the tangent at B,
and the perpendicular OM from O on AB, it is possible to draw from O a straight
line OFP, meeting the chord AB in F, the circle in P and the tangent in G, such
that
$$FP : BG = D : E,$$
where $D : E$ is any given ratio less than $BM : MO$.

If OT be drawn parallel to AB meeting the tangent at B in T,
$$BM : MO = OB : BT,$$
so that $\qquad\qquad\qquad D : E < OB : BT.$
Take a point C on TB produced such that
$$D : E = OB : BC,$$
whence $\qquad\qquad\qquad BC > BT.$

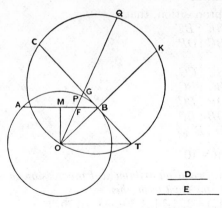

Through the points O, T, C describe a circle, and let OB be produced to meet this circle in K.

Then, since $BC > BT$, and OB is perpendicular to CT, it is possible to draw from O a straight line OGQ, meeting CT in G and the circle about OTC in Q, such that $GQ = BK$.

Let OGQ meet AB in F and the original circle in P.

Now $CG \cdot GT = OG \cdot GQ$;

and $OF : OG = BT : GT$,

so that $OF \cdot GT = OG \cdot BT$.

It follows that

$$CG \cdot GT : OF \cdot GT = OG \cdot GQ : OG \cdot BT,$$

or $CG : OF = GQ : BT$

$\qquad = BK : BT$, by construction,

$\qquad = BC : OB$

$\qquad = BC : OP$.

Hence $OP : OF = BC : CG$,

and therefore $PF : OP = BG : BC$,

or $PF : BG = OP : BC$

$\qquad = OB : BC$

$\qquad = D : E$.

PROPOSITION 9

Given a circle with centre O, a chord AB less than the diameter, the tangent at B, and the perpendicular OM from O on AB, it is possible to draw from O a straight line $OPGF$, meeting the circle in P, the tangent in G, and AB produced in F, such that

$$FP : BG = D : E,$$

where $D : E$ is any given ratio greater than $BM : MO$.

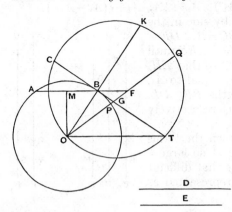

Let OT be drawn parallel to AB meeting the tangent at B in T.

Then

$D : E > BM : MO$

$\qquad > OB : BT$, by similar triangles.

Produce TB to C so that

$$D : E = OB : BC,$$

whence $BC < BT$.

Describe a circle through the points O, T, C, and produce OB to meet this circle in K.

Then, since $TB > BC$, and OB is perpendicular to CT, it is possible to draw from O a line OGQ, meeting CT in G, and the circle about OTC in Q, such that $GQ = BK$. Let OQ meet the original circle in P and AB produced in F.

We now prove, exactly as in the last proposition, that
$$CG : OF = BK : BT$$
$$= BC : OP.$$
Thus, as before,
$$OP : OF = BC : CG,$$
and
$$OP : PF = BC : BG,$$
whence
$$PF : BG = OP : BC$$
$$= OB : BC$$
$$= D : E.$$

Proposition 10

If A_1, A_2, A_3, $\cdots A_n$ be n lines forming an ascending arithmetical progression in which the common difference is equal to A_1, the least term, then
$$(n+1)A_n{}^2 + A_1(A_1 + A_2 + \cdots + A_n) = 3(A_1{}^2 + A_2{}^2 + \cdots + A_n{}^2).$$

[Archimedes' proof of this proposition is given above, pp. 456–7, and it is there pointed out that the result is equivalent to

$$1^2 + 2^2 + 3^2 + \cdots + n^2 = \frac{n(n+1)(2n+1)}{6}.]$$

Cor. 1. *It follows from this proposition that*
$$n \cdot A_n{}^2 < 3(A_1{}^2 + A_2{}^2 + \cdots + A_n{}^2),$$
and also that
$$n \cdot A_n{}^2 > 3(A_1{}^2 + A_2{}^2 + \cdots + A_{n-1}{}^2).$$

[For the proof of the latter inequality see p. 457 above.]

Cor. 2. *All the results will equally hold if similar figures are substituted for squares.*

Proposition 11

If A_1, A_2, $\cdots A_n$ be n lines forming an ascending arithmetical progression [in which the common difference is equal to the least term A_1], then
$$(n-1)A_n{}^2 : (A_n{}^2 + A_{n-1}{}^2 + \cdots + A_2{}^2) < A_n{}^2 : \{A_n \cdot A_1 + \tfrac{1}{3}(A_n - A_1)^2\};$$
but
$$(n-1)A_n{}^2 : (A_{n-1}{}^2 + A_{n-2}{}^2 + \cdots + A_1{}^2) > A_n{}^2 : \{A_n \cdot A_1 + \tfrac{1}{3}(A_n - A_1)^2\}.$$

[Archimedes sets out the terms side by side in the manner shown in the figure, where $BC = A_n$, $DE = A_{n-1}, \ldots RS = A_1$, and produces DE, FG, $\ldots RS$ until they are respectively equal to BC or A_n, so that EH, GI, $\ldots SU$ in the figure are respectively equal to A_1, $A_2 \ldots A_{n-1}$. He further measures lengths BK, DL, FM, $\ldots PV$ along BC, DE, FG, $\ldots PQ$ respectively each equal to RS.

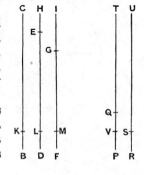

The figure makes the relations between the terms easier to see with the eye, but the use of so large a number of letters makes the proof somewhat difficult to follow, and it may be more clearly represented as follows.]

It is evident that $(A_n - A_1) = A_{n-1}$.

The following proportion is therefore obviously true, viz.
$$(n-1)A_n{}^2 : (n-1)(A_n \cdot A_1 + \tfrac{1}{3}A_{n-1}{}^2) = A_n{}^2 : \{A_n \cdot A_1 + \tfrac{1}{3}(A_n - A_1)^2\}.$$

In order therefore to prove the desired result, we have only to show that
$$(n-1)A_n \cdot A_1 + \tfrac{1}{3}(n-1)A_{n-1}{}^2 < (A_n{}^2 + A_{n-1}{}^2 + \cdots + A_2{}^2)$$
but
$$> (A_{n-1}{}^2 + A_{n-2}{}^2 + \cdots + A_1{}^2).$$

I. To prove the first inequality, we have
$$(n-1)A_n \cdot A_1 + \tfrac{1}{3}(n-1)A_{n-1}{}^2$$
$$= (n-1)A_1{}^2 + (n-1)A_1 \cdot A_{n-1} + \tfrac{1}{3}(n-1)A_{n-1}{}^2. \tag{1}$$

And
$$A_n{}^2 + A_{n-1}{}^2 + \cdots + A_2{}^2 = (A_{n-1} + A_1)^2 + (A_{n-2} + A_1)^2 + \cdots + (A_1 + A_1)^2$$
$$= (A_{n-1}{}^2 + A_{n-2}{}^2 + \cdots + A_1{}^2)$$
$$+ (n-1)A_1{}^2$$
$$+ 2A_1(A_{n-1} + A_{n-2} + \cdots + A_1)$$
$$= (A_{n-1}{}^2 + A_{n-2}{}^2 + \cdots + A_1{}^2)$$
$$+ (n-1)A_1{}^2$$
$$+ A_1\{A_{n-1} + A_{n-2} + A_{n-3} + \cdots + A_1$$
$$+ A_1 + A_2 + \cdots + A_{n-2} + A_{n-1}\}$$
$$= (A_{n-1}{}^2 + A_{n-2}{}^2 + \cdots + A_1{}^2)$$
$$+ (n-1)A_1{}^2$$
$$+ nA_1 \cdot A_{n-1}. \tag{2}$$

Comparing the right-hand sides of (1) and (2), we see that $(n-1)A_1{}^2$ is common to both sides, and
$$(n-1)A_1 \cdot A_{n-1} < nA_1 \cdot A_{n-1},$$
while, by Prop. 10, Cor. 1,
$$\tfrac{1}{3}(n-1)A_{n-1}{}^2 < A_{n-1}{}^2 + A_{n-2}{}^2 + \cdots + A_1{}^2.$$
It follows therefore that
$$(n-1)A_n \cdot A_1 + \tfrac{1}{3}(n-1)A_{n-1}{}^2 < (A_n{}^2 + A_{n-1}{}^2 + \cdots + A_2{}^2);$$
and hence the first part of the proposition is proved.

II. We have now, in order to prove the second result, to show that
$$(n-1)A_n \cdot A_1 + \tfrac{1}{3}(n-1)A_{n-1}{}^2 > (A_{n-1}{}^2 + A_{n-2}{}^2 + \cdots + A_1{}^2).$$
The right-hand side is equal to
$$(A_{n-2} + A_1)^2 + (A_{n-3} + A_1)^2 + \cdots + (A_1 + A_1)^2 + A_1{}^2$$
$$= A_{n-2}{}^2 + A_{n-3}{}^2 + \cdots + A_1{}^2$$
$$+ (n-1)A_1{}^2$$
$$+ 2A_1(A_{n-2} + A_{n-3} + \cdots + A_1)$$
$$= (A_{n-2}{}^2 + A_{n-3}{}^2 + \cdots + A_1{}^2)$$
$$+ (n-1)A_1{}^2$$
$$+ A_1\left\{\begin{array}{l} A_{n-2} + A_{n-3} + \cdots + A_1 \\ + A_1 + A_2 + \cdots + A_{n-2} \end{array}\right\}$$
$$= (A_{n-2}{}^2 + A_{n-3}{}^2 + \cdots + A_1{}^2)$$
$$+ (n-1)A_1{}^2$$
$$+ (n-2)A_1 \cdot A_{n-1}. \tag{3}$$

Comparing this expression with the right-hand side of (1) above, we see that $(n-1)A_1{}^2$ is common to both sides, and
$$(n-1)A_1 \cdot A_{n-1} > (n-2)A_1 \cdot A_{n-1},$$
while, by Prop. 10, Cor. 1,
$$\tfrac{1}{3}(n-1)A_{n-1}{}^2 > (A_{n-2}{}^2 + A_{n-3}{}^2 + \cdots + A_1{}^2).$$
Hence $\quad (n-1)A_n \cdot A_1 + \tfrac{1}{3}(n-1)A_{n-1}{}^2 > (A_{n-1}{}^2 + A_{n-2}{}^2 + \cdots + A_1{}^2);$
and the second required result follows.

COR. *The results in the above proposition are equally true if similar figures be substituted for squares on the several lines.*

DEFINITIONS

1. If a straight line drawn in a plane revolve at a uniform rate about one extremity which remains fixed and return to the position from which it started, and if, at the same time as the line revolves, a point move at a uniform rate along the straight line beginning from the extremity which remains fixed, the point will describe a *spiral* (ἕλιξ) in the plane.

2. Let the extremity of the straight line which remains fixed while the straight line revolves be called the *origin* of the spiral.

3. And let the position of the line from which the straight line began to revolve be called the *initial line* in the revolution.

4. Let the length which the point that moves along the straight line describes in one revolution be called the *first distance*, that which the same point describes in the second revolution the *second distance*, and similarly let the distances described in further revolutions be called after the number of the particular revolution.

5. Let the area bounded by the spiral described in the first revolution and the *first distance* be called the *first area*, that bounded by the spiral described in the second revolution and the *second distance* the *second area*, and similarly for the rest in order.

6. If from the origin of the spiral any straight line be drawn, let that side of it which is in the same direction as that of the revolution be called *forward* (προαγούμενα), and that which is in the other direction *backward* (ἑπόμενα).

7. Let the circle drawn with the *origin* as centre and the *first distance* as radius be called the *first circle*, that drawn with the same centre and twice the radius the *second circle*, and similarly for the succeeding circles.

Proposition 12

If any number of straight lines drawn from the origin to meet the spiral make equal angles with one another, the lines will be in arithmetical progression.

[The proof is obvious.]

Proposition 13

If a straight line touch the spiral, it will touch it in one point only.

Let *O* be the origin of the spiral, and *BC* a tangent to it.

If possible, let *BC* touch the spiral in two points *P, Q*. Join *OP, OQ*, and bisect the angle *POQ* by the straight line *OR* meeting the spiral in *R*.

Then [Prop. 12] *OR* is an arithmetic mean between *OP* and *OQ*, or

$$OP+OQ=2OR.$$

But in any triangle *POQ*, if the bisector of the angle *POQ* meets *PQ* in *K*,

$$OP+OQ>2OK.$$

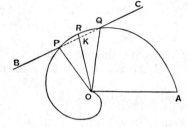

Therefore *OK* < *OR*, and it follows that some point on *BC* between *P* and *Q* lies within the spiral. Hence *BC* cuts the spiral; which is contrary to the hypothesis.

PROPOSITION 14

If O be the origin, and P, Q two points on the first turn of the spiral, and if OP, OQ produced meet the "first circle" AKP'Q' in P', Q' respectively, OA being the initial line, then

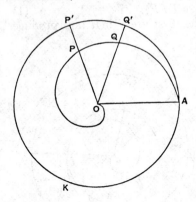

$$OP : OQ = (\text{arc } AKP') : (\text{arc } AKQ').$$

For, while the revolving line *OA* moves about *O*, the point *A* on it moves uniformly along the circumference of the circle *AKP'Q'*, and at the same time the point describing the spiral moves uniformly along *OA*.

Thus, while *A* describes the arc *AKP'*, the moving point on *OA* describes the length *OP*, and, while *A* describes the arc *AKQ'*, the moving point on *OA* describes the distance *OQ*.

Hence
$$OP : OQ = (\text{arc } AKP') : (\text{arc } AKQ').$$
[Prop. 2]

PROPOSITION 15

If P, Q be points on the second turn of the spiral, and OP, OQ meet the "first circle" AKP'Q' in P', Q', as in the last proposition, and if c be the circumference of the "first circle," then
$$OP : OQ = c + (\text{arc } AKP') : c + (\text{arc } AKQ').$$

For, while the moving point on *OA* describes the distance *OP*, the point *A* describes the whole of the circumference of the "first circle" together with the arc *AKP'*; and, while the moving point on *OA* describes the distance *OQ*, the point *A* describes the whole of the circumference of the "first circle" together with the arc *AKQ'*.

COR. Similarly, if *P, Q* are on the *n*th turn of the spiral,
$$OP : OQ = (n-1)c + (\text{arc } AKP') : (n-1)c + (\text{arc } AKQ').$$

PROPOSITIONS 16, 17

If BC be the tangent at P, any point on the spiral, PC being the "forward" part of BC, and if OP be joined, the angle OPC is obtuse while the angle OPB is acute.

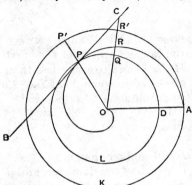

I. Suppose *P* to be on the first turn of the spiral.

Let *OA* be the initial line, *AKP'* the "first circle." Draw the circle *DLP* with centre *O* and radius *OP*, meeting *OA* in *D*. This circle must then, in the "forward" direction from *P*, fall within the spiral, and in the "backward" direction outside it, since the radii vectores of the spiral are on the "forward side" greater, and on the "backward" side less, than *OP*. Hence the angle *OPC* cannot be acute, since it cannot be less than the angle between *OP* and the tangent to the circle at P, which is a right angle.

It only remains therefore to prove that OPC is not a right angle.

If possible, let it be a right angle. BC will then touch the circle at P.

Therefore [Prop. 5] it is possible to draw a line OQC meeting the circle through P in Q and BC in C, such that

$$CQ : OQ < (\text{arc } PQ) : (\text{arc } DLP). \tag{1}$$

Suppose that OC meets the spiral in R and the "first circle" in R'; and produce OP to meet the "first circle" in P'.

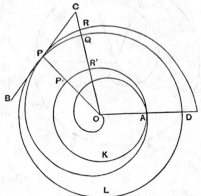

From (1) it follows, *componendo*, that

$$CO : OQ < (\text{arc } DLQ) : (\text{arc } DLP)$$
$$< (\text{arc } AKR') : (\text{arc } AKP')$$
$$< OR : OP. \qquad [\text{Prop. 14}]$$

But this is impossible, because $OQ = OP$, and $OR < OC$.

Hence the angle OPC is not a right angle. It was also proved not to be acute.

Therefore the angle OPC is obtuse, and the angle OPB consequently acute.

II. If P is on the second, or the nth turn, the proof is the same, except that in the proportion (1) above we have to substitute for the arc DLP an arc equal to $(p + \text{arc } DLP)$ or $(n-1 \cdot p + \text{arc } DLP)$, where p is the perimeter of the circle DLP through P. Similarly, in the later steps, p or $(n-1)p$ will be added to each of the arcs DLQ and DLP, and c or $(n-1)c$ to each of the arcs AKR', AKP', where c is the circumference of the "first circle" AKP'.

Propositions 18, 19

I. *If OA be the initial line, A the end of the first turn of the spiral, and if the tangent to the spiral at A be drawn, the straight line OB drawn from O perpendicular to OA will meet the said tangent in some point B, and OB will be equal to the circumference of the "first circle."*

II. *If A' be the end of the second turn, the perpendicular OB will meet the tangent at A' in some point B', and OB' will be equal to 2 (circumference of "second circle").*

III. *Generally, if A_n be the end of the nth turn, and OB meet the tangent at A_n in B_n, then* $\qquad OB_n = nc_n,$
where c_n is the circumference of the "nth circle."

I. Let AKC be the "first circle." Then, since the "backward" angle between OA and the tangent at A is acute [Prop. 16], the tangent will meet the "first circle" in a second point C. And the angles CAO, BOA are together less than two right angles; therefore OB will meet AC produced in some point B.

Then, if c be the circumference of the first circle, we have to prove that

$$OB = c.$$

If not, OB must be either greater or less than c.

(1) If possible, suppose $OB > c$.

Measure along OB a length OD less than OB but greater than c.

We have then a circle AKC, a chord AC in it less than the diameter, and a ratio $AO : OD$ which is greater than the ratio $AO : OB$ or (what is, by similar triangles, equal to it) the ratio of $\frac{1}{2}AC$ to the perpendicular from O on AC. Therefore [Prop. 7] we can draw a straight line OPF, meeting the circle in P and CA produced in F, such that

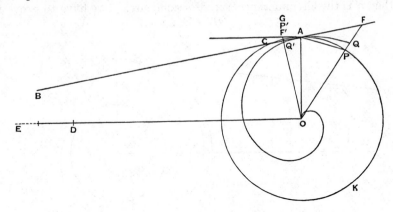

$$FP : PA = AO : OD.$$

Thus, alternately, since $\quad AO = PO,$

$$FP : PO = PA : OD$$
$$< (\text{arc } PA) : c,$$

since $(\text{arc } PA) > PA$, and $OD > c$.

Componendo,

$$FO : PO < (c + \text{arc } PA) : c$$
$$< OQ : OA,$$

where OF meets the spiral in Q. [Prop. 15]

Therefore, since $OA = OP$, $FO < OQ$; which is impossible.

Hence $\qquad\qquad\qquad OB \not> c.$

(2) If possible, suppose $\qquad OB < c.$

Measure OE along OB so that OE is greater than OB but less than c.

In this case, since the ratio $AO : OE$ is less than the ratio $AO : OB$ (or the ratio of $\frac{1}{2}AC$ to the perpendicular from O on AC), we can [Prop. 8] draw a line $OF'P'G$, meeting AC in F', the circle in P', and the tangent at A to the circle in G, such that

$$F'P' : AG = AO : OE.$$

Let $OP'G$ cut the spiral in Q'.

Then we have, alternately,

$$F'P' : P'O = AG : OE$$
$$> (\text{arc } AP') : c,$$

because $AG > (\text{arc } AP')$, and $OE < c$.

Therefore

$$F'O : P'O < (\text{arc } AKP') : c$$
$$< OQ' : OA.$$ [Prop. 14]

But this is impossible, since $OA = OP'$, and $OQ' < OF'$.

Hence $\qquad\qquad\qquad OB \not< c.$

Since therefore OB is neither greater nor less than c,

$$OB = c.$$

II. Let $A'K'C'$ be the "second circle," $A'C'$ being the tangent to the spiral at A' (which will cut the second circle, since the "backward" angle $OA'C'$ is acute). Thus, as before, the perpendicular OB' to OA' will meet $A'C'$ produced in some point B'.

If then c' is the circumference of the "second circle," we have to prove that
$$OB' = 2c'.$$

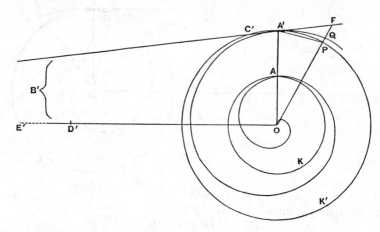

For, if not, OB' must be either greater or less than $2c'$.

(1) If possible, suppose $OB' > 2c'$.

Measure OD' along OB' so that OD' is less than OB' but greater than $2c'$.

Then, as in the case of the "first circle" above, we can draw a straight line OPF meeting the "second circle" in P and $C'A'$ produced in F, such that
$$FP : PA' = A'O : OD'.$$

Let OF meet the spiral in Q.

We now have, since $A'O = PO$,
$$FP : PO = PA' : OD'$$
$$< (\text{arc } A'P) : 2c',$$
because $(\text{arc } A'P) > A'P$ and $OD' > 2c'$.

Therefore $FO : PO < (2c' + \text{arc } A'P) : 2c'$
$$< OQ : OA'. \qquad\qquad \text{[Prop. 15, Cor.]}$$

Hence $FO < OQ$; which is impossible.

Thus $OB' \not> 2c'$.

Similarly, as in the case of the "first circle," we can prove that
$$OB' \not< 2c'.$$

Therefore $OB' = 2c'.$

III. Proceeding, in like manner, to the "third" and succeeding circles, we shall prove that
$$OB_n = nc_n.$$

PROPOSITION 20

I. *If P be any point on the first turn of the spiral and OT be drawn perpendicular to OP, OT will meet the tangent at P to the spiral in some point T; and, if the circle drawn with centre O and radius OP meet the initial line in K, then OT is equal to the arc of this circle between K and P measured in the "forward" direction of the spiral.*

II. *Generally, if P be a point on the nth turn, and the notation be as before, while p represents the circumference of the circle with radius OP,*

$$OT = (n-1)p + arc\ KP\ (measured\ "forward").$$

I. Let P be a point on the first turn of the spiral, OA the initial line, PR the tangent at P taken in the "backward" direction.

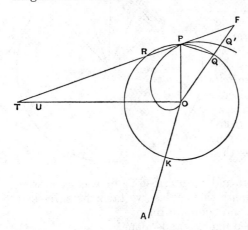

Then [Prop. 16] the angle OPR is acute. Therefore PR meets the circle through P in some point R; and also OT will meet PR produced in some point T.

If now OT is not equal to the arc KRP, it must be either greater or less.

(1) If possible, let OT be greater than the arc KRP.

Measure OU along OT less than OT but greater than the arc KRP.

Then, since the ratio $PO:OU$ is greater than the ratio $PO:OT$, or (what is, by similar triangles,

equal to it) the ratio of $\frac{1}{2}PR$ to the perpendicular from O on PR, we can draw a line OQF, meeting the circle in Q and RP produced in F, such that

$$FQ:PQ=PO:OU.\qquad\qquad\text{[Prop. 7]}$$

Let OF meet the spiral in Q'.

We have then

$$FQ:QO=PQ:OU$$
$$<(arc\ PQ):(arc\ KRP),\ \text{by hypothesis.}$$

Componendo,

$$FO:QO<(arc\ KRQ):(arc\ KRP)$$
$$<OQ':OP.\qquad\qquad\text{[Prop. 14]}$$

But $QO=OP.$

Therefore $FO<OQ'$; which is impossible.

Hence $OT \not> (arc\ KRP).$

(2) The proof that $OT \not< (arc\ KRP)$ follows the method of Prop. 18, I. (2), exactly as the above follows that of Prop. 18, I. (1).

Since then OT is neither greater nor less than the arc KRP, it is equal to it.

II. If P be on the second turn, the same method shows that

$$OT = p + (arc\ KRP);$$

and, similarly, we have, for a point P on the nth turn,

$$OT = (n-1)p + (arc\ KRP).$$

PROPOSITIONS 21, 22, 23

Given an area bounded by any arc of a spiral and the lines joining the extremities of the arc to the origin, it is possible to circumscribe about the area one figure, and to inscribe in it another figure, each consisting of similar sectors of circles, and such that the circumscribed figure exceeds the inscribed by less than any assigned area.

For let BC be any arc of the spiral, O the origin. Draw the circle with centre

O and radius OC, where C is the "forward" end of the arc.

Then, by bisecting the angle BOC, bisecting the resulting angles, and so on continually, we shall ultimately arrive at an angle COr cutting off a sector of the circle less than any assigned area. Let COr be this sector.

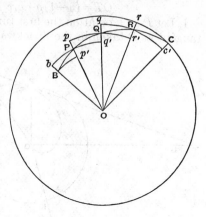

Let the other lines dividing the angle BOC into equal parts meet the spiral in P, Q, and let Or meet it in R. With O as centre and radii OB, OP, OQ, OR respectively describe arcs of circles Bp', bBq', pQr', qRc', each meeting the adjacent radii as shown in the figure. In each case the arc in the "forward" direction from each point will fall within, and the arc in the "backward" direction outside, the spiral.

We have now a circumscribed figure and an inscribed figure each consisting of similar sectors of circles. To compare their areas, we take the successive sectors of each, beginning from OC, and compare them.

The sector OCr in the circumscribed figure stands alone.

And
$$(\text{sector } ORq) = (\text{sector } ORc'),$$
$$(\text{sector } OQp) = (\text{sector } OQr'),$$
$$(\text{sector } OPb) = (\text{sector } OPq'),$$
while the sector OBp' in the inscribed figure stands alone.

Hence, if the equal sectors be taken away, the difference between the circumscribed and inscribed figures is equal to the difference between the sectors OCr and OBp'; and this difference is less than the sector OCr, which is itself less than any assigned area.

The proof is exactly the same whatever be the number of angles into which the angle BOC is divided, the only difference being that, when the arc begins from the origin, the smallest sectors OPb, OPq' in each figure are equal, and there is therefore no inscribed sector standing by itself, so that the difference between the circumscribed and inscribed figures is equal to the sector OCr itself.

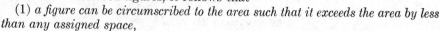

Thus the proposition is universally true.

COR. Since the area bounded by the spiral is intermediate in magnitude between the circumscribed and inscribed figures, it follows that

(1) *a figure can be circumscribed to the area such that it exceeds the area by less than any assigned space,*

(2) *a figure can be inscribed such that the area exceeds it by less than any assigned space.*

PROPOSITION 24

The area bounded by the first turn of the spiral and the initial line is equal to one-third of the "first circle" $\left[= \frac{1}{3}\pi(2\pi a)^2, \text{ where the spiral is } r = a\theta \right].$

[The same proof shows equally that, *if OP be any radius vector in the first turn of the spiral, the area of the portion of the spiral bounded thereby is equal to one-third of that sector of the circle drawn with radius OP which is bounded by the initial line and OP, measured in the "forward" direction from the initial line.*]

Let O be the origin, OA the initial line, A the extremity of the first turn.

Draw the "first circle," i.e. the circle with O as centre and OA as radius.

Then, if C_1 be the area of the first circle, R_1 that of the first turn of the spiral bounded by OA, we have to prove that
$$R_1 = \tfrac{1}{3}C_1.$$

For, if not, R_1 must be either greater or less than C_1.

I. If possible, suppose $R_1 < \tfrac{1}{3}C_1$.

We can then circumscribe a figure about R_1 made up of similar sectors of circles such that, if F be the area of this figure,
$$F - R_1 < \tfrac{1}{3}C_1 - R_1,$$
whence $F < \tfrac{1}{3}C_1$.

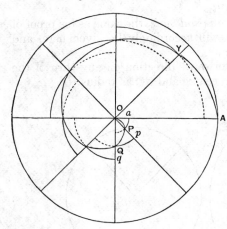

Let OP, OQ, $\cdots$ be the radii of the circular sectors, beginning from the smallest. The radius of the largest is of course OA.

The radii then form an ascending arithmetical progression in which the common difference is equal to the least term OP. If n be the number of the sectors, we have [by Prop. 10, Cor. 1]
$$n \cdot OA^2 < 3(OP^2 + OQ^2 + \cdots + OA^2);$$
and, since the similar sectors are proportional to the squares on their radii, it follows that
$$C_1 < 3F,$$
$$\text{or} \qquad F > \tfrac{1}{3}C_1.$$

But this is impossible, since F was less than $\tfrac{1}{3}C_1$.

Therefore $\qquad\qquad\qquad\qquad R_1 \not< \tfrac{1}{3}C_1$.

II. If possible, suppose $\qquad\qquad R_1 > \tfrac{1}{3}C_1$.

We can then *inscribe* a figure made up of similar sectors of circles such that, if f be its area,
$$R_1 - f < R_1 - \tfrac{1}{3}C_1,$$
whence $f > \tfrac{1}{3}C_1$.

If there are $(n-1)$ sectors, their radii, as OP, OQ, $\cdots$, form an ascending arithmetical progression in which the least term is equal to the common difference, and the greatest term, as OY, is equal to $(n-1)OP$.

Thus [Prop. 10, Cor. 1]
$$n \cdot OA^2 > 3(OP^2 + OQ^2 + \cdots + OY^2),$$
whence $\qquad\qquad\qquad\qquad C_1 > 3f,$
or $\qquad\qquad\qquad\qquad\qquad f < \tfrac{1}{3}C_1;$
which is impossible, since $\qquad f > \tfrac{1}{3}C_1$.

Therefore $\qquad\qquad\qquad\qquad R_1 \not> \tfrac{1}{3}C_1$.

Since then R_1 is neither greater nor less than $\tfrac{1}{3}C_1$,
$$R_1 = \tfrac{1}{3}C_1.$$

Propositions 25, 26, 27

[Prop. 25.] *If A_2 be the end of the second turn of the spiral, the area bounded by the second turn and OA_2 is to the area of the "second circle" in the ratio of 7 to 12, being the ratio of $\{r_2 r_1 + \frac{1}{3}(r_2 - r_1)^2\}$ to $r_2{}^2$, where r_1, r_2 are the radii of the "first" and "second" circles respectively.*

[Prop. 26.] *If BC be any arc measured in the "forward" direction on any turn of a spiral, not being greater than the complete turn, and if a circle be drawn with O as centre and OC as radius meeting OB in B', then*

$$(area\ of\ spiral\ between\ OB,\ OC) : (sector\ OB'C)$$
$$= \{OC \cdot OB + \tfrac{1}{3}(OC - OB)^2\} : OC^2.$$

[Prop. 27.] *If R_1 be the area of the first turn of the spiral bounded by the initial line, R_2 the area of the ring added by the second complete turn, R_3 that of the ring added by the third turn, and so on, then*

$$R_3 = 2R_2,\ R_4 = 3R_2,\ R_5 = 4R_2,\ \cdots,\ R_n = (n-1)R_2.$$

Also $R_2 = 6R_1.$

[Archimedes' proof of Prop. 25 is, *mutatis mutandis*, the same as his proof of the more general Prop. 26. The latter will accordingly be given here, and applied to Prop. 25 as a particular case.]

Let BC be an arc measured in the "forward" direction on any turn of the spiral, CKB' the circle drawn with O as centre and OC as radius.

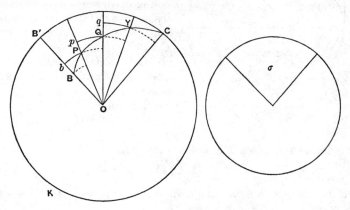

Take a circle such that the square of its radius is equal to
$$OC \cdot OB + \tfrac{1}{3}(OC - OB)^2,$$
and let σ be a sector in it whose central angle is equal to the angle BOC.
Thus $\sigma : (sector\ OB'C) = \{OC \cdot OB + \tfrac{1}{3}(OC - OB)^2\} : OC^2,$
and we have therefore to prove that
$$(area\ of\ spiral\ OBC) = \sigma.$$

For, if not, the area of the spiral OBC (which we will call S) must be either greater or less than σ.

I. Suppose, if possible, $S < \sigma$.

Circumscribe to the area S a figure made up of similar sectors of circles, such that, if F be the area of the figure,
$$F - S < \sigma - S,$$
whence $F < \sigma.$

Let the radii of the successive sectors, starting from OB, be OP, OQ, $\cdots OC$. Produce OP, OQ, $\cdots$ to meet the circle CKB', $\cdots$

If then the lines OB, OP, OQ, $\ldots OC$ be n in number, the number of sectors in the circumscribed figure will be $(n-1)$, and the sector $OB'C$ will also be divided into $(n-1)$ equal sectors. Also OB, OP, OQ, $\cdots OC$ will form an ascending arithmetical progression of n terms.

Therefore [see Prop. 11 and Cor.]
$$(n-1)OC^2 : (OP^2 + OQ^2 + \cdots + OC^2) < OC^2 : \{OC \cdot OB + \tfrac{1}{3}(OC - OB)^2\}$$
$$< (\text{sector } OB'C) : \sigma, \text{ by hypothesis.}$$

Hence, since similar sectors are as the squares of their radii,
$$(\text{sector } OB'C) : F < (\text{sector } OB'C) : \sigma,$$

so that $F > \sigma$.

But this is impossible, because $F < \sigma$.

Therefore $S \not< \sigma$.

II. Suppose, if possible, $S > \sigma$.

Inscribe in the area S a figure made up of similar sectors of circles such that, if f be its area,
$$S - f < S - \sigma,$$
whence $f > \sigma$.

Suppose OB, OP, $\ldots OY$ to be the radii of the successive sectors making up the figure f, being $(n-1)$ in number.

We shall have in this case [see Prop. 11 and Cor.]
$$(n-1)OC^2 : (OB^2 + OP^2 + \cdots + OY^2) > OC^2 : \{OC \cdot OB + \tfrac{1}{3}(OC - OB)^2\},$$
whence $(\text{sector } OB'C) : f > (\text{sector } OB'C) : \sigma,$

so that $f < \sigma$.

But this is impossible, because $f > \sigma$.

Therefore $S \not> \sigma$.

Since then S is neither greater nor less than σ, it follows that
$$S = \sigma.$$

In the particular case where B coincides with A_1, the end of the first turn of the spiral, and C with A_2, the end of the second turn, the sector $OB'C$ becomes the complete "second circle," that, namely, with OA_2 (or r_2) as radius.

Thus   (area of spiral bounded by OA_2) : ("second circle")
$$= \{r_2 r_1 + \tfrac{1}{3}(r_2 - r_1)^2\} : r_2^2$$
$$= (2 + \tfrac{1}{3}) : 4 \quad (\text{since } r_2 = 2r_1)$$
$$= 7 : 12.$$

Again, the area of the spiral bounded by OA_2 is equal to $R_1 + R_2$ (i.e. the area bounded by the first turn and OA_1, together with the ring added by the second turn). Also the "second circle" is four times the "first circle," and therefore equal to $12\,R_1$.

Hence $(R_1 + R_2) : 12R_1 = 7 : 12,$

or $R_1 + R_2 = 7R_1.$

Thus $R_2 = 6R_1.$ (1)

Next, for the third turn, we have
$$(R_1 + R_2 + R_3) : (\text{"third circle"}) = \{r_3\, r_2 + \tfrac{1}{3}(r_3 - r_2)^2\} : r_3^2$$
$$= (3 \cdot 2 + \tfrac{1}{3}) : 3^2$$
$$= 19 : 27,$$

and   ("third circle") $= 9$("first circle")
$$= 27R_1;$$

therefore $\qquad\qquad\qquad R_1+R_2+R_3=19R_1,$

and, by (1) above, it follows that

$$R_3=12R_1$$
$$=2R_2, \qquad\qquad (2)$$

and so on.

Generally, we have

$$(R_1+R_2+\cdots+R_n) : (\text{nth circle}) = \{r_n\,r_{n-1}+\tfrac13(r_n-r_{n-1})^2\} : r_n{}^2,$$
$$(R_1+R_2+\cdots+R_{n-1}) : (n-1\text{th circle}) = \{r_{n-1}\,r_{n-2}+\tfrac13(r_{n-1}-r_{n-2})^2\} : r_{n-1}{}^2,$$

and $\qquad\qquad$ (nth circle) : ($n-1$th circle) $= r_n{}^2 : r_{n-1}{}^2$.

Therefore

$$(R_1+R_2+\cdots+R_n) : (R_1+R_2+\cdots+R_{n-1})$$
$$= \{n(n-1)+\tfrac13\} : \{(n-1)(n-2)+\tfrac13\}$$
$$= \{3n(n-1)+1\} : \{3(n-1)(n-2)+1\}.$$

Dirimendo,

$$R_n : (R_1+R_2+\cdots+R_{n-1})=6(n-1) : \{3(n-1)(n-2)+1\}. \qquad (\alpha)$$

Similarly

$$R_{n-1} : (R_1+R_2+\cdots+R_{n-2})=6(n-2) : \{3(n-2)(n-3)+1\},$$

from which we derive

$$R_{n-1} : (R_1+R_2+\cdots+R_{n-1})$$
$$=6(n-2) : \{6(n-2)+3(n-2)(n-3)+1\}$$
$$=6(n-2) : \{3(n-1)(n-2)+1\}. \qquad (\beta).$$

Combining (α) and (β), we obtain

$$R_n : R_{n-1}=(n-1) : (n-2).$$

Thus

$R_2, R_3, R_4, \cdots R_n$ are in the ratio of the successive numbers $1, 2, 3 \cdots (n-1)$.

PROPOSITION 28

If O be the origin and BC any arc measured in the "forward" direction on any turn of the spiral, let two circles be drawn (1) with centre O, and radius OB, meeting OC in C', and (2) with centre O and radius OC, meeting OB produced in B'. Then, if E denote the area bounded by the larger circular arc $B'C$, the line $B'B$, and the spiral BC, while F denotes the area bounded by the smaller arc BC', the line CC' and the spiral BC,

$$E : F = \{OB+\tfrac23(OC-OB)\} : \{OB+\tfrac13(OC-OB)\}.$$

Let σ denote the area of the lesser sector OBC'; then the larger sector $OB'C$ is equal to $\sigma+F+E$. Thus [Prop. 26]

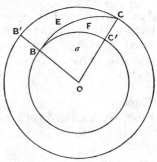

$$(\sigma+F) : (\sigma+F+E) =$$
$$\{OC\cdot OB+\tfrac13(OC-OB)^2\} : OC^2, \quad (1)$$

whence

$$E : (\sigma+F) = \{OC(OC-OB)-\tfrac13(OC-OB)^2\}$$
$$: \{OC\cdot OB+\tfrac13(OC-OB)^2\}$$
$$= \{OB(OC-OB)+\tfrac23(OC-OB)^2\}$$
$$: \{OC\cdot OB+\tfrac13(OC-OB)^2\}. \quad (2)$$

Again

$$(\sigma+F+E) : \sigma=OC^2 : OB^2.$$

Therefore, by the first proportion above, *ex aequali,*

$$(\sigma+F) : \sigma=\{OC\cdot OB+\tfrac13(OC-OB)^2\} : OB^2,$$

whence

$$(\sigma + F) : F = \{OC \cdot OB + \tfrac{1}{3}(OC - OB)^2\}$$
$$: \{OB(OC - OB) + \tfrac{1}{3}(OC - OB)^2\}.$$

Combining this with (2) above, we obtain

$$E : F = \{OB(OC - OB) + \tfrac{2}{3}(OC - OB)^2\} : \{OB(OC - OB) + \tfrac{1}{3}(OC - OB)^2\}$$
$$= \{OB + \tfrac{2}{3}(OC - OB)\} : \{OB + \tfrac{1}{3}(OC - OB)\}.$$

ON THE EQUILIBRIUM OF PLANES OR THE CENTRES OF GRAVITY OF PLANES

BOOK ONE

"I POSTULATE the following":

1. "Equal weights at equal distances are in equilibrium, and equal weights at unequal distances are not in equilibrium but incline towards the weight which is at the greater distance."

2. "If, when weights at certain distances are in equilibrium, something be added to one of the weights, they are not in equilibrium but incline towards that weight to which the addition was made."

3. "Similarly, if anything be taken away from one of the weights, they are not in equilibrium but incline towards the weight from which nothing was taken."

4. "When equal and similar plane figures coincide if applied to one another, their centres of gravity similarly coincide."

5. "In figures which are unequal but similar, the centres of gravity will be similarly situated. By points similarly situated in relation to similar figures I mean points such that, if straight lines be drawn from them to the equal angles, they make equal angles with the corresponding sides."

6. "If magnitudes at certain distances be in equilibrium, (other) magnitudes equal to them will also be in equilibrium at the same distances."

7. "In any figure whose perimeter is concave in (one and) the same direction the centre of gravity must be within the figure."

PROPOSITION 1

Weights which balance at equal distances are equal.

For, if they are unequal, take away from the greater the difference between the two. The remainders will then not balance [*Post.* 3]; which is absurd.

Therefore the weights cannot be unequal.

PROPOSITION 2

Unequal weights at equal distances will not balance but will incline towards the greater weight.

For take away from the greater the difference between the two. The equal remainders will therefore balance [*Post.* 1]. Hence, if we add the difference again, the weights will not balance but incline towards the greater [*Post.* 2].

PROPOSITION 3

Unequal weights will balance at unequal distances, the greater weight being at the lesser distance.

Let A, B be two unequal weights (of which A is the greater) balancing about C at distances AC, BC respectively.

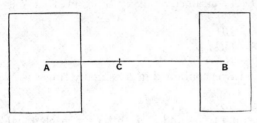

Then shall AC be less than BC. For, if not, take away from A the weight $(A-B)$. The remainders will then incline towards B [*Post.* 3]. But this is impossible, for (1) if $AC = CB$, the equal remainders will balance, or (2) if $AC > CB$, they will incline towards A at the greater distance [*Post.* 1].

Hence $AC < CB$.

Conversely, if the weights balance, and $AC < CB$, then $A > B$.

PROPOSITION 4

If two equal weights have not the same centre of gravity, the centre of gravity of both taken together is at the middle point of the line joining their centres of gravity.

[Proved from Prop. 3 by *reductio ad absurdum*.]

PROPOSITION 5

If three equal magnitudes have their centres of gravity on a straight line at equal distances, the centre of gravity of the system will coincide with that of the middle magnitude.

[This follows immediately from Prop. 4.]

COR. 1. *The same is true of any odd number of magnitudes if those which are at equal distances from the middle one are equal, while the distances between their centres of gravity are equal.*

COR. 2. *If there be an even number of magnitudes with their centres of gravity situated at equal distances on one straight line, and if the two middle ones be equal, while those which are equidistant from them (on each side) are equal respectively, the centre of gravity of the system is the middle point of the line joining the centres of gravity of the two middle ones.*

PROPOSITIONS 6, 7

Two magnitudes, whether commensurable [Prop. 6] *or incommensurable* [Prop. 7], *balance at distances reciprocally proportional to the magnitudes.*

I. Suppose the magnitudes A, B to be commensurable, and the points A, B to be their centres of gravity. Let DE be a straight line so divided at C that
$$A : B = DC : CE.$$

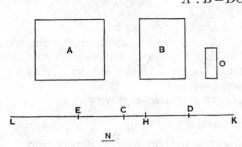

We have then to prove that, if A be placed at E and B at D, C is the centre of gravity of the two taken together.

Since A, B are commensurable, so are DC, CE. Let N be a common measure of DC, CE. Make DH, DK each equal to CE, and EL (on CE produced) equal to CD. Then $EH = CD$, since $DH = CE$. Therefore LH is bisected at E, as HK is bisected at D.

Thus LH, HK must each contain N an even number of times.

Take a magnitude O such that O is contained as many times in A as N is contained in LH, whence

$$A : O = LH : N.$$

But
$$B : A = CE : DC$$
$$= HK : LH.$$

Hence, *ex aequali*, $B : O = HK : N$, or O is contained in B as many times as N is contained in HK.

Thus O is a common measure of A, B.

Divide LH, HK into parts each equal to N, and A, B into parts each equal to O. The parts of A will therefore be equal in number to those of LH, and the parts of B equal in number to those of HK. Place one of the parts of A at the middle point of each of the parts N of LH, and one of the parts of B at the middle point of each of the parts N of HK.

Then the centre of gravity of the parts of A placed at equal distances on LH will be at E, the middle point of LH [Prop. 5, Cor. 2], and the centre of gravity of the parts of B placed at equal distances along HK will be at D, the middle point of HK.

Thus we may suppose A itself applied at E, and B itself applied at D.

But the system formed by the parts O of A and B together is a system of equal magnitudes even in number and placed at equal distances along LK. And, since $LE = CD$, and $EC = DK$, $LC = CK$, so that C is the middle point of LK. Therefore C is the centre of gravity of the system ranged along LK.

Therefore A acting at E and B acting at D balance about the point C.

II. Suppose the magnitudes to be incommensurable, and let them be $(A+a)$ and B respectively. Let DE be a line divided at C so that

$$(A+a) : B = DC : CE.$$

Then, if $(A+a)$ placed at E and B placed at D do not balance about C, $(A+a)$ is either too great to balance B, or not great enough.

Suppose, if possible, that $(A+a)$ is too great to balance B. Take from $(A+a)$ a magnitude a smaller than the deduction which would make the remainder balance B, but such that the remainder A and the magnitude B are commensurable.

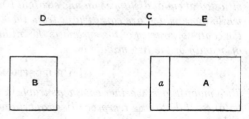

Then, since A, B are commensurable, and

$$A : B < DC : CE,$$

A and B will not balance [Prop. 6], but D will be depressed.

But this is impossible, since the deduction a was an insufficient deduction from $(A+a)$ to produce equilibrium, so that E was still depressed.

Therefore $(A+a)$ is not too great to balance B; and similarly it may be proved that B is not too great to balance $(A+a)$.

Hence $(A+a)$, B taken together have their centre of gravity at C.

Proposition 8

If AB be a magnitude whose centre of gravity is C, and AD a part of it whose centre of gravity is F, then the centre of gravity of the remaining part will be a point G on FC produced such that

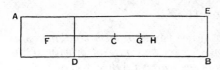

$$GC : CF = (AD) : (DE).$$

For, if the centre of gravity of the remainder (DE) be not G, let it be a point H. Then an absurdity follows at once from Props. 6, 7.

PROPOSITION 9

The centre of gravity of any parallelogram lies on the straight line joining the middle points of opposite sides.

Let $ABCD$ be a parallelogram, and let EF join the middle points of the opposite sides AD, BC.

If the centre of gravity does not lie on EF, suppose it to be H, and draw HK parallel to AD or BC meeting EF in K.

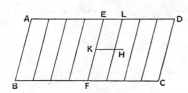

Then it is possible, by bisecting ED, then bisecting the halves, and so on continually, to arrive at a length EL less than KH. Divide both AE and ED into parts each equal to EL, and through the points of division draw parallels to AB or CD.

We have then a number of equal and similar parallelograms, and, if any one be applied to any other, their centres of gravity coincide [*Post.* 4]. Thus we have an even number of equal magnitudes whose centres of gravity lie at equal distances along a straight line. Hence the centre of gravity of the whole parallelogram will lie on the line joining the centres of gravity of the two middle parallelograms [Prop. 5, Cor. 2].

But this is impossible, for H is outside the middle parallelograms.

Therefore the centre of gravity cannot but lie on EF.

PROPOSITION 10

The centre of gravity of a parallelogram is the point of intersection of its diagonals.

For, by the last proposition, the centre of gravity lies on each of the lines which bisect opposite sides. Therefore it is at the point of their intersection; and this is also the point of intersection of the diagonals.

Alternative proof.

Let $ABCD$ be the given parallelogram, and BD a diagonal. Then the triangles ABD, CDB are equal and similar, so that [*Post.* 4], if one be applied to the other, their centres of gravity will fall one upon the other.

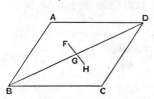

Suppose F to be the centre of gravity of the triangle ABD. Let G be the middle point of BD. Join FG and produce it to H, so that $FG = GH$.

If we then apply the triangle ABD to the triangle CDB so that AD falls on CB and AB on CD, the point F will fall on H.

But [by *Post.* 4] F will fall on the centre of gravity of CDB. Therefore H is the centre of gravity of CDB.

Hence, since F, H are the centres of gravity of the two equal triangles, the centre of gravity of the whole parallelogram is at the middle point of FH, i.e. at the middle point of BD, which is the intersection of the two diagonals.

Proposition 11

If abc, ABC be two similar triangles, and g, G two points in them similarly situated with respect to them respectively, then, if g be the centre of gravity of the triangle abc, G must be the centre of gravity of the triangle ABC.

Suppose

$$ab : bc : ca = AB : BC : CA.$$

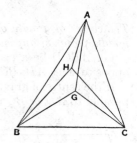

The proposition is proved by an obvious *reductio ad absurdum*. For, if G be not the centre of gravity of the triangle ABC, suppose H to be its centre of gravity.

Post. 5 requires that g, H shall be similarly situated with respect to the triangles respectively; and this leads at once to the absurdity that the angles HAB, GAB are equal.

Proposition 12

Given two similar triangles abc, ABC, and d, D the middle points of bc, BC respectively, then, if the centre of gravity of abc lie on ad, that of ABC will lie on AD.

Let g be the point on ad which is the centre of gravity of abc.

Take G on AD such that

$$ad : ag = AD : AG,$$

and join gb, gc, GB, GC.

Then, since the triangles are similar, and bd, BD are the halves of bc, BC respectively,

$$ab : bd = AB : BD,$$

and the angles abd, ABD are equal.

Therefore the triangles abd, ABD are similar, and

$$\angle bad = \angle BAD.$$

Also $$ba : ad = BA : AD,$$

while, from above, $$ad : ag = AD : AG.$$

Therefore $ba : ag = BA : AG$, while the angles bag, BAG are equal.

Hence the triangles bag, BAG are similar, and

$$\angle abg = \angle ABG.$$

And, since the angles abd, ABD are equal, it follows that

$$\angle gbd = \angle GBD.$$

In exactly the same manner we prove that

$$\angle gac = \angle GAC,$$
$$\angle acg = \angle ACG,$$
$$\angle gcd = \angle GCD.$$

Therefore g, G are similarly situated with respect to the triangles respectively; whence [Prop. 11] G is the centre of gravity of ABC.

Proposition 13

In any triangle the centre of gravity lies on the straight line joining any angle to the middle point of the opposite side.

Let ABC be a triangle and D the middle point of BC. Join AD. Then shall the centre of gravity lie on AD.

For, if possible, let this not be the case, and let H be the centre of gravity. Draw HI parallel to CB meeting AD in I.

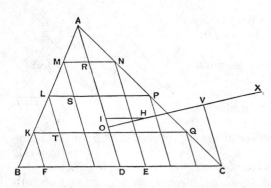

Then, if we bisect DC, then bisect the halves, and so on, we shall at length arrive at a length, as DE, less than HI. Divide both BD and DC into lengths each equal to DE, and through the points of division draw lines each parallel to DA meeting BA and AC in points as K, L, M and N, P, Q respectively.

Join MN, LP, KQ, which lines will then be each parallel to BC.

We have now a series of parallelograms as FQ, TP, SN, and AD bisects opposite sides in each. Thus the centre of gravity of each parallelogram lies on AD [Prop. 9], and therefore the centre of gravity of the figure made up of them all lies on AD.

Let the centre of gravity of all the parallelograms taken together be O. Join OH and produce it; also draw CV parallel to DA meeting OH produced in V.

Now, if n be the number of parts into which AC is divided,

$$\triangle ADC : (\text{sum of triangles on } AN,\ NP,\ \cdots) = AC^2 : (AN^2 + NP^2 + \cdots)$$
$$= n^2 : n$$
$$= n : 1$$
$$= AC : AN.$$

Similarly
$$\triangle ABD : (\text{sum of triangles on } AM,\ ML,\ \cdots) = AB : AM.$$
And
$$AC : AN = AB : AM.$$
It follows that
$$\triangle ABC : (\text{sum of all the small } \triangle \text{s}) = CA : AN$$
$$> VO : OH, \text{ by parallels.}$$
Suppose OV produced to X so that
$$\triangle ABC : (\text{sum of small } \triangle \text{s}) = XO : OH,$$
whence, *dividendo*,
$$(\text{sum of parallelograms}) : (\text{sum of small } \triangle \text{s}) = XH : HO.$$
Since then the centre of gravity of the triangle ABC is at H, and the centre of gravity of the part of it made up of the parallelograms is at O, it follows from Prop. 8 that the centre of gravity of the remaining portion consisting of all the small triangles taken together is at X.

But this is impossible, since all the triangles are on one side of the line through X parallel to AD.

Therefore the centre of gravity of the triangle cannot but lie on AD.

Alternative proof.

Suppose, if possible, that H, not lying on AD, is the centre of gravity of the triangle ABC. Join AH, BH, CH. Let E, F be the middle points of CA, AB respectively, and join DE, EF, FD. Let EF meet AD in M.

Draw FK, EL parallel to AH meeting BH, CH in K, L respectively. Join KD, HD, LD, KL. Let KL meet DH in N, and join MN.

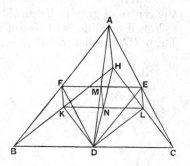

Since DE is parallel to AB, the triangles ABC, EDC are similar.

And, since $CE = EA$, and EL is parallel to AH, it follows that $CL = LH$. And $CD = DB$. Therefore BH is parallel to DL.

Thus in the similar and similarly situated triangles ABC, EDC the straight lines AH, BH are respectively parallel to EL, DL; and it follows that H, L are similarly situated with respect to the triangles respectively.

But H is, by hypothesis, the centre of gravity of ABC. Therefore L is the centre of gravity of EDC.   [Prop. 11]

Similarly the point K is the centre of gravity of the triangle FBD.

And the triangles FBD, EDC are equal, so that the centre of gravity of both together is at the middle point of KL, i.e. at the point N.

The remainder of the triangle ABC, after the triangles FBD, EDC are deducted, is the parallelogram $AFDE$, and the centre of gravity of this parallelogram is at M, the intersection of its diagonals.

It follows that the centre of gravity of the whole triangle ABC must lie on MN; that is, MN must pass through H, which is impossible (since MN is parallel to AH).

Therefore the centre of gravity of the triangle ABC cannot but lie on AD.

PROPOSITION 14

It follows at once from the last proposition that *the centre of gravity of any triangle is at the intersection of the lines drawn from any two angles to the middle points of the opposite sides respectively.*

PROPOSITION 15

If AD, BC be the two parallel sides of a trapezium $ABCD$, AD being the smaller, and if AD, BC be bisected at E, F respectively, then the centre of gravity of the trapezium is at a point G on EF such that

$$GE : GF = (2BC + AD) : (2AD + BC).$$

Produce BA, CD to meet at O. Then FE produced will also pass through O, since $AE = ED$, and $BF = FC$.

Now the centre of gravity of the triangle OAD will lie on OE, and that of the triangle OBC will lie on OF.   [Prop. 13]

It follows that the centre of gravity of the remainder, the trapezium $ABCD$, will also lie on OF.   [Prop. 8]

Join BD, and divide it at L, M into three equal parts. Through L, M draw PQ, RS parallel to BC meeting BA in P, R, FE in W, V, and CD in Q, S respectively.

Join DF, BE meeting PQ in H and RS in K respectively.

Now, since
$$BL = \tfrac{1}{3}BD,$$
$$FH = \tfrac{1}{3}FD.$$

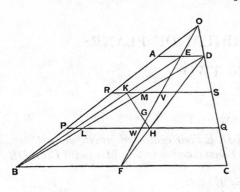

Therefore H is the centre of gravity of the triangle DBC.

Similarly, since $EK = \tfrac{1}{3}BE$, it follows that K is the centre of gravity of the triangle ADB.

Therefore the centre of gravity of the triangles DBC, ADB together, i.e. of the trapezium, lies on the line HK.

But it also lies on OF.

Therefore, if OF, HK meet in G, G is the centre of gravity of the trapezium.

Hence [Props. 6, 7]
$$\triangle DBC : \triangle ABD = KG : GH$$
$$= VG : GW.$$

But
$$\triangle DBC : \triangle ABD = BC : AD.$$

Therefore
$$BC : AD = VG : GW.$$

It follows that
$$(2BC + AD) : (2AD + BC) = (2VG + GW) : (2GW + VG)$$
$$= EG : GF.$$

Q.E.D.

ON THE EQUILIBRIUM OF PLANES

BOOK TWO

PROPOSITION 1

If P, P' be two parabolic segments and D, E their centres of gravity respectively, the centre of gravity of the two segments taken together will be at a point C on DE determined by the relation

$$P : P' = CE : CD.$$

In the same straight line with DE measure EH, EL each equal to DC, and DK equal to DH; whence it follows at once that $DK = CE$, and also that

$$KC = CL.$$

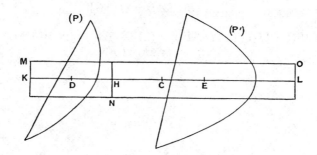

Apply a rectangle MN equal in area to the parabolic segment P to a base equal to KH, and place the rectangle so that KH bisects it, and is parallel to its base.

Then D is the centre of gravity of MN, since $KD = DH$.

Produce the sides of the rectangle which are parallel to KH, and complete the rectangle NO whose base is equal to HL. Then E is the centre of gravity of the rectangle NO.

Now
$$(MN) : (NO) = KH : HL$$
$$= DH : EH$$
$$= CE : CD$$
$$= P : P'.$$

But
$$(MN) = P.$$
Therefore
$$(NO) = P'.$$

Also, since C is the middle point of KL, C is the centre of gravity of the whole parallelogram made up of the two parallelograms (MN), (NO), which are equal to, and have the same centres of gravity as, P, P' respectively.

Hence C is the centre of gravity of P, P' taken together.

DEFINITION AND LEMMAS PRELIMINARY TO PROPOSITION 2

"If in a segment bounded by a straight line and a section of a right-angled cone [a parabola] a triangle be inscribed having the same base as the segment and equal height, if again triangles be inscribed in the remaining segments having the same bases as the segments and equal height, and if in the remaining segments triangles be inscribed in the same manner, let the resulting figure be said to be *inscribed in the recognised manner* in the segment.

"And it is plain"

(1) "that *the lines joining the two angles of the figure so inscribed which are nearest to the vertex of the segment, and the next pairs of angles in order, will be parallel to the base of the segment*,"

(2) "that *the said lines will be bisected by the diameter of the segment*, and"

(3) "that *they will cut the diameter in the proportions of the successive odd numbers, the number one having reference to [the length adjacent to] the vertex of the segment.*

"And these properties will have to be proved in their proper places."

PROPOSITION 2

If a figure be "inscribed in the recognised manner" in a parabolic segment, the centre of gravity of the figure so inscribed will lie on the diameter of the segment.

For, in the figure of the foregoing lemmas, the centre of gravity of the trapezium $BRrb$ must lie on XO, that of the trapezium $RQqr$ on WX, and so on, while the centre of gravity of the triangle PAp lies on AV.

Hence the centre of gravity of the whole figure lies on AO.

PROPOSITION 3

If BAB', bab' be two similar parabolic segments whose diameters are AO, ao respectively, and if a figure be inscribed in each segment "in the recognised manner," the number of sides in each figure being equal, the centres of gravity of the inscribed figures will divide AO, ao in the same ratio.[1]

Suppose $BRQPAP'Q'R'B'$, $brqpap'q'r'b'$ to be the two figures inscribed "in the recognised manner." Join PP', QQ', RR' meeting AO in L, M, N, and pp', qq', rr' meeting ao in l, m, n.

Then [Lemma (3)]

$$AL : LM : MN : NO = 1 : 3 : 5 : 7$$
$$= al : lm : mn : no,$$

so that AO, ao are divided in the same proportion.

Also, by reversing the proof of Lemma (3), we see that

$$PP' : pp' = QQ' : qq' = RR' : rr' = BB' : bb'.$$

Since then $RR' : BB' = rr' : bb'$, and these ratios respectively determine the proportion in which NO, no are divided by the centres of gravity of the trapezia $BRR'B'$, $brr'b'$ [I. 15], it follows that the centres of gravity of the trapezia divide NO, no in the same ratio.

Similarly the centres of gravity of the trapezia $RQQ'R'$, $rqq'r'$ divide MN, mn in the same ratio respectively, and so on.

---

[1]Archimedes enunciates this proposition as true of *similar* segments, but it is equally true of segments which are not similar, as the course of the proof will show.

Lastly, the centres of gravity of the triangles PAP', pap' divide AL, al respectively in the same ratio.

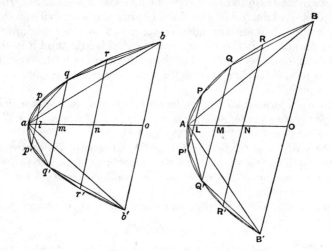

Moreover the corresponding trapezia and triangles are, each to each, in the same proportion (since their sides and heights are respectively proportional), while AO, ao are divided in the same proportion.

Therefore the centres of gravity of the complete inscribed figures divide AO, ao in the same proportion.

PROPOSITION 4

The centre of gravity of any parabolic segment cut off by a straight line lies on the diameter of the segment.

Let BAB' be a parabolic segment, A its vertex and AO its diameter.

Then, if the centre of gravity of the segment does not lie on AO, suppose it to be, if possible, the point F. Draw FE parallel to AO meeting BB' in E.

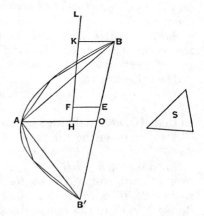

Inscribe in the segment the triangle ABB' having the same vertex and height as the segment, and take an area S such that

$$\triangle ABB' : S = BE : EO.$$

We can then inscribe in the segment "in the recognised manner" a figure such that the segments of the parabola left over are together less than S.[1]

---

[1]For Prop. 20 of the *Quadrature of the Parabola* proves that, if in any segment the triangle with the same base and height be inscribed, the triangle is greater than half the segment; whence it appears that, each time that we increase the number of the sides of the figure inscribed "in the recognised manner," we take away more than half of the remaining segments.

Let the inscribed figure be drawn accordingly; its centre of gravity then lies on AO [Prop. 2]. Let it be the point H.

Join HF and produce it to meet in K the line through B parallel to AO. Then we have

$$(\text{inscribed figure}) : (\text{remainder of segmt.}) > \triangle ABB' : S$$
$$> BE : EO$$
$$> KF : FH.$$

Suppose L taken on HK produced so that the former ratio is equal to the ratio $LF : FH$.

Then, since H is the centre of gravity of the inscribed figure, and F that of the segment, L must be the centre of gravity of all the segments taken together which form the remainder of the original segment.   [I. 8]

But this is impossible, since all these segments lie on one side of the line drawn through L parallel to AO (Cf. *Post.* 7].

Hence the centre of gravity of the segment cannot but lie on AO.

PROPOSITION 5

If in a parabolic segment a figure be inscribed "in the recognised manner," the centre of gravity of the segment is nearer to the vertex of the segment than the centre of gravity of the inscribed figure is.

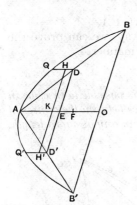

Let BAB' be the given segment, and AO its diameter. *First,* let ABB' be the *triangle* inscribed "in the recognised manner."

Divide AO in F so that $AF = 2FO$; F is then the centre of gravity of the triangle ABB'.

Bisect AB, AB' in D, D' respectively, and join DD' meeting AO in E. Draw DQ, $D'Q'$ parallel to OA to meet the curve. $QD, Q'D'$ will then be the diameters of the segments whose bases are AB, AB', and the centres of gravity of those segments will lie respectively on QD, $Q'D'$ [Prop. 4]. Let them be H, H', and join HH' meeting AO in K.

Now QD, $Q'D'$ are equal,[1] and therefore the segments of which they are the diameters are equal [*On Conoids and Spheroids*, Prop. 3].

Also, since QD, $Q'D'$ are parallel, and $DE = ED'$, K is the middle point of HH'.

Hence the centre of gravity of the equal segments AQB, $AQ'B'$ taken together is K, where K lies between E and A. And the centre of gravity of the triangle ABB' is F.

It follows that the centre of gravity of the whole segment BAB' lies between K and F, and is therefore nearer to the vertex A than F is.

Secondly, take the *five-sided* figure $BQAQ'B'$ inscribed "in the recognised manner," QD, $Q'D'$ being, as before, the diameters of the segments AQB, $AQ'B'$.

Then, by the first part of this proposition, the centre of gravity of the segment AQB (lying of course on QD) is nearer to Q than the centre of gravity of

[1]This may either be inferred from Lemma (1) above (since QQ', DD' are both parallel to BB'), or from Prop. 19 of the *Quadrature of the Parabola*, which applies equally to Q or Q'.

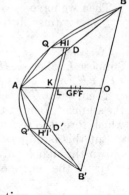

the triangle AQB is. Let the centre of gravity of the segment be H, and that of the triangle I.

Similarly let H' be the centre of gravity of the segment $AQ'B'$, and I' that of the triangle $AQ'B'$.

It follows that the centre of gravity of the two segments AQB, $AQ'B'$ taken together is K, the middle point of HH', and that of the two triangles AQB, $AQ'B'$ is L, the middle point of II'.

If now the centre of gravity of the triangle ABB' be F, the centre of gravity of the whole segment BAB' (i.e. that of the triangle ABB' and the two segments AQB, $AQ'B'$ taken together) is a point G on KF determined by the proportion

(sum of segments AQB, $AQ'B'$) : $\triangle ABB' = FG : GK$.

[I. 6, 7]

And the centre of gravity of the inscribed figure $BQAQ'B'$ is a point F' on LF determined by the proportion

$$(\triangle AQB + \triangle AQ'B') : \triangle ABB' = FF' : F'L. \qquad \text{[I. 6, 7]}$$

[Hence $\qquad FG : GK > FF' : F'L$,

or $\qquad GK : FG < F'L : FF'$,

and, *componendo*, $FK : FG < FL : FF'$, while $FK > FL$.]

Therefore $FG > FF'$, or G lies nearer than F' to the vertex A.

Using this last result, and proceeding in the same way, we can prove the proposition for *any* figure inscribed "in the recognised manner."

PROPOSITION 6

Given a segment of a parabola cut off by a straight line, it is possible to inscribe in it "in the recognised manner" a figure such that the distance between the centres of gravity of the segment and of the inscribed figure is less than any assigned length.

Let BAB' be the segment, AO its diameter, G its centre of gravity, and ABB' the triangle inscribed "in the recognised manner."

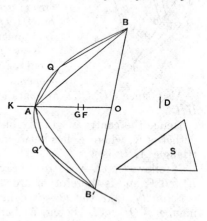

Let D be the assigned length and S an area such that

$$AG : D = \triangle ABB' : S.$$

In the segment inscribe "in the recognised manner" a figure such that the sum of the segments left over is less than S. Let F be the centre of gravity of the inscribed figure.

We shall prove that $FG < D$.

For, if not, FG must be either equal to, or greater than, D.

And clearly

(inscribed fig.) : (sum of remaining segmts.)

$> \triangle ABB' : S$

$> AG : D$

$> AG : FG$, by hypothesis (since $FG \not< D$).

Let the first ratio be equal to the ratio $KG : FG$ (where K lies on GA produced); and it follows that K is the centre of gravity of the small segments taken together.   [I. 8]

But this is impossible, since the segments are all on the same side of a line drawn through K parallel to BB'.

Hence FG cannot but be less than D.

PROPOSITION 7

If there be two similar parabolic segments, their centres of gravity divide their diameters in the same ratio.

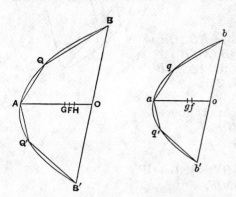

Let BAB', bab' be the two similar segments, AO, ao their diameters, and G, g their centres of gravity respectively.

Then, if G, g do not divide AO, ao respectively in the same ratio, suppose H to be such a point on AO that
$$AH : HO = ag : go;$$
and inscribe in the segment BAB' "in the recognised manner" a figure such that, if F be its centre of gravity,
$$GF < GH. \qquad \text{[Prop. 6]}$$

Inscribe in the segment bab' "in the recognised manner" a similar figure; then, if f be the centre of gravity of this figure,
$$ag < af. \qquad \text{[Prop. 5]}$$
And, by Prop. 3, $af : fo = AF : FO$.
But $AF : FO < AH : HO$
$$< ag : go, \text{ by hypothesis.}$$
Therefore $af : fo < ag : go$; which is impossible.

It follows that G, g cannot but divide AO, ao in the same ratio.

PROPOSITION 8

If AO be the diameter of a parabolic segment, and G its centre of gravity, then
$$AG = \tfrac{3}{2}GO.$$

Let the segment be BAB'. Inscribe the triangle ABB' "in the recognised manner," and let F be its centre of gravity.

Bisect AB, AB' in D, D', and draw DQ, $D'Q'$ parallel to OA to meet the curve, so that QD, $Q'D'$ are the diameters of the segments AQB, $AQ'B'$ respectively.

Let H, H' be the centres of gravity of the segments AQB, $AQ'B'$ respectively. Join QQ', HH' meeting AO in V, K respectively.

K is then the centre of gravity of the two segments AQB, $AQ'B'$ taken together.

Now $AG : GO = QH : HD$,   [Prop. 7]
whence $AO : OG = QD : HD$.
But $AO = 4QD$ [as is easily proved by means of Lemma (3), p. 511].
   Therefore $OG = 4HD$;
and, by subtraction, $AG = 4QH$.

Also, by Lemma (2), QQ' is parallel to BB' and therefore to DD'. It follows from Prop. 7 that HH' is also parallel to QQ' or DD',

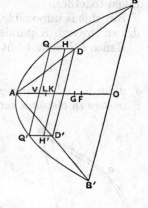

and hence $QH = VK$.

  Therefore $AG = 4VK$,

and $AV + KG = 3VK$.

Measuring VL along VK so that $VL = \frac{1}{3}AV$, we have

$$KG = 3LK. \qquad\qquad (1)$$

Again $AO = 4AV$ [Lemma (3)]

         $= 3AL$, since $AV = 3VL$,

whence $AL = \frac{1}{3}AO = OF.$ (2)

 Now, by I. 6, 7,

$\triangle ABB'$: (sum of segmts. AQB, $AQ'B'$) $= KG : GF$,

and $\triangle ABB' = 3$(sum of segments AQB, $AQ'B'$)

[since the segment ABB' is equal to $\frac{4}{3}\triangle ABB'$ (*Quadrature of the Parabola*, Props. 17, 24)].

  Hence $KG = 3GF.$

  But $KG = 3LK$, from (1) above.

  Therefore $LF = LK + KG + GF$

            $= 5GF.$

And, from (2),

$$LF = (AO - AL - OF) = \frac{1}{3}AO = OF.$$

  Therefore $OF = 5GF,$

and $OG = 6GF.$

But $AO = 3OF = 15GF.$

  Therefore, by subtraction,

$$AG = 9GF$$
$$= \frac{3}{2}GO.$$

PROPOSITION 9 (LEMMA)

If a, b, c, d be four lines in continued proportion and in descending order of magnitude, and if

$$d : (a-d) = x : \tfrac{3}{5}(a-c),$$

and $(2a+4b+6c+3d) : (5a+10b+10c+5d) = y : (a-c),$

it is required to prove that

$$x + y = \tfrac{2}{5}a.$$

[The following is the proof given by Archimedes, with the only difference that it is set out in algebraical instead of geometrical notation. This is done in the particular case simply in order to make the proof easier to follow. Archimedes exhibits his lines in the figure reproduced in the margin, but, now that it is possible to use algebraical notation, there is no advantage in using the figure and the more cumbrous notation which only obscures the course of the proof. The relation between Archimedes' figure and the letters used below is as follows:

AB $= a$, ΓB $= b$, ΔB $= c$, EB $= d$, ZH $= x$, H$\theta = y$, ΔO $= z$.]

  We have $\dfrac{a}{b} = \dfrac{b}{c} = \dfrac{c}{d}$ (1)

whence
$$\frac{a-b}{b}=\frac{b-c}{c}=\frac{c-d}{d},$$

and therefore
$$\frac{a-b}{b-c}=\frac{b-c}{c-d}=\frac{a}{b}=\frac{b}{c}=\frac{c}{d} \tag{2}$$

Now
$$\frac{2(a+b)}{2c}=\frac{a+b}{c}=\frac{a+b}{b}\cdot\frac{b}{c}=\frac{a-c}{b-c}\cdot\frac{b-c}{c-d}=\frac{a-c}{c-d}$$

And, in like manner,
$$\frac{b+c}{d}=\frac{b+c}{c}\cdot\frac{c}{d}=\frac{a-c}{c-d}.$$

It follows from the last two relations that
$$\frac{a-c}{c-d}=\frac{2a+3b+c}{2c+d} \tag{3}$$

Suppose z to be so taken that
$$\frac{2a+4b+4c+2d}{2c+d}=\frac{a-c}{z} \tag{4}$$

so that $z<(c-d)$.

Therefore
$$\frac{a-c+z}{a-c}=\frac{2a+4b+6c+3d}{2(a+d)+4(b+c)}.$$

And, by hypothesis,
$$\frac{a-c}{y}=\frac{5(a+d)+10(b+c)}{2a+4b+6c+3d},$$

so that
$$\frac{a-c+z}{y}=\frac{5(a+d)+10(b+c)}{2(a+d)+4(b+c)}=\frac{5}{2} \tag{5}$$

Again, dividing (3) by (4) crosswise, we obtain
$$\frac{z}{c-d}=\frac{2a+3b+c}{2(a+d)+4(b+c)},$$

whence
$$\frac{c-d-z}{c-d}=\frac{b+3c+2d}{2(a+d)+4(b+c)} \tag{6}$$

But, by (2),
$$\frac{c-d}{d}=\frac{a-b}{b}=\frac{3(b-c)}{3c}=\frac{2(c-d)}{2d},$$

so that
$$\frac{c-d}{d}=\frac{(a-b)+3(b-c)+2(c-d)}{b+3c+2d} \tag{7}$$

Combining (6) and (7), we have
$$\frac{c-d-z}{d}=\frac{(a-b)+3(b-c)+2(c-d)}{2(a+d)+4(b+c)},$$

whence
$$\frac{c-z}{d}=\frac{3a+6b+3c}{2(a+d)+4(b+c)} \tag{8}$$

And, since [by (1)]
$$\frac{c-d}{c+d}=\frac{b-c}{b+c}=\frac{a-b}{a+b},$$

we have
$$\frac{c-d}{a-c}=\frac{c+d}{b+c+a+b},$$

whence
$$\frac{a-d}{a-c}=\frac{a+2b+2c+d}{a+2b+c}=\frac{2(a+d)+4(b+c)}{2(a+c)+4b} \tag{9}$$

Thus
$$\frac{a-d}{\frac{3}{5}(a-c)}=\frac{2(a+d)+4(b+c)}{\frac{3}{5}\{2(a+c)+4b\}},$$
and therefore, by hypothesis,
$$\frac{d}{x}=\frac{2(a+d)+4(b+c)}{\frac{3}{5}\{2(a+c)+4b\}}.$$
But, by (8),
$$\frac{c-z}{d}=\frac{3a+6b+3c}{2(a+d)+4(b+c)};$$
and it follows, *ex aequali*, that
$$\frac{c-z}{x}=\frac{3(a+c)+6b}{\frac{3}{5}\{2(a+c)+4b\}}=\frac{5}{3}\cdot\frac{3}{2}=\frac{5}{2}.$$
And, by (5),
$$\frac{a-c+z}{y}=\frac{5}{2}.$$
Therefore
$$\frac{5}{2}=\frac{a}{x+y},$$
or
$$x+y=\tfrac{2}{5}a.$$

Proposition 10

If $PP'B'B$ be the portion of a parabola intercepted between two parallel chords PP', BB' bisected respectively in N, O by the diameter ANO (N being nearer than O to A, the vertex of the segments), and if NO be divided into five equal parts of which LM is the middle one (L being nearer than M to N), then, if G be a point on LM such that
$$LG : GM = BO^2\cdot(2PN+BO) : PN^2\cdot(2BO+PN),$$
G will be the centre of gravity of the area $PP'B'B$.

Take a line ao equal to AO, and an on it equal to AN. Let p, q be points on the line ao such that
$$ao : aq = aq : an, \tag{1}$$
$$ao : an = aq : ap, \tag{2}$$
[whence $ao : aq = aq : an = an : ap$, or ao, aq, an, ap are lines in continued proportion and in descending order of magnitude].

Measure along GA a length GF such that
$$op : ap = OL : GF. \tag{3}$$
Then, since PN, BO are ordinates to ANO,
$$BO^2 : PN^2 = AO : AN$$
$$= ao : an$$
$$= ao^2 : aq^2, \text{ by (1)},$$
so that
$$BO : PN = ao : aq, \tag{4}$$
and
$$BO^3 : PN^3 = ao^3 : aq^3$$
$$= (ao : aq)\cdot(aq : an)\cdot(an : ap)$$
$$= ao : ap. \tag{5}$$
Thus
$$(\text{segment } BAB') : (\text{segment } PAP')$$
$$= \triangle BAB' : \triangle PAP'$$
$$= BO^3 : PN^3$$
$$= ao : ap,$$
whence
$$(\text{area } PP'B'B) : (\text{segment } PAP') = op : ap$$

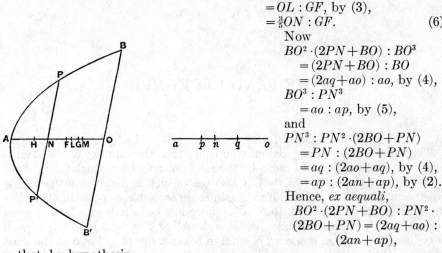

$= OL : GF$, by (3),

$= \tfrac{3}{5}ON : GF.$ (6)

Now

$BO^2 \cdot (2PN + BO) : BO^3$

$= (2PN + BO) : BO$

$= (2aq + ao) : ao$, by (4),

$BO^3 : PN^3$

$= ao : ap$, by (5),

and

$PN^3 : PN^2 \cdot (2BO + PN)$

$= PN : (2BO + PN)$

$= aq : (2ao + aq)$, by (4),

$= ap : (2an + ap)$, by (2).

Hence, *ex aequali*,

$BO^2 \cdot (2PN + BO) : PN^2 \cdot$
$(2BO + PN) = (2aq + ao) :$
$(2an + ap),$

so that, by hypothesis,

$$LG : GM = (2aq + ao) : (2an + ap).$$

Componendo, and multiplying the antecedents by 5,

$$ON : GM = \{5(ao + ap) + 10(aq + an)\} : (2an + ap).$$

But

$$ON : OM = 5 : 2 = \{5(ao + ap) + 10(aq + an)\} : \{2(ao + ap) + 4(aq + an)\}.$$

It follows that

$$ON : OG = \{5(ao + ap) + 10(aq + an)\} : (2ao + 4aq + 6an + 3ap).$$

Therefore

$$(2ao + 4aq + 6an + 3ap) : \{5(ao + ap) + 10(aq + an)\} = OG : ON$$
$$= OG : on.$$

And $ap : (ao - ap) = ap : op$

$$= GF : OL, \text{ by hypothesis,}$$
$$= GF : \tfrac{3}{5}on,$$

while ao, aq, an, ap are in continued proportion.

Therefore, by Prop. 9,

$$GF + OG = OF = \tfrac{2}{5}ao = \tfrac{2}{5}OA.$$

Thus F is the centre of gravity of the segment BAB'.   [Prop. 8]

Let H be the centre of gravity of the segment PAP', so that $AH = \tfrac{3}{5}AN$.

And, since $AF = \tfrac{3}{5}AO,$

we have, by subtraction, $HF = \tfrac{3}{5}ON.$

But, by (6) above,

$$(\text{area } PP'B'B) : (\text{segment } PAP') = \tfrac{3}{5}ON : GF$$
$$= HF : FG.$$

Thus, since F, H are the centres of gravity of the segments BAB', PAP' respectively, it follows [by I. 6, 7] that G is the centre of gravity of the area $PP'B'B$.

THE SAND-RECKONER

"THERE are some, King Gelon, who think that the number of the sand is infinite in multitude; and I mean by the sand not only that which exists about Syracuse and the rest of Sicily but also that which is found in every region whether inhabited or uninhabited. Again there are some who, without regarding it as infinite, yet think that no number has been named which is great enough to exceed its multitude. And it is clear that they who hold this view, if they imagined a mass made up of sand in other respects as large as the mass of the earth, including in it all the seas and the hollows of the earth filled up to a height equal to that of the highest of the mountains, would be many times further still from recognising that any number could be expressed which exceeded the multitude of the sand so taken. But I will try to show you by means of geometrical proofs, which you will be able to follow, that, of the numbers named by me and given in the work which I sent to Zeuxippus, some exceed not only the number of the mass of sand equal in magnitude to the earth filled up in the way described, but also that of a mass equal in magnitude to the universe. Now you are aware that 'universe' is the name given by most astronomers to the sphere whose centre is the centre of the earth and whose radius is equal to the straight line between the centre of the sun and the centre of the earth. This is the common account (τὰ γραφόμενα), as you have heard from astronomers. But Aristarchus of Samos brought out a book consisting of some hypotheses, in which the premises lead to the result that the universe is many times greater than that now so called. His hypotheses are that the fixed stars and the sun remain unmoved, that the earth revolves about the sun in the circumference of a circle, the sun lying in the middle of the orbit, and that the sphere of the fixed stars, situated about the same centre as the sun, is so great that the circle in which he supposes the earth to revolve bears such a proportion to the distance of the fixed stars as the centre of the sphere bears to its surface. Now it is easy to see that this is impossible; for, since the centre of the sphere has no magnitude, we cannot conceive it to bear any ratio whatever to the surface of the sphere. We must however take Aristarchus to mean this: since we conceive the earth to be, as it were, the centre of the universe, the ratio which the earth bears to what we describe as the 'universe' is the same as the ratio which the sphere containing the circle in which he supposes the earth to revolve bears to the sphere of the fixed stars. For he adapts the proofs of his results to a hypothesis of this kind, and in particular he appears to suppose the magnitude of the sphere in which he represents the earth as moving to be equal to what we call the 'universe.'

"I say then that, even if a sphere were made up of the sand, as great as Aristarchus supposes the sphere of the fixed stars to be, I shall still prove that, of the numbers named in the *Principles*,[1] some exceed in multitude the number of the sand which is equal in magnitude to the sphere referred to, provided that the following assumptions be made."

1. *"The perimeter of the earth is about* 3,000,000 *stadia and not greater.*

"It is true that some have tried, as you are of course aware, to prove that the said perimeter is about 300,000 stadia. But I go further and, putting the magnitude of the earth at ten times the size that my predecessors thought it, I suppose its perimeter to be about 3,000,000 stadia and not greater."

2. *"The diameter of the earth is greater than the diameter of the moon, and the diameter of the sun is greater than the diameter of the earth.*

"In this assumption I follow most of the earlier astronomers."

3. *"The diameter of the sun is about* 30 *times the diameter of the moon and not greater.*

"It is true that, of the earlier astronomers, Eudoxus declared it to be about nine times as great, and Pheidias my father twelve times, while Aristarchus tried to prove that the diameter of the sun is greater than 18 times but less than 20 times the diameter of the moon. But I go even further than Aristarchus, in order that the truth of my proposition may be established beyond dispute, and I suppose the diameter of the sun to be about 30 times that of the moon and not greater."

4. *"The diameter of the sun is greater than the side of the chiliagon inscribed in the greatest circle in the* (*sphere of the*) *universe.*

"I make this assumption because Aristarchus discovered that the sun appeared to be about $\frac{1}{720}$th part of the circle of the zodiac, and I myself tried, by a method which I will now describe, to find experimentally (ὀργανικῶς) the angle subtended by the sun and having its vertex at the eye."

[Up to this point the treatise has been literally translated because of the historical interest attaching to the *ipsissima verba* of Archimedes on such a subject. The rest of the work can now be more freely reproduced, and, before proceeding to the mathematical contents of it, it is only necessary to remark that Archimedes next describes how he arrived at a higher and a lower limit for the angle subtended by the sun. This he did by taking a long rod or ruler, fastening on the end of it a small cylinder or disc, pointing the rod in the direction of the sun just after its rising (so that it was possible to look directly at it), then putting the cylinder at such a distance that it just concealed, and just failed to conceal, the sun, and lastly measuring the angles subtended by the cylinder. He explains also the correction which he thought it necessary to make because "the eye does not see from one point but from a certain area."]

The result of the experiment was to show that the angle subtended by the diameter of the sun was less than $\frac{1}{164}$th part, and greater than $\frac{1}{200}$th part, of a right angle.

To prove that (*on this assumption*) *the diameter of the sun is greater than the side of a chiliagon, or figure with* 1000 *equal sides, inscribed in a great circle of the* "*universe.*"

Suppose the plane of the paper to be the plane passing through the centre of the sun, the centre of the earth and the eye, at the time when the sun has

---

[1] A lost work of Archimedes.

just risen above the horizon. Let the plane cut the earth in the circle EHL and
the sun in the circle FKG, the centres of the earth and sun being C, O respectively, and E being the position of the eye.

Further, let the plane cut the sphere of the "universe" (i.e. the sphere whose
centre is C and radius CO) in the great circle AOB.

Draw from E two tangents to the circle FKG touching it at P, Q, and from
C draw two other tangents to the same circle touching it in F, G respectively.

Let CO meet the sections of the earth and sun in H, K respectively; and let
CF, CG produced meet the great circle AOB in A, B.

Join EO, OF, OG, OP, OQ, AB, and let AB meet CO in M.

Now $CO > EO$, since the sun is just above the horizon.

Therefore $\angle PEQ > \angle FCG$.

And $\angle PEQ > \frac{1}{200}R$⎫
but $< \frac{1}{164}R$⎭ where R represents a right angle.

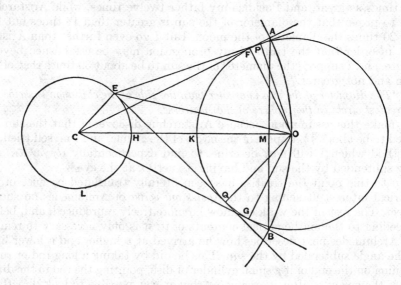

Thus $\angle FCG < \frac{1}{164}R$, *a fortiori*,
and the chord AB subtends an arc of the great circle which is less than $\frac{1}{656}$th
of the circumference of that circle, i.e.

            $AB < $ (side of 656-sided polygon inscribed in the circle).

Now the perimeter of any polygon inscribed in the great circle is less than
$\frac{44}{7}CO$.   [Cf. *Measurement of a circle*, Prop. 3.]

Therefore $AB : CO < 11 : 1148$,
and, *a fortiori*, $AB < \frac{1}{100}CO$.   (α)

Again, since $CA = CO$, and AM is perpendicular to CO, while OF is perpendicular to CA, $AM = OF$.

Therefore $AB = 2AM = $ (diameter of sun).

Thus   (diameter of sun) $< \frac{1}{100}CO$, by (α),
and, *a fortiori*,   (diameter of earth) $< \frac{1}{100}CO$.   [Assumption 2]

Hence $CH + OK < \frac{1}{100}CO$,
so that $HK > \frac{99}{100}CO$,

or $CO : HK < 100 : 99.$
And $CO > CF,$
while $HK < EQ.$
    Therefore $CF : EQ < 100 : 99.$ (β)

Now in the right-angled triangles CFO, EQO, of the sides about the right angles, $OF = OQ$, but $EQ < CF$ (since $EO < CO$).

Therefore $\angle OEQ : \angle OCF > CO : EO,$
but $< CF : EQ.$[1]

Doubling the angles,
$$\angle PEQ : \angle ACB < CF : EQ$$
$$< 100 : 99, \text{ by } (\beta) \text{ above.}$$

But $\angle PEQ > \frac{1}{200}R$, by hypothesis.

Therefore $\angle ACB > \frac{99}{20000}R$
$$> \frac{1}{203}R.$$

It follows that the arc AB is greater than $\frac{1}{812}$th of the circumference of the great circle AOB.

Hence, *a fortiori,*
$$AB > (\text{side of chiliagon inscribed in great circle}),$$
and AB is equal to the diameter of the sun, as proved above.

The following results can now be proved:
$$(\text{diameter of ``universe''}) < 10,000 \ (\text{diameter of earth}),$$
and $(\text{diameter of ``universe''}) < 10,000,000,000 \text{ stadia.}$

(1) Suppose, for brevity, that d_u represents the diameter of the "universe," d_s that of the sun, d_e that of the earth, and d_m that of the moon.

By hypothesis, $d_s \not> 30 d_m,$ [Assumption 3]
and $d_e > d_m;$ [Assumption 2]
therefore $d_s < 30 d_e.$

Now, by the last proposition,
$$d_s > (\text{side of chiliagon inscribed in great circle}),$$
so that $(\text{perimeter of chiliagon}) < 1000 d_s$
$$< 30,000 d_e.$$

But the perimeter of any regular polygon with more sides than 6 inscribed in a circle is greater than that of the inscribed regular hexagon, and therefore greater than three times the diameter. Hence
$$(\text{perimeter of chiliagon}) > 3 d_u.$$

It follows that $d_u < 10,000 d_e.$

(2) $(\text{Perimeter of earth}) \not> 3,000,000 \text{ stadia.}$ [Assumption 1]
and $(\text{perimeter of earth}) > 3 d_e.$

Therefore $d_e < 1,000,000 \text{ stadia,}$
whence $d_u < 10,000,000,000 \text{ stadia.}$

Assumption 5

Suppose a quantity of sand taken not greater than a poppy-seed, and suppose that it contains not more than 10,000 grains.

---

[1]The proposition here assumed is of course equivalent to the trigonometrical formula which states that, if α, β are the circular measures of two angles, each less than a right angle, of which α is the greater, then
$$\frac{\tan \alpha}{\tan \beta} > \frac{\alpha}{\beta} > \frac{\sin \alpha}{\sin \beta}.$$

Next suppose the diameter of the poppy-seed to be not less than $\frac{1}{40}$th of a finger-breadth.

ORDERS AND PERIODS OF NUMBERS

I. We have traditional names for numbers up to a myriad (10,000); we can therefore express numbers up to a myriad myriads (100,000,000). Let these numbers be called numbers of the *first order*.

Suppose the 100,000,000 to be the unit of the *second order*, and let the *second order* consist of the numbers from that unit up to $(100,000,000)^2$.

Let this again be the unit of the *third order* of numbers ending with $(100,000,000)^3$; and so on, until we reach the 100,000,000*th order* of numbers ending with $(100,000,000)^{100,000,000}$, which we will call P.

II. Suppose the numbers from 1 to P just described to form the *first period*.

Let P be the unit of the *first order of the second period*, and let this consist of the numbers from P up to 100,000,000P.

Let the last number be the unit of the *second order of the second period*, and let this end with $(100,000,000)^2 P$.

We can go on in this way till we reach the 100,000,000*th order of the second period* ending with $(100,000,000)^{100,000,000} P$, or P^2.

III. Taking P^2 as the unit of the *first order of the third period*, we proceed in the same way till we reach the 100,000,000*th order of the third period* ending with P^3.

IV. Taking P^3 as the unit of the *first order of the fourth period*, we continue the same process until we arrive at the 100,000,000*th order of the* 100,000,000*th period* ending with $P^{100,000,000}$. This last number is expressed by Archimedes as "a myriad-myriad units of the myriad-myriad-th order of the myriad-myriad-th period (αἱ μυριακισμυριοστᾶς περιόδου μυριακισμυριοστῶν ἀριθμῶν μυρίαι μυριάδες)," which is easily seen to be 100,000,000 times the product of (100,000,000) ^{99,999,999} and $P^{99,999,999}$, i.e. $P^{100,000,000}$.

OCTADS

Consider the series of terms in continued proportion of which the first is 1 and the second 10 [i.e. the geometrical progression 1, 10^1, 10^2, 10^3, $\cdots$]. The *first octad* of these terms [*i.e.* 1, 10^1, 10^2, $\cdots 10^7$] fall accordingly under the *first order of the first period* above described, the *second octad* [i.e. 10^8, 10^9, $\cdots 10^{15}$] under the *second order of the first period*, the first term of the octad being the unit of the corresponding order in each case. Similarly for the *third octad*, and so on. We can, in the same way, place any number of octads.

THEOREM

If there be any number of terms of a series in continued proportion, say A_1, A_2, A_3, $\cdots A_m$, $\cdots A_n$, $\cdots A_{m+n-1}$, $\cdots$ of which $A_1=1$, $A_2=10$ [so that the series forms the geometrical progression 1, 10^1, 10^2, $\cdots 10^{m-1}$, $\cdots 10^{n-1}$, $\cdots 10^{m+n-2}$, $\cdots$], and if any two terms as A_m, A_n be taken and multiplied, the product $A_m \cdot A_n$ will be a term in the same series and will be as many terms distant from A_n as A_m is distant from A_1; also it will be distant from A_1 by a number of terms less by one than the sum of the numbers of terms by which A_m and A_n respectively are distant from A_1.

Take the term which is distant from A_n by the same number of terms as A_m

is distant from A_1. This number of terms is m (the first and last being both counted). Thus the term to be taken is m terms distant from A_n, and is therefore the term A_{m+n-1}.

We have therefore to prove that
$$A_m \cdot A_n = A_{m+n-1}.$$

Now terms equally distant from other terms in the continued proportion are proportional.

Thus
$$\frac{A_m}{A_1} = \frac{A_{m+n-1}}{A_n}.$$

But $\qquad\qquad A_m = A_m \cdot A_1$, since $A_1 = 1$.

Therefore $\qquad\qquad A_{m+n-1} = A_m \cdot A_n.$ (1)

The second result is now obvious, since A_m is m terms distant from A_1, A_n is n terms distant from A_1, and A_{m+n-1} is $(m+n-1)$ terms distant from A_1.

APPLICATION TO THE NUMBER OF THE SAND

By Assumption 5 [p. 523],
$$\text{(diam. of poppy-seed)} \not< \tfrac{1}{40}(\text{finger-breadth})\,;$$
and, since spheres are to one another in the triplicate ratio of their diameters, it follows that

(sphere of diam. 1 finger-breadth) $\not>$ 64,000 poppy-seeds

$\not>$ 64,000 × 10,000

$\not>$ 640,000,000

$\not>$ 6 units of *second order* + 40,000,000 units of *first order* grains of sand.

(*a fortiori*) $<$ 10 units of *second order* of numbers.

We now gradually increase the diameter of the supposed sphere, multiplying it by 100 each time. Thus, remembering that the sphere is thereby multiplied by 100^3 or 1,000,000, the number of grains of sand which would be contained in a sphere with each successive diameter may be arrived at as follows.

Diameter of sphere.	Corresponding number of grains of sand.
(1) 100 finger-breadths	$<$ 1,000,000 × 10 units of *second order*
	$<$ (7th term of series) × (10th term of series)
	$<$ 16th term of series $\qquad$ [i.e. 10^{15}]
	$<$ [10^7 or] 10,000,000 units of the *second order*.
(2) 10,000 finger-breadths	$<$ 1,000,000 × (last number)
	$<$ (7th term of series) × (16th term)
	$<$ 22nd term of series $\qquad$ [i.e. 10^{21}]
	$<$ [10^5 or] 100,000 units of *third order*.
(3) 1 stadium	$<$ 100,000 units of *third order*.
$\quad$ ($<$ 10,000 finger-breadths)	
(4) 100 stadia	$<$ 1,000,000 × (last number)
	$<$ (7th term of series) × (22nd term)
	$<$ 28th term of series $\qquad$ [10^{27}]
	$<$ [10^3 or] 1,000 units of *fourth order*.
(5) 10,000 stadia	$<$ 1,000,000 × (last number)
	$<$ (7th term of series) × (28th term)
	$<$ 34th term of series $\qquad$ [10^{33}]
	$<$ 10 units of *fifth order*.

(6) 1,000,000 stadia	$<$(7th term of series)$\times$(34th term)	
	$<$40th term	$[10^{39}]$
	$<[10^7$ or] 10,000,000 units of *fifth order*.	
(7) 100,000,000 stadia	$<$(7th term of series)$\times$(40th term)	
	$<$46th term	$[10^{45}]$
	$<[10^5$ or] 100,000 units of *sixth order*.	
(8) 10,000,000,000 stadia	$<$(7th term of series)$\times$(46th term)	
	$<$52nd term of series	$[10^{51}]$
	$<[10^3$ or] 1,000 units of *seventh order*.	

But, by the proposition above [p. 523],

(diameter of "universe") $< 10,000,000,000$ stadia.

Hence *the number of grains of sand which could be contained in a sphere of the size of our "universe" is less than* 1,000 *units of the seventh order of numbers* [or 10^{51}].

From this we can prove further that *a sphere of the size attributed by Aristarchus to the sphere of the fixed stars would contain a number of grains of sand less than* 10,000,000 *units of the eighth order of numbers* [or $10^{56+7} = 10^{63}$].

For, by hypothesis,

(earth) : ("universe") = ("universe") : (sphere of fixed stars).

And [p. 523]

(diameter of "universe") $< 10,000$ (diam. of earth);

whence

(diam. of sphere of fixed stars) $< 10,000$ (diam. of "universe").

Therefore

(sphere of fixed stars) $< (10,000)^3 \cdot$ ("universe").

It follows that the number of grains of sand which would be contained in a sphere equal to the sphere of the fixed stars

$< (10,000)^3 \times 1,000$ units of *seventh order*

$< $(13th term of series)$\times$(52nd term of series)

$<$64th term of series   [i.e. 10^{63}]

$<[10^7$ or] 10,000,000 units of *eighth order* of numbers.

CONCLUSION.

"I conceive that these things, King Gelon, will appear incredible to the great majority of people who have not studied mathematics, but that to those who are conversant therewith and have given thought to the question of the distances and sizes of the earth, the sun and moon and the whole universe, the proof will carry conviction. And it was for this reason that I thought the subject would be not inappropriate for your consideration."

QUADRATURE OF THE PARABOLA

"Archimedes to Dositheus greeting.

"When I heard that Conon, who was my friend in his lifetime, was dead, but that you were acquainted with Conon and withal versed in geometry, while I grieved for the loss not only of a friend but of an admirable mathematician, I set myself the task of communicating to you, as I had intended to send to Conon, a certain geometrical theorem which had not been investigated before but has now been investigated by me, and which I first discovered by means of mechanics and then exhibited by means of geometry. Now some of the earlier geometers tried to prove it possible to find a rectilineal area equal to a given circle and a given segment of a circle; and after that they endeavoured to square the area bounded by the section of the whole cone and a straight line, assuming lemmas not easily conceded, so that it was recognised by most people that the problem was not solved. But I am not aware that any one of my predecessors has attempted to square the segment bounded by a straight line and a section of a right-angled cone [a parabola], of which problem I have now discovered the solution. For it is here shown that every segment bounded by a straight line and a section of a right-angled cone [a parabola] is four-thirds of the triangle which has the same base and equal height with the segment, and for the demonstration of this property the following lemma is assumed: that the excess by which the greater of (two) unequal areas exceeds the less can, by being added to itself, be made to exceed any given finite area. The earlier geometers have also used this lemma; for it is by the use of this same lemma that they have shown that circles are to one another in the duplicate ratio of their diameters, and that spheres are to one another in the triplicate ratio of their diameters, and further that every pyramid is one third part of the prism which has the same base with the pyramid and equal height; also, that every cone is one third part of the cylinder having the same base as the cone and equal height they proved by assuming a certain lemma similar to that aforesaid. And, in the result, each of the aforesaid theorems has been accepted no less than those proved without the lemma. As therefore my work now published has satisfied the same test as the propositions referred to, I have written out the proof and send it to you, first as investigated by means of mechanics, and afterwards too as demonstrated by geometry. Prefixed are, also, the elementary propositions in conics which are of service in the proof. Farewell."

PROPOSITION 1

If from a point on a parabola a straight line be drawn which is either itself the axis or parallel to the axis, as PV, and if QQ′ be a chord parallel to the tangent to the parabola at P and meeting PV in V, then

$$QV = VQ'.$$

Conversely, *if QV = VQ′, the chord QQ′ will be parallel to the tangent at P.*

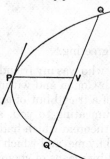

PROPOSITION 2

If in a parabola QQ′ be a chord parallel to the tangent at P, and if a straight line be drawn through P which is either itself the axis or parallel to the axis, and which meets QQ′ in V and the tangent at Q to the parabola in T, then

$$PV = PT.$$

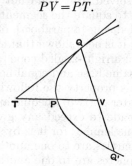

PROPOSITION 3

If from a point on a parabola a straight line be drawn which is either itself the axis or parallel to the axis, as PV, and if from two other points Q, Q′ on the parabola straight lines be drawn parallel to the tangent at P and meeting PV in V, V′ respectively, then $PV : PV' = QV^2 : Q'V'^2.$

"And these propositions are proved in the elements of conics.¹"

PROPOSITION 4

If Qq be the base of any segment of a parabola, and P the vertex of the segment, and if the diameter through any other point R meet Qq in O and QP (produced if necessary) in F, then   QV : VO = OF : FR.

Draw the ordinate RW to PV, meeting QP in K.

Then $PV : PW = QV^2 : RW^2;$

whence, by parallels, $PQ : PK = PQ^2 : PF^2.$

---

¹i.e. in the treatises on conics by Euclid and Aristaeus.

In other words, PQ, PF, PK are in continued proportion; therefore

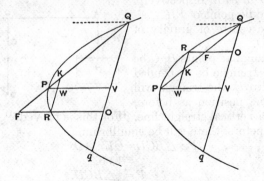

$$PQ : PF = PF : PK$$
$$= PQ \pm PF : PF \pm PK$$
$$= QF : KF.$$

Hence, by parallels, $\quad QV : VO = OF : FR.$

PROPOSITION 5

If Qq be the base of any segment of a parabola, P the vertex of the segment, and PV its diameter, and if the diameter of the parabola through any other point R meet Qq in O and the tangent at Q in E, then

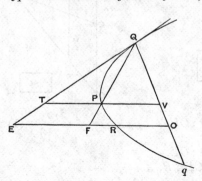

$$QO : Oq = ER : RO.$$

Let the diameter through R meet QP in F.

Then, by Prop. 4,
$$QV : VO = OF : FR.$$
Since $QV = Vq$, it follows that
$$QV : qO = OF : OR. \tag{1}$$
Also, if VP meet the tangent in T,
$$PT = PV, \text{ and therefore } EF = OF.$$
Accordingly, doubling the antecedents in (1), we have
$$Qq : qO = OE : OR,$$
whence $\quad QO : Oq = ER : RO.$

PROPOSITIONS 6, 7[1]

Suppose a lever AOB placed horizontally and supported at its middle point O. Let a triangle BCD in which the angle C is right or obtuse be suspended from B and O, so that C is attached to O and CD is in the same vertical line with O. Then, if P be such an area as, when suspended from A, will keep the system in equilibrium,
$$P = \tfrac{1}{3} \triangle BCD.$$

---

[1] In Prop. 6 Archimedes takes the separate case in which the angle BCD of the triangle is a right angle so that C coincides with O in the figure and F with E. He then proves, in Prop. 7, the same property for the triangle in which BCD is an obtuse angle, by treating the triangle as the difference between two right-angled triangles BOD, BOC and using the result of Prop. 6. I have combined the two propositions in one proof, for the sake of brevity. The same remark applies to the propositions following Props. 6, 7.

Take a point E on OB such that $BE = 2OE$, and draw EFH parallel to OCD meeting BC, BD in F, H respectively.

Let G be the middle point of FH.

Then G is the centre of gravity of the triangle BCD.

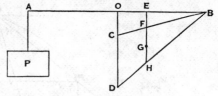

Hence, if the angular points B, C be set free and the triangle be suspended by attaching F to E, the triangle will hang in the same position as before, because EFG is a vertical straight line. "For this is proved."[1]

Therefore, as before, there will be equilibrium.

Thus
$$P : \triangle BCD = OE : AO$$
$$= 1 : 3,$$
or
$$P = \tfrac{1}{3}\triangle BCD.$$

PROPOSITIONS 8, 9

Suppose a lever AOB placed horizontally and supported at its middle point O. Let a triangle BCD, right-angled or obtuse-angled at C, be suspended from the points B, E on OB, the angular point C being so attached to E that the side CD is in the same vertical line with E. Let Q be an area such that
$$AO : OE = \triangle BCD : Q.$$

Then, if an area P suspended from A keep the system in equilibrium,
$$P < \triangle BCD \ but > Q.$$

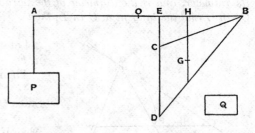

Take G the centre of gravity of the triangle BCD, and draw GH parallel to DC, i.e. vertically, meeting BO in H.

We may now suppose the triangle BCD suspended from H, and, since there is equilibrium,

$$\triangle BCD : P = AO : OH, \qquad (1)$$
whence $\qquad\qquad P < \triangle BCD.$

Also $\qquad\qquad \triangle BCD : Q = AO : OE.$

Therefore, by (1), $\qquad \triangle BCD : Q > \triangle BCD : P,$

and $\qquad\qquad\qquad P > Q.$

PROPOSITIONS 10, 11

Suppose a lever AOB placed horizontally and supported at O, its middle point. Let $CDEF$ be a trapezium which can be so placed that its parallel sides CD, FE are vertical, while C is vertically below O, and the other sides CF, DE meet in B. Let EF meet BO in H, and let the trapezium be suspended by attaching F to H and C to O. Further, suppose Q to be an area such that
$$AO : OH = (trapezium\ CDEF) : Q.$$
Then, if P be the area which, when suspended from A, keeps the system in equilibrium,
$$P < Q.$$

---

[1]Doubtless in the lost book περὶ ζυγῶν.

The same is true in the particular case where the angles at C, F are right, and consequently C, F coincide with O, H respectively.

Divide *OH* in *K* so that

$$(2CD + FE) : (2FE + CD) = HK : KO.$$

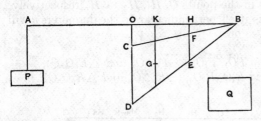

Draw *KG* parallel to *OD*, and let *G* be the middle point of the portion of *KG* intercepted within the trapezium. Then *G* is the centre of gravity of the trapezium [*On the equilibrium of planes*, I. 15].

Thus we may suppose the trapezium suspended from *K*, and the equilibrium will remain undisturbed.

Therefore $AO : OK = $ (trapezium *CDEF*) $: P$,

and, by hypothesis, $AO : OH = $ (trapezium *CDEF*) $: Q$.

Since $OK < OH$, it follows that

$$P < Q.$$

PROPOSITIONS 12, 13

If the trapezium CDEF be placed as in the last propositions, except that CD is vertically below a point L on OB instead of being below O, and the trapezium is suspended from L, H, suppose that Q, R are areas such that

$$AO : OH = (\text{trapezium } CDEF) : Q,$$

and $\qquad AO : OL = (\text{trapezium } CDEF) : R.$

If then an area P suspended from A keep the system in equilibrium,

$$P > R \text{ but} < Q.$$

Take the centre of gravity *G* of the trapezium, as in the last propositions, and let the line through *G* parallel to *DC* meet *OB* in *K*.

Then we may suppose the trapezium suspended from *K*, and there will still be equilibrium.

Therefore $\qquad$ (trapezium *CDEF*) $: P = AO : OK$.

Hence $\qquad$ (trapezium *CDEF*) $: P > $ (trapezium *CDEF*) $: Q$,

but $\qquad\qquad\qquad\qquad < $ (trapezium *CDEF*) $: R$.

It follows that $\qquad\qquad P < Q \text{ but } > R$.

PROPOSITIONS 14, 15

Let *Qq* be the base of any segment of a parabola. Then, if two lines be drawn from *Q, q*, each parallel to the axis of the parabola and on the same side of *Qq* as the segment is, either (1) the angles so formed at *Q, q* are both right angles, or (2) one is acute and the other obtuse. In the latter case let the angle at *q* be the obtuse angle.

Divide *Qq* into any number of equal parts at the points $O_1, O_2, \cdots O_n$. Draw through $q, O_1, O_2, \cdots O_n$ diameters of the parabola meeting the tangent at Q in $E, E_1, E_2, \cdots E_n$ and the parabola itself in $q, R_1, R_2, \cdots R_n$. Join $QR_1, QR_2, \cdots QR_n$ meeting $qE, O_1E_1, O_2E_2, \cdots O_{n-1}E_{n-1}$ in $F, F_1, F_2, \cdots F_{n-1}$.

Let the diameters $Eq, E_1O_1, \cdots E_nO_n$ meet a straight line QOA drawn through Q perpendicular to the diameters in the points $O, H_1, H_2, \cdots H_n$ respectively. (In the particular case where Qq is itself perpendicular to the diameters q will coincide with O, O_1 with H_1, and so on.)

It is required to prove that

    (1) $\triangle EqQ < 3$(*sum of trapezia* $FO_1, F_1O_2, \cdots F_{n-1}O_n$ *and* $\triangle E_nO_nQ$),

    (2) $\triangle EqQ > 3$(*sum of trapezia* $R_1O_2, R_2O_3, \cdots R_{n-1}O_n$ *and* $\triangle R_nO_nQ$).

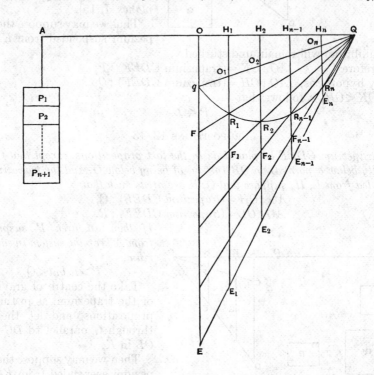

Suppose AO made equal to OQ, and conceive QOA as a lever placed horizontally and supported at O. Suppose the triangle EqQ suspended from OQ in the position drawn, and suppose that the trapezium EO_1 in the position drawn is balanced by an area P_1 suspended from A, the trapezium E_1O_2 in the position drawn is balanced by the area P_2 suspended from A, and so on, the triangle E_nO_nQ being in like manner balanced by P_{n+1}.

Then $P_1+P_2+\cdots+P_{n+1}$ will balance the whole triangle EqQ as drawn, and therefore $P_1+P_2+\cdots+P_{n+1}=\frac{1}{3}\triangle EqQ.$ [Props. 6, 7]

Again $AO : OH_1 = QO : OH_1$

                $= Qq : qO_1$

                $= E_1O_1 : O_1R_1$ [by means of Prop. 5]

                $=$ (trapezium EO_1) : (trapezium FO_1);

whence [Props. 10, 11] $(FO_1) > P_1.$

Next $\qquad AO:OH_1=E_1O_1:O_1R_1$

$$=(E_1O_2):(R_1O_2),\qquad\qquad(\alpha)$$

while $\qquad AO:OH_2=E_2O_2:O_2R_2$

$$=(E_1O_2):(F_1O_2);\qquad\qquad(\beta)$$

and, since (α) and (β) are simultaneously true, we have, by Props. 12, 13,

$$(F_1O_2)>P_2>(R_1O_2).$$

Similarly it may be proved that

$$(F_2O_3)>P_3>(R_2O_3),$$

and so on.

Lastly [Props. 8, 9] $\qquad \triangle E_nO_nQ>P_{n+1}>\triangle R_nO_nQ.$

By addition, we obtain

(1) $\quad (FO_1)+(F_1O_2)+\cdots+(F_{n-1}O_n)+\triangle E_nO_nQ>P_1+P_2+\cdots+P_{n+1}$
$$>\tfrac{1}{3}\triangle EqQ,$$

or $\qquad \triangle EqQ<3(FO_1+F_1O_2+\cdots+F_{n-1}O_n+\triangle E_nO_nQ).$

(2) $\quad (R_1O_2)+(R_2O_3)+\cdots+(R_{n-1}O_n)+\triangle R_nO_nQ<P_2+P_3+\cdots+P_{n+1}$
$$<P_1+P_2+\cdots+P_{n+1},\ a\ fortiori,$$
$$<\tfrac{1}{3}\triangle EqQ,$$

or $\qquad \triangle EqQ>3(R_1O_2+R_2O_3+\cdots+R_{n-1}O_n+\triangle R_nO_nQ).$

PROPOSITION 16

Suppose Qq to be the base of a parabolic segment, q being not more distant than Q from the vertex of the parabola. Draw through q the straight line qE parallel to the axis of the parabola to meet the tangent at Q in E. It is required to prove that

$$(\textit{area of segment})=\tfrac{1}{3}\triangle EqQ.$$

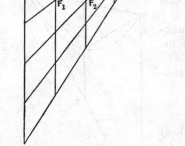

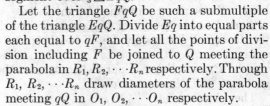

For, if not, the area of the segment must be either greater or less than $\tfrac{1}{3}\triangle EqQ$.

I. Suppose the area of the segment greater than $\tfrac{1}{3}\triangle EqQ$. Then the excess can, if continually added to itself, be made to exceed $\triangle EqQ$. And it is possible to find a submultiple of the triangle EqQ less than the said excess of the segment over $\tfrac{1}{3}\triangle EqQ$.

Let the triangle FqQ be such a submultiple of the triangle EqQ. Divide Eq into equal parts each equal to qF, and let all the points of division including F be joined to Q meeting the parabola in $R_1, R_2, \cdots R_n$ respectively. Through $R_1, R_2, \cdots R_n$ draw diameters of the parabola meeting qQ in $O_1, O_2, \cdots O_n$ respectively.

Let O_1R_1 meet QR_2 in F_1.

Let O_2R_2 meet QR_1 in D_1 and QR_3 in F_2.

Let O_3R_3 meet QR_2 in D_2 and QR_4 in F_3, and so on.

We have, by hypothesis,

$$\triangle FqQ<(\textit{area of segment})-\tfrac{1}{3}\triangle EqQ,$$

or $\qquad (\textit{area of segment})-\triangle FqQ>\tfrac{1}{3}\triangle EqQ.\qquad\qquad(\alpha)$

Now, since all the parts of qE, as qF and the rest, are equal, $O_1R_1=R_1F_1$, $O_2D_1=D_1R_2=R_2F_2$, and so on; therefore

$$\triangle FqQ = (FO_1 + R_1O_2 + D_1O_3 + \cdots)$$
$$= (FO_1 + F_1D_1 + F_2D_2 + \cdots + F_{n-1}D_{n-1} + \triangle E_nR_nQ). \qquad (\beta)$$

But   (area of segment) $< (FO_1 + F_1O_2 + \cdots + F_{n-1}O_n + \triangle E_nO_nQ)$.

Subtracting, we have

     (area of segment) $- \triangle FqQ < (R_1O_2 + R_2O_3 + \cdots + R_{n-1}O_n + \triangle R_nO_nQ)$,

whence, *a fortiori*, by (α),

$$\tfrac{1}{3}\triangle EqQ < (R_1O_2 + R_2O_3 + \cdots + R_{n-1}O_n + \triangle R_nO_nQ).$$

But this is impossible, since [Props. 14, 15]

$$\tfrac{1}{3}\triangle EqQ > (R_1O_2 + R_2O_3 + \cdots + R_{n-1}O_n + \triangle R_nO_nQ).$$

Therefore   (area of segment) $\not< \tfrac{1}{3}\triangle EqQ$.

II. If possible, suppose the area of the segment less than $\tfrac{1}{3}\triangle EqQ$.

Take a submultiple of the triangle EqQ, as the triangle FqQ, less than the excess of $\tfrac{1}{3}\triangle EqQ$ over the area of the segment, and make the same construction as before.

Since $\triangle FqQ < \tfrac{1}{3}\triangle EqQ - (\text{area of segment})$,

it follows that

$$\triangle FqQ + (\text{area of segment}) < \tfrac{1}{3}\triangle EqQ$$
$$< (FO_1 + F_1O_2 + \cdots + F_{n-1}O_n + \triangle E_nO_nQ).$$
$$\text{[Props. 14, 15]}$$

Subtracting from each side the area of the segment, we have

$$\triangle FqQ < (\text{sum of spaces } qFR_1,\ R_1F_1R_2,\ \cdots E_nR_nQ)$$
$$< (FO_1 + F_1D_1 + \cdots + F_{n-1}D_{n-1} + \triangle E_nR_nQ),\ a\ fortiori;$$

which is impossible, because, by (β) above,

$$\triangle FqQ = FO_1 + F_1D_1 + \cdots + F_{n-1}D_{n-1} + \triangle E_nR_nQ.$$

Hence   (area of segment) $\not< \tfrac{1}{3}\triangle EqQ$.

Since then the area of the segment is neither less nor greater than $\tfrac{1}{3}\triangle EqQ$, it is equal to it.

Proposition 17

It is now manifest that *the area of any segment of a parabola is four-thirds of the triangle which has the same base as the segment and equal height.*

Let Qq be the base of the segment, P its vertex. Then PQq is the inscribed triangle with the same base as the segment and equal height.

Since P is the vertex of the segment, the diameter through P bisects Qq. Let V be the point of bisection.

Let VP, and qE drawn parallel to it, meet the tangent at Q in T, E respectively.

Then, by parallels,

$$qE = 2VT,$$

and $PV = PT$,   [Prop. 2]

so that $VT = 2PV$.

Hence $\triangle EqQ = 4\triangle PQq$.

But, by Prop. 16, the area of the segment is equal to $\tfrac{1}{3}\triangle EqQ$.

Therefore (area of segment) $= \tfrac{4}{3}\triangle PQq$.

Def. "In segments bounded by a straight line and any curve I call the straight line the *base*, and the *height* the greatest perpendicular drawn from the curve to the base of the segment, and the *vertex* the point from which the greatest perpendicular is drawn."

PROPOSITION 18

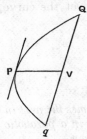

If Qq be the base of a segment of a parabola, and V the middle point of Qq, and if the diameter through V meet the curve in P, then P is the vertex of the segment.

For Qq is parallel to the tangent at P [Prop. 1]. Therefore, of all the perpendiculars which can be drawn from points on the segment to the base Qq, that from P is the greatest. Hence, by the definition, P is the vertex of the segment.

PROPOSITION 19

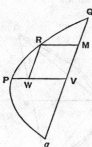

If Qq be a chord of a parabola bisected in V by the diameter PV, and if RM be a diameter bisecting QV in M, and RW be the ordinate from R to PV, then
$$PV = \tfrac{4}{3}RM.$$
For, by the property of the parabola,
$$PV : PW = QV^2 : RW^2$$
$$= 4RW^2 : RW^2,$$
so that $\qquad\qquad PV = 4PW,$
whence $\qquad\qquad PV = \tfrac{4}{3}RM.$

PROPOSITION 20

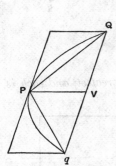

If Qq be the base, and P the vertex, of a parabolic segment, then the triangle PQq is greater than half the segment PQq.

For the chord Qq is parallel to the tangent at P, and the triangle PQq is half the parallelogram formed by Qq, the tangent at P, and the diameters through Q, q.

Therefore the triangle PQq is greater than half the segment.

COR. It follows that *it is possible to inscribe in the segment a polygon such that the segments left over are together less than any assigned area.*

PROPOSITION 21

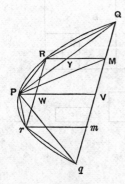

If Qq be the base, and P the vertex, of any parabolic segment, and if R be the vertex of the segment cut off by PQ, then
$$\triangle PQq = 8 \triangle PRQ.$$
The diameter through R will bisect the chord PQ, and therefore also QV, where PV is the diameter bisecting Qq. Let the diameter through R bisect PQ in Y and QV in M. Join PM.

By Prop. 19, $\qquad\qquad PV = \tfrac{4}{3}RM.$
Also $\qquad\qquad\qquad PV = 2YM.$
Therefore $\qquad\qquad YM = 2RY,$

and $\triangle PQM = 2\triangle PRQ.$
Hence $\triangle PQV = 4\triangle PRQ,$
and $\triangle PQq = 8\triangle PRQ.$

Also, if RW, the ordinate from R to PV, be produced to meet the curve again in r, $RW = rW,$
and the same proof shows that

$$\triangle PQq = 8\triangle Prq.$$

PROPOSITION 22

If there be a series of areas $A, B, C, D, \cdots$ each of which is four times the next in order, and if the largest, A, be equal to the triangle PQq inscribed in a parabolic segment PQq and having the same base with it and equal height, then

$$(A+B+C+D+\cdots) < (area\ of\ segment\ PQq).$$

For, since $\triangle PQq = 8\triangle PRQ = 8\triangle Pqr$, where R, r are the vertices of the segments cut off by PQ, Pq, as in the last proposition,

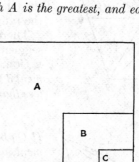

$$\triangle PQq = 4(\triangle PQR + \triangle Pqr).$$
Therefore, since $\triangle PQq = A,$
$$\triangle PQR + \triangle Pqr = B.$$

In like manner we prove that the triangles similarly inscribed in the remaining segments are together equal to the area C, and so on.

Therefore $A+B+C+D+\cdots$ is equal to the area of a certain inscribed polygon, and is therefore less than the area of the segment.

PROPOSITION 23

Given a series of areas $A, B, C, D, \cdots Z$, of which A is the greatest, and each is equal to four times the next in order, then

$$A+B+C+\cdots+Z+\tfrac{1}{3}Z = \tfrac{4}{3}A.$$

Take areas $b, c, d, \cdots$ such that
$$b = \tfrac{1}{3}B,$$
$$c = \tfrac{1}{3}C,$$
$$d = \tfrac{1}{3}D,\text{ and so on.}$$

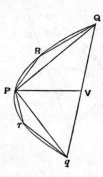

Then, since $b = \tfrac{1}{3}B,$
and $B = \tfrac{1}{4}A,$
$$B + b = \tfrac{1}{3}A.$$
Similarly $C + c = \tfrac{1}{3}B.$
....

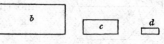

Therefore
$$B+C+D+\cdots+Z+b+c+d+\cdots+z =$$
$$\tfrac{1}{3}(A+B+C+\cdots+Y).$$
But
$$b+c+d+\cdots+y = \tfrac{1}{3}(B+C+D+\cdots+Y).$$
Therefore, by subtraction,
$$B+C+D+\cdots+Z+z = \tfrac{1}{3}A$$
or
$$A+B+C+\cdots+Z+\tfrac{1}{3}Z = \tfrac{4}{3}A.$$

PROPOSITION 24

Every segment bounded by a parabola and a chord Qq is equal to four-thirds of the triangle which has the same base as the segment and equal height.

Suppose
$$K = \tfrac{4}{3}\triangle PQq,$$
where P is the vertex of the segment; and we have then to prove that the area of the segment is equal to K.

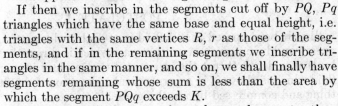

For, if the segment be not equal to K, it must either be greater or less.

I. Suppose the area of the segment greater than K.

If then we inscribe in the segments cut off by PQ, Pq triangles which have the same base and equal height, i.e. triangles with the same vertices R, r as those of the segments, and if in the remaining segments we inscribe triangles in the same manner, and so on, we shall finally have segments remaining whose sum is less than the area by which the segment PQq exceeds K.

Therefore the polygon so formed must be greater than the area K; which is impossible, since [Prop. 23]
$$A + B + C + \cdots + Z < \tfrac{4}{3}A,$$
where
$$A = \triangle PQq.$$

Thus the area of the segment cannot be greater than K.

II. Suppose, if possible, that the area of the segment is less than K.

If then $\triangle PQq = A$, $B = \tfrac{1}{4}A$, $C = \tfrac{1}{4}B$, and so on, until we arrive at an area X such that X is less than the difference between K and the segment, we have
$$A + B + C + \cdots + X + \tfrac{1}{3}X = \tfrac{4}{3}A \qquad \text{[Prop. 23]}$$
$$= K.$$

Now, since K exceeds $A + B + C + \cdots + X$ by an area less than X, and the area of the segment by an area greater than X, it follows that
$$A + B + C + \cdots + X > (\text{the segment});$$
which is impossible, by Prop. 22 above.

Hence the segment is not less than K.

Thus, since the segment is neither greater nor less than K,
$$(\text{area of segment } PQq) = K = \tfrac{4}{3}\triangle PQq.$$

ON FLOATING BODIES

BOOK ONE

POSTULATE 1

"Let it be supposed that a fluid is of such a character that, its parts lying evenly and being continuous, that part which is thrust the less is driven along by that which is thrust the more; and that each of its parts is thrust by the fluid which is above it in a perpendicular direction if the fluid be sunk in anything and compressed by anything else."

PROPOSITION 1

If a surface be cut by a plane always passing through a certain point, and if the section be always a circumference [of a circle] whose centre is the aforesaid point, the surface is that of a sphere.

For, if not, there will be some two lines drawn from the point to the surface which are not equal.

Suppose O to be the fixed point, and A, B to be two points on the surface such that OA, OB are unequal. Let the surface be cut by a plane passing through OA, OB. Then the section is, by hypothesis, a circle whose centre is O.

Thus $OA = OB$; which is contrary to the assumption. Therefore the surface cannot but be a sphere.

PROPOSITION 2

The surface of any fluid at rest is the surface of a sphere whose centre is the same as that of the earth.

Suppose the surface of the fluid cut by a plane through O, the centre of the earth, in the curve $ABCD$.

$ABCD$ shall be the circumference of a circle.

For, if not, some of the lines drawn from O to the curve will be unequal. Take one of them, OB, such that OB is greater than some of the lines from O to the curve and less than others. Draw a circle with OB as radius. Let it be EBF, which will therefore fall partly within and partly without the surface of the fluid.

Draw OGH making with OB an angle equal to the angle EOB, and meeting the surface in H and the circle in G. Draw also in the plane an arc of a circle PQR with centre O and within the fluid.

Then the parts of the fluid along PQR are uniform and continuous, and the part PQ is compressed by the part between it and AB, while the part QR is compressed by the part between QR and BH.

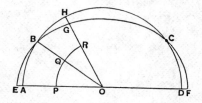

538

Therefore the parts along PQ, QR will be unequally compressed, and the part which is compressed the less will be set in motion by that which is compressed the more.

Therefore there will not be rest; which is contrary to the hypothesis.

Hence the section of the surface will be the circumference of a circle whose centre is O; and so will all other sections by planes through O.

Therefore the surface is that of a sphere with centre O.

PROPOSITION 3

Of solids those which, size for size, are of equal weight with a fluid will, if let down into the fluid, be immersed so that they do not project above the surface but do not sink lower.

If possible, let a certain solid $EFHG$ of equal weight, volume for volume, with the fluid remain immersed in it so that part of it, $EBCF$, projects above the surface.

Draw through O, the centre of the earth, and through the solid a plane cutting the surface of the fluid in the circle $ABCD$.

Conceive a pyramid with vertex O and base a parallelogram at the surface of the fluid, such that it includes the immersed portion of the solid. Let this

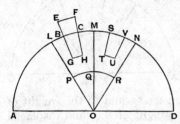

pyramid be cut by the plane of $ABCD$ in OL, OM. Also let a sphere within the fluid and below GH be described with centre O, and let the plane of $ABCD$ cut this sphere in PQR.

Conceive also another pyramid in the fluid with vertex O, continuous with the former pyramid and equal and similar to it. Let the pyramid so described be cut in OM, ON by the plane of $ABCD$.

Lastly, let $STUV$ be a part of the fluid within the second pyramid equal and similar to the part $BGHC$ of the solid, and let SV be at the surface of the fluid.

Then the pressures on PQ, QR are unequal, that on PQ being the greater. Hence the part at QR will be set in motion by that at PQ, and the fluid will not be at rest; which is contrary to the hypothesis.

Therefore the solid will not stand out above the surface.

Nor will it sink further, because all the parts of the fluid will be under the same pressure.

PROPOSITION 4

A solid lighter than a fluid will, if immersed in it, not be completely submerged, but part of it will project above the surface.

In this case, after the manner of the previous proposition, we assume the solid, if possible, to be completely submerged and the fluid to be at rest in that position, and we conceive (1) a pyramid with its vertex at O, the centre of the earth, including the solid, (2) another pyramid continuous with the former and equal and similar to it, with the same vertex O, (3) a portion of the fluid within this latter pyramid equal to the immersed solid in the other pyramid, (4) a sphere with centre O whose surface is below the immersed solid and the part of the fluid in the second pyramid corresponding thereto. We suppose a plane to be drawn through the centre O cutting the surface of the fluid in the circle

ABC, the solid in *S*, the first pyramid in *OA*, *OB*, the second pyramid in *OB*, *OC*, the portion of the fluid in the second pyramid in *K*, and the inner sphere in *PQR*.

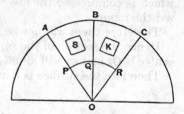

Then the pressures on the parts of the fluid at *PQ*, *QR* are unequal, since *S* is lighter than *K*. Hence there will not be rest; which is contrary to the hypothesis.

Therefore the solid *S* cannot, in a condition of rest, be completely submerged.

PROPOSITION 5

Any solid lighter than a fluid will, if placed in the fluid, be so far immersed that the weight of the solid will be equal to the weight of the fluid displaced.

For let the solid be *EGHF*, and let *BGHC* be the portion of it immersed when the fluid is at rest. As in Prop. 3, conceive a pyramid with vertex *O* including the solid, and another pyramid with the same vertex continuous with the former and equal and similar to it. Sup-

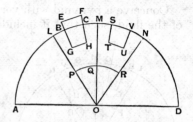

pose a portion of the fluid *STUV* at the base of the second pyramid to be equal and similar to the immersed portion of the solid; and let the construction be the same as in Prop. 3.

Then, since the pressure on the parts of the fluid at *PQ*, *QR* must be equal in order that the fluid may be at rest, it follows that the weight of the portion *STUV* of the fluid must be equal to the weight of the solid *EGHF*. And the former is equal to the weight of the fluid displaced by the immersed portion of the solid *BGHC*.

PROPOSITION 6

If a solid lighter than a fluid be forcibly immersed in it, the solid will be driven upwards by a force equal to the difference between its weight and the weight of the fluid displaced.

For let *A* be completely immersed in the fluid, and let *G* represent the weight of *A*, and (*G+H*) the weight of an equal volume of the fluid. Take a solid *D*, whose weight is *H* and add it to *A*. Then the weight of (*A+D*) is less than that of an equal volume of the fluid; and, if (*A+D*) is immersed in the fluid, it will project so that its weight will be equal to the weight of the fluid displaced. But its weight is (*G+H*).

Therefore the weight of the fluid displaced is (*G+H*), and hence the volume of the fluid displaced is the volume of the solid *A*. There will accordingly be rest with *A* immersed and *D* projecting.

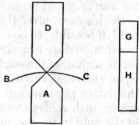

Thus the weight of *D* balances the upward force exerted by the fluid on *A*, and therefore the latter force is equal to *H*, which is the difference between the weight of *A* and the weight of the fluid which *A* displaces.

PROPOSITION 7

A solid heavier than a fluid will, if placed in it, descend to the bottom of the fluid, and the solid will, when weighed in the fluid, be lighter than its true weight by the weight of the fluid displaced.

(1) The first part of the proposition is obvious, since the part of the fluid under the solid will be under greater pressure, and therefore the other parts will give way until the solid reaches the bottom.

(2) Let A be a solid heavier than the same volume of the fluid, and let $(G+H)$ represent its weight, while G represents the weight of the same volume of the fluid.

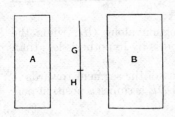

Take a solid B lighter than the same volume of the fluid, and such that the weight of B is G, while the weight of the same volume of the fluid is $(G+H)$.

Let A and B be now combined into one solid and immersed. Then, since $(A+B)$ will be of the same weight as the same volume of fluid, both weights being equal to $(G+H)+G$, it follows that $(A+B)$ will remain stationary in the fluid.

Therefore the force which causes A by itself to sink must be equal to the upward force exerted by the fluid on B by itself. This latter is equal to the difference between $(G+H)$ and G [Prop. 6]. Hence A is depressed by a force equal to H, i.e. its weight in the fluid is H, or the difference between $(G+H)$ and G.

POSTULATE 2

"Let it be granted that bodies which are forced upwards in a fluid are forced upwards along the perpendicular [to the surface] which passes through their centre of gravity."

PROPOSITION 8

If a solid in the form of a segment of a sphere, and of a substance lighter than a fluid, be immersed in it so that its base does not touch the surface, the solid will rest in such a position that its axis is perpendicular to the surface; and, if the solid be forced into such a position that its base touches the fluid on one side and be then set free, it will not remain in that position but will return to the symmetrical position.

PROPOSITION 9

If a solid in the form of a segment of a sphere, and of a substance lighter than a fluid, be immersed in it so that its base is completely below the surface, the solid will rest in such a position that its axis is perpendicular to the surface.

[The proof of this proposition has only survived in a mutilated form. It deals moreover with only one case out of three which are distinguished at the beginning, viz. that in which the segment is greater than a hemisphere. . . .]

Suppose, first, that the segment is greater than a hemisphere. Let it be cut by a plane through its axis and the centre of the earth; and, if possible, let it be at rest in the position shown in the figure, where AB is the intersection of the plane with the base of the segment, DE its axis, C the centre of the sphere of which the segment is a part, O the centre of the earth.

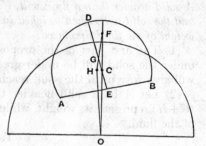

The centre of gravity of the portion of the segment outside the fluid, as F, lies on OC produced, its axis passing through C.

Let G be the centre of gravity of the segment. Join FG, and produce it to H so that

$$FG : GH = \text{(volume of immersed portion)} :$$
$$\text{(rest of solid)}.$$

Join OH.

Then the weight of the portion of the solid outside the fluid acts along FO, and the pressure of the fluid on the immersed portion along OH, while the weight of the immersed portion acts along HO and is by hypothesis less than the pressure of the fluid acting along OH.

Hence there will not be equilibrium, but the part of the segment towards A will ascend and the part towards B descend, until DE assumes a position perpendicular to the surface of the fluid.

ON FLOATING BODIES

BOOK TWO

PROPOSITION 1

If a solid lighter than a fluid be at rest in it, the weight of the solid will be to that of the same volume of the fluid as the immersed portion of the solid is to the whole.

Let $(A+B)$ be the solid, B the portion immersed in the fluid.

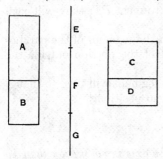

Let $(C+D)$ be an equal volume of the fluid, C being equal in volume to A and B to D.

Further suppose the line E to represent the weight of the solid $(A+B)$, $(F+G)$ to represent the weight of $(C+D)$, and G that of D.

Then

$$\text{weight of } (A+B) : \text{weight of } (C+D) = E : (F+G). \tag{1}$$

And the weight of $(A+B)$ is equal to the weight of a volume B of the fluid [I. 5], i.e. to the weight of D.

That is to say, $E = G$.

Hence, by (1),

$$\text{weight of } (A+B) : \text{weight of } (C+D) = G : F+G$$
$$= D : C+D$$
$$= B : A+B.$$

PROPOSITION 2

If a right segment of a paraboloid of revolution whose axis is not greater than $\frac{3}{4}p$ (where p is the principal parameter of the generating parabola), and whose specific gravity is less than that of a fluid, be placed in the fluid with its axis inclined to the vertical at any angle, but so that the base of the segment does not touch the surface of the fluid, the segment of the paraboloid will not remain in that position but will return to the position in which its axis is vertical.

Let the axis of the segment of the paraboloid be AN, and through AN draw a plane perpendicular to the surface of the fluid. Let the plane intersect the paraboloid in the parabola BAB', the base of the segment of the paraboloid in BB', and the plane of the surface of the fluid in the chord QQ' of the parabola.

Then, since the axis AN is placed in a position not perpendicular to QQ', BB' will not be parallel to QQ'.

Draw the tangent PT to the parabola which is parallel to QQ', and let P be the point of contact.[1]

[1]The rest of the proof . . . is given in brackets as supplied by Commandinus.

543

[From P draw PV parallel to AN meeting QQ' in V. Then PV will be a diameter of the parabola, and also the axis of the portion of the paraboloid immersed in the fluid.

Let C be the centre of gravity of the paraboloid BAB', and F that of the portion
immersed in the fluid. Join FC and produce
it to H so that H is the centre of gravity of
the remaining portion of the paraboloid
above the surface.

Then, since $AN = \frac{3}{2}AC$,
and $AN \not> \frac{3}{4}p$,

it follows that $AC \not> \dfrac{p}{2}$.

Therefore, if CP be joined, the angle CPT
is acute. Hence, if CK be drawn perpendicular to PT, K will fall between P
and T. And, if FL, HM be drawn parallel to CK to meet PT, they will each
be perpendicular to the surface of the fluid.

Now the force acting on the immersed portion of the segment of the paraboloid will act upwards along LF, while the weight of the portion outside the
fluid will act downwards along HM.

Therefore there will not be equilibrium, but the segment will turn so that B
will rise and B' will fall, until AN takes the vertical position.]

PROPOSITION 3

*If a right segment of a paraboloid of revolution whose axis is not greater than $\frac{3}{4}p$
(where p is the parameter), and whose specific gravity is less than that of a fluid,
be placed in the fluid with its axis inclined at any angle to the vertical, but so that
its base is entirely submerged, the solid will not remain in that position but will
return to the position in which the axis is vertical.*

Let the axis of the paraboloid be AN, and through AN draw a plane perpendicular to the surface of the fluid intersecting the paraboloid in the parabola
BAB', the base of the segment in BNB', and the plane of the surface of the
fluid in the chord QQ' of the parabola.

Then, since AN, as placed, is not perpendicular to the surface of the fluid, QQ' and
BB' will not be parallel.

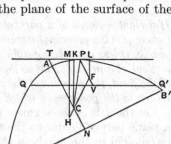

Draw PT parallel to QQ' and touching the
parabola at P. Let PT meet NA produced in
T. Draw the diameter PV bisecting QQ' in V.
PV is then the axis of the portion of the
paraboloid above the surface of the fluid.

Let C be the centre of gravity of the whole
segment of the paraboloid, F that of the portion above the surface. Join FC and produce
it to H so that H is the centre of gravity of the immersed portion.

Then, since $AC \not> \dfrac{p}{2}$, the angle CPT is an acute angle, as in the last proposition.

Hence, if CK be drawn perpendicular to PT, K will fall between P and T. Also, if HM, FL be drawn parallel to CK, they will be perpendicular to the surface of the fluid.

And the force acting on the submerged portion will act upwards along HM, while the weight of the rest will act downwards along LF produced.

Thus the paraboloid will turn until it takes the position in which AN is vertical.

PROPOSITION 4

Given a right segment of a paraboloid of revolution whose axis AN is greater than $\frac{3}{4}p$ (where p is the parameter), and whose specific gravity is less than that of a fluid but bears to it a ratio not less than $(AN-\frac{3}{4}p)^2 : AN^2$, if the segment of the paraboloid be placed in the fluid with its axis at any inclination to the vertical, but so that its base does not touch the surface of the fluid, it will not remain in that position but will return to the position in which its axis is vertical.

Let the axis of the segment of the paraboloid be AN, and let a plane be drawn through AN perpendicular to the surface of the fluid and intersecting

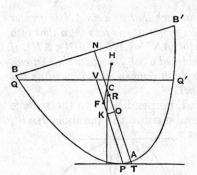

the segment in the parabola BAB', the base of the segment in BB', and the surface of the fluid in the chord QQ' of the parabola.

Then AN, as placed, will not be perpendicular to QQ'.

Draw PT parallel to QQ' and touching the parabola at P. Draw the diameter PV bisecting QQ' in V. Thus PV will be the axis of the submerged portion of the solid.

Let C be the centre of gravity of the whole solid, F that of the immersed portion. Join FC and produce it to H so that H is the centre of gravity of the remaining portion.

Now, since $AN=\frac{3}{2}AC$,
and $AN>\frac{3}{4}p$,

it follows that $AC>\dfrac{p}{2}$.

Measure CO along CA equal to $\dfrac{p}{2}$, and OR along OC equal to $\frac{1}{2}AO$.

Then, since $AN=\frac{3}{2}AC$,
and $AR=\frac{3}{2}AO$,
we have, by subtraction, $NR=\frac{3}{2}OC$.
That is, $AN-AR=\frac{3}{2}OC$
                                   $=\frac{3}{4}p$,
or $AR=(AN-\frac{3}{4}p)$.
Thus $(AN-\frac{3}{4}p)^2 : AN^2=AR^2 : AN^2$,
and therefore the ratio of the specific gravity of the solid to that of the fluid is, by the enunciation, not less than the ratio $AR^2 : AN^2$.

But, by Prop. 1, the former ratio is equal to the ratio of the immersed portion to the whole solid, i.e. to the ratio $PV^2 : AN^2$ [*On Conoids and Spheroids*, Prop. 24].

Hence $PV^2 : AN^2 \not< AR^2 : AN^2$, or $$PV \not< AR.$$

It follows that $$PF(=\tfrac{2}{3}PV) \not< \tfrac{2}{3}AR$$
$$\not< AO.$$

If, therefore, OK be drawn from O perpendicular to OA, it will meet PF between P and F.

Also, if CK be joined, the triangle KCO is equal and similar to the triangle formed by the normal, the subnormal and the ordinate at P (since $CO = \tfrac{1}{2}p$ or the subnormal, and KO is equal to the ordinate).

Therefore CK is parallel to the normal at P, and therefore perpendicular to the tangent at P and to the surface of the fluid.

Hence, if parallels to CK be drawn through F, H, they will be perpendicular to the surface of the fluid, and the force acting on the submerged portion of the solid will act upwards along the former, while the weight of the other portion will act downwards along the latter.

Therefore the solid will not remain in its position but will turn until AN assumes a vertical position.

Proposition 5

Given a right segment of a paraboloid of revolution such that its axis AN is greater than $\tfrac{3}{4}p$ (where p is the parameter), and its specific gravity is less than that of a fluid but in a ratio to it not greater than the ratio $\{AN^2 - (AN - \tfrac{3}{4}p)^2\} : AN^2$, if the segment be placed in the fluid with its axis inclined at any angle to the vertical, but so that its base is completely submerged, it will not remain in that position but will return to the position in which AN is vertical.

Let a plane be drawn through AN, as placed, perpendicular to the surface of the fluid and cutting the segment of the paraboloid in the parabola BAB', the base of the segment in BB', and the plane of the surface of the fluid in the chord QQ' of the parabola.

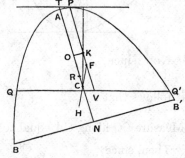

Draw the tangent PT parallel to QQ', and the diameter PV, bisecting QQ', will accordingly be the axis of the portion of the paraboloid above the surface of the fluid.

Let F be the centre of gravity of the portion above the surface, C that of the whole solid, and produce FC to H, the centre of gravity of the immersed portion.

As in the last proposition, $AC > \dfrac{p}{2}$, and we measure CO along CA equal to $\dfrac{p}{2}$, and OR along OC equal to $\tfrac{1}{2}AO$.

Then $$AN = \tfrac{3}{2}AC, \text{ and } AR = \tfrac{3}{2}AO;$$
and we derive, as before, $$AR = (AN - \tfrac{3}{4}p).$$

Now, by hypothesis,

(spec. gravity of solid) : (spec. gravity of fluid)
$$\not> \{AN^2 - (AN - \tfrac{3}{4}p)^2\} : AN^2$$
$$\not> (AN^2 - AR^2) : AN^2.$$

Therefore

(portion submerged) : (whole solid)
$$\not> (AN^2 - AR^2) : AN^2,$$

and   (whole solid) : (portion above surface)
$$\not> AN^2 : AR^2.$$
Thus $AN^2 : PV^2 \not> AN^2 : AR^2,$
whence $PV \not< AR,$
and $PF \not< \frac{2}{3}AR$
                             $\not< AO.$

Therefore, if a perpendicular to AC be drawn from O, it will meet PF in some point K between P and F.

And, since $CO = \frac{1}{2}p$, CK will be perpendicular to PT, as in the last proposition.

Now the force acting on the submerged portion of the solid will act upwards through H, and the weight of the other portion downwards through F, in directions parallel in both cases to CK; whence the proposition follows.

PROPOSITION 6

If a right segment of a paraboloid lighter than a fluid be such that its axis AM is greater than $\frac{3}{4}p$, but $AM : \frac{1}{2}p < 15 : 4$, and if the segment be placed in the fluid with its axis so inclined to the vertical that its base touches the fluid, it will never remain in such a position that the base touches the surface in one point only.

Suppose the segment of the paraboloid to be placed in the position described, and let the plane through the axis AM perpendicular to the surface of the fluid intersect the segment of the paraboloid in the parabolic segment BAB' and the plane of the surface of the fluid in BQ.

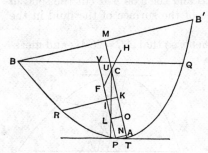

Take C on AM such that $AC = 2CM$ (or so that C is the centre of gravity of the segment of the paraboloid), and measure CK along CA such that
$$AM : CK = 15 : 4.$$

Thus $AM : CK > AM : \frac{1}{2}p$, by hypothesis; therefore $CK < \frac{1}{2}p$.

Measure CO along CA equal to $\frac{1}{2}p$. Also draw KR perpendicular to AC meeting the parabola in R.

Draw the tangent PT parallel to BQ, and through P draw the diameter PV bisecting BQ in V and meeting KR in I.

Then $PV : PI \underset{\text{or} >}{=} KM : AK,$

"for this is proved."

And $CK = \frac{4}{15}AM = \frac{2}{5}AC;$
whence $AK = AC - CK = \frac{3}{5}AC = \frac{2}{5}AM.$
Thus $KM = \frac{3}{5}AM.$
Therefore $KM = \frac{3}{2}AK.$
It follows that $PV \underset{\text{or} >}{=} \frac{3}{2}PI,$
so that $PI \underset{\text{or} <}{=} 2IV.$

Let F be the centre of gravity of the immersed portion of the paraboloid, so that $PF = 2FV$. Produce FC to H, the centre of gravity of the portion above the surface.

Draw OL perpendicular to PV.

Then, since $CO = \frac{1}{2}p$, CL must be perpendicular to PT and therefore to the
surface of the fluid.

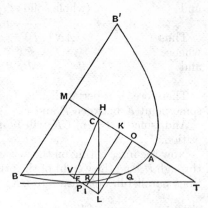

And the forces acting on the immersed
portion of the paraboloid and the portion
above the surface act respectively upwards
and downwards along lines through F and
H parallel to CL.

Hence the paraboloid cannot remain in
the position in which B just touches the
surface, but must turn in the direction of
increasing the angle PTM.

The proof is the same in the case where
the point I is not on VP but on VP produced, as in the second figure.

PROPOSITION 7

*Given a right segment of a paraboloid of revolution lighter than a fluid and such
that its axis AM is greater than $\frac{3}{4}p$, but $AM : \frac{1}{2}p < 15 : 4$, if the segment be placed
in the fluid so that its base is entirely submerged, it will never rest in such a position that the base touches the surface of the fluid at one point only.*

Suppose the solid so placed that one point of the base only (B) touches the
surface of the fluid. Let the plane through B and the axis AM cut the solid in
the parabolic segment BAB' and the plane of the surface of the fluid in the
chord BQ of the parabola.

Let C be the centre of gravity of the segment, so that $AC = 2CM$; and measure CK along CA such that

$$AM : CK = 15 : 4.$$

It follows that $\quad CK < \frac{1}{2}p$.

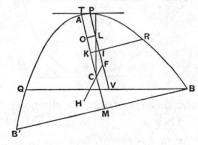

Measure CO along CA equal to $\frac{1}{2}p$.
Draw KR perpendicular to AM meeting
the parabola in R.

Let PT, touching at P, be the tangent
to the parabola which is parallel to BQ,
and PV the diameter bisecting BQ, i.e.
the axis of the portion of the paraboloid
above the surface.

Then, as in the last proposition, we prove that

$$PV \underset{\text{or}>}{=} \tfrac{3}{2}PI,$$

and

$$PI \underset{\text{or}<}{=} 2IV.$$

Let F be the centre of gravity of the portion of the solid above the surface; join
FC and produce it to H, the centre of gravity of the portion submerged.

Draw OL perpendicular to PV; and, as before, since $CO = \frac{1}{2}p$, CL is perpendicular to the tangent PT. And the lines through H, F parallel to CL are perpendicular to the surface of the fluid; thus the proposition is established as
before.

The proof is the same if the point I is not on VP but on VP produced.

PROPOSITION 8

Given a solid in the form of a right segment of a paraboloid of revolution whose axis
AM is greater than $\frac{3}{4}p$, but such that $AM : \frac{1}{2}p < 15 : 4$, and whose specific gravity
bears to that of a fluid a ratio less than $(AM - \frac{3}{4}p)^2 : AM^2$, then, if the solid be
placed in the fluid so that its base does not touch the fluid and its axis is inclined
at an angle to the vertical, the solid will not return to the position in which its axis
is vertical and will not remain in any position except that in which its axis makes
with the surface of the fluid a certain angle to be described.

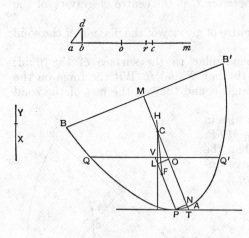

Let am be taken equal to the axis
AM, and let c be a point on am
such that $ac = 2cm$. Measure co
along ca equal to $\frac{1}{2}p$, and or along
oc equal to $\frac{1}{2}ao$.

Let $X + Y$ be a straight line such
that

(spec. gr. of solid) : (spec. gr. of
$\qquad$ fluid) $= (X + Y)^2 : am^2,$ $\qquad$ (α)

and suppose $X = 2Y$.

Now $ar = \frac{3}{2}ao = \frac{3}{2}(\frac{2}{3}am - \frac{1}{2}p)$
$\qquad = am - \frac{3}{4}p$
$\qquad = AM - \frac{3}{4}p.$

Therefore, by hypothesis,

$\qquad (X + Y)^2 : am^2 < ar^2 : am^2,$

whence $(X + Y) < ar$, and therefore
$X < ao.$

Measure ob along oa equal to X, and draw bd perpendicular to ab and of such
length that $\qquad\qquad bd^2 = \frac{1}{2}co \cdot ab.$ $\qquad\qquad\qquad$ (β)
Join ad.

Now let the solid be placed in the fluid with its axis AM inclined at an angle
to the vertical. Through AM draw a plane perpendicular to the surface of the
fluid, and let this plane cut the paraboloid in the parabola BAB' and the plane
of the surface of the fluid in the chord QQ' of the parabola.

Draw the tangent PT parallel to QQ', touching at P, and let PV be the
diameter bisecting QQ' in V (or the axis of the immersed portion of the solid),
and PN the ordinate from P.

Measure AO along AM equal to ao, and OC along OM equal to oc, and draw
OL perpendicular to PV.

I. Suppose the angle OTP greater than the angle dab.

Thus $\qquad\qquad PN^2 : NT^2 > db^2 : ba^2.$
But $\qquad\qquad PN^2 : NT^2 = p : 4AN$
$\qquad\qquad\qquad\qquad = co : NT,$
and $\qquad\qquad db^2 : ba^2 = \frac{1}{2}co : ab$, by ($\beta$).
$\quad$ Therefore $\qquad\qquad NT < 2ab,$
or $\qquad\qquad\qquad AN < ab,$
whence $\qquad\qquad NO > bo$ (since $ao = AO$)
$\qquad\qquad\qquad\qquad > X.$
$\quad$ Now $\qquad (X + Y)^2 : am^2 = $ (spec. gr. of solid) : (spec. gr. of fluid)
$\qquad\qquad\qquad\qquad = $ (portion immersed) : (rest of solid)

$$= PV^2 : AM^2,$$

so that $\qquad X + Y = PV.$

But $\qquad PL(=NO) > X$

$$> \tfrac{2}{3}(X + Y), \text{ since } X = 2Y,$$
$$> \tfrac{2}{3}PV,$$

or $\qquad\qquad PV < \tfrac{3}{2}PL,$

and therefore $\qquad PL > 2LV.$

Take a point F on PV so that $PF = 2FV$, i.e. so that F is the centre of gravity of the immersed portion of the solid.

Also $AC = ac = \tfrac{2}{3}am = \tfrac{2}{3}AM$, and therefore C is the centre of gravity of the whole solid.

Join FC and produce it to H, the centre of gravity of the portion of the solid above the surface.

Now, since $CO = \tfrac{1}{2}p$, CL is perpendicular to the surface of the fluid; therefore so are the parallels to CL through F and H. But the force on the immersed portion acts upwards through F and that on the rest of the solid downwards through H.

Therefore the solid will not rest but turn in the direction of diminishing the angle MTP.

II. Suppose the angle OTP less than the angle dab. In this case, we shall have, instead of the above results, the following,

$$AN > ab,$$
$$NO < X.$$

Also $\qquad PV > \tfrac{3}{2}PL,$

and therefore $\quad PL < 2LV.$

Make PF equal to $2FV$, so that F is the centre of gravity of the immersed portion.

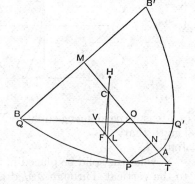

And, proceeding as before, we prove in this case that the solid will turn in the direction of *increasing* the angle MTP.

III. When the angle MTP is equal to the angle dab, equalities replace inequalities in the results obtained, and L is itself the centre of gravity of the immersed portion. Thus all the forces act in one straight line, the perpendicular CL; therefore there is equilibrium, and the solid will rest in the position described.

Proposition 9

Given a solid in the form of a right segment of a paraboloid of revolution whose axis AM is greater than $\tfrac{3}{4}p$, but such that $AM : \tfrac{1}{2}p < 15 : 4$, and whose specific gravity bears to that of a fluid a ratio greater than $\{AM^2 - (AM - \tfrac{3}{4}p)^2\} : AM^2$, then, if the solid be placed in the fluid with its axis inclined at an angle to the vertical but so that its base is entirely below the surface, the solid will not return to the position in which its axis is vertical and will not remain in any position except that in which its axis makes with the surface of the fluid an angle equal to that described in the last proposition.

Take am equal to AM, and take c on am such that $ac = 2cm$. Measure co along ca equal to $\tfrac{1}{2}p$, and ar along ac such that $ar = \tfrac{3}{2}ao$.

Let $X + Y$ be such a line that

(spec. gr. of solid) : (spec. gr. of fluid) $= \{am^2 - (X+Y)^2\} : am^2$,
and suppose $X = 2Y$.

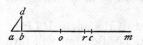

Now $ar = \frac{3}{2}ao$
$= \frac{3}{2}(\frac{2}{3}am - \frac{1}{2}p)$
$= AM - \frac{3}{4}p$.

Therefore, by hypothesis,
$am^2 - ar^2 : am^2 < \{am^2 - (X+Y)^2\} : am^2$,
whence $X + Y < ar$,
and therefore $X < ao$.

Make ob (measured along oa) equal
to X, and draw bd perpendicular to ba
and of such length that
$$bd^2 = \tfrac{1}{2}co \cdot ab.$$
Join ad.

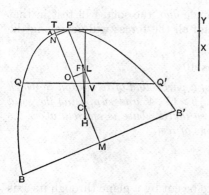

Now suppose the solid placed as in
the figure with its axis AM inclined to
the vertical. Let the plane through AM
perpendicular to the surface of the
fluid cut the solid in the parabola BAB'
and the surface of the fluid in QQ'.

Let PT be the tangent parallel to QQ', PV the diameter bisecting QQ' or)
the axis of the portion of the paraboloid above the surface), PN the ordinate
from P.

I. Suppose the angle MTP greater than the angle dab. Let AM be cut as
before in C and O so that $AC = 2CM$, $OC = \frac{1}{2}p$, and accordingly AM, am are
equally divided. Draw OL perpendicular to PV.

Then, we have, as in the last proposition,
$$PN^2 : NT^2 > db^2 : ba^2,$$
whence $co : NT > \frac{1}{2}co : ab$,
and therefore $AN < ab$.
It follows that $NO > bo$
$> X$.

Again, since the specific gravity of the solid is to that of the fluid as the
immersed portion of the solid to the whole,

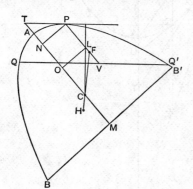

$$AM^2 - (X+Y)^2 : AM^2 = AM^2 - PV^2 : AM^2,$$
or $(X+Y)^2 : AM^2 = PV^2 : AM^2$.
That is, $X + Y = PV$.
And PL (or $NO) > X$
$> \frac{2}{3}PV$,
so that $PL > 2LV$.

Take F on PV so that $PF = 2FV$. Then F
is the centre of gravity of the portion of the
solid above the surface.

Also C is the centre of gravity of the whole
solid. Join FC and produce it to H, the centre of gravity of the immersed portion.

Then, since $CO = \frac{1}{2}p$, CL is perpendicular
to PT and to the surface of the fluid; and
the force acting on the immersed portion of the solid acts upwards along the

parallel to CL through H, while the weight of the rest of the solid acts downwards along the parallel to CL through F.

Hence the solid will not rest but turn in the direction of diminishing the angle MTP.

II. Exactly as in the last proposition, we prove that, if the angle MTP be less than the angle dab, the solid will not remain in its position but will turn in the direction of increasing the angle MTP.

III. If the angle MTP is equal to the angle dab, the solid will rest in that position, because L and F will coincide, and all the forces will act along the one line CL.

PROPOSITION 10

Given a solid in the form of a right segment of a paraboloid of revolution in which the axis AM is of a length such that $AM : \frac{1}{2}p > 15 : 4$, and supposing the solid placed in a fluid of greater specific gravity so that its base is entirely above the surface of the fluid, to investigate the positions of rest.

(PRELIMINARY)

Suppose the segment of the paraboloid to be cut by a plane through its axis AM in the parabolic segment BAB_1 of which BB_1 is the base.

Divide AM at C so that $AC = 2CM$, and measure CK along CA so that
$$AM : CK = 15 : 4, \qquad (\alpha)$$
whence, by the hypothesis, $CK > \frac{1}{2}p$.

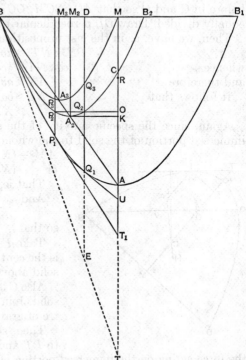

Suppose CO measured along CA equal to $\frac{1}{2}p$, and take a point R on AM such that
$$MR = \tfrac{3}{2}CO.$$
Thus $AR = AM - MR$
$$= \tfrac{3}{2}(AC - CO)$$
$$= \tfrac{3}{2}AO.$$

Join BA, draw KA_2 perpendicular to AM meeting BA in A_2, bisect BA in A_3, and draw A_2M_2, A_3M_3 parallel to AM meeting BM in M_2, M_3 respectively.

On A_2M_2, A_3M_3 as axes describe parabolic segments similar to the segment BAB_1. (It follows, by similar triangles, that BM will be the base of the segment whose axis is A_3M_3 and BB_2 the base of that whose axis is A_2M_2, where $BB_2 = 2BM_2$.)

The parabola BA_2B_2 will then pass through C.

[For
$$BM_2 : M_2M = BM_2 : A_2K$$
$$= KM : AK$$

$$=CM+CK : AC-CK$$
$$=(\tfrac{1}{3}+\tfrac{4}{15})AM : (\tfrac{2}{3}-\tfrac{4}{15})AM$$
$$=9:6 \qquad\qquad\qquad\qquad (\beta)$$
$$=MA : AC.$$

Thus C is seen to be on the parabola BA_2B_2 by the converse of Prop. 4 of the *Quadrature of the Parabola*.]

Also, if a perpendicular to AM be drawn from O, it will meet the parabola BA_2B_2 in two points, as Q_2, P_2. Let $Q_1Q_2Q_3D$ be drawn through Q_2 parallel to AM meeting the parabolas BAB_1, BA_3M respectively in Q_1, Q_3 and BM in D; and let $P_1P_2P_3$ be the corresponding parallel to AM through P_2. Let the tangents to the outer parabola at P_1, Q_1 meet MA produced in T_1, U respectively.

Then, since the three parabolic segments are similar and similarly situated, with their bases in the same straight line and having one common extremity, and since $Q_1Q_2Q_3D$ is a diameter common to all three segments, it follows that
$$Q_1Q_2 : Q_2Q_3=(B_2B_1 : B_1B)\cdot(BM : MB_2).$$

Now $\qquad\qquad B_2B_1 : B_1B=MM_2 : BM \qquad\qquad$ (dividing by 2)
$$=2:5, \qquad\qquad \text{by means of } (\beta) \text{ above.}$$

And $\qquad\qquad BM : MB_2=BM : (2BM_2-BM)$
$$=5:(6-5), \qquad\qquad \text{by means of } (\beta),$$
$$=5:1.$$

It follows that $\qquad\qquad Q_1Q_2 : Q_2Q_3=2:1,$

or $\qquad\qquad\qquad\qquad Q_1Q_2=2Q_2Q_3.\Big\}$

Similarly $\qquad\qquad\qquad P_1P_2=2P_2P_3.$

Also, since $\qquad\qquad MR=\tfrac{3}{2}CO=\tfrac{3}{4}p,$
$$AR=AM-MR$$
$$=AM-\tfrac{3}{4}p.$$

(ENUNCIATION)

If the segment of the paraboloid be placed in the fluid with its base entirely above the surface, then

(I.) *if*
$$(\textit{spec. gr. of solid}) : (\textit{spec. gr. of fluid}) \nless AR^2 : AM^2$$
$$[\nless (AM-\tfrac{3}{4}p)^2 : AM^2],$$
the solid will rest in the position in which its axis AM is vertical;

(II.) *if*
$$(\textit{spec. gr. of solid}) : (\textit{spec. gr. of fluid}) < AR^2 : AM^2$$
$$\text{but} > Q_1Q_3{}^2 : AM^2,$$
the solid will not rest with its base touching the surface of the fluid in one point only, but in such a position that its base does not touch the surface at any point and its axis makes with the surface an angle greater than U;

(III. *a*) *if*
$$(\textit{spec. gr. of solid}) : (\textit{spec. gr. of fluid}) = Q_1Q_3{}^2 : AM^2,$$
the solid will rest and remain in the position in which the base touches the surface of the fluid at one point only and the axis makes with the surface an angle equal to U;

(III. *b*) *if*
$$(\textit{spec. gr. of solid}) : (\textit{spec. gr. of fluid}) = P_1P_3{}^2 : AM^2,$$
the solid will rest with its base touching the surface of the fluid at one point only and with its axis inclined to the surface at an angle equal to T_1;

(IV.) *if*

$$(spec.\ gr.\ of\ solid) : (spec.\ gr.\ of\ fluid) > P_1P_3{}^2 : AM^2,$$
$$but < Q_1Q_3{}^2 : AM^2,$$

the solid will rest and remain in a position with its base more submerged;

(V.) *if*

$$(spec.\ gr.\ of\ solid) : (spec.\ gr.\ of\ fluid) < P_1P_3{}^2 : AM^2,$$

the solid will rest in a position in which its axis is inclined to the surface of the fluid at an angle less than T_1, but so that the base does not even touch the surface at one point.

(PROOF)

(I.) Since $AM > \frac{3}{4}p$, and

$$(spec.\ gr.\ of\ solid) : (spec.\ gr.\ of\ fluid) \nless (AM - \tfrac{3}{4}p)^2 : AM^2,$$

it follows, by Prop. 4, that the solid will be in stable equilibrium with its axis vertical.

(II.) In this case

$$(spec.\ gr.\ of\ solid) : (spec.\ gr.\ of\ fluid) < AR^2 : AM^2$$
$$but > Q_1Q_3{}^2 : AM^2.$$

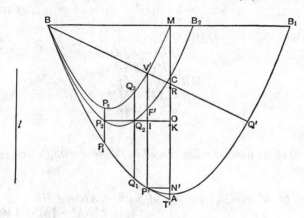

Suppose the ratio of the specific gravities to be equal to $l^2 : AM^2$, so that

$$l < AR\ but > Q_1Q_3.$$

Place $P'V'$ between the two parabolas BAB_1, BP_3Q_3M equal to l and parallel to AM; and let $P'V'$ meet the intermediate parabola in F'.

Then, by the same proof as before, we obtain

$$P'F' = 2F'V'.$$

Let $P'T'$, the tangent at P' to the outer parabola, meet MA in T', and let $P'N'$ be the ordinate at P'.

Join BV' and produce it to meet the outer parabola in Q'. Let OQ_2P_2 meet $P'V'$ in I.

Now, since, in two similar and similarly situated parabolic segments with bases BM, BB_1 in the same straight line, BV', BQ' are drawn making the same angle with the bases,

$$BV' : BQ' = BM : BB_1$$
$$= 1 : 2,$$

so that $\qquad\qquad\qquad\qquad BV' = V'Q'.$

Suppose the segment of the paraboloid placed in the fluid, as described, with

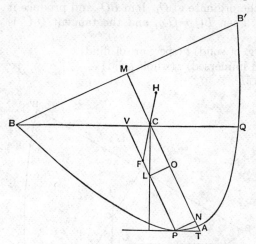

its axis inclined at an angle to the vertical, and with its base touching the surface at one point B only. Let the solid be cut by a plane through the axis and perpendicular to the surface of the fluid, and let the plane intersect the solid in the parabolic segment BAB' and the plane of the surface of the fluid in BQ.

Take the points C, O on AM as before described. Draw the tangent parallel to BQ touching the parabola in P and meeting AM in T; and let PV be the diameter bisecting BQ (i.e. the axis of the immersed portion of the solid).

Then $l^2 : AM^2 =$ (spec. gr. of solid) : (spec. gr. of fluid)
                        $=$ (portion immersed) : (whole solid)
                        $= PV^2 : AM^2$,
whence $P'V' = l = PV$.

Thus the segments in the two figures, namely $BP'Q'$, BPQ, are equal and similar.

Therefore $\angle PTN = \angle P'T'N'$.
Also $AT = AT'$, $AN = AN'$, $PN = P'N'$.

Now, in the first figure, $P'I < 2IV'$.

Therefore, if OL be perpendicular to PV in the second figure,
$$PL < 2LV.$$

Take F on LV so that $PF = 2FV$, i.e. so that F is the centre of gravity of the immersed portion of the solid. And C is the centre of gravity of the whole solid. Join FC and produce it to H, the centre of gravity of the portion above the surface.

Now, since $CO = \frac{1}{2}p$, CL is perpendicular to the tangent at P and to the surface of the fluid. Thus, as before, we prove that the solid will not rest with B touching the surface, but will turn in the direction of increasing the angle PTN.

Hence, in the position of rest, the axis AM must make with the surface of the fluid an angle greater than the angle U which the tangent at Q_1 makes with AM.

(III. a) In this case
        (spec. gr. of solid) : (spec. gr. of fluid) $= Q_1Q_3^2 : AM^2$.

Let the segment of the paraboloid be placed in the fluid so that its base nowhere touches the surface of the fluid, and its axis is inclined at an angle to the vertical.

Let the plane through AM perpendicular to the surface of the fluid cut the paraboloid in the parabola BAB' and the plane of the surface of the fluid in QQ'. Let PT be the tangent parallel to QQ', PV the diameter bisecting QQ', PN the ordinate at P.

Divide AM as before at C, O.

In the other figure let Q_1N' be the ordinate at Q_1. Join BQ_3 and produce it to meet the outer parabola in q. Then $BQ_3 = Q_3q$, and the tangent Q_1U is parallel to Bq. Now

$$Q_1Q_3{}^2 : AM^2 = (\text{spec. gr. of solid}) : (\text{spec. gr. of fluid})$$
$$= (\text{portion immersed}) : (\text{whole solid})$$
$$= PV^2 : AM^2.$$

Therefore $Q_1Q_3 = PV$; and the segments QPQ', BQ_1q of the paraboloid are equal in volume. And the base of one passes through B, while the base of the other passes through Q, a point nearer to A than B is.

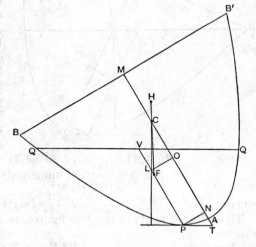

It follows that the angle between QQ' and BB' is less than the angle B_1Bq.

Therefore

$$\angle U < \angle PTN,$$

whence $AN' > AN$, and therefore

$$N'O(\text{or } Q_1Q_2) < PL,$$

where OL is perpendicular to PV.

It follows, since $Q_1Q_2 = 2Q_2Q_3$, that

$$PL > 2LV.$$

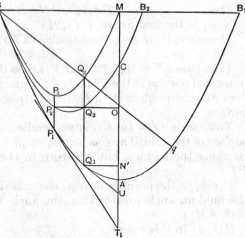

Therefore F, the centre of gravity of the immersed portion of the solid, is between P and L, while, as before, CL is perpendicular to the surface of the fluid.

Producing FC to H, the centre of gravity of the portion of the solid above the surface, we see that the solid must turn in the direction of diminishing the angle PTN until one point B of the base just touches the surface of the fluid.

When this is the case, we shall have a segment BPQ equal and similar to the segment BQ_1q, the angle PTN will be equal to the angle U, and AN will be equal to AN'.

Hence in this case $PL = 2LV$, and F, L coincide, so that F, C, H are all in one vertical straight line.

Thus the paraboloid will remain in the position in which one point B of the base touches the surface of the fluid, and the axis makes with the surface an angle equal to U.

(III. *b*) In the case where

(spec. gr. of solid) : (spec. gr. of fluid) $= P_1P_3{}^2 : AM^2$,

we can prove in the same way that, if the solid be placed in the fluid so that its axis is inclined to the vertical and its base does not anywhere touch the surface of the fluid, the solid will take up and rest in the position in which one point only of the base touches the surface, and the axis is inclined to it at an angle equal to T_1 (in the figure on p. 552).

(IV.) In this case

$$\text{(spec. gr. of solid)} : \text{(spec. gr. of fluid)} > P_1P_3{}^2 : AM^2$$
$$\text{but} < Q_1Q_3{}^2 : AM^2.$$

Suppose the ratio to be equal to $l^2 : AM^2$, so that l is greater than P_1P_3 but less than Q_1Q_3.

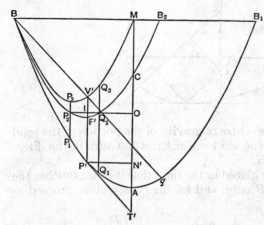

Place $P'V'$ between the parabolas BP_1Q_1, BP_3Q_3 so that $P'V'$ is equal to l and parallel to AM, and let $P'V'$ meet the intermediate parabola in F' and OQ_2P_2 in I.

Join BV' and produce it to meet the outer parabola in q.

Then, as before, $BV' = V'q$, and accordingly the tangent $P'T'$ at P' is parallel to Bq. Let $P'N'$ be the ordinate of P'.

1. Now let the segment be placed in the fluid, *first*, with its axis so inclined to the vertical that its base does not anywhere touch the surface of the fluid.

Let the plane through AM perpendicular to the surface of the fluid cut the paraboloid in the parabola BAB' and the plane of the surface of the fluid in

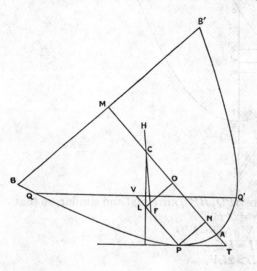

QQ'. Let PT be the tangent parallel to QQ', PV the diameter bisecting QQ'. Divide AM at C, O as before, and draw OL perpendicular to PV.

Then, as before, we have $PV = l = P'V'$.

Thus the segments $BP'q$, QPQ' of the paraboloid are equal in volume; and it follows that the angle between QQ' and BB' is less than the angle B_1Bq.

Therefore

$$\angle P'T'N' < \angle PTN,$$

and hence $AN' > AN$,

so that $NO > N'O$,

i.e. $PL > P'I$

$$> P'F', \textit{ a fortiori}.$$

Thus $PL > 2LV$, so that F, the centre of gravity of the immersed portion of the solid, is between L and P, while CL is perpendicular to the surface of the fluid.

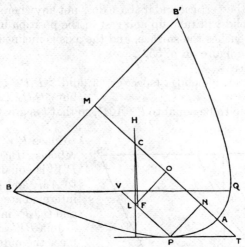

If then we produce FC to H, the centre of gravity of the portion of the solid above the surface, we prove that the solid will not rest but turn in the direction of diminishing the angle PTN.

2. Next let the paraboloid be so placed in the fluid that its base touches the surface of the fluid at one point B only, and let the construction proceed as before.

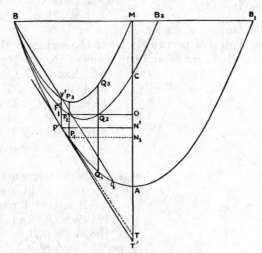

Then $PV = P'V'$, and the segments BPQ, $BP'q$ are equal and similar, so that
$$\angle PTN = \angle P'T'N'.$$
It follows that $AN = AN', \ NO = N'O,$
and therefore $P'I = PL,$
whence $PL > 2LV.$

Thus F again lies between P and L, and, as before, the paraboloid will turn in the direction of diminishing the angle PTN, i.e. so that the base will be more submerged.

(V.) In this case

(spec. gr. of solid) : (spec. gr. of fluid) $< P_1P_3{}^2 : AM^2.$

If then the ratio is equal to $l^2 : AM^2$, $l < P_1P_3$. Place $P'V'$ between the parabolas BP_1Q_1 and BP_3Q_3 equal in length to l and parallel to AM. Let $P'V'$ meet the intermediate parabola in F' and OP_2 in I.

Join BV' and produce it to meet the outer parabola in q. Then, as before, $BV' = V'q$, and the tangent $P'T'$ is parallel to Bq.

1. Let the paraboloid be so placed in the fluid that its base touches the surface at one point only.

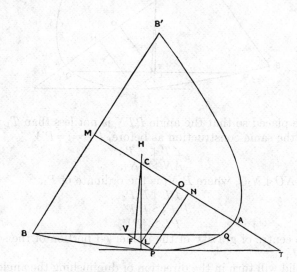

Let the plane through AM perpendicular to the surface of the fluid cut the paraboloid in the parabolic section BAB' and the plane of the surface of the fluid in BQ.

Making the usual construction, we find
$$PV = l = P'V',$$
and the segments BPQ, BP_1q are equal and similar.

Therefore $\angle PTN = \angle P'T'N',$
and $AN = AN', \ N'O = NO.$
Therefore $PL = P'I,$
whence it follows that $PL < 2LV.$

Thus F, the centre of gravity of the immersed portion of the solid, lies between L and V, while CL is perpendicular to the surface of the fluid.

Producing FC to H, the centre of gravity of the portion above the surface, we prove, as usual, that there will not be rest, but the solid will turn in the direction of increasing the angle PTN, so that the base will not anywhere touch the surface.

2. The solid will however rest in a position where its axis makes with the surface of the fluid an angle less than T_1.

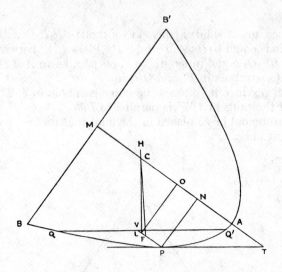

For let it be placed so that the angle PTN is not less than T_1.

Then, with the same construction as before, $PV = l = P'V'$.

And, since

$$\angle T \not< \angle T_1,$$
$$AN \not> AN_1,$$

and therefore $NO \not< N_1O$, where P_1N_1 is the ordinate of P_1.

Hence $PL \not< P_1P_2$.

But $P_1P_2 > P'F'$.

Therefore $PL > \frac{2}{3}PV$,

so that F, the centre of gravity of the immersed portion of the solid, lies between P and L.

Thus the solid will turn in the direction of diminishing the angle PTN until that angle becomes less than T_1.

BOOK OF LEMMAS

PROPOSITION 1

If two circles touch at A, and if BD, EF be parallel diameters in them, ADF is a straight line.

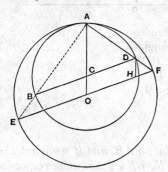

Let O, C be the centres of the circles, and let OC be joined and produced to A. Draw DH parallel to AO meeting OF in H.

Then, since $\qquad OH = CD = CA$,

and $\qquad\qquad\qquad OF = OA$,

we have, by subtraction, $\quad HF = CO = DH$.

Therefore $\qquad\qquad \angle HDF = \angle HFD$.

Thus both the triangles CAD, HDF are isosceles, and the third angles ACD, DHF in each are equal. Therefore the equal angles in each are equal to one another, and

$$\angle ADC = \angle DFH.$$

Add to each the angle CDF, and it follows that

$$\angle ADC + \angle CDF = \angle CDF + \angle DFH$$
$$= \text{(two right angles)}.$$

Hence ADF is a straight line.

The same proof applies if the circles touch externally.

PROPOSITION 2

Let AB be the diameter of a semicircle, and let the tangents to it at B and at any other point D on it meet in T. If now DE be drawn perpendicular to AB, and if AT, DE meet in F,

$$DF = FE.$$

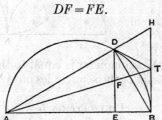

Produce AD to meet BT produced in H. Then the angle ADB in the semicircle is right; therefore the angle BDH is also right. And TB, TD are equal.

Therefore T is the centre of the semicircle on BH as diameter, which passes through D.

Hence $\qquad\qquad\qquad HT = TB$.

And, since DE, HB are parallel, it follows that $DF = FE$.

PROPOSITION 3

Let P be any point on a segment of a circle whose base is AB, and let PN be perpendicular to AB. Take D on AB so that AN = ND. If now PQ be an arc equal to the arc PA, and BQ be joined,

$$BQ, BD \text{ shall be equal.}$$

Join PA, PQ, PD, DQ.

Then, since the arcs PA, PQ are equal,
$$PA = PQ.$$

But, since $AN = ND$, and the angles at N are right,
$$PA = PD.$$

Therefore $\qquad PQ = PD,$

and $\qquad\qquad \angle PQD = \angle PDQ.$

Now, since A, P, Q, B are concyclic,
$$\angle PAD + \angle PQB = \text{(two right angles)},$$

whence $\qquad \angle PDA + \angle PQB = \text{(two right angles)}$
$$= \angle PDA + \angle PDB.$$

Therefore $\qquad\qquad \angle PQB = \angle PDB;$

and, since the parts, the angles PQD, PDQ, are equal,
$$\angle BQD = \angle BDQ,$$

and $\qquad\qquad\qquad BQ = BD.$

PROPOSITION 4

If AB be the diameter of a semicircle and N any point on AB, and if semicircles be described within the first semicircle and having AN, BN as diameters respectively, the figure included between the circumferences of the three semicircles is "what Archimedes called an ἄρβηλος";[1] and its area is equal to the circle on PN as diameter, where PN is perpendicular to AB and meets the original semicircle in P.

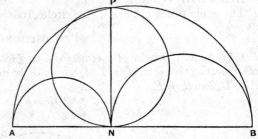

For
$$AB^2 = AN^2 + NB^2 + 2AN \cdot NB$$
$$= AN^2 + NB^2 + 2PN^2.$$

But circles (or semicircles) are to one another as the squares of their radii (or diameters).

Hence

(semicircle on AB) = (sum of semicircles on AN, NB) + 2(semicircle on PN).

That is, the circle on PN as diameter is equal to the difference between the semicircle on AB and the sum of the semicircles on AN, NB, i.e. is equal to the area of the ἄρβηλος.

PROPOSITION 5

Let AB be the diameter of a semicircle, C any point on AB, and CD perpendicular to it, and let semicircles be described within the first semicircle and having AC, CB as diameters. Then, if two circles be drawn touching CD on different sides and each touching two of the semicircles, the circles so drawn will be equal.

Let one of the circles touch CD at E, the semicircle on AB in F, and the semicircle on AC in G.

[1] ἄρβηλος is literally "a shoemaker's knife."

Draw the diameter EH of the circle, which will accordingly be perpendicular to CD and therefore parallel to AB.

Join FH, HA, and FE, EB. Then, by Prop. 1, FHA, FEB are both straight lines, since EH, AB are parallel.

For the same reason AGE, CGH are straight lines.

Let AF produced meet CD in D, and let AE produced meet the outer semi-circle in I. Join BI, ID.

Then, since the angles AFB, ACD are right, the straight lines AD, AB are such that the perpendiculars on each from the extremity of the other meet in the point E. Therefore, by the properties of triangles, AE is perpendicular to the line joining B to D.

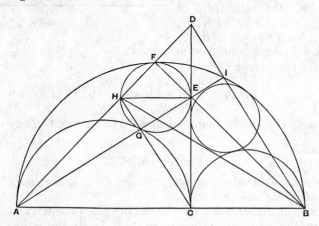

But AE is perpendicular to BI.

Therefore BID is a straight line.

Now, since the angles at G, I are right, CH is parallel to BD.

Therefore $AB : BC = AD : DH$
                                   $= AC : HE,$
so that $AC \cdot CB = AB \cdot HE.$

In like manner, if d is the diameter of the other circle, we can prove that
$$AC \cdot CB = AB \cdot d.$$
Therefore $d = HE$, and the circles are equal.

PROPOSITION 6

Let AB, the diameter of a semicircle, be divided at C so that $AC = \frac{3}{2}CB$ [or in any ratio]. Describe semicircles within the first semicircle and on AC, CB as diameters, and suppose a circle drawn touching all three semicircles. If GH be the diameter of this circle, to find the relation between GH and AB.

Let GH be that diameter of the circle which is parallel to AB, and let the circle touch the semicircles on AB, AC, CB in D, E, F respectively.

Join AG, GD and BH, HD. Then, by Prop. 1, AGD, BHD are straight lines.

For a like reason AEH, BFG are straight lines, as also are CEG, CFH.

Let AD meet the semicircle on AC in I, and let BD meet the semicircle on CB in K. Join CI, CK meeting AE, BF respectively in L, M, and let GL, HM produced meet AB in N, P respectively.

Now, in the triangle AGC, the perpendiculars from A, C on the opposite sides meet in L. Therefore, by the properties of triangles, GLN is perpendicular to AC.

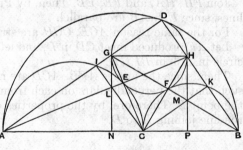

Similarly HMP is perpendicular to CB.

Again, since the angles at I, K, D are right, CK is parallel to AD, and CI to BD.

Therefore $AC : CB = AL : LH$
$$= AN : NP,$$
and $\qquad BC : CA = BM : MG$
$$= BP : PN.$$

Hence $\quad AN : NP = NP : PB$, or AN, NP, PB are in continued proportion.

Now, in the case where $\qquad AC = \frac{3}{2}CB$,
$$AN = \frac{3}{2}NP = \frac{9}{4}PB,$$
whence $\qquad BP : PN : NA : AB = 4 : 6 : 9 : 19$.

Therefore $\qquad GH = NP = \frac{6}{19}AB$.

And similarly GH can be found when $AC : CB$ is equal to any other given ratio.

PROPOSITION 7

If circles be circumscribed about and inscribed in a square, the circumscribed circle is double of the inscribed circle.

For the ratio of the circumscribed to the inscribed circle is equal to that of the square on the diagonal to the square itself, i.e. to the ratio $2 : 1$.

PROPOSITION 8

If AB be any chord of a circle whose centre is O, and if AB be produced to C so that BC is equal to the radius; if further CO meet the circle in D and be produced to meet the circle a second time in E, the arc AE will be equal to three times the arc BD.

Draw the chord EF parallel to AB, and join OB, OF.

Then, since the angles OEF, OFE are equal,
$$\angle COF = 2 \angle OEF$$
$$= 2 \angle BCO, \text{ by parallels,}$$
$$= 2 \angle BOD, \text{ since } BC = BO.$$

Therefore
$$\angle BOF = 3 \angle BOD,$$
so that the arc BF is equal to three times the arc BD.

Hence the arc AE, which is equal to the arc BF, is equal to three times the arc BD.

PROPOSITION 9

If in a circle two chords AB, CD which do not pass through the centre intersect at right angles, then

$$(\text{arc } AD) + (\text{arc } CB) = (\text{arc } AC) + (\text{arc } DB).$$

Let the chords intersect at O, and draw the diameter EF parallel to AB intersecting CD in H. EF will thus bisect CD at right angles in H, and

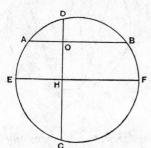

$$(\text{arc } ED) = (\text{arc } EC).$$

Also EDF, ECF are semicircles, while

$$(\text{arc } ED) = (\text{arc } EA) + (\text{arc } AD).$$

Therefore

(sum of arcs CF, EA, AD) = (arc of a semicircle).

And the arcs AE, BF are equal.

Therefore

$$(\text{arc } CB) + (\text{arc } AD) = (\text{arc of a semicircle}).$$

Hence the remainder of the circumference, the sum of the arcs AC, DB, is also equal to a semicircle; and the proposition is proved.

PROPOSITION 10

Suppose that TA, TB are two tangents to a circle, while TC cuts it. Let BD be the chord through B parallel to TC, and let AD meet TC in E. Then, if EH be drawn perpendicular to BD, it will bisect it in H.

Let AB meet TC in F, and join BE.

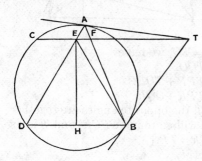

Now the angle TAB is equal to the angle in the alternate segment, i.e.

$$\angle TAB = \angle ADB$$
$$= \angle AET, \text{ by parallels.}$$

Hence the triangles EAT, AFT have one angle equal and another (at T) common. They are therefore similar, and

$$FT : AT = AT : ET.$$

Therefore $\quad ET \cdot TF = TA^2$
$$= TB^2.$$

It follows that the triangles EBT, BFT are similar.

Therefore $\qquad\qquad \angle TEB = \angle TBF$
$$= \angle TAB.$$

But the angle TEB is equal to the angle EBD, and the angle TAB was proved equal to the angle EDB.

Therefore $\qquad\qquad \angle EDB = \angle EBD.$

And the angles at H are right angles.

It follows that $\qquad\qquad BH = HD.$

PROPOSITION 11

If two chords AB, CD in a circle intersect at right angles in a point O, not being the centre, then

$$AO^2 + BO^2 + CO^2 + DO^2 = (diameter)^2.$$

Draw the diameter CE, and join AC, CB, AD, BE.

Then the angle CAO is equal to the angle CEB in the same segment, and the angles AOC, EBC are right; therefore the triangles AOC, EBC are similar, and

$$\angle ACO = \angle ECB.$$

It follows that the subtended arcs, and therefore the chords AD, BE, are equal.

Thus
$$(AO^2+DO^2)+(BO^2+CO^2)=AD^2+BC^2$$
$$=BE^2+BC^2$$
$$=CE^2.$$

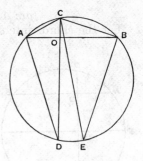

PROPOSITION 12

If AB be the diameter of a semicircle, and TP, TQ the tangents to it from any point T, and if AQ, BP be joined meeting in R, then TR is perpendicular to AB.

Let TR produced meet AB in M, and join PA, QB.

Since the angle APB is right,
$$\angle PAB+\angle PBA = \text{(a right angle)}$$
$$=\angle AQB.$$

Add to each side the angle RBQ, and
$$\angle PAB+\angle QBA = \text{(exterior)}\ \angle PRQ.$$

But
$$\angle TPR = \angle PAB,\ \text{and}\ \angle TQR = \angle QBA,$$
in the alternate segments;

therefore $\angle TPR+\angle TQR = \angle PRQ.$

It follows from this that
$$TP=TQ=TR.$$

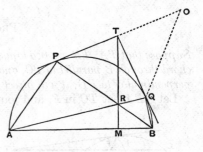

[For, if PT be produced to O so that $TO=TQ$, we have
$$\angle TOQ = \angle TQO.$$

And, by hypothesis, $\angle PRQ = \angle TPR+TQR.$

By addition, $\angle POQ+\angle PRQ = \angle TPR+OQR.$

It follows that, in the quadrilateral $OPRQ$, the opposite angles are together equal to two right angles. Therefore a circle will go round $OPQR$, and T is its centre, because $TP=TO=TQ$. Therefore $TR=TP$.]

Thus $\angle TRP = \angle TPR = \angle PAM.$

Adding to each the angle PRM,
$$\angle PAM+\angle PRM = \angle TRP+\angle PRM$$
$$= \text{(two right angles)}.$$

Therefore $\angle APR+\angle AMR = \text{(two right angles)},$

whence $\angle AMR = \text{(a right angle)}.$

PROPOSITION 13

If a diameter AB of a circle meet any chord CD, not a diameter, in E, and if AM, BN be drawn perpendicular to CD, then

$$CN=DM.$$

Let O be the centre of the circle, and OH perpendicular to CD. Join BM, and produce HO to meet BM in K.

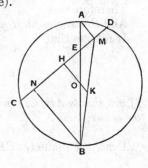

Then $CH=HD.$

And, by parallels, since $\qquad BO=OA,$
$\qquad\qquad\qquad\qquad\qquad BK=KM.$
Therefore $\qquad\qquad\qquad NH=HM.$
Accordingly $\qquad\qquad\quad CN=DM.$

PROPOSITION 14

Let ACB be a semicircle on AB as diameter, and let AD, BE be equal lengths measured along AB from A, B respectively. On AD, BE as diameters describe semicircles on the side towards C, and on DE as diameter a semicircle on the opposite side. Let the perpendicular to AB through O, the centre of the first semicircle, meet the opposite semicircles in C, F respectively.

Then shall the area of the figure bounded by the circumferences of all the semicircles be equal to the area of the circle on CF as diameter.

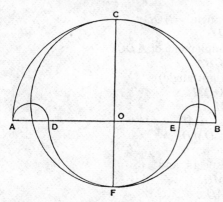

By Eucl. ɪɪ. 10, since ED is bisected at O and produced to A,
$$EA^2+AD^2=2(EO^2+OA^2),$$
and $\qquad CF=OA+OE=EA.$
Therefore
$$AB^2+DE^2=4(EO^2+OA^2)=$$
$$2(CF^2+AD^2).$$

But circles (and therefore semicircles) are to one another as the squares on their radii (or diameters).
Therefore
(sum of semicircles on AB, DE)
$=$(circle on CF)$+$(sum of semicircles on AD, BE).

Therefore
$\qquad$(area of "salinon")$=$(area of circle on CF as diam.).

PROPOSITION 15

Let AB be the diameter of a circle, AC a side of an inscribed regular pentagon, D the middle point of the arc AC. Join CD and produce it to meet BA produced in E; join AC, DB meeting in F, and draw FM perpendicular to AB. Then
$$EM=(radius\ of\ circle).$$

Let O be the centre of the circle, and join DA, DM, DO, CB.

Now $\qquad\qquad\qquad\qquad \angle ABC=\frac{2}{5}\text{(right angle)},$
and $\qquad\qquad \angle ABD=\angle DBC=\frac{1}{5}\text{(right angle)},$
whence $\qquad\qquad\qquad \angle AOD=\frac{2}{5}\text{(right angle)}.$

Further, the triangles FCB, FMB are equal in all respects.

Therefore, in the triangles DCB, DMB, the sides CB, MB being equal and BD common, while the angles CBD, MBD are equal,
$$\angle BCD=\angle BMD=\tfrac{6}{5}\text{(right angle)}.$$

But $\qquad\qquad \angle BCD+\angle BAD=\text{(two right angles)}$
$$=\angle BAD+\angle DAE$$
$$=\angle BMD+\angle DMA,$$
so that $\qquad\qquad\qquad \angle DAE=\angle BCD,$
and $\qquad\qquad\qquad\qquad \angle BAD=\angle AMD.$
Therefore $\qquad\qquad\qquad AD=MD.$

Now, in the triangle DMO,
$$\angle MOD = \tfrac{2}{5}(\text{right angle}),$$
$$\angle DMO = \tfrac{6}{5}(\text{right angle}).$$

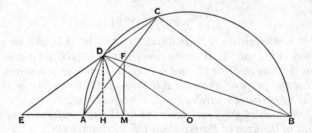

Therefore $\angle ODM = \tfrac{2}{5}(\text{right angle}) = AOD;$
whence $OM = MD.$
    Again $\angle EDA = (\text{supplement of } ADC)$
$$= \angle CBA$$
$$= \tfrac{2}{5}(\text{right angle})$$
$$= \angle ODM.$$
Therefore, in the triangles EDA, ODM,
$$\angle EDA = \angle ODM,$$
$$\angle EAD = \angle OMD,$$
and the sides AD, MD are equal.
    Hence the triangles are equal in all respects, and
$$EA = MO.$$
Therefore $EM = AO.$

Moreover $DE = DO$; and it follows that, since DE is equal to the side of an
inscribed hexagon, and DC is the side of an inscribed decagon, EC is divided
at D in extreme and mean ratio [i.e. $EC : ED = ED : DC$]; "and this is proved
in the book of the *Elements*." [Eucl. XIII. 9: "If the side of the hexagon and the
side of the decagon inscribed in the same circle be put together, the whole
straight line is divided in extreme and mean ratio, and the greater segment is
the side of the hexagon."]

THE METHOD TREATING OF MECHANICAL PROBLEMS

"Archimedes to Eratosthenes greeting.

"I sent you on a former occasion some of the theorems discovered by me, merely writing out the enunciations and inviting you to discover the proofs, which at the moment I did not give. The enunciations of the theorems which I sent were as follows:

1. "If in a right prism with a parallelogrammic base a cylinder be inscribed which has its bases in the opposite parallelograms,[1] and its sides [i.e. four generators] on the remaining planes (faces) of the prism, and if through the centre of the circle which is the base of the cylinder and (through) one side of the square in the plane opposite to it a plane be drawn, the plane so drawn will cut off from the cylinder a segment which is bounded by two planes and the surface of the cylinder, one of the two planes being the plane which has been drawn and the other the plane in which the base of the cylinder is, and the surface being that which is between the said planes; and the segment cut off from the cylinder is one sixth part of the whole prism.

2. "If in a cube a cylinder be inscribed which has its bases in the opposite parallelograms[2] and touches with its surface the remaining four planes (faces), and if there also be inscribed in the same cube another cylinder which has its bases in other parallelograms and touches with its surface the remaining four planes (faces), then the figure bounded by the surfaces of the cylinders, which is within both cylinders, is two-thirds of the whole cube.

"Now these theorems differ in character from those communicated before; for we compared the figures then in question, conoids and spheroids and segments of them, in respect to size, with figures of cones and cylinders: but none of those figures have yet been found to be equal to a solid figure bounded by planes; whereas each of the present figures bounded by two planes and surfaces of cylinders is found to be equal to one of the solid figures which are bounded by planes. The proofs then of these theorems I have written in this book and now send to you. Seeing moreover in you, as I say, an earnest student, a man of considerable eminence in philosophy, and an admirer [of mathematical inquiry], I thought fit to write out for you and explain in detail in the same book the peculiarity of a certain method, by which it will be possible for you to get a start to enable you to investigate some of the problems in mathematics by means of mechanics. This procedure is, I am persuaded, no less useful even for the proof of the theorems themselves; for certain things first became clear to me by a mechanical method, although they had to be demonstrated by geom-

[1]The parallelograms are apparently *squares*.
[2]i.e. squares.

569

etry afterwards because their investigation by the said method did not furnish an actual demonstration. But it is of course easier, when we have previously acquired, by the method, some knowledge of the questions, to supply the proof than it is to find it without any previous knowledge. This is a reason why, in the case of the theorems the proof of which Eudoxus was the first to discover, namely that the cone is a third part of the cylinder, and the pyramid of the prism, having the same base and equal height, we should give no small share of the credit to Democritus who was the first to make the assertion with regard to the said figure though he did not prove it. I am myself in the position of having first made the discovery of the theorem now to be published [by the method indicated], and I deem it necessary to expound the method partly because I have already spoken of it and I do not want to be thought to have uttered vain words, but equally because I am persuaded that it will be of no little service to mathematics; for I apprehend that some, either of my contemporaries or of my successors, will, by means of the method when once established, be able to discover other theorems in addition, which have not yet occurred to me.

"First then I will set out the very first theorem which became known to me by means of mechanics, namely that

"*Any segment of a section of a right-angled cone (i.e. a parabola) is four-thirds of the triangle which has the same base and equal height,*

and after this I will give each of the other theorems investigated by the same method. Then, at the end of the book, I will give the geometrical" [proofs of the propositions]...

[I premise the following propositions which I shall use in the course of the work.]

1. "If from [one magnitude another magnitude be subtracted which has not the same centre of gravity, the centre of gravity of the remainder is found by] producing [the straight line joining the centres of gravity of the whole magnitude and of the subtracted part in the direction of the centre of gravity of the whole] and cutting off from it a length which has to the distance between the said centres of gravity the ratio which the weight of the subtracted magnitude has to the weight of the remainder." [*On the Equilibrium of Planes*, I. 8]

2. "If the centres of gravity of any number of magnitudes whatever be on the same straight line, the centre of gravity of the magnitude made up of all of them will be on the same straight line." [Cf. *Ibid*. I. 5]

3. "The centre of gravity of any straight line is the point of bisection of the straight line." [Cf. *Ibid*. I. 4]

4. "The centre of gravity of any triangle is the point in which the straight lines drawn from the angular points of the triangle to the middle points of the (opposite) sides cut one another." [*Ibid*. I. 13, 14]

5. "The centre of gravity of any parallelogram is the point in which the diagonals meet." [*Ibid*. I. 10]

6. "The centre of gravity of a circle is the point which is also the centre [of the circle]."

7. "The centre of gravity of any cylinder is the point of bisection of the axis."

8. "The centre of gravity of any cone is [the point which divides its axis so that] the portion [adjacent to the vertex is] triple [of the portion adjacent to the base]."

[All these propositions have already been] proved.[1] [Besides these I require also the following proposition, which is easily proved:

If in two series of magnitudes those of the first series are, in order, proportional to those of the second series and further], "the magnitudes [of the first series], either all or some of them, are in any ratio whatever [to those of a third series], and if the magnitudes of the second series are in the same ratio to the corresponding magnitudes [of a fourth series], then the sum of the magnitudes of the first series has to the sum of the selected magnitudes of the third series the same ratio which the sum of the magnitudes of the second series has to the sum of the (correspondingly) selected magnitudes of the fourth series." [*On Conoids and Spheroids*, Prop. 1.]

PROPOSITION 1

Let ABC be a segment of a parabola bounded by the straight line AC and the parabola ABC, and let D be the middle point of AC. Draw the straight line DBE parallel to the axis of the parabola and join AB, BC.

Then shall the segment ABC be $\frac{4}{3}$ of the triangle ABC.

From A draw AKF parallel to DE, and let the tangent to the parabola at C meet DBE in E and AKF in F. Produce CB to meet AF in K, and again produce CK to H, making KH equal to CK.

Consider CH as the bar of a balance, K being its middle point.

Let MO be any straight line parallel to ED, and let it meet CF, CK, AC in M, N, O and the curve in P.

Now, since CE is a tangent to the parabola and CD the semi-ordinate,
$$EB = BD;$$
"for this is proved in the Elements [of Conics]."[2]

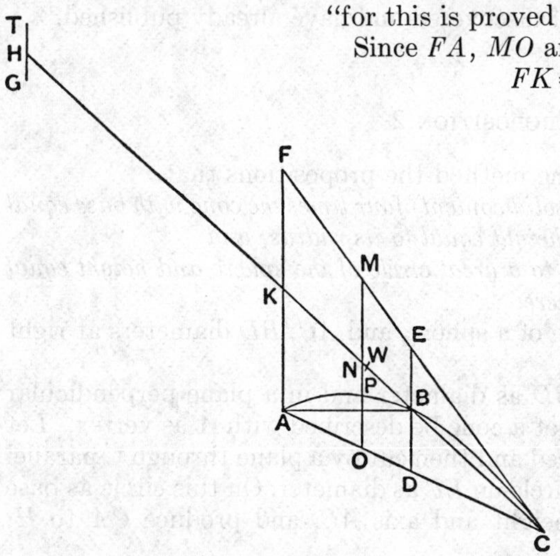

Since FA, MO are parallel to ED, it follows that
$$FK = KA, \quad MN = NO.$$

Now, by the property of the parabola, "proved in a lemma,"
$$MO : OP = CA : AO \text{ [Cf. } Quad-rature of Parabola, \text{ Prop. 5]}$$
$$= CK : KN$$
[Eucl. VI. 2]
$$= HK : KN.$$

Take a straight line TG equal to OP, and place it with its centre of gravity at H, so that $TH = HG$; then, since N is the centre of gravity of the straight line MO, and
$$MO : TG = HK : KN,$$
it follows that TG at H and MO at N will be in equilibrium about K. [*On the Equilibrium of Planes*, I. 6, 7]

---

[1] The problem of finding the centre of gravity of a cone is not solved in any extant work of Archimedes.

[2] i.e. the works on conics by Aristaeus and Euclid.

Similarly, for all other straight lines parallel to DE and meeting the arc of the parabola, (1) the portion intercepted between FC, AC with its middle point on KC and (2) a length equal to the intercept between the curve and AC placed with its centre of gravity at H will be in equilibrium about K.

Therefore K is the centre of gravity of the whole system consisting (1) of all the straight lines as MO intercepted between FC, AC and placed as they actually are in the figure and (2) of all the straight lines placed at H equal to the straight lines as PO intercepted between the curve and AC.

And, since the triangle CFA is made up of all the parallel lines like MO, and the segment CBA is made up of all the straight lines like PO within the curve,

it follows that the triangle, placed where it is in the figure, is in equilibrium about K with the segment CBA placed with its centre of gravity at H.

Divide KC at W so that $CK = 3KW$;

then W is the centre of gravity of the triangle ACF; "for this is proved in the books on equilibrium" (ἐν τοῖς ἰσορροπικοῖς).

[Cf. *On the Equilibrium of Planes* I. 15]

Therefore $\triangle ACF$: (segment ABC) $= HK : KW$
                                                    $= 3 : 1$.

Therefore   segment $ABC = \frac{1}{3} \triangle ACF$.

But $\triangle ACF = 4 \triangle ABC$.

Therefore   segment $ABC = \frac{4}{3} \triangle ABC$.

"Now the fact here stated is not actually demonstrated by the argument used; but that argument has given a sort of indication that the conclusion is true. Seeing then that the theorem is not demonstrated, but at the same time suspecting that the conclusion is true, we shall have recourse to the geometrical demonstration which I myself discovered and have already published."

PROPOSITION 2

We can investigate by the same method the propositions that

(1) *Any sphere is (in respect of solid content) four times the cone with base equal to a great circle of the sphere and height equal to its radius; and*

(2) *the cylinder with base equal to a great circle of the sphere and height equal to the diameter is $1\frac{1}{2}$ times the sphere.*

(1) Let $ABCD$ be a great circle of a sphere, and AC, BD diameters at right angles to one another.

Let a circle be drawn about BD as diameter and in a plane perpendicular to AC, and on this circle as base let a cone be described with A as vertex. Let the surface of this cone be produced and then cut by a plane through C parallel to its base; the section will be a circle on EF as diameter. On this circle as base let a cylinder be erected with height and axis AC, and produce CA to H, making AH equal to CA.

Let CH be regarded as the bar of a balance, A being its middle point.

Draw any straight line MN in the plane of the circle $ABCD$ and parallel to BD. Let MN meet the circle in O, P, the diameter AC in S, and the straight lines AE, AF in Q, R respectively. Join AO.

Through MN draw a plane at right angles to AC;

this plane will cut the cylinder in a circle with diameter MN, the sphere in a circle with diameter OP, and the cone in a circle with diameter QR.

Now, since $MS = AC$, and $QS = AS$,
$$MS \cdot SQ = CA \cdot AS$$
$$= AO^2$$
$$= OS^2 + SQ^2.$$
And, since $HA = AC$,
$$HA : AS = CA : AS$$
$$= MS : SQ$$
$$= MS^2 : MS \cdot SQ$$
$$= MS^2 : (OS^2 + SQ^2),$$
from above,
$$= MN^2 : (OP^2 + QR^2)$$
$$= (\text{circle, diam. } MN) : (\text{circle, diam. } OP$$
$$+ \text{circle, diam. } QR).$$

That is,

$HA : AS = (\text{circle in cylinder}) : (\text{circle in sphere} + \text{circle in cone}).$

Therefore the circle in the cylinder, placed where it is, is in equilibrium, about A, with the circle in the sphere together with the circle in the cone, if both the latter circles are placed with their centres of gravity at H.

Similarly for the three corresponding sections made by a plane perpendicular to AC and passing through any other straight line in the parallelogram LF parallel to EF.

If we deal in the same way with all the sets of three circles in which planes perpendicular to AC cut the cylinder, the sphere and the cone, and which make up those solids respectively, it follows that the cylinder, in the place where it is, will be in equilibrium about A with the sphere and the cone together, when both are placed with their centres of gravity at H.

Therefore, since K is the centre of gravity of the cylinder,
$$HA : AK = (\text{cylinder}) : (\text{sphere} + \text{cone } AEF).$$

But $HA = 2AK$;

therefore $\text{cylinder} = 2(\text{sphere} + \text{cone } AEF).$

Now $\text{cylinder} = 3(\text{cone } AEF);$ [Eucl. XII. 10]

therefore $\text{cone } AEF = 2(\text{sphere}).$

But, since $EF = 2BD$,
$$\text{cone } AEF = 8(\text{cone } ABD);$$

therefore $\text{sphere} = 4(\text{cone } ABD).$

(2) Through B, D draw VBW, XDY parallel to AC;

and imagine a cylinder which has AC for axis and the circles on VX, WY as diameters for bases.

Then   cylinder $VY = 2$(cylinder VD)

$$= 6(\text{cone } ABD) \qquad [\text{Eucl. xii. 10}]$$

$$= \tfrac{3}{2}(\text{sphere}), \text{ from above.}$$

Q.E.D.

"From this theorem, to the effect that a sphere is four times as great as the cone with a great circle of the sphere as base and with height equal to the radius of the sphere, I conceived the notion that the surface of any sphere is four times as great as a great circle in it; for, judging from the fact that any circle is equal to a triangle with base equal to the circumference and height equal to the radius of the circle, I apprehended that, in like manner, any sphere is equal to a cone with base equal to the surface of the sphere and height equal to the radius."

PROPOSITION 3

By this method we can also investigate the theorem that

A cylinder with base equal to the greatest circle in a spheroid and height equal to the axis of the spheroid is $1\tfrac{1}{2}$ times the spheroid;

and, when this is established, it is plain that

If any spheroid be cut by a plane through the centre and at right angles to the axis, the half of the spheroid is double of the cone which has the same base and the same axis as the segment (i.e. the half of the spheroid).

Let a plane through the axis of a spheroid cut its surface in the ellipse $ABCD$, the diameters (i.e. axes) of which are AC, BD; and let K be the centre.

Draw a circle about BD as diameter and in a plane perpendicular to AC; imagine a cone with this circle as base and A as vertex produced and cut by a plane through C parallel to its base; the section will be a circle in a plane at right angles to AC and about EF as diameter.

Imagine a cylinder with the latter circle as base and axis AC; produce CA to H, making AH equal to CA.

Let HC be regarded as the bar of a balance, A being its middle point.

In the parallelogram LF draw any straight line MN parallel to EF meeting the ellipse in O, P and AE, AF, AC in Q, R, S respectively.

If now a plane be drawn through MN at right angles to AC, it will cut the cylinder in a circle with diameter MN, the spheroid in a circle with diameter OP, and the cone in a circle with diameter QR.

Since $HA = AC$,
$$HA : AS = CA : AS$$
$$= EA : AQ$$
$$= MS : SQ.$$

Therefore
$$HA : AS = MS^2 : MS \cdot SQ.$$

But, by the property of the ellipse,
$$AS \cdot SC : SO^2 = AK^2 : KB^2$$
$$= AS^2 : SQ^2;$$
therefore
$$SQ^2 : SO^2 = AS^2 : AS \cdot SC$$
$$= SQ^2 : SQ \cdot QM,$$
and accordingly
$$SO^2 = SQ \cdot QM.$$

Add SQ^2 to each side, and we have
$$SO^2 + SQ^2 = SQ \cdot SM.$$

Therefore, from above, we have
$$HA : AS = MS^2 : (SO^2 + SQ^2)$$
$$= MN^2 : (OP^2 + QR^2)$$
$$= \text{(circle, diam. } MN) : \text{(circle, diam. } OP + \text{circle, diam. } QR).$$

That is,
$$HA : AS = \text{(circle in cylinder)} : \text{(circle in spheroid} + \text{circle in cone).}$$

Therefore the circle in the cylinder, in the place where it is, is in equilibrium, about A, with the circle in the spheroid and the circle in the cone together, if both the latter circles are placed with their centres of gravity at H.

Similarly for the three corresponding sections made by a plane perpendicular to AC and passing through any other straight line in the parallelogram LF parallel to EF.

If we deal in the same way with all the sets of three circles in which planes perpendicular to AC cut the cylinder, the spheroid and the cone, and which make up those figures respectively, it follows that the cylinder, in the place where it is, will be in equilibrium about A with the spheroid and the cone together, when both are placed with their centres of gravity at H.

Therefore, since K is the centre of gravity of the cylinder,
$$HA : AK = \text{(cylinder)} : \text{(spheroid} + \text{cone } AEF).$$

But $HA = 2AK$;
therefore   cylinder $= 2(\text{spheroid} + \text{cone } AEF)$.

And   cylinder $= 3(\text{cone } AEF)$;   [Eucl. xii. 10]
therefore   cone $AEF = 2(\text{spheroid})$.

But, since $EF = 2BD$,
            cone $AEF = 8(\text{cone } ABD)$;
therefore   spheroid $= 4(\text{cone } ABD)$,
and   half the spheroid $= 2(\text{cone } ABD)$.

Through B, D draw VBW, XDY parallel to AC;
and imagine a cylinder which has AC for axis and the circles on VX, WY as diameters for bases.

Then   cylinder $VY = 2(\text{cylinder } VD)$
$$= 6(\text{cone } ABD)$$
$$= \tfrac{3}{2}(\text{spheroid}), \text{ from above.}   \text{Q.E.D.}$$

Proposition 4

Any segment of a right-angled conoid (i.e. a paraboloid of revolution) cut off by a plane at right angles to the axis is $1\frac{1}{2}$ times the cone which has the same base and the same axis as the segment.

This can be investigated by our method, as follows.

Let a paraboloid of revolution be cut by a plane through the axis in the parabola BAC;

and let it also be cut by another plane at right angles to the axis and intersecting the former plane in BC. Produce DA, the axis of the segment, to H, making HA equal to AD.

Imagine that HD is the bar of a balance, A being its middle point.

The base of the segment being the circle on BC as diameter and in a plane perpendicular to AD,

imagine (1) a cone drawn with the latter circle as base and A as vertex, and (2) a cylinder with the same circle as base and AD as axis.

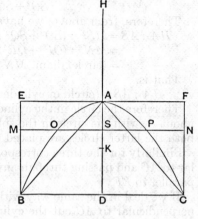

In the parallelogram EC let any straight line MN be drawn parallel to BC, and through MN let a plane be drawn at right angles to AD; this plane will cut the cylinder in a circle with diameter MN and the paraboloid in a circle with diameter OP.

Now, BAC being a parabola and BD, OS ordinates,

$$DA : AS = BD^2 : OS^2,$$

or $\qquad HA : AS = MS^2 : SO^2.$

Therefore

$$HA : AS = (\text{circle, rad. } MS) : (\text{circle, rad. } OS)$$
$$= (\text{circle in cylinder}) : (\text{circle in paraboloid}).$$

Therefore the circle in the cylinder, in the place where it is, will be in equilibrium about A with the circle in the paraboloid, if the latter is placed with its centre of gravity at H.

Similarly for the two corresponding circular sections made by a plane perpendicular to AD and passing through any other straight line in the parallelogram which is parallel to BC.

Therefore, as usual, if we take all the circles making up the whole cylinder and the whole segment and treat them in the same way, we find that the cylinder, in the place where it is, is in equilibrium about A with the segment placed with its centre of gravity at H.

If K is the middle point of AD, K is the centre of gravity of the cylinder; therefore $\qquad HA : AK = (\text{cylinder}) : (\text{segment}).$

Therefore $\qquad$ cylinder $= 2(\text{segment}).$

And $\qquad$ cylinder $= 3(\text{cone } ABC);$ $\qquad\qquad$ [Eucl. XII. 10]

therefore $\qquad$ segment $= \frac{3}{2}(\text{cone } ABC).$

PROPOSITION 5

The centre of gravity of a segment of a right-angled conoid (i.e. a paraboloid of revolution) cut off by a plane at right angles to the axis is on the straight line which is the axis of the segment, and divides the said straight line in such a way that the portion of it adjacent to the vertex is double of the remaining portion.

This can be investigated by the method, as follows.

Let a paraboloid of revolution be cut by a plane through the axis in the parabola BAC;
and let it also be cut by another plane at right angles to the axis and intersecting the former plane in BC.

Produce DA, the axis of the segment, to H, making HA equal to AD; and imagine DH to be the bar of a balance, its middle point being A.

The base of the segment being the circle on BC as diameter and in a plane perpendicular to AD,
imagine a cone with this circle as base and A as vertex, so that AB, AC are generators of the cone.

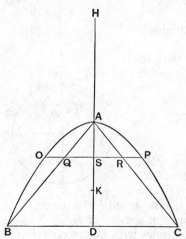

In the parabola let any double ordinate OP be drawn meeting AB, AD, AC in Q, S, R respectively.

Now, from the property of the parabola,
$$BD^2 : OS^2 = DA : AS$$
$$= BD : QS$$
$$= BD^2 : BD \cdot QS.$$

Therefore $\quad OS^2 = BD \cdot QS,$

or $\quad\quad\quad BD : OS = OS : QS,$

whence $\quad BD : QS = OS^2 : QS^2.$

But $\quad\quad\quad BD : QS = AD : AS$
$$= HA : AS.$$

Therefore $HA : AS = OS^2 : QS^2$
$$= OP^2 : QR^2.$$

If now through OP a plane be drawn at right angles to AD, this plane cuts the paraboloid in a circle with diameter OP and the cone in a circle with diameter QR.

We see therefore that $HA : AS = $ (circle, diam. OP) : (circle, diam. QR)
$$= \text{(circle in paraboloid)} : \text{(circle in cone)};$$
and the circle in the paraboloid, in the place where it is, is in equilibrium about A with the circle in the cone placed with its centre of gravity at H.

Similarly for the two corresponding circular sections made by a plane perpendicular to AD and passing through any other ordinate of the parabola.

Dealing therefore in the same way with all the circular sections which make up the whole of the segment of the paraboloid and the cone respectively, we see that the segment of the paraboloid, in the place where it is, is in equilibrium about A with the cone placed with its centre of gravity at H.

Now, since A is the centre of gravity of the whole system as placed, and the centre of gravity of part of it, namely the cone, as placed, is at H, the centre of gravity of the rest, namely the segment, is at a point K on HA produced such that $\quad\quad\quad HA : AK = $ (segment) : (cone).

But $\quad\quad\quad\quad\quad$ segment $= \frac{3}{2}$(cone). $\quad\quad\quad\quad\quad\quad\quad$ [Prop. 4]

Therefore $\qquad\qquad HA = \frac{3}{2}AK$;

that is, K divides AD in such a way that $AK = 2KD$.

PROPOSITION 6

*The centre of gravity of any hemisphere [is on the straight line which] is its axis,
and divides the said straight line in such a way that the portion of it adjacent to the
surface of the hemisphere has to the remaining portion the ratio which 5 has to 3.*

Let a sphere be cut by a plane through its centre in the circle $ABCD$;
let AC, BD be perpendicular diameters of this circle,
and through BD let a plane be drawn at right angles to AC.

The latter plane will cut the sphere in a circle on BD as diameter.

Imagine a cone with the latter circle as base and A as vertex.

Produce CA to H, making AH equal to CA, and let HC be regarded as the
bar of a balance, A being its middle point.

In the semicircle BAD, let any straight line OP be
drawn parallel to BD and cutting AC in E and the two
generators, AB, AD of the cone in Q, R respectively.
Join AO.

Through OP let a plane be drawn at right angles to
AC;

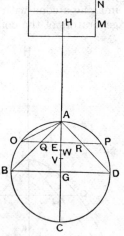

this plane will cut the hemisphere in a circle with diameter OP and the cone in a circle with diameter QR.

Now

$$
\begin{aligned}
HA : AE &= AC : AE \\
&= AO^2 : AE^2 \\
&= (OE^2 + AE^2) : AE^2 \\
&= (OE^2 + QE^2) : QE^2 \\
&= (\text{circle, diam. } OP + \text{circle, diam. } QR) : \\
&\qquad\qquad (\text{circle, diam. } QR).
\end{aligned}
$$

Therefore the circles with diameters OP, QR, in the
places where they are, are in equilibrium about A with the circle with
diameter QR if the latter is placed with its centre of gravity at H.

And, since the centre of gravity of the two circles with diameters OP, QR
taken together, in the place where they are, is . . .

[There is a lacuna here; but the proof can easily be completed on the lines
of the corresponding but more difficult case in Prop. 8.

We proceed thus from the point where the circles with diameters OP, QR,
in the place where they are, balance, about A, the circle with diameter QR
placed with its centre of gravity at H.

A similar relation holds for all the other sets of circular sections made by
other planes passing through points on AG and at right angles to AG.

Taking then all the circles which fill up the hemisphere BAD and the cone
ABD respectively, we find that
the hemisphere BAD and the cone ABD, in the places where they are, together
balance, about A, a cone equal to ABD placed with its centre of gravity at H.

Let the cylinder $M + N$ be equal to the cone ABD.

Then, since the cylinder $M + N$ placed with its centre of gravity at H balances the hemisphere BAD and the cone ABD in the places where they are,
suppose that the portion M of the cylinder, placed with its centre of gravity at

H, balances the cone ABD (alone) in the place where it is; therefore the portion N of the cylinder placed with its centre of gravity at H balances the hemisphere (alone) in the place where it is.

Now the centre of gravity of the cone is at a point V such that $AG = 4GV$; therefore, since M at H is in equilibrium with the cone,
$$M : (\text{cone}) = \tfrac{3}{4}AG : HA = \tfrac{3}{8}AC : AC,$$
whence $\qquad\qquad\qquad\qquad M = \tfrac{3}{8}(\text{cone}).$

But $M + N = (\text{cone})$; therefore $N = \tfrac{5}{8}(\text{cone})$.

Now let the centre of gravity of the hemisphere be at W, which is somewhere on AG.

Then, since N at H balances the hemisphere alone,
$$(\text{hemisphere}) : N = HA : AW.$$

But the hemisphere $BAD =$ twice the cone ABD;
$$[\textit{On the Sphere and Cylinder } \text{i. } 34 \text{ and Prop. 2 above}]$$
and $N = \tfrac{5}{8}(\text{cone})$, from above.

Therefore $\qquad\qquad\qquad 2 : \tfrac{5}{8} = HA : AW$
$$= 2AG : AW,$$
whence $AW = \tfrac{5}{8}AG$, so that W divides AG in such a way that
$$AW : WG = 5 : 3.]$$

Proposition 7

We can also investigate by the same method the theorem that

[*Any segment of a sphere has*] *to the cone* [*with the same base and height the ratio which the sum of the radius of the sphere and the height of the complementary segment has to the height of the complementary segment.*]

[There is a lacuna here; but all that is missing is the construction, and the construction is easily understood by means of the figure. BAD is of course the

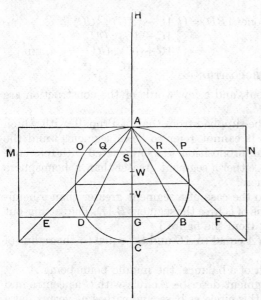

segment of the sphere the volume of which is to be compared with the volume of a cone with the same base and height.]

The plane drawn through MN and at right angles to AC will cut the cylinder in a circle with diameter MN, the segment of the sphere in a circle with diameter OP, and the cone on the base EF in a circle with diameter QR.

In the same way as before [cf. Prop. 2] we can prove that the circle with diameter MN, in the place where it is, is in equilibrium about A with the two circles with diameters OP, QR if these circles are both moved and placed with their centres of gravity at H.

The same thing can be proved of all sets of three circles in which the cylinder, the segment of the sphere, and the cone with the common height AG are all cut by any plane perpendicular to AC.

Since then the sets of circles make up the whole cylinder, the whole segment of the sphere and the whole cone respectively, it follows that the cylinder, in the place where it is, is in equilibrium about A with the sum of the segment of the sphere and the cone if both are placed with their centres of gravity at H.

Divide AG at W, V in such a way that
$$AW = WG, \quad AV = 3VG.$$

Therefore W will be the centre of gravity of the cylinder, and V will be the centre of gravity of the cone.

Since, now, the bodies are in equilibrium as described,
$$(\text{cylinder}) : (\text{cone } AEF + \text{segment } BAD \text{ of sphere}) = HA : AW.$$

. . . .

[The rest of the proof is lost; but it can easily be supplied thus:
We have
$$(\text{cone } AEF + \text{segmt. } BAD) : (\text{cylinder}) = AW : AC$$
$$= AW \cdot AC : AC^2.$$

But $\qquad (\text{cylinder}) : (\text{cone } AEF) = AC^2 : \tfrac{1}{3}EG^2$
$$= AC^2 : \tfrac{1}{3}AG^2.$$

Therefore, *ex aequali*,
$$(\text{cone } AEF + \text{segmt. } BAD) : (\text{cone } AEF) = AW \cdot AC : \tfrac{1}{3}AG^2$$
$$= \tfrac{1}{2}AC : \tfrac{1}{3}AG,$$

whence $\qquad (\text{segmt. } BAD) : (\text{cone } AEF) = (\tfrac{1}{2}AC - \tfrac{1}{3}AG) : \tfrac{1}{3}AG.$

Again $\qquad (\text{cone } AEF) : (\text{cone } ABD) = EG^2 : DG^2$
$$= AG^2 : AG \cdot GC$$
$$= AG : GC$$
$$= \tfrac{1}{3}AG : \tfrac{1}{3}GC.$$

Therefore, *ex aequali*,
$$(\text{segment } BAD) : (\text{cone } ABD) = (\tfrac{1}{2}AC - \tfrac{1}{3}AG) : \tfrac{1}{3}GC$$
$$= (\tfrac{3}{2}AC - AG) : GC$$
$$= (\tfrac{1}{2}AC + GC) : GC. \qquad \text{Q.E.D.}]$$

PROPOSITION 8

[The enunciation, the setting-out, and a few words of the construction are missing.

The enunciation however can be supplied from that of Prop. 9, with which it must be identical except that it cannot refer to "*any* segment," and the presumption therefore is that the proposition was enunciated with reference to one kind of segment only, i.e. either a segment greater than a hemisphere or a segment less than a hemisphere.

Heiberg's figure corresponds to the case of a segment greater than a hemisphere. The segment investigated is of course the segment BAD. The setting-out and construction are self-evident from the figure.]

Produce AC to H, O, making HA equal to AC and CO equal to the radius of the sphere;

and let HC be regarded as the bar of a balance, the middle point being A.

In the plane cutting off the segment describe a circle with G as centre and radius (GE) equal to AG; and on this circle as base, and with A as vertex, let a cone be described. AE, AF are generators of this cone.

Draw KL, through any point Q on AG, parallel to EF and cutting the segment in K, L, and AE, AF in R, P respectively. Join AK.

Now

$$HA : AQ = CA : AQ$$
$$= AK^2 : AQ^2$$
$$= (KQ^2 + QA^2) : QA^2$$
$$= (KQ^2 + PQ^2) : PQ^2$$
$$= (\text{circle, diam. } KL + \text{circle, diam. } PR) : (\text{circle, diam. } PR).$$

Imagine a circle equal to the circle with diameter PR placed with its centre of gravity at H; therefore the circles on diameters KL, PR, in the places where they are, are in equilibrium about A with the circle with diameter PR placed with its centre of gravity at H.

Similarly for the corresponding circular sections made by any other plane perpendicular to AG.

Therefore, taking all the circular sections which make up the segment ABD of the sphere and the cone AEF respectively, we find that the segment ABD of the sphere and the cone AEF, in the places where they are, are in equilibrium with the cone AEF assumed to be placed with its centre of gravity at H.

Let the cylinder $M + N$ be equal to the cone AEF which has A for vertex and the circle on EF as diameter for base.

Divide AG at V so that

$$AG = 4VG;$$

therefore V is the centre of gravity of the cone AEF; "for this has been proved before."

Let the cylinder $M + N$ be cut by a plane perpendicular to the axis in such a way that the cylinder M (alone), placed with its centre of gravity at H, is in equilibrium with the cone AEF.

Since $M + N$ suspended at H is in equilibrium with the segment ABD of the sphere and the cone AEF in the places where they are,

while M, also at H, is in equilibrium with the cone AEF in the place where it is,

it follows that

N at H is in equilibrium with the segment ABD of the sphere in the place where it is.

Now   (segment ABD of sphere) : (cone ABD) $= OG : GC$;

"for this is already proved" [Cf. *On the Sphere and Cylinder* II. 2 Cor. as well as Prop. 7 *ante*].

And

$$\text{(cone } ABD) : (\text{cone } AEF)$$
$$= (\text{circle, diam. } BD) : (\text{circle, diam. } EF)$$
$$= BD^2 : EF^2$$
$$= BG^2 : GE^2$$
$$= CG \cdot GA : GA^2$$
$$= CG : GA.$$

Therefore, *ex aequali,*

(segment ABD of sphere) : (cone AEF) = $OG : GA$.

Take a point W on AG such that

$AW : WG = (GA + 4GC) : (GA + 2GC)$.

We have then, inversely,

$GW : WA = (2GC + GA) : (4GC + GA)$,

and, *componendo,*

$GA : AW = (6GC + 2GA) : (4GC + GA)$.

But $GO = \frac{1}{4}(6GC + 2GA)$,   [for $GO - GC = \frac{1}{2}(CG + GA)$]

and $CV = \frac{1}{4}(4GC + GA)$;

therefore $GA : AW = OG : CV$,

and, alternately and inversely,

$OG : GA = CV : WA$.

It follows, from above, that

(segment ABD of sphere) : (cone AEF) = $CV : WA$.

Now, since the cylinder M with its centre of gravity at H is in equilibrium about A with the cone AEF with its centre of gravity at V,

(cone AEF) : (cylinder M) = $HA : AV$
$$= CA : AV;$$

and, since the cone AEF = the cylinder $M + N$, we have, *dividendo* and *invertendo,*   (cylinder M) : (cylinder N) = $AV : CV$.

Hence, *componendo,*

(cone AEF) : (cylinder N) = $CA : CV$
$$= HA : CV.$$

But it was proved that

(segment ABD of sphere) : (cone AEF) = $CV : WA$;

therefore, *ex aequali,*

(segment ABD of sphere) : (cylinder N) = $HA : AW$.

And it was above proved that the cylinder N at H is in equilibrium about A with the segment ABD, in the place where it is;

therefore, since H is the centre of gravity of the cylinder N, W is the centre of gravity of the segment ABD of the sphere.

Proposition 9

In the same way we can investigate the theorem that

The centre of gravity of any segment of a sphere is on the straight line which is the axis of the segment, and divides this straight line in such a way that the part of it adjacent to the vertex of the segment has to the remaining part the ratio which the sum of the axis of the segment and four times the axis of the complementary segment has to the sum of the axis of the segment and double the axis of the complementary segment.

[As this theorem relates to "*any* segment" but states the same result as that proved in the preceding proposition, it follows that Prop. 8 must have related to one kind of segment, either a segment greater than a semicircle (as in Heiberg's figure of Prop. 8) or a segment less than a semicircle; and the present proposition completed the proof for both kinds of segments. It would only require a slight change in the figure, in any case.]

PROPOSITION 10

By this method too we can investigate the theorem that

[*A segment of an obtuse-angled conoid (i.e. a hyperboloid of revolution) has to the cone which has*] *the same base* [*as the segment and equal height the same ratio as the sum of the axis of the segment and three times*] *the "annex to the axis" (i.e. half the transverse axis of the hyperbolic section through the axis of the hyperboloid, or, in other words, the distance between the vertex of the segment and the vertex of the enveloping cone) has to the sum of the axis of the segment and double of the "annex"* [this is the theorem proved in *On Conoids and Spheroids*, Prop. 25], "and also many other theorems, which, as the method has been made clear by means of the foregoing examples, I will omit, in order that I may now proceed to compass the proofs of the theorems mentioned above."

PROPOSITION 11

If in a right prism with square bases a cylinder be inscribed having its bases in opposite square faces and touching with its surface the remaining four parallelogrammic faces, and if through the centre of the circle which is the base of the cylinder and one side of the opposite square face a plane be drawn, the figure cut off by the plane so drawn is one sixth part of the whole prism.

"This can be investigated by the method, and, when it is set out, I will go back to the proof of it by geometrical considerations."

[The investigation by the mechanical method is contained in the two Propositions, 11, 12. Prop. 13 gives another solution which, although it contains no mechanics, is still of the character which Archimedes regards as inconclusive, since it assumes that the solid is actually *made up* of parallel plane sections and that an auxiliary parabola is actually *made up* of parallel straight lines in it. Prop. 14 added the conclusive geometrical proof.]

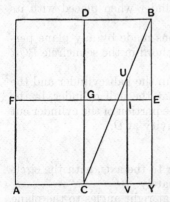

Let there be a right prism with a cylinder inscribed as stated.

Let the prism be cut through the axis of the prism and cylinder by a plane perpendicular to the plane which cuts off the portion of the cylinder; let this plane make, as section, the parallelogram *AB*, and let it cut the plane cutting off the portion of the cylinder (which plane is perpendicular to *AB*) in the straight line *BC*.

Let *CD* be the axis of the prism and cylinder, let *EF* bisect it at right angles, and through *EF* let a plane be drawn at right angles to *CD*; this plane will cut the prism in a square and the cylinder in a circle.

Let *MN* be the square and *OPQR* the circle, and let the circle touch the sides of the square in *O*, *P*, *Q*, *R* [*F*, *E* in the first figure are identical with *O*, *Q* respectively]. Let *H* be the centre of the circle.

Let *KL* be the intersection of the plane through *EF* perpendicular to the axis of the cylinder and the plane cutting off the portion of the cylinder; *KL* is bisected by *OHQ* [and passes through the middle point of *HQ*].

Let any chord of the circle, as ST, be drawn perpendicular to HQ, meeting HQ in W;

and through ST let a plane be drawn at right angles to OQ and produced on both sides of the plane of the circle $OPQR$.

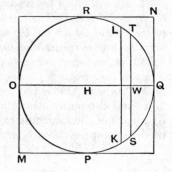

The plane so drawn will cut the half cylinder having the semicircle PQR for section and the axis of the prism for height in a parallelogram, one side of which is equal to ST and another is a generator of the cylinder; and it will also cut the portion of the cylinder cut off in a parallelogram, one side of which is equal to ST and the other is equal and parallel to UV (in the first figure).

UV will be parallel to BY and will cut off, along EG in the parallelogram DE, the segment EI equal to QW.

Now, since EC is a parallelogram, and VI is parallel to GC,

$$EG : GI = YC : CV$$
$$= BY : UV$$
$$= (\square \text{ in half cyl.}) : (\square \text{ in portion of cyl.}).$$

And $EG = HQ$, $GI = HW$, $QH = OH$;

therefore $OH : HW = (\square \text{ in half cyl.}) : (\square \text{ in portion}).$

Imagine that the parallelogram in the portion of the cylinder is moved and placed at O so that O is the centre of gravity, and that OQ is the bar of a balance, H being its middle point.

Then, since W is the centre of gravity of the parallelogram in the half cylinder, it follows from the above that the parallelogram in the half cylinder, in the place where it is, with its centre of gravity at W, is in equilibrium about H with the parallelogram in the portion of the cylinder when placed with its centre of gravity at O.

Similarly for the other parallelogrammic sections made by any plane perpendicular to OQ and passing through any other chord in the semicircle PQR perpendicular to OQ.

If then we take all the parallelograms making up the half cylinder and the portion of the cylinder respectively, it follows that the half cylinder, in the place where it is, is in equilibrium about H with the portion of the cylinder cut off when the latter is placed with its centre of gravity at O.

PROPOSITION 12

Let the parallelogram (square) MN perpendicular to the axis, with the circle $OPQR$ and its diameters OQ, PR, be drawn separately.

Join HG, HM, and through them draw planes at right angles to the plane of the circle, producing them on both sides of that plane.

This produces a prism with triangular section GHM and height equal to the axis of the cylinder; this prism is $\frac{1}{4}$ of the original prism circumscribing the cylinder.

Let LK, UT be drawn parallel to OQ and equidistant from it, cutting the circle in K, T, RP in S, F, and GH, HM in W, V respectively.

Through LK, UT draw planes at right angles to PR, producing them on both sides of the plane of the circle;

these planes produce as sections in the half cylinder PQR and in the prism GHM four parallelograms in which the heights are equal to the axis of the cylinder, and the other sides are equal to KS, TF, LW, UV respectively · · · · ·
· ·

[The rest of the proof is missing, but, as Zeuthen says, the result obtained and the method of arriving at it are plainly indicated by the above.

Archimedes wishes to prove that the half cylinder PQR, in the place where it is, balances the prism GHM, in the place where it is, about H as fixed point.

He has first to prove that the elements (1) the parallelogram with side $= KS$ and (2) the parallelogram with side $= LW$, in the places where they are, balance about S, or, in other words that the straight lines SK, LW, in the places where they are, balance about S.

Now   (radius of circle $OPQR$)$^2 = SK^2 + SH^2$,

or $SL^2 = SK^2 + SW^2$.

Therefore $LS^2 - SW^2 = SK^2$,

and accordingly $(LS + SW) \cdot LW = SK^2$,

whence $\frac{1}{2}(LS + SW) : \frac{1}{2}SK = SK : LW$.

And $\frac{1}{2}(LS + SW)$ is the distance of the centre of gravity of LW from S, while $\frac{1}{2}SK$ is the distance of the centre of gravity of SK from S.

Therefore SK and LW, in the places where they are, balance about S.

Similarly for the corresponding parallelograms.

Taking all the parallelogrammic elements in the half cylinder and prism respectively, we find that
the half cylinder PQR and the prism GHM, in the places where they are respectively, balance about H.

From this result and that of Prop. 11 we can at once deduce the volume of the portion cut off from the cylinder. For in Prop. 11 the portion of the cylinder, placed with its centre of gravity at O, is shown to balance (about H) the half-cylinder in the place where it is. By Prop. 12 we may substitute for the half-cylinder in the place where it is the prism GHM of that proposition turned the opposite way relatively to RP. The centre of gravity of the prism as thus placed is at a point (say Z) on HQ such that $HZ = \frac{2}{3}HQ$.

Therefore, assuming the prism to be applied at its centre of gravity, we have
(portion of cylinder) : (prism) $= \frac{2}{3}HQ : OH$
$= 2 : 3$;

therefore   (portion of cylinder) $= \frac{2}{3}$(prism GHM)
$= \frac{1}{6}$(original prism).

PROPOSITION 13

Let there be a right prism with square bases, one of which is $ABCD$;
in the prism let a cylinder be inscribed, the base of which is the circle $EFGH$ touching the sides of the square $ABCD$ in E, F, G, H.

Through the centre and through the side corresponding to CD in the square face *opposite* to $ABCD$ let a plane be drawn; this will cut off a prism equal to $\frac{1}{4}$ of the original prism and formed by three parallelograms and two triangles, the triangles forming opposite faces.

In the semicircle EFG describe the parabola which has FK for axis and passes through E, G; draw MN parallel to KF meeting GE in M, the parabola in L, the semicircle in O and CD in N.

Then $MN \cdot NL = NF^2;$

"for this is clear."   [Cf. Apollonius, *Conics* I. 11]

[The parameter is of course equal to GK or KF.]

Therefore $MN : NL = GK^2 : LS^2.$

Through MN draw a plane at right angles to EG;

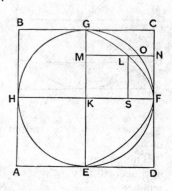

this will produce as sections (1) in the prism cut off from the whole prism a right-angled triangle, the base of which is MN, while the perpendicular is perpendicular at N to the plane $ABCD$ and equal to the axis of the cylinder, and the hypotenuse is in the plane cutting the cylinder, and (2) in the portion of the cylinder cut off a right-angled triangle the base of which is MO, while the perpendicular is the generator of the cylinder perpendicular at O to the plane KN, and the hypotenuse is $\cdots\cdots$

. . . .

[There is a lacuna here, to be supplied as follows.

Since $MN : NL = GK^2 : LS^2$
$$= MN^2 : LS^2,$$
it follows that $MN : ML = MN^2 : (MN^2 - LS^2)$
$$= MN^2 : (MN^2 - MK^2)$$
$$= MN^2 : MO^2.$$

But the triangle (1) in the prism is to the triangle (2) in the portion of the cylinder in the ratio of $MN^2 : MO^2$.

Therefore   ($\triangle$ in prism) : ($\triangle$ in portion of cylinder)
$$= MN : ML$$
= (straight line in rect. DG) : (straight line in parabola).

We now take all the corresponding elements in the prism, the portion of the cylinder, the rectangle DG and the parabola EFG respectively];
and it will follow that

(all the $\triangle$s in prism) : (all the $\triangle$s in portion of cylinder)
= (all the str. lines in $\square DG$) : (all the straight lines between parabola and EG).

But the prism is made up of the triangles in the prism, [the portion of the cylinder is made up of the triangles in it], the parallelogram DG of the straight lines in it parallel to KF, and the parabolic segment of the straight lines parallel to KF intercepted between its circumference and EG;

therefore   (prism) : (portion of cylinder)
$$= (\square GD) : (\text{parabolic segment } EFG).$$

But $\square GD = \frac{3}{2}(\text{parabolic segment } EFG);$

"for this is proved in my earlier treatise."   [*Quadrature of Parabola*]

Therefore   prism $= \frac{3}{2}$(portion of cylinder).

If then we denote the portion of the cylinder by 2, the prism is 3, and the original prism circumscribing the cylinder is 12 (being 4 times the other prism); therefore the portion of the cylinder = $\frac{1}{6}$(original prism).   Q.E.D.

[The above proposition and the next are peculiarly interesting for the fact that the parabola is an auxiliary curve introduced for the sole purpose of analytically reducing the required cubature to the known quadrature of the parabola.]

PROPOSITION 14

Let there be a right prism with square bases [and a cylinder inscribed therein having its base in the square $ABCD$ and touching its sides at E, F, G, H; let the cylinder be cut by a plane through EG and the side corresponding to CD in the square face opposite to $ABCD$.]

This plane cuts off from the prism a prism, and from the cylinder a portion of it.

It can be proved that the portion of the cylinder cut off by the plane is $\frac{1}{6}$ of the whole prism.

But we will first prove that it is possible to inscribe in the portion cut off from the cylinder, and to circumscribe about it, solid figures made up of prisms which have equal height and similar triangular bases, in such a way that the circumscribed figure exceeds the inscribed by less than any assigned magnitude.....

.   .   .   .

But it was proved that

(prism cut off by oblique plane) $< \frac{3}{2}$(figure inscribed in portion of cylinder).

Now   (prism cut off) : (inscribed figure)

= $\square DG$: ($\square$s inscribed in parabolic segment);

therefore $\square DG < \frac{3}{2}$($\square$s in parabolic segment):

which is impossible, since "it has been proved elsewhere" that the parallelogram DG is $\frac{3}{2}$ of the parabolic segment.

Consequently...................

....not greater.

.   .   .   .

And   (all the prisms in prism cut off)
                    : (all prisms in circumscr. figure)

= (all $\square$s in $\square DG$) : (all $\square$s in fig. circumscr. about parabolic segmt.);

therefore

(prism cut off) : (figure circumscr. about portion of cylinder)

= ($\square DG$) : (figure circumscr. about parabolic segment).

But the prism cut off by the oblique plane is $> \frac{3}{2}$ of the solid figure circumscribed about the portion of the cylinder.....

.   .   .   .

[There are large gaps in the exposition of this geometrical proof, but the way in which the method of exhaustion was applied, and the parallelism between this and other applications of it, are clear. The first fragment shows that solid figures made up of prisms were circumscribed and inscribed to the portion of the cylinder. The parallel triangular faces of these prisms were perpendicular to GE in the figure of Prop. 13; they divided GE into equal portions of the requisite smallness; each section of the portion of the cylinder by such a plane was a triangular face common to an inscribed and a circumscribed right prism. The planes also produced prisms in the prism cut off by the same oblique plane as cuts off the portion of the cylinder and standing on GD as base.

The number of parts into which the parallel planes divided GE was made great enough to secure that the circumscribed figure exceeded the inscribed figure by less than a small assigned magnitude.

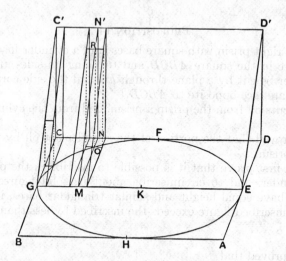

The second part of the proof began with the assumption that the portion of the cylinder is $> \frac{2}{3}$ of the prism cut off; and this was proved to be impossible, by means of the use of the auxiliary parabola and the proportion

$$MN : ML = MN^2 : MO^2$$

which are employed in Prop. 13.

We may supply the missing proof as follows.

In the accompanying figure are represented (1) the first element-prism circumscribed to the portion of the cylinder, (2) two element-prisms adjacent to the ordinate OM, of which that on the left is circumscribed and that on the right (equal to the other) inscribed, (3) the corresponding element-prisms forming part of the prism cut off ($CC'GEDD'$) which is $\frac{1}{4}$ of the original prism.

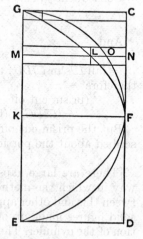

In the second figure are shown element-rectangles circumscribed and inscribed to the auxiliary parabola, which rectangles correspond exactly to the circumscribed and inscribed element-prisms represented in the first figure (the length of GM is the same in both figures, and the breadths of the element-rectangles are the same as the heights of the element-prisms); the corresponding element-rectangles forming part of the rectangle GD are similarly shown.

For convenience we suppose that GE is divided into an even number of equal parts, so that GK contains an integral number of these parts.

For the sake of brevity we will call each of the two element-prisms of which OM is an edge "el. prism (O)" and each of the element-prisms of which MNN' is a common face "el. prism (N)." Similarly we will use the corresponding abbreviations "el. rect. (L)" and "el. rect. (N)" for the corresponding elements in relation to the auxiliary parabola as shown in the second figure.

Now it is easy to see that the figure made up of all the inscribed prisms is less than the figure made up of the circumscribed prisms by twice the final circumscribed prism adjacent to FK, i.e. by twice "el. prism (N)"; and, as the height of this prism may be made as small as we please by dividing GK into sufficiently small parts, it follows that inscribed and circumscribed solid figures made up of element-prisms can be drawn differing by less than any assigned solid figure.

(1) Suppose, if possible, that

$$\text{(portion of cylinder)} > \tfrac{2}{3}\text{(prism cut off)},$$

or

$$\text{(prism cut off)} < \tfrac{3}{2}\text{(portion of cylinder)}.$$

Let $\quad$ (prism cut off) $= \tfrac{3}{2}$(portion of cylinder$-X$), say.

Construct circumscribed and inscribed figures made up of element-prisms, such that

$$\text{(circumscr. fig.)} - \text{(inscr. fig.)} < X.$$

Therefore $\qquad$ (inscr. fig.) $>$ (circumscr. fig. $-X$),

and *a fortiori* $\qquad\qquad\quad$ $>$ (portion of cyl. $-X$).

It follows that

$$\text{(prism cut off)} < \tfrac{3}{2}\text{(inscribed figure)}.$$

Considering now the element-prisms in the prism cut off and those in the inscribed figure respectively, we have

$$\text{el. prism } (N) : \text{el. prism } (O) = MN^2 : MO^2$$
$$= MN : ML \qquad\qquad \text{[as in Prop. 13]}$$
$$= \text{el. rect. } (N) : \text{el. rect. } (L).$$

It follows that

$$\Sigma\{\text{el. prism } (N)\} : \Sigma\{\text{el. prism } (O)\} = \Sigma\{\text{el. rect. } (N)\} : \Sigma\{\text{el. rect. } (L)\}.$$

(There are really two more prisms and rectangles in the first and third than there are in the second and fourth terms respectively; but this makes no difference because the first and third terms may be multiplied by a common factor as $n/(n-2)$ without affecting the truth of the proportion. Cf. the proposition from *On Conoids and Spheroids* quoted on p. 571 above.)

Therefore

$$\text{(prism cut off)} : \text{(figure inscr. in portion of cyl.)}$$
$$= \text{(rect. } GD) : \text{(fig. inscr. in parabola)}.$$

But it was proved above that

$$\text{(prism cut off)} < \tfrac{3}{2}\text{(fig. inscr. in portion of cyl.)};$$

therefore $\qquad$ (rect. GD) $< \tfrac{3}{2}$(fig. inscr. in parabola),

and, *a fortiori* $\quad$ (rect. GD) $< \tfrac{3}{2}$(parabolic segmt.):

which is impossible, since

$$\text{(rect. } GD) = \tfrac{3}{2}\text{(parabolic segmt.)}.$$

Therefore (portion of cyl.) is *not* greater than $\tfrac{2}{3}$(prism cut off).

(2) In the second lacuna must have come the beginning of the next *reductio ad absurdum* demolishing the other possible assumption that the portion of the cylinder is $< \tfrac{2}{3}$ of the prism cut off.

In this case our assumption is that

$$(\text{prism cut off}) > \tfrac{3}{2}(\text{portion of cylinder});$$

and we circumscribe and inscribe figures made up of element-prisms, such that

$$(\text{prism cut off}) > \tfrac{3}{2}(\text{fig. circumscr. about portion of cyl.}).$$

We now consider the element-prisms in the prism cut off and in the circumscribed figure respectively, and the same argument as above gives

$$(\text{prism cut off}) : (\text{fig. circumscr. about portion of cyl.})$$
$$= (\text{rect. } GD) : (\text{fig. circumscr. about parabola}),$$

whence it follows that

$$(\text{rect. } GD) > \tfrac{3}{2}(\text{fig. circumscribed about parabola}),$$

and, *a fortiori*,

$$(\text{rect. } GD) > \tfrac{3}{2}(\text{parabolic segment}):$$

which is impossible, since

$$(\text{rect. } GD) = \tfrac{3}{2}(\text{parabolic segmt.}).$$

Therefore

$$(\text{portion of cyl.}) \text{ is } not \text{ less than } \tfrac{2}{3}(\text{prism cut off}).$$

But it was also proved that neither is it greater;
therefore
$$(\text{portion of cyl.}) = \tfrac{2}{3}(\text{prism cut off})$$
$$= \tfrac{1}{6}(\text{original prism}).]$$

[PROPOSITION 15]

[This proposition, which is lost, would be the mechanical investigation of the second of the two special problems mentioned in the preface to the treatise, namely that of the cubature of the figure included between two cylinders, each of which is inscribed in one and the same cube so that its opposite bases are in two opposite faces of the cube and its surface touches the other four faces.

Zeuthen has shown how the mechanical method can be applied to this case.

In the accompanying figure $VWYX$ is a section of the cube by a plane (that of the paper) passing through the axis BD of one of the cylinders inscribed in the cube and parallel to two opposite faces.

The same plane gives the circle $ABCD$ as the section of the other inscribed cylinder with axis perpendicular to the plane of the paper and extending on each side of the plane to a distance equal to the radius of the circle or half the side of the cube.

AC is the diameter of the circle which is perpendicular to BD.

Join AB, AD and produce them to meet the tangent at C to the circle in E, F.

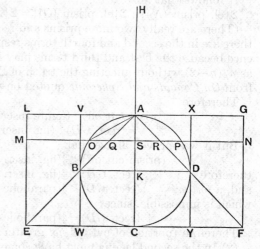

Then $EC = CF = CA$.

Let LG be the tangent at A, and complete the rectangle $EFGL$.

Draw straight lines from A to the four corners of the section in which the plane through BD perpendicular to AK cuts the cube. These straight lines, if produced, will meet the plane of the face of the cube opposite to A in four points forming the four corners of a square in that plane with sides equal to EF or double of the side of the cube, and we thus have a pyramid with A for vertex and the latter square for base.

Complete the prism (parallelepiped) with the same base and height as the pyramid.

Draw in the parallelogram LF any straight line MN parallel to EF, and through MN draw a plane at right angles to AC.

This plane cuts—

(1) the solid included by the two cylinders in a square with side equal to OP,

(2) the prism in a square with side equal to MN, and

(3) the pyramid in a square with side equal to QR.

Produce CA to H, making HA equal to AC, and imagine HC to be the bar of a balance.

Now, as in Prop. 2, since $MS = AC$, $QS = AS$,

$$MS \cdot SQ = CA \cdot AS$$
$$= AO^2$$
$$= OS^2 + SQ^2.$$

Also $HA : AS = CA : AS$
$$= MS : SQ$$
$$= MS^2 : MS \cdot SQ$$
$$= MS^2 : (OS^2 + SQ^2), \text{ from above,}$$
$$= MN^2 : (OP^2 + QR^2)$$
$$= (\text{square, side } MN) : (\text{sq., side } OP + \text{sq., side } QR).$$

Therefore the square with side equal to MN, in the place where it is, is in equilibrium about A with the squares with sides equal to OP, QR respectively placed with their centres of gravity at H.

Proceeding in the same way with the square sections produced by other planes perpendicular to AC, we finally prove that the prism, in the place where it is, is in equilibrium about A with the solid included by the two cylinders and the pyramid, both placed with their centres of gravity at H.

Now the centre of gravity of the prism is at K.

Therefore $HA : AK = (\text{prism}) : (\text{solid} + \text{pyramid})$

or $2 : 1 = (\text{prism}) : (\text{solid} + \frac{1}{3} \text{ prism}).$

Therefore $2 (\text{solid}) + \frac{2}{3}(\text{prism}) = (\text{prism}).$

It follows that

$(\text{solid included by cylinders}) = \frac{1}{6}(\text{prism})$
$$= \frac{2}{3}(\text{cube}).$$ Q.E.D.

There is no doubt that Archimedes proceeded to, and completed, the rigorous geometrical proof by the method of exhaustion.

As observed by Prof. C. Juel (Zeuthen *l.c.*), the solid in the present proposition is made up of 8 pieces of cylinders of the type of that treated in the preceding proposition. As however the two propositions are separately stated, there is no doubt that Archimedes' proofs of them were distinct.

In this case AC would be divided into a very large number of equal parts and planes would be drawn through the points of division perpendicular to AC. These planes cut the solid, and also the cube VY, in square sections. Thus we can inscribe and circumscribe to the solid the requisite solid figures made up of element-prisms and differing by less than any assigned solid magnitude; the prisms have square bases and their heights are the small segments of AC. The element-prism in the inscribed and circumscribed figures which has the square equal to OP^2 for base corresponds to an element-prism in the cube which has for base a square with side equal to that of the cube; and as the ratio of the element-prisms is the ratio $OS^2 : BK^2$, we can use the same auxiliary parabola, and work out the proof in exactly the same way, as in Prop. 14.]

CONICS

BIOGRAPHICAL NOTE

APOLLONIUS, *c.* 262–*c.* 200 B.C.

APOLLONIUS was born at Perga in Pamphylia, Asia Minor, some twenty-five years after the birth of Archimedes, which would place his birth around the year 262 B.C. He seems to have gone when quite young to Alexandria, where, according to Pappus, the fourth century mathematician, he was attracted by the reputation of the astronomer, Aristarchus of Samos. Apollonius studied under the successors of Euclid at Alexandria and continued to reside there during the reigns of Ptolemy Euergetes and of Ptolemy Philopator (247–203 B.C.). He was also for some time in Pergamum, where he made the acquaintance of the mathematician, Eudemus, to whom he dedicated the first three books of his *Conics*, and of King Attalus I (269–197 B.C.), to whom the remaining five books of the *Conics* were dedicated.

Apollonius appears to have been associated with the leading mathematicians of his day. In the dedicatory epistles of the *Conics* he records that he met Philonides while on a trip to Ephesus and that he undertook the composition of this work in the first instance for Naucrates, who was staying in Alexandria. Speaking in the same place of the preceding writers on conics, Apollonius points out their limitations and inadequacies in such a way that some of his readers, such as Pappus, have considered him boastful and envious, but it would seem that Apollonius is only trying to explain the appearance of a new text-book on the elements of conics (Books I–IV) and the publication of his own original and more advanced investigations (Books V–VIII).

The *Conics* were at once recognized as the authoritative treatise on the subject, winning for their author the name of "the great geometer." They are regularly cited by later writers. Pappus added a group of lemmas, and Eutocius (*fl.* 500 A.D.) edited and commented on the first four books. These books are extant in the original Greek; the fifth, sixth, and seventh books exist in an Arabic translation; the eighth book is known only indirectly.

Although the titles and a general indication of the contents of other works by Apollonius are given by later writers, especially by Pappus, only one, the *Cutting of a Ratio*, has survived, and that, like parts of the *Conics*, only in an Arabic version. All of the original work, with the exception of the second half of the *Conics*, has perished. Books not extant but known through Pappus are: *Cutting of an Area, Determinate Section, Tangencies, Inclinations*, and *Plane Loci*. He wrote on irrationals and, like Archimedes, devised a system of multiplication for counting large numbers and calculated an approximate value for the ratio of the circumference of a circle to the diameter. The ancient writers also record that Apollonius wrote *On the Burning-Glass*, in which he probably treated the properties of the parabola, a work comparing the dodecahedron and the icosahedron inscribed in the same sphere, and a book, perhaps on the general principles of mathematics, in which he criticized and suggested improvements for Euclid's *Elements*. Lastly, in astronomy he is credited by Ptolemy with an explanation of the motion of the planets by means of epicycles and eccentric circles. He seems to have been especially interested in the theory of the moon, and the Alexandrians are said to have called him Epsilon from the resemblance of that Greek letter to the lunar crescent.

CONTENTS

TRANSLATOR'S NOTE

If on first appearance this treatise should seem to the reader a jumble of propositions, rigorous indeed, but without much rhyme or reason in their sequence, then he can be sure he has not read aright, and as with the planets, he must look further to save the appearances. There are one or two hypotheses at least that can order the apparent wanderings of parabolas, hyperbolas, and ellipses through the first four books. Such hypotheses are the analogies between the three sections, and especially the development of the analogy between the hyperbola and the ellipse reaching its culmination, in the first book, with the final theorem, the construction of conjugate opposite sections.

In First Definitions I.5, Apollonius innocently defines two kinds of diameters, the transverse and the upright. Each one, in a conic section, bisects all the straight lines parallel to the other. But the upright diameter, defined here only as to position, has, in the case of the ellipse, natural bounds fixed by the section itself, and in Proposition I.15 we find it is the mean proportional between the corresponding transverse diameter (or conjugate diameter) and its parameter. The transverse diameter, in turn, is the mean proportional between the upright diameter (or conjugate) and its parameter, so "upright" and "transverse" become meaningless terms, in the case of the ellipse, for something better expressed by the symmetrical relation "conjugate" (First Def. I.6). Immediately, in Proposition I. 16, as if arbitrarily, the upright diameter of the hyperbola is bounded in the same way, given a definite magnitude, and becomes "the second diameter." But so far transverse and upright diameters, or transverse and second diameters, are distinct things in the case of the hyperbola, and there seems to be little reason for giving this second diameter in magnitude νομός has not yet become φύσις. That the upright diameter should be given even in position for the hyperbola becomes only very significant with two pairs of propositions—Propositions I.37 and 38, and I.39 and 40—where it is shown that certain properties holding for ordinates to the transverse diameter of the hyperbola and ellipse hold also for the ordinates to their conjugates. But it is only with the final proposition of the first book (I.60) that the magnitude of the hyperbola's second diameter is justified in magnitude as well as position. It is the corresponding diameter of the opposite sections conjugate to the first. And this analogy between the hyperbola

599

and ellipse now stands on the threshold of a vast development. For this theorem, coming as a climax to the first book, makes possible the main theme of the second book: the asymptotes, those strange lines all but touching each opposite section (II. 2, 13, 14) and forming a single bound between each adjacent pair (II. 15, 17), so making the hyperbola an all but closed section, a puckered ellipse, a mouth turned inside out. And in the third book, the fruits of this analogy are gathered as in the especially nice case of Proposition III.15.

Although this translation is literal, we have not hesitated to use such symbols and abbreviations as, without prejudicing any Greek number theory or introducing any modern theory of symbols, would yet make the reading and the mechanic of study easier and at the same time preserve all the rigor of Greek mathematics.

As for the Greek text, we have used Heiberg, and have constantly referred to the *editio princeps* of Halley. In certain instances we have been glad to consult the very excellent French translation of Paul Ver Eecke (Desclée de Brouwer, Bruges, 1923). We have also deferred, at all relevant points, to the English usage of T. L. Heath's translation of Euclid's *Elements*.

EXAMPLES OF ABBREVIATIONS
AND SYMBOLS USED

$A = B$ *for* A is equal to B.

$A + B$ *for* A added to B.

$A - B$ *for* B subtracted from A.

$A : B :: C : D$ *for* A is to B as C is to D.

rect. AB, BC *for* rectangle AB, BC.

sq. AB *for* square on AB.

ar. *for* area.

pllg. *for* parallelogram.

trgl. *for* triangle.

quadr. *for* quadrilateral.

rect. AB, BC : rect. CD, DE comp. $AB : CD, BC : DE$ *for* ratio of rectangle AB, BC to rectangle CD, DE is compounded of the ratio of AB to CD and of BC to DE.

ratio comp. $AB : BC, CD : DE =$ ratio comp. $XY : YZ, ZW : WV$ *for* ratio compounded of AB to BC and of CD to DE is the same as the ratio compounded of XY to YZ and of ZW to WV.

$A > B$ *for* A is greater than B.

$A < B$ *for* A is less than B.

rt. angle *for* right angle.

BOOK ONE

Apollonius to Eudemus, greetings.

If you are restored in body, and other things go with you to your mind, well and good; and we too fare pretty well. At the time I was with you in Pergamum, I observed you were quite eager to be kept informed of the work I was doing in conics. And so I have sent you this first book revised, and we shall dispatch the others when we are satisfied with them. For I don't believe you have forgotten hearing from me how I worked out the plan for these conics at the request of Naucrates, the geometer, at the time he was with us in Alexandria lecturing, and how on arranging them in eight books we immediately communicated them in great haste because of his near departure, not revising them but putting down whatever came to us with the intention of a final going over. And so finding now the occasion of correcting them, one book after another, we publish them. And since it happened that some others among those frequenting us got acquainted with the first and second books before the revision, don't be surprised if you come upon them in a different form.

Of the eight books the first four belong to a course in the elements. The first book contains the generation of the three sections and of the opposite branches, and the principal properties (τὰ ἀρχικὰ συμπτώματα) in them worked out more fully and universally than in the writings of others. The second book contains the properties (τὰ συμβαίνοντα) having to do with the diameters and axes and also the asymptotes, and other things of a general and necessary use for limits of possibility (πρὸς τοὺς διορισμούς). And what I call diameters and what I call axes you will know from this book. The third book contains many incredible theorems of use for the construction of solid loci and for limits of possibility of which the greatest part and the most beautiful are new. And when we had grasped these, we knew that the three-line and four-line locus had not been constructed by Euclid, but only a chance part of it and that not very happily. For it was not possible for this construction to be completed without the additional things found by us. The fourth book shows in how many ways the sections of a cone intersect with each other and with the circumference of a circle, and contains other things in addition none of which has been written up by our predecessors, that is in how many points the section of a cone or the circumference of a circle and the opposite branches meet the opposite branches. The rest of the books are fuller in treatment. For there is one dealing more fully with maxima and minima, and one with equal and similar sections of a cone, and one with limiting theorems, and one with determinate conic problems. And so indeed, with all of them published, those happening upon them can judge them as they see fit. Good-bye.

First Definitions

1. If from a point a straight line is joined to the circumference of a circle which is not in the same plane with the point, and the line is produced in both directions, and if, with the point remaining fixed, the straight line being rotated about the circumference of the circle returns to the same place from which it began, then the generated surface composed of the two surfaces lying vertically opposite one another, each of which increases indefinitely as the generating straight line is produced indefinitely, I call a conic surface, and I call the fixed point the vertex, and the straight line drawn from the vertex to the center of the circle the axis.

2. And the figure contained by the circle and by the conic surface between the vertex and the circumference of the circle I call a cone, and the point which is also the vertex of the surface I call the vertex of the cone, and the straight line drawn from the vertex to the center of the circle the axis, and the circle the base of the cone.

3. I call right cones those having axes perpendicular to their bases, and oblique those not having axes perpendicular to their bases.

4. Of any curved line which is in one plane I call that straight line the diameter which, drawn from the curved line, bisects all straight lines drawn to this curved line parallel to some straight line; and I call the end of that straight line (the diameter) situated on the curved line the vertex of the curved line, and I say that each of these parallels is drawn ordinatewise to the diameter (τεταγμένως ἐπὶ τὴν διάμετρον κατῆχθαι).[1]

5. Likewise of any two curved lines lying in one plane I call that straight line the transverse diameter (διάμετρος πλαγία) which cuts the two curved lines and bisects all the straight lines drawn to either of the curved lines parallel to some straight line; and I call the ends of the diameter situated on the curved lines the vertices of the curved lines; and I call that straight line the upright diameter (διάμετρος ὀρθία) which, lying between the two curved lines, bisects all the straight lines intercepted between the curved lines and drawn parallel to some straight line; and I say that each of the parallels is drawn ordinatewise to the diameter.

6. The two straight lines each of which being a diameter bisects the straight lines parallel to the other I call the conjugate diameters (συζυγεῖς διάμετροι) of a curved line and of two curved lines.

7. And I call that straight line the axis of a curved line and of two curved lines which being a diameter of the curved line or lines cuts the parallel straight lines at right angles.

8. And I call those straight lines the conjugate axes of a curved line and of two curved lines which being conjugate diameters cut the straight lines parallel to each other at right angles.

Proposition 1

The straight lines drawn from the vertex of the conic surface to points on the surface are on that surface.

Let there be a conic surface whose vertex is the point A, and let there be

---

[1] We shall follow modern usage and generally call these parallels ordinates.

taken some point B on the conic surface, and let a straight line ACB be joined. I say that the straight line ACB is on the conic surface.

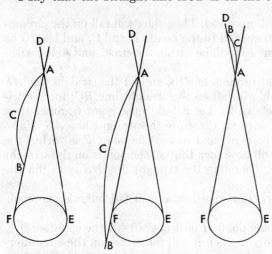

For if possible, let it not be, and let the straight line DE be the line generating the surface, and EF be the circle along which ED is moved. Then if, the point A remaining fixed, the straight line DE is moved along the circumference of the circle EF, it will also go through the point B (Def. 1), and two straight lines will have the same ends. And this is absurd.

Therefore the straight line joined from A to B cannot not be on the surface. Therefore it is on the surface.

PORISM

It is also evident that, if a straight line is joined from the vertex to some point among those within the surface, it will fall within the conic surface; and if it is joined to some point among those without, it will be outside the surface.

PROPOSITION 2

If on either one of the two vertically opposite surfaces two points are taken, and the straight line joining the points does not verge to the vertex, then it will fall within the surface, and produced it will fall outside.

Let there be a conic surface whose vertex is the point A, and a circle BC

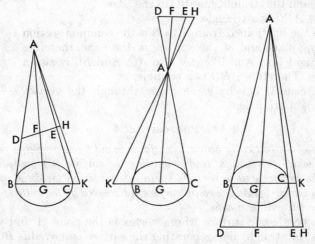

along whose circumference the generating straight line is moved, and let two points D and E be taken on either one of the two vertically opposite surfaces, and let the joining straight line DE not verge to the point A.

I say that the straight line DE will be within the surface, and produced will be without.

Let AE and AD be joined and produced. Then they will fall on the circumference of the circle (I. 1). Let them fall to the points B and C, and let BC be joined. Therefore the straight line BC will be within the circle, and so too within the conic surface.

Then let a point F be taken at random on DE, and let the straight line AF be joined and produced. Then it will fall on the straight line BC; for the triangle BCA is in one plane (Eucl. XI. 2). Let it fall to the point G. Since then the point G is within the conic surface, therefore the straight line AG is also within the conic surface (I. 1, porism), and so too the point F is within the conic surface. Then likewise it will be shown that all the points on the straight line DE are within the surface. Therefore the straight line DE is within the surface.

Then let DE be produced to H. I say then it will fall outside the conic surface.

For if possible, let there be some point H of it not outside the conic surface, and let AH be joined and produced. Then it will fall either on the circumference of the circle or within (I. 1 and porism). And this is impossible, for it falls on BC produced, as for example to the point K. Therefore the straight line EH is outside the surface.

Therefore the straight line DE is within the conic surface, and produced is outside.

PROPOSITION 3

If a cone is cut by a plane through the vertex, the section is a triangle.

Let there be a cone whose vertex is the point A and whose base is the circle BC; and let it be cut by some plane through the point A; and let it make, as sections, lines AB and AC on the surface, and the straight line BC in the base.

I say that ABC is a triangle.

For since the line joined from A to B is the common section of the cutting plane and of the surface of the cone, therefore AB is a straight line. And likewise also AC. And BC is also a straight line. Therefore ABC is a triangle.

If then a cone is cut by some plane through the vertex, the section is a triangle.

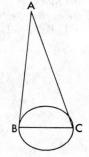

PROPOSITION 4

If either one of the vertically opposite surfaces is cut by some plane parallel to the circle along which the straight line generating the surface is moved, the plane cut off within the surface will be a circle having its center on the axis, and the figure contained by the circle and the conic surface intercepted by the cutting plane on the side of the vertex will be a cone.

Let there be a conic surface whose vertex is the point A and whose circle along which the straight line generating the surface is moved is BC; and let it be cut by some plane parallel to the circle BC, and let it make on the surface as a section the line DE.

I say that the line DE is a circle having its center on the axis.

For let the point F be taken as the center of the circle BC, and let AF be joined. Therefore AF is the axis (Def. 1) and meets the cutting plane. Let it meet it at the point G, and let some plane be produced through AF. Then the

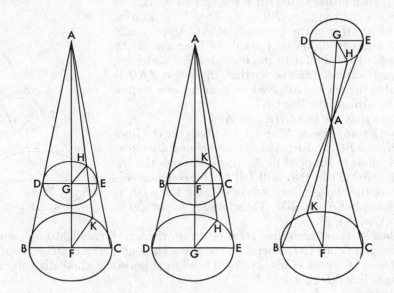

section will be the triangle ABC (i. 3). And since the points D, G, E are points in the cutting plane, and are also in the plane of the triangle ABC, therefore DGE is a straight line (Eucl. xi. 3).

Then let some point H be taken on the line DE, and let AH be joined and produced. Then it falls on the circumference BC (i. 1). Let it meet it at K, and let GH and FK be joined. And since two parallel planes, DE and BC, are cut by a plane ABC, their common sections are parallel (Eucl. xi. 16). Therefore the straight line DE is parallel to the straight line BC. Then for the same reason the straight line GH is also parallel to the straight line KF. Therefore

$$FA : AG :: FB : DG :: FC : GE :: FK : GH \text{ (Eucl. vi. 4).}$$

And $$BF = KF = FC$$

Therefore also $$DG = GH = GE \text{ (Eucl. v. 9).}$$

Then likewise we could show also that all the straight lines falling from the point G on the line DE are equal to each other.

Therefore the line DE is a circle having its center on the axis.

And it is evident that the figure contained by the circle DE and the conic surface cut off by it on the side of the point A is a cone.

And it is therewith proved that the common section of the cutting plane and of the axial triangle (triangle through the axis) is a diameter of the circle.

Proposition 5

If an oblique cone is cut by a plane through the axis at right angles to the base, and is also cut by another plane on the one hand at right angles to the axial triangle, and on the other cutting off on the side of the vertex a triangle similar to the axial triangle and lying subcontrariwise, then the section is a circle, and let such a section be called subcontrary.

Let there be an oblique cone whose vertex is the point A and whose base is the circle BC, and let it be cut by a plane through the axis perpendicular to the circle BC, and let it make as a section the triangle ABC (I. 3). Then let it also be cut by another plane perpendicular to the triangle ABC and cutting off on the side of the point A the triangle AKG similar to the triangle ABC and lying subcontrariwise, that is, so that the angle AKG is equal to the angle ABC. And let it make as a section on the surface, the line GHK.

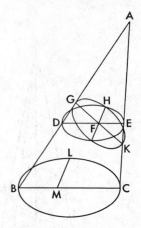

I say that the line GHK is a circle.

For let any points H and L be taken on the lines GHK and BC, and from the points H and L let perpendiculars be dropped to the plane through the triangle ABC. Then they will fall to the common sections of the planes (Eucl. XI. def. 6). Let them fall as for example FH and LM. Therefore FH is parallel to LM (Eucl. XI. 6).

Then let the straight line DFE be drawn through F parallel to BC; and FH is also parallel to LM. Therefore the plane through FH and DE is parallel to the base of the cone (Eucl. XI. 15). Therefore it is a circle whose diameter is the straight line DE (I. 4).

Therefore

rect. DF, FE = sq. FH (Eucl. III. 31 and VI. 8, porism).

And since ED is parallel to BC, angle ADE is equal to angle ABC. And angle AKG is supposed equal to angle ABC. And therefore angle AKG is equal to angle ADE. And the vertical angles at the point F are also equal. Therefore triangle DFG is similar to triangle KFE, and therefore

$$EF : FK :: GF : FD \text{ (Eucl. VI. 4).}$$

Therefore

rect. EF, FD = rect. KF, FG (Eucl. VI. 16).

But it has been shown that

sq. FH = rect. EF, FD;

and therefore

rect. KF, FG = sq. FH.

Likewise then all the perpendiculars drawn from the line GHK to the straight line GK could also be shown to be equal in square to the rectangle, in each case, contained by the segments of the straight line GK.

Therefore the section is a circle whose diameter is the straight line GK.

PROPOSITION 6

If a cone is cut by a plane through the axis, and some point is taken on the surface of the cone which is not on a side of the axial triangle, and from it is drawn a straight line parallel to some straight line which is a perpendicular from the circumference of the circle to the base of the triangle, then it meets the axial triangle, and on being produced to the other side of the surface it will be bisected by the triangle.

Let there be a cone whose vertex is the point A and whose base is the circle BC, and let the cone be cut by a plane through the axis, and let it make a common section the triangle ABC (I. 3); and from some point M of those on the

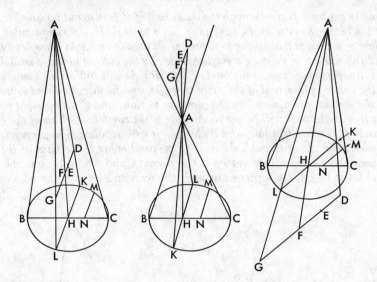

circumference, let the straight line MN be drawn perpendicular to the straight line BC. Then let some point D be taken on the surface of the cone, and through D let the straight line DE be drawn parallel to MN.

I say that the straight line DE produced will meet the plane of the triangle ABC, and, if further produced toward the other side of the cone until it meet its surface, will be bisected by the triangle ABC.

Let the straight line AD be joined and be produced. Therefore it will meet the circumference of the circle BC (I. 1). Let it meet it at K and from K let the straight line KHL be drawn perpendicular to the straight line BC. Therefore KH is parallel to MN, and therefore to DE (Eucl. XI. 9).

Let the straight line AH be joined from A to H. Since then in the triangle AHK the straight line DE is parallel to the straight line HK, therefore DE produced will meet AH. But AH is in the plane of ABC; therefore DE will meet the plane of the triangle ABC.

For the same reasons it also meets AH; let it meet it at F, and let DF be produced in a straight line until it meet the surface of the cone. Let it meet it at G.

I say that DF is equal to FG.

For since A, G, L are points on the surface of the cone, but also in the plane extended through the straight lines AH, AK, DG, KL, which is a triangle through the vertex of the cone (I. 3), therefore A, G, L are points on the common section of the cone's surface and of the triangle. Therefore the line through A, G, L is a straight line. Since then in the triangle ALK the straight line DG has been drawn parallel to the base KHL and some straight line AFH has been drawn across them from the point A, therefore

$$KH : HL : : DF : FG \text{ (Eucl. VI. 2)}.$$

But *KH* is equal to *HL*, since *KL* is a chord in circle *BC* perpendicular to the diameter (Eucl. iii. 3). Therefore *DF* is equal to *FG*.

If a cone is cut by a plane through the axis, and if it is also cut by another plane cutting the plane the base of the cone is in, in a straight line perpendicular either to the base of the axial triangle or to it produced, then the straight lines drawn from the resulting section on the cone's surface, made by the cutting plane, parallel to the straight line perpendicular to the base of the triangle will fall on the common section of the cutting plane and of the axial triangle, and further produced to the other side of the section, are bisected by the common section; and if it is a right cone the straight line in the base will be perpendicular to the common section of the cutting plane and of the axial triangle, and if oblique, it will not always be perpendicular, but whenever the plane through the axis is perpendicular to the base of the cone.

Let there be a cone whose vertex is the point *A* and whose base is the circle *BC*, and let it be cut by a plane through the axis and let it make as a section

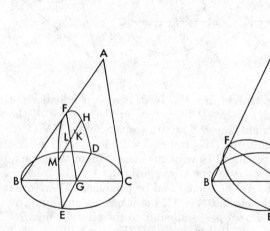

the triangle *ABC* (i. 3). And let it also be cut by another plane cutting the plane the circle *BC* is in, in the straight line *DE* perpendicular either to the straight line *BC* or to it produced, and let it make as a section on the surface of the cone the line *DFE*. Then the straight line *FG* is the common section of the cutting plane and of the triangle *ABC*. And let any point *H* be taken on the section *DFE*, and let the straight line *HK* be drawn through *H* parallel to the straight line *DE*.

I say that the straight line *HK* meets the straight line *FG*, and, on being produced to the other side of the section *DFE*, will be bisected by *FG*.

For since a cone whose vertex is the point *A* and whose base is the circle *BC* has been cut by a plane through its axis, and makes as a section the triangle *ABC*, and some point *H* on the surface, not on a side of the triangle *ABC*, has been taken, and since the straight line *DG* is perpendicular to the straight line *BC*, therefore the straight line drawn through *H* parallel to *DG*, that is *HK*, meets the triangle *ABC*, and if further produced to the other side of the surface, will be bisected by the triangle (i. 6).

Then since the straight line drawn through H parallel to the straight line DE meets the triangle ABC and is in the plane of the section DFE, therefore

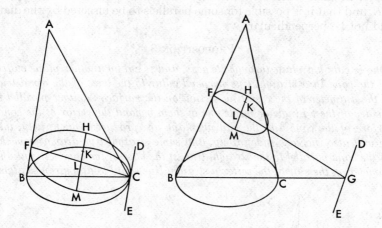

it will fall on the common section of the cutting plane and of the triangle ABC. But the straight line FG is the common section of the planes. Therefore the straight line drawn through H parallel to DE will fall on FG, and, if further produced to the other side of the section DFE, will be bisected by the straight line FG.

Then either the cone is a right cone, or the axial triangle ABC is perpendicular to the circle BC, or neither.

First let the cone be a right cone. Then the triangle ABC would be perpendicular to the circle BC (Def. 3; Eucl. XI. 18). Since then the plane ABC is perpendicular to the plane BC, and the straight line DE has been drawn in one of the planes, BC, perpendicular to their common section the straight line BC, therefore the straight line DE is perpendicular to the triangle ABC (Eucl. XI. def. 4), and therefore to all the straight lines touching it and in the triangle ABC (Eucl. XI. def. 3). And so it is also perpendicular to the straight line FG.

Then let the cone not be a right cone. If now the axial triangle is perpendicular to the circle BC, we could likewise show that DE is perpendicular to FG.

Then let the axial triangle ABC not be perpendicular to the circle BC. — I say that DE is not perpendicular to FG. For if possible, let it be. And it is also perpendicular to the straight line BC. Therefore DE is perpendicular to both BC and FG, and therefore it will be perpendicular to the plane through BC and FG. But the plane through BC and GF is the triangle ABC, and therefore DE is perpendicular to the triangle ABC. And therefore all the planes through it are perpendicular to the triangle ABC. But one of the planes through DE is the circle BC; therefore the circle BC is perpendicular to the triangle ABC. And so the triangle ABC will also be perpendicular to the circle BC. And this is not supposed. Therefore the straight line DE is not perpendicular to the straight line FG.

PORISM

Then from this it is evident that the straight line *FG* is the diameter of the section *DFE*, since it bisects the straight lines drawn parallel to some straight line *DE*, and that it is possible for some parallels to be bisected by the diameter *FG* and not be perpendicular.

PROPOSITION 8

If a cone is cut by a plane through its axis, and is cut by another plane cutting the base of the cone in a straight line perpendicular to the base of the axial triangle, and if the diameter of the resulting section on the surface is either parallel to one of the sides of the triangle or meets one of them beyond the vertex of the cone, and the surface of the cone and the cutting plane are produced indefinitely, then the section will also increase indefinitely, and some straight line drawn from the section of the cone parallel to the straight line in the base of the cone will cut off from the diameter on the side of the vertex a straight line equal to any given straight line.

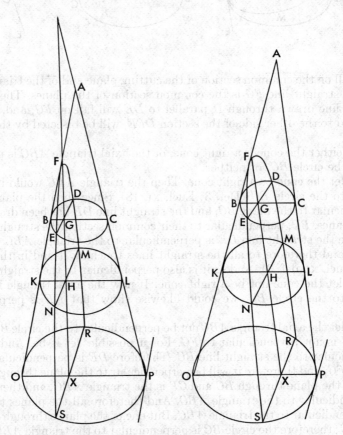

Let there be a cone whose vertex is the point *A* and whose base is the circle *BC*, and let it be cut by a plane through its axis, and let it make as a section the triangle *ABC* (I. 3). And let it be cut also by another plane cutting the circle BC in a straight line DE perpendicular to the straight line BC, and let it make as a section on the surface the line DFE. And let the diameter FG of the section DFE be either parallel to the straight line AC or on being produced meet it beyond the point A (I. 7 and porism).

I say that, if both the surface of the cone and the cutting plane are produced indefinitely, the section DFE also will increase indefinitely.

For let both the surface of the cone and the cutting plane be produced. Then it is evident that also the straight lines AB, AC, FG will be therewith produced. Since the straight line FG is either parallel to AC or produced meets it beyond the point A, therefore the straight lines FG and AC on being produced in the direction of C and G will never meet. Then let them be produced and let some point H be taken at random on the straight line FG, and let the straight line KHL be drawn through the point H parallel to the straight line BC, and MHN parallel to DE. Therefore the plane through KL and MN is parallel to the plane through BC and DE (Eucl. XI. 15). Therefore the plane $KLMN$ is a circle (I. 4).

And since the points D, E, M, N are in the cutting plane and also on the surface of the cone, therefore they are on the common section. Therefore the section DFE has increased to the points M and N. Therefore, with the surface of the cone and the cutting plane increased to the circle $KLMN$, the section DFE has also increased to the points M and N. Then likewise we could show also, that if the surface of the cone and the cutting plane are extended indefinitely, the section $MDFEN$ will also increase indefinitely.

And it is evident that some straight line will cut off on straight line FH on the side of point F a straight line equal to any given straight line. For if we lay down the straight line FX equal to the given straight line, and draw a parallel to DE through X, it will meet the section, just as the straight line through H was also proved to meet the section in the points M and N. And so some straight line is drawn meeting the section, parallel to DE, and cutting off on FG on the side of point H a straight line equal to the given straight line.

PROPOSITION 9

If a cone is cut by a plane meeting both sides of the axial triangle, and neither parallel to the base nor situated subcontrariwise, then the section will not be a circle.

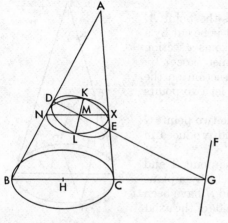

Let there be a cone whose vertex is the point A and whose base is the circle BC, and let it be cut by some plane neither parallel to the base nor situated subcontrariwise, and let it make as a section on the surface the line DKE.

I say that the line DKE will not be a circle.

For if possible, let it be, and let the cutting plane meet the base, and let the straight line FG be the common section of the planes, and let the point H be the center of the circle BC, and let the straight line HG be drawn from it perpendicular to the straight line FG. And let a plane be extended through GH and the axis and let it make as sections on the conic surface the straight lines BA and AC (I. 1). Since then D, E, G are points in the plane through the line DKE, and also in the plane through the points A, B, C, therefore D, E, G are points on the common section of the planes. Therefore GED is a straight line (Eucl. XI. 3).

Then let some point K be taken on the line DKE, and through K let the straight line KL be drawn parallel to the straight line FG; then KM will be equal to ML (I. 7). Therefore the straight line DE is the diameter of the circle $DKLE$ (Def. 4). Then let the straight line NMX be drawn through M parallel to the straight line BC. But KL is also parallel to FG. And so the plane through the straight lines NX and KM is parallel to the plane through the straight lines BC and FG, that is to the base (Eucl. XI. 15), and the section will be a circle (I. 4). Let it be the circle NKX.

And since the straight line FG is perpendicular to the straight line BG, the straight line KM is also perpendicular to the straight line NX (Eucl. XI. 10). And so

$$\text{rect. } NM, MX = \text{sq. } KM \text{ (Eucl. III. 31; VI. 8, porism)}$$

But

$$\text{rect. } DM, ME = \text{sq. } KM,$$

for the line $DKEL$ is supposed a circle, and the straight line DE is its diameter. Therefore

$$\text{rect. } NM, MX = \text{rect. } DM, ME.$$

Therefore

$$MN : MD :: EM : MX \text{ (Eucl. VI. 16).}$$

Therefore triangle DMN is similar to triangle XME (Eucl. VI. 6; VI. def. 1), and angle DNM is equal to angle MEX. But angle DNM is equal to angle ABC, for the straight line NX is parallel to the straight line BC. And therefore angle ABC is equal to angle MEX. Therefore the section is subcontrary (I. 5). And this is not supposed. Therefore the line DKE is not a circle.

PROPOSITION 10

If two points are taken on the section of a cone, the straight line joining the two points will fall within the section, and produced in a straight line it will fall outside.

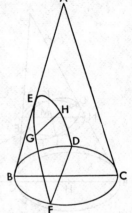

Let there be a cone whose vertex is the point A, and whose base is the circle BC, and let it be cut by a plane through the axis, and let it make as a section the triangle ABC (I. 3). Then let it also be cut by another plane, and let it make as a section on the surface of the cone the line DEF, and let two points G and H be taken on the line DEF.

I say that the straight line joining the two points G and H will fall within the line DEF, and produced in a straight line it will fall outside.

For since a cone, whose vertex is the point A and whose base is the circle BC, has been cut by a plane through the axis, and some points G and H have been taken on its surface which are not on a side of the axial triangle, and since the straight line joining G and H does not verge to the point A, therefore the straight line joining G and H will fall within the cone, and produced in a straight line it will fall outside (I. 2); consequently also outside the section DFE.

PROPOSITION 11

If a cone is cut by a plane through its axis, and also cut by another plane cutting the base of the cone in a straight line perpendicular to the base of the axial triangle, and if further the diameter of the section is parallel to one side of the axial triangle, then any straight line which is drawn from the section of the cone to its diameter parallel to the common section of the cutting plane and of the cone's base, will equal in square the rectangle contained by the straight line cut off by it on the diameter beginning from the section's vertex and by another straight line which has the ratio to the straight line between the angle of the cone and the vertex of the section that the square on the base of the axial triangle has to the rectangle contained by the remaining two sides of the triangle. And let such a section be called a parabola (παραβολή).

Let there be a cone whose vertex is the point A, and whose base is the circle BC, and let it be cut by a plane through its axis, and let it make as a section the triangle ABC (I. 3). And let it also be cut by another plane cutting the base of the cone in the straight line DE perpendicular to the straight line BC, and let it make as a section on the surface of the cone the line DFE, and let the diameter of the section FG (I. 7, and def. 4) be parallel to one side AC of the axial triangle. And let the straight line FH be drawn from the point F perpendicular to the straight line FG, and let it be contrived that

$$\text{sq. } BC : \text{rect. } BA, AC :: FH : FA.$$

And let some point K be taken at random on the section, and through K let the straight line KL be drawn parallel to the straight line DE.

I say that sq. $KL = \text{rect. } HF, FL$.

For let the straight line MN be drawn through L parallel to the straight line BC. And the straight line DE is also parallel to the straight line KL. Therefore the plane through KL and MN is parallel to the plane through BC and DE (Eucl. XI. 15), that is to the base of the cone. Therefore the plane through KL and MN is a circle whose diameter is MN (I. 4). And KL is perpendicular to MN since DE is also perpendicular to BC (Eucl. XI. 10). Therefore

rect. $ML, LN = \text{sq. } KL$ (Eucl. III. 31; VI. 8, porism).

And since

$$\text{sq. } BC : \text{rect. } BA \cdot AC :: HF : FA,$$

and

$$\text{sq. } BC : \text{rect. } BA, AC \text{ comp. } BC : CA, BC : BA \text{ (Eucl. VI. 23)},$$

therefore

$$HF : FA \text{ comp. } BC : CA, BC : BA.$$

But

$$BC : CA :: MN : NA :: ML : LF \text{ (Eucl. VI. 4)},$$

and

$$BC : BA :: MN : MA :: LM : MF :: NL : FA \text{ (Eucl. VI. 2)}.$$

Therefore

$$HF : FA \text{ comp. } ML : LF, NL : FA.$$

But

rect. ML, LN : rect. LF, FA comp. $ML : LF, LN : FA$ (Eucl. VI. 23).

Therefore

$$HF : : FA : : \text{rect. } ML, LN : \text{rect. } LF, FA$$

But, with the straight line FL taken as common height,

$$HF : FA : : \text{rect. } HF, FL : \text{rect. } LF, FA \text{ (Eucl. VI. 1),}$$

therefore

rect. ML, LN : rect. LF, FA : : rect. HF, FL : rect. LF, FA (Eucl. v. 11).

Therefore

$$\text{rect. } ML, LN = \text{rect. } HF, FL \text{ (Eucl. v. 9).}$$

But

$$\text{rect. } ML, LN = \text{sq. } KL,$$

therefore also

$$\text{sq. } KL = \text{rect. } HF, FL.$$

And let such a section be called a parabola, and let HF be called the straight line to which the straight lines drawn ordinatewise to the diameter FG are applied in square ($\pi\alpha\rho$ ἥν δύναται αἱ καταγόμεναι τεταγμένως ἐπὶ τὴν ZH διάμετρον), and let it also be called the upright side (ὀρθία).[1]

PROPOSITION 12

If a cone is cut by a plane through its axis, and also by another plane cutting the base of the cone in a straight line perpendicular to the base of the axial triangle, and if the diameter of the section produced meets one side of the axial triangle beyond the vertex of the cone, then any straight line which is drawn from the section to its diameter parallel to the common section of the cutting plane and of the cone's base, will equal in square some area applied to a straight line to which the straight line added along the diameter of the section and subtending the exterior angle of the triangle has the ratio that the square on the straight line drawn from the cone's vertex to the triangle's base parallel to the section's diameter has to the rectangle contained by the sections of the base which this straight line makes when drawn, this area having as breadth the straight line cut off on the diameter beginning from the section's vertex by this straight line from the section to the diameter and exceeding (ὑπερβάλλον) by a figure (εἶδος), similar and similarly situated to the rectangle contained by the straight line subtending the exterior angle of the triangle and by the parameter. And let such a section be called an hyperbola (ὑπερβολή).

Let there be a cone whose vertex is the point A and whose base is the circle BC, and let it be cut by a plane through its axis, and let it make as a section the triangle ABC (I. 3). And let it also be cut by another plane cutting the base of the cone in the straight line DE perpendicular to BC the base of the triangle ABC, and let it make as a section on the surface of the cone the line DFE, and

[1] The Greek of the phrase "the straight line to which the straight lines drawn ordinatewise to the diameter are applied in square," that is ἡ παρ ἥν δύνανται αἱ καταγόμεναι τεταγμένως ἐπὶ τὴν διάμετρον, soon becomes abbreviated to ἡ παρ ἥν δύνανται αἱ καταγόμεναι and to ἡ παρ ἥν δύνανται. We shall translate these abbreviations by the word "parameter." And we shall later on, after proposition XIV shorten the long expression to "the parameter of the ordinates to the diameter."

The Latin translation of ὀρθία (πλευρά) is *latus rectum* which has become an English term too.

let *FG* the diameter of the section (I. 7 and def. 4) when produced meet *AC* one side of the triangle *ABC* beyond the vertex of the cone at the point *H*. And let

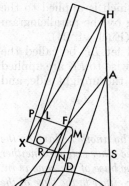

the straight line *AK* be drawn through *A* parallel to the diameter of the section *FG*, and let it cut *BC*. And let the straight line *FL* be drawn from *F* perpendicular to *FG*, and let it be contrived that

sq. *KA* : rect. *BK,KC* : : *FH* : *FL*.

And let some point *M* be taken at random on the section, and through *M* let the straight line *MN* be drawn parallel to *DE*, and through *N* let the straight line *NOX* be drawn parallel to *FL*. And let the straight line *HL* be joined and produced to *X*, and let the straight lines *LO* and *XP* be drawn through *L* and *X* parallel to *FN*.

I say that *MN* is equal in square to the parallelogram *FX* which is applied to *FL*, having *FN* as breadth, and exceeding by a figure *LX* similar to the rectangle contained by *HF* and *FL*.

For let the straight line *RNS* be drawn through *N* parallel to *BC*; and *NM* is also parallel to *DE*. Therefore the plane through *MN* and *RS* is parallel to the plane through *BC* and *DE*, that is to the base of the cone (Eucl. XI. 15). Therefore if the plane is produced through *MN* and *RS*, the section will be a circle whose diameter is the straight line *RNS* (I. 4). And *MN* is perpendicular to it. Therefore

rect. *RN, NS* = sq. *MN*.

And since

sq. *AK* : rect. *BK,KC* : : *FH* : *FL*,

and

sq. *AK* : rect. *BK,KC* comp. *AK* : *KC, AK* : *KB* (Eucl. VI. 23),

therefore also

FH : *FL* comp. *AK* : *KC, AK* : *KB*.

But

AK : *KC* : : *HG* : *GC* : : *HN* : *NS* (Eucl. VI. 4),

and

AK : *KB* : : *FG* : *GB* : : *FN* : *NR*.

Therefore

HF : *FL* comp. *HN* : *NS, FN* : *NR*.

And

rect. *HN, NF* : rect. *SN, NR* comp. *HN* : *NS, FN* : *NR* (Eucl. VI. 23).

Therefore also

rect. *HN, NF* : rect. *SN, NR* : : *HF* : *FL* : : *HN* : *NX* (Eucl. VI. 4).

But, with the straight line *FN* taken as common height,

HN : *NX* : : rect. *HN, NF* : rect. *FN, NX* (Eucl. VI. 1).

Therefore also

rect. *HN, NF* : rect. *SN, NR* : : rect. *HN, NF* : rect. *XN, NF* (Eucl. V. 11).

Therefore

rect. *SN, NR* = rect. *XN, NF* (Eucl. V. 9).

But it was shown

sq. *MN* = rect. *SN, NR*;

therefore also

$$\text{sq. } MN = \text{rect. } XN, NF.$$

But the rectangle contained by XN and NF is the parallelogram XF. Therefore the straight line MN is equal in square to XF which is applied to the straight line FL, having FN as breadth, and exceeding by the parallelogram LX similar to the rectangle contained by HF and FL (Eucl. VI. 24).

And let such a section be called an hyperbola, and let LF be called the straight line to which the straight lines drawn ordinatewise to FG are applied in square; and let the same straight line also be called the upright side, and the straight line FH the transverse side.

Proposition 13

If a cone is cut by a plane through its axis, and is also cut by another plane on the one hand meeting both sides of the axial triangle, and on the other extended neither parallel to the base nor subcontrariwise, and if the plane the base of the cone is in, and the cutting plane meet in a straight line perpendicular either to the base of the axial triangle or to it produced, then any straight line which is drawn from the section of the cone to the diameter of the section parallel to the common section of the planes, will equal in square some area applied to a straight line to which the diameter of the section has the ratio that the square on the straight line drawn from the cone's vertex to the triangle's base parallel to the section's diameter has to the rectangle contained by the intercepts of this straight line (on the base) from the sides of the triangle, an area having as breadth the straight line cut off on the diameter beginning from the section's vertex by this straight line from the section to the diameter, and deficient (ἐλλεῖπον) by a figure similar and similarly situated to the rectangle contained by the diameter and parameter. And let such a section be called an ellipse (ἔλλειψις).

Let there be a cone whose vertex is the point A and whose base is the circle BC, and let it be cut by a plane through its axis, and let it make as a section

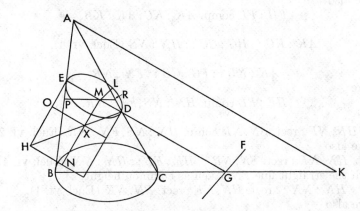

the triangle ABC. And let it also be cut by another plane on the one hand meeting both sides of the axial triangle and on the other extended neither parallel to the base of the cone nor subcontrariwise, and let it make as a section on the surface of the cone the line DE. And let the common section of the cutting plane and of the plane the base of the cone is in, be the straight line FG perpendicular to the straight line BC, and let the diameter of the section be the straight line ED (I. 7 and Def. 4). And let the straight line EH be drawn from E perpendicular to ED, and let the straight line AK be drawn through A parallel to ED, and let it be contrived that

$$\text{sq. } AK : \text{rect. } BK \cdot KC :: DE : EH.$$

And let some point L be taken on the section, and let the straight line LM be drawn through L parallel to FG.

I say that the straight line LM is equal in square to some area which is applied to EH, having EM as breadth and deficient by a figure similar to the rectangle contained by DE and EH.

For let the straight line DH be joined, and on the one hand let the straight line MXN be drawn through M parallel to HE, and on the other let the straight lines HN and XO be drawn through H and X parallel to EM, and let the straight line PMR be drawn through M parallel to BC.

Since then PR is parallel to BC, and LM is also parallel to FG, therefore the plane through LM and PR is parallel to the plane through FG and BC, that is to the base of the cone (Eucl. XI. 15). If therefore a plane is extended through LM and PR, the section will be a circle whose diameter is PR (I. 4). And LM is perpendicular to it. Therefore

$$\text{rect. } PM,MR = \text{sq. } LM.$$

And since

$$\text{sq. } AK : \text{rect. } BK, KC :: ED : EH,$$

and

$$\text{sq. } AK : \text{rect. } BK, KC \text{ comp. } AK : KB, AK : KC \text{ (Eucl. VI. 23)},$$

but

$$AK : KB :: EG : GB :: EM : MP \text{ (Eucl. VI. 4)},$$

and

$$AK : KC :: DG : GC :: DM : MR,$$

therefore

$$DE : EH \text{ comp. } EM : MP, DM : MR.$$

But

$$\text{rect. } EM, MD : \text{rect. } PM, MR \text{ comp. } EM : MP, DM : MR \text{ (Eucl. VI. 23)}.$$

Therefore

$$\text{rect. } EM,MD : \text{rect. } PM,MR :: DE : EH :: DM : MX \text{ (Eucl. VI. 4)}.$$

And, with the straight line ME taken as common height,

$$DM : MX :: \text{rect. } DM, ME \text{ rect. } XM, ME \text{ (Eucl. VI. 1)}.$$

Therefore also

rect. DM, ME : rect. PM, MR :: rect. DM, ME : rect. XM, ME (Eucl. V. 11).

Therefore

$$\text{rect. } PM, MR = \text{rect. } XM, ME \text{ (Eucl. V. 9)}.$$

But it was shown

$$\text{rect. } PM, MR = \text{sq. } LM;$$

therefore also

$$\text{rect. } XM, ME = \text{sq. } LM.$$

Therefore the straight line LM is equal in square to the parallelogram MO which is applied to the straight line HE, having EM as breadth and deficient by the figure ON similar to the rectangle contained by DE and EH (Eucl. VI. 24).

And let such a section be called an ellipse, and let EH be called the straight line to which the straight lines drawn ordinatewise to DE are applied in square, and let the same straight line also be called the upright side, and the straight line ED the transverse side.

PROPOSITION 14

If the vertically opposite surfaces are cut by a plane not through the vertex, the section on each of the two surfaces will be that which is called the hyperbola; and the diameter of the two sections will be the same straight line; and the straight lines, to which the straight lines drawn to the diameter parallel to the straight line in the cone's base are applied in square, are equal; and the transverse side of the figure, that between the vertices of the sections, is common. And let such sections be called opposite (ἀντικείμεναι).

Let there be the vertically opposite surfaces whose vertex is the point A, and let them be cut by a plane not through the vertex, and let it make as sections on the surface the lines DEF and GHK.

I say that each of the two sections DEF and GHK is the so-called hyperbola.

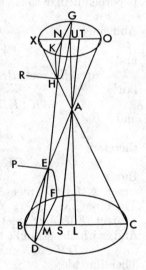

For let there be the circle $BDCF$ along which the line generating the surface moves, and let the plane $XGOK$ be extended parallel to it on the vertically opposite surface; and the straight lines FD and GK are common sections of the sections GHK and FED, and of the circles (i. 4). Then they will be parallel (Eucl. xi. 16). And let the straight line LAU be the axis of the conic surface, and the points L and U be the centers of the circles, and let a straight line drawn from L perpendicular to the straight line FD be produced to the points B and C, and let a plane be produced through the straight line BC and the axis. Then it will make as sections in the circles the parallel straight lines XO and BC (Eucl. xi. 16), and on the surface the straight lines BAO and CAX (i. 1 and Def. 4).

Then the straight line XO will be perpendicular to the straight line GK, since the straight line BC is also perpendicular to the straight line FD, and each of the two is parallel to the other (Eucl. xi. 10). And since the plane through the axis meets the sections in the points M and N within the lines, it is clear that the plane also cuts the lines. Let it cut them at H and E; therefore M, E, H, and N are points on the plane through the axis and in the plane the lines are in; therefore the line $MEHN$ is a straight line (Eucl. xi. 3). It is also evident both that X, H, A, and C are in a straight line and B, E, A, and O also. For they are both on the conic surface and in the plane through the axis (i. 1).

Let then the straight lines HR and EP be drawn from H and E perpendicular to HE, and let the straight line SAT be drawn through A parallel to $MEHN$, and let it be contrived that

$$HE : EP :: \text{sq. } AS : \text{rect. } BS, SC,$$

and

$$EH : HR :: \text{sq. } AT : \text{rect. } OT, TX.$$

Since then a cone, whose vertex is the point A and whose base is the circle BC, has been cut by a plane through its axis, and it has made as a section the triangle ABC; and it has also been cut by another plane cutting the base of the cone in the straight line DMF perpendicular to the straight line BC, and it has made as a section on the surface the line DEF; and the diameter ME produced has met one side of the axial triangle beyond the vertex of the cone, and through the point A the straight line AS has been drawn parallel to the diameter of the section EM, and from E the straight line EP has been drawn perpendicular to the straight line EM, and

$$EH : EP : : \text{sq. } AS : \text{rect. } BS, SC,$$

therefore the section DEF is an hyperbola (I. 12), and EP is the straight line to which the straight lines drawn ordinatewise to EM are applied in square, and the straight line HE is the transverse side of the figure. And likewise GHK is also an hyperbola whose diameter is the straight line HN and whose straight line to which the straight lines drawn ordinatewise to HN are applied is HR, and the transverse side of whose figure is HE.

I say that the straight line HR is equal to the straight line EP.

For since BC is parallel to XO,

$$AS : SC : : AT : TX$$

and

$$AS : SB : : AT : TO.$$

But

$$\text{sq. } AS : \text{rect. } BS, SC \text{ comp. } AS : SC, AS : SB \text{ (Eucl. VI. 23)}$$

and

$$\text{sq. } AT : \text{rect. } XT, TO \text{ comp. } AT : TX, AT : TO;$$

therefore

$$\text{sq. } AS : \text{rect. } BS, SC : : \text{sq. } AT : \text{rect. } XT, TO.$$

Also

$$\text{sq. } AS : \text{rect. } BS, SC : : HE : EP,$$

and

$$\text{sq. } AT : \text{rect. } XT, TO : : HE : HR.$$

Therefore also

$$HE : EP : : EH : HR \text{ (Eucl. V. 11).}$$

Therefore

$$EP = HR \text{ (Eucl. V. 9).}$$

PROPOSITION 15

If in an ellipse a straight line, drawn ordinatewise from the midpoint of the diameter, is produced both ways to the section, and if it is contrived that, as the straight line so produced is to the diameter, so is the diameter to some straight line, then any straight line which is drawn, from the section to the straight line produced, parallel to the diameter, will equal in square the area applied to this third proportional and having as breadth the straight line cut off by it beginning from the section and deficient by a figure similar to the rectangle contained by the straight line to which the straight lines are drawn and by the parameter; and if further produced to the other side of the section, will be bisected by the straight line to which it has been drawn.

Let there be an ellipse whose diameter is the straight line AB, and let AB be bisected at the point C, and through C let the straight line DCE be drawn ordinatewise and produced both ways to the section, and from the point D let the straight line DF be drawn perpendicular to DE. And let it be contrived that

$$DE : AB :: AB : DF$$

And let some point G be taken on the section, and through G let the straight line GH be drawn parallel to AB, and let EF be joined, and through H let the straight line HL be drawn parallel to DF, and through F and L let the straight lines FK and LM be drawn parallel to HD.

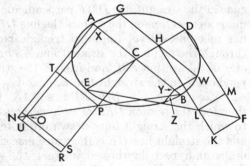

I say that the straight line GH is equal in square to the area DL which is applied to the straight line DF, having as breadth the straight line DH and deficient by a figure LF similar to the rectangle contained by ED and DF.

For let AN be the parameter of the ordinates to AB, and let BN be joined; and through G let the straight line GX be drawn parallel to DE, and through X and C let the straight lines XO and CP be drawn parallel to AN, and through N, O, and P let the straight lines NU, OS, and TP be drawn parallel to AB. Therefore

$$\text{sq. } DC = \text{ar. } AP, \quad \text{sq. } GX = \text{ar. } AO \text{ (i. 13).}$$

And since

$$BA : AN :: BC : CP :: PT : TN \text{ (Eucl. vi. 4),}$$

and

$$BC = CA = TP,$$

and

$$CP = TA,$$

therefore

$$\text{ar. } AP = \text{ar. } TR,$$

and

$$\text{ar. } XT = \text{ar. } TU.$$

Since also

$$\text{ar. } OT = \text{ar. } OR \text{ (Eucl. i. 43),}$$

and area NO is common, therefore

$$\text{ar. } TU = \text{ar. } NS.$$

But

$$\text{ar. } TU = \text{ar. } TX,$$

and TS is common. Therefore

$$\text{ar. } NP = \text{ar. } PA = \text{ar. } AO + \text{ar. } PO;$$

and so

$$\text{ar. } PA - \text{ar. } AO = \text{ar. } PO.$$

Also

$$\text{ar. } AP = \text{sq. } CD, \quad \text{ar. } AO = \text{sq. } XG,$$

and

$$\text{ar. } OP = \text{rect. } OS, SP;$$

therefore

$$\text{sq. } CD - \text{sq. } GX = \text{rect. } OS, SP.$$

Since also the straight line DE has been cut into equal parts at C, and into unequal parts at H, therefore

$$\text{rect. } EH, HD + \text{sq. } CH = \text{sq. } CD \text{ (Eucl. \textsc{ii}. 5)},$$

or

$$\text{rect. } EH, HD + \text{sq. } XG = \text{sq. } CD.$$

Therefore

$$\text{sq. } CD - \text{sq. } XG = \text{rect. } EH, HD;$$

but

$$\text{sq. } CD - \text{sq. } XG = \text{rect. } OS, SP;$$

therefore

$$\text{rect. } EH, HD = \text{rect. } OS, SP.$$

And since

$$DE : AB :: AB : DF,$$

therefore

$$DE : DF :: \text{sq. } DE : \text{sq. } AB \text{ (Eucl. \textsc{vi}. 20)},$$

that is

$$DE : DF :: \text{sq. } CD : \text{sq. } CB \text{ (Eucl. \textsc{v}. 15)};$$

And

$$\text{rect. } PC, CA = \text{rect. } PC, CB = \text{sq. } CD \text{ (\textsc{i}. 13)};$$

and since

$$DE : DF :: EH : HL \text{ (Eucl. \textsc{vi}. 4)},$$

or

$$DE : DF :: \text{rect. } EH, HD : \text{rect. } DH, HL \text{ (Eucl. \textsc{vi}. 1)},$$

and since

$$DE : DF :: \text{rect. } PC, CB : \text{sq. } CB,$$

and

$$\text{rect. } PC, CB : \text{sq. } CB :: \text{rect. } OS, SP : \text{sq. } OS,[1]$$

therefore also

$$\text{rect. } EH, HD : \text{rect. } DH, HL :: \text{rect. } OS, SP : \text{sq. } OS.$$

And

$$\text{rect. } EH, HD = \text{rect. } OS, SP;$$

therefore

$$\text{rect. } DH, HL = \text{sq. } OS = \text{sq. } GH.$$

Therefore the straight line GH is equal in square to the area DL which is applied to the straight line DF, deficient by a figure FL similar to the rectangle contained by ED and DF (Eucl. \textsc{vi}. 24).

I say then that also, if produced to the other side of the section, the straight line GH will be bisected by the straight line DE.

For let it be produced and let it meet the section at W, and let the straight line WY be drawn through Y parallel to GX, and through Y let the straight line YZ be drawn parallel to AN. And since

$$GX = WY,$$

therefore also

$$\text{sq. } GX = \text{sq. } WY.$$

---

[1]This follows from the proportions
$$PC : CB :: PS : OS \text{ (Eucl. \textsc{vi}. 4)},$$
and
$$PC : CB :: \text{rect. } PC, CB : \text{sq. } CB,$$
and
$$PS : OS :: \text{rect. } PS, OS : \text{sq. } OS \text{ (Eucl. \textsc{vi}. 1)}.$$

But
$$\text{sq. } GX = \text{rect. } AX, XO \text{ (i. 13)},$$
and
$$\text{sq. } WY = \text{rect. } AY, YZ \text{ (i. 13)}.$$
Therefore
$$OX : ZY :: YA : AX \text{ (Eucl. vi. 16)}.$$
And
$$OX : ZY :: XB : BY \text{ (Eucl. vi. 4)};$$
therefore also
$$YA : AX :: XB : BY.$$
And *separando*
$$YX : AX :: YX : BY \text{ (Eucl. v. 17)}.$$
Therefore
$$AX = YB.$$
And also
$$AC = CB;$$
therefore also the remainders
$$XC = CY;$$
and so also
$$GH = HW.$$
Therefore the straight line HG, produced to the other side of the section, is bisected by the straight line DH.

Proposition 16

If through the midpoint of the transverse side of the opposite sections a straight line be drawn parallel to a straight line drawn ordinatewise, it will be a diameter of the opposite sections conjugate to the diameter just mentioned.

Let there be the opposite sections whose diameter is the straight line AB,

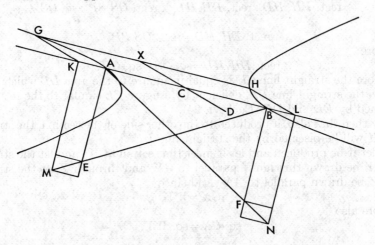

and let AB be bisected at C, and through C let the straight line CD be drawn parallel to a straight line drawn ordinatewise.

I say that the straight line CD is a diameter conjugate to AB.

For let the straight lines AE and BF be the parameters, and let the straight lines AF and BE be joined and produced, and let some point G be taken at random on either section, and through G let the straight line GH be drawn parallel to AB, and from G and H let the straight lines GK and HL be drawn ordinatewise, and through K and L let the straight lines KM and LN be drawn parallel to AE and BF. Since then

$$GK = HL \text{ (Eucl. I. 34),}$$

therefore also

$$\text{sq. } GK = \text{sq. } HL,$$

But

$$\text{sq. } GK = \text{rect. } AK, KM \text{ (I. 12),}$$

and

$$\text{sq. } HL = \text{rect. } BL, LN \text{ (I. 12);}$$

therefore

$$\text{rect. } AK, KM = \text{rect. } BL, LN.$$

And since

$$AE = BF,$$

therefore

$$AE : AB :: BF : BA \text{ (Eucl. V. 7).}$$

But

$$AE : AB :: MK : KB \text{ (Eucl. VI. 4),}$$

and as

$$BF : BA :: NL : LA \text{ (Eucl. VI. 4).}$$

And therefore

$$MK : KB :: NL : LA.$$

But, with KA taken as common height,

$$MK : KB :: \text{rect. } MK, KA : \text{rect. } BK, KA,$$

and, with BL taken as common height,

$$NL : LA :: \text{rect. } NL, LB : \text{rect. } AL, LB.$$

And therefore

$$\text{rect. } MK, KA : \text{rect. } BK, KA :: \text{rect. } NL, LB : \text{rect. } AL, LB.$$

And alternately

$$\text{rect. } MK, KA : \text{rect. } NL, LB :: \text{rect. } BK, KA : \text{rect. } AL, LB \text{ (Eucl. V. 16).}$$

And

$$\text{rect. } AK, KM = \text{rect. } BL, LN;$$

therefore

$$\text{rect. } BK, KA = \text{rect. } AL, LB;$$

therefore

$$AK = LB.[1]$$

But also

$$AC = CB,$$

and therefore

$$KC = CL;$$

and so also

$$GX = XH.$$

---

[1]The intermediary steps to this conclusion are as follows. If
$$\text{rect. } BK, KA = \text{rect. } AL, LB$$
then $BK : LB :: AL : KA,$
or $BA + AK : LB :: BA + LB : AK$
and *componendo* $BA + AK + LB : LB :: BA + LB + AK : AK.$

Therefore the straight line GH has been bisected by the straight line XCD; and is parallel to the straight line AB. Therefore the straight line XCD is a diameter and conjugate to the straight line AB (Defs. 4, 6).

SECOND DEFINITIONS

9. Let the midpoint of the diameter of both the hyperbola and the ellipse be called the center of the section, and let the straight line drawn from the center to meet the section be called the radius of the section.

10. And likewise let the midpoint of the transverse side of the opposite sections be called the center.

11. And let the straight line drawn from the center parallel to an ordinate, being a mean proportional to the sides of the figure (τὸ ἔιδος) and bisected by the center, be called the second diameter.

PROPOSITION 17

If in a section of a cone a straight line is drawn from the vertex of the line, and parallel to an ordinate, it will fall outside the section (Cf. Eucl. III. 16).

Let there be a section of a cone, whose diameter is the straight line AB.

I say that the straight line drawn from the vertex, that is from the point A, parallel to an ordinate, will fall outside the section.

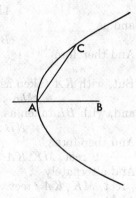

For if possible, let it fall within as AC. Since then a point C has been taken at random on a section of a cone, therefore the straight line drawn from the point C within the section parallel to an ordinate will meet the diameter AB and will be bisected by it (I. 7). Therefore the straight line AC produced will be bisected by the straight line AB. And this is absurd. For the straight line AC, if produced, will fall outside the section (I. 10). Therefore the straight line drawn from the point A parallel to an ordinate will not fall within the line; therefore it will fall outside; and therefore it is tangent to the section.

PROPOSITION 18

If a straight line, meeting a section of a cone and produced both ways, falls outside the section, and some point is taken within the section, and through it a parallel to the straight line meeting the section is drawn, the parallel so drawn, if produced both ways, will meet the section.

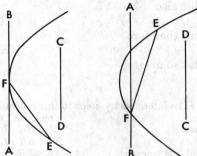

Let there be a section of a cone and the straight line AFB meeting it, and let it fall, when produced both ways, outside the section. And let some point C be taken within the section, and through C let the straight line CD be drawn parallel to the straight line AB.

I say that the straight line CD produced both ways will meet the section.

For let some point E be taken on the

section, and let the straight line EF be joined. And since the straight line AB is parallel to CD, and some straight line EF meets AB, therefore CD produced will also meet EF. And if it meets EF between the points E and F, it is evident that it also meets the section, but if beyond the point E, that it will first meet the section. Therefore CD produced to the side of points D and E meets the section. Then likewise we could show that, produced to the side of points F and B, it also meets it. Therefore the straight line CD produced both ways will meet the section.

PROPOSITION 19

In every section of a cone, any straight line drawn from the diameter parallel to an ordinate, will meet the section.

Let there be a section of a cone whose diameter is the straight line AB, and let some point B be taken on the diameter, and through B let the straight line BC be drawn parallel to an ordinate.

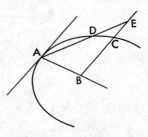

I say that the straight line BC produced will meet the section.

For let some point D be taken on the section. But A is also on the section; therefore the straight line joined from A to D will fall within the section (I. 10). And since the straight line drawn from A parallel to an ordinate falls outside the section (I. 17), and the straight line AD meets it, and the straight line BC is parallel to the ordinate, therefore BC will also meet AD. And if it meets AD between the points A and D, it is evident that it will also meet the section, but, if beyond point D as at E, that it will first meet the section. Therefore the straight line drawn from B parallel to an ordinate will meet the section.

PROPOSITION 20

If in a parabola two straight lines are dropped ordinatewise to the diameter, the squares on them will be to each other as the straight lines cut off by them on the diameter beginning from the vertex[1] are to each other.

Let there be a parabola whose diameter is the straight line AB, and let some points C and D be taken on it, and from the points C and D let the straight lines CE and DF be dropped ordinatewise to AB.

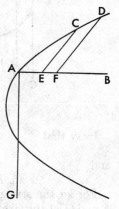

I say that

$$\text{sq. } DF : \text{sq. } CE :: FA : AE.$$

For let AG be the parameter; therefore

$$\text{sq. } DF = \text{rect. } FA, AG,$$

and

$$\text{sq. } CE = \text{rect. } EA, AG \quad (\text{I. } 11).$$

Therefore

$$\text{sq. } DF : \text{sq. } CE :: \text{rect. } FA, AG : \text{rect. } EA, AG.$$

But

$$\text{rect. } FA, AG : \text{rect. } EA, AG :: FA : AE \quad (\text{Eucl. } \text{VI. } 1);$$

---

[1] These are usually called "abscissas" from the Latin *abscindere*, to cut off.

and therefore

$$\text{sq. } DF : \text{sq. } CE :: FA : AE.$$

PROPOSITION 21

If in an hyperbola or ellipse or in the circumference of a circle straight lines are dropped ordinatewise to the diameter, the squares on them will be to the areas contained by the straight lines cut off by them beginning from the ends of the transverse side of the figure, as the upright side of the figure is to the transverse, and to each other as the areas contained by the straight lines cut off (abscissas), as we have said.

Let there be an hyperbola or ellipse or circumference of a circle whose diam-

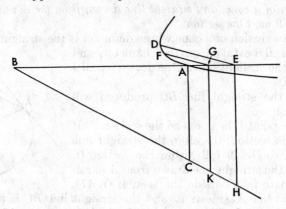

eter is AB and whose parameter is the straight line AC, and let the straight lines DE and FG be dropped ordinatewise to the diameter.

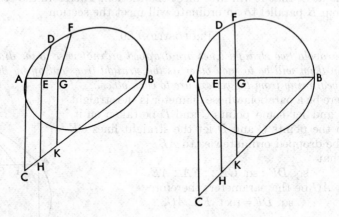

I say that

$$\text{sq. } FG : \text{rect. } AG, GB :: AC : AB$$

and

$$\text{sq. } FG : \text{sq. } DE :: \text{rect. } AG, GB : \text{rect. } AE, EB.$$

For let the straight line BC determining the figure be joined, and through E and G let the straight lines EH and GK be drawn parallel to the straight line AC. Therefore

$$\text{sq. } FG = \text{rect. } KG, GA$$
$$\text{sq. } DE = \text{rect. } HE, EA \text{ (I. 12, 13)}.$$

And since
$$KG : GB :: CA : AB;$$
and, with AG taken as common height,
$$KG : GB :: \text{rect. } KG, GA : \text{rect. } BG, GA,$$
therefore
$$CA : AB :: \text{rect. } KG, GA : \text{rect. } BG, GA.$$
or
$$CA : AB :: \text{sq. } FG : \text{rect. } BG, GA.$$
Then also for the same reasons
$$CA : AB :: \text{sq. } DE : \text{rect. } BE, EA.$$
And therefore
$$\text{sq. } FG : \text{rect. } BG, GA :: \text{sq. } DE : \text{rect. } BE, EA;$$
alternately
$$\text{sq. } FG : \text{sq. } DE :: \text{rect. } BG, GA : \text{rect. } BE, EA.[1]$$

PROPOSITION 22

If a straight line cuts a parabola or hyperbola in two points, not meeting the diameter inside, it will, if produced, meet the diameter of the section outside the section.

Let there be a parabola or hyperbola whose diameter is the straight line AB, and let some straight line cut the section in two points C and D.

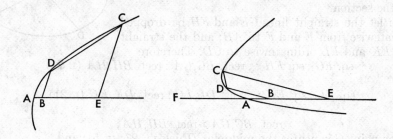

I say that the straight line DC, if produced, will meet the straight line AB outside the section.

For let the straight lines CE and DB be dropped ordinatewise from C and D; and first let the section be a parabola. Since then in the parabola
$$\text{sq. } CE : \text{sq. } DB :: EA : AB \text{ (I. 20)},$$
and
$$EA > AB,$$

[1] Eutocius commenting says: "It is to be noted that the parameter, that is the upright side, in the case of the circle is equal to the diameter. For if
$$\text{sq. } DE : \text{rect. } AE, EB :: CA, AB,$$
and only in the case of the circle
$$\text{sq. } DE = \text{rect. } AE, EB,$$
therefore also $\qquad CA = AB.$

"And this must also be noted that the ordinates on the circumference of the circle are in every case perpendicular to the diameter and are in a straight line with the parallels to AC (Eucl. III. 3, 4)."

therefore also

$$\text{sq. } CE > \text{sq. } DB \text{ (Eucl. v. 14).}$$

And so also

$$CE > DB.$$

And they are parallel; therefore CD produced will meet the diameter AB outside the section (i. 10; Eucl. i. 33).

But then let it be an hyperbola. Since then in the hyperbola

$$\text{sq. } CE : \text{sq. } DB : : \text{rect. } FE, EA : \text{rect. } FB, BA \text{ (i. 21),}$$

therefore also

$$\text{sq. } CE > \text{sq. } DB.$$

And they are parallel; therefore the straight line CD produced will meet the diameter of the section outside the section.

Proposition 23

If a straight line lying between the two (conjugate) diameters[1] cuts the ellipse, it will, when produced, meet each of the diameters outside the section.

Let there be an ellipse whose diameters are the straight lines AB and CD (i. 15), and let some straight line EF lying between the diameters AB and CD cut the section.

I say that the straight line EF, when produced, will meet each of the straight lines AB and CD outside the section.

For let the straight lines GE and FH be dropped ordinatewise from E and F to AB; and the straight lines EK and FL ordinatewise to CD. Therefore

$$\text{sq. } EG : \text{sq. } FH : : \text{rect. } BG, GA : \text{rect. } BH, HA \text{ (i. 21)}$$

and

$$\text{sq. } FL : \text{sq. } EK : : \text{rect. } DL, LC : \text{rect. } DK, KC \text{ (i. 21).}$$

And

$$\text{rect. } BG, GA > \text{rect. } BH, HA;$$

for the point G is nearer the midpoint (Eucl. vi. 27; ii. 5); and

$$\text{rect. } DL, LC > \text{rect. } DK, KC;$$

therefore also

$$\text{sq. } GE > \text{sq. } FH,$$

and

$$\text{sq. } FL > \text{sq. } EK;$$

therefore also

$$GE > FH,$$

and

$$FL > EK.$$

And GE is parallel to FH, and FL to EK; therefore the straight line EF produced will meet each of the diameters AB and CD outside the section (i. 10; Eucl. i. 33).

---

[1]So far Apollonius, by theorems i. 6, 13, 15, has shown, for every ellipse, the existence of at least one diameter and of one set of conjugate diameters, but of no more. He can therefore now speak of "the two diameters." Later on he will show the existence of an infinite number of such sets. The same is true of hyperbolas.

PROPOSITION 24

If a straight line, meeting a parabola or hyperbola at a point, when produced both ways, falls outside the section, then it will meet the diameter.

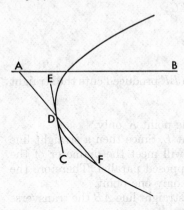

Let there be a parabola or hyperbola whose diameter is the straight line AB, and let the straight line CDE meet it at D, and, when produced both ways, let it fall outside the section.

I say that it will meet the diameter AB.

For let some point F be taken on the section, and let the straight line DF be joined; therefore DF produced will meet the diameter of the section (I. 22). Let it meet it at A; and the straight line CDE lies between the section and the straight line FDA. And therefore the line CDE produced will meet the diameter outside the section.

PROPOSITION 25

If a straight line, meeting an ellipse between the two (conjugate) diameters and produced both ways, falls outside the section, it will meet each of the diameters.

Let there be an ellipse whose diameters are the straight lines AB and CD

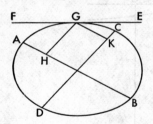

(I. 15), and let EF, some straight line between the two diameters, meet it at G, and produced both ways fall outside the section.

I say that the straight line EF will meet each of the straight lines AB and CD.

Let the straight lines GH and GK be dropped ordinatewise to the straight lines AB and CD respectively. Since GK is parallel to AB (I. 15), and some straight line GF has met GK, therefore it will also meet AB. Then likewise EF will also meet CD.

PROPOSITION 26

If in a parabola or hyperbola a straight line is drawn parallel to the diameter of the

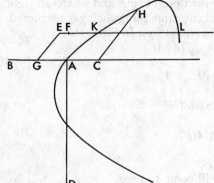

section, it will meet the section in one point only.

Let there first be a parabola whose diameter is the straight line ABC, and whose upright side is the straight line AD, and let the straight line EF be drawn parallel to AB.

I say that the straight line EF produced will meet the section.

For let some point E be taken on EF, and from E let the straight line EG be drawn parallel to an ordinate, and let

$$\text{rect. } DA, AC > \text{sq. } GE,$$

and from C let CH be erected ordinatewise (I. 19). Therefore

$$\text{sq. } HC = \text{rect. } DA, AC \text{ (I. 11)}.$$

But

$$\text{rect. } DA, AC > \text{sq. } EG;$$

therefore

$$\text{sq. } HC > \text{sq. } EG;$$

therefore

$$HC > EG.$$

And they are parallel; therefore the straight line EF produced cuts the straight line HC; and so it will also meet the section.

Let it meet it at the point K.

Then I say also that it will meet it in the one point K only.

For if possible, let it also meet it in the point L. Since then a straight line cuts a parabola in two points, if produced it will meet the diameter of the section (I. 22). And this is absurd, for it is supposed parallel. Therefore the straight line EF produced meets the section in only one point.

Next let the section be an hyperbola, and the straight line AB the transverse

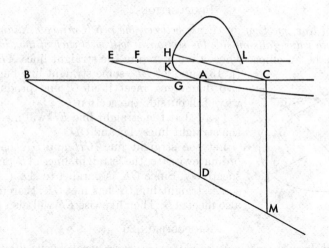

side of the figure, and the straight line AD the upright side, and let the straight line DB be joined and produced. Then with the same things being constructed, let the straight line CM be drawn from C parallel to AD. Since then

$$\text{rect. } MC, CA > \text{rect. } DA, AC,$$

and

$$\text{sq. } CH = \text{rect. } MC, CA,$$

and

$$\text{rect. } DA, AC > \text{sq. } GE,$$

therefore also

$$\text{sq. } CH > \text{sq. } GE.$$

And so also

$$CH > GE,$$

and the same things as in the first case will come to pass.

PROPOSITION 27

If a straight line cuts the diameter of a parabola, then produced both ways it will meet the section.

Let there be a parabola whose diameter is the straight line AB, and let some straight line CD cut it within the section.

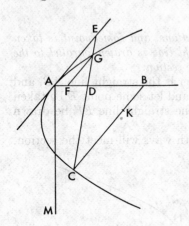

I say that the straight line CD produced both ways will meet the section.

For let some straight line AE be drawn from A parallel to an ordinate; therefore the straight line AE will fall outside the section (I. 17).

Then either the straight line CD is parallel to the straight line AE or not.

If now it is parallel to it, it has been dropped ordinatewise, so that produced both ways it will meet the section (I. 18).

Next let it not be parallel to AE, but produced let it meet AE at E. Then it is evident that it meets the section the side the point E is on; for if it meets AE, *a fortiori* it cuts the section.

I say that, produced the other way, it also meets the section. For let the straight line MA be the parameter and the straight line GF an ordinate, and let

$$\text{sq. } AD = \text{rect. } BA, AF \text{ (Eucl. VI. 11)},$$

and let the straight line BK, parallel to the ordinate, meet the straight line DC at C. Since

$$\text{rect. } BA, AF = \text{sq. } AD,$$

hence

$$AB : AD : : AD : AF;$$

and therefore,

$$BD : DF : : AB : AD \text{ (Eucl. V. 19)}.$$

Therefore also

$$\text{sq. } BD : \text{sq. } DF : : \text{sq. } AB : \text{sq. } AD.$$

But since

$$\text{sq. } AD = \text{rect. } BA, AF,$$

hence

$$AB : AF : : \text{sq. } AB : \text{sq. } AD : : \text{sq. } BD : \text{sq. } FD.$$

But

$$\text{sq. } BD : \text{sq. } DF : : \text{sq. } BC : \text{sq. } FG,$$

and

$$AB : AF : : \text{rect. } BA, AM : \text{rect. } FA, AM.$$

Therefore

$$\text{sq. } BC : \text{sq. } FG : : \text{rect. } BA, AM : \text{rect. } FA, AM;$$

and alternately

$$\text{sq. } BC : \text{rect. } BA, AM : : \text{sq. } FG : \text{rect. } FA, AM.$$

But

$$\text{sq. } FG = \text{rect. } FA, AM$$

because of the section (I. 11). Therefore also

$$\text{sq. } BC = \text{rect. } BA, AM.$$

But the straight line AM is the upright side,[1] and the straight line BC is parallel to an ordinate. Therefore the section passes through the point C (I. 20), and the straight line CD meets the section at the point C.

PROPOSITION 28

If a straight line touches one of the opposite sections, and some point is taken within the other section, and through it a straight line is drawn parallel to the tangent, then produced both ways, it will meet the section.

Let there be opposite sections whose diameter is the straight line AB, and let some straight line CD touch the section A, and let some point E be taken within the other section, and through E let the straight line EF be drawn parallel to the straight line CD.

I say that the straight line EF produced both ways will meet the section.

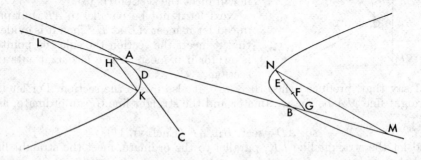

Since then it has been proved that the straight line CD produced will meet the diameter AB (I. 24), and EF is parallel to it, therefore EF produced will meet the diameter. Let it meet it at G, and let AH be made equal to GB, and through H let HK (I. 18) be drawn parallel to EF, and let the straight line KL be dropped ordinatewise, and let GM be made equal to LH, and let the straight line MN be drawn parallel to an ordinate and let GN be further produced in the same straight line. And since KL is parallel to MN, and KH to GN, and LM is one straight line, triangle KHL is similar to triangle HMN. And

$$LH = GM;$$

therefore

$$KL = MN.$$

And so also

$$\text{sq. } KL = \text{sq. } MN.$$

And since

$$LH = GM,$$

and

$$AH = BG,$$

and AB is common, therefore

$$BL = AM;$$

[1]The text reads πλαγία which is impossible. I have corrected to 'ορθία.

therefore
$$\text{rect. } BL, LA = \text{rect. } AM, MB.$$
Therefore
$$\text{rect. } BL, LA : \text{sq. } LK :: \text{rect. } AM, MB : \text{sq. } MN.$$
And
$$\text{rect. } BL, LA : \text{sq. } LK :: \text{the transverse : the upright (I. 21);}$$
therefore also
$$\text{rect. } AM, MB : \text{sq. } MN :: \text{the transverse : the upright.}$$
Therefore the point N is on the section. Therefore the straight line EF produced will meet the section at the point N (I. 21).

Likewise then it could be shown that produced to the other side it will meet the section.

PROPOSITION 29

If in opposite sections a straight line is drawn through the center to meet either of the sections, then produced it will cut the other section.

Let there be opposite sections whose diameter is the straight line AB, and whose center is the point C, and let the straight line CD cut the section AD.

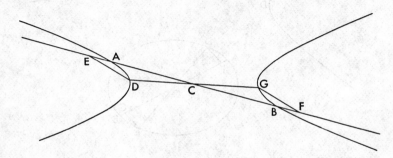

I say that it will also cut the other section.

For let the straight line ED be dropped ordinatewise, and let the straight line BF be made equal to the straight line AE, and let the straight line FG be drawn ordinatewise (I. 19). And since
$$EA = BF,$$
and AB is common, therefore
$$\text{rect. } BE, EA = \text{rect. } BF, FA.$$
And since
$$\text{rect. } BE, EA : \text{sq. } DE :: \text{the transverse : the upright (I. 21),}$$
but also
$$\text{rect. } BF, FA : \text{sq. } FG :: \text{the transverse : the upright (I. 21),}$$
therefore also
$$\text{rect. } BE, EA : \text{sq. } DE :: \text{rect. } BF, FA : \text{sq. } FG \text{ (I. 14).}$$
But
$$\text{rect. } BE, EA = \text{rect. } BF, FA;$$
therefore also
$$\text{sq. } DE = \text{sq. } FG.$$
Since then
$$EC = CF,$$

and

$$DE = FG,$$

and EF is a straight line, and ED is parallel to FG, therefore DG is also a straight line (Eucl. VI. 32). And therefore CD will also cut the other section.

PROPOSITION 30

If in an ellipse or in opposite sections a straight line is drawn in both directions from the center, meeting the section, it will be bisected at the center.

Let there be an ellipse or opposite sections, and their diameter the straight line AB, and their center C, and through C let some straight line DCE be drawn (I. 29).

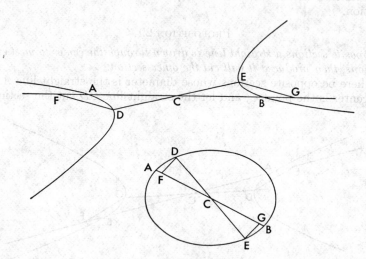

I say that the straight line CD is equal to the straight line CE.

For let the straight lines DF and EG be drawn ordinatewise. And since

       rect. BF,FA : sq. FD : : the transverse : the upright (I. 21),

but also

       rect. AG,GB : sq. GE : : the transverse : the upright (I. 21),

therefore also

       rect. BF,FA : sq. FD : : rect. AG,GB : sq. GE (I. 14).

And alternately

       rect. BF,FA : rect. AG,GB : : sq. FD : sq. GE.

But

       sq. FD : sq. GE : : sq. FC : sq. CG (Eucl. VI. 4);

therefore alternately

       rect. BF,FA : sq. FC : : rect. AG,GB : sq. CG.

Therefore also, *componendo* in the case of the ellipse, and inversely and *convertendo* in the case of the opposite sections (Eucl. V. Defs. 14,13,16),

       sq. AC : sq. CF : : sq. BC : sq. CG (Eucl. II. 5,6);

and alternately. But

       sq. CB = sq. AC;

therefore also

       sq. CG = sq. CF.

Therefore
$$CG = CF.$$
And the straight lines DF and GE are parallel; therefore also
$$DC = CE.$$

Proposition 31

If on the transverse side of the figure of an hyperbola some point be taken cutting off from the vertex of the section not less than half of the transverse side of the figure, and a straight line be drawn from it to meet the section, then, when further produced, it will fall within the section on the near side of the section.

Let there be an hyperbola whose diameter is the straight line AB, and let C some point on the diameter be taken cutting off the straight line CB not less

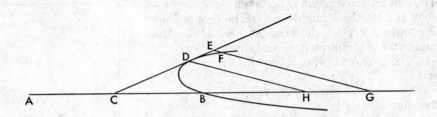

than half of AB, and let some straight line CD be drawn to meet the section.
I say that the straight line CD produced will fall within the section.

For if possible, let it fall outside the section as the line CDE (i. 24), and from E a point at random let the straight line EG be dropped ordinatewise, also DH; and first let
$$AC = CB.$$
And since
$$\text{sq. } EG : \text{sq. } DH > \text{sq. } FG : \text{sq. } DH \quad (\text{Eucl. v. 8}),$$
but
$$\text{sq. } EG : \text{sq. } DH :: \text{sq. } CG : \text{sq. } CH$$
because of EG's being parallel to DH, and
$$\text{sq. } FG : \text{sq. } DH :: \text{rect. } AG,GB : \text{rect. } AH,HB$$
because of the section (i. 21),
therefore
$$\text{sq. } CG : \text{sq. } CH > \text{rect. } AG,GB : \text{rect. } AH,HB.^{[1]}$$
Alternately therefore
$$\text{sq. } CG : \text{rect. } AG,GB > \text{sq. } CH : \text{rect. } AH,HB$$
Therefore *separando*
$$\text{sq. } CB : \text{rect. } AG,GB > \text{sq. } CB : \text{rect. } AH,HB;$$
and this is impossible (Eucl. v. 8). Therefore the straight line CDE will not fall outside the section; therefore inside. And for this reason the straight line from some one of the points on the straight line AC will *a fortiori* fall inside, since it will also fall inside CD.

[1] The rules governing operations on inequalities in proportions are not developed by Euclid in Book V of the *Elements*. But they can be deduced on Euclid's principles.

*If a straight line is drawn through the vertex of a section of a cone, parallel to an
ordinate, then it touches the section, and another straight line will not fall into the
space between the conic section and this straight line.*

Let there be a section of a cone, first the so-called parabola whose diameter
is the straight line AB, and from A let the straight line AC be drawn parallel
to an ordinate.

Now it has been shown that it falls outside the
section (I. 17).

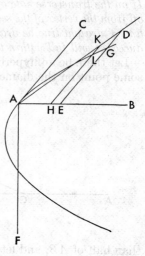

Then I say that also another straight line will not
fall into the space between the straight line AC
and the section.

For if possible, let it fall in, as the straight line
AD, and let some point D be taken on it at random, and let the straight line DE be dropped ordinatewise, and let the straight line AF be the
parameter of the ordinates. And since

sq. DE : sq. $EA >$ sq. GE : sq. EA (Eucl. v. 8),
and

$\qquad$ sq. $GE =$ rect. FA, AE (I. 11),
therefore also

$\qquad$ sq. DE : sq. $EA >$ rect. FA, AE : sq. EA,
or

$\qquad\qquad\qquad > FA : EA$.
Let it be contrived then that

$\qquad\qquad$ sq. DE : sq. EA : : $FA : HA$ (Eucl. vi. 20, 11),
and through the point H let the straight line HLK be drawn parallel to ED.
Since then

$\qquad\qquad$ sq. DE : sq. EA : : $FA : AH$: : rect. FA, AH : sq. AH,
and

$\qquad\qquad$ sq. DE : sq. EA : : sq. KH : sq. HA (Eucl. vi. 22),
and

$\qquad\qquad$ sq. $HL =$ rect. FA, AH (I. 11),
therefore also

$\qquad\qquad$ sq. KH : sq. HA : : sq. LH : sq. HA.
Therefore

$\qquad\qquad\qquad KH = HL$;
and this is absurd. Therefore another straight line will not fall into the space
between the straight line AC and the section.

Next let the section be an hyperbola or ellipse or circumference of a circle
whose diameter is the straight line AB, and whose upright side is the straight
line AF; and let the straight line BF be joined and produced, and from the
point A let the straight line AC be drawn parallel to an ordinate.

Now it has been shown that it falls outside the section (I. 17).

Then I say that also another straight line will not fall into the space between the straight line AC and the section.

For if possible, let it fall, as the straight line AD, and let some point D be
taken at random on it, and from it let the straight line DE be dropped ordi-

natewise, and through E let the straight line EM be drawn parallel to the straight line AF.

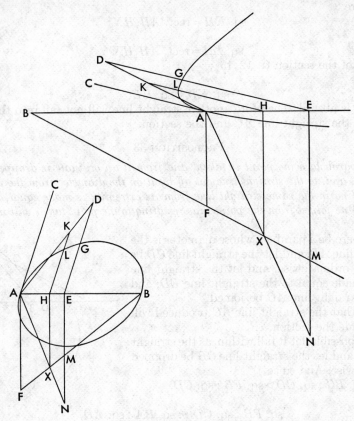

And since

$$\text{sq. } GE = \text{rect. } AE, EM \text{ (i. 12,13)}$$

let it be contrived that

$$\text{rect. } AE, EN = \text{sq. } DE,$$

and let the straight line joining AN cut the straight line FM at X, and through X let the straight line XH be drawn parallel to FA, and through H, HLK parallel to AC. Since then

$$\text{sq. } DE = \text{rect. } AM, EN,$$

hence

$$NE : ED :: DE : EA;$$

and therefore

$$NE : EA :: \text{sq. } DE : \text{sq. } EA \text{ (Eucl. vi. 20)}.$$

But

$$NE : EA :: XH : HA,$$

and

$$\text{sq. } DE : \text{sq. } EA :: \text{sq. } KH : \text{sq. } HA.$$

Therefore

$$XH : HA :: \text{sq. } KH : \text{sq. } HA;$$

therefore

$$XH : HK :: KH : HA \text{ (Eucl. vi. 20)}.$$

Therefore

$$\text{sq. } KH = \text{rect. } AH, HX;$$

but also

$$\text{sq. } LH = \text{rect. } AH, HX$$

because of the section (i. 12,13);
therefore

$$\text{sq. } KH = \text{sq. } HL;$$

and this is absurd. Therefore another straight line will not fall into the space between the straight line AC and the section.

PROPOSITION 33

If in a parabola some point is taken, and from it an ordinate is dropped to the diameter, and, to the straight line cut off by it on the diameter from the vertex, a straight line in the same straight line from its extremity is made equal, then the straight line joined from the point thus resulting to the point taken will touch the section.

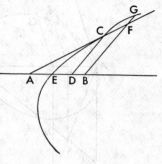

Let there be a parabola whose diameter is the straight line AB, and let the straight line CD be dropped ordinatewise, and let the straight line AE be made equal to the straight line ED, and let the straight line AC be joined.

I say that the straight line AC produced will fall outside the section.

For if possible, let it fall within, as the straight line CF, and let the straight line GB be dropped ordinatewise. And since

$$\text{sq. } BG : \text{sq. } CD > \text{sq. } FB : \text{sq. } CD,$$

but

$$\text{sq. } FB : \text{sq. } CD :: \text{sq. } BA : \text{sq. } AD,$$

and

$$\text{sq. } BG : \text{sq. } CD :: BE : DE \text{ (i. 20)},$$

therefore

$$BE : DE > \text{sq. } BA : \text{sq. } AD.$$

But

$$BE : DE :: 4 \text{ rect. } BE, EA : 4 \text{ rect. } DE, EA;$$

therefore also

$$4 \text{ rect. } BE, EA : 4 \text{ rect. } DE, EA > \text{sq. } AB : \text{sq. } AD.$$

Therefore alternately

$$4 \text{ rect. } BE, EA : \text{sq. } AB > 4 \text{ rect. } DE, EA : \text{sq. } AD;$$

and this is absurd; for since

$$AE = DE,$$

hence

$$4 \text{ rect. } DE, EA = \text{sq. } AD.$$

But

$$4 \text{ rect. } BE, EA < \text{sq. } AB;$$

for E is not the midpoint of AB (Eucl. vi. 27; ii. 5). Therefore the straight line AC does not fall within the section; therefore it touches it.

PROPOSITION 34

If on an hyperbola or ellipse or circumference of a circle some point is taken, and from it a straight line is dropped ordinatewise to the diameter, and whatever ratio the straight lines cut off by the ordinate from the ends of the figure's transverse side have to each other, that ratio have the segments of the transverse side to each other so that the segments from the vertex are corresponding, then the straight line joining the point taken on the transverse side and that taken on the section will touch the section.

Let there be an hyperbola or ellipse or circumference of a circle whose diam-

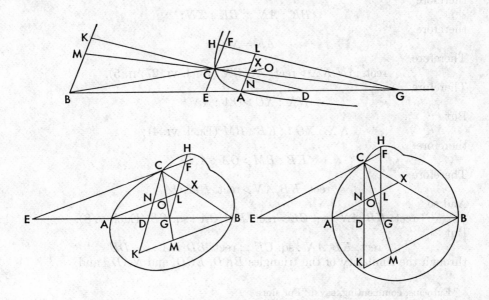

eter is the straight line AB, and let some point C be taken on the section, and from C let the straight line CD be drawn ordinatewise, and let it be contrived that

$$BD : DA :: BE : EA,[1]$$

and let the straight line EC be joined.

I say that the straight line CE touches the section.

[1]This construction is easy. In the case of the hyperbola, *componendo*.

$$BD+DA : DA :: BA : EA;$$

and in the case of the ellipse, *separando*

$$BD-DA : DA :: BA : EA.$$

This proportion is the same as the harmonic proportion defined by Nicomachus in his *Introduction to Arithmetic*. For if

$$BD : DA :: BE : EA,$$

then $BD+DA : BD :: BA : BE$

and $BA : BD :: BE-EA : BE.$

Hence $BD+DA : BA :: BA : BE-EA,$

But $DA = BD-BA, \ EA = BA-BE.$

Therefore $2BD-BA : BA :: BA : 2BE-BA.$

And so BA is the harmonic mean between BD and BE.

For if possible, let it cut it, as the straight line ECF, and let some point F be taken on it, and let the straight line GFH be dropped ordinatewise, and let the straight lines AL and BK be drawn through A and B parallel to the straight line EC, and let the straight lines DC, BC, and GC be joined and produced to the points M, X, and K. And since

$$BD : DA :: BE : EA,$$

but

$$BD : DA :: BK : AN,$$

and

$$BE : AE :: BC : CX :: BK : XN \text{ (Eucl. vi. 4)},$$

therefore

$$BK : AN :: BK : XN;$$

therefore

$$AN = NX.$$

Therefore

$$\text{rect. } AN, NX > \text{rect. } AO, OX \text{ (Eucl. vi. 27; ii. 5)}.$$

Therefore

$$NX : XO > OA : AN.^1$$

But

$$NX : XO :: KB : BM \text{ (Eucl. vi. 4)};$$

therefore

$$KB : BM > OA : AN.$$

Therefore

$$\text{rect. } KB, AN > \text{rect. } BM, OA.$$

And so

$$\text{rect. } KB, AN : \text{sq. } CE > \text{rect. } BM, OA : \text{sq. } CE \text{ (Eucl. v. 8)}.$$

But

$$\text{rect. } KB, AN : \text{sq. } CE :: \text{rect. } BD, DA : \text{sq. } DE$$

through the similarity of the triangles BKD, ECD, and NAD,[2] and

---

[1] Eutocius, commenting, says: "For since

$$\text{rect. } AN, NX > \text{rect. } AO, OX,$$

let

$$\text{rect. } AN, NX = \text{rect. } AO, XP$$

where XP is some line such that $XP > XC$;

therefore

$$OA : AN :: NX : XP.$$

But

$$NX : XO > NX : XP \text{ (Eucl. v. 8)}$$

and therefore

$$NX : XO > OA : AN.$$

"Then the converse is also evident that, if

$$NX : XO > OA : AN,$$

then

$$\text{rect. } XN, NA > \text{rect. } AO, OX.$$

"For let it be that

$$OA : AN :: NX : XP,$$

where $XP > XO$;

therefore

$$\text{rect. } XN, NA = \text{rect. } AO, XP;$$

and so

$$\text{rect. } XN, NA > \text{rect. } AO, OX."$$

[2] Eutocius, commenting, says: "Since then, because AN, EC, and KB are parallel,

$$AN : EC :: AD : DE,$$

and

$$EC : KB :: ED : DB,$$

therefore ex aequali

$$AN : KB :: AD : DB;$$

therefore also

$$\text{sq. } AN : \text{rect. } AN, KB :: \text{sq. } AD : \text{rect. } AD, DB.$$

But

$$\text{sq. } EC : \text{sq. } AN :: \text{sq. } ED : \text{sq. } AD;$$

therefore ex aequali

$$\text{sq. } EC : \text{rect. } AN, KB :: \text{sq. } ED : \text{rect. } AD, DB;$$

and inversely

$$\text{rect. } KB, AN : \text{sq. } EC :: \text{rect. } AD, DB : \text{sq. } ED."$$

A similar proof holds for the proportion following.

rect. BM, OA : sq. CE : : rect. BG, GA : sq. GE;

therefore

rect. BD, DA : sq. DE > rect. BG, GA : sq. GE.

Therefore alternately

rect. BD, DA : rect. BG, GA > sq. DE : sq. GE.

But

rect. BD, DA : rect. AG, GB : : sq. CD : sq. GH (I. 21),

and

sq. DE : sq. EG : : sq. CD : sq. FG (Eucl. VI. 4),

therefore also

sq. CD : sq. HG > sq. CD : sq. FG.

Therefore

$HG < FG$ (Eucl. V. 10);

and this is impossible. Therefore the straight line EC does not cut the section; therefore it touches it.

PROPOSITION 35

If a straight line touches a parabola, meeting the diameter outside the section, the straight line drawn from the point of contact ordinatewise to the diameter will cut off on the diameter beginning from the vertex of the section a straight line equal to the straight line between the vertex and the tangent, and no straight line will fall into the space between the tangent and the section.

Let there be a parabola whose diameter is the straight line AB, and let the straight line BC be erected ordinatewise, and let the straight line AC be tangent to the section.

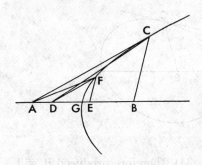

I say that the straight line AG is equal to the straight line GB.

For if possible, let it be unequal to it, and let the straight line GE be made equal to AG, and let the straight line EF be erected ordinatewise, and let the straight line AF be joined. Therefore AF produced will meet the straight line AC (I. 33); and this is impossible. For two straight lines will have the same ends. Therefore the straight line AG is not unequal to the straight line GB; therefore it is equal.

Then I say that no straight line will fall into the space between the straight line AC and the section.

For if possible, let the straight line CD fall in between, and let GE be made equal to GD, and let the straight line EF be erected ordinatewise. Therefore the straight line joined from D to F touches the section (I. 33); therefore produced it will fall outside it. And so it will meet DC, and two straight lines will have the same ends; and this is impossible. Therefore a straight line will not fall into the space between the section and the straight line AC.

PROPOSITION 36

If some straight line, meeting the transverse side of the figure touches an hyperbola or ellipse or circumference of a circle, and a straight line is dropped from the point of contact ordinatewise to the diameter, then as the straight line cut off by the tangent from the end of the transverse side is to the straight line cut off by the tangent from the other end of that side, so will the straight line cut off by the ordinate from the end of the side be to the straight line cut off by the ordinate from the other end of the side in such a way that the corresponding straight lines are continuous; and another straight line will not fall into the space between the tangent and the section of the cone.

Let there be an hyperbola or ellipse or circumference of a circle whose diameter is the straight line AB, and let the straight line CD be tangent, and let the straight line CE be dropped ordinatewise.

I say that

$$BE : EA : : BD : DA.$$

For if it is not, let it be

$$BD : DA : : BG : GA,$$

and let the straight line GF be erected ordinatewise; therefore the straight line

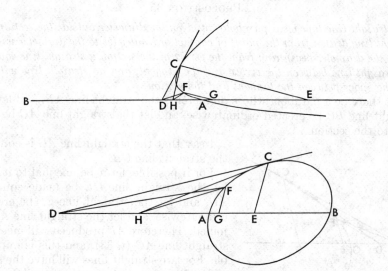

joined from D to F will touch the section (I. 34); therefore produced it will meet CD. Therefore two straight lines will have the same ends; and this is impossible.

I say that no straight line will fall between the section and the straight line CD.

For if possible, let it fall between, as the straight line CH, and let it be contrived that

$$BH : HA : : BG : GA,$$

and let the straight line GF be erected ordinatewise; therefore the straight line joined from H to F, when produced, will meet HC (I. 34). Therefore two straight lines will have the same ends; and this is impossible. Therefore a straight line will not fall into the space between the section and the straight line CD.

PROPOSITION 37

If a straight line touching an hyperbola or ellipse or circumference of a circle meets the diameter, and from the point of contact to the diameter a straight line is dropped ordinatewise, then the straight line cut off by the ordinate from the center of the section with the straight line cut off by the tangent from the center of the section will contain an area equal to the square on the radius of the section, and with the straight line between the ordinate and the tangent will contain an area having the ratio to the square on the ordinate which the transverse has to the upright.

Let there be an hyperbola or ellipse or circumference of a circle whose diameter is the straight line AB, and let the straight line CD be drawn tangent, and let the straight line CE be dropped ordinatewise, and let the point F be the center.

I say that

$$\text{rect. } DF, FE = \text{sq. } FB,$$

and

$$\text{rect. } DE, EF : \text{sq. } EC : : \text{the transverse} : \text{the upright}.$$

For since CD touches the section, and CE has been dropped ordinatewise, hence

$$AD : DB : : AE : EB \text{ (i. 36)}.$$

Therefore *componendo*

$$AD + DB : DB : : AE + EB : EB.$$

And let the halves of the antecedents be taken (Eucl. v. 15); in the case of the

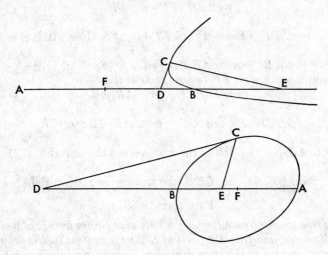

hyperbola we shall say: but

$$\text{half } (AE + EB) = FE,$$

and

$$\text{half } AB = FB;$$

therefore

$$FE : EB : : FB : BD.$$

Therefore *convertendo*

$$FE : FB : : FB : FD,$$

therefore
$$\text{rect. } EF, FD = \text{sq. } FB.$$
And since
$$FE : EB :: FB : BD :: AF : BD,$$
alternately
$$AF : FE :: DB : BE;$$
componendo
$$AE : EF :: DE : EB;$$
and so
$$\text{rect. } AE, EB = \text{rect. } FE, ED.$$
But
$$\text{rect. } AE, EB : \text{sq. } CE :: \text{the transverse : the upright (i. 21);}$$
therefore also
$$\text{rect. } FE, ED : \text{sq. } CE :: \text{the transverse : the upright.}$$
And in the case of the ellipse and of the circle we shall say: but
$$\text{half } (AD + DB) = DF,$$
and
$$\text{half } AB = FB;$$
therefore
$$FD : DB :: FB : BE.$$
Therefore *convertendo*
$$DF : FB :: BF : FE.$$
Therefore
$$\text{rect. } DF, FE = \text{sq. } BF.$$
But
$$\text{rect. } DF, FE = \text{rect. } DE, EF + \text{sq. } FE \text{ (Eucl. ii. 3),}$$
and
$$\text{sq. } BF = \text{rect. } AE, EB + \text{sq. } FE \text{ (Eucl. ii. 5).}$$
Let the common square on EF be subtracted; therefore
$$\text{rect. } DE, EF = \text{rect. } AE, EB.$$
Therefore
$$\text{rect. } DE, EF : \text{sq. } CE :: \text{rect. } AE, EB : \text{sq. } CE.$$
But
$$\text{rect. } AE, EB : \text{sq. } CE :: \text{the transverse : the upright (i. 21).}$$
Therefore
$$\text{rect. } DE, EF : \text{sq. } CE :: \text{the transverse : the upright.}$$

Proposition 38

*If a straight line touching an hyperbola or ellipse or circumference of a circle meets
the second diameter, and from the point of contact a straight line is dropped to the
same diameter parallel to the other diameter, then the straight line cut off by the
dropped straight (κατηγμένη)[1] line from the center of the section with the straight*

---

[1] When this word κατηγμένη is used in connection with the first diameter we translate it as
"ordinate," but we have preferred to stick more closely to the original when it is referred
to the second diameter. For, although it is certainly an ordinate in the case of the ellipse, yet
in the case of the hyperbola it is only analogically an ordinate. This analogy, however, becomes stronger and stronger as the treatise moves on. It is, therefore, no accident that
κατηγμένη is used in both cases. On the other hand in First Definitions, i. 5, Apollonius definitely calls both cases ordinates as if announcing the culmination of an analogy to be worked
out in the course of the treatise.

line cut off by the tangent from the center of the section will contain an area equal to the square on the half of the second diameter, and with the straight line between the dropped straight line and the tangent will contain an area having a ratio to the square on the dropped straight line which the upright side of the figure has to the transverse.

Let there be an hyperbola or ellipse or circumference of a circle whose diameter is the straight line AGB, and whose second diameter is the straight line CGD, and let the straight line ELF, meeting CD at F, be a tangent to the section, and let the straight line HE be parallel to AB.

I say that

$$\text{rect. } FG, GH = \text{sq. } GC,$$

and

$$\text{rect. } GH, HF : \text{sq. } HE :: \text{the upright : the transverse.}$$

Let the straight line ME be drawn ordinatewise; therefore

$$\text{rect. } GM, ML : \text{sq. } ME :: \text{the transverse : the upright (I. 37).}$$

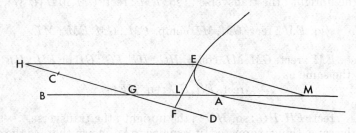

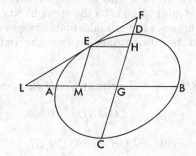

But

$$\text{the transverse } BA : CD :: CD : \text{the upright (see Def. 11);}$$

and therefore

$$\text{the transverse : the upright } :: \text{sq. } BA : \text{sq. } CD \text{ (Eucl. VI. 20);}$$

and as the quarters of them, that is

$$\text{the transverse : the upright } :: \text{sq. } GA : \text{sq. } GC;$$

therefore also

$$\text{rect. } GM, ML : \text{sq. } ME :: \text{sq. } GA : \text{sq. } GC.$$

But

$$\text{rect. } GM, ML : \text{sq. } ME \text{ comp. } GM : ME, LM : ME,$$

or

$$\text{rect. } GM, ML : \text{sq. } ME \text{ comp. } GM : GH, LM : ME.$$

Therefore inversely

sq. CG : sq. GA comp. $EM : MG$ or $HG : GM, EM : ML$ or $FG : GL$.

Therefore

sq. GC : sq. GA comp. $HG : GM, FG : GL$,

which is the same as

rect. FG, GH : rect. MG, GL.

Therefore

rect. FG, GH : rect. MG, GL : : sq. CG : sq. GA.

And alternately therefore

rect. FG, GH : sq. CG : : rect. MG, GL : sq. GA.

But

rect. $MG, GL = $ sq. GA (I. 37),

therefore also

rect. $FG, GH = $ sq. CG.

Again since

the upright : the transverse : : sq. EM : rect. GM, ML (I. 37),

and

sq. EM : rect. GM, ML comp. $EM : GM, EM : ML$

or

sq. EM : rect. GM, ML comp. $HG : HE, FG : GL$ or $FH : HE$

which is the same as

rect. FH, HG : sq. HE;

therefore

rect. FH, HG : sq. HE : : the upright : the transverse.

With the same things supposed, it remains to be shown that, as the straight line between the tangent and the end of the (second) diameter on the same side with the dropped straight line is to the straight line between the tangent and the second diameter, so is the straight line between the other end and the dropped straight line to the straight line between the first end and the dropped straight line.

For since

rect. $FG, GH = $ sq. $GC = $ rect. CG, GD (2 para. above),

for

$CG = GD$,

therefore

rect. $FG, GH = $ rect. CG, GD;

therefore

$FG : GD : : CG : GH$.

And *convertendo*

$GF : FD : : GC : CH$.

And let the doubles of the antecedents be taken; but

$2GF = CF + FD$

because

$CG = GD$,

and

$2GC = CD$;

therefore

$CF + FD : FD : : DC : CH$.

And *separando*

$$CF : FD : : DH : HC;$$

and this was to be shown.

Then it is clear from what has been said that the straight line *EF* touches the section, either if

$$\text{rect. } FG,GH = \text{sq. } GC,$$

or if

$$\text{rect. } FH,HG : \text{sq. } GC$$

in the ratio we said; for it could be shown conversely.

PROPOSITION 39

If a straight line touching an hyperbola or ellipse or circumference of a circle meets the diameter, and from the point of contact a straight line is dropped ordinatewise to the diameter, then whichever of the two straight lines is taken of which one is the straight line between the ordinate and the center of the section, and the other is between the ordinate and the tangent, then the ordinate will have to it the ratio compounded of the ratio of the other of the two straight lines to the ordinate and of the ratio of the upright side of the figure to the transverse.

Let there be an hyperbola or ellipse or circumference of a circle whose diameter is the straight line *AB*, and let the center of it be the point *F*, and let the straight line *CD* be drawn tangent to the section, and the straight line *CE* be dropped ordinatewise.

I say that

$$CE : FE \text{ comp. the upright} : \text{the transverse}, ED : EC,$$

and

$$CE : ED \text{ comp. the upright} : \text{the transverse}, FE : EC.$$

For let

$$\text{rect. } FE,ED = \text{rect. } EC,G.$$

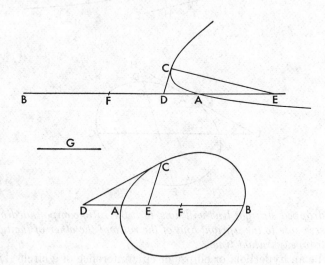

And since

$$\text{rect. } FE,ED : \text{sq. } CE : : \text{the transverse} : \text{the upright (I. 37)},$$

and
$$\text{rect. } FE, ED = \text{rect. } CE, G,$$
therefore
$$\text{rect. } CE, G : \text{sq. } CE :: G : CE :: \text{the transverse : the upright.}$$
And since
$$\text{rect. } FE, ED = \text{rect. } CE, G,$$
hence
$$FE : EC :: G : ED.$$
And since
$$CE : ED \text{ comp. } CE : G, G : ED,$$
but
$$CE : G :: \text{the upright : the transverse,}$$
therefore
$$CE : ED \text{ comp. the upright : the transverse, } FE : EC.$$

PROPOSITION 40

If a straight line touching an hyperbola or ellipse or circumference of a circle meets the second diameter, and from the point of contact a straight line is dropped to the same diameter parallel to the other diameter, then whichever of the two straight lines is taken of which one is the straight line between the dropped straight line and the center of the section, and the other is between the dropped straight line and the

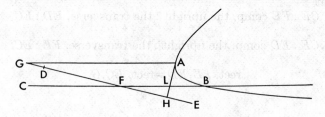

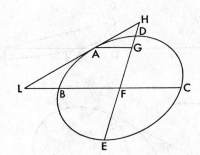

tangent, the dropped straight line will have to it the ratio compounded of the ratio of the transverse side to the upright and of the ratio of the other of the two straight lines to the dropped straight line.

Let there be an hyperbola or ellipse or circumference of a circle AB, and its diameter the straight line BFC, and its second diameter the straight line DFE, and let the straight line HLA be drawn tangent, and the straight line AG parallel to the straight line BC.

I say that
$$AG : HG \text{ comp. the transverse : the upright, } FG : GA,$$
and
$$AG : FG \text{ comp. the transverse : the upright, } HG : GA.$$
Let
$$\text{rect. } GA, K = \text{rect. } HG, GF.$$
And since
the upright : the transverse : : rect. HG, GF : sq. GA (I. 38),
and
$$\text{rect. } GA, K = \text{rect. } HG, GF,$$
therefore also
rect. GA, K : sq. GA : : $K : AG$: : the upright : the transverse.
And since
$$AG : GF \text{ comp. } AG : K, K : GF,$$
but
$$AG : K \text{ : : the transverse : the upright,}$$
and
$$K : GF \text{ : : } HG : GA$$
because
$$\text{rect. } HG, GF = \text{rect. } AG, K,$$
therefore
$$AG : GF \text{ comp. the transverse : the upright, } GH : GA.$$

PROPOSITION 41

If in an hyperbola or ellipse or circumference of a circle a straight line is dropped ordinatewise to the diameter, and equiangular parallelogrammic figures are described both on the ordinate and on the radius, and the ordinate side has to the remaining side of the figure the ratio compounded of the ratio of the radius to the remaining side of its figure, and of the ratio of the upright side of the section's figure to the transverse, then the figure on the straight line between the center and the ordinate, similar to the figure on the radius, is in the case of the hyperbola greater than the figure on the ordinate by the figure on the radius, and, in the case of the ellipse and circumference of a circle, together with the figure on the ordinate is equal to the figure on the radius.

Let there be an hyperbola or ellipse or circumference of a circle whose diameter is the straight line AB, and center the point E, and let the straight line CD be dropped ordinatewise, and on the straight lines EA and CD let the equiangular figures AF and DG be described, and let
$$CD : CG \text{ comp. } AE : EF, \text{ the upright : the transverse.}$$
I say that, with the figure on ED similar to AF, in the base of the hyperbola,
$$\text{figure on } ED = AF + GD,$$
and in the case of the ellipse and circle,
$$\text{figure on } ED + GD = AF.$$
For let it be contrived that
the upright : the transverse : : $DC : CH$.
And since
$$DC : CH \text{ : : the upright : the transverse,}$$
but
$$DC : CH \text{ : : sq. } DC \text{ : rect. } DC, CH$$

and

the upright : the transverse : : sq. DC : rect. BD, DA (I. 21),

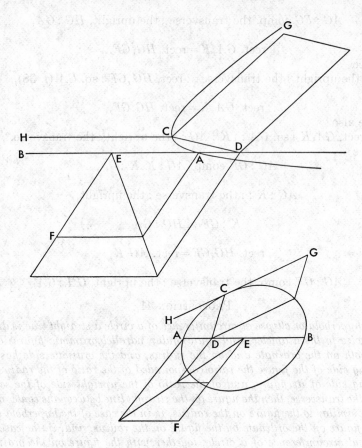

therefore

rect. BD, DA = rect. DC, CH.

And since

$DC : CG$ comp. $AE : EF$, the upright : the transverse

or

$DC : CG$ comp. $AE : EF, DC : CH$,

and further

$DC : CG$ comp. $DC : CH, CH : CG$,

therefore

ratio comp. $AE : EF, DC : CH$ = ratio comp. $DC : CH, CH : CG$.

Let the common ratio, $DC : CH$, be taken away; therefore

$AE : EF : : CH : CG.$

But

$HC : CG : : $ rect. HC, CD : rect. GC, CD,

and

$AE : EF : : $ sq. AE : rect. AE, EF;

therefore
$$\text{rect. } HC,CD : \text{rect. } GC,CD : : \text{sq. } AE : \text{rect. } AE,EF.$$
And it has been shown that
$$\text{rect. } HC,CD = \text{rect. } BD,DA;$$
therefore
$$\text{rect. } BD,DA : \text{rect. } GC,CD : : \text{sq. } AE : \text{rect. } AE,EF.$$
Alternately
$$\text{rect. } BD,DA : \text{sq. } AE : : \text{rect. } GC,CD : \text{rect. } AE,EF.$$
And
$$\text{rect. } GC,CD : \text{rect. } AE,EF : : \text{pllg. } DG : \text{pllg. } FA;$$
for they are equiangular and have to one another the ratio compounded of their sides, $GC : AE$ and $CD : EF$ (Eucl. vi. 23); and therefore
$$\text{rect. } BD,DA : \text{sq. } EA : : \text{pllg. } DG : \text{pllg. } FA.$$
Moreover in the case of the hyperbola we are to say: *componendo*
$$\text{rect. } BD,DA + \text{sq. } AE : \text{sq. } AE : : \text{pllg. } GD + \text{pllg. } AF : \text{pllg. } AF,$$
or
$$\text{sq. } DE : \text{sq. } EA : : \text{pllg. } GD + \text{pllg. } AF : \text{pllg. } AF \text{ (Eucl. ii. 6).}$$
And as the square on DE is to the square on EA, so is the figure described on ED, similar and similarly situated to the parallelogram AF, to the parallelogram AF (Eucl. vi. 20, porism); therefore, with the figure on ED similar to the parallelogram AF,
$$\text{pllg. } GD + \text{pllg. } AF : \text{pllg. } AF : : \text{figure on } ED : \text{pllg. } AF.$$
Therefore
$$\text{figure on } ED = \text{pllg. } GD + \text{pllg. } AF,$$
the figure on ED being similar to the parallelogram AF.

And in the case of the ellipse and of the circumference of a circle we shall say: since then
$$\text{whole sq. } AE : \text{whole pllg. } AF : :$$
$$\text{rect. } AD,DB \text{ subtracted} : \text{pllg. } DG \text{ subtracted,}$$
also remainder is to remainder as whole to whole (Eucl. v. 19).
And
$$\text{sq. } AE - \text{rect. } BD,DA = \text{sq. } DE \text{ (Eucl. ii. 5);}$$
therefore
$$\text{sq. } DE : \text{pllg. } AF - \text{pllg. } DG : : \text{sq. } AE : \text{pllg. } AF.$$
But
$$\text{sq. } AE : \text{pllg. } AF : : \text{sq. } DE : \text{figure on } DE \text{ (Eucl. vi. 20, porism)}$$
the figure on DE being similar to the parallelogram AF. Therefore, the figure on DE being similar to the parallelogram AF,
$$\text{sq. } DE : \text{pllg. } AF - DG : : \text{sq. } DE : \text{figure on } DE.$$
Therefore, the figure on DE being similar to the parallelogram AF,
$$\text{figure on } DE = \text{pllg. } AF - \text{pllg. } DG.$$
Therefore
$$\text{figure on } DE + \text{pllg. } DG = \text{pllg. } AF.$$

PROPOSITION 42

If a straight line touching a parabola meets the diameter, and from the point of contact a straight line is dropped ordinatewise to the diameter, and, some point being taken on the section, two straight lines are dropped to the diameter, one of them parallel to the tangent, and the other parallel to the straight line dropped from the point of contact, then the triangle resulting from them is equal to the parallelogram contained by the straight line dropped from the point of contact and by the straight line cut off by the parallel from the vertex of the section.

Let there be a parabola, whose diameter is the straight line AB, and let the straight line AC be drawn tangent to the section, and let the straight line CH be dropped ordinatewise, and from some point at random let the straight line DF be dropped ordinatewise, and through the point D let the straight line DE be drawn parallel to the straight line AC, and through the point C the straight line CG parallel to the straight line BF, and through the point B the straight line BG parallel to the straight line HC.

I say that

$$\text{trgl. } DEF = \text{pllg. } GF.$$

For since the straight line AC touches the section, and the straight line CH has been dropped ordinatewise,

$$AB = BH \text{ (i. 35)};$$

therefore

$$AH = 2BH.$$

Therefore

$$\text{trgl. } AHC = \text{pllg. } BC \text{ (Eucl. i. 41).}$$

And since

$$\text{sq. } CH : \text{sq. } DF :: HB : BF$$

because of the section (i. 20), but

$$\text{sq. } CH : \text{sq. } DF :: \text{trgl. } ACH : \text{trgl. } EDF \text{ (Eucl. vi. 19),}$$

and

$$HB : BF :: \text{pllg. } GH : \text{pllg. } GF \text{ (Eucl. vi. 1),}$$

therefore

$$\text{trgl. } ACH : \text{trgl. } EDF :: \text{pllg. } HG : \text{pllg. } FG.$$

Therefore alternately

$$\text{trgl. } AHC : \text{pllg. } BC :: \text{trgl. } EDF : \text{pllg. } GF.$$

But

$$\text{trgl. } ACH = \text{pllg. } GH;$$

therefore

$$\text{trgl. } EDF = \text{pllg. } GF.$$

PROPOSITION 43

If a straight line touching an hyperbola or ellipse or circumference of a circle meets the diameter, and from the point of contact a straight line is dropped ordinatewise to the diameter, and a parallel to it is drawn through the vertex meeting the straight line drawn through the point of contact and the center, and, some point being taken on the section, two straight lines are drawn to the diameter, one of which is parallel to the tangent and the other parallel to the straight line dropped from the point of contact, then the triangle resulting from them, in the case of the hyperbola, will be less than the triangle the straight line through the center and the point of contact cuts off, by the triangle on the radius similar to the triangle cut off; and in the case of the ellipse and the circumference of the circle, together with the triangle cut off from the center, will be equal to the triangle on the radius similar to the triangle cut off.

Let there be an hyperbola or ellipse or circumference of a circle whose diameter is the straight line AB, and center the point C, and let the straight line DE be drawn tangent to the section, and let the straight line CE be joined, and let the straight line EF be dropped ordinatewise, and let some point G be taken on the section, and let the straight line GH be drawn parallel to the tangent, and let the straight line GK be dropped ordinatewise, and through B let the straight line BL be erected ordinatewise.

I say that triangle KMC differs from triangle CLB by triangle GKH.

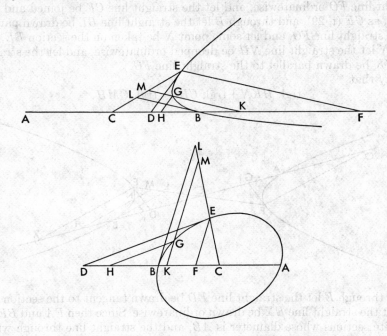

For since the straight line ED touches, and the straight line EF has been dropped, hence
$$EF : FD \text{ comp. } CF : FE, \text{ the upright : the transverse (I. 39).}$$
But
$$EF : FD :: GK : KH,$$
and
$$CF : FE :: CB : BL \text{ (Eucl. VI. 4);}$$
therefore
$$GK : KH \text{ comp. } BC : BL, \text{ the upright : the transverse.}$$
And through those things shown in the forty-first theorem (I. 41), triangle CKM differs from triangle BCL by triangle GHK; for the same things have also been shown in the case of the parallelograms, their doubles.

PROPOSITION 44

If a straight line touching one of the opposite sections meets the diameter, and from the point of contact some straight line is dropped ordinatewise to the diameter, and a parallel to it is drawn through the vertex of the other section meeting the straight line drawn through the point of contact and the center, and, some point being taken at random on the section, let straight lines be dropped to the diameter, one of which

is parallel to the tangent and the other parallel to the straight line dropped ordinate-
wise from the point of contact, then the triangle resulting from them will be less than
the triangle the dropped straight line cuts off from the center of the section, by the
triangle on the radius similar to the triangle cut off.

Let there be the opposite sections AF and BE, and let their diameter be the straight line AB, and center the point C, and from some point F of those on the section FA let the straight line FG be drawn tangent to the section, and the straight line FO ordinatewise, and let the straight line CF be joined and pro-duced, as CE (I. 29), and through B let the straight line BL be drawn parallel to the straight line FO, and let some point N be taken on the section BE, and from N let the straight line NH be dropped ordinatewise, and let the straight line NK be drawn parallel to the straight line FG.

I say that

$$\text{trgl. } HKN + \text{trgl. } CBL = \text{trgl. } CMH$$

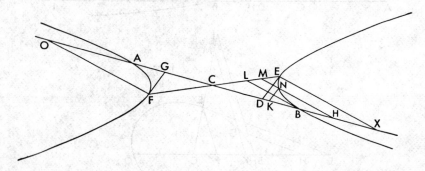

For through E let the straight line ED be drawn tangent to the section BE, and let the straight line EX be drawn ordinatewise. Since then FA and BE are opposite sections whose diameter is AB, and the straight line through whose center is FCE, and FG and ED are tangents to the section, hence DE is parallel to FG.[1] And the straight line NK is parallel to FG; therefore NK is also parallel to ED, and the straight line MH to BL. Since then BE is an hyperbola, whose diameter is the straight line AB, and whose center is C, and the straight line DE is tangent to the section, and EX drawn ordinatewise, and BL is parallel to EX, and N has been taken on the section as the point from which NH has

---

[1] Eutocius, commenting, says: "For since AF is an hyperbola, and BG a tangent, and FO
an ordinate,   rect. $OC,CG = $ sq. CA
(I. 37) likewise then also   rect. $XC,CD = $ sq. CB.
Therefore   rect. $OC,CG : $ sq. $AC :: $ rect. $XC,CD : $ sq. BC,
and alternately,   rect. $OC,CG : $ rect. $XC,CD :: $ sq. $AC : $ sq. CB.
But   sq. $AC = $ sq. CB;
therefore also   rect. $OC,CG = $ rect. XC,CD.
And $OC = CX$ (I. 14,30);
and therefore $GC = CD$;
and also $FC = CE$ (I. 30);
therefore $FC = EC, CG = CD$.
And they contain equal angles at the point C; for they are vertical. And so also
                                       $FG = ED$
and   angle $CFG = $ angle CED.
And they are alternate; therefore the straight line FG is parallel to the straight line ED."

been dropped ordinatewise, and KN has been drawn parallel to DE, therefore
$$\text{trgl. } NHK + \text{trgl. } BCL = \text{trgl. } HMC;$$
for this has been shown in the forty-third theorem (I. 43).

PROPOSITION 45

If a straight line touching an hyperbola or ellipse or circumference of a circle meets
the second diameter, and from the point of contact some straight line is dropped to
the same diameter parallel to the other diameter, and through the point of contact
and the center a straight line is produced, and, some point being taken at random
on the section, two straight lines are drawn to the second diameter one of which is
parallel to the tangent and the other parallel to the dropped straight line, then the
triangle resulting from them is greater, in the case of the hyperbola, than the tri-
angle the dropped straight line cuts off from the center, by the triangle whose base
is the tangent and vertex is the center of the section, and, in the case of the ellipse
and circle, together with the triangle cut off will be equal to the triangle whose base
is the tangent and whose vertex is the center of the section.

Let there be an hyperbola or ellipse or circumference of a circle ABC, whose

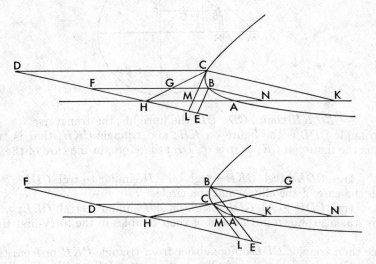

diameter is the straight line AH, and second diameter HD, and center H, and
let the straight line CML touch it at C, and let the straight line CD be drawn
parallel to AH, and let the straight line HC be joined and produced, and let
some point B be taken at random on the section, and from B let the straight
lines BE and BF be drawn from B parallel to the straight lines LC and CD.

I say that, in the case of the hyperbola,
$$\text{trgl. } BEF = \text{trgl. } GHF + \text{trgl. } LCH,$$
and, in the case of the ellipse and circle,
$$\text{trgl. } BEF + \text{trgl. } FGH = \text{trgl. } CLH.$$

For let the straight lines CK and BN be drawn parallel to DH. Since then
the straight line CM is tangent, and the straight line CK has been dropped
ordinatewise, hence
$$CK : KH \text{ comp. } MK : KC, \text{ the upright : the transverse (I. 39),}$$

and

$$MK : KC :: CD : DL \text{ (Eucl. vi. 4)};$$

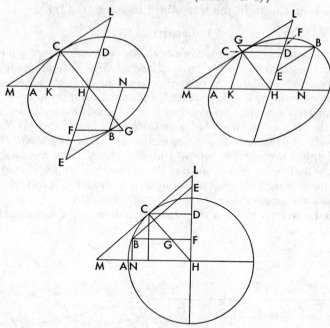

therefore

$CK : KH$ comp. $CD : DL$, the upright : the transverse.

And triangle CDL is the figure on KH; and triangle CKH, that is triangle CDH, is the figure on CK, that is on DH; therefore, in the case of the hyperbola,

trgl. $CDL = $ trgl. $CKH + $ trgl. on AH similar to trgl. CDL,

and, in the case of the ellipse and the circle,

trgl. $CDH + $ trgl. $CDL = $ trgl. on AH similar to trgl. CDL;

for this was also shown in the case of their doubles in the forty-first theorem (i. 41).

Since then triangle CDL differs either from triangle CKH or from triangle CDH by the triangle on AH similar to triangle CDL, and it also differs by triangle CHL therefore

trgl. $CHL = $ trgl. on AH similar to trgl. CDL.

Since then triangle BFE is similar to triangle CDL, and triangle GFH to triangle CDH, therefore they have the same ratio.[1] And triangle BFE is described on NH between the ordinate and the center, and triangle GFH on the ordinate BN, that is on FH; and by things already shown (i. 41) triangle BFE differs from triangle GHF by the triangle on AH similar to CDL, and so also by triangle CHL.

---

[1] That is (Eucl. vi. 4). $BF : FE :: CD : DL$
and $GF : FH :: CD : DH :: CK : KH.$
Therefore these first ratios can be substituted in the central proportion of the theorem
        $CK : KH$ comp. $CD : DL$, the upright : the transverse,
and so satisfy i. 41.

Proposition 46

If a straight line touching a parabola meets the diameter, the straight line drawn through the point of contact parallel to the diameter in the direction of the section bisects the straight lines drawn in the section parallel to the tangent.

Let there be a parabola whose diameter is the straight line ABD, and let the

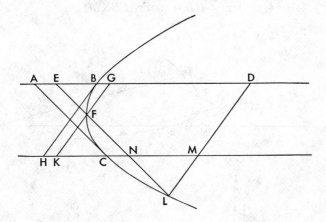

straight line AC touch the section (i. 24), and through C let the straight line HCM be drawn parallel to the straight line AD (i. 26), and let some point L be taken at random on the section, and let the straight line $LNFE$ (i. 18,22) be drawn parallel to AC.

I say that

$$LN = NF.$$

Let the straight lines BH, KFG, and LMD be drawn ordinatewise. Since then by the things already shown in the forty-second theorem (i. 42)

$$\text{trgl. } ELD = \text{pllg. } BM,$$

and

$$\text{trgl. } EFG = \text{pllg. } BK,$$

therefore the remainders

$$\text{pllg. } GM = \text{quadr. } LFGD.$$

Let the common pentagon $MDGFN$ be subtracted; therefore the remainders

$$\text{trgl. } KFN = \text{trgl. } LMN.$$

And KF is parallel to LM; therefore

$$FN = LN \quad \text{(Eucl. vi. 22, lemma).}$$

Proposition 47

If a straight line touching an hyperbola or ellipse or circumference of a circle meets the diameter, and through the point of contact and the center a straight line is drawn in the direction of the section, it bisects the straight lines drawn in the section parallel to the tangent.

Let there be an hyperbola or ellipse or circumference of a circle whose diameter is the straight line AB and center C, and let the straight line DE be drawn tangent to the section, and let the straight line CE be joined and produced, and let a point N be taken at random on the section, and through N let the straight line $HNOG$ be drawn parallel.

I say that
$$NO = OG.$$
For let the straight lines XNF, BL, and GMK be dropped ordinatewise. Therefore by things already shown in the forty-third theorem (I. 43)

trgl. HNF = quadr. $LBFX$,

and   trgl. GHK = quadr. $LBKM$.

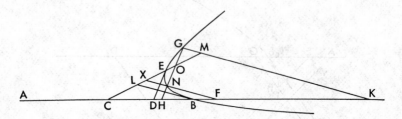

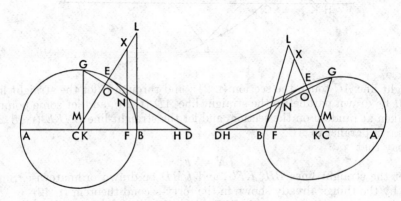

Therefore the remainders

quadr. $NGKF$ = quadr. $MKFX$;

Let the common pentagon $ONFKM$ be subtracted;
therefore the remainders

trgl. OMG = trgl. NXO.

And the straight line MG is parallel to the straight line NX; therefore
$$NO = OG \text{ (Eucl. VI. 22, lemma)}.$$

PROPOSITION 48

If a straight line touching one of the opposite sections meets the diameter, and through the point of contact and the center a straight line produced cuts the other section, then whatever line is drawn in the other section parallel to the tangent, will be bisected by the straight line produced.

Let there be opposite sections whose diameter is the straight line AB and center C, and let the straight line KL touch the section A, and let the straight line LC be joined and produced (I. 29), and let some point N be taken on the section B, and through N let the straight line NG be drawn parallel to the straight line LK.

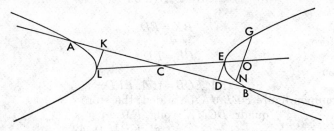

I say that
$$NO = OG.$$
For let the straight line ED be drawn through E tangent to the section; therefore ED is parallel to LK (I. 44, note). And so also to NG. Since then BNG is an hyperbola whose center is C and tangent DE, and since CE has been joined and a point N has been taken on the section and through it NG has been drawn parallel to DE, by a theorem already shown (I. 47) for the hyperbola
$$NO = OG.$$

PROPOSITION 49

If a straight line touching a parabola meets the diameter, and through the point of contact a parallel to the diameter is drawn, and from the vertex a straight line is drawn parallel to an ordinate, and it is contrived that as the segment of the tangent between the erected straight line and the point of contact is to the segment of the parallel between the point of contact and the erected straight line, so is some straight line to the double of the tangent, then whatever straight line is drawn [parallel to the tangent] from the section to the straight line drawn through the point of contact parallel to the diameter, will equal in square the rectangle contained by the straight line found and by the straight line cut off by it from the point of contact.

Let there be a parabola whose diameter is the straight line MBC, and CD its tangent, and through D let the straight line FDN be drawn parallel to the straight line BC, and let the straight line FB be erected ordinatewise (I. 17),

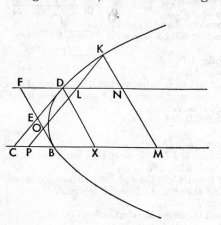

and let it be contrived that
$$ED : DF :: \text{some straight line}$$
$$G : 2CD,$$
and let some point K be taken on the section, and let the straight line KLP be drawn through K parallel to CD.

I say that
$$\text{sq. } KL = \text{rect. } G, DL$$
that is that, with the straight line DL as diameter, the straight line G is the upright side.

For let the straight lines DX and KNM be dropped ordinatewise. And since the straight line

CD touches the section, and the straight line DX has been dropped ordinatewise, then

$$CB = BX \text{ (i. 35)}.$$

But

$$BX = FD$$

and therefore

$$CB = FD.$$

And so also

$$\text{trgl. } ECB = \text{trgl. } EFD.$$

Let the common figure $DEBMN$ be added; therefore

$$\text{quadr. } DCMN = \text{pllg. } FM$$
$$= \text{trgl. } KPM \text{ (i. 42)}.$$

Let the common quadrilateral $LPMN$ be subtracted; therefore the remainders

$$\text{trgl. } KLN = \text{pllg. } LC.$$

And

$$\text{angle } DLP = \text{angle } KLN;$$

therefore

$$\text{rect. } KL, LN = 2 \text{ rect. } LD, DC.[1]$$

And since

$$ED : DF : : G : 2CD,$$

and

$$ED : DF : : KL : LN,$$

therefore also

$$G : 2CD : : KL : LN.$$

But

$$KL : LN : \text{sq. } KL : \text{rect. } KL, LN,$$

and

$$G : 2CD : : \text{rect. } G, DL : 2\text{rect. } LD, DC;$$

therefore

---

[1] Eutocius, commenting, says: "For let the triangle KLN and the parallelogram $DLPC$ be set out. And since $\qquad$ trgl. KLN = pllg. DP, let the straight line NR be drawn through N parallel to LK, and through K, KR parallel to LN; therefore LR is a parallelogram and
$$\text{pllg. } LR = 2 \text{ trgl. } KLN;$$
and so also $\qquad$ pllg. $LR = 2$ pllg. DP.
Then let the straight lines DC and LP be produced to S and T, and let CS be made equal to DC, and PT to LP, and let ST be joined; therefore
$$\text{pllg. } DT = 2 \text{ pllg. } DP;$$
and so $\qquad$ pllg. LR = pllg. LS.
But it is also equiangular with it because of the angles at L being vertical; but in equal and equiangular parallelograms the sides about the equal angles are reciprocally proportional; therefore $\qquad KL : LT$ or $DS : : DL : LN$,
and $\qquad$ rect. KL, LN = rect. LD, DS.
And since $\qquad DS = 2DC$,
hence $\qquad$ rect. $KL, LN = 2$ rect. LD, DC.
"And if DC is parallel to LP, and CP is not parallel to LD, it is clear $DCPL$ is a trapezoid, and so I say that $\qquad$ rect. KL, LN = rect. $DL, CD + LR$.
For if LP is filled out, as we have said before, and the straight lines DC and LP are produced, and CS is made equal to LP, and PT to DC, and the straight line ST is joined, then
$$\text{pllg. } DT = 2DP,$$
and the same demonstration will fit. And this will be useful in what follows (i. 50)."

sq. KL : rect. KL, LN : : rect. G, DL : 2rect. CD, DL.

And alternately; but

rect. $KL, LN = 2$rect. CD, DL;

therefore also

sq. $KL = $ rect. G, DL.

PROPOSITION 50

If a straight line touching an hyperbola or ellipse or circumference of a circle meets the diameter, and a straight line is produced through the point of contact and the center, and from the vertex a straight line erected parallel to an ordinate meets the straight line drawn through the point of contact and the center, and if it is contrived that as the segment of the tangent between the point of contact and the straight line erected is to the segment of the straight line, drawn through the point of contact and the center, between the point of contact and the straight line erected, so some straight line is to the double of the tangent, then whatever straight line is drawn from the section to the straight line drawn through the point of contact and the center, parallel to the tangent, will equal in square a rectangular area applied to the straight line found, having as breadth the straight line cut off by it from the

CASES I

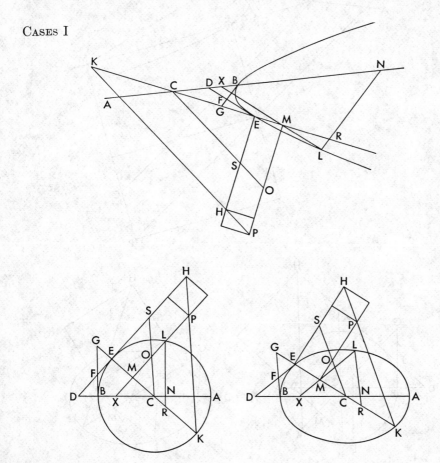

*point of contact, and exceeding, in the case of the hyperbola, by a figure similar to
the rectangle contained by the double of the straight line between the center and the
point of contact and by the straight line found; but in the case of the ellipse and
circle, defective by it.*

Let there be an hyperbola or ellipse or circumference of a circle whose diameter is the straight line AB, and center C, and let the straight line DE be a
tangent, and let the straight line CE be joined and produced both ways, and
let the straight line CK be made equal to the straight line EC, and through B
let the straight line BFG be erected ordinatewise, and through E let the
straight line EH be drawn perpendicular to EC, and let it be that

$$FE : EG : : EH : 2ED,$$

Cases II

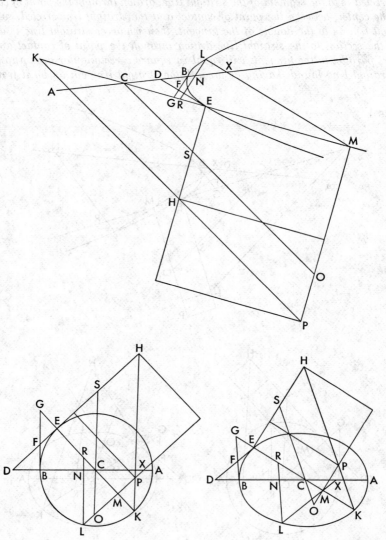

and let the straight line HK be joined and produced, and let some point L be taken on the section, and through it let the straight line LMX be drawn parallel to ED, and the straight line LRN parallel to BG, and the straight line MP parallel to EH.

I say that
$$\text{sq. } LM = \text{rect. } EM, MP.$$

For let the straight line CSO be drawn through C parallel to KP. And since
$$EC = CK,$$
and

Cases I
$$EC : KC :: ES : SH$$
therefore also
$$ES = SH.$$

Cases II
And since
$$FE : EG :: HE : 2ED,$$
and
$$2ES = EH,$$
therefore also
$$FE : EG :: SE : ED.$$
And
$$FE : EG :: LM : MR;$$
therefore
$$LM : MR :: SE : ED.$$
And since it was shown (I. 43) that, in the case of the hyperbola,
$$\text{trgl. } RNC = \text{trgl. } LNX + \text{trgl. } GBC,$$
$$= \text{trgl. } LNX + \text{trgl. } CDE,[1]$$
and, in the case of the ellipse and circle,
$$\text{trgl. } RNC + \text{trgl. } LNX = \text{trgl. } GBC$$
$$= \text{trgl. } CDE;$$
therefore, in the case of the hyperbola with the common triangle ECD and the common quadrilateral $NRMX$ subtracted, and in the case of the ellipse and circle with the common triangle MXC subtracted,[2]

[1]That
$$\text{trgl. } GBC = \text{trgl. } CDE$$
is proved by Apollonius in the course of another proof of I. 43, reported by Eutocius. It is also proved in III. 1, without the help of intervening propositions.

[2]The position of point L furnishes different cases which at times, as in the present theorem, require a change in the course of the proof. The figures marked "Cases I" are drawn to fit the proof as set down, but we have added figures marked "Cases II" as an example of the possible differences.

For the hyperbola of Case II, instead of the subtraction in the theorem above, we have
$$\text{trgl. } RNC = \text{trgl. } LNX + \text{trgl. } CDE$$
$$\text{quadr. } MCNL = \text{quadr. } MCNL.$$
Subtracting the first equals from the second identity, we have
$$\text{trgl. } LMR = \text{quadr. } MEDX.$$
The rest of the proof is the same.

For the ellipse and circle of Case II, we have as in the theorem above
$$\text{trgl. } RNC + \text{trgl. } LNX = \text{trgl. } CDE,$$
and subtracting the common triangle CMX,
$$\text{trgl. } LMR = \text{trgl. } CDE - \text{trgl. } CMX;$$
therefore
$$\text{rect. } LM, MR = \text{rect. } EM, ED + MX.$$
For let CM be made equal to CM' and CX to CX'. Then

$$\text{trgl. } LMR = \text{quadr. } MEDX.$$

And MX is parallel to DE, and

$$\text{angle } LMR = \text{angle } EMX;$$

therefore

rect. LM, MR = rect. $EM, ED + MX$ (I. 49, note, para. 2).

And since

$$MC : CE : : MX : ED$$

and

$$MC : CE : : MO : ES,$$

therefore

$$MO : ES : : MX : ED$$

And *componendo*

$$MO + ES : ES : : MX + ED : ED;$$

alternately

$$MO + ES : MX + ED : : ES : ED$$

But

$$MO + ES : MX + ED : : \text{rect. } MO + ES, EM : \text{rect. } MX + ED, EM,$$

and

$$ES : ED : : LM : MR : : FE : EG \text{ (Eucl. VI. 4)}$$

or

$$ES : ED : : \text{sq. } LM : \text{rect. } LM, MR;$$

therefore

rect. $MO + ES, ME :$ rect. $MX + ED, EM : :$ sq. $LM :$ rect. LM, MR.

And alternately

rect. $MO + ES, ME :$ sq. $LM : :$ rect. $MX + ED, EM :$ rect. LM, MR.

But

$$\text{rect. } LM, MR = \text{rect. } ME, MX + ED \text{ (above)};$$

therefore

$$\text{sq. } LM = \text{rect. } EM, MO + ES.$$

And

$$SE = SH,$$

and

$$SH = OP;$$

therefore

$$\text{sq. } LM = \text{rect. } EM, MP.$$

Proposition 51

If a straight line touching either of the opposite sections meets the diameter, and through the point of contact and the center some straight line is produced to the other section, and from the vertex a straight line is erected parallel to an ordinate and meets the straight line drawn through the point of contact and the center, and if it is contrived that, as the segment of the tangent between the straight line erected

---

     trgl. $CDE -$ trgl. $CMX =$ quadr. $M'EDX'$,
and $M'X'$ is parallel to ED, and
         angle $EM'X' =$ angle RML.

    These cases will come up again in Book III, and in general
it is convenient to think of quadrilateral $MEDX$ as standing for the difference of the two
triangles when one pair of its sides cross each other.

and the point of contact is to the segment of the straight line, drawn through the point of contact and the center, between the point of contact and the straight line erected, so is some straight line to the double of the tangent, then whatever straight line in the other of the sections is drawn to the straight line through the point of contact and the center, parallel to the tangent, will equal in square the rectangle applied to the straight line found, having as breadth the straight line cut off by it from the point of contact and exceeding by a figure similar to the rectangle contained by the straight line between the opposite sections and the straight line found.

Let there be opposite sections whose diameter is the straight line AB and

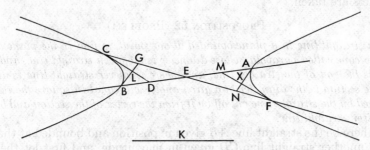

center E, and let the straight line CD be drawn tangent to the section B and the straight line CE joined and produced (I. 29), and let the straight line BLG be drawn ordinatewise (I. 17), and let it be contrived that

$$LC : CG : : \text{ some straight line } K : 2CD.$$

Now it is evident that the straight lines in the section BC, parallel to CD and drawn to EC produced are equal in square to the areas applied to K, having as breadths the straight line cut off by them from the point of contact, and exceeding by a figure similar to the rectangle CF, K; for

$$FC = 2CE.$$

I say then that in section FA the same thing will come about.

For let the straight line MF be drawn through F tangent to the section AF, and let the straight line AXN be erected ordinatewise. And since BC and AF are opposite sections, and CD and MF are tangents to them, therefore CD is equal and parallel to MF (I. 44, note). But also

$$CE = EF;$$

therefore also

$$ED = EM.$$

And since

$$LC : CG : : K : 2CD \text{ or } 2MF,$$

therefore also

$$XF : FN : : K : 2MF.$$

Since then AF is an hyperbola whose diameter is AB and tangent MF, and AN has been drawn ordinatewise, and

$$XF : FN : : K : 2FM,$$

hence any lines drawn from the section to EF produced, parallel to FM, will equal in square the rectangle contained by the straight line K and the line cut off by them from F, exceeding by a figure similar to the rectangle CF, K (I. 50).

And with these things shown, it is at once evident that in the parabola each of the straight lines drawn off parallel to the original diameter is a diameter

(I. 46), but in the hyperbola and ellipse and opposite sections each of the straight lines drawn through the center is a diameter (I. 47–48); and that in the parabola the straight lines dropped to each of the diameters parallel to the tangents will equal in square the rectangles applied to it (I. 49), but in the hyperbola and opposite sections they will equal in square the areas applied to it and exceeding by the same figure (I. 50–51), but in the ellipse the areas applied to it and defective by the same figure (I. 50); and that all the things which have been already proved about the sections as following when the principal diameters are used,[1] will also, those very same things, follow when the other diameters are taken.

PROPOSITION 52 (PROBLEM)

Given a straight line in a plane bounded at one point, to find in the plane the section of a cone called parabola, whose diameter is the given straight line, and whose vertex is the end of the straight line, and where whatever straight line is dropped from the section to the diameter at a given angle, will equal in square the rectangle contained by the straight line cut off by it from the vertex of the section and by some other given straight line.

Let there be the straight line AB given in position and bounded at the point A, and another straight line CD given in magnitude, and first let the given

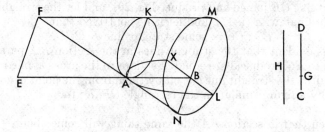

angle be a right angle; it is required then to find a parabola in the plane of reference whose diameter is the straight line AB and whose vertex is the point A, and whose upright side is the straight line CD, and where the straight lines dropped ordinatewise will be dropped at a right angle, that is so that AB is the axis (First Def. I. 7).

Let AB be produced to E, and let CG be taken as the fourth part of CD, and let

$$EA > CG,$$

and let

$$CD : H :: H : EA.$$

Therefore

$$CD : EA :: \text{sq. } H : \text{sq. } EA,$$

and

$$CD < 4EA;$$

therefore also

$$\text{sq. } H < 4 \text{ sq. } EA.$$

---

[1]The principal diameter (διάμετρος ἀρχική) is that whose being is established in I.7, porism.

Therefore
$$H < 2EA;$$
and so the two straight lines EA are greater than H. It is therefore possible for a triangle to be constructed from H and two straight lines EA. Then let the triangle EAF be constructed on EA at right angles to the plane of reference so that
$$EA = AF,$$
and
$$H = FE,$$
and let the straight line AK be drawn parallel to FE, and FK to EA, and let a cone be conceived whose vertex is the point F and whose base is the circle about diameter KA, at right angles to the plane through AFX. Then the cone will be a right cone (First Def. I. 3); for
$$AF = FK.$$
And let the cone be cut by a plane parallel to the circle KA, and let it make as a section the circle MNX (I. 4), at right angles clearly to the plane through MFN, and let the straight line MN be the common section of the circle MNX and of the triangle MFN; therefore it is the diameter of the circle. And let the straight line XL be the common section of the plane of reference and of the circle. Since then circle MNX is at right angles to triangle MFN, and the plane of reference also at right angles to triangle MFN, therefore the straight line LX, their common section, is at right angles to triangle MFN, that is to triangle KFA (Eucl. XI. 19); and therefore it is perpendicular to all the straight lines touching it and in the triangle; and so it is perpendicular to both MN and AB.

Again since a cone, whose base is the circle MNX and whose vertex is the point F, has been cut by a plane at right angles to the triangle MFN and makes as a section circle MNX, and since it has also been cut by another plane, the plane of reference, cutting the base of the cone in a straight line XL at right angles to MN which is the common section of the circle MNX and the triangle MFN, and the common section of the plane of reference and of the triangle MFN, the straight line AB, is parallel to the side of the cone FKM, therefore the resulting section of the cone in the plane of reference is a parabola, and its diameter AB (I. 11), and the straight lines dropped ordinatewise from the section to AB will be dropped at right angles; for they are parallel to XL which is perpendicular to AB. And since
$$CD : H : : H : EA,$$
and
$$EA = AF = FK$$
and
$$H = EF = AK,$$
therefore
$$CD : AK : : AK : AF.$$
And therefore
$$CD : AF : : \text{sq. } AK : \text{sq. } AF \text{ or rect. } AF, FK.$$
Therefore CD is the upright side of the section; for this has been shown in the eleventh theorem (I. 11).

PROPOSITION 53 (PROBLEM)

With the same things supposed, let the given angle not be right, and let the angle HAE be made equal to it and let

$$AH = \text{half } CD,$$

and from H let the straight line HE be drawn perpendicular to AE, and through E let the straight line EL be drawn parallel to BH, and from A let the straight line AL be drawn perpendicular to EL, and let EL be bisected at
K, and from K let the straight line
KM be drawn perpendicular to EL
and produced to F and G, and let
rect. $LK, KM = $ sq. AL. And given the
two straight lines LK and KM, KL in
position and bounded at K, and KM
in magnitude, and let a parabola be
described with a right angle whose
diameter is the straight line KL, and
whose vertex is the point K, and
whose upright side is the straight line
KM, as has been shown before (I. 52);
and it will pass through the point A
because

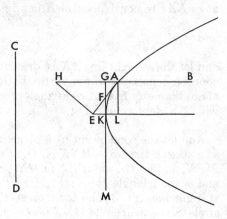

$$\text{sq. } AL = \text{rect. } LK, KM \text{ (I. 11)},$$

and the straight line EA will touch the section because

$$EK = KL \text{ (I. 33)}.$$

And HA is parallel to EKL; therefore HAB is the diameter of the section, and the straight lines dropped to it parallel to AE will be bisected by AB (I. 46). And they will be dropped at angle HAE. And since

$$\text{angle } AEH = \text{angle } AGF,$$

and angle at A is common, therefore triangle AHE is similar to triangle AGF. Therefore

$$HA : EA :: FA : AG;$$

therefore

$$2AH : 2AE :: FA : AG.$$

But

$$CD = 2AH;$$

therefore

$$FA : AG :: CD : 2AE.$$

Then by things already shown in the forty-ninth theorem (I. 49) the straight line CD is the upright side.

PROPOSITION 54

*Given two bounded straight lines perpendicular to each other, one of them being
produced on the side of the right angle, to find on the straight line produced the
section of a cone called hyperbola in the same plane with the straight lines, so that
the straight line produced is a diameter of the section and the point at the angle is
the vertex, and where whatever straight line is dropped from the section to the diameter, making an angle equal to the given angle, will equal in square the rectangle
applied to the other straight line having as breadth the straight line cut off by the
dropped straight line beginning with the vertex and exceeding by a figure similar
and similarly situated to that contained by the original straight lines.*

Let there be the two bounded straight lines AB and BC perpendicular to

each other, and let AB be produced to D; it is required then to find in the plane
through the lines AB, BC an hyperbola whose diameter will be the straight

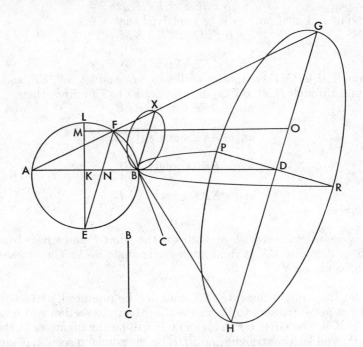

line ABD and vertex B, and upright side the straight line BC, and where the
straight lines dropped from the section to BD at the given angle will equal in
square the rectangles applied to BC having as breadths the straight lines cut
off by them from B and exceeding by a figure similar and similarly situated to
the rectangle AB, BC.

First let the given angle be a right angle, and on AB let a plane be erected at
right angles to the plane of reference, and let the circle $AEBF$ be described in it
about AB, so that the segment of the circle's diameter within the sector AEB
has to the segment of the diameter within the sector AFB a ratio not greater
than that of AB to BC,[1] and let AEB be bisected at E, and let the straight line

---

[1]Eutocius, commenting, adds: "Let there be two straight lines AB and BC, and let it be
required to describe a circle on AB so that its diameter is cut by AB in such a way that the
part of it on the side of C has to the remainder a ratio not
greater than that of AB to BC.

"Now let it be supposed that they have the same ratio,
and let AB be bisected at D, and through it let the straight
line EDF be drawn perpendicular to AB, and let it be contrived that $\qquad AB : BC : : ED : DF$,
and let EF be bisected; then it is clear that if
$$AB = BC$$
and $\qquad\qquad\qquad\qquad ED = DF,$
the point D will be the midpoint of EF, and if
$$AB > BC$$
and $\qquad\qquad\qquad\qquad ED > DF,$
the midpoint will be below D, and if

EK be drawn perpendicular from E to the straight line AB and let it be produced to L; therefore the straight line EL is a diameter (Eucl. III. 1). If then

$$AB : BC : : EK : KL$$

we use point L, but if not, let it be contrived that

$$AB : BC : : EK : KM$$

with

$$KM < KL \text{ (Eucl. v. 8)},$$

and through M let MF be drawn parallel to AB, and let AF, EF, and FB be joined, and through B let BX be drawn parallel to FE. Since then

$$\text{angle } AFE = \text{angle } EFB,$$

but

$$\text{angle } AFE = \text{angle } AXB,$$

and

$$\text{angle } EFB = \text{angle } XBF,$$

therefore also

$$\text{angle } XBF = \text{angle } FXB;$$

therefore also

$$FB = FX.$$

Let a cone be conceived whose vertex is the point F and whose base is the circle about diameter BX at right angles to triangle BFX. Then the cone will be a right cone; for

$$FB = FX.$$

Then let the straight lines BF, FX, and MF be produced, and let the cone be cut by a plane parallel to the circle BX; then the section will be a circle (I. 4). Let it be the circle GPR; and so GH will be the diameter of the circle (I. 4, end). And let the straight line PDR be the common section of circle GH and of the plane of reference; then PDR will be perpendicular to both of the straight lines GH and DB; for both of the circles XB and HG are perpendicular to triangle FGH, and the plane of reference is perpendicular to triangle FGH; and therefore their common section the straight line PDR is perpendicular to triangle FGH; therefore it makes right angles also with all the straight lines touching it and in the same plane.

$$AB < BC,$$

it will be above D.

"And now let it be below as G, and with center G and radius GF let a circle be described; then it will have to pass either within or without the points A and B. And if it should pass through the points A and B, what was enjoined would be done; but let it fall beyond the points A and B, and let the straight line AB, produced both ways, meet the circumference at H and K, and let FH, HE, EK and KF be joined, and let MB be drawn through B parallel to FK, and BL parallel to KE, and let MA and AL be joined; then these will also be parallel to FH and HE because $AD = DB$
and $DH = DK$
and FDE is perpendicular to HK. And since the angle at K is a right angle, and MB and BL are parallel to FK and KE, therefore the angle at B is a right angle; then for the same reasons also the angle at A. And so the circle described on ML will pass through the points A and B (Eucl. III. 31). Let the circle $MALB$ be described. And since MB is parallel to FK,

$$FD : DM : : KD : DB.$$

Then likewise also $KD : DB : : ED : DL.$
And therefore $FD : DM : : ED : DL.$
And alternately, $ED : DF : : AB : BC : : LD : DM.$

"And likewise if the circle described on FE cuts AB, the same thing could be shown."

And since a cone whose base is circle GH and vertex F, has been cut by a plane perpendicular to triangle FGH, and has also been cut by another plane, the plane of reference, in the straight line PDR perpendicular to the straight line GDH, and the common section of the plane of reference and of triangle GFH, that is the straight line DB, produced in the direction of B, meets the straight line GF at A, therefore by things already shown before (I. 12) the section PBR will be an hyperbola whose vertex is the point B, and where the straight lines dropped ordinatewise to BD will be dropped at a right angle; for they are parallel to straight line PDR. And since

$$AB : BC :: EK : KM,$$

and

$$EK : KM :: EN : NF :: \text{rect. } EN, NF : \text{sq. } NF,$$

therefore

$$AB : BC :: \text{rect. } EN, NF : \text{sq. } NF.$$

And

$$\text{rect. } EN, NF = \text{rect. } AN, NB;$$

therefore

$$AB : CB :: \text{rect. } AN, NB : \text{sq. } NF.$$

But

$$\text{rect. } AN, NB : \text{sq. } NF \text{ comp. } AN : NF, BN : NF;$$

but

$$AN : NF :: AD : DG :: FO : OG,$$

and

$$BN : NF :: FO : OH;$$

therefore

$$AB : BC \text{ comp. } FO : OG, FO : OH,$$

that is

$$\text{sq. } FO : \text{rect. } OG, OH.$$

Therefore

$$AB : BC :: \text{sq. } FO : \text{rect. } OG, OH.$$

And the straight line FO is parallel to the straight line AD; therefore the straight line AB is the transverse side, and BC the upright side; for these things have been shown in the twelfth theorem (I. 12).

PROPOSITION 55 (PROBLEM)

Then let the given angle not be a right angle, and let there be the two given straight lines AB and AC, and let the given angle be equal to angle BAH; then it is required to describe an hyperbola whose diameter will be the straight line AB, and upright side AC, and where the ordinates will be dropped at angle HAB.

Let the straight line AB be bisected at D, and let the semicircle AFD be described on AD, and let some straight line FG, parallel to AH, be drawn to the semicircle making

$$\text{sq. } FG : \text{rect. } DG, GA :: AC : AB,^{1}$$

---

[1] Eutocius, commenting, gives this construction: "Let there be the semicircle ABC on the diameter AC, and the given ratio EF to FG, and let it be required to do what is proposed.

"Let FH be made equal to EF, and let HG be bisected at K, and let the straight line CB be drawn in the semicircle at angle ACB (the required angle), and from the center L let the straight line LS be drawn perpendicular to it, and produced let it meet the circumference at and let the straight line *FHD* be joined and produced to *D*, and let

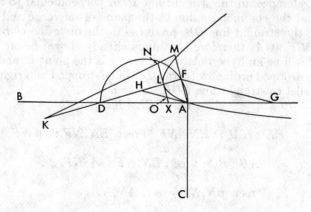

$$FD : DL :: DL : DH,$$

and let *DK* be made equal to *DL*, and let

$$\text{rect. } LF, FM = \text{sq. } AF,$$

and let *KM* be joined, and through *L* let *LN* be drawn perpendicular to *KF* and let it be produced towards *X*. And with two given bounded straight lines *KL* and *LN* perpendicular to each other, let an hyperbola be described whose transverse side is *KL*, and upright side *LN*, and where the straight lines dropped from the section to the diameter will be dropped at a right angle and will equal in square the rectangle applied to *LN* having as breadths the straight lines cut off by them from *L* and exceeding by a figure similar to rectangle *KL*, *LN* (I. 54); and the section will pass through *A*; for

$$\text{sq. } AF = \text{rect. } LF, FM \text{ (I. 12)}.$$

N, and through *N* let *NM* be drawn parallel to *CB*; therefore it will touch the circle. And let it be contrived that

$$FH : HK :: MX : XN,$$

and let *NO* be made equal to *XN*, and let the straight lines *LX* and *LO* cutting the semicircle at *P* and *R* be joined, and let the straight line *PRD* be joined.

Since then $XN = NO$, and *NL* is common and perpendicular, therefore

$$LO = LX.$$

And also $\qquad LP = LR;$

and therefore the remainders $\qquad PO = RX.$

Therefore *PRD* is parallel to *MO*. And

$$FH : HK :: MX : NX;$$

and $\qquad HK : HG :: NX : XO;$

therefore *ex aequali* $\qquad FH : HG :: MX : XO;$

inversely $\qquad HG : FH :: XO : MX;$

componendo $\qquad GF : FH :: OM : MX$

or $\qquad GF : FE :: PD : DR.$

And $\qquad PD : DR :: \text{rect. } PD, DR : \text{sq. } DR,$

but $\qquad \text{rect. } PD, DR = \text{rect. } AD, DC \text{ (Eucl. III. 36)};$

therefore $\qquad GF : FE :: \text{rect. } AD, DC : \text{sq. } DR.$

Therefore inversely $\qquad FE : GF :: \text{sq. } DR : \text{rect. } AD, DC.\text{''}$

And AH will touch it; for
$$\text{rect. } FD, DH = \text{sq. } DL \text{ (i. 37).}$$
And so AB is a diameter of the section (i. 51). And since
$$CA : 2AD \text{ or } AB :: \text{sq. } FG : \text{rect. } DG, GA,$$
but
$$CA : 2AD \text{ comp. } CA : 2AH, 2AH : 2AD$$
or
$$CA : 2AD \text{ comp. } CA : 2AH, AH : AD$$
and
$$AH : AD :: FG : GD,$$
therefore
$$CA : AB \text{ comp. } CA : 2AH, FG : GD.$$
But also
$$\text{sq. } FG : \text{rect. } DG, GA \text{ comp. } FG : GD, FG : GA;$$
therefore
ratio comp. $CA : 2AH, FG : GD = $ ratio comp. $FG : GA, FG : GD$.
Let the common ratio $FG : GD$ be taken away; therefore
$$CA : 2AH :: FG : GA.$$
But
$$FG : GA :: OA : AX,$$
therefore
$$CA : 2AH :: OA : AX.$$
But whenever this is so, the straight line AC is a parameter; for this has been shown in the fiftieth theorem (i. 50).

Proposition 56 (Problem)

Given two bounded straight lines perpendicular to each other, to find about one of them as diameter and in the same plane with the two straight lines the section of a cone called ellipse, whose vertex will be the point at the right angle, and where the straight lines dropped ordinatewise from the section to the diameter at a given angle will equal in square the rectangles applied to the other straight line, having as breadth the straight line cut off by them from the vertex of the section and defective by a figure similar and similarly situated to the rectangle contained by the given straight lines.

Let there be two given straight lines AB and AC perpendicular to each other,

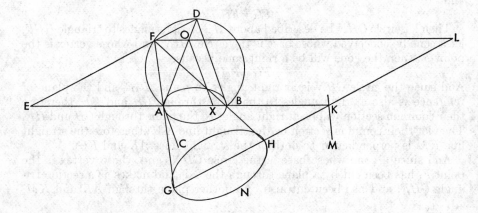

of which the greater is the straight line AB; then it is required to describe in the plane of reference an ellipse whose diameter will be the straight line AB and vertex A, and upright side AC, and where the ordinates will be dropped from the section to the diameter at a given angle and will equal in square the rectangles applied to AC having as breadths the straight lines cut off by them from A and defective by a figure similar and similarly situated to rectangle BA,AC.

And first let the given angle be a right angle, and let a plane be erected from AB at right angles to the plane of reference, and in it, on AB, let the sector of a circle ADB be described, and its midpoint be D, and let the straight lines DA and DB be joined, and let the straight line AX be made equal to AC, and through X let the straight line XO be drawn parallel to DB, and through O let OF be drawn parallel to AB, and let DF be joined and let it meet AB produced at E; then we will have

$$AB : AC :: AB : AX :: DA : AO :: DE : EF.$$

And let the straight lines AF and FB be joined and produced, and let some point G be taken at random on FA, and through it let the straight line GL be drawn parallel to DE and let it meet AB produced at K; then let FO be produced and let it meet GK at L. Since then

$$\text{arc } AD = \text{arc } DB,$$
$$\text{angle } ABD = \text{angle } DFB \text{ (Eucl. iii. 27)}.$$

And since

$$\text{angle } EFA = \text{angle } FDA + \text{angle } FAD,$$

but

$$\text{angle } FAD = \text{angle } FBD,$$

and

$$\text{angle } FDA = \text{angle } FBA,$$

therefore also

$$\text{angle } EFA = \text{angle } DBA = \text{angle } DFB.$$

And also DE is parallel to LG; therefore

$$\text{angle } EFA = \text{angle } FGH,$$

and

$$\text{angle } DFB = \text{angle } FHG$$

And so also

$$\text{angle } FGH = \text{angle } FHG,$$

and

$$FG = FH.$$

Then let circle GHN be described about HG at right angles to triangle HGF, let a cone be conceived whose base is the circle GHN, and whose vertex is the point F; then the cone will be a right cone because

$$FG = FH.$$

And since the circle GHN is at right angles to plane HGF, and the plane of reference is also at right angles to the plane through GH and HF, therefore their common section will be at right angles to the plane through GH and HF. Then let their common section be the straight line KM; therefore the straight line KM is perpendicular to both of the straight lines AK and KG.

And since a cone whose base is the circle GHN, and whose vertex is the point F, has been cut by a plane through the axis and makes as a section triangle GHF, and has been cut also by another plane through AK and KM,

which is the plane of reference, in the straight line KM which is perpendicular to GK, and the plane meets the sides of the cone FG and FH, therefore the resulting section is an ellipse whose diameter is AB and where the ordinates will be dropped at a right angle (I. 13); for they are parallel to KM. And since
$$DE : EF : : \text{rect. } DE, EF \text{ or rect. } BE, EA : \text{sq. } EF,$$
and
$$\text{rect. } BE, EA : \text{sq. } EF \text{ comp. } BE : EF, AE : EF,$$
but
$$BE : EF : : BK : KH,$$
and
$$AE : EF : : AK : KG : : FL : LG,$$
therefore
$$BA : AC \text{ comp. } FL : LG, FL : LH \text{ (see above)},$$
which is the same as
$$\text{sq. } FL : \text{rect. } GL, LH;$$
therefore
$$BA : AC : : \text{sq. } FL : \text{rect. } GL, LH.$$
And whenever this is so, the straight line AC is the upright side of the figure, as has been shown in the thirteenth theorem (I. 13).

PROPOSITION 57 (PROBLEM)

With the same things supposed let the straight line AB be less than AC, and let it be required to describe an ellipse about diameter AB so that AC is the upright.

Let AB be bisected at D, and from D let the straight line EDF be drawn perpendicular to AB, and let
$$\text{sq. } FE = \text{rect. } BA, AC$$
so that
$$FD = DE,$$
and let FG be drawn parallel to AB, and let it be contrived that
$$AC : AB : : EF : FG;$$
therefore also
$$EF > FG.$$
And since
$$\text{rect. } CA, AB = \text{sq. } EF,$$
hence
$$CA : AB : : \text{sq. } FE : \text{sq. } AB : : \text{sq. } DF : \text{sq. } DA.$$
But
$$CA : AB : : EF : FG,$$
therefore
$$EF : FG : : \text{sq. } FD : \text{sq. } DA.$$
But
$$\text{sq. } FD = \text{rect. } FD, DE;$$
therefore
$$EF : FG : : \text{rect. } ED, DF : \text{sq. } AD.$$

Then with two bounded straight lines situated at right angles to each other and with EF greater, let an ellipse be described whose diameter is EF and upright side FG (I. 56); then the section will pass through A because rect. FD, DE : sq. DA : : $EF : FG$ (I. 21).

And
$$AD = DB;$$
then it will also pass through B. Then an ellipse has been described about AB. And since
$$CA : AB :: \text{sq. } FD : \text{sq. } DA,$$
and
$$\text{sq. } DA = \text{rect. } AD, DB,$$
therefore
$$CA : AB :: \text{sq. } DF : \text{rect. } AD, DB.$$
And so the straight line AC is an upright side (I. 21).

PROPOSITION 58 (PROBLEM)

But then let the given angle not be a right angle, and let the angle BAD be equal to it, and let the straight line AB be bisected at E, and let the semicircle AFE be described on AE, and in it let the straight line FG be drawn parallel to AD making
$$\text{sq. } FG : \text{rect. } AG, GE :: CA : AB,[1]$$
and let the straight lines AF and EF be joined and produced, and let
$$DE : EH :: EH :: EF,$$

[1] Eutocius, commenting, gives this construction: "Let there be the semicircle ABC and within it some straight line AB (at the required angle to AC), and let two unequal straight lines DE and EF be laid down, and let EF be produced to G, and let FG be made equal to DE, and let the whole line EG be bisected at H, and let the center of the circle, K, be taken, and from it let a perpendicular be drawn to AB and let it meet the circumference at L, and through L let LM be drawn parallel to AB, and let KA produced meet LM at M, and let it be contrived that $\qquad HF : FG :: LM : MN,$
and let $\qquad\qquad\qquad LX = LN,$
and let the straight lines NK and KX be joined and produced, and let the circle, finished out, cut them at P and O, and let the straight line ORP be joined.

"Since then $\quad FH : FG :: LM : MN,$
componendo $\quad HG : GF :: LN : NM;$
inversely $\quad FG : GH :: NM : NL,$
and $\quad FG : GE :: MN : NX;$
separando $\quad FG : FE :: NM : MX.$
And since $\quad NL = LX,$
and the straight line LK is common and at right angles, therefore also
$$KN = KX.$$
And also $\quad KO = KP;$
therefore NX is parallel to OP. Therefore triangle KMN is similar to triangle OKR and triangle KMX to triangle PRK.
Therefore $\quad KM : KR :: MN : RO.$
But also $\quad KM : KR :: MX : PR;$
and therefore $\quad NM : RO :: MX : PR;$
and alternately $\quad NM : MX :: RO : RP.$
But $\qquad NM : MX :: GF : FE :: DE : EF,$
and $\qquad OR : RP :: \text{sq. } OR : \text{rect. } OR, RP;$
and therefore
$$DE : EF :: \text{sq. } OR : \text{rect. } OR, RP.$$
And rect. $OR, RP = \text{rect. } AR, RC$ (Eucl. III. 35).
Therefore $DE : EF :: \text{sq. } OR : \text{rect. } AR, RC.$"

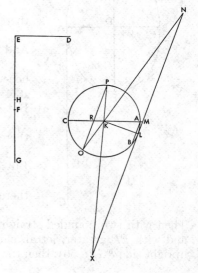

and let
$$EK = EH,$$
and let it be contrived that
$$\text{rect. } HF, FL = \text{sq. } AF,$$
and let the straight line KL be joined, and from
H let the straight line HMX be drawn perpendicular to HF and so parallel to the straight line
AFL; for the angle at F is right. And with the
two given bounded straight lines KH, and HM
perpendicular to each other, let an ellipse be
described whose transverse diameter is KH,
and the upright side of whose figure is HM,
and where the ordinates to HK will be dropped
at right angles (I. 56–57); then the section will
pass through A because sq. $FA = $ rect. HF, FL
(I. 13). And since
$$HE = EK,$$
and
$$AE = EB,$$
the section will also pass through B, and E will be the center, and the straight
line AEB the diameter. And the straight line DA will touch the section because
$$\text{rect. } DE, EF = \text{sq. } EH.$$
And since
$$CA : AB :: \text{sq. } FG : \text{rect. } AG, GE,$$
but
$$CA : AB \text{ comp. } CA : 2AD, 2AD : AB \text{ or } DA : AE,$$
and
$$\text{sq. } FG. = \text{rect. } AG, GE \text{ comp. } FG : GE, FG : GA,$$
therefore
$$\text{ratio comp. } CA : 2AD, DA : AE = \text{ratio comp. } FG : GE, FG : GA.$$
But
$$DA : AE :: FG : GE;$$
and the common ratio being taken away, we will have
$$CA : 2AD :: FG : GA$$
or
$$CA : 2AD :: XA : AN.$$
And whenever this is so, the straight line AC is the upright side of the figure
(I. 50).

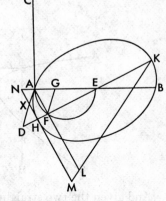

PROPOSITION 59 (PROBLEM)

*Given two bounded straight lines perpendicular to each other, to find opposite
sections whose diameter is one of the given straight lines, and whose vertex is the
ends of the straight line, and where the straight lines dropped in each of the sections at a given angle will equal in square the rectangles applied to the other of the
straight lines and exceeding by a figure similar to the rectangle contained by the
given straight lines.*

Let there be the two given bounded straight lines BE and BH, perpendicular
to each other, and let the given angle be G; then it is required to describe

opposite sections about one of the straight lines *BE* and *BH*, so that the ordinates are dropped at an angle *G*.

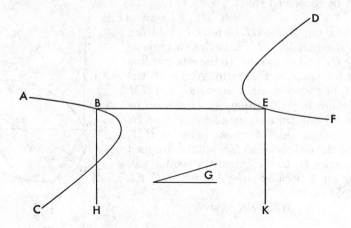

And given the two straight lines *BE* and *BH*, let an hyperbola be described whose transverse diameter will be the straight line *BE*, and the upright side of whose figure will be *HB*, and where the ordinates to *BE* produced will be at an angle *G*, and let it be the line *ABC*; for we have already described how this must be done (I. 55). Then let the straight line *EK* be drawn through *E* perpendicular to *BE* and equal to *BH*, and let another hyperbola *DEF* be likewise described whose diameter is *BE* and the upright side of whose figure is *EK*, and where the ordinates from the section will be dropped at a same angle *G*. Then it is evident that *B* and *E* are opposite sections, and there is one diameter for them, and their uprights are equal.

PROPOSITION 60 (PROBLEM)

Given two straight lines bisecting each other, to describe about each of them opposite sections, so that the straight lines are their conjugate diameters and the diameter of one pair of opposite sections is equal in square to the figure of the other pair, and likewise the diameter of the second pair of opposite sections is equal in square to the figure of the first pair.

Let there be the two given straight lines *AC* and *DE* bisecting each other; then it is required to describe opposite sections about each of them as a diameter so that the straight lines *AC* and *DE* are conjugates in them, and *DE* is equal in square to the figure about *AC*, and *AC* is equal in square to the figure about *DE*.

Let

$$\text{rect. } AC, CL = \text{sq. } DE,$$

and let *LC* be perpendicular to *CA*. And given two straight lines *AC* and *CL* perpendicular to each other, let the opposite sections *RAG* and *HCK* be described whose transverse diameter will be *CA* and whose upright side will be *CL*, and where the ordinates from the sections to *CA* will be dropped at the given angle (I. 59). Then the straight line *DE* will be a second diameter of the opposite sections (Sec. Def., I. 11); for it is the mean proportion between the sides of the figure, and, parallel to an ordinate, it has been bisected at *B*.

Then again let

$$\text{rect. } DE, DF = \text{sq. } AC,$$

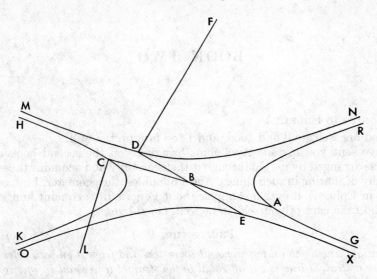

and let DF be perpendicular to DE. And given two straight lines ED and DF lying perpendicular to each other, let the opposite sections MDN and OEX be described, whose transverse diameter will be DE and the upright side of whose figure will be DF, and where the ordinates from the sections will be dropped to DE at the given angle (I. 59); then the straight line AC will also be a second diameter of the sections MDN and XEO. And so AC bisects the parallels to DE between the sections RAG and HCK, and DE the parallels to AC; and this it was required to do.

And let such sections be called conjugate.

BOOK TWO

Apollonius to Eudemus,

If you are well, well and good, and I too fare pretty well.

I have sent you my son Apollonius bringing you the second book of the conics as arranged by us. Go through it then carefully and acquaint those with it worthy of sharing in such things. And Philonides, the geometer, I introduced to you in Ephesus, if ever he happen about Pergamum, acquaint him with it too. And take care of yourself, to be well. Good-bye.

PROPOSITION 1

If a straight line touch an hyperbola at its vertex, and from it on both sides of the diameter a straight line is cut off equal to the straight line equal in square to the fourth of the figure, then the straight lines drawn from the center of the section to the ends thus taken on the tangent will not meet the section.

Let there be an hyperbola whose diameter is the straight line AB and center C, and upright the straight line BF; and let the straight line DE touch the

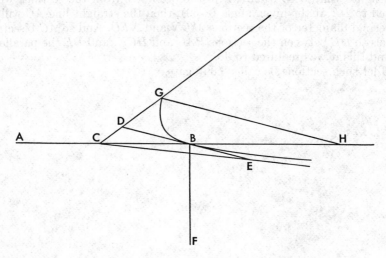

section at B, and let the squares on BD and BE each be equal to the fourth of the figure AB, BF, and the straight lines CD and CE be joined and produced.

I say that they will not meet the section.

For if possible, let CD meet the section at G, and from G let the straight line GH be dropped ordinatewise; therefore it is parallel to DB (i. 17). Since then

$$AB : BF :: \text{sq. } AB : \text{rect. } AB, BF,$$

682

but
$$\text{sq. } CB = \text{fourth sq. } AB,$$
and
$$\text{sq. } BD = \text{fourth rect. } AB, BF,$$
therefore
$$AB : BF :: \text{sq. } CB : \text{sq. } DB :: \text{sq. } CH : \text{sq. } HG.$$
And also
$$AB : BF :: \text{rect. } AH, HB : \text{sq. } HG \text{ (i. 21)};$$
therefore
$$\text{sq. } CH : \text{sq. } HG :: \text{rect. } AH, HB : \text{sq. } HG.$$
Therefore
$$\text{rect. } AH, HB = \text{sq. } CH;$$

and this is absurd (Eucl. ii. 6). Therefore the straight line CD will not meet the section. Then likewise we could show that neither does CE; therefore the straight lines CD and CE are asymptotes (ἀσύμπτωτοι)[1] to the section.

PROPOSITION 2

With the same things it is to be shown that a straight line cutting the angle contained by the straight lines DC and CE is not another asymptote.

For if possible, let CH be it, and let the straight line BH be drawn through B parallel to CD and let it meet CH at H, and let DG be made equal to BH and

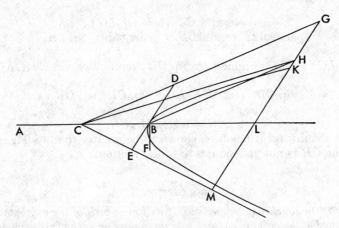

let GH be joined and produced to the points K, L, and M. Since then BH and DG are equal and parallel, DB and HG are also equal and parallel. And since AB is bisected at C and a straight line BL is added to it,
$$\text{rect. } AL, LB + \text{sq. } CB = \text{sq. } CL \text{ (Eucl. ii. 6).}$$
Likewise then, since GM is parallel to DE, and
$$DB = BE,$$

[1] The word ἀσύμπτωτος means literally "not capable of meeting" and is used in a general way in Euclid to refer to any non-secant lines or planes. In Apollonius it is also used in this way, as for instance in ii. 14, porism, where it refers to any straight lines not meeting the hyperbola. The special case where in English the lines are spoken of as asymptotes is the one defined here. Book II, proposition 14, porism further declares their peculiar property and significance.

therefore also
$$GL = LM.$$
And since
$$GH = DB,$$
therefore
$$GK > DB.$$
And also
$$KM > BE,$$
since also
$$LM > BE;$$
therefore
$$\text{rect. } MK, KG > \text{rect. } DB, BE$$
$$> \text{sq. } DB.$$
Since then
$$AB : BF :: \text{sq. } CB : \text{sq. } BD \text{ (II. 1)},$$
but
$$AB : BF :: \text{rect. } AL, LB : \text{sq. } LK \text{ (I. 21)},$$
and
$$\text{sq. } CB : \text{sq. } BD :: \text{sq. } CL : \text{sq. } LG,$$
therefore also
$$\text{sq. } CL : \text{sq. } LG :: \text{rect. } AL, LB : \text{sq. } LK.$$
Since then
$$\text{whole sq. } LC : \text{whole sq. } LG ::$$
$$\text{part subtr. rect. } AL, LB : \text{part subtr. sq. } LK,$$
therefore also
$$\text{sq. } LC : \text{sq. } LG :: \text{remainder sq. } CB : \text{remainder rect. } MK, KG,$$
that is
$$\text{sq. } CB : \text{rect. } MK, KG :: \text{sq. } CB : \text{sq. } DB.$$
Therefore
$$\text{sq. } DB = \text{rect. } MK, KG;$$
and this is absurd; for it has been shown to be greater than it. Therefore the straight line CH is not an asymptote to the section.

PROPOSITION 3

If a straight line touches an hyperbola, it will meet both of the asymptotes and it will be bisected at the point of contact, and the square on each of its segments will be equal to the fourth of the figure resulting on the diameter drawn through the point of contact.

Let there be the hyperbola ABC, and its center E, and asymptotes FE and EG, and let some straight line HK touch it at B.

I say that the straight line HK produced will meet the straight lines FE and EG.

For if possible, let it not meet them, and let EB be joined and produced, and let ED be made equal to EB; therefore the straight line BD is a diameter. Then let the squares on HB and BK each be made equal to the fourth of the figure on BD, and let EH and EK be joined. Therefore they are asymptotes (II. 1); and this is absurd (II. 2); for FE and EG are supposed asymptotes. Therefore KH produced will meet the asymptotes EF and EG at F and G.

I say then also that the squares on BF and BG will each be equal to the fourth of the figure on BD.

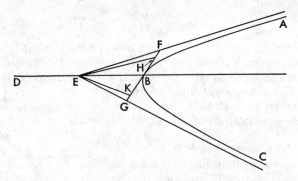

For let it not be, but if possible, let the squares on BH and BK each be equal to the fourth of the figure. Therefore HE and EK are asymptotes (II. 1); and this is absurd (II. 2). Therefore the squares on FB and BG will each be equal to the fourth of the figure on BD.

PROPOSITION 4 (PROBLEM)

Given two straight lines containing an angle and a point within the angle, to describe through the point the section of a cone called hyperbola so that the given straight lines are its asymptotes.

Let there be the two straight lines AC and AB containing a chance angle at A, and let some point D be given, and let it be required to describe through D an hyperbola to the asymptotes CA and AB.

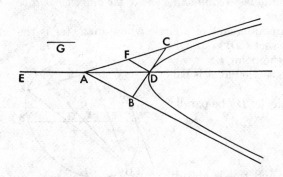

Let the straight line AD be joined and produced to E, and let AE be made equal to DA, and let the straight line DF be drawn through D parallel to AB, and let FC be made equal to AF, and let CD be joined and produced to B, and let it be contrived that

$$\text{rect. } DE, G = \text{sq. } CB,$$

and with AD extended let an hyperbola be described about it through D so that the ordinates equal in square the areas applied to G and exceeding by a figure similar to rectangle DE, G. Since then DF is parallel to BA, and

$$CF = FA,$$

therefore

$$CD = DB;$$

and so

$$\text{sq. } CB = 4 \text{ sq. } CD.$$

And

$$\text{sq. } CB = \text{rect. } DE, G;$$

therefore the squares on CD and DB are each equal to the fourth part of the figure DE, G. Therefore the straight lines AB and AC are asymptotes to the hyperbola described.

PROPOSITION 5

If the diameter of a parabola or hyperbola bisects some straight line, the tangent to the section at the end of the diameter will be parallel to the bisected straight line.

Let there be the parabola or hyperbola ABC whose diameter is the straight line DBE, and let the straight line FBG touch the section, and let some straight line AEC be drawn in the section making AE equal to EC.

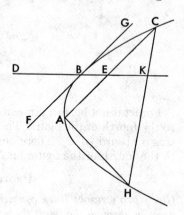

I say that AC is parallel to FG.

For if not, let the straight line CH be drawn through C parallel to FG and let HA be joined. Since then ABC is a parabola or hyperbola whose diameter is DE, and tangent FG, and CH is parallel to it, therefore
$$CK = KH \text{ (I. 46, 47).}$$
But also
$$CE = EA.$$
Therefore AH is parallel to KE; and this is absurd; for produced it meets BD (I. 22).

PROPOSITION 6

If the diameter of an ellipse or circumference of a circle bisects some straight line not through the center, the tangent to the section at the end of the diameter will be parallel to the bisected straight line.

Let there be an ellipse or circumference of a circle whose diameter is the straight line AB, and let AB bisect CD, a straight line not through the center, at the point E.

I say that the tangent to the section at A is parallel to CD.

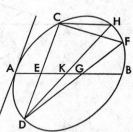

For let it not be, but if possible, let DF be parallel to the tangent at A; therefore
$$DG = FG.$$
But also
$$DE = EC;$$
therefore CF is parallel to GE; and this is absurd. For if G is the center of the section AB, the straight line CF will meet the straight line AB (I. 23); and if it is not, suppose it to be K, and let DK be joined and produced to H, and let CH be joined. Since then
$$DK = KH,$$
and also
$$DE = EC,$$
therefore CH is parallel to AB. But also CF; and this is absurd. Therefore the tangent at A is parallel to CD.

Proposition 7

If a straight line touches a section of a cone or circumference of a circle, and a parallel to it is drawn in the section and bisected, the straight line joined from the point of contact to the midpoint will be a diameter of the section.

Let there be a section of a cone or circumference of a circle ABC, and FG tangent to it, and AC parallel to FG and bisected at E, and let BE be joined.

I say that BE is a diameter of the section.

For let it not be, but, if possible, let BH be a diameter of the section. Therefore

$$AH = HC \text{ (First Def. i. 4)};$$

and this is absurd; for

$$AE = EC.$$

Therefore BH will not be a diameter of the section. Then likewise we could show that there is no other than BE.

Proposition 8

If a straight line meets an hyperbola in two points, produced both ways it will meet the asymptotes, and the straight lines cut off on it by the section from the asymptotes will be equal.

Let there be the hyperbola ABC, and the asymptotes ED and DF, and let some straight line AC meet ABC.

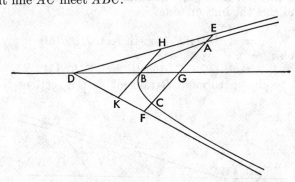

I say that produced both ways it will meet the asymptotes.

Let AC be bisected at G and let DG be joined. Therefore it is a diameter of the section (ii. 7); therefore the tangent at B is parallel to AC (ii. 5, 6). Then let HBK be the tangent (i. 32); then it will meet ED and DF (ii. 3). Since then AC is parallel to KH, and KH meets DK and DH, therefore also AC will meet DE and DF.

Let it meet them at E and F; and

$$HB = BK \text{ (ii. 3)};$$

therefore also

$$FG = GE.$$

And so also

$$CF = AE.$$

PROPOSITION 9

If a straight line meeting the asymptotes is bisected by the hyperbola, it will touch
the section in one point only.

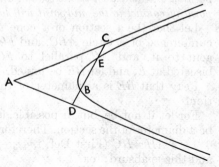

For let the straight line CD meeting
the asymptotes CA, AD be bisected by
the hyperbola at the point E.

I say that it touches the hyperbola
at no other point.

For if possible, let it touch it at B.
Therefore

$$CE = BD \text{ (II. 8)};$$

and this is absurd; for CE is supposed
equal to ED. Therefore it will not touch
the section at another point.

PROPOSITION 10

If some straight line cutting the section meet both of the asymptotes, the rectangle
contained by the straight lines cut off between the asymptotes and the section is
equal to the fourth of the figure resulting on the diameter bisecting the straight lines
drawn parallel to the drawn straight line.

Let there be the hyperbola ABC, and let DE, EF be its asymptotes, and let
some straight line DF be drawn cutting the section and the asymptotes, and
let AC be bisected at G, and let GE be joined, and let EH be made equal to BE,
and let BM be drawn from B perpendicular to HEB; therefore BH is a diameter (II. 7), and BM the upright side.

I say that

rect. DA, AF = fourth rect. HB, BM,

then likewise also

rect. DC, CF = fourth rect. HB, BM.

For let KL be drawn through B tangent to the section; therefore it is

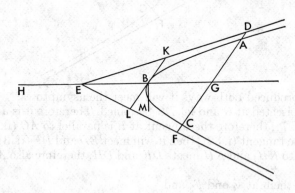

parallel to DF (II. 6). And since it has been shown

$HB : BM :: $ sq. $EB : $ sq. $BK :: $ sq. $EG : $ sq. GD (II. 1, 3),

and

$HB : BM :: $ rect. $HG, GB : $ sq. GA (I. 21),

therefore
$$\text{sq. } EG : \text{sq. } GD :: \text{rect. } HG, GB : \text{sq. } GA.$$
Since then
$$\text{whole sq. } EG : \text{whole sq. } GD ::$$
$$\text{part subtr. rect. } HG, GB : \text{part subtr. sq. } AG,$$
therefore also
$$\text{remainder sq. } EB : \text{remainder rect. } DA, AF :: \text{sq. } EG : \text{sq. } GD,$$
or
$$\text{remainder sq. } EB : \text{remainder rect. } DA, AF :: \text{sq. } EB : \text{sq. } BK.$$
Therefore
$$\text{rect. } FA, AD = \text{sq. } BK.$$
Then likewise it could be shown also that
$$\text{rect. } DC, CF = \text{sq. } BL;$$
therefore also
$$\text{rect. } FA, AD = \text{rect. } DC, CF.$$

PROPOSITION 11

If some straight line cut each of the straight lines containing the angle adjacent to the angle containing the hyperbola, it will meet the section in one point only, and the rectangle contained by the straight lines cut off between the containing straight lines and the section will be equal to the fourth part of the square on the diameter drawn parallel to the cutting straight line.

Let there be an hyperbola whose asymptotes are CA, AD, and let DA be produced to E, and through some point E let EF be drawn cutting EA and AC.

Now it is evident that it meets the section in one point only; for the straight line drawn through A parallel to EF as AB will cut angle CAD and will meet the section (II. 2) and be its diameter (I. 50); therefore EF will meet the section in one point only (I. 26).

Let it meet it at G.

I say then also that
$$\text{rect. } EG, GF = \text{sq. } AB.$$
For let the straight line $HGLK$ be drawn ordinatewise through G; therefore

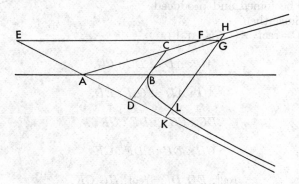

the tangent through B is parallel to GH (II. 5). Let it be CD. Since then
$$CB = BD \text{ (II. 3),}$$
therefore
$$\text{sq. } CB \text{ or rect. } CB, BD : \text{sq. } BA \text{ comp. } CB : BA, DB : BA.$$

But
$$CB : BA : : HG : GF,$$
and
$$DB : BA : : GK : GE;$$
therefore
$$\text{sq. } CB : \text{sq. } BA \text{ comp. } HG : GF, KG : GE.$$
But also
$$\text{rect. } KG, GH : \text{rect. } EG, GF \text{ comp. } HG : GF, KG : GE;$$
therefore
$$\text{rect. } KG, GH : \text{rect. } EG, GF : : \text{sq. } CB : \text{sq. } BA.$$
Alternately
$$\text{rect. } KG, GH : \text{sq. } CB : : \text{rect. } EG, GF : \text{sq. } BA.$$
But it was shown
$$\text{rect. } KG, GH = \text{sq. } CB \text{ (II. 10)};$$
therefore also
$$\text{rect. } EG, GF = \text{sq. } AB.$$

PROPOSITION 12

If two straight lines at chance angles are drawn to the asymptotes from some point of those on the section, and parallels are drawn to them from some point of those on the section, then the rectangle contained by the parallels will be equal to that contained by those straight lines to which they were drawn parallel.

Let there be an hyperbola whose asymptotes are AB and BC, and let some point D be taken on the section, and from it let DE and DF be dropped to AB and BC, and let some other point on the section G be taken, and through G let GH and GK be drawn parallel to ED and DF.

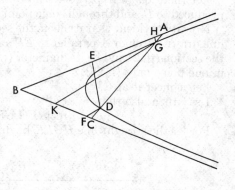

I say that
$$\text{rect. } ED, DF = \text{rect. } HG, GK.$$
For let DG be joined and produced to A and C. Since then
$$\text{rect. } AD, DC = \text{rect. } AG, GC \text{ (II. 8)},$$
therefore
$$AG : AD : : DC : CG.$$
But
$$AG : AD : : GH : ED,$$
and
$$DC : CG : : DF : GK;$$
therefore
$$GH : DE : : DF : GK$$
Therefore
$$\text{rect. } ED, DF = \text{rect. } HG, GK.$$

PROPOSITION 13

If in the place bounded by the asymptotes and the section some straight line is drawn parallel to one of the asymptotes, it will meet the section in one point only.

Let there be an hyperbola whose asymptotes are CA and AB, and let some point E be taken, and through it let EF be drawn parallel to AB.

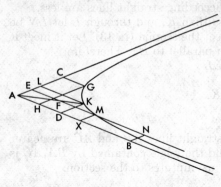

I say that it will meet the section.

For if possible, let it not meet it, and let some point G on the section be taken, and through G let GC and GH be drawn parallel to CA and AB, and let

rect. $CG,GH =$ rect. AE,EF,

and let AF be joined and produced; then it will meet the section (I. 2). Let itmeet it at K, and through K parallel to CA and AB let KL and KD be drawn; therefore

rect. $CG,GH =$ rect. LK,KD (II. 12).

And it is supposed that also

rect. $CG,GH =$ rect. AE,EF;

therefore

rect. LK,KD or rect. $KL,LA =$ rect. AE,EF;

and this is impossible; for both

$$KL > EF$$

and

$$LA > AE.$$

Therefore EF will meet the section.

Let it meet it at M.

I say then that it will not meet it at any other point.

For if possible, let it also meet it at N, and through M and N let MX and NB be drawn parallel to CA. Therefore

rect. $EM,MX =$ rect. EN,NB (II. 12);

and this is impossible. Therefore it will not meet the section in another point.

PROPOSITION 14

The asymptotes and the section, if produced indefinitely, draw nearer to each other and they reach a distance less than any given distance.

Let there be an hyperbola whose asymptotes are AB and AC, and a given distance K.

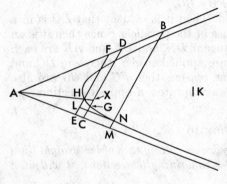

I say that AB and AC and the section, if produced, draw nearer to each other and will reach a distance less than K.

For let EHF and CGD be drawn parallel to the tangent, and let AH be joined and produced to X. Since then

rect. $CG,GD =$ rect. FH,HE (II. 10),

therefore

$$DG : FH :: HE : CG.$$

But

$$DG > FH \text{ (I. 8, 26)};$$

therefore also
$$HE > CG.$$
Then likewise we could show that the succeeding straight lines are less.

Then let the distance EL be taken less than K, and through L let LN be drawn parallel to AC; therefore it will meet the section (II. 13). Let it meet it at N, and through N let MNB be drawn parallel to EF. Therefore
$$MN = EL$$
and so
$$MN < K.$$

PORISM

Then from this it is evident that the straight lines AB and AC are nearer than all the asymptotes to the section, and the angle contained by BA, AC is clearly less than that contained by other asymptotes to the section.

PROPOSITION 15

The asymptotes of opposite sections are common.

Let there be opposite sections whose diameter is AB and center C.

I say that the asymptotes of the sections A and B are common.

Let the straight lines DAE and FBG be drawn tangent to the sections through the points A and B; they are therefore parallel (I. 44, note). Then let

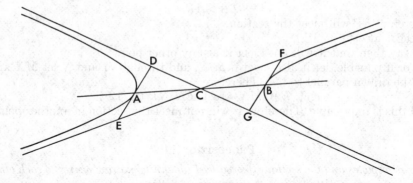

each of the straight lines DA, AE, FB, and BG be cut off equal in square to the fourth of the figure applied to AB; therefore
$$DA = AE = FB = BG.$$
Then let CD, CE, CF, and CG be joined. Then it is evident that DC is in a straight with CG and CE with CF because of the parallels. Since then it is an hyperbola whose diameter is AB and tangent DE, and DA and AE are each equal in square to the fourth of the figure applied to AB, therefore DC and CE are asymptotes (II. 1). For the same reasons then FC and CG are also asymptotes to section B. Therefore the asymptotes of opposite sections are common.

PROPOSITION 16

If in opposite sections some straight line is drawn cutting each of the straight lines containing the angle adjacent to the angles containing the sections, it will meet

each of the opposite sections in one point only, and the straight lines cut off on it
by the sections from the asymptotes will be equal.

For let there be the opposite sections A and B whose center is C and
asymptotes DCG and ECF, and let some straight line HK be drawn through
cutting each of the straight lines DC and CF.

I say that produced it will meet each of the sections in one point only.

For since DC and CE are asymptotes of section A, and some straight line
HK has been drawn across cutting both of the straight lines containing the
adjacent angle DCF, therefore HK produced will meet the section (II. 11).
Then likewise also B.

Let it meet them at L and M.

Let the straight line ACB be drawn through C parallel to LM; therefore

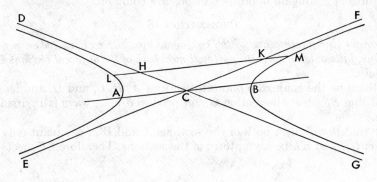

$$\text{rect. } KL, LH = \text{sq. } AC \text{ (II. 11)}$$

and

$$\text{rect. } HM, MK = \text{sq. } CB \text{ (II. 11)}.$$

And so also

$$\text{rect. } KL, LH = \text{rect. } HM, MK,$$

and

$$LH = KM.$$

PROPOSITION 17

The asymptotes of conjugate opposite sections are common.

Let there be conjugate opposite sections whose conjugate diameters are AB
and CD, and whose center is E.

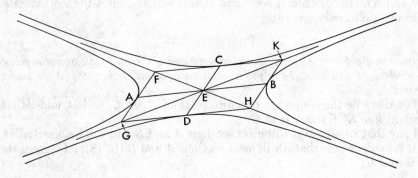

I say that their asymptotes are common.

For let the straight lines FAG, GDH, HBK, and KCF be drawn through the points A, B, C, and D touching the sections; therefore $FGHK$ is a parallelogram (I. 44, note). Then let FEH and KEG be joined; therefore they are straight lines (II. 15) and diagonals of the parallelogram, and they are all bisected at the point E. And since the figure on AB is equal to the square on CD (I. 60), and

$$CE = ED,$$

therefore each of the squares on FA, AG, KB, and BH is equal to a fourth of the figure on AB. Therefore the straight lines FEH and KEG are asymptotes of the sections A and B (II. 1). Then likewise we could show that the same straight lines are also asymptotes of the sections C and D. Therefore the asymptotes of conjugate opposite sections are common.

PROPOSITION 18

If a straight line meeting one of the conjugate opposite sections, when produced both ways, falls outside the section, it will meet both of the adjacent sections in one point only.

Let there be the conjugate opposite sections A, B, C, and D, and let some straight line EF meet the section C and produced both ways fall outside the section.

I say that it will meet both of the sections A and B in one point only.

For let GH and KL be asymptotes of the sections. Therefore EF meets both

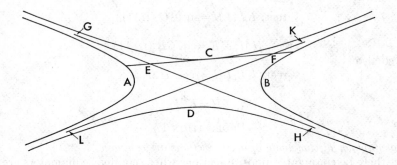

GH and KL (II. 3). Then it is evident that it will also meet the sections A and B in one point only (II. 16).

PROPOSITION 19

If some straight line is drawn touching some one of the conjugate opposite sections at random, it will meet the adjacent sections and will be bisected at the point of contact.

Let there be the conjugate opposite sections A, B, C, and D, and let some straight line ECF touch it at C.

I say that produced it will meet sections A and B and will be bisected at C.

It is evident now that it will meet sections A and B (II. 18); let it meet them at G and H.

I say that
$$CG = CH.$$

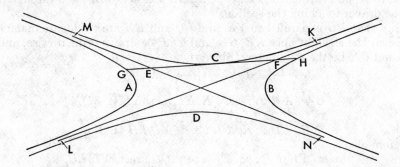

For let the asymptotes of the sections KL and MN be drawn. Therefore
$$EG = FH \text{ (ii. 16),}$$
and
$$CE = CF \text{ (ii. 3),}$$
and
$$CG = CH.$$

PROPOSITION 20

If a straight line touches one of the conjugate opposite sections, and two straight lines are drawn through their center, one through the point of contact, and one parallel to the tangent until it meet one of the adjacent sections, then the straight line touching the section at the point of meeting will be parallel to the straight line drawn through the point of contact and the center, and those through the points of contact and the center will be conjugate diameters of the opposite sections.

Let there be conjugate opposite sections whose conjugate diameters are the

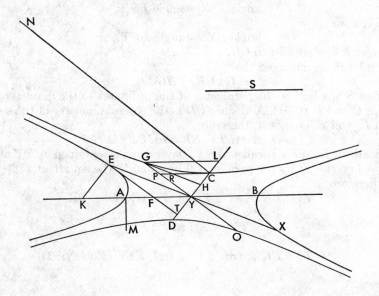

straight lines AB and CD, and center Y, and let EF be drawn touching the section A, and produced let it meet CY at T, and let EY be joined and produced to X, and through Y let YG be drawn parallel to EF, and through G let HG be drawn touching the section.

I say that HG is parallel to YE, and GO and EX are conjugate diameters.

For let the straight lines KE, GL, and CRP be drawn ordinatewise, and let AM and CN be the parameters. Since then
$$BA : AM : : NC : CD \text{ (i. 60)},$$
but
$$BA : AM : : \text{rect. } YK,KF : \text{sq. } KE \text{ (i. 37)},$$
and
$$NC : CD : : \text{sq. } GL : \text{rect. } YL,LH \text{ (i. 37)},$$
therefore also
$$\text{rect. } YK,KF : \text{sq. } EK : : \text{sq. } GL : \text{rect. } YL,LH.$$
But
$$\text{rect. } YK,KF : \text{sq. } EK \text{ comp. } YK : KE,FK : KE,$$
and
$$\text{sq. } GL : \text{rect. } YL,LH \text{ comp. } GL : LY, GL : LH;$$
therefore
$$\text{ratio comp. } YK : KE,FK : KE = \text{ratio comp. } GL : LY, GL : LH;$$
and of these
$$FK : KE : : GL : LY;$$
for each of the straight lines EK, KF, and FE is parallel to each of the straight lines YL, LG, and GY respectively. Therefore as remainder
$$YK : KE : : GL : LH.$$
Also the sides about the equal angles at K and L are proportional; therefore triangle EKY is similar to triangle GHL and will have equal the angles the corresponding sides subtend. Therefore
$$\text{angle } EYK = \text{angle } LGH.$$
But also
$$\text{angle } KYG = \text{angle } LGY;$$
and therefore
$$\text{angle } EYG = \text{angle } HGY.$$
Therefore EY is parallel to GH.

Then let it be contrived that
$$PG : GR : : HG : S;$$
therefore S is a half of the parameter of the ordinates to the diameter GO in sections C and D (i. 51). And since CD is the second diameter of the sections A and B, and ET meets it, therefore
$$\text{rect. } TY, EK = \text{sq. } CY;$$
for if we draw from E a parallel to KY, the rectangle contained by TY and the straight line cut off by the parallel will be equal to the square on CY (i. 38). And therefore
$$TY : EK : : \text{sq. } TY : \text{sq. } YC \text{ (Eucl. vi. 20)}.$$
But
$$TY : EK : : TF : FE$$
or
$$TY : EK : : \text{trgl. } TYF : \text{trgl. } EFY \text{ (Eucl. vi. 1)},$$
and

sq. TY : sq. CY : : trgl. YTF : trgl. YCP (Eucl. vi. 19)

or

sq. TY : sq. CY : : trgl. YTF : trgl. GHY (iii. 1).

Therefore

trgl. TYF : trgl. EFY : : trgl. TFY : trgl. YGH.

Therefore

trgl. GHY = trgl. YEF.

But they also have

angle HGY = angle YEF;

for EY is parallel to GH, and EF to GY. Therefore the sides about the equal angles are reciprocally proportional (Eucl. vi. 15). Therefore

$GH : EY : : EF : GY$;

therefore

rect. HG,GY = rect. YE,EF.

And since

$S : HG : : RG : GP$,

and

$RG : GP : : YE : EF$;

for they are parallel; therefore also

$S : HG : : YE : EF$.

But, with YG taken as common height,

$S : HG :$ rect. $S,YG :$ rect. HG,GY,

and

$YE : EF : :$ sq. $YE :$ rect. YE,EF.

And therefore

rect. $S,YG :$ rect. $HG,GY : :$ sq. $YE :$ rect. YE,EF.

Alternately

rect. $S,GY :$ sq. $EY : :$ rect. $HG,GY :$ rect. FE,EY.

But

rect. HG,GY = rect. YE,EF (above),

therefore also

rect. S,GY = sq. EY.

And rectangle S,GY is a fourth of the figure on GO; for

GY = half GO,

and S is the parameter; and

sq. EY = fourth sq. EX;

for

$EY = YX$.

Therefore the square on EY is equal to the figure on GO. Then likewise we could show also that GO is equal in square to the figure on EX. Therefore EX and GO are conjugate diameters of the opposite sections A, B, C, and D.

Proposition 21

The same things being supposed it is to be shown that the point of meeting of the tangents is on one of the asymptotes.

Let there be conjugate opposite sections, whose diameters are the straight lines AB and CD, and let the straight lines AE and EC be drawn tangent.

I say that the point E is on the asymptote.

For since the square on CY is equal to the fourth of the figure on AB (I. 60), and

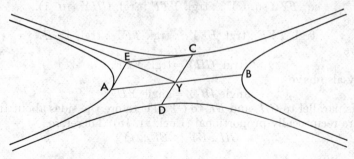

$$\text{sq. } AE = \text{sq. } CY \text{ (II. 17),}$$

therefore also the square on AE is equal to the fourth part of the figure on AB. Let EY be joined; therefore EY is an asymptote (II. 1); therefore the point E is on the asymptote.

PROPOSITION 22

If in conjugate opposite sections a radius is drawn to any one of the sections, and a parallel is drawn to it meeting one of the adjacent sections and meeting the asymptotes, then the rectangle contained by the segments produced between the section and the asymptotes on the straight line drawn is equal to the square on the radius.

Let there be the conjugate opposite sections A, B, C and D, and let there be the asymptotes of the sections YEF and YGH, and from the center Y let some straight line YCD be drawn across, and let HE be drawn parallel to it cutting both the adjacent section and the asymptotes.

I say that

$$\text{rect. } EK, KH = \text{sq. } CY.$$

Let KL be bisected at M, and let MY be joined and produced; therefore AB is the diameter of the sections A and B (I. 51, end). And since the tangent at A is parallel to EH (II. 5), therefore EH has been dropped ordinatewise to AB (I. 17). And the center is Y; therefore AB and CD are conjugate diameters (First Def. I. 6). Therefore the square on CY is equal to the fourth of the figure

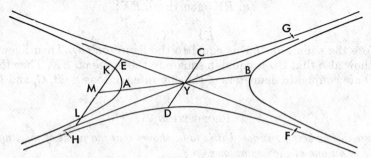

on AB (I. 60). And the rectangle HK, KE is equal to the fourth part of the figure on AB (II. 10); therefore also

$$\text{rect. } HK, KE = \text{sq. } CY.$$

Proposition 23

If in conjugate opposite sections some radius is drawn to any one of the sections, and a parallel is drawn to it meeting the three adjacent sections, then the rectangle contained by the segments produced between the three sections on the straight line drawn is twice the square on the radius.

Let there be the conjugate opposite sections A, B, C, and D, and let the center of the section be Y, and from the point Y let some straight line CY be drawn to meet any one of the sections, and let KL be drawn parallel to CY cutting the three adjacent sections.

I say that

$$\text{rect. } KM, ML = 2 \text{ sq. } CY.$$

Let the asymptotes to the sections, EF and GH, be drawn; therefore

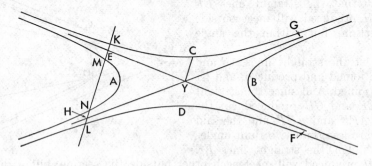

$$\text{sq. } CY = \text{rect. } HM, ME \text{ (II. 22)} = \text{rect. } HK, KE \text{ (II. 11).}$$

And

$$\text{rect. } HM, ME + \text{rect. } HK, KE = \text{rect. } LM, MK$$

because of the straight lines on the ends being equal (II. 8, 16). Therefore also

$$\text{rect. } LM, MK = 2 \text{ sq. } CY.$$

Proposition 24

If two straight lines meet a parabola each at two points, and if a point of meeting of neither one of them is contained by the points of meeting of the other, then the straight lines will meet each other outside the section.

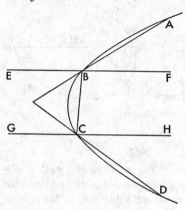

Let there be the parabola $ABCD$, and let the two straight lines AB and CD meet $ABCD$, and let a point of meeting of neither of them be contained by the points of meeting of the other.

I say that the straight lines produced will meet each other.

Let the diameters of the section, EBF and GCH, be drawn through the points B and C; therefore they are parallel (I. 51, end) and each one cuts the section in one point only (I. 26). Then let BC be joined; therefore

angle EBC + angle BCG = 2 rt. angles,

and DC and BA produced make angles less than two right angles. Therefore they will meet each other outside the section (I. 10; Eucl. Post. 5).

PROPOSITION 25

If two straight lines meet an hyperbola each at two points, and if a point of meeting of neither of them is contained by the points of meeting of the other, then the straight lines will meet each other outside the section, but within the angle containing the section.

Let there be an hyperbola, whose asymptotes are AB and AC, and let the two straight lines EF and GH cut the section, and let a point of meeting of neither of them be contained by the points of meeting of the other.

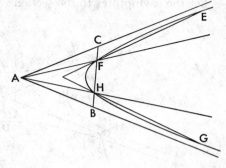

I say that the straight lines EF and GH produced will meet outside the section, but within the angle CAB.

For let the straight lines AF and AH be joined and produced, and let FH be joined. And since the straight lines EF and GH produced cut the angles AFH and AHF, and the said angles are less than two right angles (Eucl. I. 17), the straight lines EF and GH produced will meet each other outside the section, but within the angle BAC.

Then we could likewise show it, even if the straight lines EF and GH are tangents to the sections.

PROPOSITION 26

If in an ellipse or circumference of a circle two straight lines not through the center cut each other, then they do not bisect each other.

For if possible, in the ellipse or circumference of a circle let the two straight lines CD and EF not through the center bisect each other at G, and let the point H be the center of the section, and let GH be joined and produced to A and B.

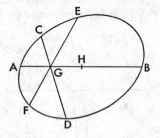

Since then the straight line AB is a diameter bisecting EF, therefore the tangent at A is parallel to EF (II. 6). We could then likewise show that it is also parallel to CD. And so also EF is parallel to CD. And this is impossible. Therefore CD and EF do not bisect each other.

PROPOSITION 27

If two straight lines touch an ellipse or circumference of a circle, and if the straight line joining the points of contact is through the center of the section, the tangents will be parallel; but if not, they will meet on the same side of the center.

Let there be the ellipse or circumference of a circle AB, and let the straight lines CAD and EBF touch it, and AB be joined, and first let it be through the center.

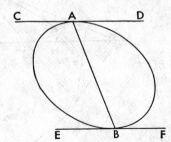
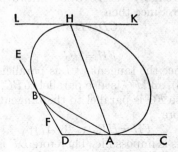

I say that CD is parallel to EF.

For since AB is a diameter of the section, and CD touches it at A, therefore CD is parallel to the ordinates to AB (I. 17). Then for the same reasons BF is also parallel to the same ordinates. Therefore CD is also parallel to EF.

Then let AB not be through the center, as in the second drawing, and let the diameter AH be drawn, and let KHL be drawn tangent through H; therefore KL is parallel to CD. Therefore EF produced will meet CD on the same side of the center as AB.

Proposition 28

If in a section of a cone or circumference of a circle some straight line bisects two parallel straight lines, then it will be a diameter of the section.

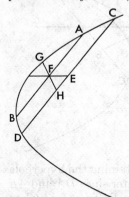

For let AB and CD, two parallel straight lines in a conic section, be bisected at E and F, and let EF be joined and produced.

I say that it is a diameter of the section.

For if not, let the straight line GFH be so if possible. Therefore the tangent at G is parallel to AB (II. 5, 6). And so the same straight line is parallel to CD. And GH is a diameter; therefore

$$CH = HD \text{ (First Def. I. 4)}$$

and this is impossible; for it is supposed

$$CE = ED$$

Therefore GH is not a diameter. Then likewise we could show that there is no other except EF. Therefore EF will be a diameter of the section.

Proposition 29

If in a section of a cone or circumference of a circle two tangents meet, the straight line drawn from their point of meeting to the midpoint of the straight line joining the points of contact is a diameter of the section.

Let there be a section of a cone or circumference of a circle to which let the straight lines AB and AC, meeting at A, be drawn tangent, and let BC be joined and bisected at D, and let AD be joined.

I say that it is a diameter of the section.

For if possible, let DE be a diameter, and let EC be joined; then it will cut the section (I. 35, 36). Let it cut it at F, and through F let FKG be drawn parallel to CDB. Since then

$$CD = DB$$

also

$$FH = HG$$

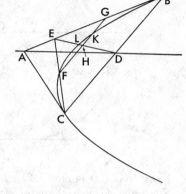

And since the tangent at L is parallel to BC (II. 5, 6), and FG is also parallel to BC, therefore also FG is parallel to the tangent at L. Therefore

$$FH = HK \quad (\text{I. 46, 47});$$

and this is impossible. Therefore DE is not a diameter. Then likewise we could show that there is no other except AD.

PROPOSITION 30

If two straight lines tangent to a section of a cone or to a circumference of a circle meet, the diameter drawn from the point of meeting will bisect the straight line joining the points of contact.

Let there be the section of a cone or circumference of a circle BC, and let two tangents BA and AC be drawn to it meeting at A, and let BC be joined and let AD be drawn through A as a diameter of the section.

I say that

$$DB = DC$$

For let it not be, but if possible, let

$$BE = EC,$$

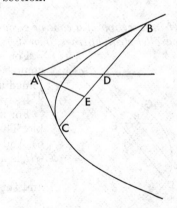

and let AE be joined; therefore AE is a diameter of the section (II. 29). But AD is also a diameter; and this is absurd. For if the section is an ellipse, the point A at which the diameters meet each other, will be a center outside the section; and this is impossible; and if the section is a parabola, the diameters meet each other (I. 51, end); and if it is an hyperbola, and the straight lines BA and AC meet the section without containing one another's points of meeting, then the center is within the angle containing the hyperbola (II. 25); but it is also on it, for it has been supposed a center since DA and AE are diameters (I. 51, end); and this is absurd. Therefore BE is not equal to EC.

PROPOSITION 31

If two straight lines touch each of the opposite sections, then if the straight line joining the points of contact falls through the center, the tangents will be parallel, but if not, they will meet on the same side as the center.

Let there be the opposite sections A and B, and let the straight lines CAD and EBF be tangent to them at A and B, and let the straight line joined from

A to *B* fall first through the center of the sections.

I say that *CD* is parallel to *EF*.

For since they are opposite sections of which *AB* is a diameter, and *CD* touches one of them at *A*, therefore the straight line drawn through *B* parallel

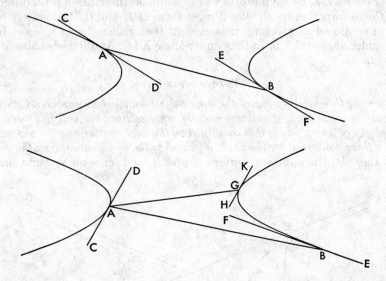

to *CD* touches the section (I. 44, note). But *EF* also touches it; therefore *CD* is parallel to *EF*.

Then let the straight line from *A* to *B* not be through the center of the sections, and let *AG* be drawn as a diameter of the sections, and let *HK* be drawn tangent to the section; therefore *HK* is parallel to *CD*, and since the straight lines *EF* and *HK* touch an hyperbola, therefore they will meet (II. 25, end). And *HK* is parallel to *CD*; therefore also the straight lines *CD* and *EF* produced will meet. And it is evident they are on the same side as the center.

PROPOSITION 32

If straight lines meet each of the opposite sections, in one point when touching or in two points when cutting, and, when produced, the straight lines meet, then their point of meeting will be in the angle adjacent to the angle containing the section.

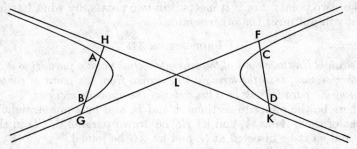

Let there be opposite sections and the straight lines *AB* and *CD* either touching the opposite sections in one point or cutting them in two points, and let them meet when produced.

I say that their point of meeting will be in the angle adjacent to the angle containing the section.

Let *FG* and *HK* be asymptotes to the sections; therefore *AB* produced will meet the asymptotes (ii. 8). Let it meet them at *H* and *G*. And since *FK* and *HG* are supposed as meeting, it is evident that either they will meet in the place under angle *HLF* or in that under angle *KLG*. And likewise also, if they touch (ii. 3).

PROPOSITION 33

If a straight line meeting one of the opposite sections, when produced both ways, falls outside the section, it will not meet the other section, but will fall through the three places of which one is that contained by the angle containing the section, and two are those contained by the angle adjacent to the angle containing the section.

Let there be the opposite sections *A* and *B*, and let some straight line *CD*

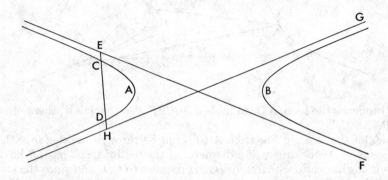

cut *A*, and, when produced both ways, let it fall outside the section.

I say that the straight line *CD* does not meet the section *B*.

For let *EF* and *GH* be drawn as asymptotes to the sections; therefore *CD* produced will meet the asymptotes (ii. 8). And it only meets them in the points *E* and *H*. And so it will not meet the section *B*.

And it is evident that it will fall through the three places. For if some straight line meets both of the opposite sections, it will meet neither of the opposite sections in two points. For if it meets it in two points, by what has just been proved it will not meet the other section.

PROPOSITION 34

If some straight line touch one of the opposite sections and a parallel to it be drawn in the other section, then the straight line drawn from the point of contact to the midpoint of the parallel will be a diameter of the opposite sections.

Let there be the opposite sections *A* and *B*, and let some straight line *CD* touch one of them *A*, at *A*, and let *EF* be drawn parallel to *CD* in the other section, and let it be bisected at *G*, and let *AG* be joined.

I say that *AG* is a diameter of the opposite sections.

For if possible, let *AHK* be. Therefore the tangent at *H* is parallel to *CD*

(II. 31). But *CD* is also parallel to *EF*; and therefore the tangent at *H* is parallel to *EF*. Therefore

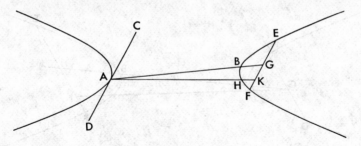

$$EK = KF \text{ (I. 47)};$$

and this is impossible; for

$$EG = GF$$

Therefore *AH* is not a diameter of the opposite sections.
Therefore *AB* is.

PROPOSITION 35

If a diameter in one of the opposite sections bisects some straight line, the straight line touching the other section at the end of the diameter will be parallel to the bisected straight line.

Let there be the opposite sections *A* and *B*, and let their diameter *AB* bisect the straight line *CD* in section *B* at *E*.

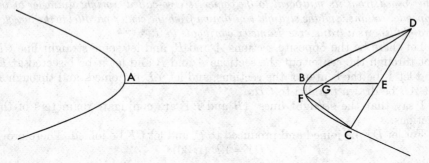

I say that the tangent to the section at *A* is parallel to *CD*.
For if possible, let *DF* be parallel to the tangent to the section at *A*; therefore

$$DG = GF \text{ (I. 48)}.$$

But also

$$DE = EC.$$

Therefore *CF* is parallel to *EG*; and this is impossible; for produced it meets it (I. 22). Therefore *DF* is not parallel to the tangent to the section at *A* nor is any other straight line except *CD*.

PROPOSITION 36

If parallel straight lines are drawn, one in each of the opposite sections, then the straight line joining their midpoints will be a diameter of the opposite sections.

Let there be the opposite sections A and B, and let the straight lines CD and EF be drawn, one in each of them, and let them be parallel, and let them both

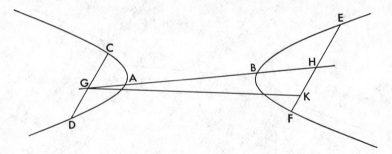

be bisected at points G and H, and let GH be joined.

I say that GH is a diameter of the opposite sections.

For if not, let GK be one. Therefore the tangent to A is parallel to CD (II. 5); and so also to EF. Therefore

$$EK = KF \text{ (I. 48)};$$

and this is impossible, since also

$$EH = HF$$

Therefore GK is not a diameter of the opposite sections. Therefore GH is.

PROPOSITION 37

If a straight line not through the center cuts the opposite sections, then the straight line joined from its midpoint to the center is a so-called upright diameter of the opposite sections, and the straight line drawn from the center parallel to the bisected straight line is a transverse diameter conjugate to it.

Let there be the opposite sections A and B, and let some straight line CD not through the center cut the sections A and B and let it be bisected at E, and let Y be the center of the sections, and let YE be joined, and through Y let AB be drawn parallel to CD.

I say that the straight lines AB and EY are conjugate diameters of the sections.

For let DY be joined and produced to F, and let CF be joined. Therefore

$$DY = YF \text{ (I. 30)}.$$

But also

$$DE = EC;$$

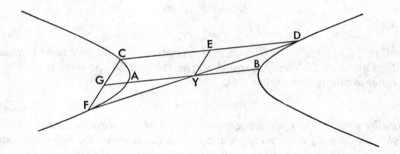

therefore EY is parallel to FC. Let BA be produced to G. And since
$$DY = YF,$$
therefore also
$$EY = FG;$$
and so also
$$CG = FG.$$
Therefore the tangent at A is parallel to CF (II. 5); and so also to EY. Therefore EY and AB are conjugate diameters (I. 16).

PROPOSITION 38

If two straight lines meeting touch opposite sections, the straight line joined from the point of meeting to the midpoint of the straight line joining the points of contact will be a so-called upright diameter of the opposite sections, and the straight line drawn through the center parallel to the straight line joining the points of contact is a transverse diameter conjugate to it.

Let there be the opposite sections A and B, and CY and YD touching the sections, and let CD be joined and bisected at E, and let EY be joined.

I say that the diameter EY is a so-called upright, and the straight line drawn through the center parallel to CD is a transverse diameter conjugate to it.

For if possible, let EF be a diameter, and let F be a point taken at random; therefore DY will meet EF. Let it meet it at F, and let CF be joined; therefore

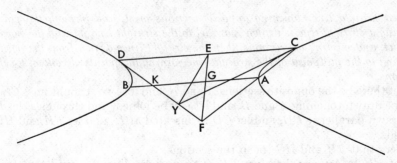

CF will hit the section (I. 32). Let it hit it at A, and through A let AB be drawn parallel to CD. Since then EF is a diameter, and bisects CD, it also bisects the parallels to it (First Def. I. 4). Therefore
$$AG = GB.$$
And since
$$CE = ED,$$
and is on triangle CFD, therefore also
$$AG = GK.$$
And so also
$$GK = GB;$$
and this is impossible. Therefore EF will not be a diameter.

PROPOSITION 39

If two straight lines meeting touch opposite sections, the straight line drawn through the center and the point of meeting of the tangents bisects the straight line joining the points of contact.

Let there be the opposite sections A and B, and let two straight lines CE and

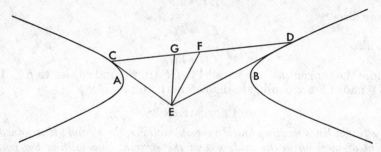

ED be drawn touching A and B, and let CD be joined, and let EF be drawn as a diameter.

I say that

$$CF = FD.$$

For if not, let CD be bisected at G, and let GE be joined; therefore GE is a diameter (II. 38). But EF is also; therefore E is the center (I. 31, end). Therefore the point of meeting of the tangents is at the center of the sections; and this is absurd (II. 32). Therefore CF is not unequal to FD. Therefore equal.

PROPOSITION 40

If two straight lines touching opposite sections meet, and through the point of meeting a straight line is drawn, parallel to the straight line joining the points of contact, and meeting the sections, then the straight lines drawn from the points of meeting to the midpoint of the straight line joining the points of contact touch the sections.

Let there be the opposite sections A and B, and let two straight lines CE and ED be drawn touching A and B, and let CD be joined, and through E let FEG be drawn parallel to CD, and let CD be bisected at H, and let FH and HG be joined.

I say that FH and HG touch the sections.

Let EH be joined; therefore EH is an upright diameter, and the straight line drawn through the center parallel to CD a transverse diameter conjugate to it (II. 38). And let the center Y be taken, and let AYB be drawn parallel to CD; therefore HE and AB are conjugate diameters. And CH has been drawn

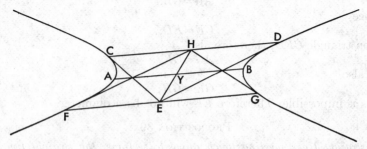

ordinatewise to the second diameter, and CE has been drawn touching the section and meeting the second diameter. Therefore the rectangle EY, YH is equal to the square on the half of the second diameter (I. 38), that is to the fourth part of the figure on AB (Second Def. I. 10). And since FE has been drawn ordinatewise and FH joined, therefore FH touches the section A (I. 38). Likewise then also GH touches section B. Therefore FH and HG touch sections A and B.

PROPOSITION 41

If in opposite sections two straight lines not through the center cut each other, then they do not bisect each other.

Let there be the opposite sections A and B, and in A and B let the two straight lines CB and AD not through the center cut each other at E.

I say that they do not bisect each other.

For if possible, let them bisect each other, and let Y be the center of the sections, and let EY be joined; therefore EY is a diameter (II. 37). Let YF be drawn through Y parallel to BC; therefore YF is a diameter and conjugate to

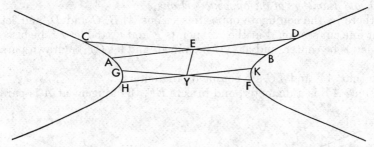

EY (II. 37). Therefore the tangent at F is parallel to EY (First Def. I. 6). Then for the same reasons, with HK drawn parallel to AD, the tangent at H is parallel to EY; and so also the tangent at F is parallel to the tangent at H; and this is absurd; for it has been shown it also meets it (II. 31). Therefore the straight lines CB and AD not being through the center do not bisect each other.

PROPOSITION 42

If in conjugate opposite sections two straight lines not through the center cut each other, they do not bisect each other.

Let there be the conjugate opposite sections A, B, C and D, and in A, B, C

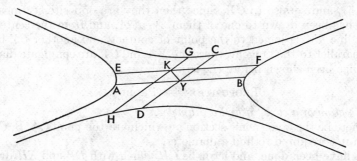

and D let the two straight lines not through the center, EF and GH, cut each other at K.

I say that they do not bisect each other.

For if possible, let them bisect each other, and let the center of the sections be Y, and let AB be drawn parallel to EF and CD to HG, and let KY be joined; therefore KY and AB are conjugate diameters (II. 37). Likewise YK and CD are also conjugate diameters. And so also the tangent at A is parallel to the tangent at C; and this is impossible; for it meets it, since the tangent at C cuts the sections A and B (II. 19), and the tangent at A sections C and D; it is evident also that their point of meeting is in the place under angle AYC (II. 21). Therefore the straight lines EF and GH not being through the center do not bisect each other.

PROPOSITION 43

If a straight line cuts one of the conjugate opposite sections in two points, and through the center one straight line is drawn to the midpoint of the cutting straight line and another straight line is drawn parallel to the cutting straight line, they will be conjugate diameters of the opposite sections.

Let there be the conjugate opposite sections A, B, C and D, and let some straight line cut section A at the two points E and F, and let FE be bisected at G, and let Y be center, and let YG be joined, and let CY be drawn parallel to EF.

I say that AY and YC are conjugate diameters.

For since AY is a diameter, and bisects EF, the tangent at A is parallel to

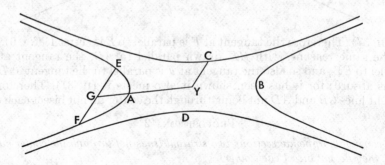

EF (II. 5); and so also to CY. Since then they are opposite sections, and a tangent has been drawn to one of them, A, at A, and from the center Y one straight line YA is joined to the point of contact, and another CY has been drawn parallel to the tangent, therefore YA and CY are conjugate diameters; for this has been shown before (II. 20).

PROPOSITION 44 (PROBLEM)

Given a section of a cone, to find a diameter.

Let there be the given conic section on which are the points A, B, C, D and E. Then it is required to find a diameter.

Let it have been done, and let it be CH. Then with DF and EH drawn ordinatewise and produced

$$DF = FB,$$

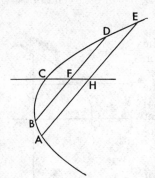

and
$$EH = HA \quad \text{(First Def. i. 4).}$$
If then we fix the straight lines BD and EA in
position to be parallel, the points H and F will
be given. And so HFC will be given in position.

Then it will be constructed (συντεθήσεται) thus:
let there be the given conic section on which are
the points A, B, C, D and E, and let the straight
lines BD and AE be drawn parallel, and be bisected
at F and H. And the straight line FH joined will
be a diameter of the section (First Def. i. 4). And
in the same way we could also find an indefinite
number of diameters.

PROPOSITION 45 (PROBLEM)

Given an ellipse or hyperbola, to find the center.

And this is evident; for if two diameters of the section, AB and CD, are

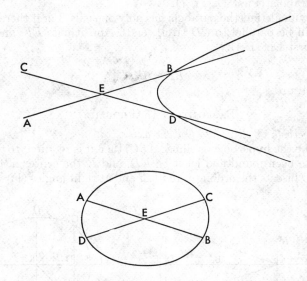

drawn through (ii. 44), the point at which they cut each other will be the center
of the section, as indicated below.

PROPOSITION 46 (PROBLEM)

Given a section of a cone, to find the axis.

Let the given section of a cone first be a parabola, on which are the points
F, C and E. Then it is required to find its axis.

For let AB be drawn as a diameter of it (i. 44). If then AB is an axis, what
was enjoined would have been done; but if not, let it have been done, and let
CD be the axis; therefore the axis CD is parallel to AB (i. 51, end) and bisects
the straight lines drawn perpendicular to it (First Def. i. 7). And the perpendiculars to CD are also perpendiculars to AB; and so CD bisects the perpendic-

ulars to AB. If then I fix EF, the perpendicular to AB, it will be given in position, and therefore
$$ED = DF;$$
therefore the point D is given. Therefore through the given point D, CD has been drawn parallel in position to AB; therefore CD is given in position.

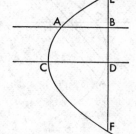

Then it will be constructed thus: let there be the given parabola on which are the points F, E and A, and let AB, a diameter of it, be drawn (II. 44), and let BE be drawn perpendicular to it and let it be produced to F. If then
$$EB = BF,$$
it is evident that AB is the axis (First Def. I. 7); but if not, let EF be bisected by D, and let CD be drawn parallel to AB. Then it is evident that CD is the axis of the section; for being parallel to a diameter, that is being a diameter (I. 51, end), it bisects EF at right angles. Therefore CD has been found as the axis of the given parabola (First Def. I. 7).

And it is evident that the parabola has only one axis. For if there is another, as AB, it will be parallel to CD (I. 51, end). And it cuts EF, and so it also bisects it (First Def. I. 4).
Therefore
$$BE = BF;$$
and this is absurd.

PROPOSITION 47 (PROBLEM)

Given an hyperbola or ellipse, to find the axis.

Let there be the hyperbola or ellipse ABC; then it is required to find its axis.

Let it have been found and let it be KD, and K the center of the section; therefore KD bisects the ordinates to itself and at right angles (First Def. I. 7).

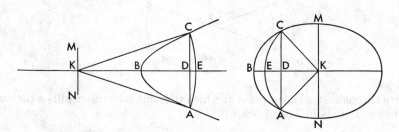

Let the perpendicular CDA be drawn, and let KA and KC be joined. Since then
$$CD = DA,$$
therefore
$$CK = KA.$$
If then we fix the given point C, CK will be given. And so the circle described with center K and radius KC will also pass through A and will be given in position. And the section ABC is also given in position; therefore the point A

is given. But the point C is also given; therefore CA is given in position. Also
$$CD = DA,$$
therefore the point D is given. But also K is given; therefore DK is given in position.

Then it will be constructed thus: let there be the given hyperbola or ellipse ABC, and let K be taken as its center; and let a point C be taken at random on the section, and let the circle CEA, with center K and radius KC, be described, and let CA be joined and bisected at D, and let KC, KD, and KA be joined, and let KD be drawn through to B.

Since then
$$AD = DC$$
and DK is common, therefore the two straight lines CD and DK are equal to the two straight lines AD and DK, and
$$\text{base } KA = \text{base } KC.$$
Therefore KBD bisects ADC at right angles. Therefore KD is an axis (First Def. i. 7).

Let MKN be drawn through K parallel to CA; therefore MN is the axis of the section conjugate to BK (First Def. i. 8).

PROPOSITION 48 (PROBLEM)

Then with these things shown, let it be next in order to show that there are no other axes of the same sections.

For if possible, let there also be another axis KG. Then in the same way as before, with AH drawn perpendicular,
$$AH = HL \text{ (First Def. i. 4)};$$

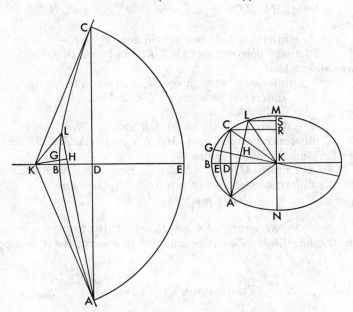

and so also
$$AK = KL.$$

But also
$$AK = KC;$$
therefore
$$KL = KC;$$
and this is absurd.

Now that the circle AEC does not hit the section also in another point between the points A, B and C, is evident in the case of the hyperbola; and in the case of the ellipse let the perpendiculars CR and LS be drawn. Since then
$$KC = KL;$$
for they are radii; also
$$\text{sq. } KC = \text{sq. } KL.$$
But
$$\text{sq. } CR + \text{sq. } RK = \text{sq. } CK,$$
and
$$\text{sq. } KS + \text{sq. } SL = \text{sq. } LK;$$
therefore
$$\text{sq. } CR + \text{sq. } RK = \text{sq. } KS + \text{sq. } SL.$$
Therefore
$$\text{difference between sq. } CR \text{ and sq. } SL =$$
$$\text{difference between sq. } KS \text{ and sq. } RK.$$
Again since
$$\text{rect. } MR, RN + \text{sq. } RK = \text{sq. } KM,$$
and also
$$\text{rect. } MS, SN + \text{sq. } SK = \text{sq. } KM \text{ (Eucl. II. 5),}$$
therefore
$$\text{rect. } MR, RN + \text{sq. } RK = \text{rect. } MS, SN + \text{sq. } SK.$$
Therefore
$$\text{difference between sq. } SK \text{ and sq. } KR =$$
$$\text{difference between rect. } MR, RN \text{ and rect. } MS, SN.$$
And it was shown that
$$\text{difference between sq. } SK \text{ and sq. } KR =$$
$$\text{difference between sq. } CR \text{ and sq. } SL;$$
therefore
$$\text{difference between sq. } CR \text{ and sq. } SL =$$
$$\text{difference between rect. } MR, RN \text{ and rect. } MS, SN.$$
And since CR and LS are ordinates
$$\text{sq. } CR : \text{rect. } MR, RN :: \text{sq. } SL : \text{rect. } MS, SN \text{ (I. 21).}$$
But the same difference was also shown for both; therefore
$$\text{sq. } CR = \text{rect. } MR, RN,$$
and
$$\text{sq. } SL = \text{rect. } MS, SN \text{ (Eucl. V. 16, 17, 9).}$$
Therefore the line LCM is a circle; and this is absurd; for it is supposed an ellipse.

PROPOSITION 49 (PROBLEM)

Given a section of a cone and a point not within the section, to draw from the point a straight line touching the section in one point.

Let the given section of a cone first be a parabola whose axis is BD. Then it is required to draw a straight line as prescribed from the given point which is not within the section.

Then the given point is either on the line or on the axis or somewhere else outside.

Now let it be on the line, and let it be A, and let it have been done, and let it be AE, and let AD be drawn perpendicular; then it will be given in position. And
$$BE = BD \ (\text{i. } 35);$$
and BD is given; therefore BE is also given. And the point B is given; therefore E is also given. But A also; therefore AE is given in position.

Then it will be constructed thus: let AD be drawn perpendicular from A, and let BE be made equal to BD, and let AE be joined. Then it is evident that it touches the section (i. 33).

Again let the given point E be on the axis, and let it have been done, and let AE be drawn tangent, and let AD be drawn perpendicular; therefore
$$BE = BD \ (\text{i. } 35).$$
And BE is given; therefore also BD is given. And the point B is given; therefore D is also given. And DA is perpendicular; therefore DA is given in position. Therefore the point A is given. But also E; therefore AE is given in position.

Then it will be constructed thus: let BD be made equal to BE, and from D let DA be drawn perpendicular to ED, and let AE be joined. Then it is evident that AE touches (i. 33).

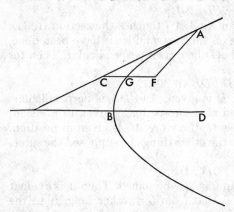

And it is evident also that, even if the given point is the same as B, the straight line drawn from B perpendicular touches the section (i. 17).

Then let C be the given point, and let it have been done, and let CA be it, and through C let CF be drawn parallel to the axis, that is to BD; therefore CF is given in position. And from A let AF be drawn ordinatewise to CF; then
$$CG = FG \ (\text{i. } 35).$$
And the point G is given; therefore F is also given. And FA has been erected ordinatewise, that is, parallel to the tangent at G (i. 32); therefore FA is given in position. Therefore A is also given; but also C. Therefore CA is given in position.

It will be constructed thus: let CF be drawn through C parallel to BD, and let FG be made equal to CG, and let FA be drawn parallel to the tangent at G (above), and let AC be joined. It is evident then that this will do the problem (i. 33).

Again let it be an hyperbola whose axis is DBC and center H, and asymptotes HE and HF. Then the given point will be given either on the section or

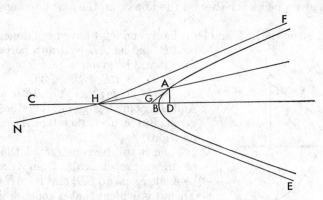

on the axis or within angle EHF or in the adjacent place or on one of the asymptotes containing the section or in the place between the straight lines containing the angle vertical to angle EHF.

Let the point A first be on the section, and let it have been done, and let AG be tangent, and let AD be drawn perpendicular, and let BC be the transverse side of the figure; then

$$CD : DB :: CG : GB \text{ (i. 36)}.$$

And the ratio of CD to DB is given; for both the straight lines are given; therefore also the ratio of CG to GB is given. And BC is given; therefore point G is given. But also A; therefore AG is given in position.

It will be constructed thus: let AD be drawn perpendicular from A, and let

$$CG : GB :: CD : DB;$$

and let AG be joined. Then it is evident that AG touches the section (i. 34).

Then again let the given point G be on the axis, and let it have been done, and let AG be drawn tangent, and let AD be drawn perpendicular. Then for the same reasons

$$CG : GB :: CD : DB \text{ (i. 36)}.$$

And BC is given; therefore the point D is given. And DA is perpendicular; therefore DA is given in position. And also the section is given in position; therefore the point A is given. But also G; therefore AG is given in position.

Then it will be constructed thus: let the other things be supposed the same, and let it be contrived that

$$CG : GB :: CD : DB,$$

and let DA be drawn perpendicular, and let AG be joined. Then it is evident that AG does the problem (i. 34), and that from G another tangent to the section could be drawn on the other side.

With the same things supposed let the given point K be in the place inside angle EHF, and let it be required to draw a tangent to the section from K. Let it have been done, and it be KA, and let KH be joined and produced, and let HN be made equal to LH, therefore they are all given. Then also LN will be given. Then let AM be drawn ordinatewise to MN; then also

$$NK : KL :: MN : ML$$

And the ratio of NK to KL is given; therefore also the ratio of NM to ML is given. And the point L is given, therefore also M is given. And MA has been

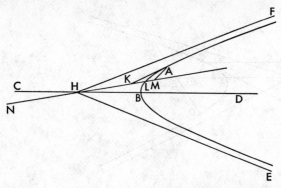

erected parallel to the tangent at L; therefore MA is given in position. And also the section ALB is given in position; therefore the point A is given. But K is also given; therefore AK is given.

Then it will be constructed thus: let the other things be supposed the same, and the given point K, and KH be joined and produced, and let HN be made equal to HL, and let it be contrived that

$$NK : KL :: NM : ML$$

and let MA be drawn parallel to the tangent at L (above), and let KA be joined; therefore KA touches the section (I. 34).

And it is evident that a tangent to the section could also be drawn to the other side.

With the same things supposed let the given point F be on one of the asymptotes containing the section, and let it be required to draw from F a tangent to the section. And let it have been done, and let it be FAE, and through A let AD be drawn parallel to EH; then

$$DH = DF,$$

since also

$$FA = AE \text{ (II. 3).}$$

And FH is given; therefore also point D is given. And through the given point

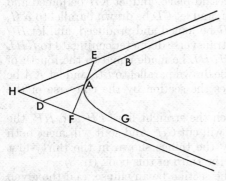

D, DA has been drawn parallel in position to EH; therefore DA is given in position. And the section is also given in position; therefore the point A is given. But F is also given; therefore the straight line FAE is given in position.

Then it will be constructed thus: let there be the section AB, and asymptotes EH and HF, and the given point F on one of the asymptotes containing the section, and let FH be bisected at D, and through D let DA be drawn parallel to HE, and let FA be joined. And since

$$FD = DH,$$

therefore also

$$FA = AE.$$

And so by things shown before, the straight line FAE touches the section (II. 9).

With the same things supposed, let the given point be in the place under the

angle adjacent to the straight lines containing the section, and let it be K; it is
required then to draw a tangent to the section from K. And let it have been

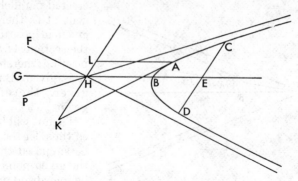

done, and let it be KA, and let KH be joined and produced; then it will be
given in position. If then a given point C is taken on the section, and through
C, CD is drawn parallel to KH, it will be given in position. And if CD is
bisected at E, and HE is joined and produced, it will be, in position, a diameter
conjugate to KH (First Def. I. 6). Then let HG be made equal to BH, and
through A let AL be drawn parallel to BH; then because KL and BG are conjugate diameters, and AK a tangent, and AL a straight line drawn parallel to
BG, therefore rectangle KH, HL is equal to the fourth part of the figure on BG
(I. 38). Therefore rectangle KH, HL is given. And KH is given; therefore HL
is also given. But it is also given in position; and the point H is given; therefore
L is also given. And through L, LA has been drawn parallel in position to BG;
therefore LA is given in position. And the section is also given in position;
therefore the point A is given. But also K; therefore AK is given in position.

Then it will be constructed thus: let the other things be supposed the same,
and let the given point K be in the aforesaid place, and let KH be joined and
produced, and let some point C be taken, and let CD be drawn parallel to KH,
and let CD be bisected by E and let EH be joined and produced, and let HG
be made equal to BH; therefore GB is a transverse diameter conjugate to KHL
(First Def. I. 6). Then let rectangle KH, HL be made equal to the fourth of
the figure on BG, and through L let LA be drawn parallel to BG, and let KA be
joined; then it is clear that KA touches the section by the converse of the
theorem (I. 38).

And if it is given in the place between the straight lines FH and HP, the
problem is impossible. For the tangent will cut GH. And so it will meet both
FH and HP; and this is impossible by the things shown in the thirty-first
theorem of the first book (I. 31) and in the third of this book (II. 3).

With the same things supposed let the section be an ellipse, and the given
point A on the section, and let it be required to draw from A a tangent to the
section. Let it have been done, and let it be AG, and let AD be drawn from A
ordinatewise to the axis BC; then the point D will be given, and
$$CD : DB : : CG : GB \text{ (I. 36)}.$$
And the ratio of CD to DB is given; therefore the ratio of CG to GB is also
given. Therefore the point G is given. But also A; therefore AG is given in
position.

Then it will be constructed thus: let AD be drawn perpendicular, and let
$$CG : GB :: CD : DE,$$

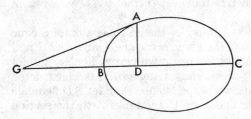

and let AG be joined. Then it is evident that AG touches, as also in the case of the hyperbola (ɪ. 34).

Then again let the given point be K, and let it be required to draw a tangent. Let it have been done, and let it be KA, and let the straight line KLH be joined to the center H and produced to N; then it will be given in position. And if AM is drawn ordinatewise, then
$$NK : KL :: NM : ML \text{ (ɪ. 36)}.$$

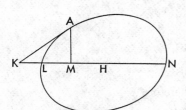

And the ratio of $NK : KL$ is given; therefore the ratio of MN to LM is also given. Therefore the point M is given. And MA has been erected ordinatewise; for it is parallel to the tangent at L; therefore MA is given in position. Therefore the point A is given. But also K; therefore KA is given in position.

And the construction (σύνθεσις) is the same as for the preceding.

PROPOSITION 50 (PROBLEM)

Given the section of a cone, to draw a tangent which will make with the axis, on the same side as the section, an angle equal to a given acute angle.

Let the section of a cone first be a parabola whose axis is AB; then it is required to draw a tangent to the section which will make with the axis AB, on the same side as the section, an angle equal to the given acute angle.

Let it have been done, and let it be CD; therefore angle BDC is given. Let BC

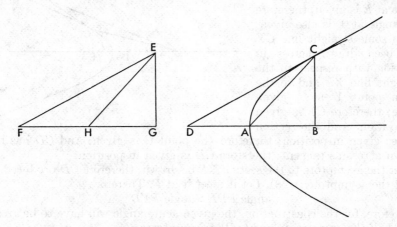

be drawn perpendicular; then the angle at B is also given. Therefore the ratio of DB to BC is given. But the ratio of BD to BA is given; therefore also the ratio of AB to BC is given. And the angle at B is given; therefore angle BAC

is also given. And it is in position with respect to BA and the given point A; therefore CA is given in position. And the section is also given in position; therefore the point C is given. And CD touches; therefore CD is given in position.

Then the problem will be constructed thus: let the given section of a cone first be a parabola whose axis is AB, and the given acute angle, angle EFG, and let some point E be taken on EF, and let EG be drawn perpendicular, and let FG be bisected by H, and let HE be joined, and let angle BAC be constructed equal to angle GHE, and let BC be drawn perpendicular, and let AD be made equal to BA, and let CD be joined. Therefore CD is tangent to the section (I. 33).

I say then that

$$\text{angle } CDB = \text{angle } EFG.$$

For since

$$FG : GH : : DB : BA$$

and

$$HG : GE : : AB : BC,$$

therefore *ex aequali*

$$FG : GE : : DB : BC,$$

And the angles at G and B are right angles, therefore

$$\text{angle at } F = \text{angle at } D.$$

Let the section be an hyperbola, and let it have been done, and let CD be tangent, and let the center of the section Y be taken, and let CY be joined, and let CE be perpendicular; therefore the ratio of rectangle YE, ED to the square on CE is given; for it is the same as the transverse to the upright (I. 37). And the ratio of the square on CE to the square on ED is given; for each of the rectangles CD, DE and DE, EC is given. Therefore the ratio of rectangle YE, ED to the square on ED is given; and so also the ratio of YE to ED is given. And the angle at E is given; therefore the angle at Y is also given. Then some straight line CY has been drawn across in position with respect to the straight line YE and to the given point Y at a given angle; therefore CY is given in position. And the section

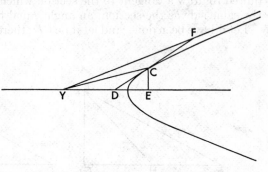

is also given in position; therefore the point C is given. And CD has been drawn across as tangent; therefore CD is given in position.

Let the asymptote to the section YF be drawn; therefore CD produced will meet the asymptote (II. 3). Let it meet it at F. Therefore

$$\text{angle } FDE > \text{angle } FYD$$

Therefore, for the construction, the given acute angle will have to be greater than half the angle contained by the asymptotes.

Then the problem will be constructed thus: let there be the given hyperbola whose axis is AB, and asymptote YF, and the given acute angle KHG greater than angle AYF, and let angle KHL = angle AYF,

and let AF be drawn from A perpendicular to AB, and let some point G be

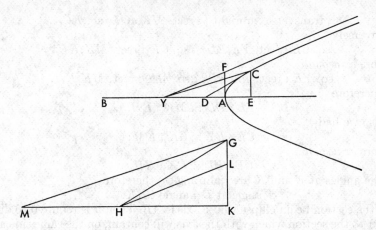

taken on GH, and let GK be drawn from it perpendicular to HK. Since then

angle FYA = angle LHK,

and also the angles at A and K are right, therefore

$$YA : AF :: HK : KL$$
$$HK : KL > HK : KG;$$

therefore also

$$YA : AF > HK : KG.$$

And so also

$$\text{sq. } YA : \text{sq. } AF > \text{sq. } HK : \text{sq. } KG.$$

But

$$\text{sq. } YA : \text{sq. } AF :: \text{transverse} : \text{upright} \ (\text{II. 1});$$

therefore also

$$\text{transverse} : \text{upright} > \text{sq. } HK : \text{sq. } KG.$$

If then we shall contrive that

$$\text{sq. } YA : \text{sq. } AF :: \text{some other} : \text{sq. } KG,$$

it will be greater than the square on HK. Let it be the rectangle MK, KH; and let GM be joined. Since then

$$\text{sq. } MK > \text{rect. } MK, KH,$$

therefore

$$\text{sq. } MK : \text{sq. } KG > \text{rect. } MK, KH : \text{sq. } KG$$
$$> \text{sq. } YA : \text{sq. } AF.$$

And if we shall contrive that

$$\text{sq. } MK : \text{sq. } KG :: \text{sq. } YA : \text{some other},$$

it will be to a magnitude less than the square on AF; and the straight line joined from Y to the point taken will make similar triangles, and therefore

angle FYA > angle GMK.

Let angle AYC be made equal to angle GMK; therefore YC will cut the section (II. 2). Let it cut it at C, and from C let CD be drawn tangent to the section (II. 49), and CE drawn perpendicular; therefore triangle CYE is similar to triangle GMK. Therefore

$$\text{sq. } YE : \text{sq. } EC :: \text{sq. } MK : \text{sq. } KG.$$

But also

$$\text{transverse : upright :: rect. } YE,ED : \text{sq. } EC \ (\text{I. } 37),$$

and

$$\text{transverse : upright :: rect. } MK,KH : \text{sq. } KG.$$

And inversely

$$\text{sq. } CE : \text{rect. } YE,ED :: \text{sq. } GK : \text{rect. } MK,KH;$$

therefore *ex aequali*

$$\text{sq. } YE : \text{rect. } YE,ED :: \text{sq. } MK : \text{rect. } MK,KH.$$

And therefore

$$YE : ED :: MK : KH.$$

But also we had

$$CE : EY :: GK : KM;$$

therefore *ex aequali*

$$CE : ED :: GK : KH.$$

And the angles at E and K are right angles; therefore

$$\text{angle at } D = \text{angle } GHK.$$

Let the section be an ellipse whose axis is AB. Then it is required to draw a tangent to the section which with the axis will contain, on the same side as the section, an angle equal to the given acute angle.

Let it have been done, and let it be CD. Therefore angle CDA is given. Let CE be drawn perpendicular; therefore the ratio of the square on DE to the square on EC is given. Let Y be the center of the section, and let CY be joined. Then the ratio of the square on CE to the rectangle DE, EY is given; for it is the same as the ratio of the upright to the transverse (I. 37), and therefore the ratio of the square on DE to rectangle DE, EY is given; and therefore the ratio of DE to EY is given. And of DE to EC; therefore also the ratio of CE to EY is given. And the angle at E is right; therefore the angle at Y is given. And it is given with respect to a straight line given in position and to a given point; therefore the point C is given. And from the given point C let CD be drawn tangent; therefore CD is given in position.

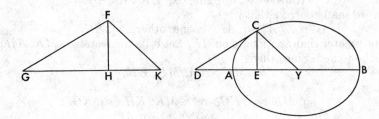

Then the problem will be constructed thus: let there be the given acute angle FGH, and let some point F be taken on FG, and let FH be drawn perpendicular, and let it be contrived that

$$\text{upright : transverse :: sq. } FH : \text{rect. } GH,HK,$$

and let KF be joined, and let Y be the center of the section, and let angle AYC be constructed equal to angle GKF, and let CD be drawn tangent to the section (II. 49).

I say that CD does the problem, that is,

$$\text{angle } CDE = \text{angle } FGH.$$

For since
$$YE : EC :: KH : FH,$$
therefore also
$$\text{sq. } YE : \text{sq. } EC :: \text{sq. } KH : \text{sq. } FH.$$
But also
$$\text{sq. } EC : \text{rect. } DE, EY :: \text{sq. } FH : \text{rect. } KH, HG;$$
for each is the same ratio as that of the upright to the transverse (i. 37, and above). And *ex aequali*; therefore
$$\text{sq. } YE : \text{rect. } DE, EY :: \text{sq. } KH : \text{rect. } KH, HG.$$
And therefore
$$YE : ED :: KH : HG.$$
But also
$$YE : EC :: KH : FH;$$
ex aequali, therefore
$$DE : EC :: HG : FH.$$
And the sides about the right angles are proportional; therefore
$$\text{angle } CDE = \text{angle } FGH.$$
Therefore CD does the problem.

Proposition 51 (Problem)

Given a section of a cone, to draw a tangent which with the diameter drawn through the point of contact will contain an angle equal to a given acute angle.

Let the given section of a cone first be a parabola whose axis is AB, and the given angle H; then it is required to draw a tangent to the parabola which with

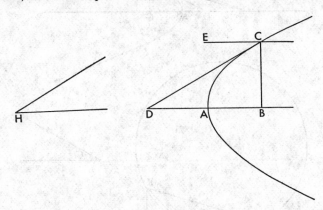

the diameter from the point of contact will contain an angle equal to the angle at H.

Let it have been done, and let CD be drawn a tangent making with the diameter EC drawn through the point of contact angle ECD equal to angle H, and let CD meet the axis at D (i. 24). Since then AD is parallel to EC (i. 51, end),
$$\text{angle } ADC = \text{angle } ECD.$$
But angle ECD is given; for it is equal to angle H; therefore angle ADC is also given.

Then it will be constructed thus: let there be a parabola whose axis is AB, and the given angle H. Let CD be drawn a tangent to the section making with the axis the angle ADC equal to angle H (II. 50), and through C let EC be drawn parallel to AB. Since then

$$\text{angle } H = \text{angle } ADC,$$

and

$$\text{angle } ADC = \text{angle } ECD,$$

therefore also

$$\text{angle } H = \text{angle } ECD.$$

Let the section be an hyperbola whose axis is AB, and center E, and asymptote ET, and the given acute angle Q, and let CD be tangent, and let CE be joined doing the problem, and let CG be drawn perpendicular. Therefore the ratio of the transverse to the upright is given; and so also the ratio of rectangle EG, GD to the square on CG (I. 37). Then let some given straight line FH be laid out, and on it let there be described a segment of a circle admitting an angle equal to angle Q (Eucl. III. 33); therefore it will be greater than a semicircle (Eucl. III. 31). And from some point K of those on the circumference let KL be drawn perpendicular making

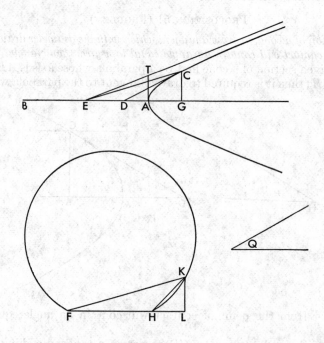

rect. FL, LH : sq. LK : : transverse : upright,

and let FK and KH be joined. Since then

$$\text{angle } FKH = \text{angle } ECD,$$

but also

rect. EG, GD : sq. GC : : transverse : upright,

and

rect. FL, LH : sq. LK : : transverse : upright,

therefore triangle KFL is similar to triangle ECG, and triangle FHK to triangle ECD.[1] And so

$$\text{angle } HFK = \text{angle } CED.$$

Then it will be constructed thus: let there be the given hyperbola AC, and axis AB, and center E, and given acute angle Q, and let the given ratio of the transverse to the upright be the same as YZ to YW, and let WZ be bisected at

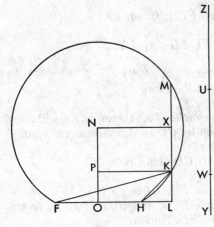

U, and let a given straight line FH be laid out, and on it let there be described a segment of a circle, greater than semicircle and admitting an angle equal to angle Q (Eucl. III. 31, 33), and let it be FKH, and let the center of the circle N be taken, and from N let NO be drawn perpendicular to FH, and let NO be cut at P in the ratio of UW to WY, and through P let PK be drawn parallel to FH, and from K let KL be drawn perpendicular to FH produced, and let FK and KH be joined, and let LK be produced to M, and from N let NX be drawn perpendicular to it; therefore it is parallel to FH. And therefore

$$NP : PO \text{ or } UW : WY :: XK : KL.$$

And doubling the antecedents

$$ZW : WY : MK : KL;$$

componendo

$$ZY : YW :: ML : LK.$$

But

$$ML : LK :: \text{rect. } ML, LK : \text{sq. } LK;$$

therefore

$$ZY : YW :: \text{rect. } ML, LK : \text{sq. } LK :: \text{rect. } FL, LH : \text{sq. } LK \text{ (Eucl. III. 36)}.$$

---

[1] Pappus, in lemma IX to this book: "Let triangle ABC be similar to triangle DEF, and triangle AGB to DEH; the result is

$$\text{rect. } BC, CG : \text{sq. } CA :: \text{rect. } EF, FH : \text{sq. } DF.$$

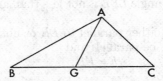

"For since because of similarity

$$\text{whole angle } A = \text{whole angle } D,$$

and

$$\text{angle } BAG = \text{angle } EDH,$$

therefore

$$\text{remaining angle } GAC = \text{remaining angle } HDF.$$

But also

$$\text{angle } C = \text{angle } F;$$

therefore

$$GC : CA :: HF : FD$$

But also

$$BC : CA :: EF : FD;$$

therefore also compounded ratio is the same with compounded. Therefore

$$\text{rect. } BC, CG : \text{sq. } CA :: \text{rect. } EF, FH : \text{sq. } FD."$$

But
$$ZY : YW :: \text{transverse} : \text{upright};$$
therefore also
$$\text{rect. } FL,LH : \text{sq. } LK :: \text{transverse} : \text{upright.}$$
Then let AT be drawn from A perpendicular to AB. Since then
$$\text{sq. } EA : \text{sq. } AT :: \text{transverse} : \text{upright (II. 1),}$$
and also
$$\text{transverse} : \text{upright} :: \text{rect. } FL,LH : \text{sq. } LK,$$
and
$$\text{sq. } FL : \text{sq. } LK > \text{rect. } FL,LH : \text{sq. } LK,$$
therefore also
$$\text{sq. } FL : \text{sq. } LK > \text{sq. } EA : \text{sq. } AT.$$
And the angles at A and L are right angles; therefore
$$\text{angle } F < \text{angle } E.$$
Then let angle AEC be constructed equal to angle LFK; therefore EC will meet the section (II. 2). Let it meet it at C. Then let CD be drawn tangent from C (II. 49), and let CG be drawn perpendicular; then
$$\text{transverse} : \text{upright} :: \text{rect. } EG,GD : \text{sq. } CG \text{ (I. 37).}$$
Therefore also
$$\text{rect. } FL,LH : \text{sq. } LK :: \text{rect. } EG,GD : \text{sq. } CG$$
therefore triangle KFL is similar to triangle ECG, and triangle KHL to triangle CGD, and triangle KFH to triangle CED. And so
$$\text{angle } ECD = \text{angle } FKH = \text{angle } Q.$$
And if the ratio of the transverse to the upright is equal to equal, KL touches the circle FKH (Eucl. III. 37), and the straight line joined from the center to K will be parallel to FH and itself will do the problem.

PROPOSITION 52

If a straight line touches an ellipse making an angle with the diameter drawn through the point of contact, it is not less than the angle adjacent to the one contained by the straight lines deflected at the middle of the section.

Let there be an ellipse whose axes are AB and CD, and center E, and let AB be the major axis, and let the straight line GFL touch the section, and let AC, CB, and FE be joined, and let BC be produced to L.

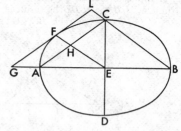

I say that angle LFE is not less than angle LCA.

For FE is either parallel to LB or not.

Let it first be parallel; and
$$AE = EB;$$
therefore also
$$AH = HC.$$
And FE is a diameter; therefore the tangent at F is parallel to AC (II. 6). But also FE is parallel to LB; therefore $FHCL$ is a parallelogram, and therefore
$$\text{angle } LFH = \text{angle } LCH.$$
And since AE and EB are each greater than EC, angle ACB is obtuse; therefore angle LCA is acute. And so also angle LFE. And therefore angle GFE is obtuse.

Then let EF not be parallel to LB, and let FK be drawn perpendicular;

therefore LBE is not equal to angle FEA. But

$$\text{rt. angle at } E = \text{rt. angle at } K;$$

therefore it is not true that

$$\text{sq. } BE : \text{sq. } EC : : \text{sq. } EK : \text{sq. } KF.$$

But

sq. BE : sq. EC : : rect. AE, EB : sq. EC : : transverse : upright (I. 21)

and

$$\text{transverse : upright : : rect. } GK, KE : \text{sq. } KF \text{ (I. 37)}.$$

Therefore it is not true that

$$\text{rect. } GK, KE : \text{sq. } KF : : \text{sq. } KE : \text{sq. } KF.$$

Therefore GK is not equal to KE. Let there be laid out a segment of a circle

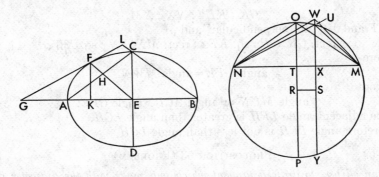

MUN admitting an angle equal to angle ACB (Eucl. III. 33); and angle ACB is obtuse; therefore MUN is a segment less than a semicircle (Eucl. III. 31). Then let it be contrived that

$$GK : KE : : NX : XM,$$

and from X let UXY be drawn at right angles, and let NU and UM be joined, and let MN be bisected at T, and let OTP be drawn at right angles; therefore it is a diameter. Let the center be R, and from it let RS be drawn perpendicular, and ON and OM be joined. Since then

$$\text{angle } MON = \text{angle } ACB,$$

and AB and MN have been bisected, the one at E and the other at T, and the angles at E and T are right angles, therefore triangles OTN and BEC are similar. Therefore

$$\text{sq. } TN : \text{sq. } TO : : \text{sq. } BE : \text{sq. } EC.$$

And since

$$TR = SX,$$

and

$$RO > SU,$$

therefore

$$RO : TR > SU : SX;$$

and *convertendo*

$$RO : OT < SU : UX.$$

And, doubling the antecedents, therefore

$$PO : TO < YU : UX.$$

And *separando*

$$PT : TO < YX : UX.$$

But

$PT : TO :: $ sq. $TN : $ sq. $TO :: $ sq. $BE : $ sq. $EC :: $ transverse : upright (I. 21), and

transverse : upright :: rect. $GK,KE : $ sq. KF (I. 37);

therefore

rect. $GK,KE : $ sq. $KF < YX : XU$
$< $ rect. $YX,XU : $ sq. XU
$< $ rect. $NX,XM : $ sq. $XU.$

If then we contrive it that

rect. $GK,KE : $ sq. $KF :: $ rect. $MX,XN : $ some other,

it will be greater than the square on XU. Let it be to the square on XW. Since then

$$GK : KE :: NX : XM,$$

and KF and YW are perpendicular, and

rect. $GK,KE : $ sq. $KF :: $ rect. $MX,XN : $ sq. $XW,$

therefore

angle $GFE = $ angle $MWN.$

Therefore

angle MUN or angle $ACB > $ angle $GFE,$

and the adjacent angle LFH is greater than angle $LCH.$

Therefore angle LFH is not less than angle $LCH.$

PROPOSITION 53 (PROBLEM)

Given an ellipse, to draw a tangent which will make with the diameter drawn through the point of contact an angle equal to a given acute angle; then it is required that the given acute angle be not less than the angle adjacent to the angle contained by the straight lines deflected at the middle of the section.

Let there be the given ellipse whose major axis is AB and minor axis CD, and center E, and let AC and CB be joined, and let angle U be the given angle

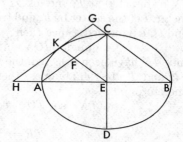

not less than angle ACG; and so also angle ACB is not less than angle $Y.$

Therefore angle U is either greater than or equal to angle $ACG.$

Let it first be equal; and through E let EK be drawn parallel to BC, and through K let KH be drawn tangent to the section (II. 49). Since then

$$AE = EB,$$

and

$$AE : EB :: AF : FC,$$

therefore

$$AF = FC.$$

And KE is a diameter; therefore the tangent to the section at K, that is HKG, is parallel to CA (II. 6). And also EK is parallel to GB; therefore $KFCG$ is a parallelogram; and therefore

$$\text{angle } GKF = \text{angle } GCF.$$

And angle GCF is equal to the given angle, that is U; therefore also

$$\text{angle } GKE = \text{angle } U.$$

Then let

$$\text{angle } U > \text{angle } ACG;$$

then inversely

$$\text{angle } Y < \text{angle } ACB.$$

Let a circle be laid out, and let a segment be taken from it, and let it be MNP admitting an angle equal to angle Y, and let MP be bisected at O, and from O let NOR be drawn at right angles to MP, and let NM and NP be joined; therefore

$$\text{angle } MNP < \text{angle } ACB.$$

But

$$\text{angle } MNO = \text{half angle } MNP,$$

and

$$\text{angle } ACE = \text{half angle } ACB;$$

therefore

$$\text{angle } MNO < \text{angle } ACE.$$

And the angles at E and O are right angles, therefore

$$AE : EC > OM : ON.$$

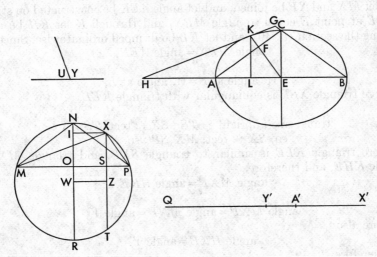

And so also

$$\text{sq. } AE : \text{sq. } EC > \text{sq. } MO : \text{sq. } NO.$$

But

$$\text{sq. } AE = \text{rect. } AE, EB,$$

and

$$\text{sq. } MO = \text{rect. } MO, OP = \text{rect. } NO, OR \text{ (Eucl. III. 35)};$$

therefore

$$\text{rect. } AE, EB : \text{sq. } EC \text{ or transverse : upright (I. 21)} > RO : ON.$$

Then let it be that
$$\text{transverse : upright} :: QA' : A'X',$$
and let QX' be bisected at Y'. Since then
$$\text{transverse : upright} > RO : ON,$$
also
$$QA' : A'X' > RO : ON.$$
And *componendo*
$$QX' : X'A' > RN : NO.$$
Let the center of the circle be W; and so also
$$Y'X' : X'A' > WN : NO.$$
And *separando*
$$A'Y' : A'X' > WO : ON.$$
Then let it be contrived that
$$A'Y' : A'X' :: WO : \text{less than } ON$$
such as IO, and let IX and XT and WZ be drawn parallel. Therefore
$$A'Y' : A'X' :: WO : OI :: ZS : SX;$$
and *componendo*
$$Y'X' : X'A' :: ZX : XS.$$
And doubling the antecedents,
$$QX' : X'A' :: TX : XS.$$
And *separando*
$$QA' : A'X' \text{ or transverse: upright} :: TS : SX.$$
Then let MX and XP be joined, and let angle AEK be constructed on straight line AE at point E equal to angle MPX, and through K let KH be drawn touching the section (II. 49), and let KL be dropped ordinatewise. Since then
$$\text{angle } MPX = \text{angle } AEK,$$
and
$$\text{rt. angle at } S = \text{rt. angle at } L,$$
therefore triangle XSP is equiangular with triangle KEL.
And
$$\text{transverse : upright} :: TS : SX :: \text{rect. } TS,SX :$$
$$\text{sq. } SX :: \text{rect. } MX,SP : \text{sq. } SX;$$
therefore triangle KLE is similar to triangle SXP, and triangle MXP to triangle KHE, and therefore
$$\text{angle } MXP = \text{angle } HKE.$$
But
$$\text{angle } MXP = \text{angle } MNP = \text{angle } Y;$$
therefore also
$$\text{angle } HKE = \text{angle } Y.$$
And therefore
$$\text{adjacent angle } GKE = \text{adjacent angle } U.$$
Therefore GH has been drawn across tangent to the section and making with the diameter KE, drawn through the point of contact, angle GKE equal to the given angle U; and this it was required to do.

BOOK THREE

PROPOSITION 1

If straight lines, touching a section of a cone or circumference of a circle, meet, and diameters are drawn through the points of contact meeting the tangents, the resulting vertically related triangles will be equal.

Let there be the section of a cone or circumference of a circle AB, and let AC and BD, meeting at E, touch AB, and let the diameters of the section CB and

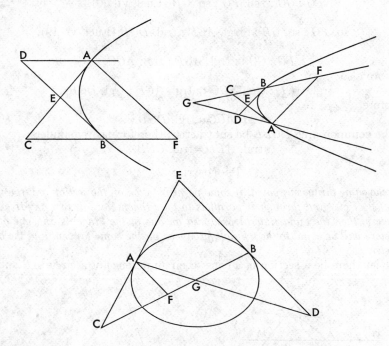

DA be drawn through A and B, meeting the tangents at C and D.

I say that

$$\text{trgl. } ADE = \text{trgl. } EBC.$$

For let AF be drawn from A parallel to BD; therefore it has been dropped ordinatewise (I. 32). Then in the case of the parabola

$$\text{pllg. } ADBF = \text{trgl. } ACF \ (\text{I. 42}),$$

and, with the common area $AEBF$ subtracted,

$$\text{trgl. } ADE = \text{trgl. } CBE.$$

And in the case of the others let the diameters meet at center G. Since then

AF has been dropped ordinatewise, and AC touches,
rect. $FG, GC =$ sq. BG (I. 37).

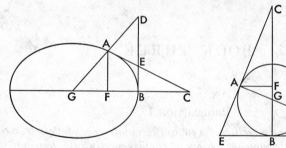

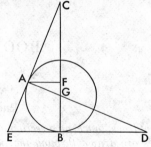

Therefore
$$FG : GB : : BG : GC;$$
therefore also
$$FG : GC : : \text{sq. } FG : \text{sq. } GB \text{ (Eucl. vi. 20)}.$$
But
$$\text{sq. } FG : \text{sq. } GB : : \text{trgl. } AGF : \text{trgl. } DGB \text{ (Eucl. vi. 19)},$$
and
$$FG : GC : : \text{trgl. } AGF : \text{trgl. } AGC;$$
therefore also
$$\text{trgl. } AGF : \text{trgl. } AGC : : \text{trgl. } AGF : \text{trgl. } DGB.$$
Therefore
$$\text{trgl. } AGC = \text{trgl. } DGB.$$
Let the common area $DGBE$ be subtracted; therefore as remainders,
$$\text{trgl. } AED = \text{trgl. } CEB.$$

PROPOSITION 2

*With the same things supposed, if some point is taken on the section or circumfer-
ence of a circle, and through it parallels to the tangents are drawn as far as the
diameters, then the quadrilateral produced on one of the tangents and one of the
diameters will be equal to the triangle produced on the same tangent and the other
diameter.*

For let there be a section of a cone or circumference of a circle AB and let

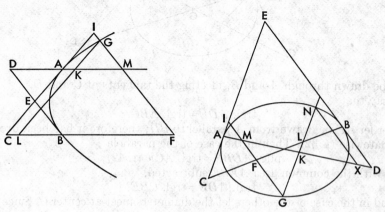

AEC and *BED* be tangents, and *AD* and *BC* diameters, and let some point *G*

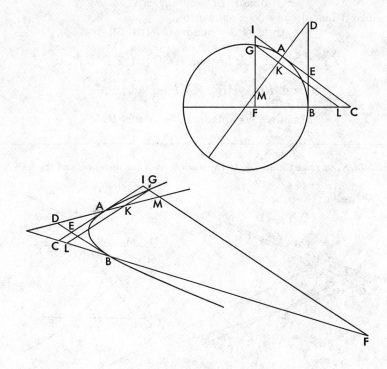

be taken on the section, and *GKL* and *GMF* be drawn parallel to the tangents.
I say that

trgl. *AIM* = quadr. *CLGI.*

For triangle *GKM* has been shown equal to quadrilateral *AL* (ɪ. 42, 43), let the common quadrilateral *IK* be added or subtracted, and

trgl. *AIM* = quadr. *CG.*[1]

PROPOSITION 3

With the same things supposed, if two points are taken on the section or circumference of a circle, and through them parallels to the tangents are drawn as far as the diameters, the quadrilaterals produced by the straight lines drawn, and standing on the diameters as bases, are equal to each other.

For let there be the section and tangents and diameters as said before, and let two points at random *F* and *G* be taken on the section, and through *F* let the straight lines *FHKL* and *NFIM* be drawn parallel to the tangents, and through *G* the straight lines *GXO* and *HPR.*
I say that

quadr. *LG* = quadr. *MH*,

[1]Eutocius, commenting, gives the proof for another and important case: "It must be remarked that, if the point *G* is taken between *A* and *B* so that the parallels are, for instance,

and
$$\text{quadr. } LN = \text{quadr. } RN.$$
For since it has already been shown that
$$\text{trgl. } RPA = \text{quadr. } CG \text{ (III. 2)},$$
and
$$\text{trgl. } AMI = \text{quadr. } CF \text{ (III. 2)},$$
and
$$\text{trgl. } RPA = \text{trgl. } AMI + \text{quadr. } PM,$$
therefore also
$$\text{quadr. } CG = \text{quadr. } CF + \text{quadr. } PM;$$

MIGI and *LGK*, one must draw *LK* to the section, at *N* for instance, and through *N* draw

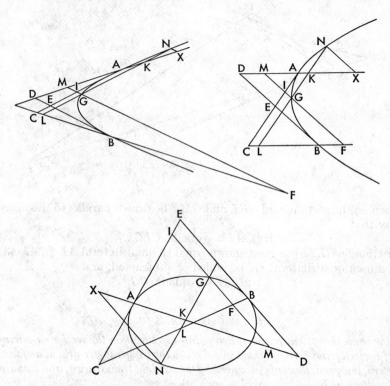

NX parallel to *BD*; for by what was said in the forty-ninth and fiftieth theorems of the first book (I. 49, 50) and in the notes to them
$$\text{trgl. } KNX = \text{quadr. } KC.$$
But triangle *KXN* is similar to triangle *KMG* because *MG* is parallel to *NX*; but it is also equal to it because *AC* is a tangent, and *GN* is parallel to it, and *MX* is a diameter, and
$$GK = KN.$$
Since then   trgl. $KNX = $ quadr. $KC = $ trgl. $KMG,$
with the common quadrilateral *AG* subtracted, as remainders
$$\text{trgl. } AIM = \text{quadr. } CG."$$
It will be noticed that, just as in the second note to I. 50, the quadrilateral *CG* is to be considered as the difference between the triangles *CIF* and *GFL*.

and so

$$\text{quadr. } CG = \text{quadr. } CH + \text{quadr. } RF.$$

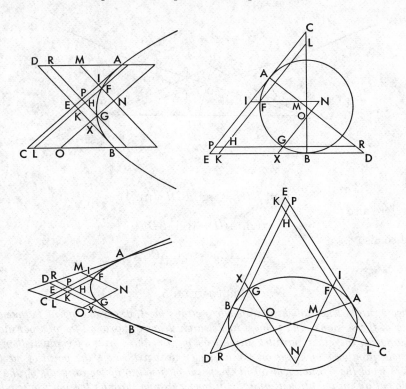

Let the common quadrilateral CH be subtracted; therefore as remainders

$$\text{quadr. } LG = \text{quadr. } HM.$$

And therefore as wholes

$$\text{quadr. } LN = \text{quadr. } RN.$$

PROPOSITION 4

If two straight lines touching opposite sections meet each other, and diameters are drawn through the points of contact meeting the tangents, then the triangles at the tangents will be equal.

Let there be the opposite sections A and B, and let the tangents to them, AC and BC, meet at C, and let D be the center of the sections and let AB and CD be joined, and CD produced to E, and let DA and BD also be joined and produced to F and G.

I say that

$$\text{trgl. } AGD = \text{trgl. } BDF,$$

and

$$\text{trgl. } ACF = \text{trgl. } BCG.$$

For let HL be drawn through H tangent to the section; therefore it is parallel to AG (I. 44, note). And since

$$AD = DH \text{ (I. 30),}$$

trgl. AGD = trgl. DHL (Eucl. vi. 19).

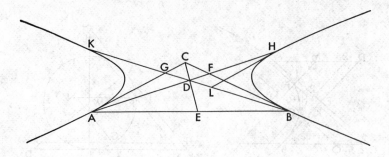

But

trgl. DHL = trgl. BDF (iii. 1);

therefore also

trgl. AGD = trgl. BDF

And so also

trgl. ACF = trgl. BCG.

Proposition 5

If two straight lines touching opposite sections meet, and some point is taken on either of the sections, and from it two straight lines are drawn, the one parallel to the tangent, the other parallel to the line joining the points of contact, then the triangle produced by them on the diameter drawn through the point of meeting differs from the triangle cut off at the point of meeting of the tangents by the triangle cut off on the tangent and the diameter drawn through the point of contact.

Let there be the opposite sections A and B whose center is C, and let tangents ED and DF meet at D, and let EF and CD be joined, and let CD be pro-

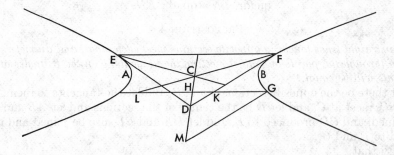

duced, and let FC and EC be joined and produced, and let some point G be taken on the section, and through it let $HGKL$ be drawn parallel to EF, and GM parallel to DF.

I say that triangle GHM differs from triangle KHD by triangle KLF.

For since CD has been shown to be a diameter of the opposite sections (ii.

39, 38), and EF to be an ordinate to it (II. 38; First Def. I. 5), and GH has been

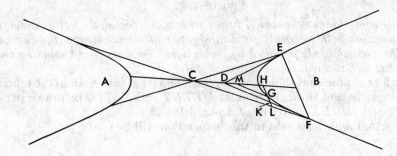

drawn parallel to EF, and MG parallel to DF, therefore triangle GHM differs from triangle CLH by triangle CDF (I. 45, or I. 44, according to the case). And so triangle GHM differs from triangle KHD by triangle KLF.

And it is evident that

$$\text{trgl. } KLF = \text{quadr. } MGKD.$$

Proposition 6

With the same things supposed, if some point is taken on one of the opposite sections, and from it parallels to the tangents are drawn meeting the tangents and the diameters, then the quadrilateral produced by them on one of the tangents and on one of the diameters will be equal to the triangle produced on the same tangent and the other diameter.

Let there be opposite sections of which AEC and BED are diameters, and let AF and BG touch the section AB meeting each other at H, and let some point K be taken on the section, and from it let KML and KNX be drawn parallel to the tangents.

I say that

$$\text{quadr. } KF = \text{trgl. } AIN.$$

Now since AB and CD are opposite sections, and AF, meeting BD, touches

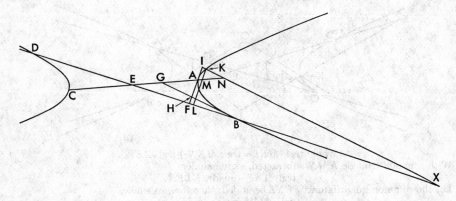

section AB, and KL has been drawn parallel to AF, therefore trgl. AIN = quadr. KF (III. 2)[1]

PROPOSITION 7

With the same things supposed, if points are taken on each of the sections, and from them parallels to the tangents are drawn meeting the tangents and the diameters, then the quadrilaterals produced by the straight lines drawn and standing on the diameters as bases will be equal to each other.

For let the aforesaid things be supposed, and let points K and L be taken on both sections, and through them let $MKPRY$ and $NSTLQ$ be drawn parallel to AF, and $NIOKX$ and $YWULZ$ parallel to BG.

I say that what was said in the enunciation will be so.

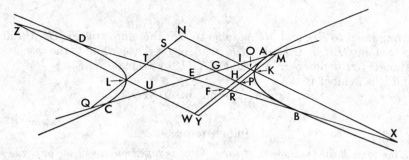

For since

$$\text{trgl. } AOI = \text{quadr. } RO \text{ (III. 2)},$$

[1] Another and important case where the point K falls between C and D is given by Eutocius in his commentary to this proposition. It is as follows: ". . . and let CPR be drawn from C tangent to the section; then it is evident that it is parallel to AF and ML (I. 44, note). And since it has been shown in the second theorem (III. 2) in the figure of the hyperbola that
$$\text{trgl. } PNC = \text{quadr. } LP \text{ (III. 2, note)},$$
let the common quadrilateral MP be added; therefore
$$\text{trgl. } MKN = \text{quadr. } MLRC.$$
Let there be added the common triangle CRE, which is equal to triangle AEF by I. 44, note (and I. 30), therefore

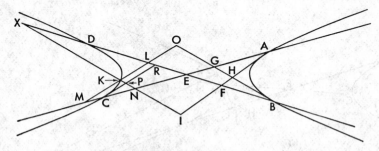

$$\text{whole trgl. } MEL = \text{trgl. } MKN + \text{trgl. } AEF.$$
With common triangle KMN subtracted, as remainders
$$\text{trgl. } AEF = \text{quadr. } KLEN.$$
Let the common quadrilateral $FENI$ be added; therefore, in whole,
$$\text{trgl. } AIN = \text{quadr. } KLFI.$$
And likewise also $\text{trgl. } BOL = \text{quadr. } KNGO.$"

let the quadrilateral EO be added to both; therefore
$$\text{whole trgl. } AEF = \text{quadr. } KE.$$
But also
$$\text{trgl. } BGE = \text{quadr. } LE \text{ (III. 5, note)};$$
and
$$\text{trgl. } AEF = \text{trgl. } BGE \text{ (III. 1)};$$
therefore
$$\text{quadr. } LE = \text{quadr. } IKRE.$$
Let the common quadrilateral NE be added; therefore as wholes
$$\text{whole quadr. } TK = \text{quadr. } IL,$$
and also
$$\text{quadr. } KU = \text{quadr. } RL.$$

PROPOSITION 8

With the same things supposed, instead of K and L let there be taken the points C and D at which the diameters hit the sections, and through them let the parallels to the tangents be drawn.

I say that
$$\text{quadr. } DG = \text{quadr. } FC$$
and
$$\text{quadr. } XI = \text{quadr. } OT.$$

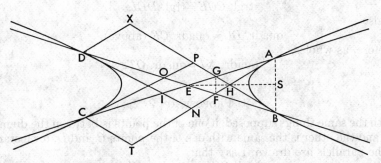

For since it was shown
$$\text{trgl. } AGH = \text{trgl. } HBF \text{ (III. 1)},$$
and the straight line from A to B is parallel to the straight line from G to F,[1] therefore
$$AE : EG :: BE : EF;$$
and *convertendo*
$$EA : AG :: EB : BF.$$
And also
$$CA : AE :: DB : BE;$$

---

[1] For the point H falls within the angle AEB (II. 25), and the straight line drawn from H to the midpoint of AB, that is S, is a diameter (II. 29), and must therefore pass through E (I. 51, end). An analogous series of propositions is found for the opposite sections: II. 32, 38, 39.

Then, since   trgl. GHA = trgl. FHB,
therefore   trgl. GFB = trgl. GFA.
Their bases are the same, therefore their heights are equal (Eucl. VI. 1).

for each is double the other; therefore *ex aequali*
$$CA : AG :: DB : BF.$$
And the triangles are similar because of the parallels; therefore
$$\text{trgl. } CTA : \text{trgl. } AHG :: \text{trgl. } XBD : \text{trgl. } HBF \text{ (Eucl. vi. 19)}.$$
And alternately; but
$$\text{trgl. } AHG = \text{trgl. } HBF \text{ (iii. 1)};$$
therefore
$$\text{trgl. } CTA = \text{trgl. } XBD.$$
As parts of these it was shown
$$\text{trgl. } AHG = \text{trgl. } HBF;$$
therefore also as remainders
$$\text{quadr. } DH = \text{quadr. } CH.$$
And so also
$$\text{quadr. } DG = \text{quadr. } CF.$$
And since CO is parallel to AF,
$$\text{trgl. } COE = \text{trgl. } AEF.$$
And likewise also
$$\text{trgl. } DEI = \text{trgl. } BEG.$$
But
$$\text{trgl. } BEG = \text{trgl. } AEF \text{ (iii. 1)};$$
therefore also
$$\text{trgl. } COE = \text{trgl. } DEI.$$
And also
$$\text{quadr. } DG = \text{quadr. } CF \text{ (above)}.$$
Therefore, as wholes,
$$\text{quadr. } XI = \text{quadr. } OT.$$

PROPOSITION 9

With the same things supposed, if one of the points is between the diameters, as K, and the other is the same with one of the points C and D, for instance C, and the parallels are drawn, I say that
$$\text{trgl. } CEO = \text{quadr. } KE,$$
and
$$\text{quadr. } LO = \text{quadr. } LM.$$

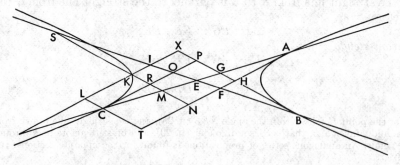

And this is evident. For since it was shown
$$\text{trgl. } CEO = \text{trgl. } AEF,$$

and
$$\text{trgl. } AEF = \text{quadr. } KE \text{ (iii. 5, note)},$$
therefore also
$$\text{trgl. } CEO = \text{quadr. } KE.$$
And so also
$$\text{trgl. } CRM = \text{quadr. } KO,$$
and
$$\text{quadr. } KC = \text{quadr. } LO.$$

PROPOSITION 10

With the same things supposed, let K and L be taken not as points at which the diameters hit the sections.

Then it is to be shown that
$$\text{quadr. } LTRY = \text{quadr. } QYKI.$$
For since the straight lines AF and BG touch, and AE and BE are diameters

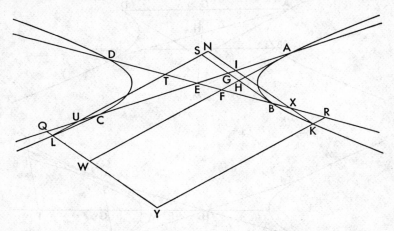

through the points of contact, and LT and KI are parallel to the tangents,
$$\text{trgl. } TUE = \text{trgl. } UQL + \text{trgl. } EFA \text{ (i. 44).}$$
And likewise also
$$\text{trgl. } XEI = \text{trgl. } XRK + \text{trgl. } BEG.$$
But
$$\text{trgl. } EFA = \text{trgl. } BEG \text{ (iii. 1);}$$
therefore
$$\text{trgl. } TUE - \text{trgl. } UQL = \text{trgl. } XEI - \text{trgl. } XRK.$$
Therefore
$$\text{trgl. } TUE + \text{trgl. } XRK = \text{trgl. } XEI + \text{trgl. } UQL.$$
Let the common area $KXEULY$ be added; therefore
$$\text{quadr. } LTRY = \text{quadr. } QYKI.$$

PROPOSITION 11

With the same things supposed, if some point is taken on either of the sections, and from it parallels are drawn, one parallel to the tangent and the other parallel to the straight line joining the points of contact, then the triangle produced by them on the diameter drawn through the point of meeting of the tangents differs from the tri-

*angle cut off on the tangent and the diameter drawn through the point of contact
by the triangle cut off at the point of meeting of the tangents.*

Let there be the opposite sections AB and CD, and let the tangents AE and
DE meet at E, and let the center be H, and let AD and EHG be joined, and let
some point B be taken at random on the section AB, and through it let BFL be
drawn parallel to AG, and BM parallel to AE.

I say that triangle BFM differs from triangle AKL by triangle KEF.

For it is evident that AD is bisected by EH (II. 39, and II. 29), and that EH is
a diameter conjugate to the diameter drawn through H parallel to AD (II. 38);
and so AG is an ordinate to EG (First Def. I. 6).

Since then GE is a diameter, and AE touches, and AG is an ordinate, and,
with point B taken on the section, BF has been dropped to EG parallel to AG,

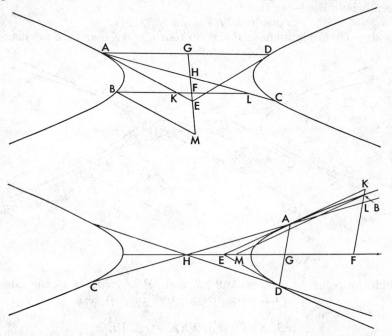

and BM parallel to AE, therefore it is clear that triangle BMF differs from
triangle LHF by triangle HAE (I. 45; I. 43).[1] And so also triangle BMF differs
from triangle AKL by triangle KFE.

And it has been proved at the same time that
$$\text{quadr. } BKEM = \text{trgl. } LKA$$

PROPOSITION 12

*With the same things being so, if on one of the sections two points are taken, and
parallels are drawn from each of them, likewise the quadrilaterals produced by
them will be equal.*

[1] That is, in the first case,
$$\text{trgl. } BMF = \text{trgl. } LHF + \text{trgl. } HAE \text{ (I. 45)};$$
in the second case, only the more general statement "differs" holds true (I. 43). It will be
noticed these are different cases of I. 43 and I. 45 from those given in the text itself.

For let there be the same things as before, and let the points B and K be taken at random on section AB, and through them let $LBMN$ and $KXOUP$

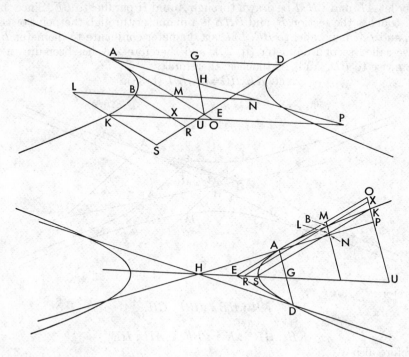

be drawn parallel to AD, and BXR and LKS parallel to AE.
  I say that

$$\text{quadr. } BP = \text{quadr. } KR.$$

For since it has been shown

$$\text{trgl. } AOP = \text{quadr. } KOES \text{ (III. 11, end)}$$

and

$$\text{trgl. } AMN = \text{quadr. } BMER \text{ (III. 11, end),}$$

therefore, as remainders, either

$$\text{quadr. } KR - \text{quadr. } BO = \text{quadr. } MP$$

or

$$\text{quadr. } KR + \text{quadr. } BO = \text{quadr. } MP.$$

And, with the common quadrilateral BO added or subtracted,

$$\text{quadr. } BP = \text{quadr. } XS.$$

PROPOSITION 13

If in conjugate opposite sections straight lines tangent to the adjacent sections meet, and diameters are drawn through the points of contact, then the triangles whose common vertex is the center of the opposite sections will be equal.

  Let there be conjugate opposite sections on which there are the points A, B, C and D, and let BE and AE, meeting at E, touch the sections A and B, and let H be the center, and let AH and BH be joined and produced to D and C.

I say that
$$\text{trgl. } BFH = \text{trgl. } AGH.$$
For let AK and LHM be drawn through A and H parallel to BE. Since then BFE touches the section B, and DHB is a diameter through the point of contact, and LM is parallel to BE, LM is a diameter conjugate to diameter BD, the so-called second diameter (II. 20); and therefore AK has been drawn ordinatewise to BD. And AG touches; therefore
$$\text{rect. } KH, HG = \text{sq. } BH \text{ (I. 38).}$$

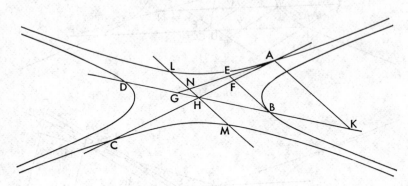

Therefore
$$KH : HB :: BH : GH.$$
But
$$KH : HB :: KA : BF :: AH : HF;$$
therefore also
$$AH : HF :: BH : GH.$$
And the angles BHF and GHF are equal to two right angles; therefore
$$\text{trgl. } AGH = \text{trgl. } BHF.$$

PROPOSITION 14

With the same things supposed, if some point is taken on any one of the sections, and from it parallels to the tangents are drawn as far as the diameters, then the triangle produced at the center will differ from the triangle produced about the same angle by the triangle having the tangent as base, and center as vertex.

Let the other things be the same, and let some point X be taken on section

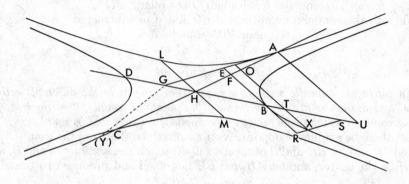

B, and through it let XRS be drawn parallel to AG and XTO parallel to BE. I say that triangle OHT differs from triangle XST by triangle HBF.

For let AU be drawn from A parallel to BF. Since then, because of the same things as before, LHM is a diameter of the section AL, and DHB is a second diameter and conjugate to it (II, 20), and AG is a tangent at A, and AU has been dropped parallel to LM, therefore

$$AU : UG \text{ comp. } HU : UA,$$
transverse side of figure on LM : upright (I. 40).

But

$$AU : UG :: XT : TS,$$

and

$$HU : UA :: HT : TO : HB : BF,$$

and

transverse side of figure on LM : upright : :
upright side of figure on BD : transverse (I. 60).

Therefore

$XT : TS$ comp. $HB : BF$, upright side of figure on BD : transverse

or

$XT : TS$ comp. $HT : TO$, upright side of figure on BD : transverse.
And by things shown in the forty-first theorem of the first book (I. 41), triangle THO differs from triangle XTS by triangle BFH.

And so also by triangle AGH (III, 13).

PROPOSITION 15

If straight lines touching one of the conjugate opposite sections meet, and diameters are drawn through the points of contact, and some point is taken on any one of the conjugate sections, and from it parallels to the tangents are drawn as far as the diameters, then the triangle produced by them at the section is greater than the triangle produced at the center by the triangle having the tangent as base and the center of the opposite sections as vertex.[1]

Let there be conjugate opposite sections AB, GS, T, and X, whose center is H, and let ADE and BDC touch the section AB, and let the diameters $AHFW$ and BHT be drawn through the points of contact A and B, and let some point S be taken on the section GS, and through it let SFL be drawn parallel to BC and SU parallel to AE.

I say that

trgl. $SLU =$ trgl. $HLF +$ trgl. HCB

For let XHG be drawn through H parallel to BC, and KIG through G parallel to AE, and SO parallel to BT; then it is evident that XG is a diameter conjugate to BT (II, 20), and that SO being parallel to BT has been dropped ordinatewise to HGO (First Def. I. 6), and that $SLHO$ is a parallelogram.

Since then BC touches, and BH is through the point of contact, and AE is another tangent, let it be contrived that

$$DB : BE :: MN : 2BC;$$
therefore MN is the so-called upright side of the figure on BT (I. 50). Let MN be bisected at P; therefore

---

[1]This proposition comes as a climax to a long series, and shows that the conjugate opposite sections taken as a unit have the same property as the other conic sections. The conjugate opposite sections seem to be a sort of fifth section.

$$DB : BE :: MP : BC.$$

Then let it be contrived that

$$XG : TB :: TB : R; \tag{α}$$

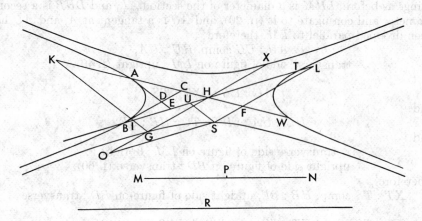

then R also will be the so-called upright side of the figure applied to XG
(I. 16, 60).

Since then

$$DB : BE :: MP : BC, \tag{β}$$

but

$$DB : BE :: \text{sq. } DB : \text{rect. } DB,BE,$$

and

$$MP : BC :: \text{rect. } MP, BH : \text{rect. } CB,BH,$$

therefore

$$\text{sq. } DB : \text{rect. } DB,BE :: \text{rect. } MP, BH : \text{rect. } CB,BH.$$

And

$$\text{rect. } MP, BH = \text{sq. } HG,$$

because

$$\text{sq. } XG = \text{rect. } TB,MN \text{ (I. 16)} \tag{γ}$$

and

$$\text{rect. } MP,BH = \text{fourth rect. } TB,MN$$

and

$$\text{sq. } HG = \text{fourth sq. } XG;$$

therefore

$$\text{sq. } DB : \text{rect. } DB,BE :: \text{sq. } HG : \text{rect. } CB,BH.$$

Alternately

$$\text{sq. } DB : \text{sq. } HG :: \text{rect. } DB,BE : \text{rect. } CB,BH.$$

But

$$\text{sq. } DB : \text{sq. } HG :: \text{trgl. } DBE : \text{trgl. } GHI;$$

for they are similar; and

$$\text{rect. } DB,BE : \text{rect. } CB,BH :: \text{trgl. } DBE : \text{trgl. } CBH;$$

therefore

$$\text{trgl. } DBE : \text{trgl. } GHI :: \text{trgl. } DBE : \text{trgl. } CBH.$$

Therefore

$$\text{trgl. } GHI = \text{trgl. } CBH.$$

Again since
$$HB : BC \text{ comp. } HB : MP, MP : BC,$$
but
$$HB : MP :: TB : MN : R : XG \text{ (above, } \alpha \text{ and } \gamma),$$
and
$$MP : BC :: DB : BE \text{ (above, } \beta)$$
therefore
$$HB : BC \text{ comp. } DB : BE, R : XG.$$
And since BC is parallel to SL, and triangle HCB is similar to triangle HLF, and
$$HB : BC :: HL : LF,$$
therefore
$$HL : LF \text{ comp. } R : XG, DB : BE$$
or
$$HL : LF \text{ comp. } R : XG, HG : HI.$$
Since then GS is an hyperbola having XG as a diameter, and R as an upright side, and, from some point S, SO has been dropped ordinatewise, and figure HIG has been described on radius HG, and figure HLF has been described on the ordinate SO or its equal HL, and on HO the straight line between the center and the ordinate or on SL its equal the figure SLU has been described similar to the figure HIG described on the radius, and there are the compounded ratios as already given, therefore
$$\text{trgl. } SLU = \text{trgl. } HLF + \text{trgl. } HCB \text{ (I. 41).}$$

PROPOSITION 16

If two straight lines touching a section of a cone or circumference of a circle meet, and from some point of those on the section a straight line is drawn parallel to one tangent and cutting the section and the other tangent, then, as the squares on the tangents are to each other, so the area contained by the straight lines between the section and the tangent will be to the square cut off at the point of contact.

Let there be the section of a cone or circumference of a circle AB, and let the straight lines AC and CB, meeting at C, touch it, and let some point D be taken on the section AB, and through it let EDF be drawn parallel to CB.

I say that
$$\text{sq. } BC : \text{sq. } AC :: \text{rect. } FE, ED : \text{sq. } EA.$$
For let the diameters AGH and KBL be drawn through A and B, and DMN through D parallel to AL; it is at once evident, that
$$DK = KF \text{ (I. 46, 47),}$$
and
$$\text{trgl. } AEG = \text{quadr. } LD \text{ (III. 2),}$$
and
$$\text{trgl. } BLC = \text{trgl. } ACH \text{ (III. 1).}$$
Since then
$$DK = KF$$
and DE is added,
$$\text{rect. } FE, ED + \text{sq. } DK = \text{sq. } KE.$$
And since triangle ELK is similar to triangle DNK,
$$\text{sq. } EK : \text{sq. } KD :: \text{trgl. } EKL : \text{trgl. } DNK.$$

And alternately

whole sq. *EK* : whole trgl. *ELK* : :
part subtracted sq. *DK* : part subtracted trgl. *DNK*.

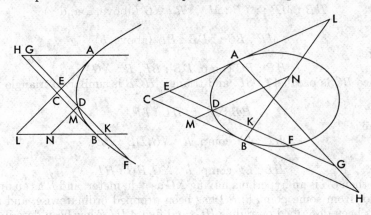

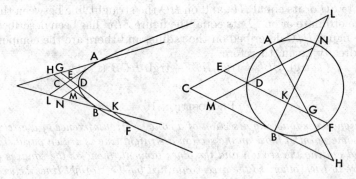

Therefore also

remainder rect. *FE,ED* : remainder quadr. *DL* : : sq. *EK* : trgl. *ELK*

But

sq. *EK* : trgl. *ELK* : : sq. *CB* : trgl. *BLC*;

therefore also

rect. *FE,ED* : quadr. *LD* : : sq. *CB* : trgl. *LCB*.

But

quadr. *LD* = trgl. *AEG*,

and

trgl. *BLC* = trgl. *ACH*;

therefore also

rect. *FE,ED* : trgl. *AEG* : : sq. *CB* : trgl. *ACH*.

Alternately

rect. *FE,ED* : sq. *CB* : : trgl. *AEG* : trgl. *ACH*.

But

trgl. *AEG* : trgl. *ACH* : : sq. *EA* : sq. *AC*;

therefore also

rect. *FE,ED* : sq. *CB* : : sq. *EA* : sq. *AC*.

And alternately.

PROPOSITION 17

*If two straight lines touching a section of a cone or circumference of a circle meet,
and two points are taken at random on the section, and from them in the section
are drawn parallel to the tangents straight lines cutting each other and the line of
the section, then as the squares on the tangents are to each other, so will the rectangles contained by the straight lines taken similarly.*

Let there be the section of a cone or circumference of a circle AB; and tangents to AB, AC and CB, meeting at C; and let points D and E be taken at
random on the section, and through them at $EFIK$ and $DFGH$ be drawn parallel to AC and CB.

I say that

$$\text{sq. } CA : \text{sq. } CB : : \text{rect. } KF, FE : \text{rect. } HF, FD.$$

For let the diameters $ALMN$ and $BOXP$ be drawn through A and B, and let
the tangents and parallels be produced to the diameters, and let DX and EM
be drawn from D and E parallel to the tangents; then it is evident that

$$KI = IE, \quad HG = GD \text{ (I. 46, 47).}$$

Since then KE has been cut equally at I and unequally at F,

$$\text{rect. } KF, FE + \text{sq. } FI = \text{sq. } EI \text{ (Eucl. II. 5)}$$

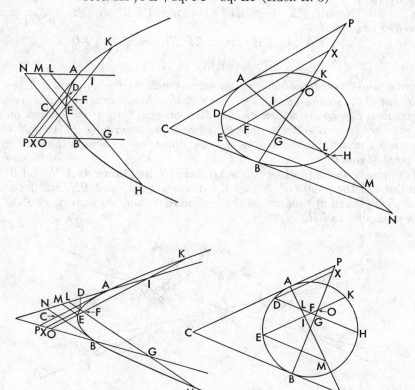

And since the triangles are similar because of the parallels,

$$\text{whole sq. } EI : \text{whole trgl. } IME : :$$

part subtracted sq. *IF* : part subtracted trgl. *FIL*.

Therefore also

  remainder rect. *KF*, *FE* : remainder quadr. *FM* : : whole

     sq. *EI* : whole trgl. *IME*

But

    sq. *EI* : trgl. *IME* : : sq. *CA* : trgl. *CAN* :

Therefore

    rect. *KF*, *FE* : quadr. *FM* : : sq. *CA* : trgl. *CAN*.

But

     trgl. *CAN* = trgl. *CPB* (III. 1),

and

     quadr. *FM* = quadr. *FX* (III. 3);

therefore

    rect. *KF*, *FE* : quadr. *FX* : : sq. *CA* : trgl. *CPB*.

Then likewise it could be shown that

    rect. *HF*, *FD* : quadr. *FX* : : sq. *CB* : trgl. *CPB*.

Since then

    rect. *KF*, *FE* : quadr. *FX* : : sq. *CA* : trgl. *CPB*,

and inversely

    quadr. *FX* : rect. *HF*, *FD* : : trgl. *CPB* : sq. *CB*,

therefore *ex aequali*

    sq. *CA* : sq. *CB* : : rect. *KF*, *FE* : rect. *HF*, *FD*.

PROPOSITION 18

If two straight lines touching opposite sections meet, and some point is taken on either one of the sections, and from it some straight line is drawn parallel to one of the tangents cutting the section and the other tangent, then as the squares on the tangents are to each other, so will the rectangle contained by the straight lines between the section and the tangent be to the square on the straight line cut off at the point of contact.

Let there be the opposite sections *AB* and *MN*, and tangents *ACL* and *BCH*, and through the points of contact the diameters *AM* and *BN*, and let some point *D* be taken at random on the section *MN*, and through it let *EDF* be drawn parallel to *BH*.

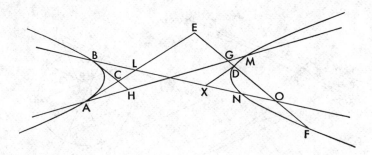

I say that

    sq. *BC* : sq. *CA* : : rect. *FE*, *ED* : sq. *AE*.

For let *DX* be drawn through *D* parallel to *AE*. Since then *AB* is an hyper-

bola and BN its diameter and BH a tangent and DF parallel to BH, therefore
$$FO = OD \text{ (I. 48)}.$$

And ED is added: therefore
$$\text{rect. } FE, ED + \text{sq. } DO = \text{sq. } EO \text{ (Eucl. II. 6)}.$$
And since EL is parallel to DX, triangle EOL is similar to triangle DXO. Therefore
$$\text{whole sq. } EO : \text{whole trgl. } EOL ::$$
$$\text{part subtracted sq. } DO : \text{part subtracted trgl. } DXO;$$
therefore also
$$\text{remainder rect. } DE, EF : \text{remainder quadr. } DL :: \text{sq. } EO : \text{trgl. } EOL.$$
But
$$\text{sq. } OE : \text{trgl. } EOL :: \text{sq. } BC : \text{trgl. } BCL;$$
therefore also
$$\text{rect. } FE, ED : \text{quadr. } DL :: \text{sq. } BC : \text{trgl. } BCL.$$
And
$$\text{quadr. } DL = \text{trgl. } AEG \text{ (III. 6, note)},$$
and
$$\text{trgl. } BCL = \text{trgl. } ACH \text{ (III. 1)};$$
therefore
$$\text{rect. } FE, ED : \text{trgl. } AEG :: \text{sq. } BC : \text{trgl. } ACH.$$
But also
$$\text{trgl. } AEG : \text{sq. } EA :: \text{trgl. } ACH : \text{sq. } AC;$$
therefore *ex aequali*
$$\text{sq. } BC : \text{sq. } AC :: \text{rect. } FE, ED : \text{sq. } EA.[1]$$

---

[1] Eutocius gives an alternative proof of Apollonius', demonstrating another and important case: "For let there be the opposite sections A and B, and tangents to them AC and CB meeting at C, and let D be taken on section B, and through it let EDF be drawn parallel to AC. I say that
$$\text{sq. } AC : \text{sq. } CB :: \text{rect. } EF, FD : \text{sq. } FB.$$
"For let AHG be drawn as a diameter through A, and through B and G, GK and BL parallel to EF. Since then BH touches the hyperbola at B, and BL has been drawn ordinatewise, $AL : LG :: AH : HG$ (I. 36).

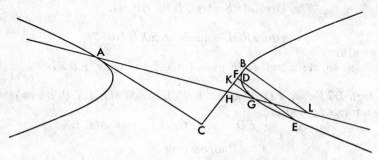

But	$AL : LG :: CB : BK,$
and	$AH : HG : AC : KG;$
therefore also	$CB : BK :: AC : KG.$
And alternately	$AC : CB :: KG : KB,$
and	sq. AC : sq. CB :: sq. GK : sq. $KB.$
But it was shown	sq. GK : sq. KB :: rect. EF, FD : sq. $FB;$
therefore also	sq. AC : sq. CB :: rect. EF, FD : sq. $FB.$"

PROPOSITION 19

If two straight lines touching opposite sections meet, and parallels to the tangents are drawn cutting each other and the section, then, as the squares on the tangents are to each other, so will the rectangle contained by the straight lines between the section and the point of meeting of the straight lines be to the rectangle contained by the straight lines taken similarly.

Let there be opposite sections whose diameters are AC and BD and center in E, and let the tangents AF and FD meet at F, and let $GHIKL$ and $MNXOL$ be drawn from any points parallel to AF and FD.

I say that

$$\text{sq. } AF : \text{sq. } FD : : \text{rect. } GL, LI : \text{rect. } ML, LX.$$

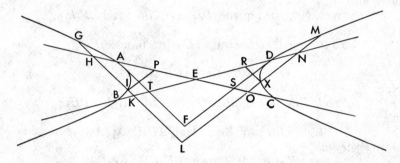

Let IP and XR be drawn through X and I parallel to AF and FD.

BH touches the hyperbola at B, and BL has been drawn ordinatewise,

$$AL : LG : : AH : HG \quad (\text{i, } 36)$$

And since

$$\text{sq. } AF : \text{trgl. } AFS : : \text{sq. } HL : \text{trgl. } HLO : : \text{sq. } HI : \text{trgl. } HIP,$$

therefore

remainder rect. GL, LI : remainder quadr. $IPOL : : \text{sq. } AF : \text{trgl. } AFS$.

But

$$\text{trgl. } AFS = \text{trgl. } DTF \quad (\text{iii. } 4),$$

and

$$\text{quadr. } IPOL = \text{quadr. } KRXL \quad (\text{iii. } 7);$$

therefore also

$$\text{sq. } AF : \text{trgl. } DTF : : \text{rect. } GL, LI : \text{quadr. } KRXL.$$

But

$$\text{trgl. } DTF : \text{sq. } FD : : \text{quadr. } KRXL : \text{rect. } ML, LX \quad (\text{likewise});$$

and therefore *ex aequali*

$$\text{sq. } AF : \text{sq. } FD : : \text{rect. } GL, LI : \text{rect. } ML, LX.$$

PROPOSITION 20

If two straight lines touching opposite sections meet, and through the point of meeting some straight line is drawn parallel to the straight line joining the points of contact and meeting each of the sections, and some other straight line is drawn parallel to the same straight line and cutting the sections and the tangents, then, as the rectangle contained by the straight lines drawn from the point of meeting to cut the sections is to the square on the tangent, so is the rectangle contained by the straight lines between the sections and the tangent to the square on the straight line cut off at the point of contact.

Let there be the opposite sections AB and CD whose center is E and tangents AF and CF, and let AC be joined, and let EF and AE be joined and produced, and let BFH be drawn through F parallel to AC, and let the point K be taken at random, and through it let $KLSMNX$ be drawn parallel to AC.

I say that

$$\text{rect. } BF, FD : \text{sq. } FA :: \text{rect. } KL, LX : \text{sq. } AL.$$

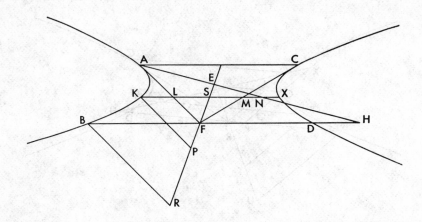

For let KP and BR be drawn from K and B parallel to AF. Since then

$$\text{sq. } BF : \text{trgl. } BFR :: \text{sq. } KS : \text{trgl. } KSP :: \text{sq. } LS : \text{trgl. } LSF,$$

and

sq. KS : trgl. KSP ::
remainder rect. KL, LX (Eucl. II. 5) :
remainder quadr. $KLFP$ (Eucl. v. 19).

and

$$\text{sq. } BF = \text{rect. } BF, FD \text{ (II. 39, 38)},$$

and

$$\text{trgl. } BRF = \text{trgl. } AFH \text{ (III. 11 and special case)},$$

and

$$\text{quadr. } KLFP = \text{trgl. } ALN \text{ (III. 5)},$$

therefore

$$\text{rect. } BF, FD : \text{trgl. } AFH :: \text{rect. } KL, LX : \text{trgl. } ALN.$$

And

$$\text{trgl. } AFH : \text{sq. } AF :: \text{trgl. } ALN : \text{sq. } AL;$$

then

$$\text{rect. } BF, FD : \text{sq. } FA :: \text{rect. } KL, LX : \text{sq. } AL.$$

PROPOSITION 21

With the same things supposed, if two points are taken on the section, and through them straight lines are drawn, the one parallel to the tangent, the other parallel to the straight line joining the points of contact, and cutting each other and the sections, then, as the rectangle contained by the straight lines drawn from the point of meeting to cut the sections is to the square on the tangent, so will the rectangle contained by the straight lines between the sections and the point of meeting be to the rectangle contained by the straight lines between the section and the point of meeting.

For let there be the same things as before, and let points G and K be taken, and through them let $NXGOPR$ and KST be drawn parallel to AF, and GLM and $KOWIYZQ$ parallel to AC.

I say that

rect. BF, FD : sq. FA : : rect. KO, OQ : rect. NO, OG.

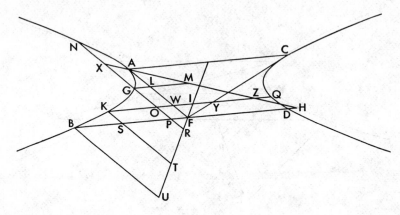

For since

sq. AF : trgl. AFH : : sq. AL : trgl. ALM : : sq. XO : trgl. XOZ

and

sq. XO : trgl. XOZ : : sq. XG : trgl. XGM,

therefore whole sq. XO : whole trgl. XOZ : :

part subtracted sq. XG : part subtracted trgl. XGM,

therefore also

remainder rect. NO, OG : remainder quadr. $GOZM$: : sq. AF : trgl. AFH.

But

trgl. AFH = trgl. BUF (iii. 11, end, special case),

and

quadr. $GOZM$ = quadr. $KORT$ (iii. 12);

therefore

sq. AF : trgl. BFU : : rect. NO, OG : quadr. $KORT$.

But it was shown (in the course of iii. 20) trgl. BUF : sq. BF or rect. BF, FD (ii. 39, 38) : : quadr. $KORT$: rect. KO, OQ;

therefore *ex aequali*

sq. AF : rect. BF, FD : : rect. NO, OG : rect. KO, OQ.

And inversely

rect. BF, FD : sq. FA : : rect. KO, OQ : rect. NO, OG.

Proposition 22

If two parallel straight lines touch opposite sections, and any straight lines are drawn cutting each other, and the sections, one parallel to the tangent, the other parallel to the straight line joining the points of contact, then as the transverse side

of the figure on the straight line joining the points of contact is to the upright,
so the rectangle contained by the straight lines between the sections and the point
of meeting will be to the rectangle contained by the straight lines between the section
and the point of meeting.

Let there be the opposite sections *A* and *B*, and let *AC* and *BD* be parallel
and tangent to them, and let *AB* be joined. Then let *EXG* be drawn across
parallel to *AB* and *KELM* parallel to *AC*.

I say that
$$AB : \text{upright side of the figure} :: \text{rect. } GE,EX : \text{rect. } KE,EM.$$
Let *XN* and *GF* be drawn through *G* and *X* parallel to *AC*.

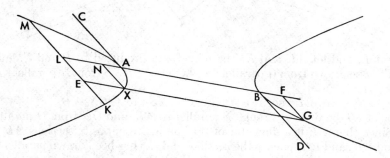

For since *AC* and *BD* are parallels tangent to the sections, *AB* is a diameter
(II. 31), and *KL*, *XN*, and *GF* are ordinates to it (I. 32); then (I. 21)
$$AB : \text{upright side} ::$$
$$\text{rect. } BL,LA : \text{sq. } LK :: \text{rect. } BN,NA : \text{sq. } NX \text{ or sq. } LK$$
Therefore
$$\text{whole rect. } BL,LA : \text{whole sq. } LK ::$$
$$\text{part subtracted rect. } BN,NA : \text{part subtracted sq. } LE,$$
or
$$\text{rect. } BL,LA : \text{sq. } LK :: \text{rect. } FA,AN : \text{sq. } LE,$$
for
$$NA = BF \text{ (I. 21)};$$
therefore also
$$\text{remainder rect. } FL,LN : \text{remainder rect. } KE,EM :: AB : \text{upright.}$$
But
$$\text{rect. } FL,LN = \text{rect. } GE,EX;$$
therefore
$$AB \text{ the transverse side of figure} : \text{upright} ::$$
$$\text{rect. } GE,EX : \text{rect. } KE,EM.$$

PROPOSITION 23

If in conjugate opposite sections two straight lines touching contrary sections meet
in any one section at random, and any straight lines are drawn parallel to the
tangents and cutting each other and the other opposite sections, then, as the squares
on the tangents are to each other, so the rectangle contained by the straight lines
between the sections and the point of meeting will be to the rectangle contained by
the straight lines similarly taken.

Let there be the conjugate opposite sections AB, CD, EF, and GH, and their center K, and let $AWCL$ and $EYDL$, tangents to the sections AB and EF

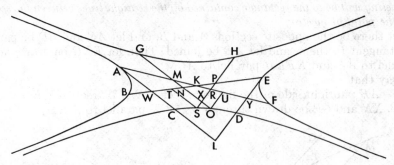

meet at L, and let AK and EK be joined and produced to B and F, and let $GMNXO$ be drawn from G parallel to AL, and $HPRXS$ from H parallel to EL.

I say that

$$\text{sq. } EL : \text{sq. } LA :: \text{rect. } HX,XS : \text{rect. } GX,XD.$$

For let ST be drawn through S parallel to AL, and OU from O parallel to EL. Since then BE is a diameter of the conjugate opposite sections AB, CD, EF and GH, and EL touches the section, and HS has been drawn parallel to it,

$$HP = PS \text{ (II. 20; First Def. I. 5)},$$

and for the same reasons

$$GM = MO$$

And since

$$\text{sq. } EL : \text{trgl. } EWL :: \text{sq. } PS : \text{trgl. } PTS :: \text{sq. } PX : \text{trgl. } PNX,$$

also

remainder rect. HX,XS : remainder quadr. $TN,XS :: \text{sq. } EL : \text{trgl. } WLE$.

But

$$\text{trgl. } EWL = \text{trgl. } ALY \text{ (III. 4)},$$

and

$$\text{quadr. } TNXS = \text{quadr. } XRUO \text{ (III. 15)};[1]$$

therefore

$$\text{sq. } EL : \text{trgl. } ALY :: \text{rect. } HX,XS : \text{quadr. } XRUO.$$

But

$$\text{trgl. } AYL : \text{sq. } AL :: \text{quadr. } XRUO : \text{rect. } GX,XO \text{ (same way)};$$

therefore *ex aequali*

$$\text{sq. } EL : \text{sq. } AL :: \text{rect. } HX,XS : \text{rect. } GX,XO.$$

PROPOSITION 24

If in conjugate opposite sections two straight lines are drawn from the center through to the sections, and one of them is taken as the transverse diameter and the other as the upright diameter, and any straight lines are drawn parallel to the two diameters and meeting each other and the sections, and the point of meeting of the straight lines is the place between the four sections, then the rectangle contained by

---

[1]This is the case of III. 15 where the tangents are one to each of the opposite sections. Compare with the two cases of III. 12 and III. 18.

For   trgl. $TSP - $trgl. $KPR = $trgl. ANK (III. 15),

and   trgl. $MOU - $trgl. $MNK = $trgl. ANK (III. 15).

the segments of the parallel to the transverse diameter together with the rectangle to which the rectangle contained by the segments of the parallel to the upright diameter has the ratio which the square on the upright diameter has to the square on the transverse, will be equal to twice the square on the half of the transverse.

Let there be the conjugate opposite sections A, B, C and D whose center is E, and from E let the transverse diameter AEC and the upright diameter DEB be drawn through, and let $FGHIKL$ and $MNXOPR$ be drawn parallel to AC and DB and meeting each other at X; and first let X be within the angle SEW or the angle UET.

I say that the rectangle FX, XL together with the rectangle to which the rectangle RX, XM has the ratio which the square on DB has to the square on AC, is equal to twice the square on AE.

For let the asymptotes of the sections SET and UEW be drawn, and through A, $SGAW$ tangent to the section.
Since then

$$\text{rect. } SA, AW = \text{sq. } DE \text{ (i. 60; ii. 1)},$$

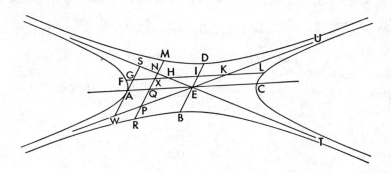

therefore

$$\text{rect. } SA, AW : \text{sq. } EA :: \text{sq. } DE : \text{sq. } EA.$$

And

$$\text{rect. } SA, AW : \text{sq. } AE \text{ comp. } SA : AE, WA : AE.$$

But

$$SA : AE :: NX : XH$$

and

$$WA : AE :: PX : XK;$$

therefore

$$\text{sq. } DE : \text{sq. } AE \text{ comp. } NX : XH, PX : XK.$$

But

$$\text{rect. } PX, XN : \text{rect. } KX, XH \text{ comp. } NX : XH, PX : XK,$$

therefore

$$\text{sq. } DE : \text{sq. } AE :: \text{rect. } PX, XN : \text{rect. } KX, XH.$$

Therefore also

$$\text{sq. } DE : \text{sq. } AE :: \text{sq. } DE + \text{rect. } PX, XN : \text{sq. } AE + \text{rect. } KX, XH.$$

And

$$\text{sq. } DE = \text{rect. } PM, MN \text{ (ii. 11)} = \text{rect. } RN, NM \text{ (ii. 16)},$$

and

$$\text{sq. } AE = \text{rect. } KF, FH \text{ (ii. 11)} = \text{rect. } LH, HF \text{ (ii. 16)};$$

therefore

$$\text{sq. } DE : \text{sq. } AE :: \text{rect. } PX, XN + \text{rect. } RN, NM :$$
$$\text{rect. } KX, XH + \text{rect. } LH, HF$$

And

$$\text{rect. } PX, XN + \text{rect. } RN, NM = \text{rect. } RX, XM ;[1]$$

therefore

$$\text{sq. } DE : \text{sq. } AE :: \text{rect. } RX, XM : \text{rect. } KX, XH + \text{rect. } KF, FH.$$

Then it must be shown that

$$\text{rect. } FX, XL + \text{rect. } KX, XH + \text{rect. } KF, FH = 2 \text{ sq. } AE.$$

Let the common square AE, that is rectangle KF, FH, be subtracted; therefore it remains to be shown that

$$\text{rect. } FX, XL + \text{rect. } KX, XH = \text{sq. } AE.$$

And this is so; for

$$\text{rect. } FX, XL + \text{rect. } KX, XH = \text{rect. } LH, HF,[\dagger]$$
$$\text{rect. } FX, XL + \text{rect. } KX, XH = \text{rect. } KF, FH \text{ (II. 16)},$$
$$= \text{sq. } AE \text{ (II. 11)}.$$

Then let the straight lines FL and MR meet on one of the asymptotes at H. Then

$$\text{rect. } FH, HL = \text{sq. } AE,$$

and

$$\text{rect. } MH, HR = \text{sq. } DE \text{ (II. 11, 16)};$$

therefore

$$\text{sq. } DE : \text{sq. } AE :: \text{rect. } MH, ER : \text{rect. } FH, HL.$$

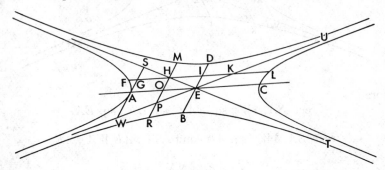

And so we want twice rectangle FH, HL to equal twice the square on AE. And it does.

[1] For $\qquad\qquad RP = NM$ (II. 8),
and $\qquad\qquad RO = OM$ (II. 3),
therefore $\qquad\qquad PO = ON$.
But $\qquad\qquad \text{rect. } PX, XN + \text{sq. } OX = \text{sq. } ON$ (Eucl. II. 5),
and, for the same reasons,

$$\text{rect. } RN, NM + \text{sq. } ON = \text{sq. } OM,$$

and $\qquad\qquad \text{rect. } RX, XM + \text{sq. } OX = \text{sq. } OM.$
Hence $\qquad \text{rect. } RN, NM + \text{sq. } ON = \text{rect. } RX, XM + \text{sq. } OX,$
and, adding equals to equals,

$$\text{rect. } RN, NM + \text{sq. } ON + \text{rect. } PX, XN + \text{sq. } OX = \text{rect. } RX, XM + \text{sq. } OX + \text{sq. } ON.$$

Subtracting the common squares,

$$\text{rect. } RN, NM + \text{rect. } PX, XN = \text{rect. } RX, XM.$$

[†] By the same manner of proof as in the note above, but using also Euclid II. 6, because of the different position of the point X.

And let the point X be within the angle SEK or angle WET. Then likewise by the composition of ratios.

$$\text{sq. } DE : \text{sq. } AE :: \text{rect. } PX, XN : \text{rect. } KX, XH.$$

And

$$\text{sq. } DE = \text{rect. } PM, RN = \text{rect. } RN, NM,$$

and

$$\text{sq. } AL = \text{rect. } FH, HL;$$

therefore

$$\text{rect. } RN, NM : \text{rect. } FH, HL ::$$

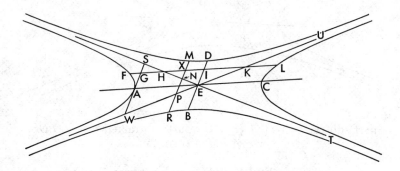

part subtracted rect. PX, XN : part subtracted rect. KX, XH. Therefore also

$$\text{rect. } RN, NM : \text{rect. } FH, HL ::$$

remainder rect. RX, XM : remainder (sq. $AE -$ rect. KX, XH)

Therefore it must be shown that

$$\text{rect. } FX, XL + (\text{sq. } AE - \text{rect. } KX, XH) = 2 \text{ sq. } AE.$$

Let the common square on AE, that is rectangle FH, HL, be subtracted; therefore it remains to be shown that

$$\text{rect. } KX, XH + (\text{sq. } AE - \text{rect. } KX, XH) = \text{sq. } AE.$$

And this is so; for

$$\text{rect. } KX, XH + \text{sq. } AE - \text{rect. } KX, XH = \text{sq. } AE.$$

PROPOSITION 25

With the same things supposed, let the point of meeting of the parallels to AC and BD be within one of the sections D and B, as set out below, at X.

I say that the rectangle contained by the segments of the parallel to the transverse, that is rectangle OX, XN, will be greater than the rectangle to which the rectangle contained by the segments of the parallel to the upright diameter, that is rectangle RX, XM, has the ratio which the square on the upright diameter has to the square on the transverse by twice the square on the half of the transverse.

For, for the same reasons,

$$\text{sq. } DE : \text{sq. } AE :: \text{rect. } PX, XH : \text{rect. } SX, XL.$$

and

$$\text{sq. } DE = \text{rect. } PM, MH,$$

and

$$\text{sq. } AE = \text{rect. } LO, OS \text{ (II. 11)};$$

therefore also

$$\text{sq. } DE : \text{sq. } AE :: \text{rect. } PM, MH : \text{rect. } LO, OS.$$

And since

$$\text{whole rect. } PX, XH : \text{whole rect. } LX, XS ::$$

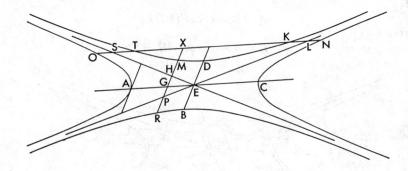

part subtracted rect. PM, MH : part subtracted rect. LO, OS,
or rect. ST, TL (II. 22),

therefore also

remainder rect. RX, SM : remainder rect. TX, XK
(first note to III. 24; II. 8) : : sq. DE : sq. AE.

Therefore it must be shown that

$$\text{rect. } OX, XN = \text{rect. } TX, XK + 2 \text{ sq. } AE.$$

Let the common rectangle TX, XK be subtracted; therefore it must be shown that

$$\text{rect. } OT, TN \text{ (first note to III. 24)} = 2 \text{ sq. } AE.$$

And it is (II. 23).

PROPOSITION 26

And if the point of meeting of the parallels at X is within one of the sections A and C, as set out below, then the rectangle contained by the segments of the parallel to the transverse, that is rectangle LX, XF, will be less than the rectangle to which the rectangle contained by the segments of the other parallel, that is rectangle RX, XG, has the ratio which the square on the upright diameter has to the square on the transverse by twice the square on half of the transverse.

For, since for the same reasons as before

$$\text{sq. } DE : \text{sq. } AE :: \text{rect. } WX, XS : \text{rect. } KX, XH,$$

therefore also

whole rect. RX, XG[1] : whole rect. $KX, XH + $ sq. AE : :
sq. upright diameter : sq. transverse.

Therefore it must be shown that

$$\text{rect. } LX, XF + 2 \text{ sq. } AE = \text{rect. } KX, XH + \text{sq. } AE.$$

---

[1]For by II. 11   rect. $WG, GS = $ sq. DE;
and $RW = GS$ (II. 16).
Therefore by the first note to III. 24, and II. 16,
      rect. $WX, XS + $ sq. $DE = $ rect. $WX, XS + $ rect. $WG, GS = $ rect. RX, XG.

Let the common square on AE be subtracted; therefore it remains to be
shown that

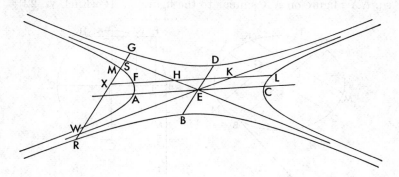

$$\text{rect. } LX, XF + \text{sq. } AE = \text{rect. } KX, XH$$

or

$$\text{rect. } LX, XF + \text{rect. } LH, HF = \text{rect. } KX, XH. \text{ (II. 16, 11).}$$

And it is, for

$$\text{rect. } LH, HF + \text{rect. } LX, XF = \text{rect. } KX, XH.[1]$$

PROPOSITION 27

*If the conjugate diameters of an ellipse or circumference of a circle are drawn, and
one of them is called the upright diameter and the other the transverse, and two
straight lines, meeting each other and the line of the section, are drawn parallel to
them, then the squares on the straight lines cut off on the straight line drawn parallel to the transverse between the point of meeting of the straight lines and the line
of the section plus the figures described on the straight lines cut off on the straight
line drawn parallel to the upright diameter between the point of meeting of the
straight lines and the line of the section, figures similar and similarly situated to
the figure on the upright diameter, will be equal to the square on the transverse
diameter.*

For let there be the ellipse or circumference of a circle $ABCD$, whose center
is E, and let two of its conjugate diameters be drawn, the upright AEC and the
transverse BED, and let $NGFH$ and $KFLM$ be drawn parallel to AC and BD.

I say that the squares on NF and FH plus the figures described on KF and
FM, similar and similarly situated to the figure on AC will be equal to the
square on BD.

Let NX be drawn from N parallel to AE; therefore it has been dropped ordinatewise to BD. And let BP be the upright side. Now since

$$BP : AC :: AC : BD \text{ (I. 15),}$$

therefore also

$$BP : BD :: \text{sq. } AC : \text{sq. } BD.$$

And

$$\text{sq. } BD = \text{figure on } AC;$$

therefore

$$BP : BD :: \text{sq. } AC : \text{figure on } AC.$$

[1]This is another case of the first note to III. 24.

And

sq. AC : figure on AC : :
sq. NX : figure on NX similar to the figure on AC (Eucl. vi. 22);

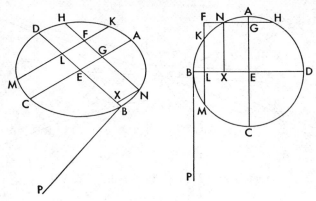

therefore also

$BP : BD$: : sq. NX : figure on NX similar to the figure on AC.

And also

$BP : BD$: : sq. NX : rect. BX,XD (i. 21);

therefore

figure on NX or FL similar to the figure on AC = rect. BX,XD.

Then likewise we could show that

figure on KL similar to the figure on AC = rect. BL,LD.

And since the straight line NH has been cut equally at G and unequally at F,

sq. HF + sq. FN = 2[sq. HG + sq. GF] = 2[sq. NG + sq. GF] (Eucl. vi. 9).

Then for the same reasons also

sq. MF + sq. FK = 2[sq. KL + sq. LF],

and the figure on MF and FK similar to the figure on AC are double the similar figures on KL and LF.

And

figure on KL + figure on FL = rect. BX,XD + rect. BL,LD (above),

and

sq. NG + sq. GF = sq. XE + sq. EL;

therefore

sq. NF + sq. FH + figures on KF and FM similar to the figure on AC =
2[rect. BX,XD + rect. BL,LD + sq. XE + sq. EL].

And since the straight line BD has been cut equally at E and unequally at X,

rect. BX,XD + sq. XE = sq. BE (Eucl. ii. 5).

And likewise also

rect. BL,LD + sq. LE = sq. BE;

and so

rect. BX,XD + rect. BL,LD + sq. XE + sq. LE = 2 sq. BE.

Therefore the squares on NF and FH together with figures on KF and FM similar to the figure on CA are double the square on BE. But also

sq. BD = 2 sq. BE;

therefore the squares on NF and FH plus the figures on KF and FM similar to the figure on AC are equal to the square on BD.

PROPOSITION 28

If in conjugate opposite sections conjugate diameters are drawn, and one of them is called the upright, and the other the transverse, and two straight lines are drawn parallel to them and meeting each other and the sections, then the squares on the straight lines cut off on the straight line drawn parallel to the upright between the point of meeting of the straight lines and the sections have to the squares on the straight lines cut off on the straight line drawn parallel to the transverse between the point of meeting of the straight lines and the sections the ratio which the square on the upright diameter has to the square on the transverse diameter.

Let there be the conjugate opposite sections A, B, C, and D and let AEC be the upright diameter and BED the transverse, and let $FGHK$ and $LGMN$

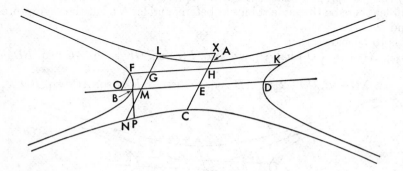

be drawn parallel to them and cutting each other and the sections.

I say that

$$\text{sq. } LG + \text{sq. } GN : \text{sq. } FG + \text{sq. } GK :: \text{sq. } AC : \text{sq. } BD.$$

For let LX and FO be drawn ordinatewise from F and L; therefore they are parallel to AC and BD. And from B let the upright side for BD, BP, be drawn; then it is evident that

$$PB : BD :: \text{sq. } AC : \text{sq. } BD \text{ (I. 15)} :: \text{sq. } AE : \text{sq. } EB ::$$
$$\text{sq. } FO : \text{rect. } BO, OD \text{ (I. 21)} :: \text{rect. } CX, XA : \text{sq. } LX \text{ (I. 60, 21).}$$

Therefore as one of the antecedents is to one of the consequents, so are all of the antecedents to all of the consequents (Eucl. v. 12); therefore

$$\text{sq. } AC : \text{sq. } BD :: \text{rect. } CX, XA + \text{sq. } AE + \text{sq. } OF : \text{rect. } DO, OB + \text{sq. } BE,$$
$$+ \text{sq. } LX$$

or

$$\text{sq. } AC : \text{sq. } BD :: \text{rect. } CX, XA + \text{sq. } AE + \text{sq. } EH :$$
$$\text{rect. } DO, OB + \text{sq. } BE + \text{sq. } ME.$$

But

$$\text{rect. } CX, XA + \text{sq. } AE = \text{sq. } XE,$$

and

$$\text{rect. } DO, OB + \text{sq. } BE = \text{sq. } OE \text{ (Eucl. II. 6);}$$

therefore

$$\text{sq. } AC : \text{sq. } BD :: \text{sq. } XE + \text{sq. } EH : \text{sq. } OE + \text{sq. } EM ::$$
$$\text{sq. } LM + \text{sq. } MG : \text{sq. } FH + \text{sq. } HG.$$

And, as has been shown,

$$\text{sq. } NG + \text{sq. } GL = 2[\text{sq. } LM + \text{sq. } MG],$$

and
$$\text{sq. } FG + \text{sq. } GK = 2[\text{sq. } FH + \text{sq. } HG] \text{ (Eucl. ii. 9)};$$
therefore also
$$\text{sq. } AC : \text{sq. } BD : : \text{sq. } NG + \text{sq. } GL : \text{sq. } FG + \text{sq. } GK.$$

PROPOSITION 29

With the same things supposed, if the parallel to the upright diameter cuts the asymptotes, then the squares on the straight lines cut off on the straight line drawn parallel to the upright between the point of meeting of the straight lines and the asymptotes plus the half of the square on the upright diameter has to the squares on the straight lines cut off on the straight line drawn parallel to the transverse between the point of meeting of the straight lines and the sections the ratio which the square on the upright diameter has to the square on the transverse.

For let there be the same things as before, and let NL cut the asymptotes at X and O.

It is to be shown that
$$\text{sq. } XG + \text{sq. } GO + \text{half sq. } AC : \text{sq. } FG + \text{sq. } GK : : \text{sq. } AC : \text{sq. } BD,$$
or
$$\text{sq. } XG + \text{sq. } GO + 2 \text{ sq. } AE : \text{sq. } FG + \text{sq. } GK : : \text{sq. } AC : \text{sq. } BD.$$

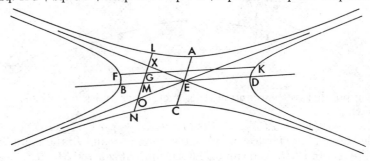

For since
$$LX = ON \text{ (ii. 16)},$$
$$\text{sq. } LG + \text{sq. } GN + 2 \text{ rect. } NX, XL = \text{sq. } XG + \text{sq. } GO;[1]$$
therefore
$$\text{sq. } XG + \text{sq. } GO + 2 \text{ sq. } AE = \text{sq. } LG + \text{sq. } GN.$$
And
$$\text{sq. } LG + \text{sq. } GN : \text{sq. } FG + \text{sq. } GK : : \text{sq. } AC : \text{sq. } BD \text{ (iii. 28)};$$
therefore also
$$\text{sq. } XG + \text{sq. } GO + 2 \text{ sq. } AE : \text{sq. } FG + \text{sq. } GK : : \text{sq. } AC : \text{sq. } BD.$$

---

[1]For
$$OM = MX.$$
Therefore, as in a lemma of Pappus, since
$$2 \text{ rect. } NX, XL + 2 \text{ sq. } MX = 2 \text{ sq. } ML \text{ (Eucl. ii. 5)},$$
adding the common square on GM,
$$2 \text{ rect. } NX, XL + 2 \text{ sq. } MX + 2 \text{ sq. } GM = 2 \text{ sq. } ML + 2 \text{ sq. } GM.$$
And
$$2 \text{ sq. } ML + 2 \text{ sq. } GM = \text{sq. } NG + \text{sq. } LG$$
and
$$2 \text{ sq. } MX + 2 \text{ sq. } GM = \text{sq. } OG + \text{sq. } GX \text{ (Eucl. ii. 9)}.$$
Therefore as above.

PROPOSITION 30

If two straight lines touching an hyperbola meet, and through the points of contact a straight line is produced, and through the point of meeting a straight line is drawn parallel to some one of the asymptotes and cutting both the section and the straight line joining the points of contact, then the straight line between the point of meeting and the straight line joining the points of contact will be bisected by the section.[1]

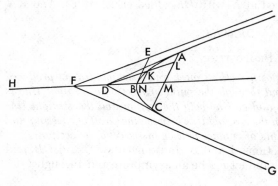

Let there be the hyperbola *ABC*, and let *AD* and *DC* be tangents and *EF* and *FG* asymptotes, and let *AC* be joined, and through *D* parallel to *FE* let *DKL* be drawn. I say that

$$DK = KL.$$

For let *FDBM* be joined and produced both ways, and let *FH* be made equal to *BF*, and through the points *B* and *K* let *BE* and *KN* be drawn parallel to *AC*; therefore they have been dropped ordinatewise (II. 30, 5, 7). And since triangle *BEF* is similar to triangle *DNK*, therefore

$$\text{sq. } DN : \text{sq. } NK : : \text{sq. } BF : \text{sq. } BE. \tag{α}$$

And

$$\text{sq. } BF : \text{sq. } BE : : HB : \text{upright (II. 1)};$$

therefore also

$$\text{sq. } DN : \text{sq. } NK : : HB : \text{upright}.$$

But

$$HB : \text{upright} : : \text{rect. } HN, NB : \text{sq. } NK \text{ (I. 21)};$$

therefore also

$$\text{sq. } DN : \text{sq. } NK : : \text{rect. } MN, NB : \text{sq. } NK. \tag{β}$$

Therefore

$$\text{rect. } HN, NB = \text{sq. } DN.$$

---

[1]The propositions from 30 to 34 inclusive are one special case, and propositions 35 and 36 are another special case of proposition 37. The first group takes the line drawn through the intersection of the tangents as parallel to an asymptote. The second group takes one of the tangents as an asymptote. Proposition 34, lying between, is special in both these ways.

In proposition 37 we have the line *CF* divided by the section at *D* and *F*, and at *E* by the straight line joining the points of contact, in such a way that

$$CF : CD : : FE : ED.$$

This is the same form of the harmonic proportion as we found in I. 34, and *DF* is the harmonic mean between *CF* and *FE*.

If we argue by analogy from this proportion, treating infinity as a definite magnitude, and two such infinities as would occur here as equal and subject to the general laws of magnitudes, we can immediately deduce the special cases of propositions 30 to 36. Thus in the case of the first group, *CF* and *FE* both become infinite, therefore *CD* is equal to *ED*.

And also
$$\text{rect. } MF,FD = \text{sq. } FB \text{ (i. 37)},$$
because AD touches and AM has been dropped ordinatewise; and so also
$$\text{rect. } HN,NB + \text{sq. } FB = \text{rect. } MF,FD + \text{sq. } DN.$$
But
$$\text{rect. } HN,NB + \text{sq. } FB = \text{sq. } FN \text{ (Eucl. ii. 6)};$$
and therefore
$$\text{rect. } MF,FD + \text{sq. } DN = \text{sq. } FN.$$
Therefore DM has been bisected at N with DF added (Eucl. ii. 6). And KN and LM are parallel; therefore
$$DK = KL.$$

PROPOSITION 31

If two straight lines touching opposite sections meet, and a straight line is produced through the points of contact, and through the point of meeting a straight line is drawn parallel to the asymptote and cutting both the section and the straight line joining the points of contact, then the straight line between the point of meeting and the straight line joining the points of contact will be bisected by the section.

Let there be the opposite sections A and B, and tangents AC and CB, and let AB be joined and produced, and let FE be an asymptote and through C let CGH be drawn parallel to FE.

I say that
$$CG = GH.$$

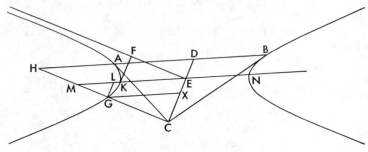

Let CE be joined and produced to D, and through E and G let $NEKM$ and GX be drawn parallel to AB, and through G and K let KF and GL be drawn parallel to CD.

Since triangle KFE is similar to triangle MLG,
$$\text{sq. } KE : \text{sq. } KF :: \text{sq. } ML : \text{sq. } LG.$$
And it has been shown
$$\text{sq. } KEKE : \text{sq. } KF :: \text{rect. } NL,LK : \text{sq. } LG \ (\alpha \text{ and } \beta \text{ of iii. 30});$$
therefore
$$\text{rect. } NL,LK = \text{sq. } ML.$$
Let the square on KE be added to each; therefore
$$\text{rect. } NL,LK + \text{sq. } KE = \text{sq. } LE = \text{sq. } GX = \text{sq. } ML + \text{sq. } KE.$$
And
$$\text{sq. } GX : \text{sq. } ML + \text{sq. } KE :: \text{sq. } XC : \text{sq. } LG + \text{sq. } KF \text{ (Eucl. vi. 4; v. 12)};$$
therefore
$$\text{sq. } XC = \text{sq. } LG + \text{sq. } KF.$$

And
$$\text{sq. } LG = \text{sq. } XE$$
and
$$\text{sq. } KF = \text{sq. on half of second diameter (II. 1),}$$
$$= \text{rect. } CE, ED \text{ (I. 38);}$$
therefore
$$\text{sq. } XC = \text{sq. } XE + \text{rect. } CE, ED.$$
Therefore the straight line CD has been cut equally at X and unequally at E (Eucl. II. 5).
And DH is parallel to GX; therefore
$$CG = GH.$$

Proposition 32

If two straight lines touching an hyperbola meet, and a straight line is produced through the points of contact, and a straight line is drawn through the point of meeting of the tangents parallel to the straight line joining the points of contact, and a straight line is drawn through the midpoint of the straight line joining the points of contact parallel to one of the asymptotes, then the straight line cut off between this midpoint and the parallel will be bisected by the section.

Let there be the hyperbola ABC, whose center is D, and asymptote DE, and let AF and FC touch, and let CA and FD be joined and produced to G and H;

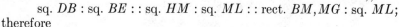

then it is evident that
$$AH = HC.$$
Then let FK be drawn through F parallel to AC, and HLK through H parallel to DE.
I say that
$$KL = HL.$$
Let LM and BE be drawn through B and L parallel to AC; then, as has been already shown (III. 30, α, β, and conclusion),

$$\text{sq. } DB : \text{sq. } BE :: \text{sq. } HM : \text{sq. } ML :: \text{rect. } BM, MG : \text{sq. } ML;$$
therefore
$$\text{rect. } GM, MB = \text{sq. } MH.$$
And also
$$\text{rect. } HD, DF = \text{sq. } DB,$$
because AF touches, and AH has been dropped ordinatewise (I. 37); therefore
rect. $GM, MB + $sq. $DB = $rect. $HD, DF + $sq. $MH = $sq. DM (Eucl. II. 6).
Therefore FH has been bisected at M with DF added. And KF and LM are parallel; therefore
$$KL = LH.$$

Proposition 33

If two straight lines touching opposite sections meet, and one straight line is produced through the points of contact, and another straight line is drawn through the point of meeting of the tangents parallel to the straight line joining the points of

*contact, and still another straight line is drawn through the midpoint of the straight
line joining the points of contact parallel to one of the asymptotes and meeting the
section, and the parallel drawn through the point of meeting, then the straight line
between the midpoint and the parallel will be bisected by the section.*

Let there be the opposite sections ABC and DEF, and tangents AG and DG
and center H, and asymptote KH, and let HG be joined and produced, and
also let ALD be joined; then it is evident that it is bisected at L (II. 30). Then
let BHE and CGF be drawn through G and H parallel to AD, and LMN
through L parallel to HK.

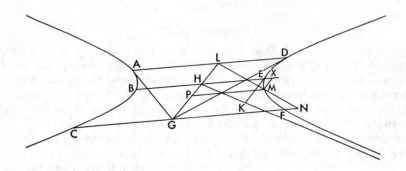

I say that
$$LM = MN.$$
For let EK and MX be dropped from E and M parallel to GH, and MP
through M parallel to AD.

Since then through things already shown (III. 30, α and β)
$$\text{sq. } HE : \text{sq. } EK :: \text{rect. } BX,XE : \text{sq. } XM,$$
therefore
$$\text{sq. } HE : \text{sq. } EK :: \text{rect. } BX,XE + \text{sq. } HE : \text{sq. } KE + \text{sq. } XM. \text{ (Eucl. v. 12)}$$
or
$$\text{sq. } HE : \text{sq. } EK :: \text{sq. } HX : \text{sq. } KE + \text{sq. } XM \text{ (Eucl. II. 6)}.$$
But it has been shown (I. 38; II. 1)
$$\text{sq. } EK = \text{rect. } GH,HL$$
and
$$\text{sq. } XM = \text{sq. } HP;$$
therefore
$$\text{sq. } HE : \text{sq. } EK :: \text{sq. } HX \text{ or sq. } MP : \text{rect. } GH,HL + \text{sq. } HP.$$
And
$$\text{sq. } HE : \text{sq. } EK :: \text{sq. } MP : \text{sq. } PL \text{ (Eucl. vi. 4)};$$
therefore
$$\text{sq. } MP : \text{sq. } PL :: \text{sq. } MP : \text{rect. } GH,HL + \text{sq. } HP.$$
Therefore
$$\text{sq. } PL = \text{rect. } GH,HL + \text{sq. } HP.$$
Therefore the straight line LG has been cut equally at P and unequally at H
(Eucl. II. 5).
And MP and GN are parallel; therefore
$$LM = MN.$$

Proposition 34

If some point is taken on one of the asymptotes of an hyperbola, and a straight line from it touches the section, and through the point of contact a parallel to the asymptote is drawn, then the straight line drawn from the point taken parallel to the other asymptote will be bisected by the section.

Let there be the hyperbola AB, and the asymptotes CD and DE, and let a point C be taken at random on CD, and through it let CBE be drawn touching

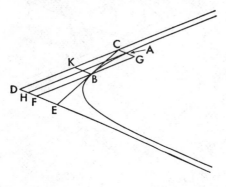

the section, and through B let FBG be drawn parallel to CD, and through C let CAG be drawn parallel to DE.

I say that
$$CA = AG.$$

For let AH be drawn through A parallel to CD, and BK through B parallel to DE. Since then
$$CB = BE \text{ (ii. 3)},$$
therefore also
$$CK = KD$$
and
$$DF = FE.$$

And since
$$\text{rect. } KB, BF = \text{rect. } CA, AH \text{ (ii. 12)},$$
and
$$BF = DK = CK,$$
and
$$AH = DC,$$
therefore
$$\text{rect. } DC, CA = \text{rect. } GC, CK.$$
Therefore
$$DC : CK :: GC : CA.$$
And
$$CD = 2CK;$$
therefore also
$$GC = 2\,CA.$$
Therefore
$$CA = AG.$$

Proposition 35

With the same things being so, if from the point taken some straight line is drawn cutting the section at two points, then as the whole straight line is to the straight line cut off outside, so will the segments of the straight line cut off inside be to each other.

For let there be the hyperbola AB and the asymptotes CD and DE, and CBE touching and HB parallel, and through C let some straight line $CALFG$ be drawn across cutting the section at A and F.

I say that
$$FC : CA :: FL : AL.$$
For let CNX, KAM, $OPBR$, and FU be drawn through C, A, B and F

parallel to DE; and APS and $TFRMX$ through A and F parallel to CD.

Since then
$$AC = FG \text{ (II. 8)},$$
therefore also
$$KA = TG \text{ (Eucl. VI. 4)}.$$ 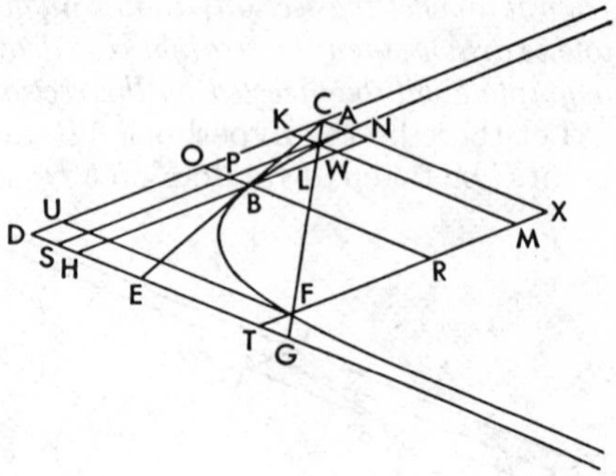
But
$$KA = DS;$$
therefore also
$$TG = DS.$$
And so also
$$CK = DU.$$
And since
$$CK = DU,$$
also
$$DK = CU;$$
therefore
$$DK : CK :: CU : CK.$$
And
$$CU : CK :: FC : AC,$$
and
$$FC : AC :: MK : KA,$$
and
$$MK : KA :: \text{pllg. } MD : \text{pllg. } DA \text{ (Eucl. VI. 1)},$$
and
$$DK : CK :: \text{pllg. } HK : \text{pllg. } KN;$$
therefore also
$$\text{pllg. } MD : \text{pllg. } DA :: \text{pllg. } HK : \text{pllg. } KN.$$
But
$$\text{pllg. } DA = \text{pllg. } DB \text{ (II. 12)} = \text{pllg. } ON;$$
for
$$CB = BE \text{ (II. 3)},$$
and
$$DO = OC;$$
therefore
$$\text{pllg. } MD : \text{pllg. } ON :: \text{pllg. } HK : \text{pllg. } KN.$$
and
remainder pllg. MH : remainder pllg. BK :: whole pllg. MD : whole pllg. ON
And since
$$\text{pllg. } DA = \text{pllg. } DB,$$
let the common parallelogram DP be subtracted;
therefore
$$\text{pllg. } KP = \text{pllg. } PH.$$
Let the common parallelogram AB be added; therefore
$$\text{whole pllg. } BK = \text{whole pllg. } AH.$$
Therefore
$$\text{pllg. } MD : \text{pllg. } DA :: \text{pllg. } MH : \text{pllg. } AH.$$
But
$$\text{pllg. } MD : \text{pllg. } DA :: MK : KA :: FC : AC,$$
and

pllg. MH : pllg. AH : : MW : WA : : FL : LA;

therefore also

$$FC : AC : : FL : LA.$$

PROPOSITION 36

*With the same things being so, if the straight line drawn across from the point
neither cuts the section at two points nor is parallel to the asymptote, it will meet the
opposite section, and as the whole straight line is to the straight line between the
section and the parallel through the point of contact, so will the straight line between the opposite section and the asymptote be to the straight line between the
asymptote and the other section.*

Let there be the opposite sections A and B whose center is C and asymptotes
DE and FG, and let some point G be taken on CG, and from it let GBE be
drawn tangent, and GH neither parallel to CE nor cutting the section in two
points (I. 26).

It has been shown that GH produced meets CD and therefore also section A.
Let it meet it at A, and let KBL be drawn through B parallel to CG.

I say that

$$AK : KH : : AG : GH.$$

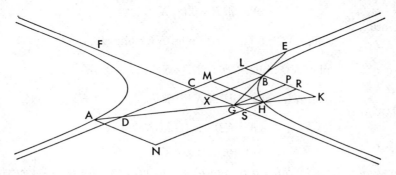

For let HM and AN be drawn from the points A and H parallel to CG, and
BX, GP, and $RHSN$ from B, G and H parallel to DE. Since then

$$AD = GH \text{ (II. 16)},$$
$$AG : GH : : DH : HG$$

But

$$AG : GH : : NS : SH,$$

and

$$DH : GH : : CS : SG;$$

And therefore

$$NS : SH : : CS : SG.$$

But

$$NS : SH : : \text{pllg. } NC : \text{pllg. } CH,$$

and

$$CS : SG : : \text{pllg. } RC : \text{pllg. } RG;$$

therefore also

$$\text{pllg. } NC : \text{pllg. } CH : : \text{pllg. } RC : \text{pllg. } RG.$$

And as one is to one so are all to all; therefore

pllg. NC : pllg. CH : : whole pllg. NL : whole pllg. CH +pllg. RG.
And since
$$EB = BG,$$
also
$$LB = BP$$
and
$$\text{pllg. } LX = \text{pllg. } BG.$$
And
$$\text{pllg. } LX = \text{pllg. } CH \text{ (ii. 12)};$$
therefore also
$$\text{pllg. } BG = \text{pllg. } CH.$$
Therefore
pllg. NC : pllg. CH : : whole pllg. NL : whole pllg. BG +pllg. RG
or
pllg. NC : pllg. CH : : pllg. NL : pllg. RX.
But
$$\text{pllg. } RX = \text{pllg. } LH,$$
since also
$$\text{pllg. } CH = \text{pllg. } BC \text{ (ii. 12)},$$
and
$$\text{pllg. } MB = \text{pllg. } XH.$$
Therefore
pllg. NC : pllg. CH : : pllg. NL : pllg. LH.
But
pllg. NC : pllg. CH : : NS : SH : : AG : GH,
and
pllg. NL : pllg. LH : : NR : RH : : AK : KH;
therefore also
$$AK : KH : : AG : GH.$$

Proposition 37

If two straight lines touching a section of a cone or circumference of a circle or opposite sections meet, and a straight line is joined to their points of contact, and from the point of meeting of the tangents some straight line is drawn across cutting the line (of the section) at two points, then as the whole straight line is to the straight line cut off outside, so will the segments produced by the straight line joining the points of contact be to each other.

Let there be the section of a cone AB and tangents AC and CB and let AB be joined, and let $CDEF$ be drawn across.

I say that
$$CF : CD : : FE : ED.$$

Let the diameters CH and AK be drawn through C and A, and through F and D, DP, FR, LFM and NDO parallel to AH and LC. Since then LFM is parallel to XDO,
$$FC : CD : : LF : XD : : FM : DO : : LM : XO;$$
and therefore
$$\text{sq. } LM : \text{sq. } XO : : \text{sq. } FM : \text{sq. } DO.$$
But
$$\text{sq. } LM : \text{sq. } XO : : \text{trgl. } LMC : \text{trgl. } XCO \text{ (Eucl. vi. 19)},$$

and
$$\text{sq. } FM : \text{sq. } DO : : \text{trgl. } FRM : \text{trgl. } DPO;$$
therefore also
$$\text{trgl. } LMC : \text{trgl. } XCO : : \text{trgl. } FRM : \text{trgl. } DPO : :$$
$$: : \text{remainder quadr. } LCRF : \text{remainder quadr. } XCP$$
But
$$\text{quadr. } LCRF = \text{trgl. } ALK \text{ (iii. 2; iii. 11)},$$
and
$$\text{quadr. } XCPD = \text{trgl. } ANX \text{ (iii. 2; iii. 11)};$$

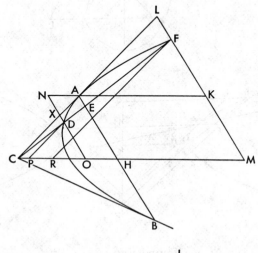

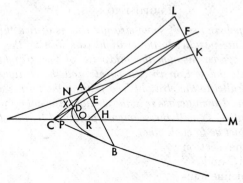

therefore
$$\text{sq. } LM : \text{sq. } XO : : \text{trgl. } ALK : \text{trgl. } ANX.$$
But
$$\text{sq. } LM : \text{sq. } XO : : \text{sq. } FC : \text{sq. } CD,$$
and
$$\text{trgl. } ALK : \text{trgl. } ANX : : \text{sq. } LA : \text{sq. } AX : : \text{sq. } FE : \text{sq. } ED;$$
therefore also
$$\text{sq. } FC : \text{sq. } CD : : \text{sq. } FE : \text{sq. } ED.$$
And therefore
$$FC : CD : : FE : ED.$$

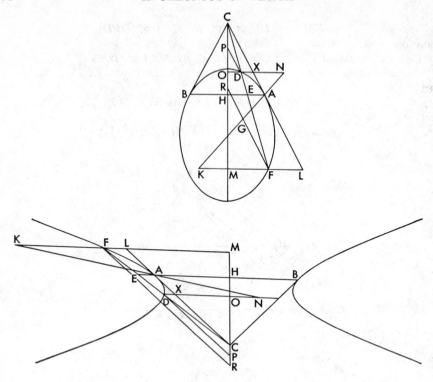

PROPOSITION 38

With the same things being so, if some straight line is drawn through the point of meeting of the tangents parallel to the straight line joining the points of contact, and a straight line drawn through the midpoint of the straight line joining the points of contact cuts the section in two points and the straight line through the point of meeting parallel to the straight line joining the points of contact, then as the whole straight line drawn across is to the straight line cut off outside between the section and the parallel, so will the segments produced by the straight line joined to the points of contact be to each other.

Let there be the section AB and tangents AC and BC and AB the straight line joining the points of contact, and AN and CM diameters; then it is evident that AB has been bisected at E (II. 30, 39).

Let CO be drawn from C parallel to AB, and let $FEDO$ be drawn across through E.

I say that
$$FO : OD :: FE : ED.$$

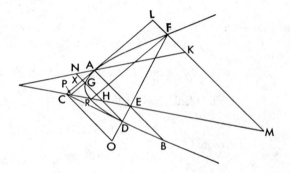

For let *LFKM* and *DHGXN* be
drawn through *F* and *D* parallel to
AB, and through *F* and *G*, *FR* and
GP parallel to *LC*. Then likewise as
before (III. 37) it will be shown that
sq. *LM* : sq. *XH* : : sq. *LA* : sq. *AX*.
And
sq. *LM* : sq. *XH* : : sq. *LC* : sq. *CX* : :
sq. *FO* : sq. *OD*,
and
 sq. *LA* : sq. *AX* : : sq. *FE* : sq. *ED*;
therefore
 sq. *FO* : sq. *OD* : : sq. *FE* : sq. *ED*,
and

$$FO : OD : : FE : ED.$$

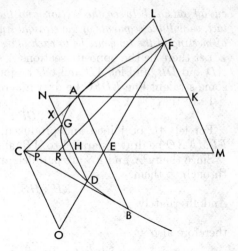

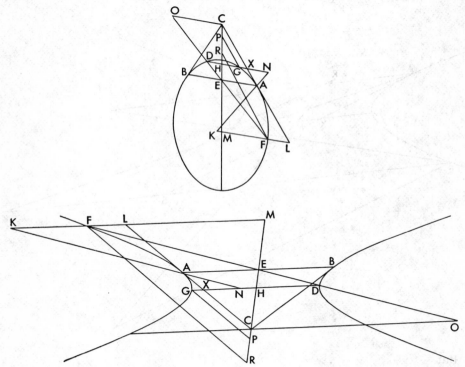

PROPOSITION 39

If two straight lines touching opposite sections meet, and a straight line is pro-
duced through the points of contact, and a straight line drawn from the point of
meeting of the tangents cuts both of the sections and the straight line joining the
points of contact, then as the whole straight line drawn across is to the straight line

cut off outside between the section and the straight line joining the points of contact, so will the segments of the straight line produced by the segments and the point of meeting of the tangents be to each other.

Let there be the opposite sections A and B whose center is C and tangents AD and DB, and let AB and CD be joined and produced, and through D let some straight line $EDFG$ be drawn across.

I say that

$$EG : GF :: ED : DF.$$

For let AC be joined and produced, and through E and F let EHS and $FLMNXO$ be drawn parallel to AB, and parallel to AD, EP and FR.

Since then FX and ES are parallel, and EF, XS, and HM have been drawn through to them,

$$EH : HS :: FM : MX.$$

And alternately

$$EH : FM :: HS : MX;$$

therefore also

$$\text{sq. } EH : \text{sq. } FM :: \text{sq. } HS : \text{sq. } MX.$$

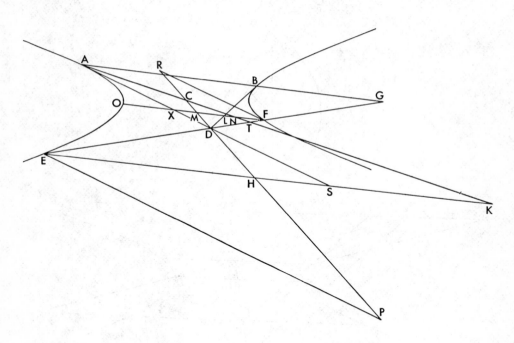

But

$$\text{sq. } EH : \text{sq. } FM :: \text{trgl. } EHP : \text{trgl. } FRM,$$

and

$$\text{sq. } HS : \text{sq. } MX :: \text{trgl. } DHS : \text{trgl. } XMD;$$

therefore also

$$\text{trgl. } EHP : \text{trgl. } FRM :: \text{trgl. } DHS : \text{trgl. } XMD.$$

And

$$\text{trgl. } EHP = \text{trgl. } ASK + \text{trgl. } DHS \text{ (iii. 11)},$$

and
$$\text{trgl. } FRM = \text{trgl. } AXN + \text{trgl. } XMD \text{ (iii. 11)};$$
therefore
$$\text{trgl. } DHS : \text{trgl. } XMD :: \text{trgl. } ASK + \text{trgl. } DHS : \text{trgl. } AXN + \text{trgl. } XMD,$$
and
$$\text{remainder trgl. } ASK : \text{remainder trgl. } ANX :: \text{trgl. } DHS : \text{trgl. } XMD.$$
But
$$\text{trgl. } ASK : \text{trgl. } ANX :: \text{sq. } KA : \text{sq. } AN :: \text{sq. } EG : \text{sq. } FG,^*$$
and
$$\text{trgl. } DHS : \text{trgl. } XMD :: \text{sq. } HD : \text{sq. } DM :: \text{sq. } ED : \text{sq. } DF.$$
Therefore also
$$EG : FG :: ED : DF.$$

PROPOSITION 40

With the same things being so, if a straight line is drawn through the point of meeting of the tangents parallel to the straight line joining the points of contact, and if a straight line drawn from the midpoint of the straight line joining the points of contact cuts both of the sections and the straight line parallel to the straight line joining the points of contact, then as the whole straight line drawn across is to the straight line cut off outside between the parallel and the section, so will the straight line's segments produced by the sections and the straight line joining the points of contact be to each other.

Let there be the opposite sections A and B whose center is C, and tangents AD and DB, and let AB and CDE be joined; therefore
$$AE = EB \text{ (ii. 39).}$$
And from D let FDG be drawn parallel to AB, and from E, LE at random.
   I say that
$$HL : LK :: HE : EK.$$
From H and K let $NMHX$ and KOP be drawn parallel to AB, and HR and KS parallel to AD, and let $XACT$ be drawn through.
   Since then XAU and MAP have been drawn across the parallels XM and KP,
$$XA : AU :: MA : AP.$$
But
$$XA : AU :: HE : EK;$$
and
$$HE : EK :: HN : KO$$
because of the similarity of the triangles HEN and KEO; therefore
$$HN : KO :: MA : AP;$$
therefore also
$$\text{sq. } HN : \text{sq. } KO :: \text{sq. } MA : \text{sq. } AP.$$

---

*For
$$EG : TG :: KA : TA,$$
and
$$TG : TF :: TA : TN,$$
and
$$TG - TF : TG :: TA - TN : TA;$$
therefore *ex aequali*
$$EG : FG :: KA : AN.$$

But

$$\text{sq. } HN : \text{sq. } KO :: \text{trgl. } HRN : \text{trgl. } KSO,$$

and

$$\text{sq. } MA : \text{sq. } AP :: \text{trgl. } XMA : \text{trgl. } AUP;$$

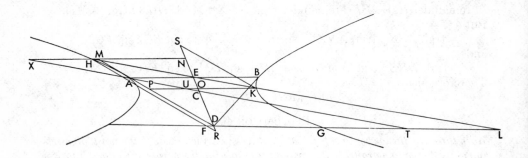

therefore also

$$\text{trgl. } HRN : \text{trgl. } KSO :: \text{trgl. } XMA : \text{trgl. } AUP.$$

And

$$\text{trgl. } HNR = \text{trgl. } XMA + \text{trgl. } MND \text{ (III. 11)},$$

and

$$\text{trgl. } KSO = \text{trgl. } AUP + \text{trgl. } DOP \text{ (III. 11)};$$

therefore also

$$\text{trgl. } XMA + \text{trgl. } MND : \text{trgl. } AUP + \text{trgl. } DOP :: \text{trgl. } XMA : \text{trgl. } AUP;$$

therefore also

$$\text{remainder trgl. } NMD : \text{remainder trgl. } DOP :: \text{whole} : \text{whole.}$$

But

$$\text{trgl. } XMA : \text{trgl. } AUP :: \text{sq. } XA : \text{sq. } AU,$$

and

$$\text{trgl. } NMD : \text{trgl. } DOP :: \text{sq. } MN : \text{sq. } PO;$$

therefore also

$$\text{sq. } MN : \text{sq. } PO :: \text{sq. } XA : \text{sq. } AU.$$

But

$$\text{sq. } MN : \text{sq. } PO :: \text{sq. } ND : \text{sq. } OD,$$

and

$$\text{sq. } XA : \text{sq. } AU :: \text{sq. } HE : \text{sq. } EK,$$

and

$$\text{sq. } ND : \text{sq. } DO :: \text{sq. } HL : \text{sq. } LK;$$

therefore also

$$\text{sq. } HE : \text{sq. } EK :: \text{sq. } HL : \text{sq. } LK.$$

Therefore

$$HE : EK :: HL : LK.$$

PROPOSITION 41

If three straight lines touching a parabola meet each other, they will be cut in the same ratio.

Let there be the parabola ABC, and tangents ADE, EFC and DBF.

I say that

$$CF : FE :: ED : DA :: FB : BD.$$

For let AC be joined and bisected at G.

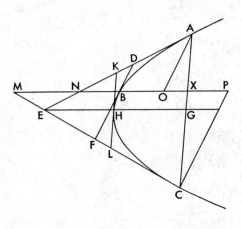

Then it is evident that the straight line from E to G is a diameter of the section. (II. 29).

If then it goes through B, DF is parallel to AC, (II. 5) and will be bisected by EG, and therefore

$$AD = DE \text{ (I. 35)},$$

and

$$CF = FE \text{ (I. 35)},$$

and what was sought is apparent.

Let it not go through B, but through H, and let KHL be drawn through H parallel to AC; therefore it will touch the section at H (I. 32), and because of things already said (I. 35),

$$AK = KE$$

and

$$LC = LE.$$

Let $MNBX$ be drawn through B parallel to EG, and AO and CP through A and C parallel to DF. Since then MB is parallel to EH, MB is a diameter (I. 40; I. 51, end); and DF touches at B; therefore AO and CP have been dropped ordinatewise (II. 5; First Def. I. 4). And since MB is a diameter, and CM a tangent, and CP an ordinate,

$$MB = BP \text{ (I. 35)},$$

and so also

$$MF = FC.$$

And since

$$MF = FC$$

and

$$EL = LC,$$
$$MC : CF :: EC : CL;$$

and alternately

$$MC : EC :: CF : CL.$$

But

$$MC : EC :: XC : CG;$$

therefore also

$$CF : CL :: XC : CG.$$

And

$$CL : EC :: CG : CA;$$

therefore *ex aequali*

$$CA : XC :: EC : CF,$$

and *convertendo*

$$EC : FE :: CA : AX;$$

separando

$$CF : FE :: XC : AX.$$

Again since MB is a diameter and AN a tangent and AO an ordinate,

$$NB = BO \text{ (i. 35)},$$

and

$$ND = DA.$$

And also

$$EK = KA;$$

therefore

$$AE : KA :: NA : DA;$$

alternately

$$AE : NA :: KA : DA.$$

But

$$AE : NA :: GA : AX;$$

therefore also

$$KA : DA :: GA : AX.$$

And also

$$AE : KA :: CA : GA;$$

therefore, *ex aequali*,

$$AE : DA :: CA : AX;$$

separando,

$$ED : DA :: XC : AX.$$

And it was also shown

$$XC : AX :: CF : FE;$$

therefore

$$CF : EF :: ED : DA.$$

Again since

$$XC : AX :: CP : AO,$$

and

$$CP = 2 \; BF,$$

and

$$CM = 2 \; MF,$$

and

$$AO = 2 \; BD,$$

and

$$AN = 2 \; ND,$$

therefore

$$XC : AX :: FB : BD :: CF : FE :: ED : DA.$$

PROPOSITION 42

If in an hyperbola or ellipse or circumference of a circle or opposite sections straight lines are drawn from the vertex of the diameter parallel to an ordinate, and some other straight line at random is drawn tangent, it will cut off from them straight lines containing a rectangle equal to the fourth part of the figure to the same diameter.

For let there be some one of the aforesaid sections, whose diameter is AB, and from A and B let AC and DB be drawn parallel to an ordinate, and let some other straight line CED be tangent at E.

I say that

$$\text{rect. } AC,BD = \text{fourth part of figure to } AB.$$

For let its center be F, and through it let FG be drawn parallel to AC and BD. Since then AC and BD are parallel, and FG is also parallel, therefore it is the diameter conjugate to AB (First Def., I. 6); and so

sq. $FG=$fourth part of figure to AB (Sec. Def. I. 3).

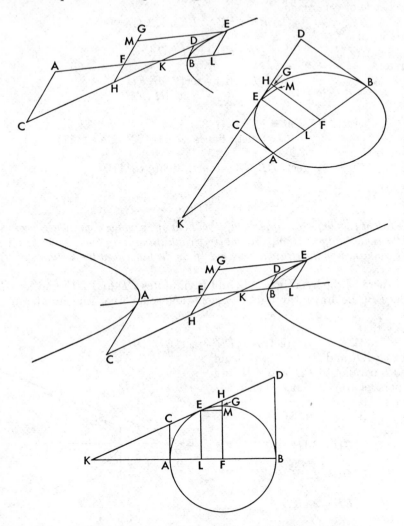

If then FG goes through E in the case of the ellipse and circle,

$$AC=FG=BD \text{ (II. 7),}$$

and it is immediately evident that

rect. $AC,BD=$sq. FG or fourth part of figure to AB.

Then let it not go through it, and let DC and BA produced meet at K, and let EL be drawn through E parallel to AC, and EM parallel to AB. Since then

$$\text{rect. } KF,FL=\text{sq. } AF \text{ (I. 37),}$$
$$KF : AF : : AF : FL,$$

and
$$KA : AL :: KF : AF \text{ or } FB \text{ (Eucl. v. 19)};$$
inversely
$$FB : KF :: AL : KA;$$
componendo or *separando*
$$BK : KF :: LK : KA.$$
Therefore also
$$DB : FH :: EL : CA.$$
Therefore
$$\text{rect. } DB, CA = \text{rect. } FH, EL,$$
$$= \text{rect. } HF, FM.$$
But
$$\text{rect. } HF, FM = \text{sq. } FG \text{ (i. 38)},$$
$$= \text{fourth figure to } AB \text{ (Sec. Def. i. 11)};$$
therefore also
$$\text{rect. } DB, CA = \text{fourth figure to } AB.$$

PROPOSITION 43

If a straight line touch an hyperbola, it will cut off from the asymptotes, beginning with the center of the section, straight lines containing a rectangle equal to the rectangle contained by the straight lines cut off by the tangent at the section's vertex at its axis.

Let there be the hyperbola AB, and asymptotes CD and DE, and axis BD, and let FBG be drawn through B tangent, and some other tangent at random, CAH.

I say that
$$\text{rect. } FD, DG = \text{rect. } CD, DH.$$
For let AK and BL be drawn from A and B parallel to DG, and AM and BN parallel to CD. Since then CAH touches,
$$CA = AH \text{ (ii. 3)};$$
and so
$$CH = 2AH$$
and
$$CD = 2AM$$
and
$$DH = 2AK.$$

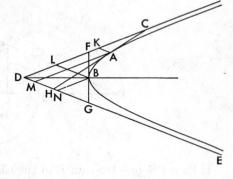

Therefore
$$\text{rect. } CD, DH = 4 \text{ rect. } KA, AM.$$
Then likewise it could be shown
$$\text{rect. } FD, DG = 4 \text{ rect. } LB, BN.$$
But
$$\text{rect. } KA, AM = \text{rect. } LB, BN \text{ (ii. 12).}$$
Therefore also
$$\text{rect. } CD, DH = \text{rect. } FD, DG.$$
Then likewise it could be shown, even if DB were some other diameter and not the axis.

PROPOSITION 44

If two straight lines touching an hyperbola or opposite sections meet the asymp-totes, then the straight lines drawn to the sections will be parallel to the straight line joining the points of contact.

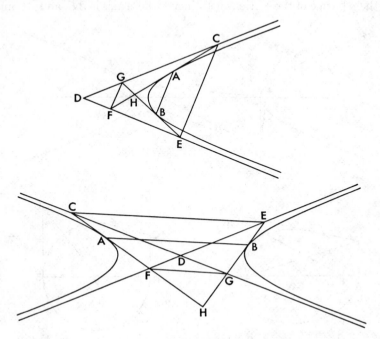

For let there be either the hyperbola or the opposite sections AB, and asymp-totes CD and DE, and tangents $CAHF$ and $EBHG$, and let AB, FG, and CE be joined.

I say that they are parallel.

For since

$$\text{rect. } CD, DF = \text{rect. } GD, DE \text{ (III. 43)},$$

therefore

$$CD : DE : : GD : DF;$$

therefore CE is parallel to FG. And therefore

$$HF : FC : : HG : GE.$$

And

$$FC : AF : : GE : GB;$$

for each is double (II. 3); therefore *ex aequali*

$$HG : GB : : HF : FA.$$

Therefore FG is parallel to AB.

PROPOSITION 45

If in an hyperbola or ellipse or circumference of a circle or opposite sections straight lines are drawn from the vertex of the axis at right angles, and a rectangle equal to the fourth part of the figure is applied to the axis on each side and exceed-

ing by a square figure in the case of the hyperbola and opposite sections, but defi-
cient in the case of the ellipse, and some straight line is drawn tangent to the section
and meeting the perpendicular straight lines, then the straight lines drawn from the
points of meeting to the points produced by the application make right angles at the
aforesaid points.[1]

Let there be one of the sections mentioned whose axis is AB, and AC and BD

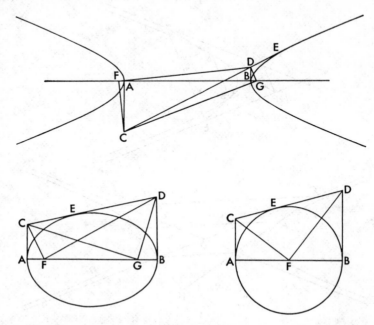

[1]"The points of application" are in modern terminology the foci of the conics. The circle
is seen here as an ellipse whose two foci or focal points coincide with the center. This theory
is, of course, a special application of Euclid VI. 28 and 29, two theorems on which depends
one whole side of Greek geometry.

Apollonius never speaks of the focus of the parabola, but it can be found by analogy with
the ellipse.

Thus in the ellipse above

rect. AF, FB = fourth rect. AB, R

where R is the parameter. Or

rect. $AF, (AB-AF)$ = fourth rect. AB, R

or

AF : fourth $R :: AB : (AB-AF)$.

Then if we consider the ellipse as its axis, AB gets as large as we please; we can think of it as
approaching as near as we please to a parabola with parameter R. The ratio $AB : (AB-AF)$
approaches as near as we please to equality and hence also the ratio
AF : fourth R. At the limit we can think of the ellipse as the parabola,
its axis AB as infinite, and AB as equal to $AB-AF$. Then AF will be
equal to a fourth R. Thus the focus of a parabola will be defined as the
point on its axis at a distance from the vertex equal to one quarter of
the parameter. Then many of the properties of the foci of the ellipse
can be proved analogously for the parabola. Thus in the case of this
proposition, FD will become parallel to CE. Hence any straight line

from the focus of a parabola parallel to a tangent will make a right angle with the straight
line drawn from the focus to the intersection of the tangent and the perpendicular to the
axis at the vertex.

at right angles, and *CED* tangent, and let the rectangle *AF,FB* and the rectangle *AG,GB* equal to the fourth part of the figure be applied on each side (Eucl. vi. 28. 29), as has been said, and let *CF, CG, DF,* and *DG* be joined.

I say that angle *CFD* and angle *CGD* are each a right angle.

For since it has been shown

$$\text{rect. } AC,BD = \text{fourth figure on } AB \text{ (iii. 42)},$$

and since also

$$\text{rect. } AF,FB = \text{fourth figure on } AB,$$

therefore

$$\text{rect. } AC,BD = \text{rect. } AF, FB.$$

Therefore

$$AC : AF : : FB : BD.$$

And the angles at points *A* and *B* are right; therefore

$$\text{angle } ACF = \text{angle } BFD \text{ (Eucl. vi. 6)},$$

and

$$\text{angle } AFC = \text{angle } FDB.$$

And since angle *CAF* is right, therefore

$$\text{angle } ACF + \text{angle } AFC = 1 \text{ rt. angle.}$$

And it has also been shown that

$$\text{angle } ACF = \text{angle } DFB;$$

therefore

$$\text{angle } AFC + \text{angle } DFB = 1 \text{ right angle.}$$

Therefore

$$\text{angle } DFC = 1 \text{ right angle.}$$

Then likewise it could also be shown

$$\text{angle } CGD = 1 \text{ right angle.}$$

Proposition 46

With the same things being so, the straight lines joined make equal angles with the tangents.

For with the same things supposed, I say that

$$\text{angle } ACF = \text{angle } DCG$$

and

$$\text{angle } CDF = \text{angle } BDG.$$

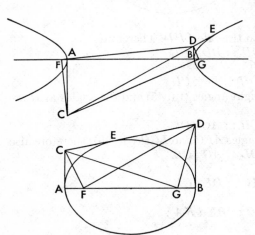

For since it has been shown that both angle *CFD* and angle *CGD* are right angles (iii.45), the circle described about *CD* as a diameter will pass through points *F* and *G*; therefore

$$\text{angle } DCG = \text{angle } DFG;$$

for they are on the same segment of the circle. And it was shown

$$\text{angle } DFG = \text{angle } ACF \text{ (iii. 45)};$$

and so

$$\text{angle } DCG = \text{angle } ACF.$$

And likewise also

$$\text{angle } CDF = \text{angle } BDG.$$

PROPOSITION 47

With the same things being so, the straight line drawn from the point of meeting of the joined straight lines to the point of contact will be perpendicular to the tangent.

For let the same things as before be supposed and let CG and FD meet each other at H, and let CD and BA produced meet at K, and let EH be joined.

I say that EH is perpendicular to CD.

For if not, let HL be drawn from H perpendicular to CD. Since then

$$\text{angle } CDF = \text{angle } GBD \text{ (iii. 46)},$$

and also

$$\text{rt. angle } DBC = \text{rt. angle } DLH,$$

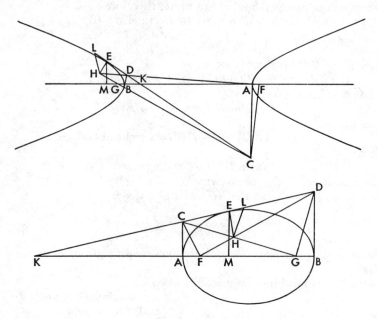

therefore triangle DGB is similar to triangle LHD. Therefore

$$GD : DH :: BD : DL.$$

But

$$GD : DH :: FC : CH$$

because the angles at F and G are right angles (iii. 45) and the angles at H are equal; but

$$FC : CH :: AC : CL$$

because of the similarity of the triangles AFC and LCH (iii. 46); therefore also

$$BD : DL :: AC : CL.$$

Alternately

$$BD : AC :: DL : CL.$$

But

$$BD : AC :: BK : KA :$$

therefore also

$$DL : CL :: BK : KA.$$

Let *EM* be drawn from *E* parallel to *AC*; therefore it will have been dropped ordinatewise to *AB* (ii. 7); and

$$BK : KA :: BM : MA.$$

And

$$BM : MA :: DE : EC;$$

therefore also

$$DL : CL :: DE : EC;$$

and this is absurd. Therefore *HL* is not perpendicular nor is any other straight line except *HE*.*

PROPOSITION 48

With the same things being so, it must be shown that the straight lines drawn from the point of contact to the points produced by the application make equal angles with the tangent.

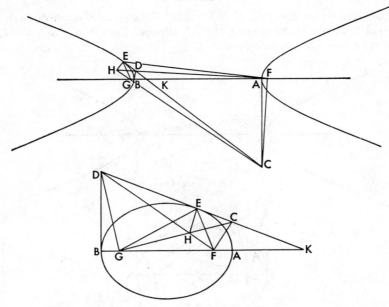

*There is the analogous theorem for the parabola. *FD* becomes a straight line parallel to

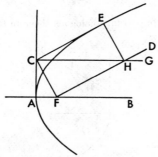

CE and *CG* a straight line parallel to *AB*. Again *HE* is perpendicular to *CE*, and this can be proved rigorously as well as understood by analogy.

For let the same things be supposed, and let EF and EG be joined.

I say that

angle CEF = angle GED.

For since angles DGH and DEH are right angles (III. 45. 47), the circle described about DH as a diameter will pass through the points E and G (Eucl. III. 31); and so

angle DHG = angle DEG (Eucl. III. 21);

for they are in the same segment. Likewise then also

angle CEF = angle CHF.

But

angle CHF = angle DHG;

for they are vertical angles; therefore also

angle CEF = angle DEG.*

PROPOSITION 49

With the same things being so, if from one of the points (of application) a perpendicular is drawn to the tangent, then the straight lines from that point to the ends of the axis make a right angle.

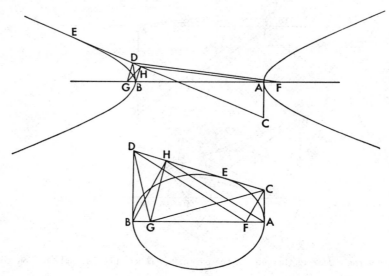

*Here there is another and important analogous theorem for the parabola. EG becomes parallel to AB, and

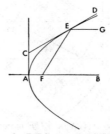

angle DEG = angle CEF.

For let the same things be supposed, and let the perpendicular GH be drawn from G to CD, and let AH and BH be joined.

I say that angle AHB is a right angle.

For since angle DBG is a right angle and also angle DHG, the circle described about DG as a diameter will pass through H and B, and

$$\text{angle } BHG = \text{angle } BDG.$$

But it was shown

$$\text{angle } AGC = \text{angle } BDG \text{ (III. 46)};$$

therefore also

$$\text{angle } BHG = \text{angle } AGC = \text{angle } AHC \text{ (Eucl. III. 21)}.$$

And so also

$$\text{angle } CHG = \text{angle } AHB.$$

But angle CHG is a right angle; therefore also angle AHB is a right angle.

PROPOSITION 50

With the same things being so, if from the center of the section there falls to the tangent a straight line parallel to the straight line drawn through the point of contact and one of the points (of application), then it will be equal to one half the axis.

For let there be the same things as before and let H be the center, and let EF be joined, and let DC and BA meet at K, and through H let HL be drawn parallel to EF.

I say that

$$HL = HB.$$

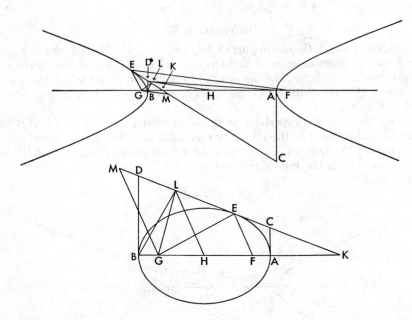

For let EG, AL, LG be joined, and through G let GM be drawn parallel to EF. Since then

$$\text{rect. } AF, FB = \text{rect. } AG, GB \text{ (See III. 45)},$$

therefore
$$AF = GB.$$
But also
$$AH = HB;$$
therefore also
$$FH = HG.$$
And so also
$$EL = LM.$$
And since it was shown (III. 48)
$$\text{angle } CEF = \text{angle } DEG,$$
and
$$\text{angle } CEF = \text{angle } EMG,$$
therefore also
$$\text{angle } EMG = \text{angle } DEG.$$
And therefore
$$EG = GM.$$
But it was also shown
$$EL = LM$$
therefore GL is perpendicular to EM. And so through what was shown before (III. 49) angle ALB is a right angle, and the circle described about AB as a diameter will pass through L. And
$$HA = HB;$$
therefore also, since HL is a radius of the semicircle,
$$HL = HB.$$

PROPOSITION 51

If a rectangle equal to the fourth part of the figure is applied from both sides to the axis of an hyperbola or opposite sections and exceeding by a square figure, and straight lines are deflected from the resulting points of application to either one of the sections, then the greater of the two straight lines exceeds the less by exactly as much as the axis.

For let there be an hyperbola or opposite sections whose axis is AB and center C, and let each of the rectangles AD, DB and AE, EB be equal to the fourth part of the figure, and from points E and D let the straight lines EF and FD be deflected to the line of the section.

I say that
$$EF = FD + AB$$

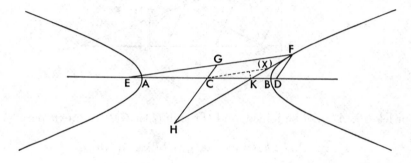

Let FKH be drawn tangent through F, and GCH through C parallel to FD; therefore

$$\text{angle } KHG = \text{angle } KFD;$$

for they are alternate. And

$$\text{angle } KFD = \text{angle } GFH \text{ (iii. 48);}$$

therefore

$$GF = GH.$$

But

$$GF = GE,$$

since also

$$AE = BD$$

and

$$AC = CB$$

and

$$EC = CD;$$

and therefore

$$GH = EG.$$

And so

$$FE = 2GH.$$

And since it has been shown (iii. 50)

$$CH = CB,^*$$

therefore

$$FE = 2(GC \; CB).$$

But

$$FD = 2GC,$$

and

$$AB = 2CB;$$

therefore

$$FE = FD + AB.$$

And so EF is greater than FD by AB.

Proposition 52

If in an ellipse a rectangle equal to the fourth part of the figure is applied from both sides to the major axis and deficient by a square figure, and from the points resulting from the application straight lines are deflected to the line of the section, then they will be equal to the axis.

Let there be an ellipse, whose major axis is AB, and let each of the rectangles AC, CB and AD, DB be equal to the fourth of the figure, and from C and D let the straight lines CE and ED have been deflected to the line of the section.

I say that

$$CE + ED = AB.$$

*For

$$GF = GH,$$

and, by iii. 50, a line $C(X)$ drawn parallel to GF is equal to CB. But also

$$C(X) = CH.$$

Hence

$$CH = CB.$$

Let *FEH* be drawn tangent, and *G* be center and through it let *GKH* be drawn parallel to *CE*. Since then

$$\text{Angle } CEF = \text{angle } HEK \text{ (III. 48)},$$

and

$$\text{angle } CEF = \text{angle } EHK,$$

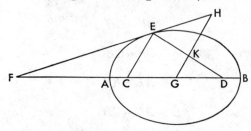

therefore also

$$\text{angle } EHK = \text{angle } HEK.$$

Therefore also

$$HK = KE.$$

And since

$$AG = GB,$$

and

$$AC = DB,$$

therefore also

$$CG = GD;$$

and so also

$$EK = KD.$$

And for this reason

$$ED = 2HK,$$

and

$$EC = 2KG,$$

and

$$ED + EC = 2GH.$$

But also

$$AB = 2GH \text{ (III. 50)};$$

therefore

$$AB = ED + EC.$$

PROPOSITION 53

If in an hyperbola or ellipse or circumference of a circle or opposite sections straight lines are drawn from the vertex of a diameter parallel to an ordinate, and straight lines drawn from the same ends to the same point on the line of the section cut the parallels, then the rectangle contained by the straight lines cut off is equal to the figure on that same diameter.

Let there be one of the aforesaid sections *ABC* whose diameter is *AC*, and let *AD* and *CE* be drawn parallel to an ordinate, and let *ABE* and *CBD* be drawn across.

I say that

$$\text{rect. } AD, EC = \text{figure on } AC.$$

For let *BF* be drawn from *B* parallel to an ordinate.

Therefore

$$\text{rect. } AF, FC : \text{sq. } FB :: \text{transverse side : upright side}$$
$$:: \text{sq. } AC : \text{the figure (I. 21).}$$

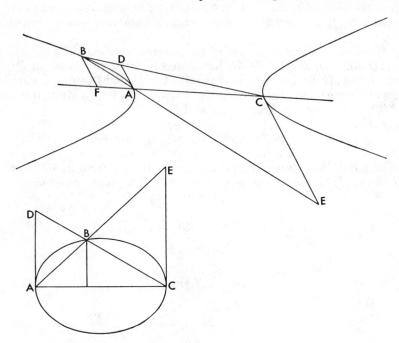

But

$$\text{rect. } AF, FC : \text{sq. } FB \text{ comp. } AF : FB, FC : FB;$$

therefore

$$\text{figure : sq. } AC \text{ comp. } FB : AF, FB : FC.$$

But

$$AF : FB :: AC : CE,$$

and

$$FC : FB :: AC : AD;$$

therefore

$$\text{figure : sq. } AC \text{ comp. } CE : AC, AD : AC.$$

And also

$$\text{rect. } AD, CE : \text{sq. } AC \text{ comp. } CE : AC, AD : AC;$$

therefore

$$\text{figure : sq. } AC :: \text{rect. } AD, CE : \text{sq. } AC.$$

Therefore

$$\text{rect. } AD, CE = \text{figure on } AC.$$

PROPOSITION 54

If two tangents to a section of a cone or to a circumference of a circle meet, and through the points of contact parallels to the tangents are drawn, and from the points of contact, to the same point of the line of the section, straight lines are drawn across cutting the parallels, then the rectangle contained by the straight lines cut off to the square on the straight line joining the points of contact has a ratio compounded of the ratio which the inside segment line joining the point of meeting of the tangents and the midpoint of the straight line joining the points of contact has in square to the remainder, and of the ratio which the rectangle contained by the tangents has to the fourth part of the square on the straight line joining the points of contact.

Let there be a section of a cone or circumference of a circle ABC and tangents AD and CD, and let AC be joined and bisected at E, and let DBE be joined, and let AF be drawn from A parallel to CD, and CG from C parallel to AD, and let some point H on the section be taken, and let the straight lines AH and CH be joined and produced to G and F.

I say that

rect. AF, CG : sq. AC comp. sq. EB : sq. BD, rect. AD, DC.

fourth sq. AC or rect. AE, EC.

For let $KHOXL$ be drawn from H parallel to AC, and from B, MBN parallel to AC; then it is evident that MN is tangent (II. 29, 5, 6). Since then

$$AE = EC,$$

also

$$MB = BN.$$

and

$$KO = OL$$

and

$$HO = OX \text{ (II. 7)}$$

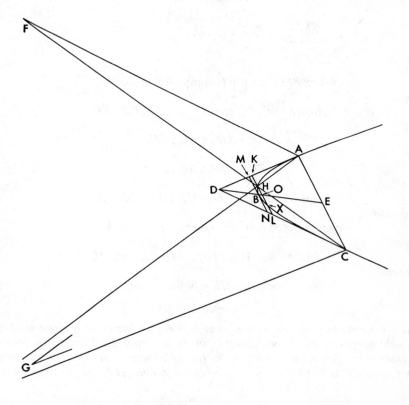

and
$$KH = XL.$$
Since then MB and MA are tangents and KHL has been drawn parallel to MB,

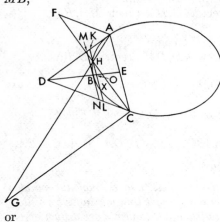

sq. AM : sq. MB : : sq. AK : rect. XK, KH (III. 16)

or

sq. AM : rect. MB, BN : : sq. AK : rect. LH, HK.

And

rect. NC, AM : sq. AM : : rect. LC, AK : sq. AK (Eucl. VI. 2; V, 18);

therefore *ex aequali*

rect. NC, AM : rect. MB, BN : : rect. LC, AK : rect. LH, HK.

But

rect. LC, AK : rect. LH, HK comp.

$$LC : LH, AK : HK$$

or

rect. LC, AK : rect. LH, HK comp. $FA : AC, GC : CA$

which is the same as

$$\text{rect. } GC, FA : \text{sq. } CA.$$

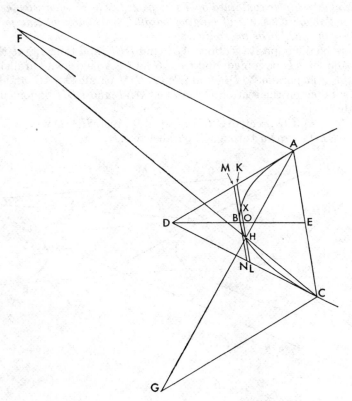

Therefore
rect. NC,AM : rect. MB,BN : : rect. GC,FA : sq. CA.
But, with the rectangle <i>ND,DM</i> taken as a mean,
rect. NC,AM : rect. MB,BN comp.
rect. NC,AM : rect. ND,DM, rect. ND,DM : rect. MB,BN;
therefore
rect. GC,FA : sq. CA comp.
rect. NC,AM : rect. ND,DM, rect. ND,DM : rect. MB,BN.
But
rect. NC,AM : rect. ND,DM : : sq. EB : sq. BD,
and
rect. ND,DM : rect. NB,BM : : rect. CD,DA : rect. CE,EA;
therefore
rect. <i>GC,FA</i> : sq. <i>CA</i> comp. sq. <i>BE</i> : sq. <i>BD</i>, rect. <i>CD,DA</i> : rect. <i>CE,EA</i>.

PROPOSITION 55

*If two straight lines touching opposite sections meet, and through the point of
meeting a straight line is drawn parallel to the straight line joining the points of
contact, and from the points of contact parallels to the tangents are drawn across,
and straight lines are produced from the points of contact to the same point of one
of the sections cutting the parallels, then the rectangle contained by the straight lines
cut off will have to the square on the straight line joining the points of contact the
ratio which the rectangle contained by the tangents has to the square on the straight
line drawn through the point of meeting parallel to the straight line joining the
points of contact, as far as the section.*

Let there be the opposite sections <i>ABC</i> and <i>DEF</i>, and tangents to them <i>AG</i>
and <i>GD</i>, and let <i>AD</i> be joined, and from <i>G</i> let <i>CGE</i> be drawn parallel to <i>AD</i>,
and from <i>A</i>, <i>AM</i> parallel to <i>DG</i>, and from <i>D</i>, <i>DM</i> parallel to <i>AG</i>, and let some
point <i>F</i> be taken on the section <i>DF</i>, and let <i>ANF</i> and <i>FDH</i> be joined.

I say that
sq. CG : rect. AG,GD : : sq. AD : rect. HA,DN.
For let <i>FLKB</i> be drawn through <i>F</i> parallel to <i>AD</i>.

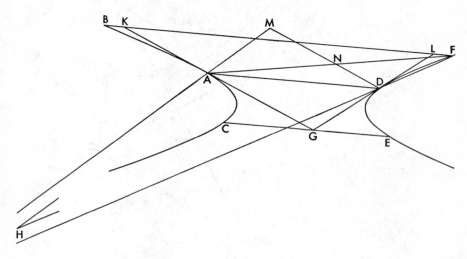

Since then it has been shown that
$$\text{sq. } EG : \text{sq. } GD : : \text{rect. } BL, LF : \text{sq. } DL \text{ (III. 20)},$$
and
$$CG = EG \text{ (II. 38)},$$
and
$$BK = LF \text{ (II. 38)},$$
therefore
$$\text{sq. } CG : \text{sq. } GD : : \text{rect. } KF, FL : \text{sq. } DL.$$
And also
$$\text{sq. } GD : \text{rect. } AG, GD : : \text{sq. } DL : \text{rect. } DL, AK \text{ (Eucl. VI. 2, 1)};$$
therefore *ex aequali*
$$\text{sq. } GC : \text{rect. } AG, GD : : \text{rect. } KF, FL : \text{rect. } DL, AK.$$
But
$$\text{rect. } KF, FL : \text{rect. } DL, AK \text{ comp. } KF : AK, \ FL : DL.$$
But
$$KF : AK : : AD : DN,$$
and
$$FL : DL : : AD : HA;$$
therefore
$$\text{sq. } CG : \text{rect. } AG, GD \text{ comp. } AD : DN, \ AD : HA.$$
And also
$$\text{sq. } AD : \text{rect. } HA, DN \text{ comp. } AD : DN, \ AD : HA;$$
therefore
$$\text{sq. } CG : \text{rect. } AG, GD : : \text{sq. } AD : \text{rect. } HA, DN.$$

Proposition 56

If two straight lines touching one of the opposite sections meet, and parallels to the tangents are drawn through the points of contact, and straight lines cutting the parallels are drawn from the points of contact to the same point of the other section, then the rectangle contained by the straight lines cut off will have to the square on the straight line joining the points of contact the ratio compounded of the ratio which, of the straight line joining the point of meeting and the midpoint, that part between the midpoint and the other section has in square to that part between the same section and the point of meeting, and of the ratio which the rectangle contained by the tangents has to the fourth part of the square on the straight line joining the points of contact.

Let there be the opposite sections AB and CD whose center is O, and tangents $AEFG$ and $BEHK$, and let AB be joined, and bisected at L, and let LE be joined and drawn across to D, and let AM be drawn from A parallel to BE, and BN from B parallel to AE, and let some point C be taken on the section CD, and let CBM and CAN be joined.

I say that
$$\text{rect. } MA, BN : \text{sq. } AB \text{ comp. sq. } LD : \text{sq. } DE, \text{ rect. } AE, EB :$$
$$\text{fourth sq. } AB \text{ or rect. } AL, LB.$$

For let GCK and HDF be drawn from C and D parallel to AB; then it is evident that
$$HD = DF,$$
and
$$KX = XG,$$

and also

$$XC = XP;$$

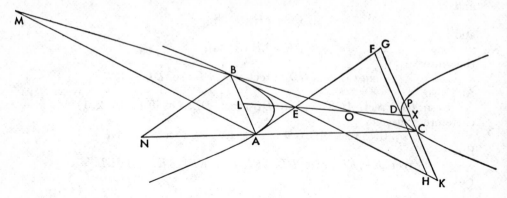

and so also

$$CK = GP.$$

And since AB and DC are opposite sections, and BEH and HD are tangents, and KG is parallel to DH, therefore

      sq. BH : sq. HD : : sq. BK : rect. PK, KC (III. 18, note).

But

             sq. HD = rect. HD, DF,
          rect. PK, KC = rect. KC, CG.

Therefore

      sq. BH : rect. HD, DF : : sq. BK : rect. KC, CG.

And also

      rect. FA, BH : sq. BH : : rect. GA, BK : sq. BK;

therefore *ex aequali*

     rect. FA, BH : rect. HD, DF : : rect. GA, BK : rect. KC, CG.

And, with rectangle HE, EF taken as a mean,

        rect. FA, BH : rect. HD, DF comp.

rect. FA, HB : rect. HE, EF, rect. HE, EF : rect. HD, DF;

and

      rect. FA, HB : rect. HE, EF : : sq. LD : sq. DE,

and

     rect. HE, EF : rect. HD, DF : : rect. AE, EB : rect. AL, LB;

therefore

    rect. GA, BK : rect. KC, CG comp. sq. LD : sq. DE, rect. AF, FB :
                   rect. AL, LB.

And

     rect. GA, BK : rect. KC, CG comp. BK : KC, GA : CG.

But

            $BK : KC : : MA : AB$,

and

            $GA : CG : : BN : AB$;

therefore

       rect. MA, BN : sq. AB comp. $MA : AB, BN : AB$
    comp. sq. LD : sq. DE, rect. AE, EB : rect. AL, LB.

TRANSLATOR'S APPENDIX ON THREE-and
FOUR-LINE LOCI

The three-line locus property of conics is easily deduced for the ellipse, hyperbola, parabola and circle from III. 54; and for the opposite sections from III. 55 and 56. The three-line locus property of conics can be stated thus. Any conic section or circle or pair of opposite sections can be considered as the locus of points whose distances from three given fixed straight lines (the distances being either perpendicular or at a given constant angle to each of the given straight lines, although the constant angle may be different for each of the three straight lines) are such that the square of one of the distances is always in a constant ratio to the rectangle contained by the other two distances.

It is shown in III. 54 that in the case of conic sections and circles

rect. *AF, CG* : sq. *AC* comp. sq. *EB* : sq. *BD*, rect. *AD, DC* : fourth sq. *AC*.

Now if we consider the straight lines *AD, DC*, and *AC* as fixed and given and therefore straight line *DE* fixed and given as bisecting *AC*, then it is evident that the straight lines *AC, EB, BD, AD, DC*, and therefore the squares on them and the rectangles contained by them, are also fixed and given. Then although as the point *H* is taken at different points along the conic, the straight lines *AF* and *CG* change in magnitude, nevertheless the magnitude of the rectangle *AF, CG*, because of the above proportion remains constant.

For let *HX* be drawn parallel to *BE*, and *HY* to *AD*, and *HZ* to *DC*. Then *HX* is the distance from *H* to *AC* at a given angle, and *AY* because of parallels

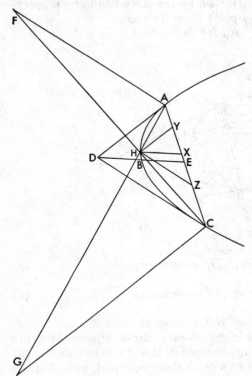

represents the distance from *H* to *AD* at another given angle, and *ZC* represents the distance from *H* to *DC* at another given angle. Then by similar triangles

$$CZ : ZH :: AC : AF,$$
$$AY : YH :: AC : CG;$$

therefore compounding

rect. *CZ, AY* : rect. *ZH, YH* :: sq. *AC* : rect. *AF, CG*.

Now we have seen that the rectangle *AF, CG* is a constant magnitude as the point *H* changes, and the square on *AC* is constant; therefore their ratio is constant. Therefore

rect. *CZ, AY* : rect. *ZH, YH* is a constant ratio . . . . (1)

Again by similar triangles

$$ZH : HX :: CD : DE,$$
$$YH : HX :: AD : DE;$$

therefore compounding

rect. *ZH, YH* : sq. *HX* :: rect. *CD, AD* : sq. *DE*.

But rectangle *CD, AD* and the square on *DE* are constant magnitudes as the point H changes; therefore their ratio is constant. Therefore

$$\text{rect. } ZH, YH : \text{sq. } HX \text{ is a constant ratio} \qquad (2)$$

Compounding (1) and (2), we get a constant ratio, that is

$$\text{rect. } CZ, AY : \text{sq. } HX \text{ is a constant ratio.}$$

In other words, as the point H
changes, the rectangle contained
by the distances from H to two of
the given straight lines (at given
angles to those straight lines) has
a constant ratio to the square on
the distance to the third straight
line (at a given angle to that
straight line). And it can easily be
proved by means of similar triangles
that if any other three angles are
chosen for the distances, than those
chosen here for the demonstration,
then the corresponding ratio will
be constant, although not equal.

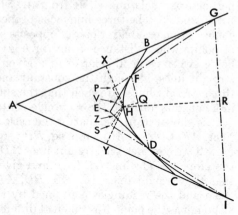

The four-line locus property can be easily deduced from the three-line. If to
any conic section we construct four tangents AG, BE, AI, and EC, and the
straight lines FG, GI, ID, and DF, joining the points of contact; and draw the
distances from any point H on the conic to these straight lines at any given
angles (perpendiculars are convenient), then by the three-line locus property
with respect to triangle FBG for any point H on the conic

$$\text{rect. } HX, HV : \text{sq. } HP \text{ is constant;} \qquad (\alpha)$$

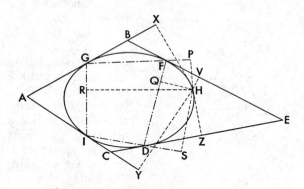

with respect to triangle AIG

$$\text{rect. } HX, HY : \text{sq. } HR \text{ is constant;} \qquad (\beta)$$

with respect to triangle DCI

$$\text{rect. } HY, HZ : \text{sq. } HS \text{ is constant;} \qquad (\gamma)$$

with respect to triangle EFD

$$\text{rect. } HZ, HV : \text{sq. } HQ \text{ is constant} \qquad (\delta)$$

It will be noticed that we have taken in succession a pair of adjacent tangents
and the straight line joining their points of contact. It will also be noticed that
the rectangles in the four ratios present a cyclical arrangement, so that if the

inverse of (α) is compounded with (β), and the inverse of (γ) with (δ), we would have two constant ratios

$$\text{pllpd. } HY, HP, HP : \text{pllpd. } HV, HR, HR, \tag{ϵ}$$
$$\text{pllpd. } HV, HS, HS : \text{pllpd. } HY, HQ, HQ \tag{ζ}$$

Again compounding the first of these with the second, we would have finally

$$\text{rect. } HP, HS : \text{rect. } HQ, HR, \text{ a constant ratio.}$$

And this is the property of the four-line locus, namely the locus of points H such that the rectangle contained by the distances from points H to any two given fixed straight lines FG and ID has to the rectangle contained by the distances from H to two other fixed straight lines, IG, FD, a constant ratio.

The rigorous method of effecting these compoundings is as follows. For inverting (α), by Eucl. XI, 32 we have the constant ratios

sq. HP : rect. HX, HV : : pllpd. HP, HP, HY : pllpd. HX, HV, HY,
rect. HX, HY : sq. HR : : pllpd. HX, HY, HV : pllpd. HR, HR, HV.

Hence, by definition, the ratio (a constant one) compounded of these two is

$$\text{pllpd. } HY, HP, HP : \text{pllpd. } HV, HR, HR.$$

And in the same way we find the constant ratio compounded of the inverse of (γ) and (δ). Now

pllpd. HY, HP, HP : pllpd. HV, HR, HR comp. $HY : HV$, sq. HP : sq. HR,
pllpd. HV, HS, HS : pllpd. HY, HQ, HQ comp. $HV : HY$, sq. HS : sq. HQ.

IF then we take two lines M and N such that

$$HP : HR : : HR : M, \tag{η}$$
$$HS : HQ : : HQ : N, \tag{θ}$$

then

$$\text{sq. } HP : \text{sq. } HR : : HP : M,$$
$$\text{sq. } HS : \text{sq. } HQ : : HS : N.$$

Hence

ratio comp. $HY : HV$, sq. HP : sq. HR ratio comp. $HY : HV$, $HP : \text{M}$
ratio comp. $HV : HY$, sq. HS : sq. HQ ratio comp. $HV : HY$, $HS : N$.

But

rect. HY, HP : rect. HV, M comp. $HY : HV$, $HP : M$,
rect. HV, HS : rect. HY, N comp. $HV : HY$, $HS : N$;

and

pllpd. HY, HP, HS : pllpd. HV, M, HS : : rect. HY, HP : rect. HV, M,
pllpd. HV, HS, M : pllpd. HY, N, M : : rect. HV, HS : rect. HY, N;

and these are constant ratios. Hence compounding, we get the constant ratio

$$\text{pllpd. } HY, HP, HS : \text{pllpd. } HY, N, M,$$

which is the same as the constant ratio

$$\text{rect. } HP, HS : \text{rect. } N, M.$$

Now, taking L and O as some constants,

$$\text{rect. } HP, HS : \text{rect. } N, M : : L : O$$

and

$$\text{rect. } HP, HS : \text{rect. } HR, HQ : : \text{rect. } HR, HQ : \text{rect. } M, N.$$

by compounding (η) and (θ). But equal ratios have equal duplicate ratios (Heath's note to Euclid, VI, 22) and hence

$$\text{rect. } HP, HS : \text{rect. } HR, HQ \text{ is constant.}$$

In the case of opposite sections, it is shown in III. 56

rect. MA, BN : sq. AB comp. sq. LD : sq. DE, rect. AE, EB : fourth sq. AB.

Then it is evident for the same reasons as before that for different points C the magnitudes MA and BN may change, but the rectangle MA, BN is a constant magnitude.

For as before, let CX be drawn parallel to DE, CY to EA, CZ to EB. By similar triangles

$$AY : YC : : AB : BN,$$
$$BZ : ZC : : AB : MA;$$

therefore compounding

$$\text{rect. } AY, BZ : \text{rect. } YC, ZC : : \text{sq. } AB : \text{rect. } MA, BN.$$

Since rectangle MA, BN is constant as C changes, and also the square on AB is constant, therefore

$$\text{rect. } AY, BZ : \text{rect. } YC, ZC \text{ is a constant ratio} \qquad (1)$$

Again by similar triangles

$$ZC : CX : : EB : EL,$$

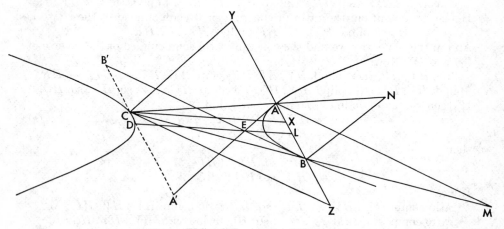

$$YC : CX : : EA : EL,$$

therefore compounding

$$\text{rect. } YC, ZC : \text{sq. } CX : : \text{rect. } EB, EA : \text{sq. } EL.$$

Hence

$$\text{rect. } YC, ZC : \text{sq. } CX \text{ is a constant ratio} \qquad (2)$$

Compounding (1) and (2) we have a constant ratio

$$\text{rect. } AY, BZ : \text{sq. } CX.$$

But AY and BZ are equal to CA' and CB', the distances from C. This is the property of the three-line locus of section C with respect to the straight lines EA and EB tangents to the other section, and EB the straight line joining their points of contact. And so one opposite section is a three line-locus to the tangents to the other of the opposite sections. That it is also a four-line locus could be shown in the same way as before.

Again from III. 55 we can conclude that both of the opposite sections together are a three-line locus to the triangle formed by a tangent to each of the sections and the straight line joining their points of contact. For by III. 55

$$\text{rect. } HA, DN : \text{sq. } AD : : \text{rect. } AG, GD : \text{sq. } CG.$$

Now since the three last terms of this proportion are evidently constants as the point F changes, therefore also, although HA and DN change with F, yet rectangle HA, DN remains constant in magnitude. Then reproducing the figure of

iii. 55, we drop YF parallel to DL, and FZ to KA, and FX to GE, where E is the midpoint of AD. Then by similar triangles

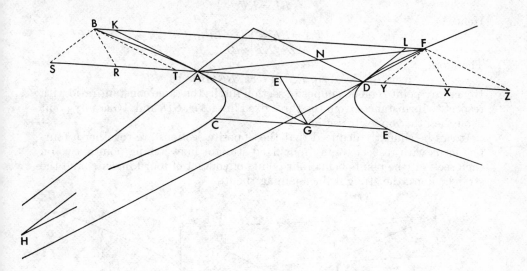

$$YD : FY :: AD : HA,$$
$$AZ : FZ :: AD : DN;$$

therefore compounding

$$\text{rect. } YD, AZ : \text{rect. } FY, FZ :: \text{sq. } AD : \text{rect. } HA, DN.$$

But the last two terms are constant, therefore

$$\text{rect. } YD, AZ : \text{rect. } FY, FZ \text{ is a constant ratio} \qquad (1)$$

Again by similar triangles

$$FY : FX :: DG : EG,$$
$$FZ : FX :: AG : EG;$$

therefore compounding

$$\text{rect. } FY, FZ : \text{sq. } FX :: \text{rect. } DG, AG : \text{rect. } ED, EG.$$

But the last two terms are constant, therefore

$$\text{rect. } FY, FZ : \text{sq. } FX \text{ is a constant ratio} \qquad (2)$$

Compounding (1) and (2), we see that

$$\text{rect. } YD, AZ : \text{sq. } FX \text{ is a constant ratio.}$$

But this is the definition of a three-line locus that the rectangle contained by the distances from any point on the locus to two fixed straight lines have to the square on the distance to a third fixed straight line a constant ratio. But

$$DY = LF,$$
$$AZ = KF,$$

and FX is the distance from F to AD. And so the ratio fulfills the definition.

Furthermore, if we consider B the point of intersection of the straight line KF, drawn parallel to AD, with the other opposite section, and draw BS parallel to FY, BR to FX, and BT to FZ, since they are parallels between parallels,

$$BR = FX,$$
$$KF = AZ,$$
$$TA = BK.$$

But it was shown in the course of III. 55 that

$$BK = LF,$$
$$BL = KF.$$

Hence

$$TA = BK = YD = LF,$$
$$AZ = KF = BL.$$

Therefore

rect. LF, KF : sq. FX : : rect. BK, BL : sq. $BR.$

Hence any point B on one opposite section fulfills the same constant ratio with respect to its distances from the three fixed lines AD, GD, and AG as any point F on the other opposite section.

It can be similarly deduced that the opposite sections are together a four-line locus with respect to any four fixed straight lines joining points, two on each section (the points being four points of contact of four tangents, and the straight lines, the straight lines joining them).

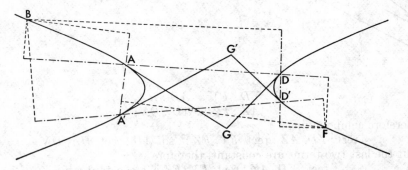

To sum up, a parabola, ellipse, circle, and hyperbola are three-line loci with respect to any two tangents to them and a straight line joining the points of contact. One opposite section is also a three-line locus with respect to any two tangents to the other section together with the straight line joining their points of contact. The two opposite sections together are a three line-locus with respect to two tangents, each to one of the sections, together with the straight line joining their points of contact.

The parabola, ellipse, circle, and hyperbola are four-line loci with respect to any inscribed quadrilateral. One opposite section is also a four-line locus with respect to any quadrilateral inscribed in the other section. The two opposite sections together are a four-line locus to any four straight lines joining four points, two lying on each opposite section.

INTRODUCTION TO ARITHMETIC

BIOGRAPHICAL NOTE
NICOMACHUS, *fl. c.* A.D. 100

NICOMACHUS OF GERASA flourished around the end of the first century of our era. In one of his surviving books, the *Introduction to Harmonics*, he mentions a certain Thrasyllus, presumably Thrasyllus of Mendes, a writer on music, who lived in the reign of Tiberius. Another book by Nicomachus, the *Introduction to Arithmetic*, was translated into Latin by Apuleius under the Antonines. This places the life of Nicomachus somewhere between the middle of the first century and the middle of the second century. Perhaps the fact that Ptolemy, whose recorded astronomical observations were made between A.D. 127 and 151, is not mentioned in the *Introduction to Harmonics* makes it probable that he was not yet famous at the time Nicomachus was writing.

The manuscripts of Nicomachus' books and the scholia call him "of Gerasa." The best known city of that name was in Palestine and was primarily Greek. However, it can hardly be supposed that Nicomachus received all of his philosophical and mathematical education at Gerasa. He probably studied at Alexandria, at this time the center of mathematical studies and of Neo-Pythagoreanism. Jamblichus says of Nicomachus: "The man is great in mathematics, and had as instructors those that were most skilled in the subject."

Nothing is known of the personal life of Nicomachus except what is said or implied in the dedication of the *Introduction to Harmonics* to an unknown lady: "But I must spur on all my zeal, most noble and august lady, since it is you that bid me. . . . And, if the gods are willing, just as soon as I shall have leisure and a rest from my journeyings, I will compile for you a better and more detailed *Introduction* dealing with this very subject . . . and, so that you may the more easily follow the argument, I will take my beginning, say, from the same point as that at which I began your instruction when I was expounding the subject to you."

Nicomachus appears to have been an important member of the Neo-Pythagorean group, though his extant writings would seem to indicate that he was a popularizer and a compiler of manuals and not the head of a school. Besides the *Introduction to Arithmetic* and the *Introduction to Harmonics*, he also wrote a book on the mystical doctrine of number called *Theologoumena Arithmeticae*, which is one of the best sources on Neo-Pythagoreanism; extracts and paraphrases of this work survive in a later anonymous work of the same name and in the *Bibliotheca*, a collection of extracts from ancient works made in the ninth century by Photius, patriarch of Constantinople. Nicomachus also wrote an *Introduction to Geometry* and a *Life of Pythagoras*, which have not survived, and a larger work on music, possibly that promised in the dedication to the *Introduction to Harmonics*, of which we have only fragments. He may have written a book on the interpretation of Plato, though the evidence for it is slight, and also an *Introduction to Astronomy*, thereby completing the quadrivial series.

The success of the *Introduction to Arithmetic* must have been immediate. It

was used as a text book throughout later antiquity and, in the Latin para-
phrase of Boethius, throughout the Middle Ages. It had a host of commentators. In the *Philopatris*, attributed to Lucian, a character says: "You reckon
like Nicomachus." This remark lends itself to more than one interpretation,
but in any case it is evidence of his fame. Nicomachus also appears to have
been considered one of the "golden chain," or succession, of true philosophers;
for Proclus, the fifth century Neo-Platonist, who belonged to that "chain,"
claimed, on the basis of a dream, that he had within him the soul of Nicomachus.

CONTENTS

BOOK ONE

CHAPTER I

[1] The ancients, who under the leadership of Pythagoras first made science systematic, defined philosophy as the love of wisdom. Indeed the name itself means this, and before Pythagoras all who had knowledge were called "wise" indiscriminately—a carpenter, for example, a cobbler, a helmsman, and in a word anyone who was versed in any art or handicraft. Pythagoras, however, restricting the title so as to apply to the knowledge and comprehension of reality, and calling the knowledge of the truth in this the only wisdom, naturally designated the desire and pursuit of this knowledge philosophy, as being desire for wisdom.

[2] He is more worthy of credence than those who have given other definitions, since he makes clear the sense of the term and the thing defined. This "wisdom" he defined as the knowledge, or science, of the truth in real things, conceiving "science" to be a steadfast and firm apprehension of the underlying substance, and "real things" to be those which continue uniformly and the same in the universe and never depart even briefly from their existence; these real things would be things immaterial, by sharing in the substance of which everything else that exists under the same name and is so called is said to be "this particular thing," and exists.

[3] For bodily, material things are, to be sure, forever involved in continuous flow and change—in imitation of the nature and peculiar quality of that eternal matter and substance which has been from the beginning, and which was all changeable and variable throughout. The bodiless things, however, of which we conceive in connection with or together with matter, such as qualities, quantities, configurations, largeness, smallness, equality, relations, actualities, dispositions, places, times, all those things, in a word, whereby the qualities found in each body are comprehended—all these are of themselves immovable and unchangeable, but accidentally they share in and partake of the affections of the body to which they belong.

[4] Now it is with such things that "wisdom" is particularly concerned, but accidentally also with things that share in them, that is, bodies.

CHAPTER II

[1] Those things, however, are immaterial, eternal, without end, and it is their nature to persist ever the same and unchanging, abiding by their own essential being, and each one of them is called real in the proper sense. But what are involved in birth and destruction, growth and diminution, all kinds of change and participation, are seen to vary continually, and while they are called real things, by the same term as the former, so far as they partake of them, they are not actually real by their own nature; for they do not abide for even the shortest moment in the same condition, but are always passing over in all sorts of changes. *[2]* To quote the words of Timaeus, in Plato,[1] "What is that which always is, and has no birth, and what is that which is always becoming but never is? The one is apprehended by the mental processes, with reasoning, and is ever the same; the other can be guessed at by opinion in company with unreasoning sense, a thing which becomes and passes away, but never really is."

[3] Therefore, if we crave for the goal that is worthy and fitting for man, namely, happiness of life[2]—and this is accomplished by philosophy alone and by nothing else, and philosophy, as I said, means for us desire for wisdom, and wisdom the science of the truth in things, and of things some are properly so called, others merely share the name—it is reasonable and most necessary to distinguish and systematize the accidental qualities of things.

[4] Things, then, both those properly so called and those that simply have the name, are some of them unified and continuous, for example, an animal, the universe, a tree, and

---

[1]*Timaeus*, 27.

[2]The word used by Nicomachus, εὐζωΐα, is once employed by Aristotle in the *Ethics*, I. 8. 1098ᵇ 20 ff.

the like, which are properly and peculiarly called "magnitudes"; others are discontinuous, in a side-by-side arrangement, and, as it were, in heaps, which are called "multitudes," a flock, for instance, a people, a heap, a chorus, and the like.

[5] Wisdom, then, must be considered to be the knowledge of these two forms. Since, however, all multitude and magnitude are by their own nature of necessity infinite—for multitude starts from a definite root and never ceases increasing; and magnitude, when division beginning with a limited whole is carried on, cannot bring the dividing process to an end, but proceeds therefore to infinity—and since sciences are always sciences of limited things, and never of infinites, it is accordingly evident that a science dealing either with magnitude, per se, or with multitude, per se, could never be formulated, for each of them is limitless in itself, multitude in the direction of the more, and magnitude in the direction of the less. A science, however, would arise to deal with something separated from each of them, with quantity, set off from multitude, and size, set off from magnitude.

CHAPTER III

[1] Again, to start afresh, since of quantity one kind is viewed by itself, having no relation to anything else, as "even," "odd," "perfect," and the like, and the other is relative to something else and is conceived of together with its relationship to another thing, like "double," "greater," "smaller," "half," "one and one-half times," "one and one-third times," and so forth, it is clear that two scientific methods will lay hold of and deal with the whole investigation of quantity; arithmetic, absolute quantity, and music, relative quantity.[1]

[2] And once more, inasmuch as part of "size" is in a state of rest and stability, and another part in motion and revolution, two other sciences in the same way will accurately treat of "size," geometry the part that abides and is at rest, astronomy that which moves and revolves.

[3] Without the aid of these, then, it is not possible to deal accurately with the forms of being nor to discover the truth in things, knowledge of which is wisdom, and evidently not even to philosophize properly, for "just as painting contributes to the menial arts toward correctness of theory, so in truth lines, numbers, harmonic intervals, and the revolutions of circles

bear aid to the learning of the doctrines of wisdom," says the Pythagorean Androcydes. [4] Likewise Archytas of Tarentum, at the beginning of his treatise On Harmony, says the same thing, in about these words: "It seems to me that they do well to study mathematics, and it is not at all strange that they have correct knowledge about each thing, what it is. For if they knew rightly the nature of the whole, they were also likely to see well what is the nature of the parts. About geometry, indeed, and arithmetic and astronomy, they have handed down to us a clear understanding, and not least also about music. For these seem to be sister sciences; for they deal with sister subjects, the first two forms of being."

[5] Plato, too, at the end of the thirteenth book of the Laws, to which some give the title The Philosopher, because he investigates and defines in it what sort of man the real philosopher should be, in the course of his summary of what had previously been fully set forth and established, adds: "Every diagram, system of numbers, every scheme of harmony, and every law of the movement of the stars, ought to appear one to him who studies rightly; and what we say will properly appear if one studies all things looking to one principle, for there will be seen to be one bond for all these things, and if any one attempts philosophy in any other way he must call on Fortune to assist him. For there is never a path without these; this is the way, these the studies, be they hard or easy; by this course must one go, and not neglect it. The one who has attained all these things in the way I describe, him I for my part call wisest, and this I maintain through thick and thin." [6] For it is clear that these studies are like ladders and bridges that carry our minds from things apprehended by sense and opinion to those comprehended by the mind and understanding, and from those material, physical things, our foster-brethren known to us from childhood, to the things with which we are unacquainted, foreign to our senses, but in their immateriality and eternity more akin to our souls, and above all to the reason which is in our souls.

[7] And likewise in Plato's Republic, when the interlocutor of Socrates appears to bring certain plausible reasons to bear upon the mathematical sciences, to show that they are useful to human life; arithmetic for reckoning, distributions, contributions, exchanges, and partnerships, geometry for sieges, the founding of cities and sanctuaries, and the partition

---

[1] Cf. Aristotle, Met., IV. 15. 1020ᵇ 26.

of land, music for festivals, entertainment, and the worship of the gods, and the doctrine of the spheres, or astronomy, for farming, navigation and other undertakings, revealing beforehand the proper procedure and suitable season, Socrates, reproaching him, says: "You amuse me, because you seem to fear that these are useless studies that I recommend; but that is very difficult, nay, impossible. For the eye of the soul, blinded and buried by other pursuits, is rekindled and aroused again by these and these alone, and it is better that this be saved than thousands of bodily eyes, for by it alone is the truth of the universe beheld."[1]

CHAPTER IV

[1] Which then of these four methods must we first learn? Evidently, the one which naturally exists before them all, is superior and takes the place of origin and root and, as it were, of mother to the others. [2] And this is arithmetic,[2] not solely because we said that it existed before all the others in the mind of the creating God like some universal and exemplary plan, relying upon which as a design and archetypal example the creator of the universe sets in order his material creations and makes them attain to their proper ends; but also because it is naturally prior in birth, inasmuch as it abolishes other sciences with itself,[3] but is not abolished together with them. For example, "animal" is naturally antecedent to "man," for abolish "animal" and "man" is abolished; but if "man" be abolished, it no longer follows that "animal" is abolished at the same time. And again, "man" is antecedent to "schoolteacher"; for if "man" does not exist, neither does "schoolteacher," but if "schoolteacher" is nonexistent, it is still possible for "man" to be. Thus since it has the property of abolishing the other ideas with itself, it is likewise the older.

[3] Conversely, that is called younger and posterior which implies the other thing with itself,[4] but is not implied by it, like "musician," for this always implies "man." Again, take "horse"; "animal" is always implied along with "horse," but not the reverse; for if "animal" exists, it is not necessary that "horse" should exist, nor if "man" exists, must "musician" also be implied.

[1]*Republic*, 527 ff.
[2]Plato, *Rep.*, 522.
[3]Cf. below II. 22. 3. Cf. Aristotle, *Met.*, 1019[a] 1 ff.
[4]Cf. Aristotle, e. g., *Top.*, VI. 6. 144[b] 17: also *Top.*, II. 4. 111[a] 25 ff.

[4] So it is with the foregoing sciences; if geometry exists, arithmetic must also needs be implied, for it is with the help of this latter that we can speak of triangle, quadrilateral, octahedron, icosahedron, double, eightfold, or one and one-half times, or anything else of the sort which is used as a term by geometry, and such things cannot be conceived of without the numbers that are implied with each one. For how can "triple" exist, or be spoken of, unless the number 3 exists beforehand, or "eightfold" without 8? But on the contrary 3, 4, and the rest might be without the figures existing to which they give names. [5] Hence arithmetic abolishes geometry along with itself, but is not abolished by it, and while it is implied by geometry, it does not itself imply geometry.

CHAPTER V

[1] And once more is this true in the case of music; not only because the absolute is prior to the relative, as "great" to "greater" and "rich" to "richer" and "man" to "father," but also because the musical harmonies, diatessaron, diapente, and diapason, are named for numbers; similarly all of their harmonic ratios are arithmetical ones, for the diatessaron is the ratio of 4:3, the diapente that of 3:2, and the diapason the double ratio; and the most perfect, the didiapason, is the quadruple ratio.

[2] More evidently still astronomy attains through arithmetic the investigations that pertain to it, not alone because it is later than geometry[5] in origin—for motion naturally comes after rest—nor because the motions of the stars have a perfectly melodious harmony, but also because risings, settings, progressions, retrogressions, increases, and all sorts of phases are governed by numerical cycles and quantities.

[3] So then we have rightly undertaken first the systematic treatment of this, as the science naturally prior, more honorable, and more venerable, and, as it were, mother and nurse of the rest; and here we will take our start for the sake of clearness.

CHAPTER VI

[1] All that has by nature with systematic method been arranged in the universe seems both in part and as a whole to have been determined and ordered in accordance with number, by the forethought and the mind of him that

[5]Cf. Plato, *Rep.*, 528.

created all things; for the pattern was fixed, like a preliminary sketch, by the domination of number preëxistent in the mind of the world-creating God, number conceptual only and immaterial in every way, but at the same time the true and the eternal essence, so that with reference to it, as to an artistic plan, should be created all these things, time, motion, the heavens, the stars, all sorts of revolutions.

[2] It must needs be, then, that scientific number, being set over such things as these, should be harmoniously constituted, in accordance with itself; not by any other but by itself. [3] Everything that is harmoniously constituted is knit together out of opposites and, of course, out of real things; for neither can non-existent things be set in harmony, nor can things that exist, but are like one another, nor yet things that are different, but have no relation one to another. It remains, accordingly, that those things out of which a harmony is made are both real, different, and things with some relation to one another.

[4] Of such things, therefore, scientific number consists; for the most fundamental species in it are two, embracing the essence of quantity, different from one another and not of a wholly different genus, odd and even, and they are reciprocally woven into harmony with each other, inseparably and uniformly, by a wonderful and divine Nature, as straightway we shall see.

CHAPTER VII

[1] Number is limited multitude or a combination of units or a flow of quantity made up of units; and the first division of number is even and odd.

[2] The even[1] is that which can be divided into two equal parts without a unit intervening in the middle; and the odd is that which cannot be divided into two equal parts because of the aforesaid intervention of a unit.

[3] Now this is the definition after the ordinary conception; by the Pythagorean doctrine, however, the even number is that which admits of division into the greatest and the smallest parts at the same operation, greatest in size and smallest in quantity, in accordance with the natural contrariety of these two genera; and the odd is that which does not allow this to be done to it, but is divided into two unequal parts.

[4] In still another way, by the ancient definition, the even is that which can be divided alike into two equal and two unequal parts, except that the dyad, which is its elementary form, admits but one division, that into equal parts; and in any division whatsoever it brings to light only one species of number, however it may be divided, independent of the other. The odd is a number which in any division whatsoever, which necessarily is a division into unequal parts, shows both the two species of number together, never without intermixture one with another, but always in one another's company.

[5] By the definition in terms of each other, the odd is that which differs by a unit from the even in either direction, that is, toward the greater or the less, and the even is that which differs by a unit in either direction from the odd, that is, is greater by a unit or less by a unit.

CHAPTER VIII

[1] Every number is at once half the sum of the two on either side of itself, and similarly half the sum of those next but one in either direction, and of those next beyond them, and so on as far as it is possible to go. [2] Unity alone, because it does not have two numbers on either side of it, is half merely of the adjoining number; hence unity is the natural starting point of all number.

[3] By subdivision of the even, there are the even-times even, the odd-times even, and the even-times odd. The even-times even and the even-times odd are opposite to one another, like extremes, and the odd-times even is common to them both like a mean term.

[4] Now the even-times even[2] is a number which is itself capable of being divided into two equal parts, in accordance with the properties of its genus, and with each of its parts similarly capable of division, and again in the same way each of their parts divisible into two equals until the division of the successive subdivisions reaches the naturally indivisible unit. [5] Take for example 64; one half of this is 32, and of this 16, and of this the half is 8, and of this 4, and of this 2, and then finally unity is half of the latter, and this is naturally indivisible and will not admit of a half.

[6] It is a property of the even-times even that, whatever part of it be taken, it is always

[1]Cf. Euclid, VII, Def. 6.

[2]Euclid's definition is: "The even-times even number is that which is measured by an even number an even number of times" *Elements*, VII, Def. 8.

even-times even in designation, and at the same time, by the quantity of the units in it, even-times even in value; and that neither of these two things will ever share in the other class. [7] Doubtless it is because of this that it is called even-times even, because it is itself even and always has its parts, and the parts of its parts down to unity, even both in name and in value; in other words, every part that it has is even-times even in name and even-times even in value.

[8] There is a method of producing the even-times even, so that none will escape, but all successively fall under it, if you do as follows: [9] As you proceed from unity, as from a root, by the double ratio to infinity, as many terms as there are will all be even-times even, and it is impossible to find others besides these; for instance, 1, 2, 4, 8, 16, 32, 64, 128, 256, 512. . . .

[10] Now each of the numbers set forth is produced by the double ratio, beginning with unity, and is in every respect even-times even, and every part that it may be found to have is always named from some one of the numbers before it in the series, and the sum of units in this part is the same as one of the numbers before it, by a system of mutual correspondence, indeed, and interchange. If there is an even number of terms of the double ratio from unity, not one mean term can be found, but always two, from which the correspondence and interchange of factors and values, values and factors, will proceed in order, going first to the two on either side of the means, then to the next on either side, until it comes to the extreme terms, so that the whole will correspond in value to unity and unity to the whole. For example, if we set down 128 as the largest term, the number of terms will be even, for there are eight in all up to this number; and they will not have one mean term, for this is impossible with an even number, but of necessity two, 8 and 16. These will correspond to each other as factors; for of the whole, 128, 16 is one eighth and conversely 8 is one sixteenth. Thence proceeding in either direction, we find that 32 is one fourth, and 4 one thirty-second, and again 64 is one half, and 2 one sixty-fourth, and finally at the extremes unity is one one-hundred-twenty-eighth, and conversely 128 is the whole, to correspond with unity.

[11] If, however, the series consists of an odd number of terms, seven for example, and we deal with 64, there will be of necessity one mean term in accordance with the nature of the odd; the mean term will correspond to it-self because it has no partner; and those on either side of it in turn will correspond to one another until this correspondence ends in the extremes. Unity, for example, will be one sixty-fourth, and 64 the whole, corresponding to unity; 32 is one half, and 2 one thirty-second; 16 is one fourth, and 4 one sixteenth; and 8 the eighth part, with nothing else to correspond to it.

[12] It is the property of all these terms when they are added together successively to be equal to the next in the series, lacking one unit, so that of necessity their summation in any way whatsoever will be an odd number, for that which fails by a unit of being equal to an even number is odd. [13] This observation will be of use to us very shortly in the construction of perfect numbers.[1] But to take an example, the terms from unity preceding 256 in the series, when added together, are within 1 of equaling 256, and all the terms before 128, the term immediately preceding, are similarly equal to 128 save for one unit; and to the next terms the sums of those below them are similarly related. Thus unity itself[2] is within one unit of equaling the next term, which is 2, and these two together fail by 1 of equaling the next, and the three together are within 1 of the next in order, and you will find that this goes on without interruption to infinity.

[14] This too it is very needful to recall: If the number of terms of the even-times even series dealt with is even, the product of the extremes will always be equal to the product of the means; if there is an odd number of terms, the product of the extremes will be equal to the square of the mean. For, in the case of an even number of terms, 1 times 128 is equal to 8 times 16 and further to 2 times 64 and again to 4 times 32, and this is so in every case; and with an odd number of terms, 1 times 64 equals 2 times 32, and this equals 4 times 16, and this again equals 8 times 8, the mean term alone multiplied by itself.

CHAPTER IX

[1] The even-times odd number is one which is by its genus itself even, but is specifically opposed to the aforesaid even-times even. It is a number of which, though it admits of the division into two equal halves, after the fashion of the genus common to it and the even-times even, the halves are not immediately divisible

[1]See Chapter 16.
[2]Cf. on I. 8. 7.

into two equals, for example, 6, 10, 14, 18, 22, 26, and the like; for after these have been divided their halves are found to be indivisible.

[2] It is the property of the even-times odd that whatever factor it may be discovered to have is opposite in name to its value, and that the quantity of every part is opposite in value to its name, and that the numerical value of its part never by any means is of the same genus as its name. To take a single example, the number 18, its half, with an even name, is 9, odd in value; its third part, again, with an odd designation, is 6, even in value; conversely, the sixth part is 3 and the ninth part 2; and in other numbers the same peculiarity will be found.

[3] It is possibly for this reason that it received such a name, that is, because, although it is even, its halves are at once odd.

[4] This number is produced from the series beginning with unity, with a difference of 2, namely, the odd numbers, set forth in proper order as far as you like and then multiplied by 2. The numbers produced would be, in order, these: 6, 10, 14, 18, 22, 26, 30, and so on, as far as you care to proceed. The greater terms always differ by 4 from the next smaller ones, the reason for which is that their original basic forms, the odd numbers, exceed one another by 2 and were multiplied by 2 to make this series, and 2 times 2 makes 4.

[5] Accordingly, in the natural series of numbers the even-times odd numbers will be found fifth from one another, exceeding one another by a difference of 4, passing over three terms, and produced by the multiplication of the odd numbers by 2.

[6] They are said to be opposite in properties to the even-times even, because of these the greatest extreme term alone is divisible, while of these former the smallest only proved to be indivisible; and in particular because in the former case the reciprocal arrangement of parts[1] from extremes to mean term or terms makes the product of the former equal to the square or product of the latter; but in this case by the same correspondence and comparison the mean term is one half the sum of the extremes, or if there should be two means, their sum equals that of the two extremes.

CHAPTER X

[1] The odd-times even number is the one which displays the third form of the even, belonging in common to both the previously mentioned species like a single mean between two extremes, for in one respect it resembles the even-times even, and in another the even-times odd, and that property wherein it varies from the one it shares with the other, and by that property which it shares with the one it differs from the other.

[2] The odd-times even number is an even number which can be divided into two equal parts, whose parts also can so be divided, and sometimes even the parts of its parts, but it cannot carry the division of its parts as far as unity. Such numbers are 24, 28, 40; for each of these has its own half and indeed the half of its half, and sometimes one is found among them that will allow the halving to be carried even farther among its parts. There is none, however, that will have its parts divisible into halves as far as the naturally indivisible unit.

[3] Now in admitting more than one division, the odd-times even is like the even-times even and unlike the even-times odd; but in that its subdivision never ends with unity, it is like the even-times odd and unlike the even-times even.

[4] It alone has at once the proper qualities of each of the former two,[2] and then again properties which belong to neither of them; for of them one had only the highest term divisible, and the other only the smallest indivisible, but this neither; for it is observed to have more divisions than one in the greater term, and more than one indivisible in the lesser.

[5] Furthermore, there are in it certain parts whose names are not opposed to their values nor of the opposite genus,[3] after the fashion of the even-times even; and there are also always other parts of a name opposite and contrary in kind to their values, after the fashion of the even-times odd. For example, in 24, there are parts not opposed in name to their values, the fourth part, 6, the half, 12, the sixth, 4, and the twelfth, 2; but the third part, 8, the eighth, 3, and the twenty-fourth, 1, are opposed; and so it is with the rest.

[6] This number is produced by a somewhat complicated method, and shows, after a fashion, even in its manner of production, that it is a mixture of both other kinds. For whereas the even-times even is made from even numbers, the doubles from unity to infinity, and the even-times odd from the odd numbers from 3, progressing to infinity, this must be woven

---

[1]Cf. I. 8. 10.

[2]Cf. I. 9. 6.
[3]Cf. I. 8. 7; 9. 2.

together out of both classes, as being common to both. *[7]* Let us then set forth the odd numbers from 3 by themselves in due order in one series:

3, 5, 7, 9, 11, 13, 15, 17, 19, . . .

and the even-times even, beginning with 4, again one after another in a second series after their own order:

4, 8, 16, 32, 64, 128, 256, . . .

as far as you please. *[8]* Now multiply by the first number of either series—it makes no difference which—from the beginning and in order all those in the remaining series and note down the resulting numbers; then again multiply by the second number of the same series the same numbers once more, as far as you can, and write down the results; then with the third number again multiply the same terms anew, and however far you go you will get nothing but the odd-times even numbers.

[9] For the sake of illustration let us use the first term of the series of odd numbers and multiply by it all the terms in the second series in order, thus: 3×4, 3×8, 3×16, 3×32, and so on to infinity. The results will be 12, 24, 48, 96, which we must note down in one line. Then taking a new start do the same thing with the second number, 5×4, 5×8, 5×16, 5×32. The results will be 20, 40, 80, 160. Then do the same thing once more with 7, the third number, 7×4, 7×8, 7×16, 7×32. The results are 28, 56,

term, or their product, should there be two. Thus this one species has the peculiar properties of them both, because it is a natural mixture of them both.

CHAPTER XI

[1] Again, while the odd is distinguished over against the even in classification and has nothing in common with it, since the latter is divisible into equal halves and the former is not thus divisible, nevertheless there are found three species of the odd,[1] differing from one another, of which the first is called the prime and incomposite,[2] that which is opposed to it the secondary and composite, and that which is midway between both of these and is viewed as a mean among extremes, namely, the variety which, in itself, is secondary and composite, but relatively is prime and incomposite.

[2] Now the first species, the prime and incomposite, is found whenever an odd number admits of no other factor save the one with the number itself as denominator, which is always unity; for example, 3, 5, 7, 11, 13, 17, 19, 23, 29, 31. None of these numbers will by any chance be found to have a fractional part with a denominator different from the number itself, but only the one with this as denominator, and this part will be unity in each case; for 3 has only a third part, which has the same denominator as the number and is of course uni-

Odd numbers		3	5	7	9	11	13	15
Even-times even		4	8	16	32	64	128	256
Odd-times even numbers,	*Breadth*	12	24	48	96	192	384	768
		20	40	80	160	320	640	1280
		28	56	112	224	448	896	1792
		36	72	144	288	576	1152	2304
		44	88	176	352	704	1408	2816

Length

112, 224; and in the same way as far as you care to go, you will get similar results.

[10] Now when you arrange the products of multiplication by each term in its proper line, making the lines parallel, in marvelous fashion there will appear along the breadth of the table the peculiar property of the even-times odd, that the mean term is always half the sum of the extremes, if there should be one mean, and the sum of the means equals the sum of the extremes if two. But along the length of the table the property of the even-times even will appear; for the product of the extremes is equal to the square of the mean, should there be one mean

ty, 5 a fifth, 7 a seventh, and 11 only an eleventh part, and in all of them these parts are unity.

[3] It has received this name because it can be measured only by the number which is first and common to all, unity, and by no other; moreover, because it is produced by no other number combined with itself save unity alone; for 5 is 5×1, and 7 is 7×1, and the others in accordance with their own quantity. To be sure, when they are combined with themselves, other

[1]Cf. Euclid, *Elem.*, VII, Deff., 11-14.
[2]Cf. Euclid, *Elem.*, VII, Def. 11; Aristotle, *Top.*, VIII. 2. 157ᵃ 39.

numbers might be produced, originating from them as from a fountain and a root, wherefore they are called "prime," because they exist beforehand as the beginnings of the others. For every origin is elementary and incomposite, into which everything is resolved and out of which everything is made, but the origin itself cannot be resolved into anything or constituted out of anything.

CHAPTER XII

[1] The secondary, composite number[1] is an odd number, indeed, because it is distinguished as a member of this same class, but it has no elementary quality, for it gets its origin by the combination of something else. For this reason it is characteristic of the secondary number to have, in addition to the fractional part with the number itself as denominator, yet another part or parts with different denominators, the former always, as in all cases, unity, the latter never unity, but always either that number or those numbers by the combination of which it was produced. For example, 9, 15, 21, 25, 27, 33, 35, 39; each one of these is measured by unity, as other numbers are, and like them has a fractional part with the same denominator as the number itself, by the nature of the class common to them all; but by exception and more peculiarly they also employ a part, or parts, with a different denominator; 9, in addition to the ninth part, has a third part besides; 15 a third and a fifth besides a fifteenth; 21 a seventh and a third besides a twenty-first, and 25, in addition to the twenty-fifth, which has as a denominator 25 itself, also a fifth, with a different denominator.

[2] It is called secondary, then, because it can employ yet another measure along with unity, and because it is not elementary, but is produced by some other number combined with itself or with something else; in the case of 9, 3; in the case of 15, 5 or, by Zeus, 3; and those following in the same fashion. And it is called composite for this, or some such, reason: that it may be resolved into those numbers out of which it was made, since it can also be measured by them. For nothing that can be broken down is incomposite, but by all means composite.

CHAPTER XIII

[1] Now while these two species of the odd are opposed to each other a third one[2] is con-

ceived of between them, deriving, as it were, its specific form from them both, namely the number which is in itself secondary and composite, but relatively to another number is prime and incomposite. This exists when a number, in addition to the common measure, unity, is measured by some other number and is therefore able to admit of a fractional part, or parts, with denominator other than the number itself, as well as the one with itself as denominator. When this is compared with another number of similar properties, it is found that it cannot be measured by a measure common to the other, nor does it have a fractional part with the same denominator as those in the other. As an illustration, let 9 be compared with 25. Each in itself is secondary and composite, but relatively to each other they have only unity as a common measure, and no factors in them have the same denominator, for the third part in the former does not exist in the latter nor is the fifth part in the latter found in the former.

[2] The production of these numbers is called by Eratosthenes the "sieve," because we take the odd numbers mingled together and indiscriminate and out of them by this method of production separate, as by a kind of instrument or sieve, the prime and incomposite by themselves, and the secondary and composite by themselves, and find the mixed class by themselves.

[3] The method of the "sieve" is as follows. I set forth all the odd numbers in order, beginning with 3, in as long a series as possible, and then starting with the first I observe what ones it can measure, and I find that it can measure the terms two places apart, as far as we care to proceed. And I find that it measures not as it chances and at random, but that it will measure the first one, that is, the one two places removed, by the quantity of the one that stands first in the series, that is, by its own quantity, for it measures it 3 times; and the one two places from this by the quantity of the second in order, for this it will measure 5 times; and again the one two places farther on by the quantity of the third in order, or 7 times, and the one two places still farther on by the quantity of the fourth in order, or 9 times, and so *ad infinitum* in the same way.

[4] Then taking a fresh start I come to the second number and observe what it can measure, and find that it measures all the terms four places apart, the first by the quantity of the first in order, or 3 times; the second by that of the second, or 5 times; the third by that of

---

[1]Cf. Euclid, *Elements*. VII, Def. 14.
[2]Cf. Euclid, *Elements*, VII, Def. 13.

the third, or 7 times; and in this order *ad infinitum*.

[5] Again, as before, the third term 7, taking over the measuring function, will measure terms six places apart, and the first by the quantity of 3, the first of the series, the second by that of 5, for this is the second number, and the third by that of 7, for this has the third position in the series.

[6] And analogously throughout, this process will go on without interruption, so that the numbers will succeed to the measuring function in accordance with their fixed position in the series; the interval separating terms measured is determined by the orderly progress of the even numbers from 2 to infinity, or by the doubling of the position in the series occupied by the measuring term, and the number of times a term is measured is fixed by the orderly advance of the odd numbers in series from 3.

[7] Now if you mark the numbers with certain signs, you will find that the terms which succeed one another in the measuring function neither measure all the same number—and sometimes not even two will measure the same one—nor do absolutely all of the numbers set forth submit themselves to a measure, but some entirely avoid being measured by any number whatsoever, some are measured by one only, and some by two or even more. [8] Now these that are not measured at all, but avoid it, are primes and incomposites, sifted out as it were by a sieve; those measured by only one measure in accordance with its own quantity will have but one fractional part with denominator different from the number itself, in addition to the part with the same denominator; and those which are measured by one measure only, but in accordance with the quantity of some other number than the measure and not its own, or are measured by two measures at the same time, will have several fractional parts with other denominators besides the one with the same as the number itself; these will be secondary and composite.

[9] The third division, the one common to both the former, which is in itself secondary and composite but primary and incomposite in relation to another, will consist of the numbers produced when some prime and incomposite number measures them in accordance with its own quantity, if one thus produced be compared to another of similar origin. For example, if 9, which was produced by 3 measuring by its own quantity, for it is 3 times 3, be compared with 25, which was produced from 5 measuring by

its own quantity, for it is 5 times 5, these numbers have no common measure except unity.

[10] We shall now investigate how we may have a method[1] of discerning whether numbers are prime and incomposite, or secondary and composite, relatively to each other, since of the former unity is the common measure, but of the latter some other number also besides unity; and what this number is.

[11] Suppose there be given us two odd numbers and some one sets the problem and directs us to determine whether they are prime and incomposite relatively to each other or secondary and composite, and if they are secondary and composite, what number is their common measure. We must compare the given numbers and subtract the smaller from the larger as many times as possible; then after this subtraction, subtract in turn from the other as many times as possible; for this changing about and subtraction from one and the other in turn will necessarily end either in unity or in some one and the same number, which will necessarily be odd. [12] Now when the subtractions terminate in unity they show that the numbers are prime and incomposite relatively to each other; and when they end in some other number, odd in quantity and twice produced, then say that they are secondary and composite relatively to each other, and that their common measure is that very number which twice appears.

For example, if the given numbers were 23 and 45, subtract 23 from 45, and 22 will be the remainder; subtracting this from 23, the remainder is 1, subtracting this from 22 as many times as possible you will end with unity. Hence they are prime and incomposite to one another, and unity, which is the remainder, is their common measure.

[13] But if one should propose other numbers, 21 and 49, I subtract the smaller from the larger and 28 is the remainder. Then again I subtract the same 21 from this, for it can be done, and the remainder is 7. This I subtract in turn from 21 and 14 remains; from which I subtract 7 again, for it is possible, and 7 will remain. But it is not possible to subtract 7 from 7; hence the termination of the process with a repeated 7 has been brought about, and you may declare the original numbers 21 and 49 secondary and composite relatively to each

[1] This mode of determining common factors is found in Euclid (VII. 1; X. 2) and is commonly termed the Euclidean method of finding the greatest common divisor of numbers.

other, and 7 their common measure in addition to the universal unit.

CHAPTER XIV

[1] To make again a fresh start, of the simple even numbers, some are superabundant, some deficient, like extremes set over against each other, and some are intermediary between them and are called perfect. *[2]* Those which are said to be opposites to one another, the superabundant and deficient, are distinguished from one another in the relation of inequality[1] in the directions of the greater and the less; for apart from these no other form of inequality could be conceived, nor could evil,[2] disease, disproportion, unseemliness, nor any such thing, save in terms of excess or deficiency. For in the realm of the greater[3] there arise excesses, overreaching, and superabundance, and in the less need, deficiency, privation, and lack; but in that which lies between the greater and the less, namely, the equal, are virtues, wealth, moderation, propriety, beauty, and the like, to which the aforesaid form of number, the perfect, is most akin.

[3] Now the superabundant number is one which has, over and above the factors which belong to it and fall to its share, others in addition, just as if an animal should be created with too many parts or limbs, with ten tongues, as the poet says,[4] and ten mouths, or with nine lips, or three rows of teeth, or a hundred hands, or too many fingers on one hand. Similarly if, when all the factors in a number are examined and added together in one sum, it proves upon investigation that the number's own factors exceed the number itself, this is called a superabundant number, for it oversteps the symmetry which exists between the perfect and its own parts. Such are 12, 24, and certain others, for 12 has a half, 6, a third, 4, a fourth, 3, a sixth, 2, and a twelfth, 1, which added together make 16, which is more than the original 12; its parts, therefore, are greater than the whole itself. *[4]* And 24 has a half, a third, fourth, sixth, eighth, twelfth, and twenty-fourth, which are 12, 8, 6, 4, 3, 2, 1. Added together they make 36, which, compared to the original number, 24, is found to be greater than it, although made up solely of its factors. Hence in this case also the parts are in excess of the whole.

[1]Cf. I. 17. 2, 4, 6; also I. 23. 4.
[2]Cf. Arist., *Ethics*, II. 6. 1106[b] 33.
[3]Cf. Arist., *Ethics*, II. 6. 1106[b] 24, 33.
[4]Homer, *Odyssey*, XII. 85 ff.

CHAPTER XV

[1] The deficient number is one which has qualities the opposite of those pointed out, and whose factors added together are less in comparison than the number itself. It is as if some animal should fall short of the natural number of limbs or parts, or as if a man should have but one eye, as in the poem, "And one round orb was fixed in his brow"; or as though one should be one-handed, or have fewer than five fingers on one hand, or lack a tongue, or some such member. Such a one would be called deficient and so to speak maimed, after the peculiar fashion of the number whose factors are less than itself, such as 8 or 14. For 8 has the factors half, fourth, and eighth, which are 4, 2, and 1, and added together they make 7, and less than the original number. The parts, therefore, fall short of making up the whole. *[2]* Again, 14 has a half, a seventh, a fourteenth, 7, 2, and 1, respectively; and all together they make 10, less than the original number. So this number also is deficient in its parts, with respect to making up the whole out of them.

CHAPTER XVI

[1] While these two varieties are opposed after the manner of extremes, the so-called perfect number[5] appears as a mean, which is discovered to be in the realm of equality, and neither makes its parts greater than itself, added together, nor shows itself greater than its parts, but is always equal to its own parts. For the equal is always conceived of as in the midground between greater and less, and is, as it were, moderation between excess and deficiency, and that which is in tune, between pitches too high and too low.

[2] Now when a number, comparing with itself the sum and combination of all the factors whose presence it will admit, neither exceeds them in multitude nor is exceeded by them, then such a number is properly said to be perfect, as one which is equal to its own parts. Such numbers are 6 and 28; for 6 has the factors half, third, and sixth, 3, 2, and 1, respectively, and these added together make 6 and are equal to the original number, and neither more nor less. Twenty-eight has the factors half, fourth, seventh, fourteenth, and twenty-eighth, which are 14, 7, 4, 2 and 1; these added together make 28, and so neither are the

[5]Euclid's definition, *Elem.*, VII. 22, is: "A perfect number is one that is equal to its own parts."

parts greater than the whole nor the whole greater than the parts, but their comparison is in equality, which is the peculiar quality of the perfect number.

[3] It comes about that even as fair and excellent things are few and easily enumerated, while ugly and evil ones are widespread, so also the superabundant and deficient numbers are found in great multitude and irregularly placed —for the method of their discovery is irregular—but the perfect numbers are easily enumerated and arranged with suitable order; for only one is found among the units, 6, only one other among the tens, 28, and a third in the rank of the hundreds, 496 alone, and a fourth within the limits of the thousands, that is, below ten thousand, 8,128. And it is their accompanying characteristic to end alternately in 6 or 8, and always to be even.

[4] There is a method of producing them,[1] neat and unfailing, which neither passes by any of the perfect numbers nor fails to differentiate any of those that are not such, which is carried out in the following way.

You must set forth the even-times even numbers from unity, advancing in order in one line, as far as you please: 1, 2, 4, 8, 16, 32, 64, 128, 256, 512, 1,024, 2,048, 4,096. . . . Then you must add them together, one at a time, and each time you make a summation observe the result to see what it is. If you find that it is a prime, incomposite number, multiply it by the quantity of the last number added, and the result will always be a perfect number. If, however, the result is secondary and composite, do not multiply, but add the next and observe again what the resulting number is; if it is secondary and composite, again pass it by and do not multiply; but add the next; but if it is prime and incomposite, multiply it by the last term added, and the result will be a perfect number; and so on to infinity. In similar fashion you will produce all the perfect numbers in succession, overlooking none.

For example, to 1 I add 2, and observe the sum, and find that it is 3, a prime and incomposite number in accordance with our previous demonstrations; for it has no factor with denominator different from the number itself, but only that with denominator agreeing. Therefore I multiply it by the last number to be taken into the sum, that is, 2; I get 6, and this I declare to be the first perfect number in actuality, and to have those parts which are beheld

in the numbers of which it is composed. For it will have unity as the factor with denominator the same as itself, that is, its sixth part; and 3 as the half, which is seen in 2, and conversely 2 as its third part.

[5] Twenty-eight likewise is produced by the same method when another number, 4, is added to the previous ones. For the sum of the three, 1, 2, and 4, is 7, and is found to be prime and incomposite, for it admits only the factor with denominator like itself, the seventh part. Therefore I multiply it by the quantity of the term last taken into the summation, and my result is 28, equal to its own parts, and having its factors derived from the numbers already adduced, a half corresponding to 2; a fourth, to 7; a seventh, to 4; a fourteenth to offset the half; and a twenty-eighth, in accordance with its own nomenclature, which is 1 in all numbers.

[6] When these have been discovered, 6 among the units and 28 in the tens, you must do the same to fashion the next. *[7]* Again add the next number, 8, and the sum is 15. Observing this, I find that we no longer have a prime and incomposite number, but in addition to the factor with denominator like the number itself, it has also a fifth and a third, with unlike denominators. Hence I do not multiply it by 8, but add the next number, 16, and 31 results. As this is a prime, incomposite number, of necessity it will be multiplied, in accordance with the general rule of the process, by the last number added, 16, and the result is 496, in the hundreds ; and then comes 8,128 in the thousands, and so on, as far as it is convenient for one to follow.

[8] Now unity is potentially a perfect number, but not actually; for taking it from the series as the very first I observe what sort it is, according to the rule, and find it prime and incomposite; for it is so in very truth, not by participation like the rest, but it is the primary number of all, and alone incomposite. *[9]* I multiply it, therefore, by the last term taken into the summation, that is, by itself, and my result is 1; for 1 times 1 equals 1. *[10]* Thus unity is perfect potentially; for it is potentially equal to its own parts, the others actually.

CHAPTER XVII

[1] Now that we have given a preliminary systematic account of absolute quantity we come in turn to relative quantity.

[2] Of relative quantity, then, the highest generic divisions are two, equality and inequal-

---

[1]Cf. Euclid (IX. 36).

ity; for everything viewed in comparison with another thing is either equal or unequal, and there is no third thing besides these.

[3] Now the equal is seen, when of the things compared one neither exceeds nor falls short in comparison with the other, for example, 100 compared with 100, 10 with 10, 2 with 2, a mina with a mina, a talent with a talent, a cubit with a cubit, and the like, either in bulk, length, weight, or any kind of quantity. [4] And as a peculiar characteristic, also this relation is of itself not to be divided or separated, as being most elementary, for it admits of no difference. For there is no such thing as this kind of equality and that kind, but the equal exists in one and the same manner. [5] And that which corresponds to an equal thing, to be sure, does not have a different name from it, but the same; like "friend," "neighbor," "comrade," so also "equal"; for it is equal to an equal.

[6] The unequal, on the other hand, is split up by subdivisions, and one part of it is the greater, the other the less, which have opposite names and are antithetical to one another in their quantity and relation. For the greater is greater than some other thing, and the less again is less than another thing in comparison, and their names are not the same, but they each have different ones, for example, "father" and "son," "striker" and "struck," "teacher" and "pupil," and the like.

[7] Moreover, of the greater, separated by a second subdivision into five species, one kind is the multiple, another the superparticular, another the superpartient, another the multiple superparticular, and another the multiple superpartient. [8] And of its opposite, the less, there arise similarly by subdivision five species, opposed to the foregoing five varieties of the greater, the submultiple, subsuperparticular, subsuperpartient, submultiple-superparticular, and submultiple-superpartient; for as whole answers to whole, smaller to greater, so also the varieties correspond, each to each, in the aforesaid order, with the prefix sub-.

CHAPTER XVIII

[1] Once more, then; the multiple is the species of the greater first and most original by nature, as straightway we shall see, and it is a number which, when it is observed in comparison with another, contains the whole of that number more than once. For example, compared with unity, all the successive numbers beginning with 2 generate in their proper order the regular forms of the multiple; for 2, in the first place, is and is called the double, 3 triple, 4 quadruple, and so on; for "more than once" means twice, or three times, and so on in succession as far as you like.

[2] Answering to this is the submultiple, which is itself primary in the smaller division of inequality. It is the number which, when it is compared with a larger, is able to measure it completely more than once, and "more than once" starts with twice and goes on to infinity. [3] If then it measures the larger number that is being compared twice only, it is properly called the subdouble, as 1 is of 2; if thrice, subtriple, as 1 of 3; if four times, subquadruple, as 1 of 4, and so on in succession.

[4] While each of these, the multiple and the submultiple, is generically infinite, the varieties by subdivision and the species also are observed naturally to make an infinite series. For the double, beginning with 2, goes on through all the even numbers, as we select alternate numbers out of the natural series; and these will be called doubles in comparison with the even and odd numbers successively placed beginning with unity. [5] All the numbers from the beginning two places apart, and third in order, are triples, for example, 3, 6, 9, 12, 15, 18, 21, 24. It is their property to be alternately odd and even, and they themselves in the regular series from unity are triples of all the numbers in succession as far as one wishes to go on with the process.

[6] The quadruples are those in the fourth places, three apart, for instance, 4, 8, 12, 16, 20, 24, 28, 32, and so on. These are the quadruples of the regular series of numbers from unity going on as far as one finds it convenient to follow. It belongs to them all to be even; for one needs only to take the alternate terms out of the even numbers already selected. Thus necessarily it is true that the even numbers, with no further designation, are all doubles, the alternate ones quadruples, those two places apart sextuples and those three places apart octuples, and this series will go on, on this same analogy, indefinitely.

[7] The quintuples will be seen to be those four places apart, placed fifth from one another, and themselves the quintuples of the successive numbers beginning with unity. Alternately they are odd and even, like the triples.

CHAPTER XIX

[1] The superparticular, the second species of the greater both naturally and in order, is a

number that contains within itself the whole of the number compared with it, and some one factor of it besides.

[2] If this factor is a half, the greater of the terms compared is called specifically sesquialter, and the smaller subsesquialter; if it is a third, sesquitertian and subsesquitertian; and as you go on throughout it will always thus agree, so that these species also will progress to infinity, even though they are species of an unlimited genus.

For it comes about that the first species, the sesquialter ratio, has as its consequents the even numbers in succession from 2, and no other at all, and as antecedents the triples in succession from 3, and no other. *[3]* These must be joined together regularly, first to first, second to second, third to third—3:2, 6:4, 9:6, 12:8—and the analogous numbers to the ones corresponding to them in position.

[4] If we care to investigate the second species of the superparticular, the sesquitertian (for the fraction naturally following after the half is the third), we shall have this definition of it—a number which contains the whole of the number compared, and a third of it in addition to the whole. We may have examples of it, in the proper order, in the successive quadruples beginning with 4 joined to the triples from 3, each term with the one in the corresponding position in the series, for example, 4: 3, 8:6, 12:9, and so on to infinity. *[5]* It is plain that that which corresponds to the sesquitertian but is called with the prefix sub-, subsesquitertian, is the number, the whole of which is contained and a third part in addition, for example, 3:4, 6:8, 9:12, and the similar pairs of numbers in the same position in the series.

[6] And we must observe the never-failing corollary of all this, that the first forms in each series, the so-called root numbers, are next to one another in the natural series; the next after the root-forms show an interval of only one number; the third two; the fourth three; the fifth four; and so on, as far as you like. *[7]* Furthermore, that the fraction after which each of the superparticulars is named is seen in the lesser of the root numbers, never in the greater.

[8] That by nature and by no disposition of ours the multiple is a more elementary and an older form than the superparticular we shall shortly learn, through a somewhat intricate process. And here, for a simple demonstration, we must prepare in regular and parallel lines the multiples specified above, according to their

varieties, first the double in one line, then in a second the triple, then the quadruple in a third, and so on as far as the tenfold multiples, so that we may detect their order and variety, their regulated progress, and which of them is naturally prior, and indeed other corollaries delightful in their exactness. Let the diagram be as follows: *[9]*

1	2	3	4	5	6	7	8	9	10
2	4	6	8	10	12	14	16	18	20
3	6	9	12	15	18	21	24	27	30
4	8	12	16	20	24	28	32	36	40
5	10	15	20	25	30	35	40	45	50
6	12	18	24	30	36	42	48	54	60
7	14	21	28	35	42	49	56	63	70
8	16	24	32	40	48	56	64	72	80
9	18	27	36	45	54	63	72	81	90
10	20	30	40	50	60	70	80	90	100

[10] Let there be set forth in the first row the natural series from unity, and then in order those species of the multiple which we were bidden to insert.

[11] Now then in comparison with the first rows beginning with unity, if we read both across and up and down in the form of the letter gamma, the next rows both ways, themselves in the form of a gamma, beginning with 4, are multiples according to the first form of the multiple, for they are doubles. The first differs by unity from the first, the second from the second by 2, the third from the third by 3, the next by 4, those following by 5, and you will find that this follows throughout.

The third rows in both directions from 9, their common origin, will be the triples of the terms in that same first row according to the second form of the multiple; the cross-lines like the letter chi, ending in the term 3 in either direction, are to be taken into consideration. *[12]* The difference, for these numbers, will progress after the series of the even numbers, being 2 for the first, 4 for the next, 6 for the third; and this difference Nature has of her own accord interpolated for us between these rows that are being examined, as is evident in the diagram.

[13] The fourth row, whose common origin in both directions is 16, and whose cross-lines end with the terms 4, exhibits the third species of multiple, the quadruple, when it is compared with that same first row according to corresponding positions, first term with first, second with second, third with third, and so on. Again, the differences of these numbers are 3, 6, then 9, then 12, and the quantities that progress by steps of 3. These numbers are detected in the

structure of the diagram in places just above the quadruples, and in the subsequent forms of the multiple the analogy will hold throughout.

[14] In comparison with the second line reading either way, which begins with the common origin 4 and runs over in cross-lines to the term 2 in each row, the lines which are next in order beneath display the first species of the superparticular, that is, the sesquialter, between terms occupying corresponding places. Thus by divine nature, not by our convention or agreement, the superparticulars are of later origin than the multiples. For illustration, 3 is the sesquialter of 2, 6 of 4, 9 of 6, 12 of 8, 15 of 10, and throughout thus. They have as a difference the successive numbers from unity, like those before them.

[15] The sesquitertians, the second species of superparticular, proceed with a regular, even advance from 4:3, 8:6, 12:9, 16:12, and so on; having also a regular increase of their differences. *[16]* And in the other multiple and superparticular relations you will see that the results are in harmony and not by any means inconsistent as you go on to infinity.

[17] The following feature of the diagram, moreover, is of no less exactness. The terms at the corners are units; the one at the beginning a simple unit, that at the end the unit of the third course, and the other two units of the second course appearing twice; so that the product (of the first two) is equal to the square (of the last). *[18]* Furthermore, in reading either way there is an even progress from unity to the tens, and again on the opposite sides two other progressions from 10 to 100.

[19] The terms on the diagonal from 1 to 100 are all square numbers, the products of equals by equals, and those flanking them on either side are all heteromecic, unequal, and the products of sides of which one is greater than the other by unity; and so the sum of two successive squares and twice the heteromecic numbers between them is always a square, and conversely a square is always produced from the two heteromecic numbers on the sides and twice the square between them.

[20] An ambitious person might find many other pleasing things displayed in this diagram, upon which it is not now the time to dwell, for we have not yet gained recognition of them from our *Introduction*, and so we must turn to the next subject. For after these two generic relations of the multiple and the superparticular and the other two, opposite to them, with the prefix sub-, the submultiple and the sub-

superparticular, there are in the greater division of inequality the superpartient, and in the less its opposite, the subsuperpartient.

CHAPTER XX

[1] It is the superpartient relation when a number contains within itself the whole of the number compared and in addition more than one part of it; and "more than one" starts with 2 and goes on to all the numbers in succession. Thus the root-form of the superpartient is naturally the one which has in addition to the whole two parts of the number compared, and as a species will be called superbipartient; after this the one with three parts besides the whole will be called supertripartient as a species; then comes the superquadripartient, the superquintipartient, and so forth.

[2] The parts have their root and origin with the third, for it is impossible in this case to begin with the half. For if we assume that any number contains two halves of the compared number, besides the whole of it, we shall inadvertently be setting up a multiple instead of a superpartient, because each whole, plus two halves of it, added together makes double the original number. Thus it is most necessary to start with two thirds, then two fifths, two sevenths, and after these two ninths, following the advance of the odd numbers; for two quarters, for example, again are a half, two sixths a third, and thus again superparticulars will be produced instead of superpartients, which is not the problem laid before us nor in accord with the systematic construction of our science.

[3] After the superpartient the subsuperpartient immediately is produced, whenever a number is completely contained in the one compared with it, and in addition several parts of it, 2, 3, 4, or 5, and so on.

CHAPTER XXI

[1] The regular arrangement and orderly production of both species are discovered when we set forth the successive even and odd numbers, beginning with 3, and compare with them simple series of odd numbers only, from 5 in succession, first to first—that is, 5 to 3,—second to second—that is, 7 to 4,—third to third—that is, 9 to 5,—fourth to fourth—that is, 11 to 6,— and so on in the same order as far as you like. In this way the forms of the superpartient and the subsuperpartient, in due order, will be disclosed through the root-forms of each species, the superbipartient first, then the supertripartient, superquadripartient, and super-

quintipartient, and further in succession in similar manner; for after the root-forms of each species the ones which follow them will be produced by doubling, or tripling, both the terms, and in general by multiplying after the regular forms of the multiple.

nerically, it will have in its subdivisions according to species a sort of diversification and change of names proper both to the first part of the name and to the second. For instance, in the first part, that is, the multiple, it will have double, triple, quadruple, quintuple, and

TABLE OF THE SUPERPARTIENTS

Root-forms	5	3	7	4	9	5	11	6	13	7
	10	6	14	8	18	10	22	12	26	14
	15	9	21	12	27	15	33	18	39	21
	20	12	28	16	36	20	44	24	52	28
	25	15	35	20	45	25	55	30	65	35
	30	18	42	24	54	30	66	36	78	42
	35	21	49	28	63	35	77	42	91	49
	40	24	56	32	72	40	88	48	104	56
	45	27	63	36	81	45	99	54	117	63

[2] It must be observed that from the two parts in addition to the whole which are contained in the greater term, we are to understand "third," in the case of three parts, "fourth," with four parts, "fifth," with five, "sixth," and so on, so that the order of nomenclature is something like this: superbipartient, supertripartient, superquadripartient, then superquintipartient, and similarly with the rest.

[3] Now the simple, uncompounded relations of relative quantity are these which have been enumerated. Those which are compounded of them and as it were woven out of two into one are the following, of which the antecedents are the multiple superparticular and multiple superpartient, and the consequents the ones that immediately arise in connection with each of the former, named with the prefix sub-; together with the multiple superparticular the submultiple superparticular, and with the multiple superpartient the submultiple superpartient. In the subdivision of the genera the species of the one will correspond to those of the other, these also having names with the prefix sub-.

CHAPTER XXII

[1] Now the multiple superparticular is a relation in which the greater of the compared terms contains within itself the lesser term more than once and in addition some one part of it, whatever this may be.

[2] As a compound, such a number is doubly diversified after the peculiarities of nomenclature of its components on either side; for inasmuch as the multiple superparticular is composed of the multiple and superparticular ge-

so forth, and in the second part, generically from the superparticular, its specific forms in due order, the sesquialter, sesquitertian, sesquiquartan, sesquiquintan, and so on, so that the combination will proceed in somewhat this order:

Double sesquialter, double sesquitertian, double sesquiquartan, double sesquiquintan, double sesquisextan, and analogously.

Beginning once more: triple sesquialter, triple sesquitertian, triple sesquiquartan, triple sesquiquintan.

Again: quadruple sesquialter, quadruple sesquitertian, quadruple sesquiquartan, quadruple sesquiquintan.

Again: quintuple sesquialter, quintuple sesquitertian, quintuple sesquiquartan, quintuple sesquiquintan, and the forms analogous to these *ad infinitum*. Whatever number of times the greater contains the whole of the smaller, by this quantity the first part of the ratio of the terms joined together in the multiple superparticular is named; and whatever may be the factor, in addition to the whole several times contained, that is, in the greater term, from this is named the second kind of ratio of which the multiple superparticular is compounded.

[3] Examples of it are these: 5 is the double sesquialter of 2; 7 the double sesquitertian of 3; 9 the double sesquiquartan of 4; 11 the double sesquiquintan of 5. You will furthermore always produce them in regular order, in this fashion, by comparing with the successive even and odd numbers from 2 the odd numbers, exclusively, from 5, first with first, second with second, third with third, and the others each with the one in the same position in the series.

The successive terms beginning with 5 and differing by 5 will be without exception double sesquialters of all the successive even numbers from 2 on, when terms in the same position in the series are compared; and beginning with 3, if all those with a difference of 3 be set forth, as 3, 6, 9, 12, 15, 18, 21, and in another series there be set forth those that differ by 7, to infinity, as 7, 14, 21, 28, 35, 42, 49, and the greater be compared with the smaller, first to first, second to second, third to third, fourth to fourth, and so on, the second species will appear, the double sesquitertian, disposed in its proper order.

[4] Then again, to take a fresh start, if the simple series of quadruples be set forth, 4, 8, 12, 16, 20, 24, 28, 32, and then there be placed beside it in another series the successive numbers beginning with 9, and increasing by 9, as 9, 18, 27, 36, 45, 54, we shall have revealed once more the multiple superparticular in a specific form, that is, the double sesquiquartan in its proper order; and any one who desires can contrive this to an unlimited extent.

[5] The second kind begins with the triple sesquialter, such as 7:2, 14:4, and in general the numbers that advance by steps of 7 compared with the even numbers in order from 2.

[6] Then once more, 10:3 is the first triple sesquitertian, 20:6 the second, and, in a word, the multiples of 10 in succession, compared with the successive triples. This indeed we can observe with greater exactitude and clearness in the table studied above, for in comparison with the first row the succeeding rows in order,[1] compared as whole rows, display the forms of the multiple in regular order up to infinity when they are all compared in each case to the same first row; and when each row is compared to all those above it, in succession, the second row being taken as our starting point, all the forms of the superparticular are produced in their proper order; and if we start with the third row, all of those beginning with the fifth that are odd in the series when they are compared with this same third row, and those following it, will show all the forms of the superpartient in proper order. In the case of the multiple superparticular, the comparisons will have a natural order of their own if we start with the second row and compare the terms from the fifth, first to first, second to second, third to third, and so on, and then the terms of the seventh row to the third, those of the ninth to the

fourth, and follow the corresponding order as far as we are able to go. *[7]* It is plain that here too the smaller terms have names corresponding to the larger ones, with the prefix sub-, according to the nomenclature given them all.

CHAPTER XXIII

[1] The multiple superpartient is the remaining relation of number. This, and the relation called by a corresponding name with the prefix sub-, exist when a number contains the whole of the number compared more than once (that is, twice, thrice, or any number of times) and certain parts of it, more than one, either two, three, or four, and so on, besides. *[2]* These parts[2] are not halves, for the reasons mentioned above, but either thirds, fourths, or fifths, and so on.

[3] From what has already been said it is not hard to conceive of the varieties of this relation, for they are differentiated in the same way as, and consistently with, those that precede, double superbipartient, double supertripartient, double superquadripartient, and so on. For example, 8 is the double superbipartient of 3, 16 of 6, and in general the numbers beginning with 8 and differing by 8 are double superbipartients of those beginning with 3 and differing by 3, when those in corresponding places in the series are compared, and in the case of the other varieties one could ascertain their proper sequence by following out what has already been said. In this case, too, we must conceive that the nomenclature of the number compared goes along and suffers corresponding changes, with the addition of the prefix sub-.

[4] Thus we come to the end of our speculation upon the ten arithmetical relations for a first *Introduction*. There is, however, a method very exact and necessary for all discussion of the nature of the universe which very clearly and indisputably presents to us the fact that that which is fair and limited, and which subjects itself to knowledge,[3] is naturally prior to the unlimited, incomprehensible, and ugly, and furthermore that the parts and varieties of the infinite and unlimited are given shape and boundaries by the former, and through it attain to their fitting order and sequence, and like objects brought beneath some seal or measure, all gain a share of likeness to it and similarity of name when they fall under its influence. For thus it is reasonable that the rational

---

[1] Referring to the table in Chapter 19.

[2] See 20. 2 above.
[3] Cf. I. 2. 5.

part of the soul will be the agent which puts in order the irrational part, and passion and appetite, which find their places in the two forms of inequality, will be regulated by the reasoning faculty as though by a kind of equality and sameness. *[5]* And from this equalizing process there will properly result for us the so-called ethical virtues, sobriety,[1] courage, gentleness, self-control, fortitude, and the like.

[6] Let us then consider the nature of the principle that pertains to these universal matters. It is capable of proving that all the complex species of inequality and the varieties of these species are produced out of equality, first and alone, as from a mother and root.

[7] Let there be given us equal numbers in three terms, first, units, then two's in another group of three, then three's, next four's, five's, and so on as far as you like. For them, as the setting forth of these terms has come about by a divine, and not human, contrivance, nay, by Nature herself, multiples will first be produced, and among these the double will lead the way, the triple after the double, the quadruple next, and then the quintuple, and, following the order we have previously recognized, *ad infinitum;* second, the superparticular, and here again the first form, the sesquialter, will lead, and the next after it, the sesquitertian, will follow, and after them the next in order, the sesquiquartan, the sesquiquintan, the sesquisextan, and so on *ad infinitum;* third, the superpartient, which once more the superbipartient will lead, the supertripartient will follow immediately upon it, and then will come the superquadripartient, the superquintipartient, and according to the foregoing as far as one may proceed.

[8] Now you must have certain rules, like invariable and inviolable natural laws, following which the whole aforesaid advance and progress from equality may go on without failure. These are the directions: Make the first equal to the first, the second equal to the sum of the first and second, and the third to the sum of the first, twice the second, and the third. For if you fashion according to these rules you would get first all the forms of the multiple in order out of the three given terms of the equality, as it were, sprouting and growing without your paying any heed or offering any aid. From equality you will first get the double; from the double the triple, from the triple successively

the quadruple, and from this the quintuple in due order, and so on. *[9]* From these same multiples in their regular order, reversed, there are immediately produced by a sort of natural necessity through the agency of the same three rules the superparticulars, and these not as it chances and irregularly but in their proper sequence; for from the first, the double, reversed, comes the first, the sesquialter, and from the second, the triple, the second in this class, the sesquitertian; then the sesquiquartan from the quadruple, and in general each one from the one of similar name. *[10]* And with a fresh start, if the superparticulars are set forth in the order of their production, but with terms reversed, the superpartients, which naturally follow them, are brought to light, the superbipartient from the sesquialter, the supertripartient from the sesquitertian, the superquadripartient from the sesquiquartan, and so on *ad infinitum.* *[11]* If, however, the superparticulars are set forth with terms not in reverse but in direct order, there are produced through the three rules the multiple superparticulars, the double sesquialter out of the first, the sesquialter; the double sesquitertian from the second, the sesquitertian, the double sesquiquartan from the third, the sesquiquartan, and so on. *[12]* From those produced by the reversal of the superparticular, that is, the superpartients, and from those produced without such reversal, the multiple superparticulars, there are once more produced, in the same way and by the same rules, both when the terms are in direct or reverse order, the numbers that show the remaining numerical relations.

[13] The following must suffice as illustrations of all that has been said hitherto, the production of these numbers and their sequence, and the use of direct and of reverse order. *[14]* From the relation and proportion in terms of the sesquialter, reversed so as to begin with the largest term, there arises a relation in superpartient ratios, the superbipartient; and from it in direct order, beginning with the smallest term, a multiple superparticular relation, the double sesquialter. For example, from 9, 6, 4, we get either 9, 15, 25 or 4, 10, 25. From the relation in terms of sesquitertians, beginning with the greatest term, is derived a superpartient, the supertripartient; beginning with the smallest term, a double sesquitertian. For example, from 16, 12, 9 comes either 16, 28, 49 or 9, 21, 49. And from the relation in terms of sesquiquartans, when it is arranged to begin with the largest term, is derived a superpar-

---

[1] Cf. Aristotle, *Ethics*, 1107^b 4 ff. See *ibid.*, 1108^a 4 ff.; 1145^b 8 ff.

tient, the superquadripartient; when it starts with the smallest term, a multiple superparticular, the double sesquiquintan; for instance, from 25, 20, 16 comes either 25, 45, 81 or 16, 36, 81.

[15] In the case of all these relations that are thus differentiated, and of the one from which both of the differentiated ones are derived, the last term is always the same and a square; the first term becomes the smallest, and invariably the extremes are squares.

[16] Moreover the multiple superpartients and superpartients of other kinds are made to appear in yet another way out of the superpartients; for example, from the superbipartient relation arranged so as to begin with the small-est term comes the double superbipartient, but, arranged so as to start with the greatest, the superpartient ratio of 8:5. Thus from 9, 15, 25 comes either 9, 24, 64 or 25, 40, 64. From the supertripartient, beginning with the smallest term, we have the double supertripartient, and, beginning with the largest, the ratio of 11:7. Thus, from 16, 28, 49 comes either 16, 44, 121 or 49, 77, 121. [17] Again, from the superquintipartient, as, for example, 25, 45, 81, beginning with the lesser term we derive the double superquintipartient in the terms 25, 70, 196, but beginning with the greater a superpartient again, the ratio of 14:9, in the terms 81, 126, 196. And you will find the results analogous and in agreement with the foregoing in all successive cases to infinity.

BOOK TWO

CHAPTER I

[1] An element is said to be, and is, the smallest thing which enters into the composition of an object and the least thing into which it can be analyzed. Letters, for example, are called the elements of literate speech, for out of them all articulate speech is composed and into them finally it is resolved. Sounds are the elements of all melody; for they are the beginning of its composition and into them it is resolved. The so-called four elements of the universe in general are simple bodies, fire, water, air, and earth; for out of them in the first instance we account for the constitution of the universe, and into them finally we conceive of it as being resolved.

We wish also to prove that equality is the elementary principle[1] of relative number; for of absolute number, number per se, unity and the dyad are the most primitive elements, the least things out of which it is constructed, even to infinity, by which it has its growth, and with which its analysis into smaller terms comes to an end. *[2]* We have, however, demonstrated that in the realm of inequality advance and increase have their origin in equality and go on to absolutely all the relations with a certain regularity through the operation of the three rules.[2] It remains, then, in order to make it an element in very truth, to prove that analyses also finally come to an end in equality. Let this then be considered our procedure.

CHAPTER II

[1] Suppose then you are given three terms, in any relation whatsoever and in any ratio, whether multiple, superparticular, superpartient, or a compound of these, multiple superparticular or multiple superpartient, provided only that the mean term is seen to be in the same ratio to the lesser as the greater to the mean, and vice versa. Subtract always from the mean the lesser term, whether it be first or last in order, and set down the lesser term itself as the first term of your new series; then put as your second term what remains from the second after the subtraction; then after having subtracted the sum of the new first term and twice the new second term from the remaining number—that is, the greater of the numbers originally given you—make the remainder your third term, and the resulting numbers will be in some other ratio, naturally more primitive. *[2]* And if again in the same way you subtract the remainder from these same terms, it will be found that your three terms have passed back into three others more primitive, and you will find that this always takes place as a consequence, until they are reduced to equality, whence by every necessity it appears evident that equality is the elementary principle of relative quantity.

[3] There follows upon this speculation a most elegant principle, extremely useful in its application to the Platonic psychogony[3] and the problem of all harmonic intervals; for in the Platonic passage we are frequently bidden, for the sake of the argument, to set up series of intervals of two, three, four, five, or an infinite number of sesquialter ratios, or two sesquitertians, sesquiquartans, sesquioctaves, or superparticulars of any kind whatsoever, and in each case three, four, or five of them, or as many as may be directed. *[4]* It is reasonable that we should do this not in an unscientific, unintelligent fashion, it may be even blunderingly, but artistically, surely, and quickly, by the following procedure.

CHAPTER III

[1] Every multiple will stand at the head[4] of as many superparticular ratios corresponding in name with itself as it itself chances to be removed from unity, and no more nor less under any circumstances.

---

[1]See on I. 23. 4.
[2]See on I. 23. 8.

[3]See Plato, *Timaeus*, 35 ff.
[4]Refers to the table in Chapter 4.

[2] The doubles, then, will produce[1] sesqui-alters, the first one, the second two, the third three, the fourth four, the fifth five, the sixth six, and neither more nor less, but by every necessity when the superparticulars that are generated attain the proper number, that is, when their number agrees with the multiples that have generated them, at that point by a divine device, as it were, there is found the

Sixteen, the fourth double, will stand at the head of four sesquialters, 24, 36, 54, and finally 81, so that they may of necessity be equal in number to what generated them; for 81 by its nature is not divisible by 2. And this, as you go on, you will find holds true in similar fashion to infinity.

[4] For the sake of illustration let there be set down the table of the doubles, thus:

The double ratio in the breadth of the table							
1	2	4	8	16	32	64	
	3	6	12	24	48	96	
The triple ratio along		9	18	36	72	144	The sesquialter ra-
the hypotenuse			27	54	108	216	tio in the depth
				81	162	324	
					243	486	
						729	

number which terminates them all because it naturally is not divisible by that factor whereby the progression of the superparticular ratios went on.

CHAPTER IV

[1] We must make a similar table in illustration of the triple:

The triple ratio in the breadth							
1	3	9	27	81	243	729	
	4	12	36	108	324	972	
The quadruple ratio		16	48	144	432	1296	The sesquitertian
on the hypotenuse			64	192	576	1728	ratio in the depth
				256	768	2304	
					1024	3072	
						4096	

From the triples all the sesquitertians will proceed, likewise equal in number to the number of the generating terms, and coming to an end, after the independence of their advance is lost, in numbers not divisible by 3. Similarly the sesquiquartans come from the quadruples, reaching a culmination after their independent progression in a number that is not divisible by 4.

[3] As an example, since doubles generate sesquialters corresponding to them in number, the first row of multiples will be 1, 2, 4, 8, 16, 32, 64. Now since 2 is the first after unity, this will be the origin of one sesquialter only, 3, which number is not divisible by 2, so that another sesquialter might arise out of it. The first double, therefore, is productive of but one sesquialter, and the second, 4, of two. For it produces its own sesquialter, 6, and that of 6, 9, but there is none for 9 because it has no half. Eight, which is the third double, is father to three sesquialters; one its own, 12; the second, 18, the sesquialter of 12; and third, 27, that of 18; there is no fourth one, however, because of the general rule, for 27 is not divisible by 2.

In the foregoing table we shall observe that in the same way the first triple, 3, stands at the head of but one sesquitertian ratio, 4, its own sesquitertian, which immediately shuts off the development of another like it; for 4 is not divisible by 3, and hence will not have a sesquitertian. The second triple is 9, and hence will begin a series of only two sesquitertian ratios, 12, its own, and 16, that of 12; but 16 cuts off further progress, for it is not divisible by 3 and hence will not have a sesquitertian. *[2]* Next in order is the triple 27, three times removed from 1, for the triples progress thus: 1, 3, 9, 27. Therefore this number will stand at the head of three sesquitertian ratios and no more. The first is its own, 36; the second the sesquitertian of 36, 48; the third that of the last, 64, and this no longer has a third part and therefore will not admit of a sesquitertian. The fourth leads a series of four sesquitertians and the fifth, of course, five.

[3] Such, then, is the illustration; and for the other multiples let the manner of your tables be the same. Observe that likewise here as we found to be true in our previous discus'

[1] See I. 19. 2.

sion, Nature shows us that the doubles are more nearly original than the triples, the triples than the quadruples, these latter than the quintuples, and so on throughout. For the highest rows of figures, across the breadth of the tables, if they are doubles, will have doubles lying parallel to them, and the numbers lying diagonally, on the hypotenuse, will be of the next succeeding variety, greater by 1, that is, triples, seen also in a series of parallel lines. If, however, there are triples across the breadth, the diagonals will by all means be quadruples; if the former are quadruples, then the latter are quintuples, and so forth.

CHAPTER V

[1] It remains, after we have explained what other ratios are produced by combination of ratios, to pass on to the succeeding topics of the *Introduction*.

[2] Now the first two ratios of the superparticular, combined, produce the first ratio of the multiple, namely, the double; for every double is a combination of sesquialter and sesquitertian, and every sesquialter and sesquitertian combined will invariably produce a double.

For example, since 3 is the sesquialter of 2, and 4 the sesquitertian of 3, 4 will be the double of 2, and is a combination of sesquialter and sesquitertian. Again, as 6 is the double of 3, we shall find between them some number that will of necessity preserve the sesquitertian ratio to the one and the sesquialter to the other; and indeed 4, lying between 6 and 3, gives the sesquitertian ratio to 3 and the sesquialter to 6.

[3] It was rightly said, then, that the double, when resolved, is resolved into the sesquialter and the sesquitertian, and that when sesquialter and sesquitertian are combined there arises the double, and that the first two forms of the superparticular combined make the first form of the multiple.

[4] But again, to take another start, this first form of the multiple which has thus been produced, together with the first form of the superparticular, will produce the next form of the same class, that is, the second multiple, the triple; for from every multiple and sesquialter combined a triple of necessity arises. For example, as the double of 6 is 12, and the sesquialter of this is 18, then immediately 18 is the triple of 6; and to take another method, if I do not care to make 12 the mean term, but rather 9, the sesquialter of 6, the same result will come about, without deviation and harmoniously;

for while 18 is the double of 9 it will preserve the triple ratio to 6. Hence from the sesquialter and the double, the first forms of the superparticular and the multiple, there arises by combination the second form of the multiple, the triple, and into them it is always resolved. *[5]* For look you; 6, which is the triple of 2, will have a mean term 3, which will exhibit two ratios, the sesquialter with regard to 2, and the double ratio of 6 to itself.

But if this triple ratio, likewise, the second form of the multiple, is combined with the sesquitertian, which is the second form of the superparticular, there would be produced from them the next form of the multiple, namely, the quadruple, and this also will of necessity be resolved into them after the same fashion as the cases previously set forth: and the quadruple, taking into combination the sesquiquartan, will make the quintuple, and, once more, the latter with the sesquiquintan will make the sextuple, and so on to the end. Thus the multiples in regular order from the beginning with the superparticulars in regular order from the beginning will be found to produce the next larger multiples. For the double with the sesquialter makes the triple, the triple with the sesquitertian the quadruple, the quadruple with the sesquiquartan the quintuple, and as far as you wish to proceed no contrary result will appear.

CHAPTER VI

[1] Up to this point then we have sufficiently discussed relative number, by a process of selection measuring out what is easily comprehended and appropriate to the nature of the matters thus far introduced. Whatever remains to be said on this topic will be filled in after we have put it aside and have first discussed certain subjects which involve a more serviceable inquiry, having to do with the properties of absolute number, not relative. For mathematical speculations are always to be interlocked and to be explained one by means of another. The subjects which we must first survey and observe are concerned with linear, plane, and solid numbers, cubical and spherical, equilateral and scalene, "bricks," "beams," "wedges," and the like, the tradition concerning which, to be sure, since they are more closely related to magnitude, is properly given in the *Geometrical Introduction*. Yet the germs of these ideas are taken over into arithmetic, as the science which is the mother of geometry and more elementary than it. For we recall that a short time ago we saw that arithmetic abolishes the other sciences

with itself, but is not abolished by them, and conversely is of necessity implied by them but does not itself imply them.

[2] First, however, we must recognize that each letter by which we indicate a number, such as iota, the sign for 10, kappa for 20, and omega for 800, designates that number by man's convention and agreement, not by nature. On the other hand, the natural, unartificial, and therefore simplest indication of numbers would be the setting forth one beside the other of the units contained in each. For example, the writing of one unit by means of one alpha will be the sign for 1; two units side by side, that is, a series of two alphas, will be the sign for 2; when three are put in a line it will be the character for 3, four in a line for 4, five for 5, and so on. For by means of such a notation and indication alone could the schematic arrangement of the plane and solid numbers mentioned be made clear and evident, thus:

The number 1, a
The number 2, a a
The number 3, a a a
The number 4, a a a a
The number 5, a a a a a

and further in similar fashion.

[3] Unity, then, occupying the place and character of a point, will be the beginning of intervals and of numbers, but not itself an interval or a number, just as the point is the beginning of a line, or an interval, but is not itself line or interval. Indeed, when a point is added to a point, it makes no increase, for when an non-dimensional thing is added to another non-dimensional thing, it will not thereby have dimension; just as if one should examine the sum of nothing added to nothing, which makes nothing. We saw[1] a similar thing also in the case of equality among the relatives; for a proportion is preserved—as the first is to the second, so the second is to the third—but no interval is generated in the relation of the extremes to each other, as there is in all the other relations with the exception of equality. In exactly the same way unity alone out of all number, when it multiplies itself, produces nothing greater than itself.

Unity, therefore, is non-dimensional and elementary, and dimension first is found and seen in 2, then in 3, then in 4, and in succession in the following numbers; for "dimension" is that

which is conceived of as between two limits.

[4] The first dimension is called "line," for "line" is that which is extended in one direction. Two dimensions are called "surface," for a "surface" is that which is extended in two directions. Three dimensions are called "solid," for a "solid" is that which is extended in three directions, and it is by no means possible to conceive of a solid which has more than three dimensions, depth, breadth, and length. By these are defined the six directions which are said to exist in connection with every body and by which motions in space are distinguished, forward, backward,[2] up, down, right and left; for of necessity two directions opposite to each other follow upon each dimension, up and down upon one, forward and backward upon the second, and right and left upon the third.

[5] The statement, also, as it happens, can be made conversely thus: If a thing is solid, it has by all means three dimensions, length, depth and breadth; and conversely, if it has the three dimensions, it is always a solid, and nothing else.

[6] That which has but two dimensions, therefore, will not be a solid, but a surface, for the latter admits of but two dimensions. Here too it is possible similarly to reverse the statement; directly stated, a surface is that which has two dimensions, and conversely, that which has two dimensions is always a surface.

[7] The surface, then, is exceeded by the solid by one dimension, and the line is exceeded by the surface by one, for the line is that which is extended in but one direction and has only one dimension, and it falls short of the solid by two dimensions. The point falls short of the latter by one dimension, and hence it has already been stated that it is non-dimensional, since it falls short of the solid by three dimensions, of the surface by two, and of the line by one.

CHAPTER VII

[1] The point, then, is the beginning of dimension, but not itself a dimension, and likewise the beginning of a line, but not itself a line; the line is the beginning of surface, but not surface; and the beginning of the two-dimensional, but not itself extended in two directions. [2] Naturally, too, surface is the beginning of body, but not itself body, and likewise the beginning of the three-dimensional, but not itself extended in three directions.

---

[1] I. 23. 7 ff.

[2] Cf. Plato, *Timaeus*, 43.

[3] Exactly the same in numbers, unity is the beginning of all number that advances unit by unit in one direction; linear number is the beginning of plane number, which spreads out like a plane in one more dimension; and plane number is the beginning of solid number, which possesses a depth[1] in the third dimension, besides the original ones. To illustrate and classify, linear numbers are all those which begin with 2 and advance by the addition of 1 in one and the same dimension; and plane numbers are those[2] that begin with 3 as their most elementary root and proceed through the next succeeding numbers. They receive their names also in the same order; for there are first the triangles, then the squares, the pentagons after these, then the hexagons, the heptagons, and so on indefinitely, and, as we said, they are named after the successive numbers beginning with 3.

[4] The triangle, therefore, is found to be the most original and elementary form of the plane number. This we can see from the fact that, among plane figures,[3] graphically represented, if lines are drawn from the angles to the centers each rectilinear figure will by all means be resolved into as many triangles as it has sides; but the triangle itself, if treated like the rest, will not change into anything else but itself. Hence the triangle is elementary among these figures; for everything else is resolved into it, but it into nothing else. From it the others likewise would be constituted, but it from no other. It is therefore the element of the others, and has itself no element. *[5]* Likewise, as the argument proceeds in the realm of numerical forms, it will confirm this statement.

CHAPTER VIII

[1] Now a triangular number is one which, when it is analyzed into units, shapes into triangular form the equilateral placement of its parts in a plane. 3, 6, 10, 15, 21, 28, and so on, are examples of it; for their regular formations, expressed graphically, will be at once triangular and equilateral. As you advance you will find that such a numerical series as far as you like takes the triangular form, if you put as the most elementary form the one that arises from unity, so that unity may appear to be potentially a triangle, and 3 the first actually.

[2] Their sides will increase by the succes-

sive numbers, for the side of the one potentially first is unity; that of the one actually first, that is, 3, is 2; that of 6, which is actually second, 3; that of the third, 4; the fourth, 5; the fifth, 6; and so on.

[3] The triangular number is produced from the natural series of number set forth in a line, and by the continued addition of successive terms, one by one, from the beginning; for by the successive combinations and additions of another term to the sum, the triangular numbers in regular order are completed. For example, from this natural series, 1, 2, 3, 4, 5, 6, 7, 8, 9, 10, 11, 12, 13, 14, 15, I take the first term and have the triangular number which is potentially first, 1,

 ; then adding the next term I get the triangle actually first, for 2 plus 1 equals 3. In its graphic representation it is thus made up: Two units, side by side, are set beneath one unit, and the number three is made a triangle:

Then when next after these the following number, 3, is added, simplified into units, and joined to the former, it gives 6, the second triangle in actuality, and furthermore, it graphically represents this number:

Again, the number that naturally follows, 4, added in and set down below the former, reduced to units, gives the one in order next after the aforesaid, 10, and takes a triangular form:

5, after this, then 6, then 7, and all the numbers in order, are added, so that regularly the sides of each triangle will consist of as many

---

[1]Cf. Plato, *Timaeus*, 53.
[2]But cf. Euclid, in *Elements*, VII, Def. 17.
[3]Cf. Plato, *Timaeus*, 53 ff.

numbers as have been added from the natural series to produce it:

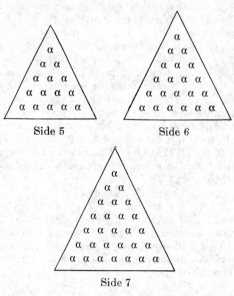

Side 5   Side 6

Side 7

CHAPTER IX

[1] The square is the next number after this, which shows us no longer 3, like the former, but 4 angles in its graphic representation, but is none the less equilateral. Take, for example, 1, 4, 9, 16, 25, 36, 49, 64, 81, 100; for the representations of these numbers are equilateral, square figures, as here shown; and it will be similar as far as you wish to go:

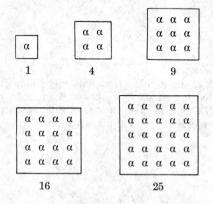

1   4   9

16   25

[2] It is true of these numbers, as it was also of the preceding, that the advance in their sides progresses with the natural series. The side of the square potentially first, 1, is 1; that of 4, the first in actuality, 2; that of 9, actually the second, 3; that of 16, the next, actually the

third, 4; that of the fourth, 5; of the fifth, 6, and so on in general with all that follow.

[3] This number also is produced if the natural series is extended in a line, increasing by 1, and no longer the successive numbers are added to the numbers in order, as was shown before, but rather all those in alternate places, that is, the odd numbers. For the first, 1, is potentially the first square; the second, 1 plus 3, is the first in actuality; the third, 1 plus 3 plus 5, is the second in actuality; the fourth, 1 plus 3 plus 5 plus 7, is the third in actuality; the next is produced by adding 9 to the former numbers, the next by the addition of 11, and so on.

[4] In these cases, also, it is a fact that the side of each consists of as many units as there are numbers taken into the sum to produce it.

CHAPTER X

[1] The pentagonal number is one which likewise upon its resolution into units and depiction as a plane figure assumes the form of an equilateral pentagon. 1, 5, 12, 22, 35, 51, 70, and analogous numbers are examples. *[2]* Each side of the first actual pentagon, 5, is 2, for 1 is the side of the pentagon potentially first, 1; 3 is the side of 12, the second of those listed; 4, that of the next, 22; 5, that of the next in order, 35, and 6 of the succeeding one, 51, and so on. In general the side contains as many units as are the numbers that have been added together to produce the pentagon, chosen out of the natural arithmetical series set forth in a row. For in a like and similar manner, there are added together to produce the pentagonal numbers the terms beginning with 1 to any extent whatever that are two places apart, that is, those that have a difference of 3.

Unity is the first pentagon, potentially, and is thus depicted:

5, made up of 1 plus 4, is the second, similarly represented:

12, the third, is made up out of the two former numbers with 7 added to them, so that it may have 3 as a side, as three numbers have been added to make it. Similarly the preceding pentagon, 5, was the combination of two numbers and had 2 as its side. The graphic representation of 12 is this:

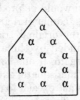

The other pentagonal numbers will be produced by adding together one after another in due order the terms after 7 that have the difference 3, as, for example, 10, 13, 16, 19, 22, 25, and so on. The pentagons will be 22, 35, 51, 70, 92, 117, and so forth.

CHAPTER XI

[1] The hexagonal, heptagonal, and succeeding numbers will be set forth in their series by following the same process, if from the natural series of number there be set forth series with their differences increasing by 1. For as the triangular number was produced by admitting into the summation the terms that differ by 1 and do not pass over any in the series; as the square was made by adding the terms that differ by 2 and are one place apart, and the pentagon similarly by adding terms with a difference of 3 and two places apart (and we have demonstrated these, by setting forth examples both of them and of the polygonal numbers made from them), so likewise the hexagons will have as their root-numbers those which differ by 4 and are three places apart in the series, which added together in succession will produce the hexagons. For example, 1, 5, 9, 13, 17, 21, and so on; so that the hexagonal numbers produced will be 1, 6, 15, 28, 45, 66, and so on, as far as one wishes to go.

[2] The heptagonals, which follow these, have as their root-numbers terms differing by 5 and four places apart in the series, like 1, 6, 11, 16, 21, 26, 31, 36, and so on. The heptagons that thus arise are 1, 7, 18, 34, 55, 81, 112, 148 and so forth.

[3] The octagonals increase after the same fashion, with a difference of 6 in their root-numbers and corresponding variation in their total constitution.

[4] In order that, as you survey all cases, you may have a rule generally applicable, note that the root-numbers of any polygonal differ by 2 less than the number of the angles shown by the name of the polygonal—that is, by 1 in the triangle, 2 in the square, 3 in the pentagon, 4 in the hexagon, 5 in the heptagon, and so on, with similar increase.

CHAPTER XII

[1] Concerning the nature of plane polygonals this is sufficient for a first *Introduction*. That, however, the doctrine of these numbers is to the highest degree in accord with their geometrical representation, and not out of harmony with it, would be evident, not only from the graphic representation in each case, but also from the following: Every square figure diagonally divided is resolved into two triangles and every square number is resolved into two consecutive triangular numbers, and hence is made up of two successive triangular numbers. For example, 1, 3, 6, 10, 15, 21, 28, 36, 45, 55, and so on, are triangular numbers and 1, 4, 9, 16, 25, 36, 49, 64, 81, 100, squares. *[2]* If you add any two consecutive triangles that you please, you will always make a square, and hence, whatever square you resolve, you will be able to make two triangles of it.

Again, any triangle joined to any square figure makes a pentagon, for example, the triangle 1 joined with the square 4 makes the pentagon 5; the next triangle, 3 of course, with 9, the next square, makes the pentagon 12; the next, 6, with the next square, 16, gives the next pentagon, 22; 10 and 25 give 35; and so on

[3] Similarly, if the triangles are added to the pentagons, following the same order, they will produce the hexagonals in due order, and again the same triangles with the latter will make the heptagonals in order, the octagonals after the heptagonals, and so on to infinity.

[4] To remind us, let us set forth rows of the polygonals, written in parallel lines, as follows: The first row, triangles, the next squares, after them pentagonals, then hexagonals, then heptagonals, then if one wishes, the succeeding polygonals.

Triangles	1	3	6	10	15	21	28	36	45	55
Squares	1	4	9	16	25	36	49	64	81	100
Pentagonals	1	5	12	22	35	51	70	92	117	145
Hexagonals	1	6	15	28	45	66	91	120	153	190
Heptagonals	1	7	18	34	55	81	112	148	189	235

You can also set forth the succeeding polygonals in similar parallel lines.

[5] In general, you will find that the squares are the sum of the triangles above those that occupy the same place in the series, plus the numbers of that same class in the next place back; for example, 4 equals 3 plus 1, 9 equals 6 plus 3, 16 equals 10 plus 6, 25 equals 15 plus 10, 36 equals 21 plus 15, and so on.

The pentagons are the sum of the squares above them in the same place in the series, plus the elementary triangles that are one place further back in the series; for example, 5 equals 4 plus 1, 12 equals 9 plus 3, 22 equals 16 plus 6, 35 equals 25 plus 10, and so on.

[6] Again, the hexagonals are similarly the sums of the pentagons above them in the same place in the series plus the triangles one place back; for instance, 6 equals 5 plus 1, 15 equals 12 plus 3, 28 equals 22 plus 6, 45 equals 35 plus 10, and as far as you like.

[7] The same applies to the heptagonals, for 7 is the sum of 6 and 1, 18 equals 15 plus 3, 34 equals 28 plus 6, and so on. Thus each polygonal number is the sum of the polygonal in the same place in the series with one less angle, plus the triangle, in the highest row, one place back in the series.

[8] Naturally, then, the triangle is the element of the polygon both in figures and in numbers, and we say this because in the table, reading either up and down or across, the successive numbers in the rows are discovered to have as differences the triangles in regular order.

CHAPTER XIII

[1] From this it is easy to see what the solid number is and how its series advances with equal sides; for the number which, in addition to the two dimensions contemplated in graphic representation in a plane, length, and breadth, has a third dimension, which some call depth, others thickness, and some height, that number would be a solid number, extended in three directions and having length, depth, and breadth.

[2] This first makes its appearance in the so-called pyramids. These are produced from rather wide bases narrowing to a sharp apex, first after the triangular form from a triangular base, second after the form of the square from a square base, and succeeding these after the pentagonal form from a pentagonal base, then similarly from the hexagon, heptagon, octagon, and so on indefinitely.

[3] Exactly so among the geometrical solid figures; if one imagines three lines from the three angles of an equilateral triangle, equal in length to the sides of the triangle, converging in the dimension height to one and the same point, a pyramid would be produced, bounded by four triangles, equilateral and equal one to the other, one the original triangle, and the other three bounded by the aforesaid three lines. [4] And again, if one conceives of four lines starting from a square, equal in length to the sides of the square, each to each, and again converging in the dimension height to one and the same point, a pyramid would be completed with a square base and diminishing in square form, bounded by four equilateral triangles and one square, the original one. [5] And starting from a pentagon, hexagon, heptagon, and however far you care to go, lines equal in number to the angles, erected in the same fashion from the angles and converging to one and the same point, will complete a pyramid named from its pentagonal, hexagonal, or heptagonal base, or similarly.

[6] So likewise among numbers, each linear number increases from unity, as from a point, as for example, 1, 2, 3, 4, 5, and successive numbers to infinity; and from these same numbers, which are linear and extended in one direction, combined in no random manner, the polygonal and plane numbers are fashioned—the triangles by the combination of root-numbers immediately adjacent, the square by adding every other term, the pentagons every third term, and so on. [7] In exactly the same way, if the plane polygonal numbers are piled one upon the other and as it were built up, the pyramids that are akin to each of them are produced, the triangular pyramid from the triangles, the square pyramid from the squares, the pentagonal from the pentagons, the hexagonal from the hexagons, and so on throughout.

[8] The pyramids with a triangular base, then, in their proper order, are these: 1, 4, 10, 20, 35, 56, 84, and so on; and their origin is the piling up of the triangular numbers one upon the other, first 1, then 1, 3, then 1, 3, 6, then 10 in addition to these, and next 15 together with the foregoing, then 21 besides these, next 28, and so on to infinity.

[9] It is clear that the greatest number is conceived of as being lowest, for it is discovered to be the base; the next succeeding one is on top of it, and the next on top of that; until unity appears at the apex and, so to speak, tapers off the completed pyramid into a point.

CHAPTER XIV

[1] The next pyramids in order are those with a square base which rise in this shape to one and the same point. These are formed in the same way as the triangular pyramids of which we have just spoken. For if I extend in series the square numbers in order beginning with unity, thus, 1, 4, 9, 16, 25, 36, 49, 64, 81, 100, and again set the successive terms, as in a pile, one upon the other in the dimension height, when I put 1 on top of 4, the first actual pyramid with square base, 5 is produced, for here again unity is potentially the first. *[2]* Once more, I put this same pyramid entire, composed of 5 units, just as it is, upon the square 9, and there is made up for me the pyramid 14, with square base and side 3—for the former pyramid had the side 2, and the one potentially first 1 as a side. For here too each side of any pyramid whatsoever must consist of as many units as there are polygonal numbers piled together to create it.

[3] Again, I place the whole pyramid 14, with the square 9 as its base, upon the square 16 and I have 30, the third actual pyramid of those that have a square base, and by the same order and procedure from a pentagonal, hexagonal, or heptagonal base, and even going on farther, we shall produce pyramids by piling upon one another the corresponding polygonal numbers, starting with unity as the smallest and going on to infinity in each case.

[4] From this too it becomes evident that triangles are the most elementary; for absolutely all of the pyramids that are exhibited and shown, with the various polygonal bases, are bounded by triangles up to the apex.

[5] But lest we be heedless of truncated, bi-truncated, and tri-truncated pyramids, the names of which we are sure to encounter in scientific writings, you may know that if a pyramid with any sort of polygon as its base, triangle, square, pentagon, or any of the succeeding polygons of the kind, when it increases by this process of piling up does not taper off into unity, it is called simply truncated when it is left without the natural apex that belongs to all pyramids; for it does not terminate in the potential polygon, unity, as in some one point, but in another polygon, and an actual one, and unity is not its apex, but its upper boundary becomes a plane figure with the same number of angles as the base. If, however, in addition to the failure to terminate in unity it does not even terminate in the polygon next to unity and

the first in actuality, such a pyramid is called bi-truncated, and if, still further, it does not have the second actual polygon at its upper limit, but only the one next beneath, it will be called tri-truncated, yes, even four times truncated, if it does not have the next one as its limit, or five times truncated at the next step, and so on as far as you care to carry the nomenclature.

CHAPTER XV

[1] While the origin, advance, increase, and nature of the equilateral solid numbers of pyramidal appearance is the foregoing, with its seed and root in the polygonal numbers and the piling up of them in their regular order, there is another series of solid numbers of a different kind, consisting of the so-called cubes, "beams," "bricks," "wedges," spheres and parallelepipedons, which has the order of its progress somewhat as follows:

[2] The foregoing squares 1, 4, 9, 16, 25, 36, 49, 64, and so on, which are extended in two directions and in their graphic representation in a plane have only length and breadth, will take on yet a third dimension and be solids and extended in three directions if each is multiplied by its own side; 4, which is 2 times 2, is again multiplied by 2, to make 8; 9, which is 3 times 3, is again increased by 3 in another dimension and gives 27; 16, which is 4 times 4, is multiplied by its own side, 4, and 64 results; and so on with the succeeding squares throughout.

[3] Here, too, the sides will be composed of as many units as were in the sides of the squares from which they arose, in each case; the sides of 8 will be 2, like those of 4; those of 27, 3, like those of 9; those of 64, 4, like those of 16; and so on, so that likewise the side of unity, the potential cube, will be 1, which is the side of the potential square, 1.

In general, each square is a single plane, and has four angles and four sides, while each several cube, having increased out of some one square multiplied by its own side, will have always six plane surfaces, each equal to the original square, and twelve edges, each equal to and containing exactly the same number of units as each side of the original square, and eight solid angles, each of which is bounded by three edges like in each case to the sides of the original square.

CHAPTER XVI

[1] Now since the cube is a solid figure with equal sides in all dimensions, in length, depth,

and breadth, and is equally extended in all the six so-called directions,[1] it follows that there is opposed to it that which has its dimensions in no case equal to one another, but its depth unequal to its breadth and its length unequal to either of these, for example 2 times 3 times 4, or 2 times 4 times 8, or 3 times 5 times 12, or a figure which follows some other scheme of inequality.

[2] Such solid figures, in which the dimensions are everywhere unequal one to another, are called scalene in general. Some, however, using other names, call them "wedges," for carpenters', house-builders' and blacksmiths' wedges and those used in other crafts, having unequal sides in every direction, are fashioned so as to penetrate; they begin with a sharp end and continually broaden out unequally in all the dimensions. Some also call them *sphekiskoi*, "wasps," because wasps' bodies also are very like them, compressed in the middle and showing the resemblance mentioned. From this also the *sphekoma*, "point of the helmet," must derive its name, for where it is compressed it imitates the waist of the wasp. Others call the same numbers "altars," using their own metaphor, for the altars of ancient style, particularly the Ionic, do not have the breadth equal to the depth, nor either of these equal to the length, nor the base equal to the top, but are of varied dimensions everywhere.

[3] Now whereas the two kinds of numbers, cube and scalene, are extremes, the one equally extended in every dimension, the other unequally, the so-called parallelepipedons are solid numbers like means between them. The plane surfaces of these are heteromecic numbers,[2] just as in the case of the cubes the faces were squares, as has been shown.

CHAPTER XVII

[1] Again, then, to take a fresh start, a number is called heteromecic if its representation, when graphically described in a plane, is quadrilateral and quadrangular, to be sure, but the sides are not equal one to another, nor is the length equal to the breadth, but they differ by 1. Examples are 2, 6, 12, 20, 30, 42, and so on, for if one represents them graphically he will always construct them thus: 1 times 2 equals 2, 2 times 3 equals 6, 3 times 4 equals 12, and the succeeding ones similarly, 4 times 5, 5 times 6, 6 times 7, 7 times 8, and thus indefinitely,

provided only that one side is greater than the other by 1 and by no other number. If, however, the sides differ otherwise than by 1, for instance, by 2, 3, 4 or succeeding numbers, as in 2 times 4, 3 times 6, 4 times 8, or however else they may differ, then no longer will such a number be properly called a heteromecic, but an oblong number. For the ancients of the school of Pythagoras and his successors saw "the other"[3] and "otherness" primarily in 2, and "the same" and "sameness" in 1, as the two beginnings of all things, and these two are found to differ from each other only by 1. Thus "the other" is fundamentally "other" by 1, and by no other number, and for this reason customarily "other" is used, among those who speak correctly, of two things and not of more than two.

[2] Moreover, it was shown that all odd number is given its specific form[4] by unity, and all even number by 2. Hence we shall naturally say that the odd partakes of the nature of "the same," and the even of that of "the other"; for indeed there are produced by the successive additions of each of these—naturally, and not by our decree—by the addition of the odd numbers from 1 to infinity the class of the squares, and by the addition of the evens from 2 to infinity, that of the heteromecic numbers.[5]

[3] There is, accordingly, every reason to think that the square once more shares in the nature of the same; for its sides display the same ratio, alike, unchanging and firmly fixed in equality, to themselves; while the heteromecic number partakes of the nature of the other; for just as 1 is differentiated from 2, differing by 1 alone, thus also the sides of every heteromecic number differ from one another, one differing from the other by 1 alone.

To illustrate, if I have set out before me the successive numbers in series beginning with 1, and select and arrange by themselves the odd numbers in the line and the even by themselves in another, there are obtained these two series:

1, 3, 5, 7, 9, 11, 13, 15, 17, 19, 21, 23, 25, 27
2, 4, 6, 8, 10, 12, 14, 16, 18, 20, 22, 24, 26, 28

[4] Now, then, the beginning of the odd series is unity, which is of the same class as the series and possesses the nature of "the same," and so whether it multiplies itself in two dimensions

[1]Cf. II. 6. 4.
[2]See the following chapter.

[3]Cf. Plato, *Timaeus*, 35 ff.
[4]Cf. I. 7. 2.
[5]Cf. II. 18. 2 and 20. 3.

or in three it is not made different, nor yet does it make any other number depart from what it was originally,[1] but keeps it just as it was. Such a property it is impossible to find in any other number. [5] Of the other series the beginning is 2, which is similar in kind to this series and imitates "otherness"; for whether it multiplies itself or another number, it causes a change,[2] for example, 2 times 2, 2 times 3.

[6] But in cases like 8 times 8 times 2, or 8 times 8 times 3, such solid forms are called "bricks," the product of a number by itself and then by a smaller number; if, however, a greater height is joined to the square, as in 3 times 3 times 7, 3 times 3 times 8, or 3 times 3 times 9, or however many times the square be taken, provided only it be a greater number of times than the square itself, then the number is a "beam," the product of a number by itself and then by a larger number. The "wedges," to be sure, were the products of three unequal numbers, and cubes of three equal ones.

[7] Among the cubes, some of them, in addition to being the product of three equal numbers, have the further property of ending at every multiplication in the same number as that from which they began; these are called spherical, and also recurrent. Such indeed are those with sides 5 or 6; for however many times I increase each one of these, it will by all means end each time in the same figure, the derivative of 6 in 6 and that of 5 in 5. For example, the product of 5 times 5 will end in 5, and so will 5 times this product and if necessary, 5 times this again, and to infinity no other concluding term will be found except 5. From 6, too, in the same fashion 6 and no other will be the concluding term; and so 1 likewise is potentially spherical and recurrent, for as is reasonable it has the same property as the spheres and circles. For each one of them, circling and turning around, ends where it begins. And so these numbers aforesaid are the only ones of the products of equal factors to return to the same starting point from which they began, in the course of all their increases. If they increase in the manner of planes, in two dimensions, they are called circular, like 1, 25, and 36, derived from 1 times 1, 5 times 5, and 6 times 6; but if they have three dimensions, or are multiplied still further than this, they are called spherical solid numbers, for example 1, 125, 216, or, again, 1, 625, 1,296.

CHAPTER XVIII

[1] Regarding the solid numbers this is for the present sufficient. The physical philosophers, however, and those that take their start with mathematics, call "the same" and "the other" the principles of the universe, and it has been shown that "the same" inheres in unity and the odd numbers, to which unity gives specific form, and to an even greater degree in the squares, made by the continued addition of odd numbers, because in their sides they share in equality; while "the other" inheres in 2 and the whole even series, which is given specific form by 2, and particularly in the heteromecic numbers, which are made by the continued addition of the even numbers, because of the share of the original inequality[3] and "otherness" which they have in the difference between their sides. Therefore it is most necessary further to demonstrate how in these two, as in origins and seeds, there are potentially existent all the peculiar properties of number, of its forms and subdivisions, of all its relations, of polygonals, and the like.

[2] First, however, we must make the distinction whereby the oblong (promecic) number differs from the heteromecic. The heteromecic is, as was stated above,[4] the product of a number multiplied by another larger than the first by 1, for example, 6, which is 2 times 3, or 12, which is 3 times 4. But the oblong is similarly the product of two differing numbers, differing, however, not by 1 but by some larger number, as 2 times 4, 3 times 6, 4 times 8, and similar numbers, which in a way exceed in length and overstep the difference of 1.

[3] Therefore, since squares are produced from the multiplication of numbers by their own length, and have their length the same as their breadth, properly speaking they would be called "idiomecic" or "tautomecic"; for example, 2 times 2, 3 times 3, 4 times 4, and the rest. And if this is true, they will admit in every way of sameness and equality, and for this reason are limited and come to an end; for "the equal" and "the same" are so in one definite way. But since the heteromecic numbers are produced by the multiplication of a number by not its own, but another number's length, they are therefore called "heteromecic," and admit of infinity and boundlessness.

[4] In this way, then, all numbers and the

---

[1]Cf. II. 6. 3.
[2]Cf. Aristotle, *On the Soul*, 406[b] 13.

[3]Cf. II. 17. 2.
[4]Cf. II. 17. 1.

objects in the universe which have been created with reference to them are divided and classified and are seen to be opposite one to another, and well do the ancients at the very beginning of their account of Nature make the first subdivision in their cosmogony on this principle. Thus Plato[1] mentions the distinction between the natures of "the same" and "the other," and again, that between the essence which is indivisible and always the same and the one which is divided; and Philolaus says that existent things must all be either limitless or limited, or limited and limitless at the same time, by which it is generally agreed that he means that the universe is made up out of limited and limitless things at the same time, obviously after the image of number, for all number is composed of unity and the dyad, even and odd, and these in truth display equality and inequality, sameness and otherness, the bounded and the boundless, the defined and the undefined.

CHAPTER XIX

[1] That we may be clearly persuaded of what is being said, namely, that things are made up of warring and opposite elements[2] and have in all likelihood taken on harmony—and harmony always arises from opposites; for harmony is the unification of the diverse and the reconciliation of the contrary-minded—let us set forth in two parallel lines no longer, as just previously, the even numbers from 2 by themselves and the odd numbers from 1, but the numbers that are produced from these by adding them successively together, the squares from the odd numbers, and the heteromecic from the even. For if we give careful attention to their setting forth, we shall admire their mutual friendship and their coöperation to produce and perfect the remaining forms, to the end that we may with probability conceive that also in the nature of the universe from some such source as this a similar thing was brought about by universal providence.

[2] Let the two series then be as follows: That of the squares, from unity, 1, 4, 9, 16, 25, 36, 49, 64, 81, 100, 121, 144, 169, 196, 225, and that of the heteromecic numbers, beginning with 2 and proceeding thus, 2, 6, 12, 20, 30, 42, 56, 72, 90, 110, 132, 156, 182, 210, 240.

[3] In the first place, then, the first square is the fundamental multiple of the first hetero-

mecic number; the second, compared to the second, is its sesquialter; the third, sesquitertian of the third; the fourth, sesquiquartan of the fourth; then sesquiquintan, sesquisextan, and so on similarly *ad infinitum*. Their differences, too, will increase according to the successive numbers from 1; the difference of the first terms is 1, of the second 2, of the third 3, and so on. Next, if first the second term of the squares be compared with the first heteromecic number, the third with the second, the fourth with the third, and the rest similarly, they will keep unchanged the same ratios as before, but their differences will begin to progress no longer from 1, but from 2, remaining the same as before, and according to the advance observed in the former comparison, the first to the first will be the first, or root-form, multiple, the second to the second the second sesquialter from the root-form, the third to the third the third sesquitertian from the root-form, and the succeeding terms will go on in similar fashion.

[4] Furthermore, the squares among themselves will have only the odd numbers as differences, the heteromecic, even numbers. And if we put the first heteromecic number as a mean term between the first two squares, the second between the next two, the third between the two following, and the fourth between the two next succeeding, therein will be seen still more regularly the numerical relations in groups of three terms. For as 4 is to 2, so is 2 to 1; and as 9 is sesquialter to 6, so is 6 to 4; and as 16 to 12, so is 12 to 9, and so on, with both numbers and ratios regularly advancing. As the greater is to the mean, so will the mean be to the lesser, and not in the same ratio, but always a different one, by an increase. In all the groupings, too, the product of the extremes is equal to the square of the mean; and the extremes, plus twice the mean, by exchange will always give a square. What is neatest of all, from the addition of both there comes about the production of the triangles in due order, showing that the nature of these is more ancient[3] than the origin of all things, thus: 1 plus 2, 2 plus 4, 4 plus 6, 6 plus 9, 9 plus 12, 12 plus 16, 16 plus 20, and by this process the triangles, which give rise to the polygons, come forth in order.

CHAPTER XX

[1] Still further, every square plus its own side becomes heteromecic, or by Zeus, if its side is subtracted from it. Thus, "the other" is con-

[1]Cf. Plato, *Timeaus*, 35.
[2]Plato, *Timaeus*, 30.

[3]Cf. II. 17. 3; 18. 1 and II. 7. 4; cf. 12. 8

ceived of as being both greater and smaller than "the same," since it is produced, both by addition and by subtraction, in the same way that the two kinds of inequality[1] also, the greater and the less, have their origin from the application of addition or subtraction to equality. [2] This also is sufficient evidence that the two forms partake of sameness and otherness, of otherness in an indefinite fashion, but of sameness definitely, 1 and 2 generically, but the odd of sameness after the manner of a subordinate species because it belongs to the same class as 1, and the even of otherness because it is homogeneous with 2.

[3] There is also a still clearer reason why the square, since it is the product of the addition of odd numbers, is akin to sameness, and the heteromecic numbers to otherness because it is made up by adding even numbers; for as though they were friends of one another, these two forms share in their two rows the same differences when they do not have the same ratios, and conversely the same ratios when they do not have the same differences. For the difference between 4 and 2 in the double ratio is found between 6 and 4 as a superparticular; and again the difference between 9 and 6, as a sesquialter, is found between 12 and 9 as a sesquitertian, and so on. What is the same in quality is different in quantity, and just the opposite, what is the same in quantity is different in quality. [4] Again, it is clear that in all their relations the same difference between two terms will necessarily be called fractions with names that differ by 1, and be the half of one and the third of the other, or the third of one and the quarter of the other, or the fourth of one and the fifth of the other, and so on.

[5] But what will most of all confirm the fact that the odd, and never the even, is preëminently the cause of sameness, is to be demonstrated in every series beginning with 1 following some ratio, for example, the double ratio, 1, 2, 4, 8, 16, 32, 64, 128, 256, or the triple, 1, 3, 9, 27, 81, 243, 729, 2,187, and as far as you like. You will find that of necessity all the terms in the odd places in the series are squares, and no others by any device whatsoever, and that no square is to be found in an even place.

But all the products of a number multiplied twice into itself, that is, the cubes, which are extended in three dimensions and seen to share in sameness to an even greater extent, are the product of the odd numbers, not the even, 1,

8, 27, 64, 125, and 216, and those that go on analogously, in a simple, unvaried progression as well. For when the successive odd numbers are set forth indefinitely beginning with 1, observe this: The first one makes the potential cube; the next two, added together, the second; the next three, the third; the four next following, the fourth; the succeeding five, the fifth; the next six, the sixth; and so on.

CHAPTER XXI

[1] After this it would be the proper time to incorporate the nature of proportions, a thing most essential for speculation about the nature of the universe and for the propositions of music, astronomy, and geometry, and not least for the study of the works of the ancients, and thus to bring the *Introduction to Arithmetic* to the end that is at once suitable and fitting.

[2] A proportion, then, is in the proper sense, the combination of two or more *ratios*, but by the more general definition the combination of two or more *relations*, even if they are not brought under the same ratio, but rather a difference, or something else.

[3] Now a ratio[2] is the relation of two terms to one another, and the combination of such is a proportion, so that three is the smallest number of terms of which the latter is composed, although it can be a series of more, subject to the same ratio or the same difference. For example, 1:2 is one ratio, where there are two terms; but 2:4 is another similar ratio; hence 1, 2, 4 is a proportion, for it is a combination of ratios, or of three terms which are observed to be in the same ratio to one another. [4] The same thing may be observed also in greater numbers and longer series of terms; for let a fourth term, 8, be joined to the former after 4, again in a similar relation, the double, and then 16 after 8 and so on.

[5] Now if the same term, one and unchanging, is compared to those on either side of it, to the greater as consequent and to the lesser as antecedent, such a proportion is called continued; for example, 1, 2, 4 is a continued proportion as regards quality[3], for 4:2 equals 2:1, and conversely 1:2 equals 2:4. In quantity, 1, 2, 3, for example, is a continued proportion, for as 3 exceeds 2, so 2 exceeds 1, and conversely, as 1 is less than 2, by so much 2 is less than 3.

[6] If, however, one term answers to the lesser term, and becomes its antecedent and a

[1]Cf. I. 17. 6.

[2]Cf. Euclid, *Elements, V, init.*
[3]Cf. II. 22. 2; 23. 4 below.

greater term, and another, not the same, takes the place of consequent and lesser term with reference to the greater, such a mean and such a proportion is called no longer continued, but disjunct; for example, as regards quality, 1, 2, 4, 8, for 2:1 equals 8:4, and conversely 1:2 equals 4:8, and again 1:4 equals 2:8 or 4:1 equals 8:2; and in quantity, 1, 2, 3, 4, for as 1 is exceeded by 2, by so much 3 is exceeded by 4, or as 4 exceeds 3, so 2 exceeds 1, and by interchange, as 3 exceeds 1, so 4 exceeds 2, or as 1 is exceeded by 3, by so much 2 is exceeded by 4.

CHAPTER XXII

[1] The first three proportions, then, which are acknowledged by all the ancients, Pythagoras, Plato, and Aristotle, are the arithmetic, geometric, and harmonic; and there are three others subcontrary to them, which do not have names of their own, but are called in more general terms the fourth, fifth, and sixth forms of mean; after which the moderns discover four others as well, making up the number ten, which, according to the Pythagorean view, is the most perfect possible. It was in accordance with this number indeed that not long ago the ten relations were observed to take their proper number, the so-called ten categories, the divisions and forms of the extremities of our hands and feet, and countless other things which we shall notice in the proper place.

[2] Now, however, we must treat from the beginning, first, that form of proportion which by quantity reconciles and binds together the comparison of the terms, which is a quantitative equality as regards the difference of the several terms to one another. This would be the arithmetic proportion, for it was previously reported that quantity is its peculiar belonging. *[3]* What, then, is the reason that we shall treat of this first, and not another? Is it not clear that Nature shows it forth before the rest? For in the natural series of simple numbers, beginning with 1, with no term passed over or omitted, the definition of this proportion alone is preserved; moreover, in our previous statements,[1] we demonstrated that the *Arithmetical Introduction* itself is antecedent to all the others, because it abolishes them together with itself, but is not abolished together with them, and because it is implied by them, but does not imply them. Thus it is natural that the mean which shares the name of arithmetic will not

unreasonably take precedence of the means which are named for the other sciences, the geometric and harmonic; for it is plain that all the more will it take precedence over the subcontraries, over which the first three hold the leadership. *[4]* As the first and original, therefore, since it is most deserving of the honor, let the arithmetic proportion have its discussion at our hands before the others.

CHAPTER XXIII

[1] It is an arithmetic proportion, then, whenever three or more terms are set forth in succession, or are so conceived, and the same quantitative difference is found to exist between the successive numbers, but not the same ratio among the terms, one to another. For example, 1, 2, 3, 4, 5, 6, 7, 8, 9, 10, 11, 12, 13; for in this natural series of numbers, examined consecutively and without any omissions, every term whatsoever is discovered to be placed between two and to preserve the arithmetic proportion to them. For its differences as compared with those ranged on either side of it are equal; the same ratio, however, is not preserved among them.

[2] And we understand that in such a series there comes about both a continued and a disjunct proportion; for if the same middle term answers to those on either side as both antecedent and consequent, it would be a continued proportion, but if there is another mean along with it, a disjunct proportion comes about.

[3] Now if we separate out of this series any three consecutive terms whatsoever, after the form of the continued proportion, or four or more terms after the disjunct form, and consider them, the difference of them all would be 1, but their ratios would be different throughout. If, however, again we select three or more terms, not adjacent, but separated, separated nevertheless by a constant interval, if one term was omitted in setting down each term, the difference in every case will be 2; and once more with three terms it will be a continued proportion; with more, disjunct. If two terms are omitted, the difference will always be 3 in all of them, continued or disjunct; if three, 4; if four, 5; and so on.

[4] Such a proportion, therefore, partakes in equal quantity in its differences, but of unequal quality; for this reason it is arithmetic. If on the contrary it partook of similar quality, but not quantity, it would be geometric instead of arithmetic.

[5] A thing is peculiar to this proportion

---

[1] Cf. I. 4. 2 ff.

that does not belong to any other, namely, the mean is either half of, or equal to, the sum of the extremes, whether the proportion be viewed as continuous or disjunct or by alternation; for either the mean term with itself, or the mean terms with one another, are equal to the sum of the extremes.

[6] It has still another peculiarity; what ratio each term has to itself, this the differences have to the differences; that is, they are equal.

Again, the thing which is most exact, and which has escaped the notice of the majority, the product of the extremes when compared to the square of the mean is found to be smaller than it by the product of the differences, whether they be 1, 2, 3, 4, or any number whatever.

In the fourth place, a thing which all previous writers also have noted, the ratios between the smaller terms are larger, as compared to those between the greater terms. It will be shown that in the harmonic proportion, on the contrary, the ratios between the greater terms are greater than those between the smaller; for this reason the harmonic proportion is subcontrary to the arithmetic, and the geometric is midway between them, as it were, between extremes, for this proportion has the ratios between the greater terms and those between the smaller equal, and we have seen that the equal is in the middle ground between the greater and the less. So much, then, about the arithmetic proportion.

CHAPTER XXIV

[1] The next proportion[1] after this one, the geometric, is the only one in the strict sense of the word to be called a proportion, because its terms are seen to be in the same ratio. It exists whenever, of three or more terms, as the greatest is to the next greatest, so the latter is to the one following, and if there are more terms, as this again is to the one following it, but they do not, however, differ from one another by the same quantity, but rather by the same quality of ratio, the opposite of what was seen to be the case with the arithmetic proportion.

[2] For an example, set forth the numbers beginning with 1 that advance by the double ratio, 1, 2, 4, 8, 16, 32, 64, and so on, or by the triple ratio, 1, 3, 9, 27, 81, 243, and so on, or by the quadruple, or in some similar way. In each one of these series three adjacent terms, or four, or any number whatever that may be taken,

will give the geometric proportion to one another; as the first is to the next smaller, so is that to the next smaller, and again that to the next smaller, and so on as far as you care to go, and also by alternation. For instance, 2, 4, 8; the ratio which 8 bears to 4, that 4 bears to 2, and conversely; they do not, however, have the same quantitative difference. Again, 2, 4, 8, 16; for not only does 16 have the same ratio to 8 as before, though not the same difference, but also by alternation it preserves a similar relation—as 16 is to 4, so 8 is to 2, and conversely, as 2 is to 8, so 4 is to 16; and disjunctly, as 2 is to 4, so 8 is to 16; and conversely and in disjunct form, as 16 is to 8 so 4 is to 2; for it has the double ratio.

[3] The geometric proportion has a peculiar property shared by none of the rest, that the differences of the terms are in the same ratio to each other as the terms to those adjacent to them, the greater to the less, and vice versa. Still another property is that the greater terms have as a difference, with respect to the lesser, the lesser terms themselves, and similarly difference differs from difference, by the smaller difference itself, if the terms are set forth in the double ratio; in the triple ratio both terms and differences will have as a difference twice the next smaller, in the quadruple ratio thrice, in the quintuple four times, and so on.

[4] Geometric proportions come about not only among the multiples, but also among all the superparticular, superpartient, and mixed forms, and the peculiar property of this proportion in all cases is preserved, that in the continued proportions the product of the extremes is equal to the square of the mean, but in disjunct proportions, or those with a greater number of terms, even if they are not continued, but with an even number of terms, that the product of the extremes equals that of the means.

[5] As an illustration of the fact that in all the relations, all kinds of multiples, superparticulars, superpartients, and mixed ratios the peculiar property of this proportion is preserved, let that suffice[2] and be sufficient for us wherein we fashioned, beginning with equality, by the three rules all the kinds of inequality out of one another, when they were in both direct and reverse order; for each act of fashioning and each series set forth is a geometric proportion with all the aforesaid properties as well as a fourth, namely, that they keep the

---

[1]Cf. Euclid, *Elements*, VII, Def. 21.   [2]Cf. I. 23. 7 ff.

same ratio in both the greater and the smaller terms. Moreover, if we set forth the series shared by both heteromecic and square numbers, one by one, containing the terms in both series, and then selecting the terms by groups of three beginning with 1, examine them, in each case setting down the last of the former group as the starting point of the next, we shall find that from the multiple relation—that is, the double—all the kinds of superparticulars appear one after the other, the sesquialter, sesquitertian, sesquiquartan, and so on.

[6] It would be most seasonable, now that we have reached this point, to mention a corollary that is of use to us for a certain Platonic theorem:[1] for plane numbers are bound together always by a single mean, solids by two, in the form of a proportion. For with two consecutive squares[2] only one mean term is discovered which preserves the geometric proportion, as antecedent to the smaller and consequent to the greater term, and never more than one. Hence we conceive of two intervals between the mean term and each extreme, in the relation of similar ratios. *[7]* Again, with two consecutive cubes[3] only two middle terms in proper ratio are found, in accordance with the geometric proportion, never more; hence there are three intervals, one, that between the mean terms compared to one another, and two between the extremes and the means on either side. *[8]* Thus the solid forms are called three-dimensional and the plane ones two-dimensional; for example, 1 and 4 are planes, and 2 a middle term in proportion, or again 4 and 9, two squares, and their middle term 6, held by the greater and holding the lesser term in the same ratio as that in which one difference holds the other. *[9]* The reason for this is that the sides of the two squares, one belonging peculiarly to each, both together produced this very number 6. In cubes, however, for example 8 and 27, no longer one but two mean terms are found, 12 and 18, which put themselves and the terms in the same ratio as that which the differences bear to one another; and the reason of this is that the two mean terms are the products of the sides of the cubes commingled, 2 times 2 times 3 and 3 times 3 times 2.

[10] In general, then, if a square takes a square, that is, multiplies it, it always makes a square; but if a square multiplies a hetero-

mecic number, or vice versa, it never makes a square; and if cube multiplies cube, a cube will always result, but if a heteromecic number multiplies a cube, or vice versa, never is the result a cube. In precisely the same way if an even number multiplies an even number, the product is always even and if odd multiplies odd always odd; but if odd multiplies even or even odd, the result will always be even and never odd. *[11]* These matters will receive their proper elucidation in the commentary on Plato, with reference to the passage on the so-called marriage number in the *Republic*[4] introduced in the person of the Muses. So then let us pass over to the third proportion, the so-called harmonic, and analyze it.

CHAPTER XXV

[1] The proportion that is placed in the third order is one called the harmonic, which exists whenever among three terms the mean on examination is observed to be neither in the same ratio to the extremes, antecedent of one and consequent of the other, as in the geometric proportion, nor with equal intervals, but an inequality of ratios, as in the arithmetic, but on the contrary, as the greatest term is to the smallest, so the difference between greatest and mean terms is to the difference between mean and smallest term. For example, take 3, 4, 6, or 2, 3, 6. For 6 exceeds 4 by one third of itself, since 2 is one third of 6, and 3 falls short of 4 by one third of itself, for 1 is one third of 3. In the first example, the extremes are in double ratio and their differences with the mean term are again in the same double ratio to one another; but in the second they are each in the triple ratio.

[2] It has a peculiar property, opposite, as we have said,[5] to that of the arithmetic proportion; for in the latter the ratios were greater among the smaller terms, and smaller among the greater terms. Here, however, on the contrary, those among the greater terms are greater and those among the smaller terms smaller, so that in the geometric proportion, like a mean between them, there may be observed the equality of ratios on either side, a midground between greater and smaller.

[3] Furthermore, in the arithmetic proportion the mean term is seen to be greater and smaller than those on either side by the same fraction of itself, but by different fractions of

[1]*Timaeus*, 32.
[2]Cf. Euclid, *Elements*, VIII, 11.
[3]Cf. Euclid, *Elements*, VIII, 12.

[4]*Republic*, 546 ff.
[5]Cf. II. 23. 6.

the terms that flank it; in the harmonic, however, it is the opposite, for the middle term is greater and less than the terms on either side by different fractions of itself, but always the same fraction of those terms at its sides, a half of them or a third; but the geometric, as if in the midground between them, shows this property neither in the mean term exclusively nor in the extremes, but in both mean and extreme.

[4] Once more, the harmonic proportion has as a peculiar property the fact that when the extremes are added together and multiplied by the mean, it makes twice the product of themselves multiplied by one another.

[5] The harmonic proportion was so called because the arithmetic proportion was distinguished by quantity, showing an equality in this respect with the intervals from one term to another, and the geometric by quality, giving similar qualitative relations between one term and another, but this form, with reference to relativity, appears now in one form, now in another, neither in its terms exclusively nor in its differences exclusively, but partly in the terms and partly in the differences; for as the greatest term is to the smallest, so also is the difference between the greatest and the next greatest, or middle, term to the difference between the least term and the middle term, and vice versa.

CHAPTER XXVI

[1] In the classification of Being previously set forth we recognized the relative [1] as a thing peculiar to harmonic theory; but the musical ratios of the harmonic intervals are also rather to be found in this proportion. The most elementary is the diatessaron, in the sesquitertian ratio, 4:3, which is the ratio of term to term[2] in the example in the double ratio, or of difference to difference in that which follows, the triple, for these differences are of 6 to 2 or again of 6 to 3. Immediately following is the diapente, which is the sesquialter, 3:2 or again, 6:4, the ratio of term to term. Then the combination[3] of both of these, sesquialter and sesquitertian, the diapason, which comes next, is in the double ratio, 6:3 in both of the examples, the ratio of term to term. The following interval, that of the diapason and diapente together, which preserves the triple ratio of the two of them together, since it is the combination of double

[1]See I. 3. 1.

[2]The examples referred to are the harmonic proportions cited in II. 25. 1.

[3]Cf. II. 5. 2.

and sesquialter, is as 6:2, the ratio of term to term in the example in the triple ratio, and likewise of difference to difference in the same, and in the proportion with double ratio it is the ratio of the greatest term to the difference between that term and the mean term, or of the difference between the extremes to the difference between the smaller terms. The last and greatest interval, the so-called di-diapason, as it were twice the double, which is in the quadruple ratio, is as the middle term in the proportion in the double ratio to the difference between the lesser terms, or as the difference between the extremes, in the example in the triple ratio, to the difference between the lesser terms.

[2] Some, however, agreeing with Philolaus, believe that the proportion is called harmonic because it attends upon all geometric harmony, and they say that "geometric harmony" is the cube because it is harmonized in all three dimensions, being the product of a number thrice multiplied together. For in every cube this proportion is mirrored; there are in every cube 12 sides, 8 angles and 6 faces; hence 8, the mean between 6 and 12, is according to harmonic proportion, for as the extremes are to each other, so is the difference between greatest and middle term to that between the middle and smallest terms, and, again, the middle term is greater than the smallest by one fraction of itself and by another is less than the greater term, but is greater and smaller by one and the same fraction of the extremes. And again, the sum of the extremes multiplied by the mean makes double the product of the extremes multiplied together. The diatessaron is found in the ratio 8:6, which is sesquitertian, the diapente in 12:8, which is sesquialter; the diapason, the combination of these two, in 12:6, the double ratio; the diapason and diapente combined, which is triple, in the ratio of the difference of the extremes to that of the smaller terms, and the di-diapason is the ratio of the middle term to the difference between itself and the lesser term. Most properly, then, has it been called harmonic.

CHAPTER XXVII

[1] Just as in the division of the musical canon, when a single string is stretched or one length of a pipe is used, with immovable ends, and the mid-point shifts in the pipe by means of the finger-holes, in the string by means of the bridge, and as in one way after another the aforesaid proportions, arithmetic, geometric,

and harmonic, can be produced, so that the fact becomes apparent that they are logically and very properly named, since they are brought about through changing and shifting the middle term in different ways, so too it is both reasonable and possible to insert the mean term that fits each of the three proportions between two arithmetic terms, which stay fixed and do not change, whether they are both even or odd. In the arithmetic proportion this mean term is one that exceeds and is exceeded by an equal amount; in the geometric proportion it is differentiated from the extremes by the same ratio, and in the harmonic it is greater and smaller than the extremes by the same fraction of those same extremes.

[2] Let there be given then, first, two even terms, between which we must find how the three means would be inserted, and what they are. Let them be 10 and 40.

[3] First, then, I fit to them the arithmetic mean. It is 25, and the attendant properties of the arithmetic proportion are all preserved; for as each term is to itself, so also is difference to difference; they are in equality, therefore. And as much as the greater exceeds the means by so much the latter exceeds the lesser term; the sum of the extremes is twice the mean; the ratio of the lesser terms is greater than that of the greater; the product of the extremes is less than the square of the mean by the amount of the square of the differences; and the middle term is greater and less than the extremes by the same fraction of itself, but by different fractions regarded as parts of the extremes.

[4] If, however, I insert 20 as a mean between the given even terms, the properties of the geometrical proportion come into view and those of the arithmetic are done away with. For as the greater term is to the middle term, so is the middle term to the lesser; the product of the extremes is equal to the square of the mean; the differences are observed to be in the same ratio to one another as that of the terms; neither in the extremes alone nor in the middle term alone does there reside the sameness of the fraction concerned in the relative excess and deficiency of the terms, but in the middle term and one of the extremes by turns; and both between greater and smaller terms there is the same ratio.

[5] But if I select 16 as the mean, again the properties of the two former proportions disappear and those of the harmonic are seen to remain fixed, with respect to the two even terms. For as the greatest term is to the least,

so is the difference of the greater terms to that of the lesser; by what fractions, seen as fractions of the greater term, the mean is smaller than the greater term, by these the same mean term is greater than the smallest term when they are looked upon as fractions of the smallest term; the ratio between the greater terms is greater, and that of the smaller terms, smaller, a thing which is not true of any other proportion; and the sum of the extremes multiplied by the mean is double the product of the extremes.

[6] If, however, the two terms that are given are not even but odd, like 5, 45, the same number, 25, will make the arithmetic proportion; and the reason for this is that the terms on either side overpass it and fail to come up to it by an equal number, keeping the same quantitative difference with respect to it. 15 substituted makes the geometric proportion, as it is the triple and subtriple of each respectively; and if 9 takes over the function of mean term it gives the harmonic; for by those parts of the smaller term by which it exceeds, namely, four fifths of the smaller, it is also less than the greater, if they be regarded as parts of the greater term, for this too is four fifths, and if you try all the previously mentioned properties of the harmonic ratio you will find that they will fit.

[7] And let this be your method whereby you might scientifically fashion the mean terms that are illustrated in the three proportions. For the two terms given you, whether odd or even, you will find the arithmetic mean by adding the extremes and putting down half of them as the mean, or if you divide by 2 the excess of the greater over the smaller, and add this to the smaller, you will have the mean. As for the geometric mean, if you find the square root of the product of the extremes, you will produce it, or, observing the ratio of the terms to one another, divide this by 2 and make the mean, for example, the double, in the case of a quadruple ratio. For the harmonic mean, you must multiply the difference of the extremes by the lesser term and divide the product by the sum of the extremes, then add the quotient to the lesser term, and the result will be the harmonic mean.

CHAPTER XXVIII

[1] So much, then, concerning the three proportions celebrated by the ancients, which we have discussed the more clearly and at length for just this reason, that they are to be met

with frequently and in various forms in the writings of those authors. The succeeding forms, however, we must only epitomize, since they do not occur frequently in the ancient writings, but are included merely for the sake of our own acquaintance with them and, so to speak, for the completeness of our reckoning. *[2]* They are set forth by us in an order based on their opposition to the three archetypes already described, since they are fashioned out of them and have the same order.

[3] The fourth, and the one called subcontrary, because it is opposite to, and has opposite properties to, the harmonic proportion, exists when, in three terms, as the greatest is to the smallest, so the difference of the smaller terms is to that of the greater, for example 3, 5, 6. For the terms compared are seen to be in the double ratio, and it is plain wherein it is opposite to the harmonic proportion; for whereas they both have the same extreme terms, and in double ratio, in the former the difference of the greater terms as compared to that of the lesser preserved the same ratio as that of the extremes, but in this proportion just the reverse, the difference of the smaller compared with that of the greater. You must know that its peculiar property is this. The product of the greater and the mean terms is twice the product of the mean and the smaller; for 6 times 5 is twice 5 times 3.

[4] The two proportions, fifth and sixth, were both fashioned after the geometrical, and they differ from each other thus.

The fifth form exists, whenever, among three terms, as the middle term is to the lesser, so their difference is to the difference between the greater and the mean, as in 2, 4, 5, for 4 is the middle term, the double of 2, the lesser, and 2 is the double of 1—the difference of the smallest terms as compared with that of the largest. That which makes it contrary to the geometric proportion is that in the former,[1] as the middle term is to the lesser, so the excess of the greater over the mean is to the excess of the mean over the lesser term, whereas in this proportion, on the contrary, it is the difference of the lesser compared to that of the greater. Nevertheless it is peculiar to this proportion that the product of the greatest by the middle term is double that of the greatest by the smallest, for 5 times 4 is twice 5 times 2.

[5] The sixth form[2] comes about when, in a group of three terms, as the greatest is to the mean, so the excess of the mean over the lesser is to the excess of the greater over the mean, for example 1, 4, 6, for both are in the sesquialter ratio. There is in this case also a reasonable cause for its opposition to the geometrical; for here, too, the likeness of the ratios reverses, as in the fifth form.

[6] These are the six proportions commonly spoken of among previous writers, the three prototypes having lasted from the times of Pythagoras down to Aristotle and Plato, and the three others, opposites of the former, coming into use among the commentators and sectarians who succeeded these men. But certain men have devised in addition, by shifting the terms and differences of the former, four more which do not much appear in the writings of the ancients, but have been sparingly touched upon as an over-nice detail. These, however, we must run over in the following fashion, lest we seem ignorant.

[7] The first of them, and the seventh in the list of them all, exists when, as the greatest term is to the least, so their difference is to the difference of the lesser terms, as 6, 8, 9, for on comparison the ratio of each is seen to be the sesquialter.

[8] The eighth proportion, which is the second of this group, comes about when, as the greatest is to the least term, so the difference of the extremes is to the difference of the greater terms, as 6, 7, 9; for this also has sesquialters for the two ratios.

[9] The ninth in the complete list, and third in the number of those subsequently invented, exists when there are three terms and whatever ratio the mean bears to the least, that also the difference of the extremes has in comparison with that of the smallest terms, as 4, 6, 7.

[10] The tenth, in the full list, which concludes them all, and the fourth in the series presented by the moderns, is seen when, among three terms, as the mean is to the lesser, so the difference of the extremes is to the difference of the greater terms, as 3, 5, 8, for it is the superbipartient ratio in each pair.

[11] To sum up, then, let the terms of the ten proportions be set forth in one illustration, for the sake of easy comprehension:

First: 1, 2, 3	Sixth: 1, 4, 6
Second: 1, 2, 4	Seventh: 6, 8, 9
Third: 3, 4, 6	Eighth: 6, 7, 9
Fourth: 3, 5, 6	Ninth: 4, 6, 7
Fifth: 2, 4, 5	Tenth: 3, 5, 8

[1] Cf. II. 24.
[2] Cf. Euclid, *Elem.*, V., Def. 16.

CHAPTER XXIX

[1] It remains for me to discuss briefly the most perfect proportion, that which is three-dimensional and embraces them all, and which is most useful for all progress in music and in the theory of the nature of the universe. This alone would properly and truly be called harmony[1] rather than the others, since it is not a plane, nor bound together by only one mean term, but with two, so as thus to be extended in three dimensions,[2] just as a while ago it was explained that the cube is harmony.

[2] When, therefore, there are two extreme terms, both of three dimensions, either numbers multiplied thrice by themselves so as to be a cube, or numbers multiplied twice by themselves and once by another number so as to be either "beams" or "bricks," or the products of three unequal numbers, so as to be scalene, and between them there are found two other terms which preserve the same ratios to the extremes alternately and together, in such a manner that, while one of them preserves the harmonic proportion, the other completes the arithmetic, it is necessary that in such a disposition of the four the geometric proportion appear, on examination, commingled with both mean terms—as the greatest is to the third removed from it, so is the second from it to the fourth; for such a situation makes the product of the means equal to the product of the extremes. And again, if the greatest term be

shown to differ from the one next beneath it by the amount whereby this latter differs from the least term, such an array becomes an arithmetic proportion and the sum of the extremes is twice the mean. But if the third term from the greatest exceeds and is exceeded by the same fraction of the extremes, it is harmonic and the product of the mean by the sum of the extremes is double the product of the extremes.

[3] Let this be an example of this proportion, 6, 8, 9, 12. 6 is a scalene number, derived from 1 times 2 times 3, and 12 comes from the successive multiplication of 2 times 2 times 3; of the mean terms the lesser is from 1 times 2 times 4, and the greater from 1 times 3 times 3. The extremes are both solid and three-dimensional, and the means are of the same class. According to the geometric proportion, as 12 is to 8, so 9 is to 6; according to the arithmetic, as 12 exceeds 9, by so much does 9 exceed 6; and by the harmonic, by the fraction by which 8 exceeds 6, viewed as a fraction of 6, 8 is also exceeded by 12, viewed as a fraction of 12.

[4] Moreover 8:6 or 12:9 is the diatessaron, in sesquitertian ratio; 9:6 or 12:8 is the diapente in the sesquialter; 12:6 is the diapason in the double. Finally, 9:8 is the interval of a tone, in the superoctave ratio, which is the common measure of all the ratios in music, since it is also the more familiar, because it is likewise the difference between the first and most elementary intervals.

[5] And let this be sufficient concerning the phenomena and properties of number, for a first *Introduction.*

[1]Cf. II. 26. 2.
[2]Cf. II. 24. 6.

THE GREAT IDEAS, Volumes 2 and 3